Principles of Modern BIOLOGY

Principles of Modern

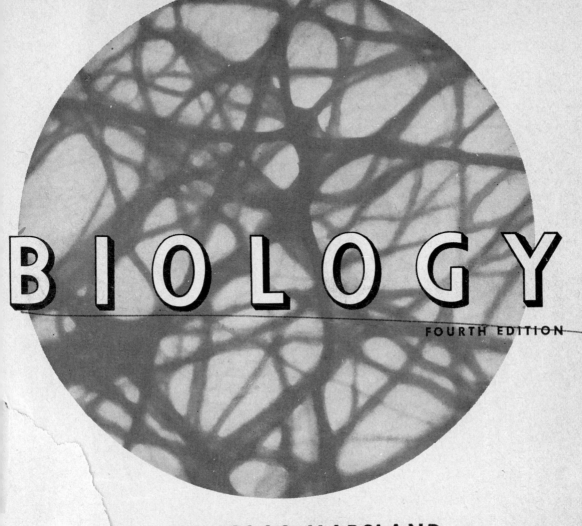

BIOLOGY

FOURTH EDITION

DOUGLAS MARSLAND

Research Professor • New York University
Washington Square College of Arts and Sciences

574
M35 pa

HOLT, RINEHART AND WINSTON

New York • Chicago • San Francisco • Toronto • London

Preface to the Fourth Edition

BIOLOGY has advanced very rapidly during the past eight years. Thus it is difficult merely to list the new material that has been incorporated into this fourth edition of *Principles of Modern Biology*. However, some main topics that have been added or brought thoroughly up-to-date may be specified as follows: (1) Electron microscopy: fine structure of the endoplasmic reticulum; centrioles; plastids; grana; mitochondria; muscle filaments; cilia; flagella; the plasma membrane; synaptic membranes; chromosomes; the mitotic apparatus; pinocytic vacuoles; ribosomes; etc. (2) Cellular metabolism: isotope tracer and chromatographic methods; the carbon path in photosynthesis; photochemical phenomena, especially photophosphorylation; thermodynamics of intracellular energy transactions; role of ATP; electron transport systems; the Krebs cycle; glycolysis and fermentation; theory of enzyme action; activation energies; enzyme-coenzyme interactions and amino acid activation. (3) Protein structure: methods of determining the amino acid sequence of the primary structure and the role of hydrogen bonds and other linkages in determining secondary and tertiary structure. (4) DNA-RNA-protein interrelationships: the Watson-Crick model; mechanisms of self-templated replication; the base-pair rule in DNA-RNA synthesis; the genetic code; messenger and transport RNA. (5) Genetics: population analysis, abnormal chromosome complexes in relation to heritable "errors of metabolism." (6) Nature of the gene: analysis of the base sequence in viral replication and in cell-free bacterial preparations; *cis-trans*

phenomena; gene-enzyme interrelationships; enzyme induction; morphogenesis and differentiation; basic nature of mutational changes. (7) Ecology: the ecosystem concept; producers, consumers, and decomposers; abiotic base; ecological succession; pioneering and climax stages. (8) New phytohormones and photoperiodism. (9) Antibody production in relation to the thymus gland. (10) Endocrine advances: the parathyroid hormone; erythropoiten; the pineal hormones; neurohumors generally; cellular and comparative endocrinology; feedback mechanisms; homeostasis in general. (11) Receptors: chemistry of vision; generator potentials; excitatory substances. (12) Effectors: newer concepts of muscle structure and function; chemistry of luminescence. (13) Central nervous system: fine structure of the synapse; neurosecretory vesicles; integrative functions of neurons; transmitter substances; pacemaker and other types of potential. (14) Excretory system: concept of homeostasis; evolution of the vertebrate kidney. Many other more specific data of recent origin have been interpolated at appropriate points in the various chapters of the book.

Considerable attention has been given to the illustrations. Many new photographs, particularly electronmicrographs, have been added and there are quite a few new drawings. A number of the old drawings have been relabeled for the sake of greater clarity, and special attention has been paid to the captions. The purpose in this connection has been to provide each figure with an independent interest without sacrificing the primary function, which is to clarify the text material.

The fourth edition continues to derive an important heritage from C. R. Plunkett's *Outlines of Modern Biology,* which was published in 1929. Most of the form and substance of the original book has changed, but the basic aim remains. This is to present biology as an integrated science—a consistently unified body of knowledge, principle, and theory that tries to explain as well as to describe the phenomena of life. Indeed, this emphasis on the essential unity of biology, as a science that derives its principles quite equally from a study of plants and animals, represents one of Plunkett's most unique and important contributions.

The problem of integrating and incorporating new developments into an existing body of facts and principles is a difficult challenge. Each "new" development is apt to represent a modified derivative of some "older" concept. It cannot, like a supernumerary limb, merely be grafted haphazardly upon the body surface. The whole system must be adjusted and accommodated to the new growth, if a harmonious integrity is to be preserved. Consequently, this fourth edition has involved an extensive amount of rewriting, as did the other three.

Another perennial problem is to develop the student's interest and to bring the complex material of modern biology into range of comprehension without sacrificing scientific standards. Most students fail to take an interest in general principles unless these are interpreted in terms of their own experience or in terms of experimental evidence clearly and fully presented. Superficial treatments, too often encountered, do not suffice. New ideas must be thoroughly developed. They must be carefully defined, explained, analyzed, and exemplified. It is necessary to challenge the intelligence of our students and to have faith in their capacity to learn. Experience has shown that general students, whose main objective is to gain a relatively broad understanding of how biology impinges upon human life and thought, are generally willing to accept the challenge. They provide excellent competition for the biology majors preparing for advanced work.

My associates at Washington Square College have been very helpful in many ways. To a large extent, the content of the book keeps originating from the lectures of our General Biology course; and over the years many members of the Biology Department have contributed to these lectures. Specifically, I want to thank Drs. Harry A. Chariper, H. Clark Dalton, Albert S. Gordon, Morris H. Harnly, Henry S. Hirshfield, Milan J. Kopac, Alexander Sandow, and Charles D. Siegel. I want also to acknowledge a special indebtedness to the late Henry J. Fry who originally planned our General Biology course and who directed our teaching in the early days at Washington Square College.

And, finally, I am happy to dedicate this book to my wife, Alice Marsland, who has helped so much.

D. M.

New York City
November, 1963

Contents

vii

Part IV. HEREDITY AND EVOLUTION

PART I-*The Cell*

1-*Life and Protoplasm*

MORE THAN a million and a quarter distinct species of plants and animals are recognized in the world at large, and quite a number of newly discovered species are reported every year. Different organisms have evolved a special fitness to live in almost every part of the environment—in the ocean, on land, and in the air—under a wide variety of conditions. Certain species thrive on dry rocks and in stagnant swamps; in hot springs and in polar ices; where oxygen is abundant, and even where oxygen is lacking entirely.

Some organisms appear to be very simple —like microscopic droplets of clear liquid. But other creatures, like man, possess an obviously complicated structure. Gigantic living things, like whales or redwood trees, stand in dramatic contrast to the puniest bacterium, which looks like the smallest speck, even under the best magnification of the microscope. In short, a very rich diversity of living creatures has been evolved upon our earth, and man is challenged to reach an understanding of their nature (Fig. 1-1).

DISTINCTIVE ACTIVITIES OF LIVING BODIES

Since *biology* is the group of sciences that *deals with life* in all its forms and in all its activities, it is necessary to distinguish as clearly as possible between living and non-living bodies. Such a distinction is not usually difficult, because living bodies are apt to

Fig. 1-1.   The size of organisms varies greatly. This whale (a sulfur bottom whale) weighs over 300,000 pounds, and the elephant weighs 20,000 pounds. But it takes more than a trillon tuberculosis bacilli to make one pound. (Redrawn from *Organic Evolution*, by Lull. The Macmillan Company.)

display several unmistakable signs of life. All typical organisms are **responsive**; that is, all living things react to stimulation—by chemical agents such as food, or by physical agents such as light. Likewise, all living things sustain themselves by some kind of **nutrition.** Each takes in food from which to derive matter for growth and energy for movement. And above all, each kind of living thing displays a capacity for **reproduction**, perpetuating itself from generation to

nonliving things display activities analogous to nutrition and growth. Water, or any other form of matter, continually alters its behavior in response to changes in temperature, pressure, light, and other factors of the environment. Water expands or contracts according to the temperature; it boils at one temperature and freezes at another. These are relatively simple reactions, hardly to be compared to the complex responses of a thinking man, or of a sprouting seed. But

Fig. 1-2. Responsiveness, nutrition, and reproduction are characteristic of living things. Incidentally, this adult female robin is a fairly rare, white (albino) specimen. (Courtesy of Hugh M. Halliday.)

generation. In fact, these three activities— *responsiveness, nutrition,* and *reproduction* —are uniquely combined in living bodies, and can be taken as the main criteria of the **living state** (Fig. 1-2).

Responsiveness. One must conclude, however, that the dividing line between the living and nonliving is not a very sharp one, because a number of nonliving systems can be found that simulate some aspects of living behavior. All bodies, nonliving as well as living, are in some degree responsive; and some

there are nonliving systems that are highly reactive—as for example, a loaded pistol responding to a touch on the trigger, or an automobile responding to pressure on the accelerator. Generally speaking, however, animate responses, in comparison with inanimate ones, are much more complex and variable.

Nutrition. Nonliving bodies may also display nutrition, although generally the nutrition of living bodies is considerably more complex. Within the living body, food always contributes both **energy**—the energy that activates the vital system—and **matter,** to form new components in the living structure. In other words, food in the living body can serve not only as a **fuel,** but also as raw material for chemical syntheses that provide for **maintenance** and lead to **growth.**

Many inanimate bodies utilize fuels, but few, if any, can grow or even maintain their existing structure. An automobile duplicates almost all the destructive phases of animate nutrition. It takes in fuel (food); it distributes the fuel to the carburetor; it sucks in (breathes) oxygen through the carburetor, which sends the fuel-oxygen mixture to the cylinders; it chemically decomposes (oxidizes) the fuel and utilizes the energy that is liberated for the development of mechanical power. Furthermore, the automobile must eliminate (excrete) the end products (waste products) of its chemical activities. But here the analogy stops. The automobile cannot grow. It cannot even replace the small structural losses that inevitably result from wear and tear. All the constructive phases of nutrition, by which new substances are synthesized and incorporated into the structure of the living body, are absent in all inanimate systems.

Growth and Reproduction: The Most Unique Activities of Living Systems. Biologists have tried to find a parallel to the characteristic **growth phenomena** of living bodies in the "growth" of crystals in a super-saturated solution. But this phenomenon seems much simpler than organic growth. Crystal growth follows a precise and characteristic pattern, but is altogether local and external. The crystal enlarges by the addition of new molecular layers at the *surface* only, and the enlargement is at the expense of molecules that exist as such in the surrounding solution. Organic growth, in contrast, pervades the entire protoplasmic mass, and depends upon an elaborate series of chemical changes leading to the formation of new components in the protoplasm. Or, from another point of view, organic growth depends upon a pre-

cisely patterned aggregation of many kinds of molecules, whereas crystals grow by the assemblage of one, or at most, two or three kinds of molecules.

The most unique characteristic of living bodies is the capacity for *reproduction;* and here it is hard to find any convincing inanimate examples. From the humblest bacterium to the mightiest mammal, each living species must maintain an unbroken line of descent, if it is to avoid extinction. The processes of reproduction are extremely complex and delicate even in the simpler forms of life. The formation of a new body, which is almost an exact replica of the old, presupposes the existence of a delicate mechanism that can sort out certain important components in each living organism and pass these on to each ensuing generation. These important *genic materials,* as we shall see (Chap. 26), possess not only the unique potential of *self-replication,* but also the capacity of providing templates for the replication of other essential components in each particular kind of living thing.

Certain inanimate bodies, namely crystals, may show an extremely simple form of "reproduction." Occasionally, while a small crystal is in the process of "growing," it will fragment spontaneously and each of the fragments will become the center around which a perfect new crystal will form. However, with the possible exception of the multiplication of the filtrable viruses (pp. 7-11), such a "reproductive" process is incomparably simpler than all cases of animate reproduction.

LIFE AND PROTOPLASM

To define life completely is scarcely possible, but the word can be used to designate the sum total of all activities—*responsiveness, nutrition, reproduction,* etc.—that are displayed by living bodies generally. Life, according to this usage, simply specifies "what living things do." It does not in any sense *explain* what they do, or *how* they do it.

Popularly the word "life" is sometimes used in a different sense: to designate a mysterious immaterial "something" that uniquely resides in living bodies, causing their activities. Science, however, has not been able to find the slightest evidence to confirm the existence of anything corresponding to this idea. Nor is such a concept useful. To say that a living body moves, responds, or grows "because it is alive" or because "it possesses life" is like saying that a motor runs "because it is motile" or "because it possesses motility." In science such so-called explanations are not admissible. The only scientifically valid kind of explanation consists in finding and describing an actual mechanism, in which the special composition, arrangement, and interaction of the component parts logically account for the observed activities.

In accordance with this important criterion of science, the aim of biology is to explain life—the activities of living bodies—in terms of the composition and structure of these bodies: what materials are present, how the component materials are uniquely organized in the living body, and how these components interact to generate the activities that are recognized as life. Just as the chemist or the physicist probes into the visible and subvisible structure of nonliving matter in seeking to understand the mechanism of its behavior, so the biologist, using essentially the same methods, investigates the ultimate structure of living matter, which is called **protoplasm.**

Protoplasm. The phenomena of life never find complete expression except in association with a particular kind of matter, namely protoplasm.

Typically protoplasm is a colorless, translucent, gelatinous fluid, which composes the living part of every living thing. All other parts of any living body—bone, cartilage, wood, etc.—are produced by the protoplasmic parts. **Protoplasm,** therefore, must be regarded as the *physical basis of life,* or, more simply, it may be referred to as **living matter.** In the ultimate composition and structure of protoplasm, the answers to life's unique riddles must be sought.

Chemical Structure. Protoplasm is not a single homogeneous substance. Rather, it is a complexly organized system in which many substances are present. Some of these substances, such as water and mineral salts, are also abundant in nonliving nature. But protoplasm is especially characterized by its rich variety of **organic substances,** especially **proteins,** which are found nowhere *in nature* except as components or products of protoplasm. The manifold chemical compounds of the protoplasm are constantly reacting and interacting. This ebb and flow of chemical activity, which is called **metabolism,** generates energy and provides for the synthesis of more organic compounds, needed as growth occurs. Moreover, the complex physical and chemical structure of protoplasm is *not stable.* It tends to disintegrate and become disorganized unless energy is constantly available for reconstruction. Just as an airplane cannot maintain altitude unless energy is available from the combustion of fuel in the motors, so the protoplasmic structure undergoes degradation unless energy is forthcoming from metabolism. The ultimate sources of metabolic energy may vary considerably in different forms of life (Chap. 9), but energy for immediate use is provided by a set of basic metabolic reactions that seem to be common to all protoplasm (Chap. 8).

Modern biologists now recognize that the physics and chemistry of protoplasm represent vitally important areas, and many research workers are active in these fields. Considerable attention will therefore be given to protoplasmic structure, particularly in Chapters 4 and 5.

Cellular Structure. It is generally recognized that protoplasm seldom, if ever, occurs in the form of any large continuous mass. Rather, it is subdivided into small unit masses, called **cells,** which usually are microscopic in dimension. Moreover, the protoplasm of every typical cell consists of two complementary and mutually dependent parts: a more or less central mass, the **nucleus** and a surrounding part, the **cytoplasm.** Both of these parts of the protoplasm possess an essentially similar chemical composition, except that certain of the proteins, namely the *DNA-nucleoproteins* (p. 90), are *distinctive of the nucleus.* This is a very important distinction, and will be explored more fully later (Chaps. 4, 8, and 27).

Each cell, essentially, is a living unit. Some small forms of life consist each of a single cell, and larger plants and animals are composed of many cells, variously modified according to their special functions in different parts of the body. Regardless of whether they are unicellular or multicellular, however, each specifically distinctive kind of living creature is designated as an **organism.**

Recognition of the **cell principle** (Chap. 2) did not reach full maturity until late in the nineteenth century. Nevertheless, this principle has had tremendous impact upon modern biology. Whatever activity is exhibited by a multicellular organism in performing the functions of responsiveness, growth, and reproduction represents the sum total of the activities of the component cells, working together as a beautifully integrated team. Accordingly, Part One of this book (Chaps. 1 to 11) will deal with single cells. This Part will attempt to analyze the structure and behavior of various basic cell types; the remaining Parts will be concerned mainly with the integrated behavior of the component cells of higher plant and animal organisms.

In the present century, particularly during the past 20 years, great advances have occurred that have enriched our knowledge of cellular structure and function. We now begin to understand the significance of many intracellular structures, or organelles. We know quite a bit about how **chromosomes** (p. 23) are constituted and how they are able to transmit coded directions in each cell; what the **nucleolus** (p. 23) is and how it is concerned with the synthesis of specific proteins in each cell; the nature of the **mito-**chondria** (p. 28), **ribosomes** (p. 25), and the **endoplasmic reticulum** (p. 23); and what roles these structures play in physiological activity. These and many other questions are being probed intensively by research workers throughout the world today. Final answers, of course, cannot be given, but the current status of the more important developments will be discussed in several later chapters.

All unequivocally living forms display a cellular structure, but there are some borderline cases, which must be mentioned now. These include two groups of exceedingly small infectious bodies—the **Rickettsia** (p. 580) and the **viruses.** Here, however, only the viruses will be discussed.

VIRUSES

Viruses are disease-inducing particles that are exceedingly small—so small in fact that their structure cannot be revealed by any type of light microscope (Fig. 2-10). Yet viruses display some properties that elsewhere are found only in association with living cells. It may be necessary, therefore, to qualify our concepts of the living unit, in light of further knowledge.

Ever since the dawn of biological curiosity, when the early cave men first began to draw pictures of the plants and animals that shared their environment, man has continued to discover and record new forms of life. Before the seventeenth century, when the microscope first revealed a whole new world of living minutiae, generation after generation of protozoans, bacteria, and other microscopic forms had lived and died without the blessing of man's cognizance. The biologists of that day were slow to admit these new organisms into the fraternity of life, and many years of research and controversy followed before the microorganisms were recognized generally. Today, it is the viruses that seem to lie at the boundary line between the living and the nonliving. If biologists finally conclude that the viruses are alive, then it will have to be admitted that a continuous intergradation exists between nonliving and living forms of matter.

The first virus was discovered by Iwanowski in 1892. Iwanowski found that juice squeezed from a tobacco plant afflicted with mosaic disease (Fig. 1-3), after passing through

Fig. 1-3. A tobaco leaf infected with the mosaic virus. Note the dark diseased patches, which give the leaf a spotted (mosaic) appearance. (Courtesy of L. O. Kunkel, The Rockefeller Institute for Medical Research, New York.)

an extremely fine porcelain filter, still could give rise to the disease if brought into contact with a healthy plant. This was surprising since the clear filtered juice did not contain any particles large enough to be seen with any existing microscope. Previously in the nineteenth century, Pasteur, Koch, Reed, and others had demonstrated that many diseases in plants and animals are caused by microscopic parasites—such as bacteria and protozoans—which invade the tissues of other plants or animals. But in the present century it soon became apparent that other diseases must involve infective bodies much

smaller and simpler than any known microorganism. Now, in fact, a fairly large number of virus diseases are recognized. These include smallpox, infantile paralysis, influenza, the common cold, and measles, for man; swine influenza, hog cholera, and bovine hoof and mouth disease for other animals; and the bacteriophages (Fig. 1-4) and mosaic infections of plants.

One unique feature of the viruses is the extreme smallness of the individual particles, each of which can be identified as being a complete virus unit. If one takes a fluid containing bacteria and forces this fluid through a porcelain filter (ultrafilter), the filtrate obtained is found to be sterile, that is, entirely free of bacteria. Apparently the pores of such a filter are so small that they prevent the bacteria from passing through. If, however, one ultrafilters a fluid containing the particles of a virus—such as the juice that can be squeezed from a tobacco plant infected with the tobacco mosaic disease, or the fluid derived from the brain of a monkey infected with infantile paralysis—the virus appears in the filtrate, quite undiminished in quantity.

Growth and Reproduction. Another important characteristic of the viruses is that each possesses, under the proper conditions, an unlimited capacity for growth and reproduction. Take, for example, the virus that gives rise to infantile paralysis in man and certain monkeys. This virus can be transmitted from monkey to monkey in endless succession, without any sign of limit. The smallest quantity of fluid from the brain of a diseased animal, implanted into the brain of a healthy monkey, leads in due time to paralytic symptoms in the inoculated animal. During the **incubation period,** the original minute quantity of virus increases to a tremendous extent. The virus spreads throughout all parts of the nervous system. Finally, every small fraction of the brain of the newly paralyzed animal contains as much of the virus as was originally introduced into the one localized site of injection.

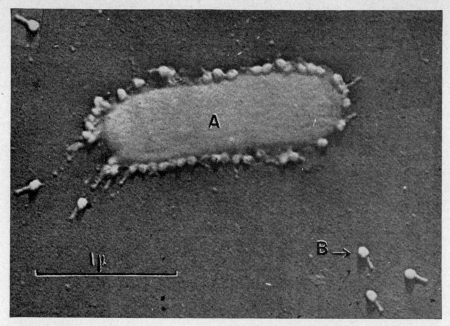

Fig. 1-4. An electronmicrograph showing a single bacterial cell (A) surrounded by many particles of bacteriophage (B). The marker (1 micron) shows the extremely small size of the bacterium *(Escherichia coli)* and the still smaller size of the bacteriophage particles (strain T$_2$). The bacteriophage destroys the bacterium when it penetrates the cell. In the present case, however, the clustering of the bacteriophage particles at the surface of the bacterium has resulted from drying the preparation—which must be done before an electronmicrograph can be taken. These specimens were shadow-cast with gold. (Courtesy of T. F. Anderson, University of Pennsylvania.)

Isolation of a Virus. In 1935 one of the viruses, the **tobacco mosaic virus,** was isolated and identified by W. M. Stanley, then at the Rockefeller Institute in New York City. To separate the virus from the many inactive components present in the total juice from an infected tobacco plant, two stages of centrifuging were employed. First, an ordinary low-speed centrifuge was used to remove all larger particles, such as bacteria and other microscopically visible bodies. This left a perfectly clear supernatant fluid that retained its infective potency in full strength. The second centrifuge was of the high-speed type, called an **ultracentrifuge.** Such a machine can develop centrifugal forces of about half a million times gravity. When a solution is subjected to this force, the larger **molecular** components tend to be thrown out of solution and to accumulate at the bottom of the

test tube. In the present case, the sedimented material proved to be the virus in a practically pure condition. In other words, this sample of virus was practically free from contamination by any inactive materials. After further simple chemical treatment, the virus was obtained in the form of **crystals** (Fig. 1-5)

Fig. 1-5. Crystals of tobacco mosaic virus (× 675). Each crystal represents an aggregate of *many* virus particles. (Courtesy of W. M. Stanley, University of California.)

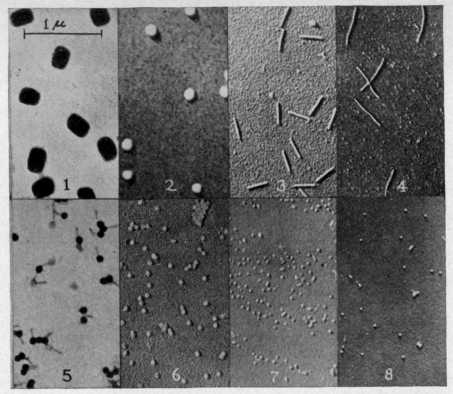

Fig. 1-6. The unit particles of different viruses vary considerably as to size and shape; and in some cases, more than one kind of molecule is represented in each virus particle. Electronmicrographs: 1. vaccinia virus, from smallpox vaccine; 2. influenza virus; 3. tobacco mosaic virus; 4. potato mosaic virus; 5. bacteriophage; 6. virus of the Shope papilloma; 7. southern bean mosaic virus; 8. bushy stunt virus of tomato. All except 1 and 5 were shadow-cast with gold. This technique permits the depth of each particle to be appreciated. (Courtesy of C. A. Knight, University of California.)

that displayed a high degree of purity. Each crystal, however, consists not of one virus particle, but of many, arranged in the orderly pattern of a **crystal structure.**

Unit Structure. Analysis of the isolated tobacco mosaic virus crystals proved that the disease is transmitted by extremely small unit particles (Fig. 1-6) composed, essentially, of a single kind of substance, **nucleoprotein.**[1]

[1] Nucleoprotein molecules are formed by combination between **nucleic acid** and **protein** (p. 83). However, two general kinds of nucleic acid are known: (1) DNA (deoxyribonucleic acid) and (2) RNA (ribonucleic acid), each having a slightly different chemical structure. The RNA proteins are present in the cytoplasm as well as in the nuclei of cells generally; but the DNA proteins, of which genes are composed, are restricted (except for viruses) almost entirely to nuclei.

The nucleic acid fraction of most viruses has proved to be of the DNA (deoxyribonucleic acid) type. Throughout all nature, such DNA proteins are recognized as the most essential components represented in the structure of the **genes,** the instruments of hereditary transmission in all organisms. The DNA proteins, indeed, show two very unique and important characteristics. Each is capable of engineering self-synthesis by providing a template that guides the synthesis of its own structure (p. 522). And in addition, the DNA elements of the cell may provide templates for the synthesis of other substances (Chap. 27).

The unit particles of different viruses are generally too small to be seen with any light microscope, but they can be resolved by the electron microscope (Fig. 1-6). Among viruses with spherical particles, the diameters range from about 17 millimicrons (mμ) for the alfalfa mosaic virus, to about 225 millimicrons (Fig. 1-6) for the vaccinia (cowpox) virus (used for vaccinations against smallpox in man). In some cases (for example, human influenza virus), traces of lipid (p. 80) and carbohydrate (p. 76) compounds are present, in addition to the nucleoprotein; and generally speaking the protein fraction of the particles is localized at the surface, forming a sort of envelope surrounding the nucleic acid.

Virus particles are much smaller and simpler than bacterial cells, which are perhaps the smallest cells. The bacterial cell is several thousand times larger and it contains a wide variety of chemical components—water, inorganic salts, lipids, and carbohydrates—in addition to proteins and nucleoproteins. In short, bacteria show a fairly typical protoplasmic structure. The simplest virus, on the other hand, may be a single large molecule of nucleoprotein or, at most, a complex of relatively few molecules. Consequently, if it ever is proved that viruses are truly alive, it will have to be admitted that the simplest forms of life are not much more complex than certain inanimate kinds of matter.

Are Viruses Alive? The crux of the question as to whether the viruses are truly alive lies in the fact that no virus has ever displayed any capacity for growth and replication, *except when the virus is inside some well-recognized kind of living cell*. When a virus particle makes contact with the proper kind of living cell, penetration occurs, but only the DNA fraction actually enters (p. 524). In the cell, the viral DNA rapidly undergoes self-replication and less than an hour later, usually, the amount of viral DNA has increased more than a hundredfold. Viral protein then begins to appear and the multiplication of complete viral particles has been achieved (p. 525). In other words, viral DNA, inside the host cell, behaves like a foreign gene, usurping the material that ordinarily would be used in the replication of the normal genes of the host cell itself (p. 522). The virus appears to provide a pattern that activates certain molecules present in the host cell to assemble and unite in such a way as to form new virus. Indeed, it sometimes happens that a certain virus may become incorporated into a chromosome of a host cell and thus be carried from cell generation to generation quite indefinitely.

The foregoing observations make it doubtful that the growth and replication of viruses represent a truly independent type of reproduction, such as is characteristic of living things generally. On the other hand, certain bacteria are obligatory parasites, which never reproduce except within some living host; yet no one is inclined to doubt the living status of these forms. Certainly viral replication bears a very close resemblance to genic replication (p. 522), which is an integral part of reproduction in all organisms. Many unsuccessful attempts[2] have been made to cultivate viruses and to induce them to reproduce in some medium in which no living cells are present. But unless or until such cultivation is achieved, we must continue to regard the viruses as more or less transitional between the living and nonliving forms of matter.

THE PROGRESS OF SCIENCE

A *science* is a systematically organized body of knowledge, based upon precise unbiased observation and integrated by logical reasoning. To the fullest possible extent, scientific knowledge is checked and counterchecked by carefully planned and strictly controlled experiments.

Without special training in scientific research, man has always been quite helpless in trying to understand the nature of his universe. In very early times man depended

[2] A recent report indicates that viral growth and replication has been observed in a cell-free medium. However, preformed DNA, extracted from cells, was provided in this medium.

upon superstition to cover his ignorance of natural events; and this led to the creation of many gods: of the wind, the sun, the harvest, and so forth. But even at the dawn of civilization, some capacity for accurate observation was gradually developing, as can be seen in the records of animal and plant life that the cave dwellers painted by torchlight on the walls of their ancient homes (Fig. 1-7).

during the past 75 years—well within the memory of our fathers and grandfathers—research laboratories have developed in every important university, in every industry, and in every part of the world. This new group of workers has been carefully trained in the scientific method, and has widely extended the frontiers of natural science. Consequently the present-day student of biology, chemistry, physics, or other science begins work with a

Fig. 1-7. Scientific observation began in prehistoric times. Cro-Magnon artists in the Cavern of Font de Gaume. (Courtesy of the American Museum of Natural History, New York.)

Early civilized men, especially the Egyptians, Greeks, and Romans, began to use direct observation rather than superstitious tradition as the basis of their thinking. In fact the ancients began to test their conclusions by experiment, and many roots of our scientific knowledge can be traced back into the classical period.

But the scientific attitude did not survive. After the decline of the Romans, superstition prevailed again for almost fourteen centuries. The scant scientific knowledge that survived the Dark Ages was "second hand" —passed on from generation to generation, chiefly by the medieval monks.

During the Renaissance, much of the ancient learning was revived, and science began to gain a new momentum. Gradually the scientific method came into its own. Especially

double heritage. He receives not only a large fund of knowledge, tested by the scientists of every nation, but also a most useful tool—the fully developed *method of science*.

The Scientific Method. Unquestionably, trial-and-error procedures play an important part in all research, especially in the early exploratory stages. Behind these probings, however, there usually stands a well-defined plan, in which the reasoning is *partly inductive* and *partly deductive*. The scientific method involves *four steps*—and the same steps are taken over and over again, as new ground is being gained and tested.

1. Observation. The primary basis of all scientific thinking is observation—precisely quantitative and, above all, *unbiased* by any preconception as to the significance of the observed data. Nowadays especially, the observation may be somewhat indirect, involving complex instruments and calculations, but the scientist must never be guilty of weighting the data in favor of his preconceptions. A current hypothesis or theory may serve to indicate an area where further observations are needed and to determine the nature of the needed experiments, but it must never be allowed to warp the observations.

2. *Interpretation.* The second step in the research technique is to formulate a logical explanation of the observed data. This involves setting up a tentative *hypothesis.* The hypothesis is usually broader than the data from which it is *induced,* and consequently the hypothesis must remain tentative until further observation either confirms or denies its validity.

3. *Prediction.* This third step of the scientific method requires that predictions be *deduced* from the working hypothesis. On the basis of such predictions new experiments are suggested for testing the hypothesis in question. If the predictions are verified by the experiments, the hypothesis is strengthened; if not, the hypothesis must be modified or discarded.

4. *Experimentation.* Each experiment is calculated to test the predictions that are deduced from a particular hypothesis. The experiment is so designed that it yields a single answer regarding the prediction in question. Accordingly, each experiment must be accompanied by a *control* in which all of the factors, except the one being investigated, are duplicated in the *strictest possible* fashion.

Experimental Control. Assume, for example, that it is necessary to test a simple hypothesis: that the loss of consciousness experienced by an aviator at high altitude depends upon a scarcity of oxygen. To prove this, it is necessary to subject the aviator to an experiment that rules out all other possibilities. At high altitude not only is the oxygen scarce, but the total atmospheric pressure and the temperature are greatly reduced. Moreover, there

may be accelerations and decelerations in the speed of flight. Therefore, to decide the issue, it is necessary to set up a control experiment, utilizing a plane equipped with a pressurized cabin, in which the temperature, the composition of the atmospheric gases, and other factors can be regulated. In the control experiment, the temperature and total air pressure would have to be lowered to the level indicated by the altitude in question, while at the same time the available oxygen would be maintained at the normal value, and the velocity of flight and other conditions would be the same as when the original blackout occurred. Under these conditions consciousness would not be lost. Consequently it could be concluded that the hypothesis was sound, and that unconsciousness does in fact depend upon a *scarcity of oxygen.*

Hypothesis, Theory, and Principle. The scientific method may be illustrated more completely by considering an early hypothesis—as to the nature of *combustion,* or burning. This **phlogiston hypothesis** held favor prior to the discovery of oxygen by Lavoisier in 1776.

The phlogiston hypothesis held that combustible material, such as wood, contains an unknown gaseous substance, called **phlogiston,** which begins to escape as soon as a material is heated sufficiently to begin burning. The hypothesis was based upon certain observations: something (the flame) appears to escape from the burning body, and the ash, or remnant of combustion, usually has a lesser weight than the unburned material. But one deducible prediction of this hypothesis is that every material must be lighter after burning; and this prediction cannot be verified by all experiments. Some materials, such as magnesium, i.e., the foil which burns with glaring speed in a photographic flashlight bulb, show an increase of weight after combustion. The ash, magnesium oxide (MgO), is significantly heavier than the unburned magnesium (Mg). In view of such exceptions, it became necessary to discard the phlogiston hypothesis. Then, with the discovery of oxygen, a new hypothesis—the **oxidation hypothesis**—was formulated. This hypothesis was tested by countless experiments that extended through many years. Gradually the oxidation hypothesis received sufficient confirmation to be called a *theory,* and finally the **oxidation principle** has taken its place as one of the established and fundamental *laws,* or *principles,* of chemical science.

The Biological Sciences. In a broad sense, all phases of science that deal with life and living things lie within the province of biology. However, it is customary to separate the biological sciences into three parts: (1) sociology (L. *socius* = society, and Gr. *logos* = study), which deals with social behavior, especially in man; (2) psychology (Gr. *psyche* =

mind), which treats of individual behavior, likewise primarily in man; and (3) biology (Gr. *bios* = life), which embraces all other vital phenomena.

Biology proper is further subdivided in complex fashion, as is shown diagrammatically in Figure 1-8. However, this diagram fails to show many of the more detailed subdivisions: bacteriology, protozoology, etc., which correspond to the various groups in the plant and animal kingdoms (see Appendix I).

Values of Biology. The study of biology provides a foundation for many specialized professions. In medicine or dentistry, for example, every phase of the training—every subject in the medical and dental curricula—is essentially a part of biology. Unless these spe-

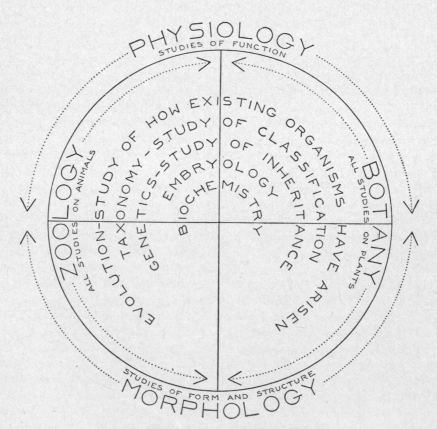

Fig. 1-8. Main subdivisions of biological science.

cial trainings are rooted in a sound conception of *general principles,* the practitioner lacks a background for critical judgment and proceeds by rule of thumb. Likewise in many other fields—in forestry, agriculture, and horticulture; in animal and plant breeding; in veterinary medicine and in the work of the fisheries—biology has great practical value.

Above and beyond the practical uses of biology, however, there lies an even more important realm of values—the contributions of biological sciences to human thinking and philosophy. All of science provides a challenge to man's intellect, but the ideas of biological sciences have a uniquely direct bearing upon our concepts of origin and destiny, and upon how that destiny may be guided and achieved.

Continuity of Life. Nonliving matter is continually converted into living matter by constructive metabolism; and living matter is continually reconverted into lifeless matter by destructive metabolism and by the death of organisms. But so far as we know, nonliving matter is converted into living matter only in intimate association with existing protoplasm—that is, in living organisms. In this present geological age, living organisms are known to originate only from other living organisms, by the processes of reproduction. It seems logically inevitable that living matter must have originated, in the remote past, from nonliving matter, without the intervention of previously living matter, but the evidence as to how and under what conditions this happened, is rather scanty.

TEST QUESTIONS

1. Specify the activities that are generally exhibited by living things. To what extent are these activities limited to living things?
2. Explain in what manner the "growth" of a crystal differs from the growth of typical living bodies.
3. Name three viruses and explain how the simplest viruses differ *structurally* from small living organisms such as bacteria.
4. Why is it necessary to reserve judgment in deciding whether the viruses are alive? Explain carefully.
5. Explain why control experiments are very important, exemplifying the discussion by a specific example.
6. Differentiate among hypothesis, theory, and principle, using specific examples.
7. Explain why hypotheses are important in scientific research.
8. Give a careful definition for each of the following terms: (a) life; (b) protoplasm; (c) biology; (d) nutrition; (e) responsiveness; (f) reproduction; (g) metabolism; (h) ultramicroscopic structure.
9. What is the basis of the statement that "protoplasm displays an unstable structure"?

FURTHER READINGS

1. *The Virus: Life's Enemy,* by K. M. Smith; New York, 1948.
2. *The Physics and Chemistry of Life,* a collection of articles from *Scientific American;* New York, 1955.
3. *Science and Common Sense,* by J. B. Conant; New Haven, 1951.

2-Protoplasm, the Cell, and the Organism

UNTIL about 125 years ago, very little was known about cells. Since then, however, biologists have come to realize that the living parts of all definitely living things are composed of cells—one or a few in smaller organisms and many millions in larger forms such as man (Figs. 2-1 and 2-2). This **cell principle** (p. 38) has had tremendous influence upon all phases of biology. Accordingly, the basic organization of this text centers around the form and function of cells, taken individually and in highly organized groups.

THE CELL

The cell may be defined as an organized unit mass of protoplasm, consisting of two complementary, mutually dependent parts: a more or less central part, the **nucleus,** and a surrounding part, the **cytoplasm.** Generally the nucleus is delimited from the surrounding cytoplasm by an exceedingly delicate **nuclear membrane** (Fig. 2-2) and the cytoplasm is bounded externally by a specialized

layer, also very thin and delicate, which is called the **plasma membrane.** However, in addition to these **intrinsic membranes,** which are specialized parts of the protoplasm proper, most cells are covered by a layer of relatively inert material, which stabilizes the protoplasmic surface. The composition of such **extrinsic,** or **nonprotoplasmic** cell coverings varies according to cell type (p. 33). But regardless of type, the boundary membrane of a cell, consisting of the plasma membrane plus such extrinsic material as may be present, is often referred to as the **cell membrane.**

Some small primitive unicellular organisms, especially the **blue-green algae** (p. 594), do not seem to show a distinct segregation of nuclear and cytoplasmic materials (Fig. 2-3). In such cells, the DNA proteins—a kind of material that in other cells is confined within the nucleus—appears to be scattered throughout the cytoplasm in the form of numerous fine granules, called **chromidia.** In other words, these cells contain nuclear material,

16

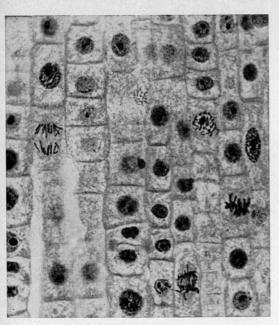

Fig. 2-1. Photomicrograph of typical cells in a stained section of the root of an onion plant. Note that each nucleus appears as a dark round body surrounded by the lighter cytoplasm. In a few cells the nuclei are not in focus. Also some of the cells are dividing, in which case the chromosomes (p. 41) are visible. (Copyright, General Biological Supply House, Inc.)

but no nuclear membrane segregates this from the cytoplasm. Some caution is necessary, however, because these cells are extremely small and the details of their structure are difficult to observe. Until about 10 years ago it was generally believed that bacterial cells possessed such a **chromidial structure,** but now it is recognized that most, if not all, bacteria do have definitive nuclei.

Another relatively rare condition is displayed by the **slime molds** (p. 602), certain green algae (p. 596), and the fibers of the **skeletal** type of muscle (Fig. 15-14). In these cases, no limiting membranes are found separating the individual "cells." Rather, several nuclei are enveloped within a common mass of cytoplasm. Such an atypical arrangement is called a **syncytium** (Fig. 2-4). Some biologists have designated both of these atypical conditions —whether chromidial or syncytial in nature —as "noncellular." But it seems more logical to regard them as variations of the normal

protoplasmic pattern, differing from the usual mainly in the lack of limiting membranes—between the nucleus and cytoplasm in the first case and between adjacent cells in the second. In any event, extensive evidence is available (p. 34) showing that no "cell" can long endure or carry on all of its vital activities in the complete absence of either its nuclear or cytoplasmic components (p. 35). The nucleus and cytoplasm, therefore, must be regarded as complementary, mutually dependent parts of one protoplasmic unit, namely the cell.

The Size of Cells. A great majority of cells are too small to be seen with the naked eye, which can resolve an object only if the diameter is not less than about 0.1 millimeter (mm). However, most cells can be seen plainly with the microscope, which extends the range of vision a thousandfold—down to diameters of about 0.1 micron (μ). Many bacteria— which are among the smallest cells—lie at the very lowest limit of microscopic visibility (Figs. 2-5 and 2-6). At the other extreme, the largest single cells are the egg cells of birds. This kind of cell—which popularly is designated as the "yolk of the egg"—may measure more than 3 centimeters (cm) in diameter, as in the case of the ostrich egg. But such examples are quite rare. Most cells, in both plants and animals, have dimensions between 1 and 100 microns, and thus most cells lie definitely within the range of the compound microscope.

There is a natural limit to the growth of any cell. To support metabolism the cell must be able to obtain an adequate supply of oxygen and other foods, and to give off carbon dioxide and other wastes fast enough to avoid accumulation. These necessary exchanges between the cell and the environment can occur only at the surface of the cell, whereas metabolic activity pervades the entire protoplasmic mass. Consequently, the surface of the cell must be kept adequately large in proportion to the protoplasmic volume. But as a cell grows larger, particularly if its shape is compact and rounded, the

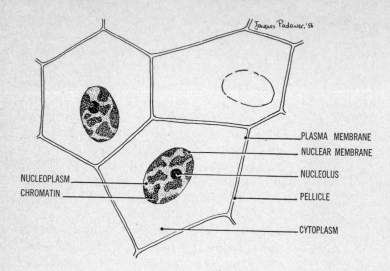

Jacques Padawer, '56

PLASMA MEMBRANE
NUCLEAR MEMBRANE
NUCLEOLUS
NUCLEOPLASM
CHROMATIN
PELLICLE
CYTOPLASM

Fig. 2-2. A typical animal cell.

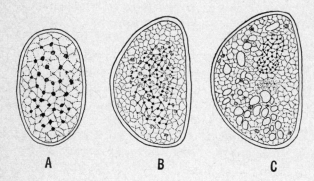

A   B   C

Fig. 2-3. In a few primitive cells the nuclear and cytoplasmic materials are not separated very distinctly; that is, no distinct nuclear membrane is present. In this case the chromatin granules, or **chromidia** (the most darkly shaded particles in the cells), are more or less scattered throughout the cytoplasm. A, B, and C, cells of different blue-green algae, showing transitional stages in the development of the delimited type of nucleus. (After Acton.)

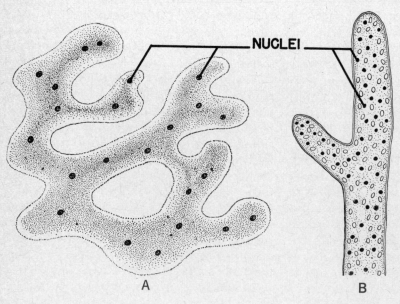

NUCLEI

Fig. 2-4. Syncytial organisms: A, a slime mold, with many nuclei scattered through the continuous mass of cytoplasm. B, small portion of filament of a green alga, with many nuclei and chloroplasts scattered through the continuous cytoplasm.

A   B

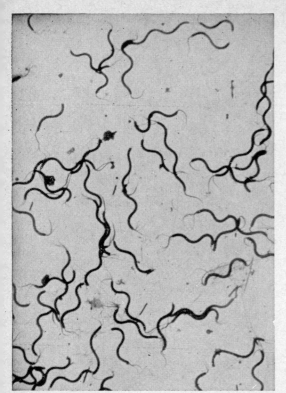

Fig. 2-5. Stained bacteria at a magnification of about 1000 diameters. (Copyright, General Biological Supply House, Inc.)

proportion of surface to volume steadily diminishes. In a sphere, for example, the surface increases merely as the square of the diameter, whereas the volume increases in proportion to the cube of the diameter. Accordingly, when a cell grows larger, it reaches a natural limit when its surface area becomes too small in proportion to its volume. This limit varies according to each particular cell shape and according to the intensity of metabolism. But when the limit is reached, the cell must either stop growing or it must divide.

The Form of Cells. Different cells assume a great variety of shapes: spherical or oval; fixed or changeable; flat or elongate; spindle-shaped or lobose; polyhedral or cylindrical; and so forth. But generally speaking, the form of each cell bears a distinct relation to its particular function. *Nerve cells,* for example, are elongate and branched, a form that enables the cells to conduct impulses from one part of the body to another (Fig. 2-7); or *epithelial cells*—which cover the surfaces of the body—take the form of overlapping tiles, as in the skin of many animals, or of variously shaped bricks, as in the lining of man's digestive tract (Fig. 2-8).

Likewise among plant cells *form varies according to function.* **Root hair cells** (Fig. 2-9), for example, collectively constitute a specialized surface layer, or **epidermis,** which covers the root in the region where the plant absorbs water and mineral salts from the soil. The *body* of a root hair cell is bricklike, and the many separate "bricks" fit together, covering the surface of the root. But each root hair cell also displays an elongate outgrowth —the *root hair proper.* Each root hair extends out among the particles of soil, making contact with the soil water. Thus the special form of the root hair cells enables them to perform a double function. Collectively they provide an epidermis for the outer surface of the root, and at the same time they absorb substances from the soil water. In fact, without root hairs the absorbing surface of the root would be reduced by almost 90 percent.

Regardless of their shape, all cells tend to become rounded into droplike spheres, if freed from various restraining factors. This behavior results from the fact that protoplasm is essentially a *liquid system.* All small liquid masses—such as droplets of mercury or water—behave in this fashion. The rounding results from surface forces that act in the boundary layers of liquids generally. The surface forces in protoplasm are small, relative to those acting upon a drop of water exposed to the air. But the typical cell is a microscopic mass, and most cells do become rounded like other liquids, unless there are restraining factors.

Many cells are rounded and droplike when first they are formed by cell division, and such cells must expend energy when they distort themselves into another shape. But after a cell has assumed its final form it may retain this shape in a variety of ways. It may

SIZE RANGE	KIND OF CELL OR PARTICLE AT STATED MAGNIFICATIONS	ACTUAL DIMENSIONS
MACROSCOPIC (NAKED EYE) ABOVE 0.1 MILLIMETER (mm) i.e. ABOVE 100 MICRONS (μ)	EGG CELL (HEN) 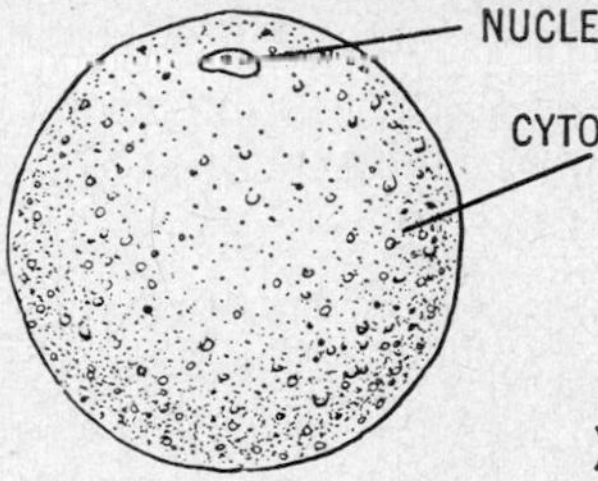 NUCLEUS CYTOPLASM x 1 EGG CELL (FROG)	ACTUAL DIAM. = 3 CENTIMETERS (cm) = 30 mm ACTUAL DIAM. = 1.75 mm
MICROSCOPIC (LIGHT MICROSCOPE) 100 MICRONS (100 μ) DOWN TO ABOUT 0.1 MICRON (0.1 μ)	AMOEBA 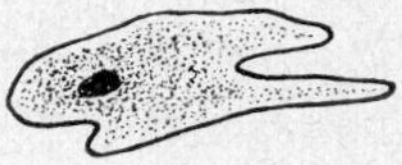 x 100 RED BLOOD CELL  x 1000 TYPHOID BACILLUS  x 10,000	ACTUAL LENGTH AVERAGES ABOUT 250 MICRONS (0.25 mm) ACTUAL DIAM. = 7-8 MICRONS ACTUAL LENGTH = 2 MICRONS
ULTRAMICROSCOPIC (ELECTRON MICROSCOPE) BELOW 0.1 MICRON, DOWN TO 0.001 μ = 1 MILLIMICRON (m μ)	ONE OF THE SMALLEST BACTERIA (BACTERIUM PNEUMOSINTES)  x 100,000 INFLUENZA VIRUS  x 100,000	ACTUAL LENGTH = 0.2 μ 200 mμ ACTUAL DIAM. = 60 mμ

Fig. 2-6. Relative sizes and size ranges of various cells and particles. The smallest unit used in biology is an Ångstrom (Å), which is equal to 0.1 millimicron.

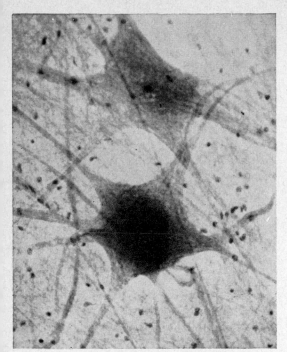

Fig. 2-7. Two nerve cells in the spinal cord. Each nerve fiber is an elongate extension from a particular nerve cell. Some fibers reach parts of the body several feet distant from the main part of the cell. The nuclei do not show clearly, due to overstaining. (Copyright, General Biological Supply House, Inc.)

surround itself with a rigid or semirigid non-living coating, which holds the protoplasm in a definite mold; or as with a few cells, it may construct a delicate internal skeleton that supports the protoplasm. Also, cells may be stabilized in shape by a gelling of the proto-

plasm (p. 94) or by pressure from surrounding cells.

Intracellular Structure. The various types of **light microscopes** available today (Fig. 2-10) enable one to observe the nucleus and other major intracellular structures in some detail; but the finer features of such structures cannot be resolved by any of these light-focusing instruments. **Cytologists,** who specialize in the study of cell structure, were greatly handicapped until quite recently, when the development of the **electron microscope** and associated techniques began to reach fruition.

The limit of resolution of a light microscope is reached when the diameter of any spherical or cylindrical structure falls slightly below 0.1 micron (Fig. 2-6). Specifically, resolution fails when the structural dimension diminishes to about half the wavelength of the type of radiation being utilized. Thus ultraviolet light, although not visible to the eye directly, permits a photographic resolution of fine structures down to about 0.06 micron. But the electron beam extends the resolution even further, down to about 0.0001 micron (1.0 millimicron). Today, therefore, the **fine structure,** or **ultrastructure,** of the protoplasmic parts can be examined, thus affording us a deeper understanding of the vital activities of living cells.

There are many pitfalls in cytology, however. Usually it is necessary to *kill* and *fix* the

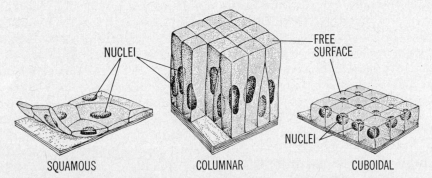

NUCLEI

FREE SURFACE

NUCLEI

SQUAMOUS   COLUMNAR   CUBOIDAL

Fig. 2-8. Note that epithelial cells display virtually no intercellular material and that they cover the surface very completely. The three types shown here are: the tall columnar epithelium; the cuboidal epithelium; and the scalelike or squamous epithelium.

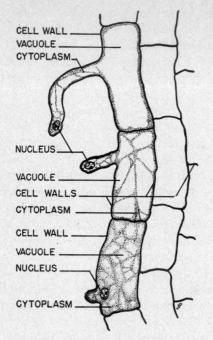

CELL WALL
VACUOLE
CYTOPLASM

NUCLEUS

VACUOLE
CELL WALLS
CYTOPLASM

CELL WALL
VACUOLE
NUCLEUS

CYTOPLASM

Fig. 2-9. Epidermal cells of root showing development of root hairs. Even the longest (uppermost) of these root hairs is not fully mature.

cell or tissue, using strong acids or toxic metals, in order to stabilize the labile protoplasmic pattern and to obtain sharp resolution of structure. In addition, the cells are frequently *stained* with special dyes, which differentially color the various protoplasmic parts. Tissues and other large masses of cells are too opaque for direct microscopic study, and such material must be cut into thin transparent slices, or **sections.** Electron microscopy not only requires that the cell be cut into exceedingly thin (usually less than 1.0 micron) sections, but also that the entire water content of the protoplasm be removed, in order to achieve an adequate transmission of the electron beam. Such drastic treatments, especially complete desiccation in vacuum, must alter the protoplasmic structure, leaving only a derivative of the original pattern. A study of these derivatives has proved most fruitful and informative, but it is always important to check and recheck such observations, comparing them, whenever possible, with studies on the living cell.

The Nucleus. In the living cell, the nucleus is hard to see, although usually a good microscopist can bring it into view. The difficulty arises from the fact that the nuclear and cytoplasmic parts of the protoplasm have many common properties. Typically both are colorless, transparent, and fluid and both have a broadly comparable chemical constitution (Chap. 4). Consequently it is not surprising to find that the optical differentiation between the nucleus and cytoplasm is often very slight.

When a nondividing cell is stained by any of the conventional techniques of cytology, the nucleus is plainly visible, since generally it takes on a deeper color than the cytoplasm (Fig. 2-1). Certain dyes, especially **hematoxylin,** display a distinct affinity for the nuclear materials. However, such nuclear dyes do not stain all parts of the nucleus with equal intensity. There appears to be a network of relatively more solid material that stains very intensely. Collectively this densely stainable material is referred to as **chromatin.** The chromatin network, however, appears to be suspended in a more fluid, nonstainable, **achromatic** material. One to several larger masses of chromatin material, the **nucleoli,** are usually found, closely associated with the chromatin network (Fig. 2-1).

The precise nature of the chromatin network of the nondividing nucleus remains somewhat debatable. However, considerable evidence (Chap. 27) indicates that the chromatin network is made up of a specific number of elongate threads looped and massed together in such a fashion that they give the appearance of a network. These threads are the **chromosomes** (p. 475). The chromatin material of the chromosomes consists, essentially, of nucleoproteins, especially DNA proteins, although some RNA proteins are also represented in the nucleus. DNA proteins occur in almost infinite variety, however, if we consider the precise pattern of their chemical structure (p. 521). In fact, the DNA proteins of each organism are uniquely distinctive of that organism. These, as we shall see, are the

genic materials. They mediate the transmission of heritable characteristics from generation to generation in the organism (Chap. 26). Each DNA unit possesses a remarkable capacity for determining its own synthesis, thus achieving *self*-replication (p. 522). Moreover each carries a *code of instructions* for the synthesis of other important components in the cell (Chap. 27).

At the time of **cell division** (Chap. 3), the elongate DNA-protein threads become tightly compacted into short rodlike bodies that are easy to recognize as chromosomes (Figs. 2-1 and 2-11A). By this time each thread has undergone replication, forming duplicate sister chromosomes, which still lie side by side (Fig. 2-11A). Then, as cell division proceeds, the duplicate chromosomes become separated from each other. Thus finally, when two new daughter cells have been formed, each receives one member of every pair of sister chromosomes. By this means the chromosomal and genic structures of the cell are perpetuated from generation to generation.

Between divisions the chromosomes energetically carry out their synthetic activities. The chromosomes become exceedingly elongate, each appearing as a delicate, complexly folded thread (Fig. 2-11B). In the uncoiled, elongate form, the chromosomes are more difficult to resolve. Moreover, since a number of such elongate threads are massed together within the confines of the nuclear membrane, it is very difficult to distinguish them individually.

DNA proteins occur almost exclusively as components of nuclei, or more particularly of chromosomes (except in the case of viruses). But RNA proteins (p. 525) are found both inside the nucleus and outside, in the surrounding cytoplasm. Both types of nucleoproteins display a generally similar chemical structure (p. 525). However, they can be distinguished on the basis of a very useful staining process, called the **Feulgen reaction.** DNA compounds, by virtue of their content of deoxyribose sugar (p. 80), yield a positive Feulgen coloration; whereas RNA compounds, in which the sugar constituent is ribose, are negative to the Feulgen reaction.

A considerable body of evidence indicates that the RNA components of the cell originate from the DNA elements. In fact DNA appears to provide a template (p. 134) for the synthesis of RNA. Temporarily, RNA may accumulate in or around a definitive center, the **nucleolus,** but eventually much of it is translocated into the cytoplasm (p. 526). The importance of RNA in relation to the synthesis of enzymes and other proteins in the cell will be considered later (p. 134).

Nucleoli are now generally recognized as definitive intranuclear organelles. Generally, nucleoli are Feulgen negative; the number present is fixed and definite in each kind of cell; they tend to disappear during each cell division; and new nucleoli originate at fixed points on specific chromosomes, after cell division has occurred.

Nuclei vary widely as to size, form, and position. Usually, however, the nucleus is rounded, and usually it lies near the center of the cell. The relative size of the nucleus also varies, from a small fraction to almost the whole cell volume. In any one kind of cell, however, the ratio between nuclear and cytoplasmic volumes appears to remain quite constant.

The Cytoplasm. All the protoplasm of a cell, exclusive of the nucleus, is the cytoplasm. Under a light microscope, the main part of the cytoplasm, which has been termed the **clear cytoplasmic matrix,** gives the appearance of an optically empty fluid, in which a variety of visible bodies—**mitochondria** (p. 28), **vacuoles** (p. 28), **fibrils** (p. 30), etc.—are suspended.

The term *clear cytoplasmic matrix,* although much used prior to the development of electron microscopy, is nonetheless misleading. The electron microscope shows that the so-called clear cytoplasm possesses a complex ultramicroscopic structure. This consists mainly of an elaborate system of exceedingly delicate interconnected double membranes, collectively called the **endoplasmic reticulum**

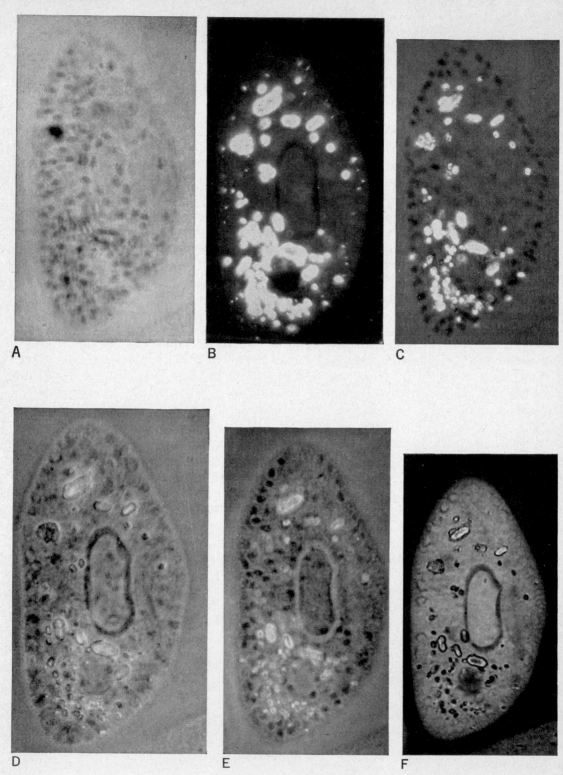

A

B

C

D

E

F

Fig. 2-10.

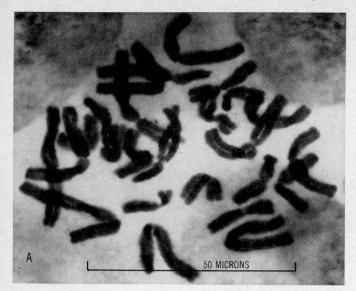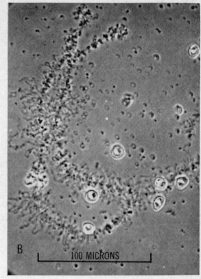

Fig. 2-11. Chromosomes from the cells of a newt (*Triturus cristatus carnifex*). A, compact, or shortened, form of the chromosomes, such as occurs during cell division. Note the pairs (sister chromosomes) that have originated by division. B, a pair of sister chromosomes (the smallest pair of A) after undergoing extension, or elongation (diplotene stage of meiosis). Active synthesis of RNA and protein (p. 524) occurs only while the chromosomes are thus "unfolded." The term "lampbrush chromosomes," often applied to such extended forms, is descriptive of the numerous looplike excrescences that come off from the central core of the chromosomal filament. (Courtesy of H. G. Callan, The University, St. Andrews, Scotland.)

(Fig. 2-12). Parts of this membrane system display a branching tubular form, but mainly it shows a pattern of numerous parallel double sheets, intricately connected with one another (Fig. 2-13). The total thickness of these double membranous sheets is only about 10 millimicrons, which, of course, precludes resolution by the ordinary microscope.

As will be apparent later (Chap. 8), the **endoplasmic reticulum** is of great importance. It provides the cell with an extensive system of surfaces (p. 95) upon which various enzymes may be localized in orderly pattern. Some of the foci of chemical activity, namely the **ribosomes,** can be identified in any good electronmicrograph of the endoplasmic reticulum. The ribosomes appear in prodigious number, as an array of electron-dense particles lined up in orderly series along the surfaces of the double membrane sheets (Figs. 2-12 and 2-13). Analysis shows that the ribosomes are composed in large part of RNA-protein material. Apparently they represent focal points for the synthesis of enzymes and other cytoplasmic protein compounds (p. 134).

Fig. 2-10 (facing). Various types of **light microscopy** are used in studying different features of cell structure. Same cell (*Paramecium bursaria*) photographed with different techniques; specimen fixed, but **not stained;** final magnification, $\times$ 900 to $\times$ 1000. A, ordinary brightfield: light transmitted vertically through the specimen. B, darkfield: light transmitted more or less horizontally across the specimen. C, polarizing microscope: polarized light transmitted vertically. D and E, phase-contrast microscopy: utilizes changes in the phase of light induced by transmission through the cell structures. F, interference microscopy: proper calibration of this instrument permits calculation of the density of the various cell parts. Note how the sharpness of the different structures varies with the technique; macronucleus, well defined in D, E, and F; refractile crystals, brightly shown in B and C; contractile vacuole (lower end) perhaps best shown in D; symbiotic algae (small round, dark bodies in periphery of cytoplasm) most clearly shown in C and E; gullet (curved structure to right of macronucleus) well defined only in F. (Photographs by Oscar W. Richards, Chief Biologist, American Optical Co.)

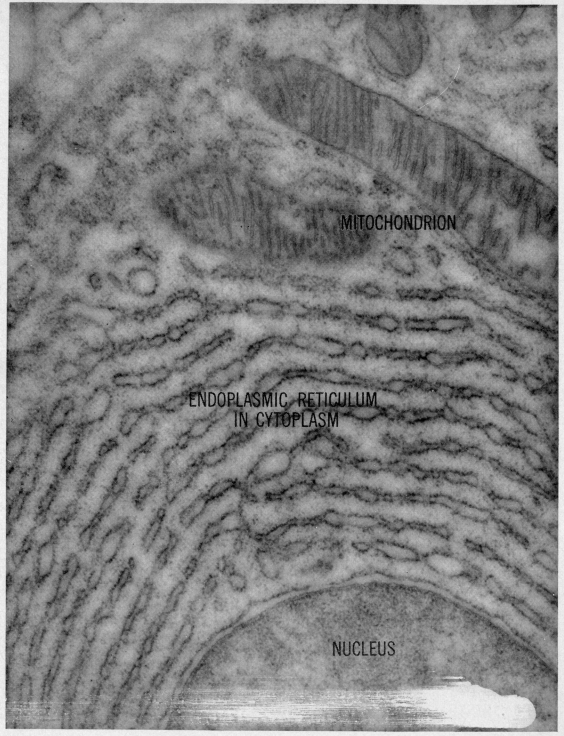

Fig. 2-12. Part of an animal cell (gland cell from pancreas of a guinea pig) as revealed by the electron microscope at relatively low magnification (40,000). (Courtesy of George E. Palade, The Rockefeller Institute, New York.)

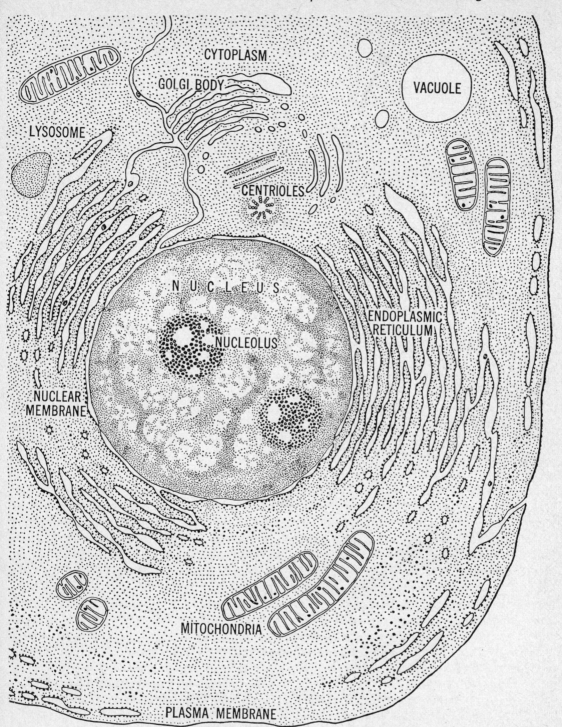

Fig. 2-13. Composite diagram of various intracellular structures that can be observed by electron microscopy. Compare this picture with the actual electronmicrograph shown in Figure 2-12. (Modified after J. Brachet; courtesy of *Scientific American*.)

Cytoplasmic Organelles. The organelles are structurally specialized parts of the cytoplasm in which certain of the activities of the cell are focalized. The **mitochondria** and **lysosomes** are stable structures, probably present in all cells; whereas **spindles, asters,** and, perhaps, **centrioles** appear only transiently, during cell division. **Vacuoles, plastids,** and **myofibrils,** on the other hand, are characteristic features found only in particular kinds of cells. All of these structures, except the lysosomes, can be seen under the light microscope, but it is necessary to use the electron microscope to resolve the details of their morphology.

Mitochondria. Usually several hundred of these sausage-shaped structures are in the cytoplasm of animal and plant cells generally. Prior to the development of electron microscopy, the mitochondria were differentiated from other small cytoplasmic bodies by virtue of their susceptibility to staining with a particular dye, *janus green.* Now, however, they are recognized on the basis of their uniquely characteristic ultrastructure (Fig. 2-12).

As may be seen in the electronmicrograph of Figure 2-12, or perhaps more clearly in the diagram of Figure 2-13, each **mitochondrion** is a vesicle bounded by a double membrane. The inner membrane displays numerous complexly arranged infoldings called **cristae.** As will be explained more fully later (Chap. 8), the mitochondria are very important organelles, especially with reference to the development of useful energy within the cell. The extensive, complexly organized membrane system of each mitochondrion provides for the patterned positioning of a whole group of oxidizing enzymes. These enzymes, working together as a team, maneuver a stepwise series of energy-yielding transactions (pp. 147 and 148).

Lysosomes. Definitive recognition of these somewhat smaller, usually round cytoplasmic vesicles, which are found in the cytoplasm of many, if not all, cells, came after the development of the electron microscope. Each lysosome (Fig. 2-13), unlike a mitochondrion, is bounded by a single membrane, and *no cristae are present.* At present, the evidence indicates that lysosomes are centers in which certain enzymes, especially **hydrolytic enzymes** (p. 102), are localized. Such enzymes may be useful to the cell, especially if reconstruction becomes necessary. The hydrolytic enzymes exert a disruptive action (p. 84) upon proteins and other large organic molecules. Presumably, therefore, they must be segregated and kept out of contact with other structures in the cytoplasm, except on special occasion.

Plastids. Typically, plastids are pigmented bodies of fixed and definite form. The most important and widely distributed kinds are the **chloroplasts** (Fig. 2-14), found in the cells of the green parts of all typical plants. The chloroplasts, with their content of the green pigment **chlorophyll,** are of tremendous importance in the economy of life. They enable plants to carry on **photosynthesis** (Chap. 9). By this process, light energy is trapped and utilized (indirectly) for the synthesis of glucose, and other organic compounds, from carbon dioxide and water (p. 161). This *primary type of organic synthesis* stores enormous amounts of energy. Eventually this energy is utilized, not only by the plants, but also by all other forms of life. Moreover, photosynthesis regenerates free oxygen, and thus it prevents a depletion of this important component of our atmosphere (Chap. 9).

Photosynthesis is not a simple process. Rather it is a complex series of interlinked reactions about which more and more is being discovered. Accordingly, it is not surprising to find that chloroplasts possess a complex internal ultrastructure, as may be seen in Figure 9.2. Inside each chloroplast are many smaller bodies, the **grana** (Fig. 9-3), each granum consisting of a system of complexly folded membranes (Fig. 9-3). Just how this highly organized system functions in coordinating and achieving the processes of photosynthesis is not entirely known, but some aspects of the problem will be considered in Chapter 9.

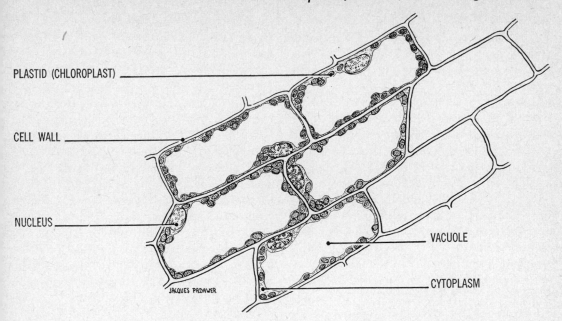

PLASTID (CHLOROPLAST)

CELL WALL

NUCLEUS

VACUOLE

CYTOPLASM

JACQUES PADAWER

Fig. 2-14. Living cells in a leaf of a plant.

Golgi Bodies. Golgi bodies are specialized areas of cytoplasmic structure that are seldom, if ever, found in plant cells; among animal cells, the **Golgi "apparatus"** is particularly conspicuous in gland cells. Usually the cell displays just one Golgi area, in the vicinity of the nucleus, differentiated on the basis of its susceptibility to staining with *neutral red* and on the basis of its ultrastructure (Fig. 2-13).

The Golgi body appears to be a specialized part of the endoplasmic reticulum. Probably it is concerned with the synthesis or elaboration of secretional products, which differ according to the particular kind of gland cell observed. Ribosomal granules appear to be absent from the boundary membranes of the Golgi organelle (Fig. 2-13).

Cytoplasmic Vacuoles. Vacuoles are of various kinds. In general, each is a fluid-filled vesicle with a definitive boundary membrane. However, certain vacuoles may contain one or more masses of solid material suspended in the fluid content.

Contractile Vacuoles. Contractile vacuoles are characteristic of one-celled *fresh-water* animals, such as *Amoeba*. In the amoeba (Fig.

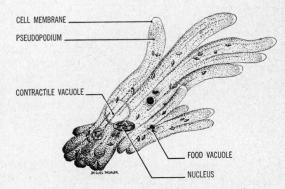

CELL MEMBRANE

PSEUDOPODIUM

CONTRACTILE VACUOLE

FOOD VACUOLE

NUCLEUS

JACQUES PADAWER

Fig. 2-15. *Amoeba, a unicellular animal.*

2-15) the contractile vacuole appears as a clear, round vesicle that gradually increases in size. Reaching a maximum, the contractile vacuole suddenly fades from view as it discharges its contents to the exterior of the cell. Apparently the contractile vacuole serves to extract water from the cytoplasm and to pump it outside the cell. This work must go on constantly, since water keeps entering the cell by osmosis (Chap. 6). Thus if the work of the contractile vacuole is stopped, as it may be by certain drugs, the amoeba begins to swell and finally it may reach the bursting point.

Cell Sap Vacuoles. Cell sap vacuoles are characteristic of large, *mature* plant cells (Figs. 2-9 and 14). Each is filled with **cell sap,** an aqueous solution of mineral salts. Frequently the large cell sap vacuole occupies all of the central part of the plant cell, so that the cytoplasm is limited to a relatively thin layer, between the vacuole and the cell wall (Fig. 2-14). Usually the nucleus lies in this thin, superficial layer of cytoplasm, although sometimes it is found at the center of the vacuole, surrounded by a small amount of cytoplasm and suspended by strands of cytoplasm that stretch across the vacuolar space (Fig. 2-16). Cell sap vacuoles play an important role in controlling the water balance in plant cells and tissues generally (Chap. 6).

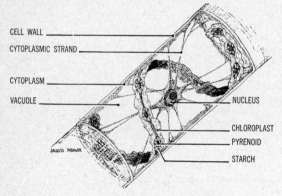

CELL WALL
CYTOPLASMIC STRAND
CYTOPLASM
VACUOLE
NUCLEUS
CHLOROPLAST
PYRENOID
STARCH

JACQUES PADAWER

Fig. 2-16.   One cell of *Spirogyra,* a colonial green alga.

Phagocytic and Pinocytic Vacuoles. Many cells are capable of engulfing materials from the fluids that surround them. Such active engulfment always involves an inpocketing of the surface membrane, followed by a pinching off into the surrounding cytoplasm of one or more vacuoles, of varying size, containing the engulfed material. If the engulfed material includes, in addition to fluid from the outside medium, microscopically visible solid material, such as bacteria or bits of organic matter, the process is called **phagocytosis** (literally "eating by the cell"). Such vacuoles are referred to as **phagocytic vacuoles,** or more simply as **food vacuoles** (Fig. 2-15). If

the entrapped fluid does not include any visible solid material, one speaks of **pinocytosis** (literally, "drinking by the cell") and the vacuoles are referred to as **pinocytic vacuoles** (Fig. 6-9).

Phagocytosis has been recognized as an important biological phenomenon since the latter part of the nineteenth century, when Metchnikoff, working at the Pasteur Institute in Paris, first observed the engulfment of bacteria by white blood-cells (Fig. 17-4). The formation of food vacuoles, indeed, represents the standard method by which amoebae (Figs. 7-1 and 7-2) and other one-celled animals ingest their food. In the food vacuoles, organic food substances are gradually digested, in preparation for absorption, from the vacuole cavity into the surrounding cytoplasm.

Pinocytosis, on the other hand, was not precisely described and named until 1931, when Warren H. Lewis of Johns Hopkins University recorded the process in tissue culture cells. It is difficult to observe pinocytosis because the tubular inpocketings (Fig. 6-9) are very delicate and the multiple pinocytic vacuoles, which pinch off internally, are very small. In fact, some cells develop channels and vacuoles that are of ultramicroscopic dimensions and cannot be demonstrated without the electron microscope. Probably pinocytosis represents an important mechanism by which cells take in substances of great molecular size, as will be discussed later (Chap. 6).

Fibrillar Structures. There are a variety of cytoplasmic structures that exhibit a pattern of precisely oriented threads, or fibrils, either microscopic or ultramicroscopic in dimension. These include **myofibrils** (p. 286), contractile elements demonstrable in all types of muscle tissue; **neurofibrils** (p. 195), conductive elements found in *Paramecium* and certain other unicellular animals; and **ciliary fibrils** (p. 197), a precisely arranged group of ultrafine, presumably contractile, threads demonstrable by electron microscopy in all **cilia** (p. 195) and **flagella** (p. 195). In addition to these persisting elements of cell structure there is the **mitotic apparatus** (Fig. 3-3), which appears transiently each time a cell divides (Chap. 3).

Granules of more or less inert materials are found in virtually every kind of cell. Many of these granules represent stored materials, such as starch grains (in plant cells), fat droplets or glycogen grains (in animal cells), and yolk granules (in egg cells). Others, particularly in gland cells, are **secretory granules.** Secretory granules are composed of special products, synthesized and accumulated in the gland cell, later to be extruded as components of some secretion. **Pigment granules** give characteristic colors to the cells and tissues containing them; still other granules merely represent waste products accumulated and precipitated in the cytoplasm. The size of the granules in the cytoplasm extends down to and beyond the limits of microscopic and ultramicroscopic resolvability to the level of relatively small molecules, such as glucose and water.

Intrinsic (Protoplasmic) Membranes. At every surface, protoplasm displays an altered structure, forming a subvisible specialized layer, or membrane, which is denser and less fluid than the rest of the protoplasm. The **plasma membrane,** at the external surface of the cytoplasm, is such a layer. In addition there are a number of other **intrinsic membranes** at internally placed surfaces in the cell: at the boundary between the nucleus and cytoplasm (the **nuclear membrane**); bordering each vacuole (**vacuolar membranes**); and at the contact surfaces between the cytoplasm and the visibly differentiated structures such as mitochondria, Golgi bodies, chloroplasts, etc. All these living membranes possess a number of unique and important properties, but these properties have been studied most extensively in the plasma membrane.

The Plasma Membrane. The plasma membrane is so thin that it is not microscopically visible as a separate structure. It appears merely as the external boundary of the cytoplasm. Nevertheless the plasma membrane has great functional importance. It plays a dominant role in controlling the passage of substances into and out of the cell.

Because the plasma membrane is not resolvable with any type of light microscope, many earlier biologists doubted its existence. These workers compared the cell to a mass of gelatin or other gelated material, in which no differentiated boundary membrane is present. To explain the fact that certain substances—particularly dyestuffs like **phenol red**—fail to penetrate the cell from a surrounding solution, it was said that the protoplasm had no "chemical affinity" for the dyes in question.

Proof for the existence of the plasma membrane was finally obtained by means of **microinjection experiments** (Fig. 2-17). If a phenol red solution is microinjected into the cytoplasm, it does color the protoplasm. In fact the injected dye spreads throughout the whole cytoplasm; but when it reaches the boundary surface, it cannot pass out of the cell. Therefore it is certain that the boundary layer is different from the internal cytoplasm, and this differentiated surface layer is called the **plasma membrane.** The plasma membrane prevents the molecules of phenol red from entering the cell from a surrounding solution, and likewise it prevents the dye from leaving the cell once it is placed inside. Such an experiment, of course, must be performed on a cell from which any extraneous coating has been removed, since otherwise it would not be possible to rule out the nonprotoplasmic membrane as a barrier to the passage of the dye.

The plasma membrane, like other parts of the living protoplasm, displays a well-defined capacity for self-repair. If the cell surface is torn—as, for example, with a microneedle—the gap seals itself spontaneously, provided the tear is not too drastic. But if a very extensive rent is torn in the plasma membrane, a visible wave of disintegration sweeps over the surface of the cell, and within a few seconds all parts of the protoplasm disintegrate.

Fig. 2-17. A modern micromanipulator with accessory equipment. This apparatus permits the operator to inject fluid reagents into the cytoplasm, or into the nucleus of a cell, and to dissect the cell in various ways. Two of the control levers that guide the microinstruments are shown (lower left). A photomicrographic camera is mounted above the microscope. Above this (not shown in the photo) there is a television screen. This enables the operator to observe the cells while they are being dissected and photographed. (Courtesy of M. J. Kopac, New York University.)

This experiment shows that the plasma membrane is an integral part of the living protoplasm without which the cell cannot remain alive.

Much is now being learned about the structure of the plasma and other intrinsic membranes of the cell, directly from electron-micrographic studies, and indirectly from studies on the special properties of such membranes. The plasma membrane (Fig. 2-13) proves to be about 8.0 millimicrons thick in the desiccated state, although probably it approximates 10.0 millimicrons in the living cell. It appears to consist of two layers of electron-dense material between which lies a layer of less dense substance. Presumably, the denser material is of protein composition, whereas the layer of lesser density is lipid (p. 80). The structural and functional characteristics of the plasma membrane and of other intrinsic protoplasmic surfaces will be considered more thoroughly in Chapter 6.

Extraneous (Nonprotoplasmic) Membranes. In most cases the cell is covered by some sort of extraneous membrane, which lies in contact with the outer surface of the plasma membrane. Such nonliving covers protect the protoplasm from mechanical injury and help to maintain the characteristic shape of the particular cell. Extraneous membranes are usually thick enough to be visible under the microscope and are composed of inert substances that have been synthesized by the protoplasm and deposited at the external surface.

The extraneous membranes of plant cells are generally quite different from those of animal cells, and consequently they are given different names. In the case of plant cells it is customary to speak of the **cell wall;** and in the case of animal cells, one speaks of the **pellicle.** In the tissues of higher animals, the pellicular covering of the cells may be very thin or even absent, although usually some sort of extraneous intercellular material can be demonstrated.

The **cell wall** (Figs. 2-14 and 2-16) of plant cells is generally stronger, more rigid, and less elastic than the **pellicle** of animal cells— as can be demonstrated by experiments. If plant and animal cells are placed in distilled water, which tends to make cells swell (Chap. 6), the results are quite different in each case. Animal cells, owing to the greater elasticity and weakness of the pellicle, continue to swell. The cells become larger and larger, until finally they burst. But plant cells swell only slightly, and then stop. The strength of the cell wall, like that of the casing of an automobile tire, prevents further swelling, despite

the fact that the inflation pressure in the plant cell may reach a value of several atmospheres.

The converse of this experiment demonstrates the greater *rigidity* of the cell wall, as compared to the pellicle. When plant and animal cells are placed in strong salt solutions, which induce the protoplasm to shrink, marked differences are again observed. As the animal cell shrinks, at first the pellicle shrinks along with the protoplasm. But as shrinkage continues, the flexible pellicle becomes wrinkled (Fig. 2-18) and distorted to

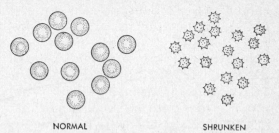

NORMAL   SHRUNKEN

Fig. 2-18. The shrinking of animal cells (human red cells). Note the wrinkled pellicle in the shrunken cells.

fit the reduced contour of the cell. In the plant cell, on the other hand, the cell wall does not shrink as the protoplasm shrinks; nor does the cell wall become wrinkled. The protoplasm merely pulls away from the rigid wall and continues to shrink by itself until it occupies only a small part of the original tightly fitting compartment (Fig. 2-19).

CELL WALL
CYTOPLASM
VACUOLE

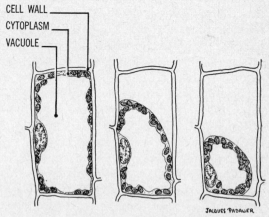

JACQUES PADAWER

Fig. 2-19. The shrinking of a plant cell. The cell wall is rigid and does not shrink as the protoplasm shrinks.

The different *physical* properties of the cell wall and pellicle reflect a fundamental difference of *chemical* constitution. The cell wall of the typical plant cell is composed mainly of a **carbohydrate** substance, **cellulose,** which is the special component of all "woody" materials. But the pellicular covering of typical animal cells is composed mainly, if not entirely, of **mucoprotein** substances (Chap. 4).

Extraneous material, found between the cells of certain tissues, is designated generally as **intercellular matrix.** In some tissues (for example, bone and cartilage) the matrix is more abundant than the protoplasm (Fig. 15-17). Like the cell wall or pellicle, the matrix is secreted by the cell it surrounds, and the matrix is not part of the protoplasm. Even in tissues possessing no visible matrix, small amounts of an analogous material, the **intercellular cement,** are usually present. This material binds the cells together—pellicle to pellicle, or cell wall to cell wall, as the case may be.

The nonliving nature of extraneous membranes and matrices generally is emphasized by the fact that they are not essential to the life of the cell. By microdissection and other techniques, the cell wall or pellicle can be removed from a number of plant or animal cells. Such naked cells are more vulnerable to mechanical injury and may fail to maintain their normal shape, but they do continue to live. In time, the naked cells may replace the missing protective material.

Functional Responsibilities of the Nucleus and Cytoplasm. By microdissection it is possible to remove the nucleus from certain cells (Fig. 2-20) or to cut the cell into two surviving pieces of roughly equal size, one with a nucleus and the other without.

The common fresh-water *amoeba,* because of its large size and ease of culture, provides a favorable cell for the performance of such microoperations. Virtually none of the cytoplasm is lost during the enucleation and the cell membrane repairs itself instantaneously when the nucleus is carefully pulled out

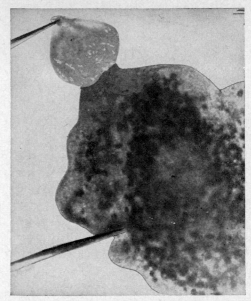

Fig. 2-20. Using microneedles to remove the nucleus from an amoeba. The bottom needle holds the amoeba while the top one pulls out the nucleus through the cell membrane. (Photograph retouched.) (Courtesy of Robert Chambers.)

through it (Fig. 2-20). Also, when the amoeba is properly cut in half, the cell membrane on both sides of the cut becomes sealed immediately.

The enucleated amoeba continues most of its vital activities for about two weeks. It can move and ingest food; it digests and *absorbs* this food; and it even shows some slight signs of *growth*. But it is *not able to reproduce.* Gradually growth and activity cease and the cytoplasm begins to waste away. Finally, usually within two to three weeks, the cell remnant disintegrates. Observations on the **anucleate halves** of cut amoebae yield similar results, except that the survival time is usually less.

The **nucleated half** of a cut amoeba has a different fate, however. Its activity and growth continue vigorously. Within a day or two it has more than regained its original size, whereupon cell division occurs and reproduction is achieved. In fact the nucleated half of a cell displays a full potential for continuing all its vital activities, including reproduction.

Further experiments with anucleate "cells," especially those in which radioactive tracer methods (p. 141) have been used as a means of following constructive metabolism, have yielded some basic conclusions, which will be discussed more fully later (Chap. 4). Suffice it to say here that the nucleus, with its content of specific DNA proteins (genic materials), provides for the continued production of complementary RNA proteins, which are passed on to the cytoplasm. In the cytoplasm, these RNA compounds provide templates for the synthesis of enzymes and other proteins, which are essential for continued growth and activity. In the absence of a nucleus to replenish RNA, the cytoplasm gradually loses its powers of synthesis and begins to waste away. Moreover, since only the DNA proteins of the nucleus display any capacity for self-replication, no reproductive potential remains in the anucleate "cell." In any event, these experiments give firm support to the conclusion that each cell, nucleus and cytoplasm together, represents a protoplasmic unit from the viewpoint not only of form, but also of function.

The importance of the nucleus in constructive metabolism is emphasized by other observations. The nucleus usually migrates to any part of a cell where active synthesis is occurring (Fig. 2-21); and gland cells—in which constructive metabolism goes on very rapidly—tend to possess exceptionally large or even lobulated nuclei, which expose a maximum of surface to the surrounding cytoplasm (Fig. 2-21D).

THE CELL AND THE ORGANISM

In the simplest organisms the whole body consists of a single cell, and within the limits of such a cell there may be a fairly complex differentiation of structures, especially in the case of animal cells. The nutrition of a typical animal (Chap. 7), even in unicellular forms, presupposes a capacity to sense the location of food, to move toward food, and to ingest, digest, and absorb the food; and

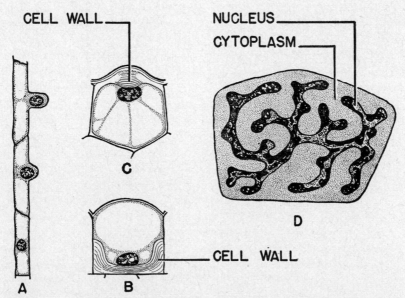

Fig. 2-21. The nucleus is concerned with synthetic processes in cells. A, growth of root hairs from epidermal cells of root of plant; note the location of the nuclei close to the points of rapid growth. B, C, plant cells synthesizing local thickenings of the cell walls, with the nuclei close to the point of special thickening in each case. D, a cell of the silk gland of a caterpillar, with a large lobulated nucleus. (A, B, and C after Haberlandt; D, after Korschelt.)

these reactions require a complex structural organization even in the single cell.

The unicellular condition has limitations, however, particularly as regards the maximum size to which the organism can grow (p. 17). Larger organisms—up to a limit, which is quite large—possess many obvious biological advantages. Large organisms are less vulnerable to small environmental forces and they are less at the mercy of smaller enemies. Bacteria, because of their smallness, are continually buffeted from side to side by the random bombardment of the molecules of the water in which they live; but the greater bulk of the larger aquatic forms makes them immune to such small forces.

When a small insect, or other animal, falls upon still water, it may be caught and torn by surface tension; but larger animals may clamber in and out of water without any fear of such a puny force. A salmon breasts the strongest stream, impossible for even the fastest swimming protozoan; while an elephant may easily uproot a tree that previously was the home of many smaller creatures.

The advantages of greater size were gained by plants and animals mainly through the evolution of **cell aggregates.** In simplest form such aggregates are mere colonies, with the individual cells independent of each other. But colonial forms were followed in evolution by **multicellular organisms,** in which

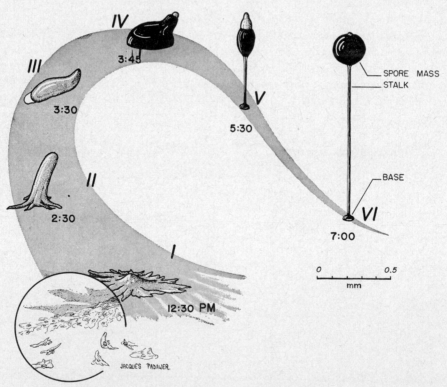

Fig. 2-22. Rare phenomenon, found only in a few slime molds. In this case a multicellular "organism" originates by the coming together of many separate cells. Most of the time this mold (*Dictyostelium*) takes the form of a multitude of separate amoebalike cells that move and multiply in the soil, among the rotting leaves. Sometimes, however, the cells all come together (stage I) forming a multicellular mass that displays integrated locomotion while it migrates for several hours (stages I-III). Then all the cells cooperate in building a complex structure with a spore capsule at the top (stages IV-VI). Finally a multitude of unicellular spores are discharged from the capsule. Each spore gives rise to another individual "amoeba." (Redrawn after J. T. Bonner, Princeton University.)

the many cells are of different kinds, each being fitted for some special function. Accordingly, the different cells of the multicellular organism are dependent upon each other to a very significant degree.

Except in rare cases (Figs. 2-22 and 2-23) multicellular organisms arise, not by the coming together of previously dissociated cells, but by the staying together of cells derived by division from a single parent cell. In fact, virtually all multicellular plants and animals return to the unicellular condition each time a new individual is conceived. Among plants and animals, generally all the cells of each offspring are derived by division from a *fertilized egg cell*.

In multicellular organisms each different kind of cell, taken *as a group* and including any intercellular matrix that may be present, constitutes a *tissue* (for example, bone and muscle, in animals; xylem and epidermis, in plants). The tissues in turn compose the **organs** (such as the stomach of an animal, or the leaf of a plant), each organ being fabricated of several different tissues. Finally, the organs themselves are grouped into **organ systems** (such as the digestive system, or the nervous system), each system subserving some general function in the nutrition, responsiveness, or reproduction of the organism as a whole.

In higher organisms, the distribution of substances is effected by body fluids (such as blood, lymph, or sap) that flow throughout

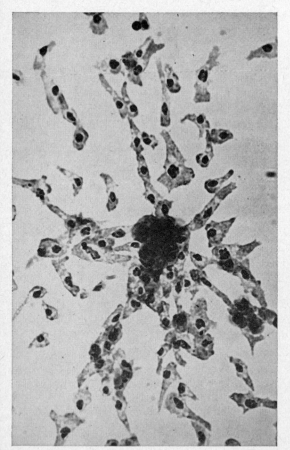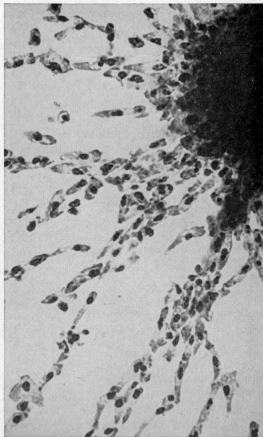

Fig. 2-23. Photographs showing the separate cells of the slime mold coming together to form a multicellular amoeboid mass (such as is shown in Fig. 2-22, stage I). Left, aggregation commencing; right, multicellular mass building up. (Courtesy of J. T. Bonner, Princeton University.)

the body in definite channels. Likewise, the nervous system effects an integrated behavior of the body parts in higher animals generally. These connections enable the cells, tissues, and organs of the multicellular body to act together as a unified whole—the **organism.** But *whatever the organism does is done by its cells,* and the noncellular parts of an organism are lifeless products and passive tools subserving the activities of the living cells. Thus the life of the organism is to be considered as the sum total of the integrated activities of its component cells. To consider that the organism is "something more than the sum of its cells" is like considering that a machine is something more than the total of its parts. Without question, the properties of the whole machine are determined by the relations, as well as by the structures, of the separate parts—and how the parts are fitted and linked together is just as important as how each is formed individually. Likewise the activities of an organism result from the interaction, rather than from the independent action, of the component cells, organs, and organ systems.

The tissue cells of a complex animal subordinate themselves to the functions of the whole organism, but all the cells are individually alive, and some retain an unlimited potential for growth and multiplication. This can be shown by the technique of tissue culture. In this technique a small piece, usually of embryonic tissue, is placed in a nutrient medium, such as the blood plasma of the same animal. Optimum conditions are provided for the cells by changing the medium at frequent intervals, meanwhile trimming away excess quantities of tissue as growth continues. The utmost care to prevent bacterial contamination must be taken during all these operations.

In tissue culture, some cells retain their characteristic form and activity and their capacity to grow quite indefinitely. At the Rockefeller Institute, for example, a piece of heart tissue, taken from a chick embryo, was cultured for more than 20 years. In this tissue some of the cells remained motile and continued to grow throughout the whole period. In fact, if all this growing tissue could have been saved and provided with good conditions, the accrued amount of new tissue would now be many times the volume of this earth.

THE CELL PRINCIPLE

The **cell principle** has gradually developed from the cell hypothesis, and now it has attained a very fundamental importance in biology. This development may be summarized as follows:

1. Plant and animal bodies, with minor exceptions, are composed of one or more cells. Among the first to emphasize this generalization were a botanist, Mathias Schleiden (1838), and a zoologist, Theodor Schwann (1839), who submitted the cell hypothesis almost simultaneously. Much earlier Robert Hooke (1665) had observed plant cells, and Anton Leeuwenhoek (1660) had observed animal cells. However, these early investigators could not have realized the general occurrence and wide significance of the cell.

2. The essential living part of every cell is its protoplasm. In the early development of the cell hypothesis, the cell wall (or the pellicle) was thought to be more important than the protoplasm; and it was not until 1861 that Max Schultze recognized that the protoplasm alone displays the essential attributes of life, in both plant and animal cells.

3. New cells arise only by division from pre-existing parent cells—at least under conditions as they exist today. Accordingly each species of plant and animal represents an unbroken cell lineage extending back into ancient time. The first of these conclusions was stated clearly by Virchow in 1855; the second derives from the work of August Weismann in the latter part of the nineteenth century.

4. Each cell—so long as it retains its capacity for growth and multiplication—must be considered as an integral living unit. This conclusion was confirmed by tissue culture experiments, which were begun by Harrison in 1912.

5. The life of the whole organism represents the sum total of the integrated life of the component cells. This conclusion is scarcely susceptible to proof, but is a viewpoint supported by a wide variety of observations and experiments.

TEST QUESTIONS

1. List the features that are possessed by typical cells generally. Make a fully labeled sketch of any cell that displays all these features.
2. Explain why each of the following is not to be regarded as a typical cell: (a) blue-green algae; (b) certain slime molds. Make labeled sketches to illustrate the points in question.
3. Cite examples (including the dimensions of):
   a. an extremely small cell
   b. an extremely large cell
   c. a cell of average size
4. Explain how and why cells generally cannot grow beyond a certain definite limit.
5. Why do cells tend to assume a droplike form when constraining factors are absent? Explain.
6. Cite two examples to illustrate the general rule that the form of a cell is generally related to its function.
7. Distinguish between:
   a. chromatin and chromosomes
   b. chromatin and chromidia
   c. chlorophyll and chloroplasts
8. Cite evidence indicating that the chromatin part of the protoplasm is very essential in every cell.
9. Specify five kinds of cytoplasmic bodies and explain how each is identified.
10. Carefully identify each of the following: (a) phase-contrast microscopy; (b) darkfield microscopy; (c) interference microscopy; (d) electron microscopy.
11. What properties of the plasma membrane distinguish it from such extraneous membranes as the pellicle and cell wall?
12. Describe the microinjection technique and explain how it has been used to prove the existence of the plasma membrane.
13. Define the terms "cell wall" and "pellicle"; specify at least three differences between these two kinds of membranes.
14. Cite an experiment that demonstrates the general importance of the nucleus in the metabolic activities of the cell. What other evidence tends to substantiate the conclusion drawn from the experiment?
15. Distinguish between an organ and an organism.
16. Explain the technique of tissue culture; what important conclusion has been derived from tissue culture experiments?
17. Carefully identify each of the following terms: (a) lysosomes; (b) chromosomes; (c) ribosomes; (d) Golgi bodies; (e) mitochondria; (f) nucleolus; (g) endoplasmic reticulum.

FURTHER READINGS

1. *Unresting Cells,* by R. W. Gerard; New York, 1949.
2. *General Cytology,* 3d ed., by E. D. P. De-Robertis, W. W. Nowinwski, and F. A. Saez; Philadelphia, 1960.
3. *Great Experiments in Biology,* Ed. by M. Gabriel and S. Fogel; Englewood Cliffs, N. J., 1955.
4. *The Cell,* ed. by J. Brachet and A. E. Mirsky, 5 vols., New York, 1961.
5. "The Living Cell," special issue of *Scientific American,* September 1961.

3=Cell Division in Relation to Reproduction

SOONER or later each kind of cell reaches a size at which it must either stop growing or divide. If it is to be division, the cell begins to undergo a drastic reorganization of both its nuclear and cytoplasmic structure. Indeed, a considerable part of the metabolic activity of the cell during its life between divisions appears to be directed toward the synthesis of new materials in preparation for the next division. The cell is thus ready to replicate itself, and all the important and dramatic events of cell division can begin to proceed without delay and with great precision.

Biologists are generally agreed that new cells arise solely by division from pre-existing parent cells, at least under conditions as they exist today. Consequently cell division provides the underlying basis for all forms of reproduction—sexual as well as asexual (p. 51)—in every kind of plant and animal. Cell division also provides a basic mechanism for the transmission of hereditary qualities from cell generation to cell generation, and from

generation to generation of the whole organism.

In man and in multicellular animals generally, all the cells of the body arise by division from a single embryonic cell, the **fertilized egg.** This fertilized egg, formed by the fusion of two cells, an egg and a sperm, likewise arises by division from the cells of the parent organisms. The same situation also holds true for most plants. However, the cells of some plants are formed by the multiplication of another kind of cell, called a **spore,** which differs somewhat from an egg cell (Chap. 12).

In both plants and animals a great majority of the cells are produced in the same way, by a type of cell division called **mitosis,** which was described briefly in Chapter 2. But it is important to realize that certain reproductive cells—especially the eggs and sperm in animals, and the spores in plants—are produced by a somewhat different type of cell division called **meiosis.** These two types of division, although somewhat modified in a few special cases, are the only normal methods of division that occur in nature. Generally speaking, the body cells of the organism are formed by mitosis, but the eggs and sperm (in animals) and the spores (in plants) are produced by meiosis.

MITOTIC CELL DIVISION

Mitosis, the more usual type of cell division, represents one of the most intricate and beautifully regulated processes in all the realm of life. Essentially, it enables the cell to produce two replicas of itself, the two **daughter cells,** each possessing a full potential for perpetuating the unique characteristics of its lineage.

To some extent the successive stages and events of mitosis can be observed sequentially in the living cell. However, a full appreciation of the detailed pattern of changing structure requires the use of cells that have been fixed, stained, and subsequently studied microscopically. In such cases, critical judgment must be used in deciding upon the proper sequence of the statically recorded events, and always it must be realized that only a derivative of the living structure is under observation.

Prophase. The mitosis of animal and plant cells is fundamentally similar. There are certain small differences, however, which will be mentioned in the course of the following general description.

One very early sign that mitosis has started is that the chromosomes, still within the confines of the nuclear membrane, become easier to identify individually. Each appears as a long, slender thread **(spireme stage)** that continues to become shorter and stouter and to stain more and more intensely (Fig. 3-1, prophases). In favorable cases, a spiral structure can be observed in each chromosome, as is indicated diagrammatically in Figure 3-2. The spirals appear to become more and more tightly coiled as the chromosome progressively shortens and thickens. Finally each chromosome attains a very compact, intensely staining form (Figs. 2-11A and 3-2). Moreover, as soon as the chromosomes become clearly visible, it can often be seen that each consists of *two* parallel threads, lying side by side. In fact, each prophase chromosome appears to be constituted, essentially, of *two[1] parallel spiral strands* of Feulgen positive material (Fig. 3-2).

Somewhere along its length, each chromosome displays a more compact section, which is designated as the **kinetochore,** or **centromere** (Figs. 2-11 and 3-2). The kinetochore seems to represent a specific anchorage point for the attachment of certain *spindle fibers.* Usually the kinetochore occupies a position more or less halfway between the ends of the chromosome, although sometimes it is very eccentric, even to the point of being terminally located. Soon after the double structure of the chromosome becomes discernible, it is possible to see that the kinetochore is also double. By the end of prophase, in fact, the two halves of each chromosome, which now are compact, rodlike, and (usually) slightly bent at the locus of the kinetochore, are separated slightly from one another (Figs. 2-11 and 3-2). Now it can be said that the process of chromosomal replication has been completed and that *each original chromosome has divided into two identical daughter chromosomes.*

While the chromosomes are shortening, thickening, and becoming sharply delineated, the **nucleoli** begin to lose their distinct outlines, and finally they fade from view completely. Also toward the end of prophase the nuclear membrane begins to fade. Soon it disappears, perhaps by fragmenting into pieces that become dispersed (Fig. 3-2).

Meanwhile dramatic events are going on in the cytoplasm. Very early, while the chromosomes are still elongate, the **mitotic apparatus** (Fig. 3-3) appears. This consists of two **mitotic centers,** between which there is a

[1] In some cases the coils themselves appear to be coiled, so that a multiple, rather than a double, spiral structure appears while the chromosomes are becoming shorter and thicker during prophase.

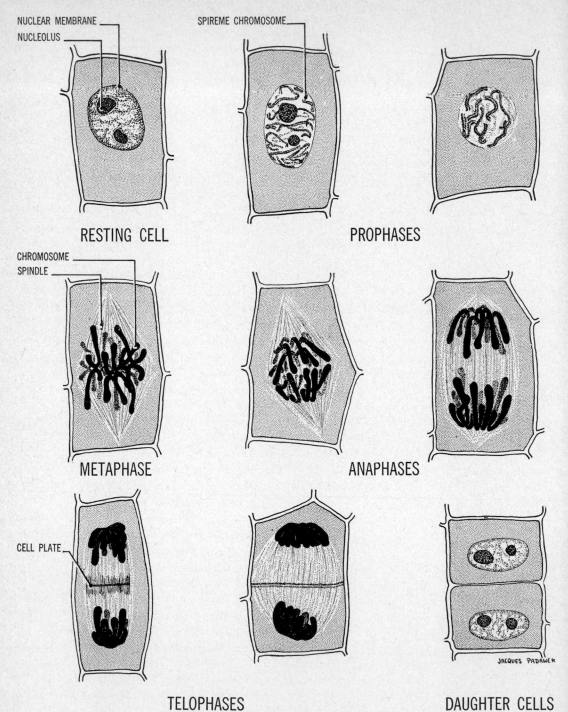

Fig. 3-1.   Mitosis in a typical **plant** cell.

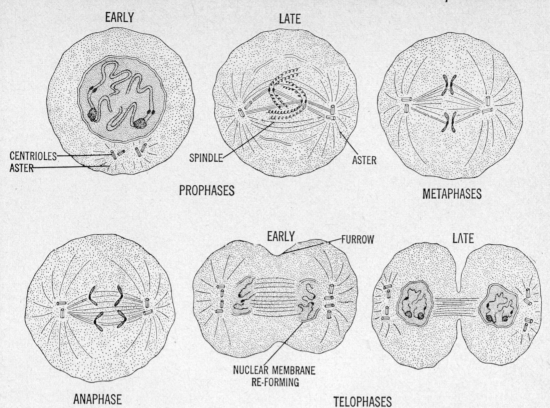

EARLY   LATE

CENTRIOLES
ASTER   SPINDLE   ASTER

PROPHASES   METAPHASES

EARLY   FURROW   LATE

NUCLEAR MEMBRANE
RE-FORMING

ANAPHASE   TELOPHASES

Fig. 3-2. Diagram depicting modern concept of mitosis as observed in a typical **animal** cell.

system of protoplasmic fibers, collectively called the **spindle.** The mitotic centers are regarded as specialized parts of the cytoplasm, situated at the ends, or *poles,* of the spindle, although these regions sometimes are not very clearly delineated, especially in plant cells. The fibers toward each end of the spindle always converge, however, toward a definitely localized center. Moreover, in larger animal cells at least, radiating from each mitotic center there is a stellate system of protoplasmic fibers, collectively designated as the **aster** (Fig. 3-2). Also in most, if not all, animal cells, a pair of short rodlike bodies, the **centrioles,** can be demonstrated occupying a focal position in the mitotic center (Figs. 3-2 and 3-5).

The centrioles are "self-replicating" structures. They appear to focalize the dynamic activities of the mitotic center during the division of animal cells generally. The spindle always stretches between the centriolar regions, and the plane of division regularly cuts across the center of the spindle at right angles to the spindle axis (Fig. 3-2). Moreover, the two short rodlike units that constitute each pair of centrioles always lie at right angles to one another. Each unit of the pair, as seen at high magnifications in favorable electronmicrographs, consists of a compact bundle of 27 fibers (perhaps tubules), arranged concentrically in groups of three (Fig. 3-5). Sometimes the units of each pair of centriolar bodies replicate themselves very early, toward the end of one mitosis, in preparation for the next; but in other cases replication is delayed until early prophase of the next division. In any event, the sister pairs of centrioles, after replication has occurred, move to opposite sides of the prophase nucleus, and the spindle begins to appear between the diverging sister pairs (Fig. 3-2).

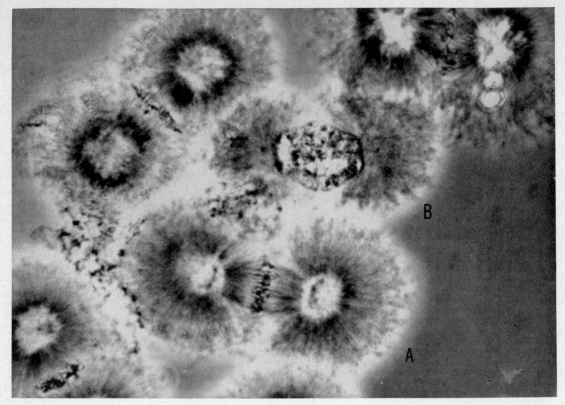

Fig. 3-3. Mitotic apparatuses, or spindle-aster-chromosome complexes, removed from dividing egg cells (sea urchin) by the method of Mazia and Dan. A, late metaphase; B, prophase, at time of breakdown of nuclear membrane. To isolate the apparatus one uses very cold (—12°C) 30 percent alcohol as a stabilizing agent; then a detergent (digitonin, 1 percent) is employed to disperse the cytoplasm. (Courtesy of Daniel Mazia, University of California.)

Moreover, as may be judged from the very precise observations of Donald Costello, of the University of North Carolina, the orientation displayed by the paired centriolar rods at one mitosis exerts a determining influence upon the plane of division in the next mitosis.

The spindle likewise displays a duplex structure. One set of fibers, collectively referred to as the **central spindle,** extends full length from pole to pole. The other set, which is usually designated as **traction fibers,** originates from the poles, but each terminates by making connection with the kinetochore of some one of the chromosomes (Fig. 3-2). When the spindle has reached full development, the nuclear membrane usually has begun to disappear (Fig. 3-2). However, in a few exceptional cases it has been observed that kinetochore connections can be established even while the membrane continues to persist. In any event, there is one important rule that is never broken, except in rare accidental cases. The members of a sister pair of kinetochores, formed as each chromosome divides into two daughters, never establish connection with the same pole of the spindle. In other words, *the two daughter chromosomes, formed by the division of each parent chromosome, become connected to opposite poles of the spindle.*

Metakinesis and Metaphase. After the disappearance of the nuclear membrane, the pairs of daughter chromosomes, each daughter lying parallel to and in contact with the other, are arranged more or less randomly

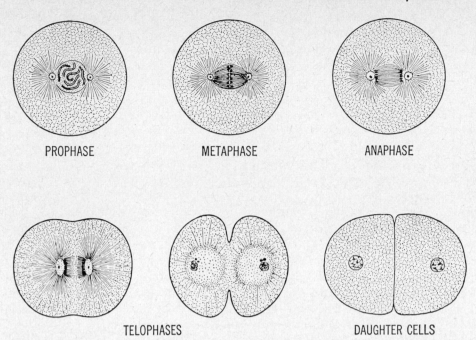

PROPHASE   METAPHASE   ANAPHASE

TELOPHASES   DAUGHTER CELLS

Fig. 3-4. Mitosis in a typical **animal** cell (egg cell of a sea urchin). Note particularly the asters, centrioles, and cleavage furrows. These structures are rarely found in plant cells.

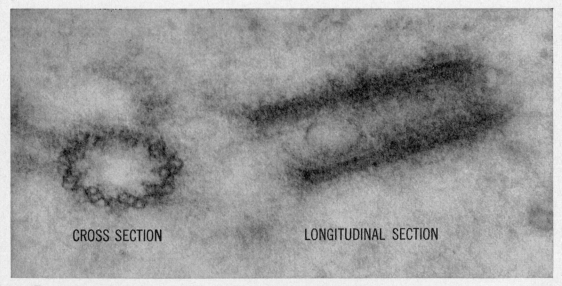

CROSS SECTION   LONGITUDINAL SECTION

Fig. 3-5. Paired **centrioles** of a human tumor cell (Desille lymphosarcoma). Final magnification, $\times$ 160,000 (approximate). Note the pattern revealed by the cross section: nine triplet groups of tubules (or perhaps fibers) arranged in a circle. This pattern appears to be general, as indicated in electronmicrographs of the centrioles of various other dividing cells. (Courtesy of Wilhelm Bernhard, Institut de Recherches Scientifiques sur le Cancer, Villejuif, France.)

around the center of the cell, near the now clearly defined spindle. Soon, however, they are moved into a precisely regimented arrangement at the exact center of the spindle —that is, halfway between the poles and regularly disposed around the spindle axis (Fig. 3-2). While the chromosomes maintain this mid-point position, the cell is said to be in the **metaphase** of mitosis. The final stages of prophase, while the chromosomes are being moved to the metaphase position, are usually referred to as **metakinesis.**

Anaphase. Anaphase is the period that embraces all stages during which the sister chromosomes are separated from one another, as they are moved toward, and finally to, opposite poles of the spindle (Figs. 3-2 and 3-4). Each of the chromosomes originally present in the parent cell has undergone replication into identical pairs of sister chromosomes, and now the sister members of each pair regularly pass to opposite poles of the mitotic apparatus.

The exact mechanism that brings about the anaphase movements of the chromosomes is still somewhat problematical. Considerable evidence exists, however, to indicate that the chromosomes are pulled along the length of the spindle by contractile processes inherent in the traction fibers. The kinetochore of each chromosome, to which a traction fiber is attached, regularly leads the way, and the limbs, on either side of the kinetochore, appear as if they were being dragged through a viscous medium. Thus during anaphase, the chromosomes display J and V shapes, depending upon whether the kinetochore is exactly centered, and the limbs of the bent chromosomes regularly trail away from the poles of the spindle. The traction fibers can be observed to become shorter and shorter as the chromosomes move from the equator to the poles. The fibers do not thicken as they shorten, however, as might be expected if the contraction were of an elastic nature. Indeed, a few biologists have postulated the existence of unknown forces—of attraction between the kinetochores and the mitotic cen-

ters, or of repulsion between sister kinetochores. According to such views the fibrous structure of the spindle would be interpreted as a molecular orientation resulting from lines of force generated by the attraction or repulsion. A less ephemeral mitotic structure appears more likely, however, especially in view of the important recent work of Mazia and Dan. These investigators have shown that the mitotic apparatus can be isolated as a stable, integral structure, to which the chromosomes remain attached, when certain cells, particularly dividing egg cells, are fixed in cold alcohol and then treated with detergents that dissolve or disperse all other parts of the cytoplasm (Fig. 3-3).

Not all of the force that operates to separate the daughter groups of chromosomes can originate in the traction fibers, however. While the traction fibers are shortening, the fibers of the central spindle are lengthening. But here again no change in the caliber of the fibers has been observed. The precise mechanisms by which these processes of shortening and lengthening are brought about remain obscure. Nevertheless, it must be recognized that the lengthening of the central spindle participates in the work of moving the daughter groups of chromosomes to opposite sides of the dividing cell.

Telophase. During telophase, the final phase of mitosis, the new nuclei of the two prospective daughter cells become organized and the cytoplasm of the parent cell becomes divided, usually in roughly equal fashion, between the two resulting daughter cells (Fig. 3-2).

Soon after reaching the poles of the spindle, the chromosomes begin to elongate and to lose their compact, densely staining form, thus making it difficult to distinguish them individually (Fig. 3-2). Meanwhile, a new nuclear membrane is formed, or perhaps assembled, around the chromosomes, and the nucleus of each daughter cell takes on the appearance of the parent nucleus before mitosis began. This telophase reorganization of the daughter nuclei probably represents a reversal of the processes that occurred in the parent nucleus during the previous prophase. Instead of coiling more and more tightly the spiral structure appears to uncoil to a considerable degree; in this **extended form** (Fig. 2-11B) the chromosomes are extremely delicate and difficult to delineate microscopically.

While nuclear reorganization is progressing, cytoplasmic division is achieved. Plant and animal cells differ, however, as to the mechanisms of cytoplasmic division. In the plant cell, a partition, called the **cell plate,** is built across the center of the cell. The cell plate passes directly across the center of the spindle, at right angles to the spindle axis (Fig. 3-1). The plate, in fact, appears to be constituted of materials derived from the middle section of the central spindle. In any event the cell plate soon splits into two parallel plates between which the *cell walls* of the new cells are deposited.

The animal cell divides its cytoplasm in another way, however—namely, by **furrowing** (Figs. 3-2 and 3-4). The **division furrow (cleavage furrow)** appears at the beginning of telophase, encircling the equator of the cell, in the plane that passes through the center of the spindle at right angles to its axis. Gradually the furrow deepens until it cuts through the cytoplasm and spindle remnant completely, thus separating the daughter cells. By now, nuclear reorganization has been consummated, the mitotic apparatus, with the exception, perhaps, of the centrioles, has faded from view, and the mitosis is complete.

The duration of the mitotic process varies in different kinds of cells. It may last a few minutes or several hours, the prophase usually being longest. The duration of the intermitotic stage is even more variable. In rapidly developing tissues, one mitosis may succeed another with practically no interval at all; but in the specialized tissues of a multicellular organism many of the mature cells may never divide again during the lifetime of the individual.

SOME CURRENT PROBLEMS

The events of mitosis have been observed and described in a wide variety of cells for more than 60 years. Yet a fundamental understanding of the intricate mitotic mechanisms remains elusive. There are many questions for which only partial answers or no answers have been obtained. What is the "trigger" that initiates mitosis and how is the precise timing of the successive mitotic stages so beautifully regulated? What is the functional role of the asters and why is it that these structures are not essential in the division of plant cells, or even of smaller animal cells? By what means do the genes, chromosomes, centrioles, and other structures effect a replication of themselves and how does the animal cell obtain energy for furrowing into two cells? These and many other problems are being studied intensively with modern research techniques and more progress can be expected soon.

Perhaps the best recent progress has been made in reference to the manner in which the DNA proteins, or genic substances, achieve their replication in the chromosomes. Such studies have been aided greatly by the development of radioactive isotopes (p. 141). These provide a means of tracing, step by step, the metabolism of self-templated synthesis, as will be explained more fully later (Chap. 27). However, it is necessary to distinguish between self-guided synthesis, which replicates the genic substances, and the division of a whole chromosome into daughter chromosomes. DNA synthesis, apparently, is completed before mitosis starts, whereas the sister chromosomes are not individually distinguishable until prophase.

Good progress can also be noted in reference to the manner in which the cell develops mechanical energy in achieving the anaphase movements of the chromosomes. The studies of Daniel Mazia and co-workers, at the University of California, hold good promise that this long-standing problem will soon be resolved.

Likewise the problem of how the division furrow develops energy for cleaving the animal cell into two daughters is receiving considerable attention. Here, however, two more or less opposite hypotheses are being tested: (1) that furrowing results from an **expansion** of the cell surface (viewpoint of M. M. Swann and M. Mitchison, in Great Britain); and (2) that furrowing results from the **contraction** of a peripheral girdle of strongly gelled (p. 94) cytoplasm that forms around the equator of the cell during telophase (viewpoint of W. H. Lewis and D. A. Marsland, in the United States). At present, final decision on this problem cannot be made, although recent developments tend to favor the contraction viewpoint.

Control of Cell Division. One very important and difficult problem in biology is to ascertain precisely how the multiplication of cells is controlled within the body so that the number of cells in each part is appropriate to the requirements of the body as a whole. In the human body, for example, mitotic activity remains at a high level in the different parts of the embryo, but as development proceeds, mitosis becomes less and less frequent. At maturity, indeed, most of the cells have stopped dividing. Mitotic activity becomes confined to certain localized regions, such as the skin, where the epithelial cells continue to multiply, replacing the surface layers as they wear away; in the gonads (p. 380), where the many prospective gametes are being formed; in wounds, while the processes of repair are going on; and in blood-forming and certain other tissues.

The Cancer Problem. Little is known about the factors that regulate cell division, but usually they are most effective in controlling the population of each kind of cell in the different organs of various animals and plants. On rare occasion, however, something goes wrong and the cells in some part of the body begin dividing without restraint. This results in an abnormally large and improperly organized mass of cells called a **tumor. Benign** types of tumor, which do not display a very high level of mitotic activity and which tend to become encapsulated by the surrounding tissues of the host, are not very serious. Eventually the benign tumor tends to stop growing and usually it is not difficult to remove surgically. But **malignant tumors, or cancers,** possess a very high mitotic rate and an unlimited capacity to spread at the expense of any surrounding tissues. Moreover, small groups of the cancerous cells may become detached from the main mass and be carried by the circulatory system to some other part of the body, where a secondary cancer, or **metastasis,** will start. Consequently, it is most important that a malignant tumor be detected and removed as soon as possible, before it has invaded some vital region, and before it has metastasized. Among higher animals generally, two main types of malignancies are distinguished: **carcinomas,** in which the cancerous cells are of an **epithelial nature;** and **sarcomas,** in which the cells are of a **connective tissue** type.

The causation of cancerous growths is a complex problem, especially since not all types originate in the same way. One type, the Rous sarcoma in chickens, appears to be initiated by a filtrable virus. This type, therefore, can be transmitted to a healthy bird merely by injecting cell-free fluid from a diseased individual. The transmission of other tumors, on the other hand, involves transplanting some of the cancerous cells. Also, it is known that certain bacteria are capable of inducing tumorous growths in plants, although once induced, such tumors can continue to grow even in the absence of the bacteria. Certain malignant tumors in animals can be induced by chemical compounds (originally isolated from tar), and once induced, such cancers likewise continue to grow after the **carcinogenic compound** has been removed. All in all, therefore, it seems probable that cancerous cells develop some intrinsic difference, possibly a change in their genic material, that makes them insensitive to hormonal (p. 400) and other factors that normally limit the multiplication of body cells. However, very little is known about these factors and cancer still remains a hideous unsolved riddle.

Primitive Forms of Mitosis. It is difficult to observe the processes of mitosis in bacteria (p. 601) and blue-green algae (p. 594) because the cells are very small. In many bacteria a single chromosome appears and divides at the time of fission, but whether there is a well-developed mitotic apparatus has not yet been determined. Among the blue-green algae, the chromidial bodies (p. 18), which may represent very small chromosomes, are carefully lined up, divided and separated into two groups that soon are walled off into separate cells (Fig. 3-6). Among many protozoans (p. 625), definite chromosomes are formed, but the mitotic apparatus lies entirely inside the nuclear membrane, which persists throughout the division (Fig. 3-7).

SIGNIFICANCE OF MITOSIS: IMPORTANCE OF CHROMOSOMES

Viewing the situation as a whole, it seems clear that the behavior of the chromosomes during mitosis is essentially the same in the cells of all multicellular plants and animals—although there are some

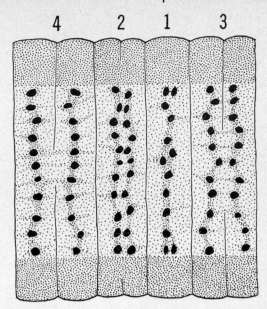

Fig. 3-6. Cells of *Oscillatoria*, a colonial blue-green alga, showing a simple type of mitotic division. 1, 2, 3, 4, successive stages of cell division. (Adapted from Olive.)

variations of detail in different kinds of cells, especially in the behavior of the nonchromatic parts. At every mitosis, each individual chromosome divides, and one of the two resulting daughter chromosomes passes to each new nucleus. Such a procedure maintains

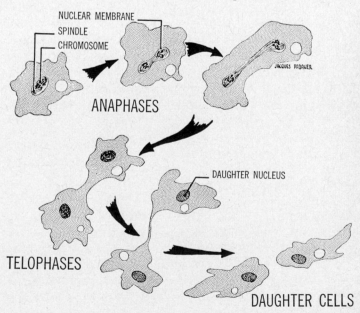

Fig. 3-7. Mitosis in an amoeba. Note that the spindle and chromosomes lie inside the *persisting* nuclear membrane.

NUCLEAR MEMBRANE
SPINDLE
CHROMOSOME

ANAPHASES

DAUGHTER NUCLEUS

TELOPHASES

DAUGHTER CELLS

(with rare exception) a constant number of chromosomes in the many cells of each different organism. This constant is usually an even number, and this number is the same for all individuals belonging to a given species. The **chromosome number** varies, in different organisms, from 2 to 200 or more, but usually it is below 50 (man has 46). Not only the number of chromosomes but also the size and shape of each chromosome remain constant. Usually the chromosomes of a given species are *individually* distinguishable, and exactly the same set appears at mitosis in all cells of the individual and of the species. The chromosomes that appear in any cell during the prophase are exactly the same as those that apparently disappeared during the preceding telophase. In some cases the separateness of the chromosomes can be seen at all times, even throughout the **intermitotic** period. But usually this cannot be seen directly, although other evidence indicates that it is true. In other words, each chromosome has a persistent individuality. Each grows and replicates its own unique genic materials during the intermitotic period and each divides at every mitosis. Thus every chromosome maintains its own peculiar composition and structure throughout innumerable cell generations. The essential function of the intricate mechanism of mitosis is to achieve an *exactly equal division of the parent chromosomes into two equivalent daughter sets* that then are segregated into the two new daughter cells. By assembling the many kinds of genic materials, each essential to the continued life of the cell, into a small, definite number of precisely packaged groups, and by having every genic unit in each group replicate itself before mitosis takes place, the cell has achieved a relatively simple, highly effective means by which it assures an exactly equal, quantitative as well as qualitative, division of these materials between the daughter cells. It is estimated (p. 496) that at least 10,000 genes are present in the average cell. If each gene had to be sorted and separated on an individual basis, the mechanisms of mitosis would doubtless have to be far more complicated than they are.

The dividing of the other parts of the cell is *not so exactly equal,* because there is no mechanism to accomplish a precise partitionment of the other parts. If a plant cell, for example, contains a certain number of chloroplasts, *about* half of these usually go to a particular daughter cell. But sometimes the numbers received by the two daughter cells may be quite unequal. The cytoplasm as a whole is divided quite equally in most cells, but in some cases, such as dividing yeasts, one of the daughter cells regularly receives by far the larger share (Fig. 10-2). The significance of mitosis becomes clear when it is realized that each chromosome carries a specific group of hereditary determinants and that these carry coded instructions (p. 134) by means of which each cell is enabled to fulfill the destinies of its own particular lineage. When a cell multiples by mitosis, its own complex of chromosomes and genes remains unchanged from generation to generation, and consequently there is no change in its intrinsic hereditary potentialities.

Amitosis. In rare instances cells have been observed to divide without forming chromosomes. The nucleus merely pinches into two parts and then the cleavage furrow or cell plate cuts through the cytoplasm. Such cases of **amitotic division** are considered to be more or less abnormal and relatively unimportant, because daughter cells produced by amitosis have lost the potential of perpetuating their lineage indefinitely.

HAPLOIDY AND DIPLOIDY IN RELATION TO FERTILIZATION

Still another important fact about the chromosomes has not been mentioned. When counted and matched against one another, it is usually found that the chromosomes make up a duplicate set. The duplicate, or **diploid,** set of chromosomes possessed by one species of animal is shown in Figure 3-8. This relatively simple case shows that the eight chro-

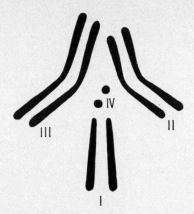

Fig. 3-8. Diploid chromosome group of the fruit fly, *Drosophila.* The numbers I, II, III, and IV indicate the four **pairs** of chromosomes.

mosomes are really four pairs. Each individual chromosome possesses a **homologous mate** that displays an identical size and shape. Similarly the 16 chromosomes of the onion plant are really 8 pairs, and the 46 chromosomes of man actually represent 23 pairs.

The reason why most of the body cells of plants and animals possess a **diploid** set of chromosomes is relatively simple. The fertilized egg from which all the body cells arise is always formed by the coming together and *fusing of two cells.* A sperm cell from the male parent always fuses with the **unfertilized** egg cell from the female parent. Thus the diploid set of chromosomes possessed by the **fertilized** egg is really constituted of two single, or **haploid** sets (Fig. 3-9). One of these haploid sets was present in the nucleus of the unfertilized egg, and the other was brought in by the nucleus of the sperm cell. When the egg and sperm *nuclei* finally fuse into one—and this is the essential event of **fertilization**—the nucleus of the fertilized egg becomes diploid, and it remains so throughout all subsequent mitotic divisions.

Fertilization. Fertilization is a very important process found in the reproductive cycles of a great majority of plant and animal organisms. The new individual that arises from the fertilized egg possesses chromosomes (and genes) contributed by both the male and female of its parents, and consequently this new individual derives its heritable qualities from both. Sexual forms of reproduction always involve fertilization, and it is only in sexual reproduction that **biparental** inheritance is found. Asexual reproductive processes never involve fertilization, and in asexual reproduction, inheritance is entirely uniparental. Asexually produced offspring tend to resemble their single parent and do not display as wide a variability as those that are generated sexually.

MEIOTIC CELL DIVISION

The real problem concerning chromosome numbers does not revolve around how the body cells come to be diploid, but how the **eggs** and **sperm** of animals, and the **spores** of plants, come to be **haploid.** This difficult question took many years to solve. Finally it was learned that these reproductive cells are produced not by mitosis, but by a highly modified type of division, which is called **meiosis.**

One difference between meiosis and mitosis is that meiosis involves two succeeding divisions, whereas each single mitotic division is complete unto itself. In meiosis, when the two divisions have been finished, four cells (or at least four nuclei) have been produced. The parent cell at the outset of meiosis is always diploid and the four final daughter cells are always haploid. In mitosis, on the other hand, the daughter cells always possess the same number of chromosomes as the parent cell, whether that original number was diploid or, as sometimes is the case, haploid. This and other differences between meiosis and mitosis serve to distinguish clearly between the two processes. Nevertheless, it is important to realize that the two types of division have much in common. In both cases the same four stages—prophase, metaphase, anaphase, and telophase—are plainly distinguishable, although in meiosis the steps occur twice. Also the same accessory mechanisms, including spindles, asters, and

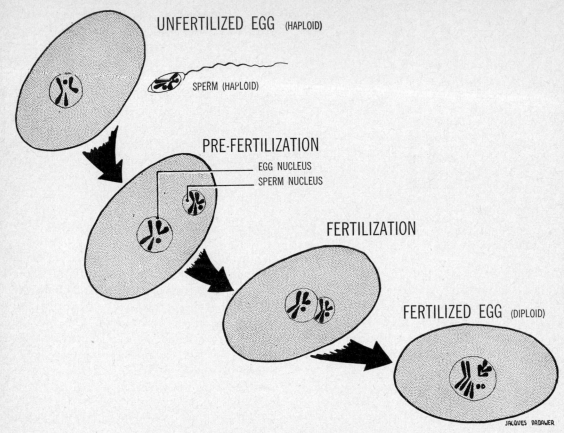

UNFERTILIZED EGG (HAPLOID)

SPERM (HAPLOID)

PRE-FERTILIZATION

EGG NUCLEUS
SPERM NUCLEUS

FERTILIZATION

FERTILIZED EGG (DIPLOID)

JACQUES PADAWER

Fig. 3-9. Fertilization: origin of diploid cells.

so forth, take part in both kinds of cell division.

The meiotic divisions take place in the **ovaries** or the **testes,** in the case of **animals,** and in the **spore capsules,** in the case of **plants.** At present it will suffice to describe meiosis as it occurs in the testis of a male animal. Later, in connection with the study of heredity, the similar development of eggs in the ovary, and of spores in the sporangium, will also be described.

The testes of man and other multicellular animals contain a group of numerous special cells, called the **spermatogonia** (Fig. 3-10). Sooner or later these cells eventually give rise to the sperm cells. The **spermatogonia** are **diploid** cells. They have arisen, along with all other cells of the organism, from the repeated mitoses of the original diploid fertilized egg. Furthermore, the spermato-

gonia in the testes may continue to multiply by mitosis, giving rise to a steady supply of more spermatogonia, all diploid.

Finally, a few at a time, the germ cells in the testes stop multiplying by mitosis. Now each begins to grow and can be recognized as a **primary spermatocyte** (Fig. 3-10). Each of the primary spermatocytes is destined to undergo only two further divisions and these will be the meiotic divisions. Consequently each primary spermatocyte will form only four sperm cells (Fig. 3-10).

The prophase of the **first meiotic division** commences almost as soon as the primary spermatocyte begins to enlarge. This prophase differs in two ways from that of an ordinary mitosis. First it endures much longer, usually for days, rather than for hours or minutes, and during all this period the elongate chromosomes are definitely vis-

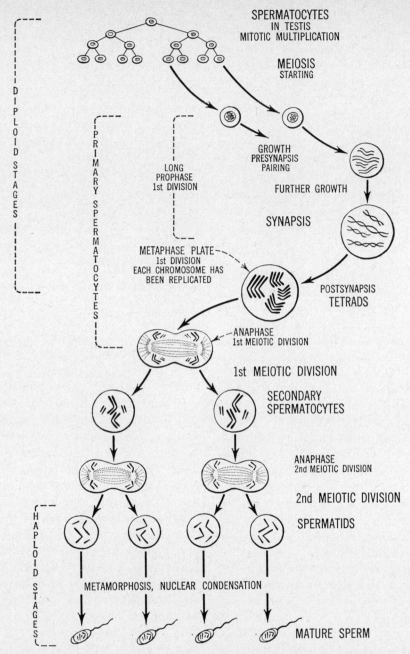

Fig. 3-10.   Diagram of meiosis as observed in a testis during the production of sperm. Note that the prophase of the first meiotic division differs in several ways from the prophase of an ordinary mitotic division: (1) it endures much longer; (2) it is accompanied by considerable cell growth; and (3) it involves synapsis between the members of each homologous pair of chromosomes. Moreover, the second division is unique in that no replication of the chromosomes takes place and the interphase between the first and second divisions is exceptionally short. Meiosis leads to the production of haploid cells (or nuclei) from diploid progenitors; whereas mitosis transmits an unchanged number of chromosomes, either diploid or haploid, to the daughter cells (or nuclei). In mitosis, moreover, the members of the homologous pairs, when pairs are present, do not associate as pairs.

ible and individually identifiable. Second, in the prophase of the first meiotic division, the two homologous chromosomes of every *pair* always lie side by side, intimately entwined one around the other one (Fig. 3-10). This pairing and entwining of homologous chromosomes, which is called **synapsis,** has very real consequences in heredity because, while the pairs of chromosomes are in the synaptic condition, they may mutually exchange a certain number of their genes (p. 491). Synapsis occurs only during the prophase of the first meiotic division. Usually during ordinary mitosis, the homologous chromosomes behave as independent units and show little or no attraction for each other.

Before metaphase, in the first meiotic division, the pairs of chromosomes have unraveled from synapsis, but still the members of each pair lie side by side. By this time each chromosome has divided lengthwise into two daughters. Consequently at the metaphase of the first meiotic division one sees the chromosomes assembled on the spindle in characteristic quadruple groupings, which are called the **tetrads** (Fig. 3-10).

The postsynaptic division of each chromosome is the only occasion when the chromosomes divide during the whole process of meiosis. In fact the two cell divisions, which follow shortly, serve merely to distribute the chromosomes that exist as soon as the tetrads have been formed (Fig. 3-10). And if later events proceed in a normal fashion, each of the four sperm cells produced by any one spermatocyte is destined finally to receive just one chromosome from every tetrad (Fig. 3-10).

After the first metaphase, the remaining events of meiosis usually proceed quite rapidly. The anaphase and telophase of the first division lead to the formation of two cells, the **secondary spermatocytes,** each receiving half of each tetrad. In other words each secondary spermatocyte receives one of the two **diads** into which each tetrad has become separated (Fig. 3-10). But the precise manner in which a tetrad separates into diads

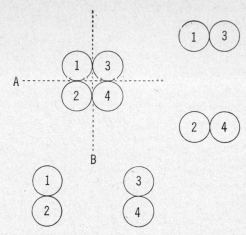

Fig. 3-11. Diagram showing how the four chromosomes of any given tetrad may separate during the first meiotic division. Regardless of which of the two possibilities (A or B) occurs, one member of each tetrad eventually reaches every sperm, when the second meiotic division occurs.

appears to be a matter of chance. The two possibilities indicated in Figure 3-11 seem to occur with equal frequency.

Without pause, the secondary spermatocytes usually launch into the second meiotic division. In fact the diad chromosomes remain visible, as they quickly pass through prophase and assume the metaphase arrangement on the spindle (Fig. 3-10). Then the anaphases and telophases are completed, and a single chromosome from each of the diads is delivered to each of the four final cells. But here again it is a matter of chance as to which member of a diad goes to a particular one of the resulting cells.

The four resulting cells are called **spermatids.** But shortly thereafter, when each has developed an elongate motile flagellum, they are called the **sperm.** As may be seen by referring to Figure 3-10, each sperm possesses the haploid set of chromosomes that later will be carried to the egg, when fertilization occurs.

Similar processes of meiosis are encountered in the development of the egg cells in female animals, and of spore cells in plants; the special features of these developments will be discussed in Chapter 26.

Significance of Meiosis. Meiosis quite obviously constitutes a mechanism whereby haploid reproductive cells are formed from diploid progenitors. During the two divisions of the original cell, only one division of the chromosomes occurs. Consequently, meiosis inevitably produces a **reduction** in the chromosome number. Meiosis and fertilization together constitute a system by which half the chromosomes of the new individual are derived from each of the parents, without at the same time leading to a progressive increase in the chromosome number of the species. In conjunction with fertilization, meiosis provides a basis for sexual reproduction, permitting the development of biparental inheritance. Biparental inheritance in turn greatly increases variability in the inherited qualities within the species. In species where the only method of cell multiplication is mitosis, the reproduction is asexual; and since the chromosomes passed on to the ensuing generations tend to be identical with those of the parent, hereditary variability in asexual forms remains at a minimum.

REPRODUCTION IN SIMPLER ORGANISMS

Strictly speaking, the term "reproduction" is restricted to processes whereby *total* new organisms are generated. Thus the mere multiplication of cells in a multicellular organism does not of itself constitute reproduction. Only when the single cell is at the same time a complete organism, as in the Protozoa and other unicellular forms, does cell division alone constitute a form of reproduction.

The reproduction of an organism may be **sexual** or **asexual,** depending upon whether **fertilization** comes into play. All forms of reproduction which involve fertilization are designated as sexual, whereas all reproductive processes not involving fertilization are, by this token, asexual.

Asexual Forms of Reproduction.
Binary Fission. Binary fission is the term employed when an organism divides directly into two approximately equal parts, each of which then grows into an individual similar to the departed parent. The commonest form of binary fission results when a unicellular organism undergoes mitosis (Fig. 3-7). However, there are some multicellular forms, like certain flatworms, that reproduce by splitting directly into two quite equal pieces (p. 395).

Among protozoans, bacteria, and algae, the two cells formed by binary fission *usually* separate soon after division, swimming or crawling away, each on its separate mission. Consequently such species remain strictly unicellular. But the cells of some nonmotile forms adhere together throughout several divisions. Thus they form **incipient colonies** of loose and indefinite form. Such colonies disintegrate readily with mechanical disturbances such as currents in the surrounding water. The formation of definite colonies depends upon a more firmly established tendency of cells to cling together through a series of divisions; and in a **true colony** the planes of division, and consequently the arrangement of the cells, become fixed and regular. In a linear colony such as *Spirogyra,* for example, all cell divisions occur at right angles to the length of the filament, and the cells remain fastened together end to end (Fig. 3-16). Such colonies cannot be dispersed except by rather violent disturbances, or by the death and disintegration of some of the cells in the chain. Many cell aggregates, even such definite colonies as *Spirogyra,* display no real distinction between the reproduction of the individual cells (cell division) and the reproduction of the whole colony. Only after further evolution—with the development of special cells that assume the reproductive function of the colony or organism—does this distinction become plain.

Although binary fission is probably the oldest and most primitive kind of reproduction, it is not restricted entirely to unicellular forms. A few multicellular animals such as *Hydra* (Fig. 3-12) and *Planaria* (Fig. 16-7) can also reproduce by fission. When a multicellular organism splits into two quite equal

Fig. 3-12. Parent *Hydra*, with two buds. (Copyright, General Biological Supply House, Inc.)

parts, each part then grows into a new individual. And even such highly organized creatures as earthworms can behave in similar fashion, if *cut* into two pieces of fairly equal size.

Budding. Budding is similar to binary fission except that the two parts into which the body divides are conspicuously unequal. A most familiar example of budding is found in dividing yeast cells (Fig. 10-0). Here it is seen that one of the daughter cells receives only a minor share of the cytoplasm, although the nucleus of the smaller is equal to that of the larger daughter cell. The smaller daughter cell, called the **bud**, thus retains a full potential for growth and activity. In time the bud may catch up with its larger sister, which meanwhile may continue to give off other buds. In an undisturbed medium the yeast cells may cling together for several generations and thus give the appearance of a small branching filament. However, their attachments are tenuous, and **permanent colonies** are not formed in this particular kind of plant.

Budding is fairly common among proto-

zoans, and it occurs also in some multicellular plants and animals. In the latter case, however, the bud is not a single cell, but an aggregate of cells derived by mitosis from the cells of the parent. In *Hydra*, for example, the bud develops into a small but complete new individual before it becomes detached and independent (Fig. 3-12).

Sporulation. The formation of **reproductive spores** is very common among simpler organisms, and practically universal among higher plants. Typically each spore-forming cell undergoes two or more divisions in rapid succession, producing four or more **spores**. Frequently the sporulation divisions are meiotic, so that usually the spores are haploid. The spore, unlike an egg or sperm, develops into a new individual *without any process of fertilization*. The sporulation divisions often occur inside the cell wall of the spore mother cell (Fig. 3-13); and usually each spore develops its own tough casing, making it resistant to dry conditions. Certain yeasts reproduce not only by budding but also by sporulation. When the medium in which the yeasts live begins to dry up, or becomes otherwise unsuitable for life, each of the cells divides into four equal spores, possessing individual protective covers, but all contained within the original cell wall (Fig. 3-13). Later this outer casing ruptures and the liberated spores may be blown about in the dry atmosphere without suffering death from loss of water. Finally the spore may chance upon a

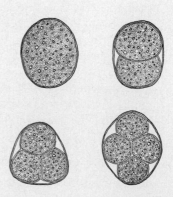

Fig. 3-13. Spore formation in yeast cells (unstained).

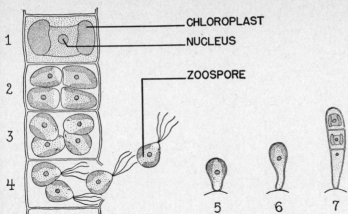

CHLOROPLAST

NUCLEUS

ZOOSPORE

Fig. 3-14. Sporulation in *Ulothrix*, a filamentous green alga. 1, nonreproducing cell of filament; 2-4, formation and liberation of zoospores; 5-7, development of a zoospore into a new filament.

suitable new medium, where it may begin to grow and bud again.

Many species of algae reproduce asexually by means of free-swimming flagellated spores, called **swarm spores,** or **zoospores.** At least four, but frequently many, zoospores are formed from a single mother cell, as in *Ulothrix* (Fig. 3-14). In this plant the zoospores free themselves and start migrating in all directions. If one finds a favorable new location, it settles down and develops into the ordinary attached (sessile) form of the plant.

Among the higher plants, including the mosses, ferns, and seed plants, asexual reproduction by means of sporulation occurs at regularly alternating periods during the life cycle of each species. In these plants the number of spores produced by each of the **spore mother cells** has become reduced to a *standard of four.* Each spore mother cell divides only twice to produce its quota of spores. These two divisions are **meiotic** in character, and consequently the *spores in all higher plants are haploid cells.* Each spore develops *without fertilization* into a form of the plant in which all the cells are haploid. Only later in the cycle do such plants produce eggs and sperm. Then fertilization occurs and the diploid condition is restored (see Chap. 12).

SEXUAL FORMS OF REPRODUCTION

A great majority of living things, including many unicellular and colonial forms, ex-

hibit sexual reproduction. In these cases, fertilization always occurs in one form or another.

The essential feature of fertilization is the fusion of two haploid nuclei that usually are recognizable as the egg nucleus and the sperm nucleus. Ordinarily the resulting diploid nucleus becomes the progenitor of all the nuclei of the new individual. In more primitive forms, however, it is not always possible to distinguish between the egg and sperm cells. Sometimes the two cells that undergo fusion appear to be identical, and therefore it is necessary to speak in broader terms. The two haploid cells that come together in fertilization, whether similar or dissimilar in appearance, are always designated as the **gamete** cells. The egg, when distinguishable, is called the **female gamete,** and the sperm, the **male gamete.** Furthermore, the diploid nucleus created by the fusion of the gamete nuclei is always called the **zygote nucleus;** and the whole cell formed at the time of fertilization is the **zygote.** In evolution apparently sexual reproduction came before any differences had developed in the external appearance of individuals of opposite sex, or between the gametes produced by the two cooperating parents.

Isogamy vs. Heterogamy. A number of examples can be found that illustrate the foregoing principles. In *Spirogyra* and closely related species, the ordinary cells of the filament are haploid cells, and any or all of these

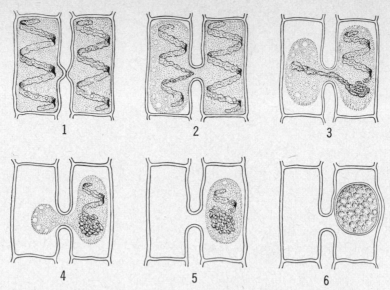

Fig. 3-15.   Conjugation of *Spirogyra*. Note how a bridge forms between the conjugating cells and how one of the cells flows over and fuses with the other. Also note the appearance of contractile vacuoles, which eliminate water from the cells, allowing them to shrink as they fuse.

filament cells may act as gametes. When *Spirogyra* engages in sexual reproduction— and this usually occurs in the fall of the year—the pairs of cells that happen to lie oppositely on two nearby filaments begin to show signs of mutual stimulation. Short tube-like processes grow out from each of the prospective gametes (Fig. 3-15). These outgrowths join in pairs, and the cell walls dissolve away at the points of contact. In this way an open tube is formed connecting the members of each pair of conjugating cells (Fig. 3-15). Soon all the protoplasm of one gamete passes through the **conjugation tube** and fuses with the protoplasm of the other. Finally—and this is the essence of fertilization—*the two* **haploid gamete nuclei** *fuse to form the* **diploid zygote nucleus.**

In the case of *Spirogyra* the gamete cells are identical in appearance. Accordingly these gametes are specified as **isogametes**, and the production of such gametes is called **isogamy.** Conversely, cases where the gametes (**heterogametes**) are obviously not alike are designated as **heterogamy.** Although isogamy is fairly widespread among primitive organ-

isms, it is not encountered in higher forms. Heterogamy became dominant early in evolution, and fully differentiated eggs and sperm are common to practically all multicellular animals and plants.

Shortly after fertilization the zygote of *Spirogyra* develops a very thick cell wall and becomes a resting cell, called the **zygospore** (Fig. 3-16). The zygospore is resistant to cold and drought and is able to survive through the winter. Then in the spring, the zygospore germinates (Fig. 3-17), but just before a new filament is formed, the zygote nucleus divides twice in rapid succession. In *Spirogyra, these are the meiotic divisions.* Four haploid nuclei are thus produced, but three of these degenerate prior to germination (Fig. 3-17, stage 8). The remaining haploid nucleus gives rise *by mitosis* to all the nuclei of the new filament, and consequently all the cells of the colony are haploid cells.

Isogamy is also encountered in many other algae, and in a few fungi and protozoans. Most higher algae, however, have specialized gametes, which are small flagellated cells, similar to but smaller than the zoospores. Some-

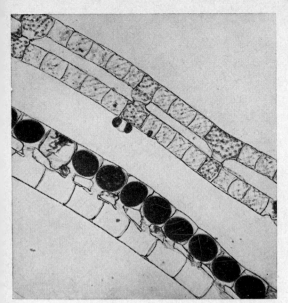

Fig. 3-16. Photograph of conjugating *Spirogyra*. The upper pair of filaments shows three pairs of cells at the outset of conjugation; and the lower filaments show a number of zygospores (dark oval bodies) which result from conjugation. (Photograph retouched. Copyright, General Biological Supply House, Inc.)

times the same cells may act either as asexual zoospores, or as gametes, as in the case of *Ulothrix,* another filamentous green alga (Fig. 3-18). In this plant the number of reproductive cells produced by each cell of the filament may vary from 4 to 64; the larger the number, the smaller the size of the cells. The larger spores soon settle down and develop asexually into a new filament by repeated mitotic division (Fig. 3-18). The smaller "spores" may also germinate in the same way, but their growth is slower and the filaments produced by them are less vigorous. More frequently these smaller cells fuse in pairs, thus acting as gametes and forming a zygote (Fig. 3-18). After fertilization has occurred, the zygote develops into a thick-walled zygospore, as in *Spirogyra*. Likewise in *Ulothrix,* the diploid zygote undergoes two divisions, the **meiotic divisions,** just before germination. At first the four resulting haploid cells lie huddled together inside the old cell wall (Fig. 3-18) but finally, after this encasement has disintegrated, each of the four

haploid cells gives rise by mitosis to a separate new filament.

The evolutionary transition between isogamy, which is very common among simpler organisms, and heterogamy, which reaches a standardized condition in the eggs and sperm of higher plants and animals, can be found in a single group of free-swimming green algal plants. This group, the Volvocaceae, is made up of many species, but only three species will be mentioned in the present connection.

All the Volvocaceae reproduce both sexually and asexually. The gametes formed by *Pandorina* (Fig. 3-19) are of two sorts, one slightly larger than the other. When fertilization takes place, one of the smaller, or **microgametes,** usually fuses with a larger, **macrogamete.** But sometimes two microgametes, or two macrogametes, will come together. In either case, a diploid zygote is formed, and this gives rise to the new colony. Accordingly it may be said that *Pandorina* shows the first beginnings of a difference between the gametes of the sexes.

In *Eudorina* (Fig. 3-19) and *Volvox* (Fig. 3-19), the differentiation between the gametes has developed much further. The macrogametes of *Eudorina* are several times larger than the microgametes, although both gametes are flagellated and motile. Moreover, fertilization always involves a fusion of the *unequal* gametes. But the climax of heterogamy is reached in *Volvox* (Fig. 3-19). The macrogamete of *Volvox,* due to its relatively large size and its inability to move, can properly be called an egg, and the very small **motile** microgamete can truly be considered a **sperm.**

The differentiation between the sperm, which is small and motile, and the egg, which is large and nonmotile, represents an efficient division of labor. The size and motility of the sperm cell makes it an effective agent for carrying the paternal chromosomes to the egg. Usually the sperm are produced in very large numbers and discharged near the eggs. Consequently at least one sperm is almost

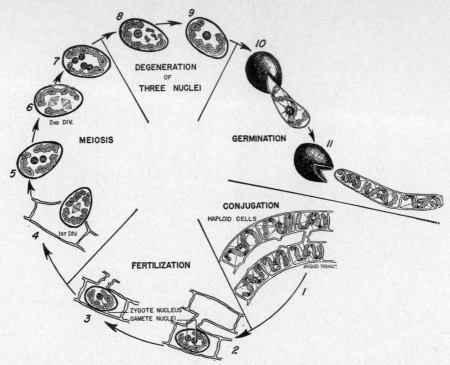

Fig. 3-17. Life cycle of *Spirogyra*. Conjugation (stage 1) usually occurs in the fall of the year, and during the winter months the zygospore (stage 3) lies dormant. In the spring, however, meiosis (stages 4-7) occurs, and soon thereafter the new haploid filament emerges from the spore capsule (stage 10-11).

sure to find and penetrate each egg. The egg cell, on the other hand, is adapted for the reception of the sperm and for assembling the maternal and paternal chromosomes to form the zygote nucleus, which will give rise to all the nuclei of the offspring. In addition, the egg is laden with yolk and other stored material to nourish the offspring during its embryonic development—that is, until the new organism is capable of obtaining food for itself. And since eggs and sperm are the agency for sexual reproduction in a large majority of plants and animals, there can be little doubt as to the efficiency of these developments.

LIFE CYCLES; HAPLOID AND DIPLOID PHASES

The complete life span of an organism, starting at any given stage, and extending to the time when the offspring reach the same

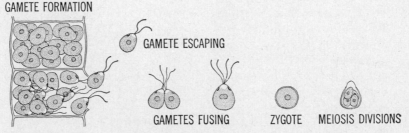

Fig. 3-18. Sexual reproduction of *Ulothrix*. Each of the four spores may develop into a new filament (as shown in Figure 3-14).

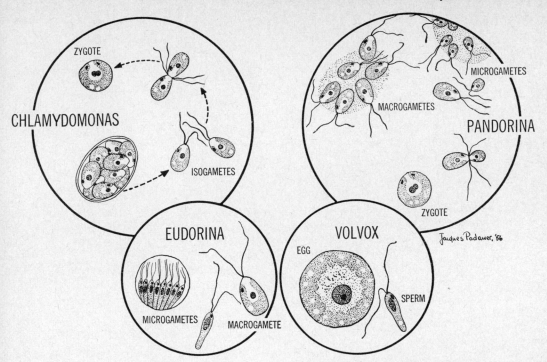

Fig. 3-19. Sexual reproduction of several Volvocaceae.

stage, constitutes the **life cycle** in each species. In some species, the life cycle is very simple, but in others, as we shall see, it is quite complex.

Some amoebae and other unicellular organisms that reproduce solely by binary fission display the very simplest type of life cycle. A young amoeba feeds, grows, and then divides, which returns the species directly to the starting point. Such a cycle is devoid of any sexual stages, and consequently the terms diploid and haploid have no real meaning. Without fertilization no diploid stage is ever formed, but by convention the cells in such species are regarded as haploid (Fig. 3-20).

Another type of life cycle, which characterizes many green algae, is exhibited by *Spirogyra*. During the *major part* of the life cycle, while the colony is multiplying asexually by mitosis, the cells remain **haploid.** The diploid stage starts at the time of fertilization and persists only until meiosis occurs. This is in the spring, just before the

zygospore germinates to form a new filament, which again is haploid (Fig. 3-20).

The opposite type of cycle is found in almost all multicellular animals, including man, and in a few primitive plants. In man, the diploid stage begins when the egg is fertilized, and persists in all the body cells, which arise from the fertilized egg by mitosis. Meiosis occurs very late in the cycle, when the eggs and sperm are being produced in the sex organs. This type of cycle is shown in Figure 3-20.

The final type of cycle, which is intermediate between the preceding two, is found in all higher plants (Chap. 12), and in a few multicellular algae. In this type of cycle (Fig. 3-20), there is a regular alternation of haploid and diploid generations. The fertilized egg always gives rise to a diploid plant body that reproduces asexually—by forming spores. This diploid asexual generation in higher plants is therefore called the **sporophyte generation.** The spores in all higher plants are produced by meiosis in groups of

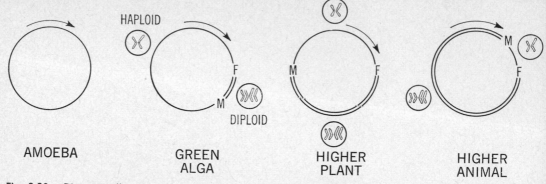

Fig. 3-20. Diagrams illustrating the relations of the haploid and diploid stages in various types of life cycles (see text). In each figure the single line represents the haploid, the double line the diploid condition. The direction of the arrows indicates the succession of generations. F, fertilization; M, meiosis.

four from the spore mother cells in the spore capsule. Consequently the spores are always haploid. Each haploid spore invariably gives rise to a haploid form of the plant, which eventually will reproduce by gametes. Thus the haploid sexual generation in higher plants is called the **gametophyte.** Finally when fertilization again takes place, the haploid gamete nuclei fuse, and the diploid con-

dition of the succeeding sporophyte generation is restored.

The early evolution of reproductive structures among plants and animals appears to have occurred by trial and error. A variety of methods first appeared among primitive organisms, but only a few were successful enough to be passed on to higher plants and animals.

TEST QUESTIONS

1. Explain three important differences and three important similarities between *mitosis* and *meiosis*.

2. What is *amitosis?* Why is amitosis *not* regarded as a *normal* kind of cell division?

3. In proper sequence list the events that occur during the prophase of mitosis: (a) in a plant cell; (b) in an animal cell.

4. How does the prophase of the *first* meiotic division differ from the prophase of mitosis?

5. How are metaphases and anaphases distinguished from the other stages of mitosis?

6. In mitosis, what invariable rule determines the movements of the members of each pair of daughter chromosomes (the two chromosomes formed by the division of each parent chromosome)?

7. What importance is attached to the fact that each chromosome divides *lengthwise,* rather than *crosswise?*

8. Specify two ways in which the *telophases* of plant and animal cells are: (a) different; and (b) similar.

9. Assuming that the chromosomes were distinctly visible, how would you decide whether a given cell were *haploid* or *diploid?*

10. Explain the term *homologous chromosomes.*

11. Is it true that any species of plant or animal can be identified by studying the chromosomes of one of its cells? Explain your answer carefully.

12. In man, most of the cells are formed by mitosis, but some are produced by meiosis. Explain this statement more specifically.

13. Identify each of the following terms: (a) spireme chromosomes; (b) spermatogonia; (c) primary spermatocytes; (d) synapsis; (e) tetrads; (f) secondary spermatocytes; (g) diads; (h) spermatids; (i) sperm.

14. In each case specify the distinguishing features and cite a specific example: (a) asexual reproduction; (b) binary fission; (c) budding; (d) sporulation; (e) zoospores.

15. Carefully define each term and in each case cite *three* specific examples: (a) a gamete cell; (b) the zygote; (c) fertilization.

16. Distinguish between isogamy and heterogamy; cite two examples in each case.
17. Divide the following cells into two lists according to whether they are haploid or diploid: (a) fertilized eggs; (b) the tissue cells of man's body; (c) sperm cells; (d) unfertilized eggs; (e) the zygospore of *Spirogyra;* (f) the zygospore of *Ulothrix;* (g) the macrogamete of *Pandorina;* (h) a spore mother cell; (i) the spore of a higher plant.
18. In the life cycle of each of the following organisms, specify where fertilization and meiosis take place: (a) man; (b) *Spirogyra;* (c) any high plant; (d) *Amoeba.*
19. Carefully explain each of the following statements: (a) certain features of mitosis very plainly indicate that among the various structures of a cell the chromosomes are of paramount importance; (b) jointly, meiosis and fertilization provide a basis for *biparental* inheritance.

FURTHER READINGS

1. "How Cells Divide," by D. Mazia, in "The Living Cell," special issue of *Scientific American,* September 1961.
2. *The Cell,* vol. 3, *Mitosis and Meiosis,* ed. by J. Brachet and A. E. Mirsky; New York, 1961.
3. *General Cytology,* 3d ed., by E. D. P. DeRobertis, W. W. Nowinski and F. A. Saetz; Philadelphia, 1960.

4 - *The Chemical and Physical Structure of Protoplasm*

VARIOUS microscopic techniques provide many clues to the functions of the different parts of the cell. But below the reach even of the electron microscope there lies a realm of smaller things: the world of molecules and atoms, which compose the ultimate structure of all matter. Biologists now realize that the visible parts of the cell are very important, but full attention must also be given to the submicroscopic **molecular pattern** of protoplasm. This means that an irreducible minimum of biochemistry and biophysics has become basic in general biology. The cell, essentially, is a delicate physicochemical mechanism; and the merest trace of a foreign chemical such as cyanide, or the slightest excess of a physical factor such as heat, may derange the finely poised molecular structure of the protoplasm, killing the cell immediately.

Each cell faces the problem of obtaining a quantity and variety of substances sufficient to *maintain* and *operate* its existing protoplasmic structure, as well as to increase the protoplasm when *growth* occurs. But before the chemistry of growth, maintenance, and operation can be considered, it is necessary to know the general composition of living matter. What substances are always present? How much of each of these essential components must there be? And how are these active molecules assembled and arranged with reference to visible structures in the cell?

No two samples of protoplasm are ever *precisely* identical; but the many differences found among various cells are mainly matters of detail. One cell utilizes a certain kind of sugar that differs slightly from the sugar used by another. Plant cells synthesize starch; whereas animal cells build glycogen, a closely related compound. But above and beyond these specific variations, there is a general pattern, and all protoplasm conforms to this pattern. Always the same types of chemical compounds are present, and these compounds play similar roles in the protoplasm of plants and animals generally.

Merely to list the specific compounds that

can be extracted from the cell would be a difficult task. The list, in fact, would take on the proportions of a telephone directory. A far simpler approach is to ascertain the **elements** out of which these many compounds are formed. What various **atoms,** combined together to form a great variety of molecules, are present in the protoplasm? Assuming that a sample of protoplasm were placed in a sealed retort and subjected to such drastic chemical treatment that each of the many compound molecules was decomposed into its elements, *what atoms would be yielded?*

ELEMENTARY CONSTITUENTS IN PROTOPLASM

Table 4-1 shows that oxygen, hydrogen, carbon, and nitrogen account for a very large proportion of the weight of the protoplasmic compounds. These same elements are also most abundant in the nonliving ma-

terials of our world. Among the elements[1] that compose all matter, carbon, hydrogen, oxygen, and nitrogen are uniquely fitted for their functions in the protoplasmic system. So far as we know, living things have arisen only on planets where these elements are very abundant—and this is probably not a coincidence (p. 187).

Among the elements, only those given in the list are generally found in protoplasm, although a few others are found in special

[1] The classical number of elements, *ninety-two,* has been modified by modern chemical research, since this classical number did not include any of the newly synthesized elements, such as plutonium, which recently have been "created" by the bombardment of certain atomic nuclei with high-speed particles, although some of these elements may have existed prior to their artificial synthesis. Modern work in atomic physics also shows that, as a result of small variations in weight, the atoms of a particular element may display several forms, called **atomic isotopes,** many of which are radioactive (p. 141). However, all the isotopes of a given element display an *identical chemical behavior.*

Table 4-1—Elements Liberated by Decomposition of Protoplasmic Compounds

Name and Symbol	Average Percentage by Weight	Combining Capacity (Valence)	Common Appearance, as the Free Element
Oxygen (O)	76.0	2	Colorless gas; supports combustion; 16 times heavier than hydrogen
Hydrogen (H)	10.0	1	Very light, flammable gas; comparative weight = unity
Nitrogen (N)	2.5	3 and 5	Colorless nonflammable gas; heavier than hydrogen
Carbon (C)	10.5	4	Black solid
Sulfur (S)	.2	2 and 6	Yellow solid
Phosphorus (P)	.3	5	Red solid
Potassium (K)	.3	1	Light metallic solid
Iron (Fe)	.01	2 and 3	Heavy metallic solid
Magnesium (Mg)	.02	2	Light, flammable metal
Calcium (Ca)	.02	2	Light metal
Sodium (Na)	.04	1	Light active metal
Chlorine (Cl)	.10	1	Heavy greenish gas
Copper (Cu)	Trace	1 and 2	Metallic solids
Cobalt (Co)	Trace	2 and 3	
Zinc (Zn)	Trace	2	
Manganese (Mn)	Trace	4	

cases. All the protoplasmic elements are very common in nonliving nature, being abundantly represented in the soil, the atmosphere and the waters of the earth. No single element is entirely peculiar to living things. However, a few—especially carbon and nitrogen—are relatively much more abundant in living than in nonliving matter.

BASIC IDEAS AND DEFINITIONS [2]

Matter and Energy. The material component of our universe—*matter in general*—is to be identified by its universal properties. Always **matter occupies space,** and always it **displays weight.** Each kind of matter may assume the form of a **solid** (like ice), or of a **liquid** (like water), or of a **gas** (like water vapor); but whatever its form, matter always retains its identifying attributes.

Energy is the other fundamental component of our universe. Energy may take a variety of forms, such as light, heat, mechanical movement, electricity, and so forth. In fact energy can only be identified in terms of what it *does,* or what it *can do. Energy is the motion of, or the capacity to produce motion in, any mass of matter.* Sometimes the energized mass is very small, as in the case of the flowing electrons of an electric current or the vibrating molecules of a heated substance;

[2] Two kinds of type are used in this section of the book. For students who have not had chemistry previously, the material in smaller type is just as important as, if not more important than, the material in larger type. For students who have had chemistry, the material in smaller type will be useful as a review.

or the material body may be larger, like a bullet hurtling from the barrel of a rifle.

All forms of energy are at least partially interconvertible [3] (Table 4-2). This can be illustrated by the electric system of an automobile. The battery of the car contains a store of **chemical energy** represented by the reactivity of the acid and other chemicals of the battery. This chemical energy is transformed to **electrical energy** whenever the headlight switch is closed, and as the electricity flows through the filament of the lamp bulb, electrical energy is converted to **heat.** Then when the temperature of the lamp filament reaches the incandescent point, the heat begins to be transformed into **light.** Or, if the starter switch is pushed and the electricity flows through the starting motor, electrical energy is converted into **mechanical energy** (the movement of the pistons, etc.) as the engine is forced to "turn over" before it "catches."

In modern science, everything that happens—every natural event and phenomenon—is to be explained and described in terms of matter and energy, in terms of some change, actual or potential, in the internal or external motion of the components of some material system. Throughout the universe, matter and energy are inseparably associated. Each acts and interacts solely through the medium of the other. Attempting to understand the general principles of biology, chemistry,

[3] As predicted by the Einstein equation ($e = MC^2$) matter and energy are also interconvertible. However, such interconversions are insignificantly small except under rare conditions (e.g., in an atomic bomb) and they seem to be unimportant in living organisms. In this equation, the energy (e) is expressed in *ergs;* the mass (M) is in *grams;* and the constant (C) represents the velocity of light, expressed in *centimeters per second.*

Table 4-2—Forms of Energy

	Kinetic	*Potential*
Polymolecular*	Movement (mechanical energy)	Weight (gravity)
Molecular	Heat	Cohesion and adhesion†
Atomic	Chemical reaction	Chemical reactivity
Electronic	Electric current	Electric charge
Radiant	Light, x-rays, etc.	

* Pertaining to masses of visible size.
† Cohesion is attraction between molecules of the same substance; adhesion is attraction between molecules of different substances.

or physics, without reference to matter and energy, would be like trying to appreciate the beauty of a landscape in a world devoid of light.

Molecular Composition of Matter. Each appreciable mass of matter, regardless of its specific kind, is composed of a great number of subvisible unit particles, the **molecules.** This knowledge has become so commonplace that many students do not pause to question its origin, although there is a large body of experimental evidence from every field of science that firmly establishes the molecular nature of matter.

Let us choose any sample of **matter,** such as water. As everyone knows, water *exists in three states:* as a **solid** (at temperatures below the freezing point, 0° C), as a **liquid** (at temperatures between 0° and 100° C), and as a **gas** (above 100° C)—assuming that the water sample is pure and that other conditions, especially the atmospheric pressure, are standardized. In the gaseous state, of course, the water is not visible. As soon as the water molecules, which in the solid and liquid states are quite closely packed into a tangible mass, have absorbed enough heat energy to escape as individuals from the common mass, their subvisible smallness is revealed. But water was chosen at random to exemplify matter generally. All other samples of matter—all other *specific chemical substances*—can undergo similar *changes* of state, although in some cases the practical conditions are hard to realize. In the **solid state** the molecules of a substance are relatively closely packed and the intermolecular attractions are strong enough to prevent the free migration of the individual molecules within the solid mass, although each is free to vibrate (due to heat energy) in the region of a relatively fixed locus. In the **liquid state** the intermolecular distances are greater and consequently the forces of attraction between the molecules are significantly smaller. Under these conditions, the individual molecules are free, not only to vibrate, but also to migrate (more and more rapidly as the absorbed heat energy increases) through the body of the liquid, although they are not free to escape en masse from the definitive boundary of the liquid. Finally, when a liquid has been energized by heat beyond a certain critical point, the molecules of the mass begin to move so rapidly that they separate themselves more or less completely from the intermolecular attractions; and in the **gaseous state,** *the subvisible* smallness of the individual molecules becomes apparent.

Molecules vs. Atoms. There are thousands of different kinds of matter, such as water, sugar, oxygen, nitrogen, etc., or—as the chemist expresses it—thousands of specifically different **substances,** each characterized by a different kind of molecule. The problem of identifying these many specific molecules belongs, of course, to the field of chemistry. But the molecules present in protoplasm also belong to biology; and it so happens that some of the protoplasmic molecules are extremely complex in their chemical structure.

The chemist designates each specific molecule by its **formula,** which specifies the atoms that are combined in definite proportion in each different molecule—as, for example; water $= H_2O$; table sugar $= C_{12}H_{22}O_{11}$; and oxygen $= O_2$. If such examples were repeated indefinitely, it would be found that the molecular formulas of all known substances can be given by using the symbols of only 92 different atoms (elements), together with their relatively rare isotopes. In other words, the same elements enter into a multitude of specific chemical combinations in forming the molecules of all substances in our universe.

The methods used by the chemist in determining that a sugar molecule is to be designated as $C_{12}H_{22}O_{11}$, or the water molecule as H_2O, are difficult and indirect; but taken as a whole, they are absolutely convincing. However, only the slightest indication of these methods can be given here.

In the case of sugar, it is not difficult to demonstrate that carbon (C) is present in the molecule. Anyone who has heated sugar and allowed it to **char** has demonstrated this point. At high temperature sugar molecules begin to decompose, liberating carbon, the familiar black solid, which is easily recognized. The presence of hydrogen (H) and oxygen (O) in the sugar molecules can also be shown by heat decomposition, at very high temperature, in a sealed retort. Under these conditions, the water (H_2O) that is liberated can be collected and identified. And finally, the water can be decomposed by means of a strong direct current, and the liberated hydrogen and oxygen can be identified (Fig. 4-1).

The molecules of a substance are the smallest unit particles of that substance; and if a substance be subdivided into particles smaller than its molecules, it no longer remains the same substance. Water, for example, becomes hydrogen and oxygen; sugar becomes carbon, hydrogen, and oxygen. **Atoms,** on the other hand, *are the*

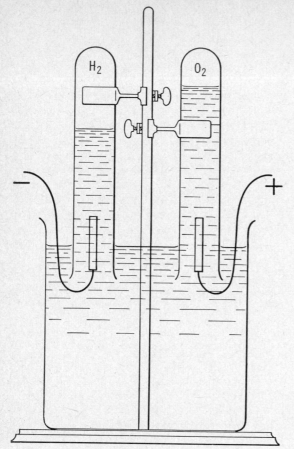

Fig. 4-1 When a direct current flows through water, the water molecules decompose into hydrogen (left test tube) and oxygen (right test tube). Note that the quantity (volume) of the hydrogen produced is twice that of the oxygen (as in H_2O).

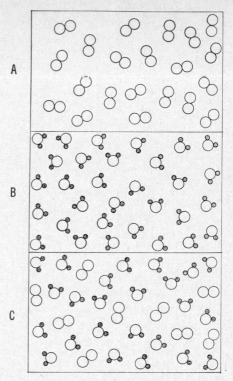

Fig. 4-2. Diagrams representing two substances (A and B), and a mixture (C) of the two. The large open circles represent oxygen atoms, the smaller dark circles hydrogen atoms. A, a free element, oxygen (O_2), in which all the molecules are alike and contain only one kind of atom. B, a compound, water (H_2O), in which all the molecules are alike, each consisting of one oxygen and two hydrogen atoms. C, a mixture of water and free oxygen (i.e., oxygen dissolved in water), which may be mixed in various proportions.

kinds of smaller particles that combine together in fixed proportion to form a countless variety of molecules.

Substances vs. Mixtures. Every sample of matter is either a **substance** or a **mixture** (Fig. 4-2). Strictly speaking, a **substance** *is a purified single kind of matter in which all the molecules are of the same species.* Purified (distilled) water, or highly refined sugar, or pure oxygen must therefore be designated as substances. **Mixtures,** *unlike* **substances,** *are made up of more than one kind of molecule.* Pond water, although it is composed chiefly of H_2O molecules, also contains molecules of various minerals as well as the molecules of nitrogen (N_2) and oxygen (O_2), dissolved from the atmosphere; air contains molecules of oxygen, nitrogen, and small amounts of other gases. Con-

sequently these latter kinds of matter are designated as mixtures.

In practice one can distinguish a substance from a mixture containing that substance in large proportion by the fact that the purified substance displays a nonvariable and standard set of physical and chemical properties. Each specific substance can be identified with absolute certainty by its known properties. A purified sample of water (H_2O) displays the same properties regardless of whether it is obtained from Siberia or Afghanistan. Its physical properties (color, taste, odor, boiling point, freezing point, etc.), and its chemical properties (see later), allow no question as to its identity as a single substance; and the same holds true for all other known substances. Table sugar, or more properly **sucrose,** $C_{12}H_{22}O_{11}$, can be distinguished from all other similar and dissimilar substances, on the basis of exact measurements of its melting point, crystalline structure, degree of sweetness, solubility, and other of its specific physical and chemical attributes.

A **mixture,** in contrast to a substance, *displays variable properties,* depending upon the proportions of the mixed components. The properties of pond water, for example, vary widely according to the locality from which it is collected. It may contain different mineral salts from the soil and various amounts of the atmospheric gases. It may display a wide variety of tastes and colors and considerable variation in the boiling and freezing points. It may even be toxic when drunk. Or crude sugar may be light or dark, strongly or weakly sweet, easy or difficult to dissolve, and so forth, depending upon the refinement of the methods used to extract it from the cane. The variations of a mixture depend upon the varying proportions of the mixed substances, and perhaps the most complex and variable of all mixtures is protoplasm itself. In protoplasm the number of components is very great, and the problem of understanding their interactions is very difficult.

Chemical Combination vs. Mixing. The fixity of the properties of a substance, as compared to the variability of the properties of a mixture, is due to the fact that *the atoms that constitute the molecules of a substance are chemically united in fixed proportion; whereas the molecules that compose a mixture may be present in any proportion.* This may be illustrated by a specific case. Take, for example, a strong gas tank containing hydrogen gas (H_2) and oxygen gas (O_2) *mixed* together (Fig. 4-3). In the tank the hydrogen and oxygen may be present in any proportion. With little hydrogen and much oxygen, the mixture as a whole will be relatively heavy and dense; or conversely, with little oxygen and much hydrogen, the mixture will be lighter and less dense. In other words, the properties of the mixture in the tank are altogether variable. But suppose that gradually the tank is heated. At a critical temperature, combustion, which represents a chemical union between the atoms of the hydrogen (H) and the oxygen (O), will start and then proceed with explosive speed. A fraction of a second later, all that can be recovered from within the tank is a small amount of water (H_2O) and a residual quantity of either oxygen or hydrogen—depending upon whether the exploded mixture contained an excess of the one or the other (Fig. 4-3). But the point to be made is that *when two or more atoms chemically unite to form a molecule, they do so in fixed proportion.* The fixed proportion that determines the specific combining power of each different kind of atom is given by its **valence** number. Consequently this number must be learned, at least for all atoms present in the protoplasmic system (Table 4-1).

Atomic Structure. The fact that the molecules of all substances are constituted by specific combinations of the atoms of a limited number of different elements, has been recognized by scientists for many years now. But it is only in the recent years of "atom smashing" that conclusive proof has been advanced that each atom is constituted of electrically charged smaller particles that are of just *two* sorts. The center of each atom is constituted mainly of **protons,** each bearing a single **positive** charge, although there are some

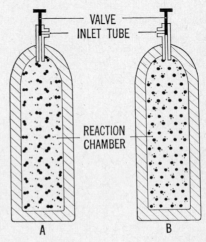

Fig. 4-3. The mixing of two substances is not the same as chemical union between them. A, reaction tank contains a **mixture** of free oxygen (O_2) and hydrogen (H_2) **before** ignition has occurred. B, same tank after the hydrogen has burned (united with oxygen). Two hydrogen atoms unite with each oxygen (i.e., the atoms unite in a **fixed** proportion). Therefore the resulting compound, water (H_2O), is a uniform product. Large dots represent oxygen atoms; small dots, hydrogen atoms.

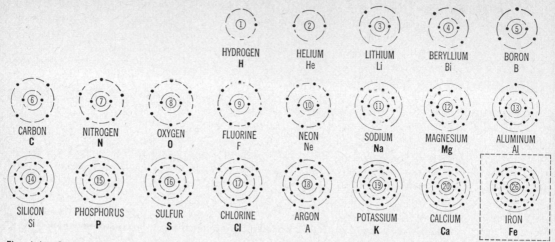

Fig. 4-4. Structure of atoms of atomic numbers 1-20 and 26. The central circle represents the atomic nucleus, the number in the circle showing the net positive charge, i.e., the atomic number; the small black circles represent planetary electrons. These figures are purely diagrammatic and do not pretend to show the actual spatial configuration of the electrons. The atoms whose symbols are printed in heavy type are those of elements generally present in living matter.

negatively charged particles, the **electrons,** also present in the **atomic center.**[4] Energetically revolving around the atomic center, like the planets of the solar system, there is another group of electrons, the **planetary electrons.** The number of protons and electrons present in the whole configuration differs for each particular kind of atom (Fig. 4-4), but *always the total number of electrons present in a given atom is exactly equal to the number of its protons.* In short, *each atom, as a whole, is an uncharged body.*

A knowledge of atomic structure provides an understanding of how various atoms enter into chemical union. One group of the atoms (the **electropositive atoms**) tends to give up one or more **planetary electrons,** transferring the electrons to the planets of atoms of another group (the **electronegative atoms**), which have a tendency to gain planetary electrons. When such an exchange occurs (Fig. 4-5), the participating atoms tend to cling together, constituting a molecule. The atom that has lost electrons now possesses a positive charge, and this makes it cling to the other atom, which having gained electrons, possesses a negative charge. Such studies also explain

[4] Actually the atomic center is composed mainly of **neutrons,** each formed by the union of one proton with one electron. In fact, the number of free protons present in the atomic center is restricted to the number of planetary electrons in each atom, and this determines the atomic number (Fig. 4-4).

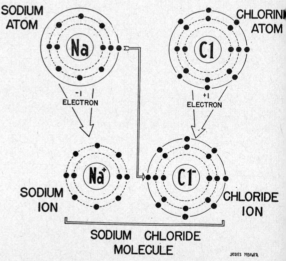

Fig. 4-5. Chemical union between an atom of sodium (Na) and an atom of chlorine (Cl) to form a molecule of salt (NaCl).

the existence of a third general group of atoms, the **inert** elements, like helium and neon (Fig. 4-4). These inert atoms never form any chemical compounds. Each possesses a very stable planetary system, which resists the gaining or losing of electrons. But among chemically active atoms, the number of planetary electrons that can be gained or lost during chemical union is specified as the **valence** of the particular atom in question.

The newer knowledge of atomic physics also provides a key to other problems. It explains, for example, the source of the energy that is liberated or bound whenever a chemical reaction takes place (see p. 78). Each atom is a system supercharged with energy—the **kinetic energy** of the vibrating and revolving electrons, and the **potential energy** of the electrical attractions between the protons and electrons. No two different atomic combinations, or molecules, ever possess precisely equal quantities of intramolecular energy. Therefore, it follows that any alteration in atomic combination, such as occurs during every chemical reaction, must involve either gain or loss of energy. Either there is an energy surplus, which is put forth, or there is a deficit, which is absorbed, with reference to the environment. Accordingly, when we witness an expenditure of energy in any cell—such as the beating of cilia or the contracting of muscle—we know that the energy arises from the chemical reactions that constitute the metabolism of the cell.

CHEMICAL COMPOSITION OF PROTOPLASM

Organic vs. Inorganic Substances. The many substances present in protoplasm fall naturally into two great classes: **organic** and **inorganic** substances. Early in the nineteenth century it was thought that some "vital factor" was distinctive of organic substances, because up to that time no organic substance had ever been obtained except from the bodies of living organisms. But in 1828, Woehler first synthesized an organic compound (urea), and since then a wide variety of organic compounds have been manufactured in the laboratory—many of which, like aspirin and sulfanilamide, never existed previously. Nevertheless an important distinction differentiates organic from inorganic substances. Excluding artificial synthesis, organic compounds, such as sugar, are found only in living bodies, or in their products and remains; whereas inorganic substances, such as water, are found *both* in living and in nonliving bodies.

Inorganic Substances. Inorganic substances make up the bulk of living as well as nonliving matter. The rocks, soil, atmosphere, and waters of the earth are composed almost entirely of a wide variety of inorganic materials. And in living matter also, the inorganic components greatly preponderate. This is due mainly to the high proportion of **water** in all protoplasm, although lesser quantities of the inorganic **salts, acids, bases,** and **gases** are likewise always present in protoplasm.

Water. Water is by far the most abundant single compound in all protoplasm. The proportion of water—in terms of the *weight* of the protoplasm—varies between 70 and 90 percent in different cells, and this water is by no means inert and unimportant. Without water, there is no such thing as protoplasm; and the life structure of any cell is immediately destroyed if the cell loses a significant proportion of its water content.

Water is so familiar that it is difficult to appraise its functions scientifically. Nevertheless, the unique physical and chemical properties of water give it a dominant role in determining protoplasmic structure and activity. In fact, water is the chief **dispersion medium** of the protoplasm. In other words, water is the liquid that *dissolves, suspends, or otherwise disperses* most of the various other substances present in the cell.

Solvent Properties of Water. One important property of water is its high efficiency as a **solvent.** No other single liquid substance is capable of dissolving so many other substances. Water is the most effective solvent for inorganic compounds generally; also, many important organic compounds are soluble in water.

When a substance (the **solute**) *dissolves* in another substance (the **solvent**), the solute tends to become *dispersed* throughout the solvent. The ideal state of **true solution** is reached when all the molecules of the solute have become individually separated from the dissolving mass and have scattered freely throughout the solvent. Thus when a crystal of sugar is dropped into a glass of water, the disappearance of the crystal indicates that the sugar molecules, which previously formed a compact and tangible mass, have become individually separated and distributed throughout the water.

The solvent capacity of water is important because the many compounds in protoplasm are dissolved in a common medium, and this intimate mixing of the different molecules greatly enhances their chemical reactivity. Dissolved substances interact together much more rapidly than mixtures in a dry state. Therefore, much of the complex metabolism of the cell would not be possible if the protoplasmic dispersion medium could not encompass such a rich variety of chemical components. Moreover, the protein components of the protoplasm require an aqueous environment if each is to maintain its molecular configuration and metabolic activity (p. 87).

Thermal Properties of Water. The freezing (0° C) and boiling (100° C) points—between which water remains in liquid state—represent the approximate extremes that are tolerable to protoplasm.[5] If temperatures in this range had not prevailed on the earth for many years, life as we know it could not have been evolved. Likewise, the exceptionally high **heat capacity**[6] of water plays an important role in the life of organisms generally. When the temperature of the environment changes rapidly, that of the living body changes much more slowly, owing to its large content of water. Accordingly, organisms have time to take measures of self-preservation when drastic changes occur in the temperature of the environment. A frog, for example, may sit on a rock in the broiling sun, while the temperature of the rock—

which has a relatively low heat capacity—rises with considerable rapidity. But the temperature of the frog rises much more slowly, and this allows ample time for the frog to seek a nearby pond.

Another important **thermal property** of water is its exceptionally high **heat of vaporization,**[7] which provides a cooling factor in organisms generally. In the case of man and other higher animals, perspiration is vaporized from the surface of the body, and this process dissipates large amounts of heat, which otherwise would elevate the body temperature. In higher plants, the process of transpiration likewise keeps the temperature of the leaves below the lethal point; and at the same time, transpiration generates a force that draws more water up from the soil (Chap. 13).

Chemical Activity of Water. Water participates in many metabolic reactions in all cells. Hydrogen and oxygen are constituents of virtually all organic compounds, and consequently water frequently appears among the initial or end products, when such compounds are metabolized in the protoplasm.

WATER IN RELATION TO DISSOCIATION. *In solution* many molecules tend to *dissociate,* or *ionize,* forming electrically charged fragments, called **ions.** Not all substances can dissociate appreciably, but the tendency, if present, always reaches a maximum when a substance is dissolved in *water.*

The dissociation of table salt (NaCl) is given in the following equation:

$$NaCl \xrightleftharpoons[\text{association}]{\text{dissociation}} Na^+ + Cl^-$$

NaCl
molecular
sodium chloride,
in aqueous
solution

Na⁺
sodium
ion

Cl⁻
chloride
ion

which shows that each molecule of NaCl, when it dissociates, liberates one sodium ion (Na+) and one chloride ion (Cl⁻).

[5] In *dormant state,* a number of cells are able to endure lengthy exposure to subzero (<° C) temperatures, but few if any can continue to function during the exposure.

[6] The heat capacity (specific heat) of a substance specifies the quantity of heat (number of calories) required to raise the temperature of 1 gram of the substance 1 degree Centigrade. For water, the heat capacity is one (cal), an exceptionally high value. Or, to use a different unit, one large calorie (1 Cal), which is designated by the capital C, is required to produce a 1° C elevation in the temperature of a liter (= 1000 g) of water.

[7] The heat of vaporization (expressed in Calories) specifies the quantity of heat required to vaporize one gram of a liquid, and the value for water (0.540 Cal) is unusually high.

The origin of the electric charges, which are characteristic of all ions, can be seen by inspecting the atomic structure of the NaCl molecule (Fig. 4-5). The sodium atom in uniting with chlorine gives up one electron, becoming the sodium ion (Na^+); and the chlorine atom becomes the chloride ion (Cl^-), by accepting an electron. So long as these ions remain united as the NaCl molecule, the electric charges neutralize each other; but if the ions separate—as they do when the salt is dissolved in water—the ionic charges become effective.

Not all ions are as simple as Na^+ and Cl^-, as may be seen in the following cases:

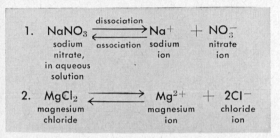

Generally speaking, *an ion is an atom, or group of atoms, that bears one or more electric charges. Positively charged ions are called cations, and negatively charged ions are called anions.*

ELECTROLYTES AND NONELECTROLYTES. Some substances, such as sugars, starches, and fats, display no appreciable tendency to ionize, and such compounds are called **nonelectrolytes;** but other substances, such as salts and proteins, dissociate more or less strongly, and these are called **electrolytes.** Among the electrolytes, some are strong and others are weak, depending upon the proportion of the molecules of the given substance that undergo dissociation in aqueous solution.

Experimentally, electrolytes are distinguished from nonelectrolytes by measuring the electrical conductivity of the substances **dissolved in water.** Water itself conducts electricity very poorly, and when pure water is placed between the poles in an electric circuit, scarcely any current flows. But if a strong electrolyte, such as sodium chloride, is added to the water, the resulting solution is a good conductor. The current, in fact, is carried by the ions of the solution. The cations (in this case Na^+) migrate toward the **cathode,** or **negative** pole; and the anions (in this case Cl^-) pass toward the **anode,** or **positive** pole. Accordingly, the conductivity of an aqueous solution is a good index to the degree of dissociation of the solute molecules. In the case of nonelectrolytes, such as sugar, the solution, as compared to pure water, displays little or no increase in conductivity.

Many compounds in the cell are strong electrolytes, which dissociate freely in the aqueous parts of the protoplasm. On this account, protoplasm itself will conduct electricity quite freely, and this fact is of considerable importance in every cell (Chap. 11).

DISSOCIATION OF WATER: HYDROGEN AND HYDROXYL IONS. The conductivity of pure water is very small, but even this small conductivity is significant. It indicates that water dissociates in small degree, as is shown in the following equation:

$$H \cdot OH(H_2O) \rightleftharpoons H^+ + OH^-$$

molecular water   hydrogen ion   hydroxyl ion

Despite the fact that the ratio of dissociated to undissociated molecules in pure water is very small (1:555,000,000), the dissociation of water cannot be overlooked. Hydrogen ions (H^+) and hydroxyl ions (OH^-) are both *extremely* active ions, which participate, directly or indirectly, in many metabolic reactions of every cell.

ACID, BASIC, AND NEUTRAL SOLUTIONS. All solutions are classified as **acid, basic,** or **neutral**—*depending upon the proportion of hydrogen* (H^+) *and hydroxyl* (OH^-) *ions they contain.* In acid solutions, the hydrogen ion is more abundant than the hydroxyl; in basic (alkaline) solutions, the hydroxyl ion is more abundant than the hydrogen; and in neutral solutions, the hydrogen and hydroxyl ions are present in equal numbers.

Pure water (HOH) displays a *neutral reaction,* because each dissociated water molecule liberates H^+ and OH^- ions in *equal*

Table 4-3—Reciprocal Relation between the Hydrogen Ion Concentration [H⁺] and the Hydroxyl Ion Concentration [OH⁻] in a Solution When the Acidity or the Alkalinity is Varied

[H⁺] Mols per Liter	[OH⁻] Mols per Liter	Log [H⁺]	−log [H⁺] = pH
1×10^{0}	1×10^{-14}	0	0
1×10^{-1}	1×10^{-13}	−1	1
1×10^{-4}	1×10^{-10}	−4	4
1×10^{-7}	1×10^{-7}	−7	7
1×10^{-10}	1×10^{-4}	−10	10
1×10^{-13}	1×10^{-1}	−13	13
1×10^{-14}	1×10^{0}	−14	14

ratio (1:1). The reaction of protoplasm, however, is not precisely neutral, since protoplasm may vary *slightly* in either an acid or a basic direction. Protoplasm contains many acid substances (p. 75), which liberate hydrogen ions, and many bases, which yield hydroxyl ions, and interactions constantly occur between these compounds. Accordingly, local changes in acidity and alkalinity occur, although these shifts are very small. In any solution the abundance of hydroxyl [OH⁻] ions *varies inversely* with the abundance of hydrogen [H⁺] ions (see Table 4-3). Consequently it is possible to designate the varying degrees of acidity-alkalinity on a single scale. This **pH scale** (Fig. 4-6) is very useful, since many metabolic reactions are exceedingly sensitive to small hydrogen ion changes occurring at localized foci in the protoplasm.

When **indicator dyes**—which change color according to the hydrogen ion concentration —are microinjected into a cell, it is found that the reaction of the **cytoplasm** is stabilized

at a point very *slightly on the acid side of neutrality* (pH 6.8); while the **nucleoplasm** is very slightly alkaline (pH 7.6). Moreover, the cell *maintains* this *approximate neutrality* of the protoplasm; and if acids or bases accumulate unduly in any cell, the protoplasmic structure deteriorates and death results.

SALTS, ACIDS, BASES, AND THEIR RESPECTIVE IONS. Many different inorganic **salts** are found in protoplasm—and the same is true of inorganic **acids** and **bases**—except that these compounds are present in *much smaller amounts*. Moreover, all the inorganic salts, acids, and bases are highly dissociated into ions; and in protoplasm, the many ions continuously unite and disunite in various ways, as may be seen in Table 4-4.

Table 4-4 also shows that the classification of inorganic compounds depends upon the presence or absence of hydrogen (H⁺) and hydroxyl (OH⁻) ions in the various compounds. An **acid sub-**

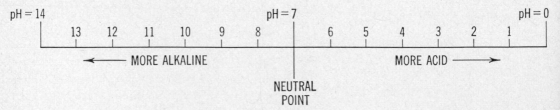

Fig. 4-6. The pH scale, by which the degree of acidity or alkalinity of a solution may be specified. Numbers *below* the neutral point (pH 7) indicate greater and greater acidity (greater abundance of hydrogen (H⁺) ions); numbers *above* 7 indicate increasing alkalinity (lesser abundance of hydrogen ions).

Table 4-4—Main Inorganic Ions in Protoplasm
(classification of inorganic compounds)

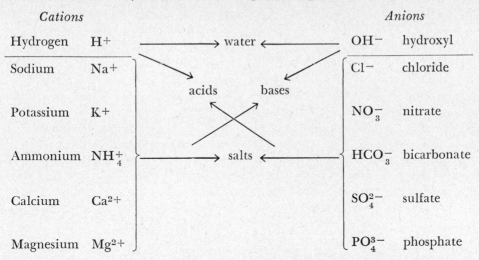

Origin of the four main kinds of inorganic compounds: water, salts, acids, and bases. Water is formed by a union between (H^+) and (OH^-) ions; acids are formed by H^+ ion uniting with any anion except OH^-; bases by OH^- ion uniting with any cation except H^+; and finally, salts are formed by any cation except H^+ uniting with any anion except OH^-.

stance represents the union of hydrogen ion with any anion, *except* the hydroxyl; a **base** represents the union of hydroxyl ion with any cation *except* the hydrogen; and a **salt** is any cation, except $H+$, combined with any anion, except OH^-. In inorganic chemistry, therefore, **water**, which represents a union between the hydrogen and hydroxyl ions, occupies a class all by itself.

The hydrogen and hydroxyl ions in protoplasm are relatively less abundant than other ions. This is because most of these ions remain *associated* as HOH (water). Consequently the manifold molecules, which momentarily are formed when oppositely charged ions come into contact, give rise mainly to **salts,** such as sodium chloride (NaCl) and sodium nitrate (NaNO$_3$) (see Table 4-4). However, some hydrogen and hydroxyl ions are always present, so that protoplasm always contains traces of the various **inorganic acids,** such as hydrochloric acid (HCl) and nitric acid (HNO$_3$); and traces of **inorganic bases,** such as sodium hydroxide (NaOH) and potassium hydroxide (KOH) (Table 4-4).

Gases in the Protoplasm. All cells are permeable to the atmospheric gases, and these gases are soluble both in water and in protoplasm. Consequently, the gases of the

air tend to enter all cells and to dissolve in the protoplasm.

Nitrogen (N_2), due to its abundance in the air (79 percent), is always present in the cell; but free nitrogen is very inert chemically, and free N_2 does not participate in the metabolism of most cells—although the compounds of nitrogen are very important in metabolism. Considerable oxygen (O_2) also enters the cell, due to its abundance (20.96 percent) in air; and oxygen takes part in many metabolic reactions. Without oxygen, in fact, most cells cannot maintain their structure and activities, except for relatively short periods. Very little (0.03 percent) carbon dioxide (CO_2) is present in the atmosphere, but CO_2 is produced in the oxidative metabolism of all cells. In the cell much of the carbon dioxide unites chemically with water, forming a weakly acidic compound, carbonic acid (H_2CO_3):

$$CO_2 + H_2O \rightleftarrows H_2CO_3 \rightleftarrows H^+ + HCO_3^-$$
$$\text{carbonic acid} \qquad \text{bicarbonate ion}$$

Organic Components of Protoplasm. Except when synthesized artificially, organic compounds occur only in living bodies, or in their products and remains. Organic molecules tend to be relatively large and complex, and usually organic molecules lack any strong tendency to ionize. However, the most important distinction between organic and inorganic compounds lies in the intrinsic composition. The element **carbon** (C), which rarely appears in inorganic chemistry, is present *in all organic compounds*. In other words, *organic chemistry is the chemistry of carbon compounds.* In fact, the commonest test to determine whether an unknown substance is organic or inorganic is the charring test. Virtually every organic compound decomposes and yields carbon if it is heated drastically in a dry condition.

The unique capacity of carbon to form a great variety of compounds—which are segregated as a separate branch of chemistry—derives from the structure and behavior of the carbon atom. Carbon differs from most other atoms in that it is intermediate between the electropositive atoms, which *lose* electrons, and the electronegative atoms, which *gain* electrons, when they unite to form their respective compounds. Carbon can combine with either type of atom, and this capacity enriches the variety of carbon compounds. Furthermore, the valence of carbon is relatively high. By gaining, losing, or sharing the *four* valence electrons, carbon can unite with *four* other univalent atoms or atomic groups.

An even more important property of carbon is its capacity to unite with other carbon atoms. This property enables carbon to form a wide variety of chainlike and ringlike "molecular skeletons," and in this way carbon is able to unite with many other atoms, forming very large complex molecules.

Table 4-5 shows a simple series of organic compounds composed entirely of carbon and hydrogen. Here it should be noted that the different molecules are constructed in similar fashion, in that: (1) every carbon atom possesses four combining points; (2) each molecule is formed by a series of carbon to carbon linkages; (3) the linkage between any two consecutive carbon atoms mutually pre-empts one valence from each carbon; and (4) each hydrogen atom occupies just one valence point of any given carbon atom.

Kinds of Organic Substances. Living cells contain a very great variety of organic compounds. These carbon compounds are continually changing by interaction with each other, but certain kinds tend to be most abundant in the protoplasm. The most abundant organic compounds are divided into three main *classes*—the **carbohydrates,** the **lipids,** and the **proteins**—which are distinguishable on the basis of their physical and chemical characteristics, and on the basis of their functions in the cell. There are still other organic compounds (p. 89), which cannot be put into any of the three major classes, although they may be very important, metabolically.

Carbohydrates. The most familiar carbohydrate compounds are the **sugars, starches, glycogens,** and **celluloses.** Chemically, all carbohydrates have much in common, although different carbohydrates may have different functions in the cell.

The chemical structure of carbohydrates can be exemplified by two specific compounds: (1) **glucose** ($C_6H_{12}O_6$), a white crystalline sugar, present in practically every cell; and (2) **sucrose** ($C_{12}H_{22}O_{11}$), the familiar sugar of the dining table. The formulas of these compounds show that (1) the only constituents of a carbohydrate are carbon, hydrogen, and oxygen; (2) the hydrogen and oxygen display a ratio of 2:1 (as in water); and (3) six (or a multiple of six) carbon atoms are present. The first two points are true for *all* carbohydrates, and the third is true for a majority. Accordingly, *typical carbohydrates are compounds solely of carbon, hydrogen, and oxygen, in which frequently carbon atoms are present to the extent of six (or a multiple of six) and the hydrogen and oxygen are in a two to one ratio.*

Table 4-5—A Series of Relatively Simple Organic Compounds

Name	Formula	Structure
Methane.........	CH_4	H | H—C—H | H
Ethane..........	C_2H_6	H H | | H—C—C—H | | H H
Propane.........	C_3H_8	H H H | | | H—C—C—C—H | | | H H H
Butane..........	C_4H_{10}	H H H H | | | | H—C C C—C—H | | | | H H H H
Pentane.........	C_5H_{12}	H H H H H | | | | | H—C—C—C—C—C—H | | | | | H H H H H
Octane..........	C_8H_{18}	H H H H H H H H | | | | | | | | H—C—C—C—C—C—C—C—C—H | | | | | | | | H H H H H H H H
or Generally........	C_nH_{2n+2}	H H H H | | | | H—C—C—C — — — C—H | | | | H H H H

GLUCOSE. Glucose is a most important carbohydrate. In every cell glucose can provide not only energy, but also matter, for the synthesis of quite a few other essential compounds.

Pure glucose, like table sugar, is a white crystalline sweet-tasting solid, which is very soluble in water. But compared to sucrose, glucose is more active chemically; and glucose, due to the smaller size of its molecules, can pass through cell membranes more easily than sucrose.

GLUCOSE AS A PROTOPLASMIC FUEL. The energy expended by a cell when it moves and performs its other activities all comes from the decomposition of organic compounds in the protoplasm. These organic compounds possess a rich fund of intramolecular energy; and in serving as fuel, large energy-rich molecules continually decompose into simpler end products, liberating the balance of energy for the useful work of the cell. Moreover, many of these decompositions are **oxidative** in nature.

Among the **fuels** used by cells generally, glucose is very important. Most cells are able to "burn" glucose, and many cells use glucose in preference to other fuels.

The oxidation of glucose proceeds in many steps (p. 148), but the *over-all* oxidation can be specified as follows:

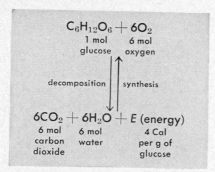

$$C_6H_{12}O_6 + 6O_2$$

1 mol glucose   6 mol oxygen

decomposition ↕ synthesis

$$6CO_2 + 6H_2O + E \text{ (energy)}$$

6 mol carbon dioxide   6 mol water   4 Cal per g of glucose

In other words, by uniting with six molecules of oxygen, each glucose molecule produces six molecules of carbon dioxide and six molecules of water; and in this oxidation, energy is liberated for the use of the cell.

Chemical Reactions in Relation to Matter and Energy. The oxidation of glucose exemplifies the nature of chemical reactions generally. In all chemical reactions one or more substances are transformed into one or more *other* substances by a *regrouping* of the same existing atoms. Accordingly, all chemical reactions display a *conservation of matter*—as is plain from two considerations. (1) The total weight of the reacting substances exactly equals the total weight of the resulting substances, and (2) the total number of each kind of atom remains unchanged when the reaction is completed. In the present case, for example, the glucose and oxygen that are consumed weigh exactly as much as the carbon dioxide and water that are produced. Also, the *equation* is *balanced,* since both the initial and the final products are constituted by 6, 12, and 18 atoms respectively, of carbon, hydrogen, and oxygen.

Virtually all chemical reactions involve some kind of *energy* transaction. On this basis, in fact, chemical reactions are generally subdivided into two groups: (1) **exothermic** reactions, which discharge energy *to* the environment; and (2) **endothermic** reactions, which absorb energy *from* the environment.

Larger and more complex molecules generally possess a greater fund of intramolecular energy than a corresponding weight of smaller and simpler molecules. Consequently most **decomposition reactions**—in which larger molecules are fragmented into smaller ones—give forth energy *to the environment*. But conversely, most **synthetic reactions**—in which larger molecules are built from smaller units—cannot proceed without absorbing energy *from the environment*.

The foregoing equation shows that the oxidation of glucose is a typical decomposition. It is exothermic to the extent of 4 Calories per gram of glucose consumed. However, the same reaction proceeding in the opposite direction—and this occurs when a green plant cell absorbs sunlight and converts carbon dioxide and water into glucose and oxygen—is a typical synthesis, namely, **photosynthesis.** Photosynthesis is an endothermic reaction, and can occur only when an equivalent fund of energy, in the form of light, is available for absorption from the environment.

Glucose is employed more universally than other protoplasmic fuels. The cells of man's body, for example, derive much of their energy, at least indirectly, by oxidizing glucose. Man's blood stream carries a very constant supply of glucose, and the "blood sugar level" must be maintained at a minimum of about 0.1 percent if serious collapse is to be avoided (p. 00).

Synthesis of Other Carbohydrates from Glucose. Cells also use glucose as a raw material from which to synthesize other carbohydrates. In this case a number of glucose molecules unite chemically, forming larger types of molecules. Accordingly, many carbohydrates are essentially aggregates, formed by the chemical union of a greater or lesser number of glucose molecules.

DEHYDRATION SYNTHESIS. One of the commonest methods by which cells synthesize larger molecules from smaller units is by the process of **dehydration synthesis.** This type of reaction is shown by the synthesis of malt sugar (maltose), which occurs in many plant cells (Fig. 4-7). Each molecule of maltose is formed from two molecules of glucose, and in the course of the reaction, one molecule of water is formed as a by-product.

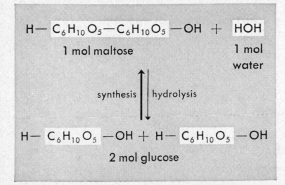

Fig. 4-7. Building one molecule of maltose from two molecules of glucose, by **dehydration synthesis.** Note that a molecule of water is formed as a by-product. Opposite reaction, termed **hydrolysis,** uses a molecule of water to split one maltose into two glucose molecules.

The synthesis of maltose may be taken as the prototype for dehydration synthesis generally. In fact, any union between smaller molecules that involves the *formation of water as a by-product* is called a dehydration synthesis. In a dehydration synthesis, water is always formed as a by-product, because one molecule of water is eliminated at each point where union occurs between two smaller molecules, as is shown in Figure 4-7.

In the cell, many large molecules, not only of carbohydrates, but also of proteins and other substances, are built by a series of dehydration syntheses, which keep adding to the length of the carbon skeleton.

HYDROLYSIS. Hydrolysis is the opposite of dehydration synthesis, as is also shown in Figure 4-7. Hydrolysis occurs when a larger molecule combines with water and fragments into smaller molecules.

Hydrolysis and dehydration synthesis occur very frequently in metabolism. Constructive metabolism involves the building of many complex substances from simpler chemical units, and frequently this involves a series of dehydration syntheses. Conversely, destructive metabolism often involves the hydrolytic splitting of larger molecules into simpler components. Hydrolysis reactions generally are exothermic, whereas dehydration syntheses are endothermic; but, with certain important exceptions (see p. 143), the quantity of energy involved is rather small.

OTHER CARBOHYDRATES. *Monosaccharides.* The formula $C_6H_{12}O_6$ is not specific for glucose. This formula designates a whole group of simple sugars, the **hexose monosaccharides,** among which **glucose, fructose,** and **galactose** are the most important (Table 4-6). These monosaccharide sugars differ from one another very slightly as regards the degree of sweetness, solubility, chemical reactivity, and so forth. In the molecules of each, the same numbers and kinds of atoms are represented, but the *arrangement* of the atoms is not quite the same (Fig. 4-8). Most of the monosaccharides are 6-carbon compounds, but a few (see p. 80) have only 5 carbon atoms.

Disaccharides. From glucose and other monosaccharides the cell synthesizes more complex carbohydrates as these are needed. Two monosaccharide molecules, chemically united, constitute a disaccharide, for which the general formula is $C_{12}H_{22}O_{11}$. The three most important disaccharides (Table 4-6) are **maltose** (malt sugar), **sucrose** (table sugar), and **lactose** (milk sugar). Each maltose molecule represents a union between two molecules of glucose; sucrose is formed from one glucose and one fructose; and lactose is constituted of glucose and galactose. Accordingly, all the disaccharides are formed by dehydration synthesis from the monosaccharides; and conversely, each disaccharide lib-

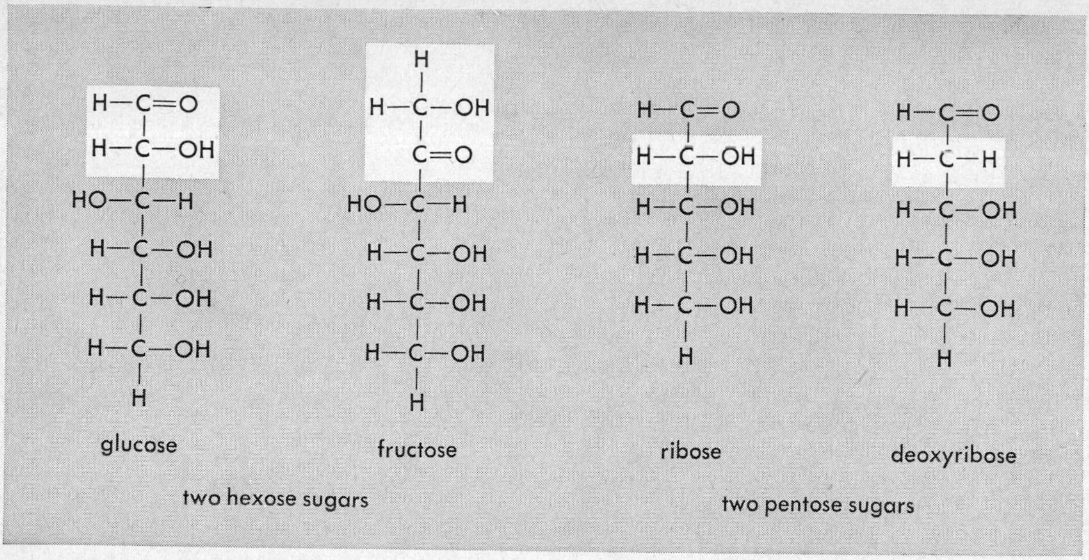

```
    H—C=O              H              H—C=O            H—C=O
    H—C—OH          H—C—OH           H—C—OH           H—C—H
   HO—C—H            C=O             H—C—OH           H—C—OH
    H—C—OH          HO—C—H           H—C—OH           H—C—OH
    H—C—OH           H—C—OH          H—C—OH           H—C—OH
    H—C—OH           H—C—OH            H                H
      H                H
      H—C—OH

   glucose          fructose          ribose        deoxyribose

  two hexose sugars                    two pentose sugars
```

Fig. 4-8. Molecular structure of *four important sugars*. Note the slight differences between glucose and fructose, although both are 6-carbon sugars (hexoses) with the same gross formula ($C_6H_{12}O_6$). Also note the difference between the two 5-carbon (pentose) sugars, which are extremely important constituents of the nucleic acids (see p. 88). As the name implies, deoxyribose has one less oxygen (O) atom than ribose.

erates the corresponding monosaccharides, when hydrolysis occurs.

Polysaccharides. The polysaccharides are important substances that include the **starches, glycogens,** and **celluloses.** All these compounds are derived from **glucose** by multiple dehydration synthesis. The starches and glycogens possess huge molecules, each representing a complex of almost a thousand glucose molecules, united chemically into a single unit; and the cellulose molecule is even larger. The exact number and arrangement of the glucose units differ somewhat in the different starches, glycogens, and celluloses found in different cells.

All polysaccharides are relatively insoluble and tasteless. The starches (in plant cells) and glycogens (in animal cells) tend to be deposited in the form of definite *grains,* which can be seen in the cytoplasm (Fig. 4-9). Cellulose is deposited on the surfaces of plant cells, as a thin but visible sheet—the *cell wall.*

Cellulose has great importance as the chief component of cell walls and of *woody* materials generally. **Starch** and **glycogen** are also important, as reserve protoplasmic fuels. The cell can hydrolyze glycogen or starch, obtaining glucose for use at any moment. Meanwhile, the deposit of fuel remains safely in reserve. Due to the size and insolubility of polysaccharide molecules, neither starch nor glycogen can escape from the cell; and the chemical inertness of these polysaccharides safeguards them from deterioration.

Lipids. All *fats* and *fatlike substances* are included among the lipids. *Physically,* the **lipids** are "greasy" substances, relatively in-

Table 4-6—Chemical Nature of Some Familiar Carbohydrates

Class	General Formula	Specific Names
Monosaccharides	$C_6H_{12}O_6$	Glucose, fructose, lactose
Disaccharides	$C_{12}H_{22}O_{11}$	Maltose (glucose-glucose), sucrose (glucose-fructose), lactose (glucose-galactose)
Polysaccharides	$(C_6H_{10}O_5)x$	Starches, glycogens, celluloses

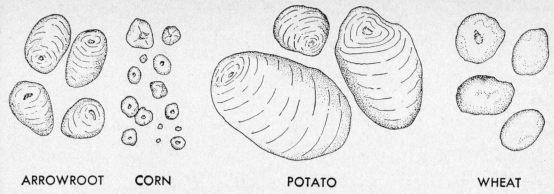

ARROWROOT   CORN   POTATO   WHEAT

Fig. 4-9.   Starch **grains** from different plants, all drawn to the same scale.

soluble in water, but readily soluble in such organic solvents as ether, chloroform, and hot alcohol. Lipids that are liquid at room temperature (about 20° C) are commonly called **oils** (olive oil, cod-liver oil, etc.); but even **fats** such as butter, lard, and tallow, which are solid or semisolid at room temperature, are generally liquid at the body temperature of the warm-blooded animals in which they occur. Generally the lipid components of the protoplasm are relatively light (low specific gravity) and tend to be thrown to the "light end" when the cell is centrifuged (Fig. 4-10).

Because of their diverse *chemical* nature, lipids are not treated as a single group, but are subdivided into three groups: (1) the **true fats**, (2) the **phospholipids**, and (3) the **steroids.**

THE TRUE FATS. The **true fats** include many familiar substances, such as olive oil, butter fat, and beef fat. Beef fat ($C_{57}H_{110}O_6$) shows the typical chemical structure of a true fat in that: (1) true fats are composed entirely of C, H, and O; and (2) the natural fats have large molecules, containing usually about 50 and 100 atoms respectively of C and H, but *only 6 atoms of O.*

The fats in protoplasm serve mainly as accessory fuels. However, fats do not oxidize as readily as glucose, although the quantity of energy per gram of oxidized fat is considerably greater (9 Cal as compared to 4). Much of the fat in complex animals such

as man is localized in special cells, which collectively make up the **adipose tissue** of the body.

A molecule of fat represents a combination of *simpler units* that can be liberated by **hydrolysis.** In practice this hydrolysis is accomplished by boiling the fat in a strongly basic solution, although cells hydrolyze fats at ordinary temperatures. When hydrolyzed, each fat molecule liberates: (1) *one* molecule **of glycerol,** which is commonly called glycerin, and (2) *three* molecules that the chemist identifies as **fatty acid.**

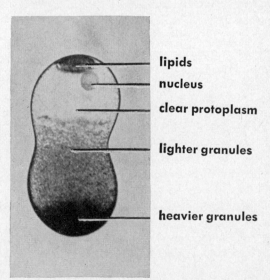

lipids

nucleus

clear protoplasm

lighter granules

heavier granules

Fig. 4-10.   The fatty materials of protoplasm are relatively light and rise to one end when a cell (such as this *Arbacia* egg) is centrifuged strongly. (Courtesy of Ethel Browne Harvey.)

Glycerol is a viscous, colorless, water-soluble liquid, possessing a formula of $C_3H_8O_3$, and the following chemical structure:

$$
\begin{array}{c}
H \\
| \\
H\text{---}C\text{---}OH \\
| \\
H\text{---}C\text{---}OH \\
| \\
H\text{---}C\text{---}OH \\
| \\
H
\end{array}
$$

1 mol glycerol

The **fatty acids** are less familiar than glycerol, although fatty acids are widely used, in the form of a water emulsion, as the "brushless" type of shaving cream. Dry crstalline fatty acids are white, waxy-feeling solids, which are not very soluble in water, although considerably more so than the fats from which they are derived. The most familiar fatty acid is **stearic acid,** $CH_3(CH_2)_{16} \cdot COOH$, which is obtained by hydrolyzing beef fat.

The formula for stearic acid shows that one end (called the **head**) of the fatty acid molecule is constituted by a special grouping of atoms (—COOH), which is the **carboxyl radical.** The carboxyl radical is written as —COOH, although its true structure is better shown by an expanded formula:

$$
\text{---}C\text{---}OH = \text{---}COOH
$$
$$
\overset{\parallel}{O}
$$

The carboxyl radical is important because all compounds possessing it are **organic acids.** The hydrogen of the carboxyl is "loosely connected," and this hydrogen dissociates as hydrogen ion (H^+) when an organic acid is dissolved in water. Thus **organic acids** may be specified by the general formula R—COOH, where the R stands for the **body** of the molecule, which varies in different compounds. The dissociation of an organic acid may be written:

$$
R \cdot COOH \rightleftarrows R \cdot COO^- + H^+
$$

organic acid   organic anion   hydrogen ion

In the fatty acids, the "body" (R) of the molecule represents a straight carbon chain in which most if not all of the available combining points are occupied by hydrogen. For example, the specific formula of **palmitic acid** (from coconut oil) is $CH_3(CH_2)_{14} \cdot COOH$. Most natural fatty acids possess rather "long chain" molecules, although a few, such as **acetic acid** ($CH_3 \cdot COOH$), are much simpler. Moreover, all naturally occurring fatty acids are constituted by an *even* number of carbon atoms (see above), since the metabolic build-up and breakdown of these molecules involves the adding or subtracting of 2-carbon pieces to the carbon chains of the molecular skeletons (Fig. 8-5).

Plant and animal cells can synthesize fat by triple dehydration synthesis, provided glycerol and fatty acids are present in the protoplasm, as is shown in Figure 4-11.

When a cell uses fat as fuel, it first hydrolyzes the fat into glycerol and fatty acids, and then gradually oxidizes the products. Since C, H, and O are the only constituents of a fatty acid, the only end products formed when a fatty acid is oxidized completely are CO_2 and H_2O. Disregarding the complex intermediary stages, the total oxidation of a fatty acid may be written:

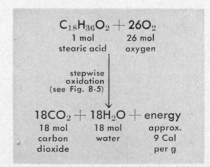

$$C_{18}H_{36}O_2 + 26O_2$$

1 mol stearic acid   26 mol oxygen

stepwise oxidation (see Fig. 8-5)

$$18CO_2 + 18H_2O + \text{energy}$$

18 mol carbon dioxide   18 mol water   approx. 9 Cal per g

PHOSPHOLIPIDS AND STEROIDS. The chemical complexity of phospholipids and steroids precludes an adequate brief description. One very common phospholipid is **lecithin,** a fat-

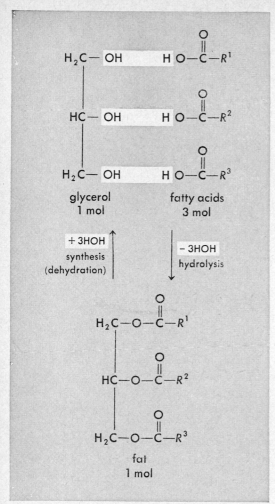

Fig. 4-11. Build-up and breakdown of fat as it occurs in cells generally.

like compound obtainable in good quantity from egg yolk. Lecithin is probably a structural component in all cells. The molecular structure of lecithin resembles that of a fat, except that one of the three fatty acids is replaced by phosphoric acid in combination with **choline** (an organic base).

The most familiar steroid substance is **cholesterol** ($C_{27}H_{45}OH$), a normal component of bile; several hormones, including the sex hormones (p. 000), likewise belong to the steroid group. Cholesterol and the other steroids are constituted entirely of C, H, and O; but the "carbon skeleton" of a steroid is a complex of several interlinked *rings,* as is shown in Figure 4-12. Steroids and phospholipids are probably represented in all protoplasm, as essential components of the intrinsic membrane systems.

Proteins. Proteins are all-important **structural components** in every cell. Each of the genes represents a *uniquely* distinctive DNA-protein complex, without which the cell loses virtually all powers of growth and replication (Chap. 27). Nor can growth occur in the absence of the RNA-protein components of the protoplasm (p. 134). Likewise enzymes, by means of which the cell carries on its other metabolic activities (Chap. 5), always possess an essential protein component; and proteins are always represented in the structure of the plasma membrane and other intrinsic membranes of the cell. In short, pro-

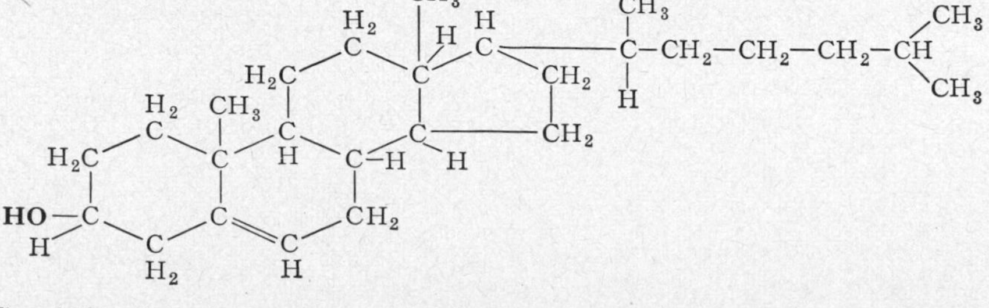

Fig. 4-12. Molecular structure of **cholesterol**, a **steroid** compound. Cholesterol is present in most, if not all, cells. Also a number of **hormones** (Chap. 22)—such as the male and female "sex hormones" (testosterone and "estrogen"), the "pregnancy hormone" (progesterone), and the adrenocortical hormones (cortisone, etc.)—are steroids, which have a similar, though not identical structure.

teins play an absolutely essential role in determining both structure and activity in every cell.

Chemically, proteins are the most complicated of all substances. The molecules— even in such relatively simple proteins as gelatin and egg albumen—are huge, consisting of thousands of atoms. The constituent atoms of natural proteins always include carbon, hydrogen, oxygen, nitrogen, and sulfur. Moreover, proteins can chemically unite with any or all of the various acidic and basic components of the protoplasm (p. 74), and consequently all the various **ions** listed in Table 4-4 can be found in affiliation with any protein molecule.

AMINO ACIDS. Protein chemistry was greatly simplified when it was discovered that each large protein molecule represents a chain of simpler units—the **amino acids.** The amino acids are liberated as separate molecules when a protein is completely broken down by **hydrolysis.** This can be achieved by boiling a protein preparation for several hours in strongly acid medium. When the protein is fully hydrolyzed, it yields 25 different amino acids in varying amounts, according to the specific composition of the initial protein.

The amino acids are relatively small molecules. Almost all may be designated by a single *general formula,* R—$CH(NH_2) \cdot$ COOH. In expanded form, this may be written as shown at top of next column.

The **body** of an amino acid molecule, designated by R, is different for each different

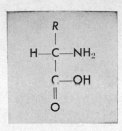

amino acid (Fig. 4-13); but the **head** is almost always the same. This head displays two important radicals: (1) the **carboxyl** (—COOH), which determines the acidic properties of the amino acid, and (2) the **amino radical** (—NH_2), which accounts for the basic behavior of the amino acid (see below).

The three simplest of the *twenty-five different amino acids* are shown in Figure 4-13. In **glycine,** R represents simply —H; in **alanine,** $R =$ —CH_3; and in **cysteine,** $R =$ —$CH_2 \cdot SH$.

The acidic behavior of the carboxyl radical is the same in an amino acid as in other organic acids (Fig. 4-14). But the basic behavior of the amino (—NH_2) group requires further explanation. Amino compounds act as bases, not by liberating hydroxyl ions in a solution, but by *removing* hydrogen (H+) ions from the solution, as may be seen in Figure 4-14.

The degree to which an amino acid acts as a base or acid depends upon the acidity or alkalinity of the solution in which it is dissolved. In acid solutions, the amino radicals tend to neutralize the acidity by accepting hydrogen ions. But in basic solutions, the

Fig. 4-13.   Three amino acids.

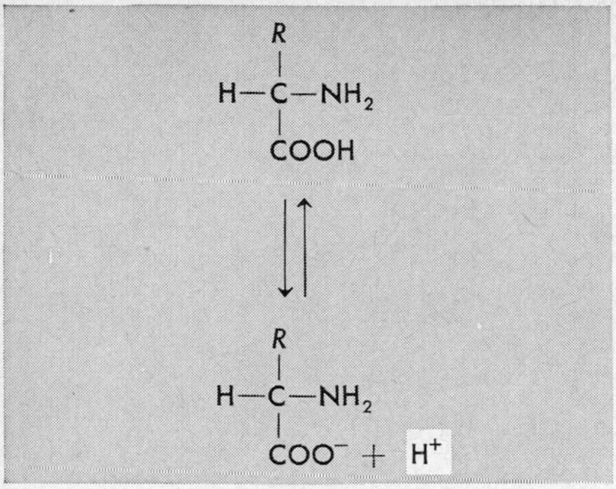

$$R$$
$$|$$
$$H-C-NH_2$$
$$|$$
$$COOH$$

$$\uparrow\downarrow$$

$$R$$
$$|$$
$$H-C-NH_2$$
$$|$$
$$COO^- + H^+$$

acidic behavior

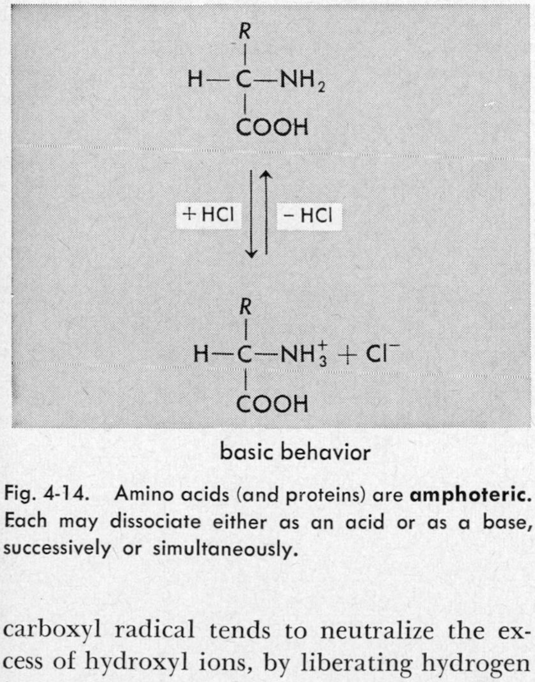

$$R$$
$$|$$
$$H-C-NH_2$$
$$|$$
$$COOH$$

$$+HCl \quad \uparrow\downarrow \quad -HCl$$

$$R$$
$$|$$
$$H-C-NH_3^+ + Cl^-$$
$$|$$
$$COOH$$

basic behavior

Fig. 4-14. Amino acids (and proteins) are **amphoteric.** Each may dissociate either as an acid or as a base, successively or simultaneously.

carboxyl radical tends to neutralize the excess of hydroxyl ions, by liberating hydrogen ions. This dual action is called an **amphoteric** behavior, and the amino acids and proteins are spoken of as **amphoteric** compounds, or **ampholytes.** Moreover, proteins and amino acids are said to exert a *buffer action,* since they tend to *stabilize the reaction of a solution,* preventing it from shifting very much in either an acid or a basic direction, when acids or bases are added to the solution.

All the amino acids derived by the hydrolysis of natural proteins are crystalline solids that dissolve very freely in water. Amino

acid molecules are all relatively small, and all can enter the cell through the boundary membranes, albeit rather slowly.

PEPTIDE BONDING IN RELATION TO PROTEIN STRUCTURE. Given a full assortment of amino acids, a cell can synthesize all of its protein components. Protein synthesis, essentially, is a multiple dehydration synthesis. The amino acids become linked into an exceedingly elongate chain, as is indicated in Figures 4-15 and 4-16. The principal linkages in such a chain are bonds that extend from the carbon atom of the carboxyl group of one amino acid to the nitrogen atom of the amino group of the next amino acid (Fig. 4-15). This type of linkage is called a **peptide bond,** and the elongate skeleton of the protein molecule, which may be more than a thousand units in length, is referred to as a **peptide chain.**

SPECIFICITY OF PROTEINS. A full complement of the various amino acids is present in most proteins, but the proportion and serial arrangement of the amino acids varies widely. And since each different arrangement represents a different protein substance (Fig. 4-16), it follows that an almost infinite variety of proteins can exist. Just as an almost infinite variety of words can be formed from the 26 letters of our alphabet, so a large number of specifically different proteins can be synthesized from the 25 kinds of amino acids.

The proteins of each different kind of cell —its genes, enzymes, ribosomal and membrane proteins, etc.—appear to be uniquely and individually self-characteristic. Similar proteins may fulfill similar functions in different cells, but perfect identity is probably never found. For example, the hormone *insulin,* which is a relatively simple protein, contains almost but not quite the same complement and arrangement of amino acids in the three different animals (beef cattle, swine, and horse) for which a detailed analysis has been accomplished (Fig. 4-16). Furthermore, it is known that a small change, involving just a single protein of a cell, may induce a large

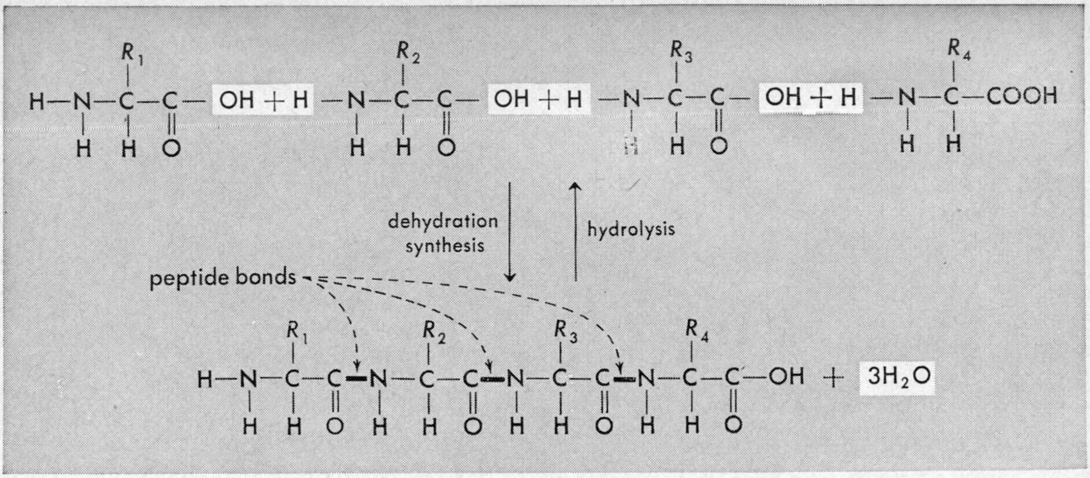

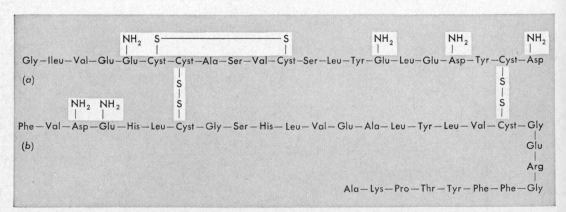

Fig. 4-15. Construction of a **tetrapeptide chain** from four separate amino acids. Note that the formation of each **peptide bond** involves the splitting off of a water molecule. Consequently the synthesis is a dehydration synthesis. In a protein molecule the peptide chain is much longer, often consisting of more than a thousand amino acid units.

change in that cell. In the case of **sickle cell anemia,** the red protein pigment, **hemoglobin,** present in the erythrocytes (p. 289), differs from the normal by just one amino acid in the peptide chain. Nevertheless, the sickle-shaped red cells of an individual suffering from this rare hereditary defect are grossly abnormal as to both form and function (p. 507).

The problem of cell replication hinges, in large measure, upon the mechanisms of protein replication. How does the cell transmit the code that determines precisely the proper amino acids and how they become bonded together in precisely the right order and arrangement, when protein synthesis takes place? This problem involves an analysis of the DNA components of the nucleus and of

Fig. 4-16. Sequence and arrangement of amino acids in a molecule of **insulin** (beef), a **protein** hormone. Horse insulin and pig insulin resemble beef insulin, but there are slight differences in the amino acid sequence. The amino acid structure of a protein molecule may be ascertained by hydrolyzing (digesting) the protein with different enzymes (see Table 5-1, digestive enzymes) and identifying the liberated amino acids by paper chromatography (Fig. 9-5), and by other means. (Amino acids designated: Ala, alanine; Arg, arginine; Asp, aspartic acid; Cyst, cysteine; Glu, glutamic acid; Gly, glycine; His, histidine; Ileu, isoleucine; Leu, leuchine; Lys, lysine; Phe, phenylalanine; Pro, proline; Ser, serine; Thr, threonine; Tyr, tyrosine; Val, valine.)

the RNA components of the cytoplasm, as will be considered in Chapters 7 and 27.

THREE-DIMENSIONAL CONFIGURATION OF PROTEIN MOLECULES: PRIMARY, SECONDARY, AND TERTIARY STRUCTURE. The primary structure of a protein molecule is constituted by one or more peptide chains. Within each chain the amino acid units are held together by peptide linkages; the peptide chains, if

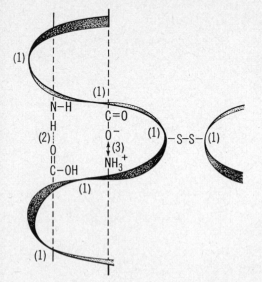

Fig. 4-17. Helical configuration of a protein molecule. Three types of bonds determine the primary, secondary, and tertiary aspects of protein structure: (1) strong bonds (**peptide** and **disulfide**), which determine primary structure; (2) weaker **hydrogen bonds**, which determine secondary structure; (3) very weak forces (e.g., electrostatic), which effect the tertiary structure. Each broad part, along the length of the spiral, represents one amino acid.

more than one is present, are united by one or more **disulfide** (—S—S—) **bridges,** as in the insulin molecule (Fig. 4-16). These chemical bonds, namely peptide and disulfide, are relatively stable. Collectively they determine what is called the **primary structure** of a protein molecule (Fig. 4-17).

Peptide chains are not straight, however. Rather, they display a coiled, or **helical structure** (Fig. 4-17). Usually each complete coil of the helix is constituted by about four amino acids, and the distance pre-empted by one coil, along the central axis of the helix,

is about 1.5 Ångstroms. However, the tightness of coiling and consequently the total length of a protein molecule may vary considerably, depending upon temperature, pH, and other factors. An *unfolded,* or *extended,* protein molecule may be several times longer than the same molecule in the *folded,* or *tightly coiled,* form.

The forces and factors that influence the helical structure of a protein molecule, especially the degree of its folding and unfolding, collectively determine what is called the **secondary** and **tertiary structure** of the protein (Fig. 4-17).

Hydrogen bonds are particularly important in relation to secondary structure. Hydrogen bonds are relatively weak linkages that result from the tendency of hydrogen to share elections with two neighboring atoms, especially O and N, when these atoms are situated very close together (Fig. 4-17). A fully folded protein molecule appears to display one hydrogen bond between every third amino acid in the coiled peptide chain. Collectively, the many hydrogen bonds, although weak individually, exert considerable force in stabilizing the helical structure. Still weaker forces, such as electrostatic attractions between oppositely ionized molecular foci (Fig. 4-17), are regarded as the determinants of tertiary structure in proteins and other macromolecular configurations.

The three-dimensional configuration of proteins and other macromolecular components of the protoplasm has great influence upon their physiological activity. For example, enzymes are mainly of protein composition (Chap. 5) and each displays a configuration that must fit the molecular form of the substrate molecules that are being activated (p. 105). Moreover, the folding of elongate, partially unfolded protein molecules may explain the property of contractility, which is exhibited by protoplasm generally (Fig. 4-23). However, in the completely unfolded state, such as is induced by abnormally high temperature, exceptionally high or low pH conditions, or other drastic

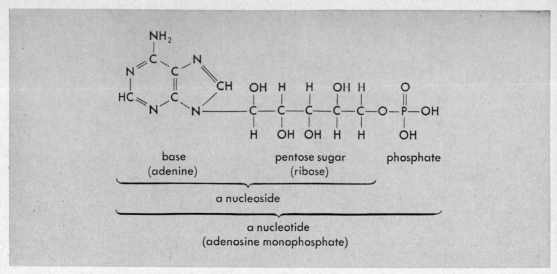

base
(adenine)

pentose sugar
(ribose)

phosphate

a nucleoside

a nucleotide
(adenosine monophosphate)

Fig. 4-18. Adenosine monophosphate, a typical nucleotide. A variety of nucleotide units, chemically linked in varying sequence into long chainlike macromolecules, determines the structure of the nucleic acids (Fig. 4-20).

changes, the proteins of the cell become inactive or, in other words, they become **denatured.**

SIMPLE VS. CONJUGATED PROTEINS. Proteins that yield only amino acids upon complete hydrolysis are designated as **simple proteins.** But if other substances are also liberated, one is dealing with a **conjugated protein.** Glucose, for example, can be derived from the **glycoproteins;** lipid, from the **lipoproteins;** or nucleic acid, from the **nucleoproteins.**

Nucleoproteins. By far the most important of the conjugated proteins are the *nucleoproteins*—not only the DNA proteins, or *genic materials,* which generally remain inside the nucleus, but also the RNA proteins, which carry on many of their functions in the cytoplasm. Essentially each nucleoprotein represents a gigantic macromolecule formed by a union between a specific protein and **nucleic acid.**

The **nucleic acids** also are very long-chained molecules. The chain of a nucleic acid, however, is constituted by a sequence of complex units, called **nucleotides** (Figs. 4-18, 4-19, and 4-20). Each nucleotide, in turn, is formed by chemical union between three constituents, namely: (1) phosphoric acid; (2) a pentose sugar; and (3) an **organic**

base. There are, however, two general and five specific kinds of organic bases, as may be seen in Figure 4-19. The pentose sugar repeatedly represented in deoxyribonucleic acid (DNA) is always deoxyribose (Fig. 4-8); whereas that of ribonucleic acid (RNA) is always ribose—as is suggested, of course, by the names.

A very large number of specifically different nucleic acids is present in any cell. Each time the nucleotides are combined in different sequence and proportion, the properties of the resulting molecule are changed. In DNA, for example, the four different bases (adenine, cytosine, guanine, and thymine) may occur in many different sequences, as is indicated in Figure 4-20. Moreover, the sugar-phosphate skeleton of a DNA is usually several thousand units in length. This means that an almost infinite variety of such macromolecules can be formed.

It is not possible to overemphasize the importance of DNA substances in the life of the organism. Between each cell division, each DNA unit replicates itself in very precise manner. Moreover, as will be seen in Chapter 7, each unit of DNA carries a set of coded instructions and this **code,** transmitted through the agency of RNA, serves to de-

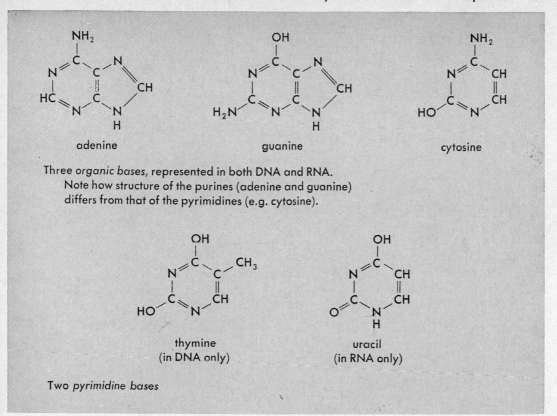

Three *organic bases*, represented in both DNA and RNA.
Note how structure of the purines (adenine and guanine)
differs from that of the pyrimidines (e.g. cytosine).

Two *pyrimidine bases*

Fig. 4-19. Organic bases **(purines** and **pyrimidines)** are important constituents of the various **nucleotides** (Fig. 4-18). The nucleotides, in turn, provide building units that go into the macromolecular structure (Fig. 4-20) of the nucleic acids (DNA and RNA).

termine the structure and activity of all protein components (including enzymes) in the cell.

Other Protoplasmic Components. In addition to the proteins, carbohydrates, lipids, and other previously mentioned substances, protoplasm always contains smaller amounts of other, usually simpler, organic compounds. This **miscellaneous group of compounds** includes: (1) various **organic wastes,** such as **urea** (p. 342); (2) metabolic **energy transmitters,** such as ATP (Fig. 4-21); (3) **hormones,** such as **adrenalin** (p. 406); and (4) **vitamins,** such as thiamine (p. 346). Many of these miscellaneous substances are of great physiological significance, as will be explained in later chapters.

Summary of Chemical Composition. All living cells are composed of water, inorganic salts, proteins (including DNA and RNA nucleoproteins), carbohydrates, and lipids, together with smaller amounts of other substances. The average amounts of these compounds are shown in Table 4-7, although certain cells may vary considerably from the average.

Table 4-7—Average Composition of Protoplasm

Kinds of Substances	Percent by Weight
Water	80
Inorganic salts	1
Proteins	15
Lipids	3
Carbohydrates *plus other substances*	1
	100

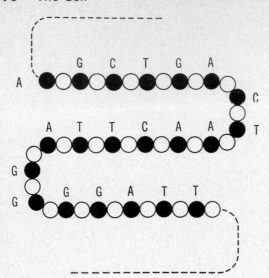

Fig. 4-20. Molecular structure of a single strand of **nucleic acid** (DNA). Black circles = sugar (deoxyribose); white circles = phosphate; A, adenine; C, cytosine; G, guanine; and T, thymine (Fig. 4-19). The chain, when broken up, yields either nucleotides (phosphate-sugar-base units) or nucleosides (slightly smaller sugar-base units, devoid of phosphate).

In the living cell the various compounds may be united into larger complexes: proteins with salts, carbohydrates, and lipids; steroids with other lipids; carbohydrates with inorganic salts, etc. Water associates with virtually all compounds dissolved in it; and in the case of such supermolecular aggregates it is not possible to distinguish clearly between chemical and physical combinations. Such linkages tend to be disrupted by the very methods usually employed to extract the protoplasmic substances from the cell, and much still remains to be learned about the chemistry of protoplasm. However, our present knowledge makes it plain that the complexity of the composition of protoplasm is sufficiently great to account for the amazingly intricate behavior of living cells.

PHYSICAL STRUCTURE OF PROTOPLASM

Protoplasm is not just a mixture of chemical components; if such were the case, one should be able to create a living cell by merely adding the proper ingredients to a test tube. This, however, would be like expecting an accurately timed watch to emerge from a randomly piled assortment of cogwheels, screws, springs, etc. Obviously the creation of any functioning mechanism depends not only upon the materials of which it is composed, but also upon how these materials are formed and fitted into a functional relationship.

In the last analysis, protoplasm, like other matter, is **particulate,** that is, composed of particles. In protoplasm, however, the particles display a tremendous variability of size and shape: from single molecules and ions, large and small, to various molecular aggregates, visible and subvisible. The size and shape of these particles greatly influence their behavior; and consequently it is necessary to study the dimensions very carefully.

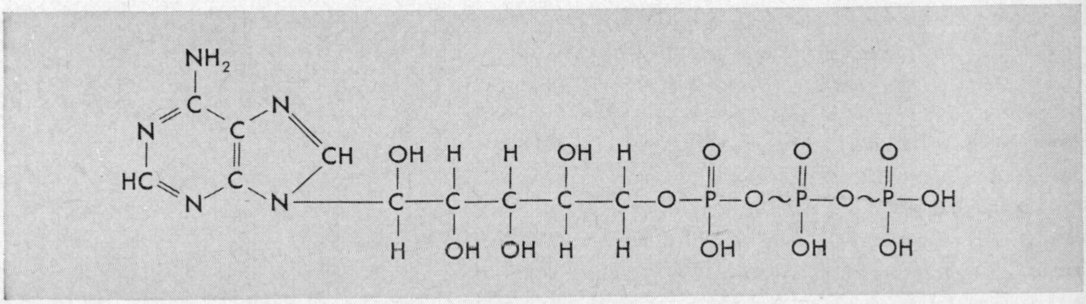

Fig. 4-21. **Adenosine triphosphate** (ATP). This energy-rich compound is certainly the most important metabolic *energy transmitter* in the cell. It can quickly transmit energy to a wide variety of cellular activities (as explained in Chapter 8). Note the special symbol ($\sim$). This denotes the two **high-energy bonds,** which transmit all of the energy (p. 143).

Coarse, Colloidal, and Crystalloidal Dimensions. Anything that is visible, either with the naked eye or with a compound microscope, is designated as **coarse;** and above this borderline of visibility, vast space exists to accommodate the familiar objects of our universe. But even below this borderline, there is ample room for great variability in the size of submicroscopic particles.

Particles that are too small to be resolved by any type of light-focusing microscope are subdivided into two categories: all larger particles—like protein and polysaccharide molecules—fall into the **colloidal size range;** and all smaller molecules—like water, salts, and monosaccharides—lie in the **crystalloidal range.** No real line divides colloidal from crystalloidal particles, and the various particles of protoplasm are finely and continuously intergraded in size. Arbitrarily, however, a line is set at 1 millimicron $(m\mu)$, which is equivalent to 10 Ångstrom units (Fig. 2-6), or 0.001 micron. Accordingly, particles having diameters extending from 100 millimicrons (the limit of resolution of an ordinary compound microscope) down to 1 millimicron are said to be **colloidal;** whereas particles with diameters of less than 1 millimicron are designated as **crystalloidal.**

On a practical basis, the appearance of a fluid indicates whether it is a colloidal or crystalloidal system. If the dispersed particles of a fluid are very small, that is, of crystalloid dimensions, the fluid as a whole is clear and *transparent*—like a sugar or salt solution. The dispersed molecules or ions of such a solution are not large enough to interfere with the light as it passes through. But if a fluid contains particles that are large enough to fall in the colloid range, the system has a cloudy or *translucent* appearance—like a starch or albumin solution. In this case the dispersed particles (large organic molecules) are not large enough to block the passage of light waves completely, but they are large enough to scatter, or diffract, the light. Finally, a *coarse* system—like milk—appears *opaque*. In this case, the dispersed globules of butter fat are aggregated masses of molecules, and such particles are large enough to reflect light. Consequently, when milk is examined with a microscope, the *coarse* dispersed particles are individually visible.

Although colloidal particles are not large enough to be *seen* with a standard microscope, most of them can be resolved by the electron microscope and many can be detected by means of the darkfield microscope (Fig. 2-10). The latter instrument resembles an ordinary microscope, except that it requires a more intense beam of light; and this beam is passed *horizontally*, rather than vertically, through the material under examination. Under the darkfield, or ultramicroscope, the colloidal particles of the protoplasm appear as a myriad of *bright specks* zigzagging in random directions against a black and empty background. Each particle may not be large enough to reflect a definite pattern of light; but the particles are sufficiently large to scatter some of the light vertically toward the ocular. Thus the ultramicroscope shows very little as regards the precise color, shape, or size of colloidal particles. It merely permits these particles to be identified and enumerated, and it reveals the nature of their movements.

Another practical method of distinguishing between colloid and crystalloid particles is to test their capacity to penetrate a membrane such as cellophane or parchment. The pores or channels through a cellophane membrane appear to be just small enough to prevent the passage of colloid particles, but these pores are large enough to permit crystalloidal particles to pass through. Thus if a closed cellophane bag, filled with an aqueous solution containing glucose and starch, is immersed in water, after a short time glucose—but not starch, will begin to escape from the bag into the surrounding water. Such permeability considerations are very important in determining the exchange of substances between cells and their surrounding media. Generally speaking, colloidal particles are not able to penetrate the plasma membrane, and crystalloidal particles *may* or *may not* penetrate, depending upon a variety of other factors (Chap. 6).

Size and the Motility of Particles: Brownian Movement. The absorption of heat by any kind of matter accelerates and intensifies the random movements of the component molecules, ions, and other particles. In fluid bodies like protoplasm, these **thermal movements** tend to scatter the particles evenly throughout the system. But the speed at which each particle moves, impelled by thermal energy at a given temperature, is governed largely by its size. When the diameter is doubled, the rate of movement is quartered. In other words, the rate of thermal movement of a particle is inversely proportional to the square of its diameter. Accordingly the random movement of colloidal particles, such as protein molecules, is very small compared to the movement of crystalloid particles, such as inorganic molecules and ions. The actual motion of the colloidal particles as seen in the ultramicroscope, and the movement of small microscopically visible particles such as bacteria and starch grains are not directly due to the thermal energy of these relatively large particles. Instead, they represent a phenomenon called **Brownian movement.** Brownian movement is exhibited by all small microscopic bodies as well as by ultramicroscopic particles generally. It arises from the bombardment of the larger particles by the surrounding multitude of smaller particles. In the protoplasm, the smaller particles responsible for this bombardment are chiefly water molecules. The bombardment is unequal from moment to moment, being heavier first on one side and then on another. Accordingly, the displacement of particles by Brownian movement is very irregular and unpredictable.

Solutions; Molecular Polarity. In an **ideal solution,** all the molecules or ions of the **solute** become individually separated and evenly dispersed throughout the dispersion medium, which is called the **solvent.** In actual solutions, however, the situation is complicated by the fact that the solute molecules or ions become associated with the molecules of the solvent; and the effective size of the dispersed particles in a solution tends to be greater than expectations based on the molecular and ionic volumes of the dissolved substances. Accordingly, in protoplasm and other **aqueous** solutions, the solute particles are associated with a greater or lesser number of **water** molecules; or in other words, each solute particle is said to be **hydrated.**

The forces that attract water to the molecules or ions of the solute are mainly electrical. In many molecules, the electrical charges (protons and electrons) do not have a symmetrical placement in the molecule as a whole. In the case of water, for example, the whole molecule is an uncharged body, but the negative charges are more concentrated toward one end, and the positive charges toward the other. This endows water molecules with an electrical **polarity,** and in fact, water is designated as a **moderately polar** compound. Water is attracted to other molecules and ions in a solution with greater or lesser force, depending upon whether these other particles are *strongly* or *weakly* **polar** in their electrical configuration. Generally speaking, water, salts, proteins, and simple carbohydrates are distinctly polar, whereas fats and polysaccharides are relatively **nonpolar** compounds.

Among the components of protoplasm, those that dissolve in water include: most inorganic substances; sugars, amino acids, and other simple organic compounds; many proteins; and to a slight extent, the phospholipids and polysaccharides. Other lipids are virtually insoluble in water, although they dissolve mutually in each other. The water-soluble components in the protoplasm are all hydrated to a greater or lesser degree, and the salts, amino acids, proteins, and phospholipids are also more or less strongly ionized. These considerations have great importance in determining chemical and physical activities in the cell.

Suspensions and Emulsions. In a suspension or emulsion, the scattered particles consist not of single molecules, but of molecular aggregates of the dispersed substance. In a **suspension** the dispersed particles are considered to be **solid**; in an **emulsion** they are **liquid**; but in practice this distinction tends to be quite arbitrary. When the dispersed particles are very small, as in **colloidal** suspensions and emulsions, it is difficult to determine whether the individual particles are in a solid or a liquid state.

The size of the dispersed particles in different emulsions and suspensions ranges from colloidal to microscopic dimensions. In fact, colloidal suspensions and emulsions are sometimes so finely subdivided that they scarcely can be distinguished from colloidal solutions. Moreover, substances emulsified or suspended in water may even be hydrated and ionized, just as in true solutions.

Diphasic and Multiphasic Dispersions. In a true solution it is customary to regard the intermingled molecules and ions of the solute and solvent as all belonging to the same **phase** of the system. But in suspensions and emulsions it is necessary to distinguish between the **discontinuous** and the **continuous phases.** The discontinuous phase consists of all the larger dispersed particles or droplets, taken collectively; whereas the continuous phase is constituted by the dispersion medium itself, considered as a homogeneous mass. Milk, for example, is an emulsion in which the discontinuous phase is comprised by the microscopically visible globules of butter fat; these globules float in the continuous phase, which is an aqueous solution containing milk sugar, various inorganic salts, and proteins.

A complex system such as protoplasm displays more than one discontinuous phase, each represented by a different kind of dispersed particle or droplet. Also in protoplasm one may find more than one continuous phase (see gel structure, below).

Emulsifying Agents; Adsorption. If olive oil and water are shaken together in a test tube, an unstable emulsion is formed that begins to break down as soon as the shaking is stopped. The agitation scatters a multitude of oil droplets throughout the water, but when the shaking ceases, these droplets begin to coalesce into larger and larger drops, and finally all the oil comes together as a separate layer, which floats on top of the water. If, however, a trace of soluble protein, or a small amount of soap solution, is added before shaking, a **stable emulsion** is obtained, and such an emulsion keeps its structure more or less indefinitely.

The foregoing example indicates that protein (or soap) can act as an **emulsifying agent.** In the stable emulsion most of the added protein accumulates at the surfaces of contact between the two phases, that is, at the **interfaces** between the oil droplets and the water. Such an accumulation coats each droplet with a protective film that prevents it from coalescing with other droplets. The tendency for certain dissolved substances to become concentrated at the interfaces of an emulsion or suspension is called **adsorption.** Many colloidal substances, particularly proteins and phospholipids, tend to be adsorbed heavily at the various protoplasmic interfaces. This stabilizes the finely emulsified droplets and delicately suspended particles that are so characteristic of living matter.

Phase Reversal. An emulsion such as is formed by shaking oil with water may take either of two stable forms: that of an **oil-in-water** emulsion (Fig. 4-22A), or that of a **water-in-oil** emulsion (Fig. 4-22C). The intermediate form (Fig. 4-22B) is unstable. It tends to pass into either of the two stable forms; or it tends to "break" the emulsion structure, with a complete separation of the phases. These differences in the form of an emulsion depend chiefly upon the chemical nature of the emulsifying agent. Any chemical change affecting the constitution of the emulsifying agent may therefore affect the stability of the emulsion and the relation of its phases. Without doubt, some of the changes in the appearance and consistency

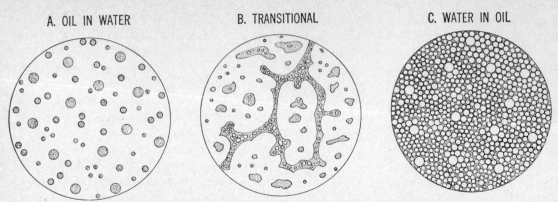

A. OIL IN WATER   B. TRANSITIONAL   C. WATER IN OIL

Fig. 4-22. Emulsion formed from olive oil and water, as seen with the microscope; the oil contains a dye to make it darker. The changes in form of an emulsion are brought about by the addition of small amounts of a substance that changes the chemical constitution of the emulsifying agent. A, water the continuous phase, oil the discontinuous (dispersed) phase. B, intermediate form, the emulsion "breaking"; this state is very unstable, the two phases being in continual rapid motion and rearrangement. C, oil the continuous phase, water the dispersed phase.

of the protoplasm are due to such **phase reversals,** which result from chemical changes wrought by the metabolism of the cell, or from chemical changes in the nearby environment.

Gelation and Solation. Protoplasm frequently alters its consistency by undergoing gelation or solation. Like a gelatin solution, the fluid protoplasm of a cell may become set at a certain moment into a semisolid elastic mass; and then later it may revert to a more fluid consistency. Recently the function of these changes has become clearer. The evidence indicates that the **contractility** of protoplasm depends upon its capacity to undergo gelation; and that many cell movements, such as **amoeboid movement,** cannot occur if the sol-gel changes in the protoplasm are inhibited.

The capacity to gelate is found in many colloidal systems, especially when the dispersed particles are elongate, like protein or polysaccharide molecules. In the sol condition such elongate particles behave more or less as separate units (Figs. 4-23A). But as gelation occurs, attractive forces come into play between the colloid particles, so that the dispersed particles of the system become interlinked, forming a colloidal network that extends throughout the gel (Fig. 4-23B). The water and other crystalloidal components are enmeshed by the gel framework and consequently the whole mass develops rigidity, elasticity, and contractility—properties that ordinarily are found only in solid systems.

The precise manner in which the elongate particles of a sol become linked together to

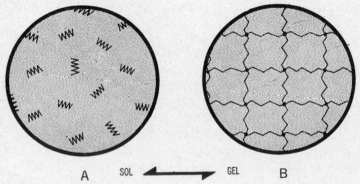

A   SOL ⟷ GEL   B

Fig. 4-23. Ultramicroscopic structure of a sol and a gel (diagrammatic). A, a sol, in which the elongate colloidal molecules or particles are folded and separate. B, same system after gelation has occurred, in which the elongate particles are unfolded and interlinked, forming a colloidal network. Gels tend to be elastic and **contractile.** The zigzag lines represent elongate colloidal particles (e.g., protein molecules); the dots represent water and other crystalloidal molecules.

form the colloidal framework of a gel is not very clearly understood. The strength and number of the interconnections, and consequently the firmness of the resulting gel are sensitive to many factors. Some of these factors are chemical, such as changes in the concentration of hydrogen ions and other substances in the solution; and some are physical, such as changes in temperature. Apparently gelation in protoplasm is under the control of metabolism, which continually alters local conditions in various parts of the cell. All protoplasmic gels that have been studied behave oppositely to gelatin, at least insofar as temperature is concerned. Instead of undergoing solation as the temperature is raised, protoplasm undergoes gelation. Such behavior is also exhibited by gels composed of **actomyosin,** the main protein present in muscle tissue. In any event, once a gel framework has been assembled in the protoplasm, contractility can develop as a result of the folding of the interlinked molecules or other particles, and such folding processes are particularly characteristic of actomyosin and other elongate protein complexes.

Protoplasmic Surfaces. It is important to realize that a colloidal system such as protoplasm possesses a tremendous expanse of surface area. Each colloidal particle, globule, membrane, or fiber exposes a large proportion of free surface at which some one (or more) metabolic reaction may be catalyzed, or speeded up (p. 101). In fact, most metabolic reactions can scarcely proceed at all in the absence of such catalytic surfaces. Consequently the extent of the protoplasmic surfaces, and the fact that their pattern may be changed from moment to moment play a very important role in determining metabolic activity in the cell.

The stupendous surface of the protoplasmic system can best be visualized by thinking of a small cube, measuring perhaps 1 centimeter per edge, that is being cut progressively into smaller and smaller cubes. Initially the total surface is, of course, only 6 square centimeters; but as the pieces become smaller and smaller, the free surface increases tremendously. Indeed, if finally the pieces measure only 0.01 micron per edge, which is about average as a colloidal dimension, the total surface of the subdivided mass would be more than 6 *million square centimeters*. In other words, if we visualize all the free surfaces in a cell—the surfaces of the microsomes, mitochondria, canaliculae, chloroplasts, grana, vacuoles, protein fibers, emulsion globules, and so forth—we begin to realize that the protoplasmic surfaces are extremely extensive, complex, and adaptable.

SUMMARY

Protoplasm represents a very complicated polyphasic dispersion in which each phase displays a complex composition. Simultaneously, protoplasm is a crystalloidal, colloidal, and coarse dispersion, partly solution, partly emulsion, and partly suspension. Sometimes protoplasm is in a gel state and sometimes it is a sol.

The complex structure of living matter is not static; that is, protoplasm ceaselessly changes, and these changes underlie the vital activities of the cell. The lipoid phases may alternately undergo coalescence and separation in a fashion that may or may not involve phase reversal. The aqueous phases may remain homogeneous, as in the sol condition, or they may give rise to colloidal networks, as when gelation occurs. Such changes continually demand an expenditure of energy, which is supplied by metabolism. When energy-liberating chemical reactions cease, the finer protoplasmic structure breaks down, becoming less complex, more stable—in other words, dead.

But even as protoplasmic structure is dependent on metabolism, so metabolism is dependent on the living structure. The separate phases of the protoplasmic system constitute a series of microscopic and ultramicroscopic **reaction foci.** The separate films and surfaces at which a variety of the reacting components may be adsorbed and concentrated limit, control, and regulate the metabolic reactions. Despite the size, each cell may be considered as a delicately organized "chemical engine." In the cell a wide variety of reactions go on simultaneously and more or less independently. When this delicate organization breaks down, the chemical activity does not cease immediately. Rather the metabolism becomes disorganized, unregulated, and purely destructive, leading to a decomposition of many of the essential protoplasmic compounds.

Because protoplasmic structure and metabolism are mutually interdependent, a cell once dead cannot be "started up" again: the metabolism cannot be resumed in the absence of the living structure; and this structure cannot be restored without the metabolism. But the "death" of a cell is not usually a very abrupt and tangible change. In fact the intergradations between disease, injury, and death are very subtle; but when the protoplasmic structure has degenerated beyond restoration, the cell is dead, however difficult it may be to determine exactly when this point of degradation is reached. From a sci-

entific standpoint, the death of a multicellular individual, such as man, is still more indefinite. The many cells of the body do not all die at once. Some of the tissues may continue to live many hours after the man is "officially" dead. The usual verdict of death is given when the heartbeat and breathing stop, but these movements can sometimes be restored many minutes later. But without respiration and circulation, no oxygen is carried to the body cells; and in the absence of oxidative metabolism, the protoplasmic structure gradually crumbles. Then sooner or later in each of the tissues the degradation becomes irreversible.

Thus all living organisms originate from the protoplasm of other living organisms; and the "endless" chain of specific structure and metabolism goes on unbroken, except when a species becomes extinct. Of the ultimate origin of the protoplasmic system, we have very little direct knowledge. Presumably protoplasm was evolved very gradually, through the millions of years of early geological time, from much simpler structures and processes (Chap. 10).

TEST QUESTIONS

1. Among the elements represented in cells generally, which of them are:
   a. never present in uncombined form
   b. present as the free element, as well as in combined form
   c. present in the merest traces
   d. exceptionally abundant
   e. univalent
   f. divalent
   g. tetravalent
2. In what way might you be able to convince your younger brother that water (and all other forms of matter) is composed of subvisibly small particles, or molecules?
3. Specify at least six kinds of energy; what are the primary distinctions between matter and energy?
4. Carefully define and exemplify each of the following terms: (a) molecules and atoms; (b) a substance and a mixture; (c) electrons and protons; (d) kinetic and potential energy.

5. Explain how the valence of an element is related to its atomic structure.
6. Distinguish between electropositive, electronegative, and inert atoms—giving an example in each case.
7. Discuss the physical properties of water in relation to the structural and functional characteristics of protoplasm.
8. Distinguish between electrolytes (strong and weak) and nonelectrolytes; what is the general importance of electrolytes in the life of a cell?
9. Distinguish between the members of each group of terms:
   a. acid, basic, and neutral solutions
   b. an acid substance and an acid solution
10. Explain a method by which the reaction (acidity or alkalinity) of the protoplasm of the nucleus and cytoplasm of certain cells has been measured. State the results of such experiments.

11. What gases are usually present in protoplasm? How do these gases enter the cells? Why are they important?

12. Distinguish between organic and inorganic compounds of the basis of
    a. occurrence in nature
    b. chemical composition
    c. molecular dimensions
    d. capacity to dissociate

13. Describe a simple test that can be used to differentiate between organic and inorganic substances. Explain.

14. Name four different carbohydrate substances and specify how each is important in various cells.

15. How are carbohydrates different from other organic substances?

16. To what extent is glucose used as a protoplasmic fuel? Explain, using the proper chemical equation.

17. Each chemical reaction represents a transformation of matter that proceeds in accordance with the law of the *conservation of matter*. Explain this statement using a specific reaction to exemplify the discussion.

18. What is the essential difference between an exothermic and an endothermic reaction? To what extent is it possible, by inspecting an equation, to decide whether a reaction is exothermic or endothermic?

19. Distinguish between:
    a. decomposition and synthesis
    b. dehydration syntheses and other syntheses
    c. hydrolysis and other decompositions

20. Specify the end products yielded by the complete hydrolysis of:
    a. starch (and cellulose)
    b. maltose
    c. sucrose
    d. a true fat
    e. any simple protein
    f. any conjugated protein

21. Provide at least one specific example, in each case, of:
    a. monosaccharide sugars
    b. disaccharide sugars
    c. fatty acids
    d. amino acids

22. As to chemical structure, how are amino acids (a) similar to, and (b) different from fatty acids?

23. Explain the relation between:
    a. digestion and hydrolysis
    b. true fats and phospholipids

24. As to the constituent atoms, how do proteins differ from carbohydrates and fats?

25. All complete proteins liberate the same amino acids when fully hydrolyzed, and yet the proteins of different animals and plants are specifically distinctive. Explain.

26. Show by formulas how an amino acid can behave: (a) as an acid, and (b) as a basic substance.

27. Carefully explain: (a) the buffer action, and (b) the amphoteric behavior of amino acids.

28. Discuss the primary structure of protein molecules. What types of chemical bonds determine this structure?

29. What is a hydrogen bond? Why are such bonds important?

30. What is meant by secondary and tertiary structure in the protein molecule? By what forces are these aspects of structure determined?

31. What may be the physiological significance of the "folding" and "unfolding" of protein molecules? What is a denatured protein? Give an example.

32. What is a conjugated protein? Name two very important kinds.

33. What is a nucleotide; a nucleoside?

34. Name five organic bases present in various nucleic acids. Which of these can be found (a) in DNA only; (b) in RNA only; and (c) in both DNA and RNA?

35. Differentiate in as many ways as possible between DNA and RNA.

36. Explain why DNA and RNA are very important in the cell.

37. Assuming that the chemical composition of protoplasm were fully known (which is far from true), what other difficulties would have to be surmounted to bring the "artificial synthesis of protoplasm" within the realm of possibility?

38. Explain how the coarse, colloidal, and crystalloidal particles of protoplasm are to be distinguished on the basis of:
    a. actual dimensions
    b. capacity to penetrate a cellophane membrane
    c. capacity to penetrate the plasma membrane

    d. microscopic visibility

    e. detectability with the ultramicroscope

    f. capacity to reflect or diffract light waves

    g. thermal movements, including Brownian movement

39. Briefly explain how the polarity of a molecule is related to its degree of hydration and its "effective size."

40. Mention three polar and two nonpolar compounds present in protoplasm.

41. Distinguish between emulsions, suspensions, and solutions; give an example in each case.

42. Explain why phase reversal is possible in emulsion but not in suspensions.

43. Define the terms: (a) adsorption; (b) emulsifying agent; and (c) stable emulsion. Explain how these terms are interrelated.

44. Differentiate between a sol and a gel, using a gelatin "solution" to exemplify the discussion.

45. How does a gelatin gel differ from actomyosin and other "protoplasmic gels"?

46. Explain the relation between gelation and the contractility of protoplasm.

FURTHER READINGS

1. *Dynamic Aspects of Biochemistry,* 3d ed., by E. Baldwin; New York, 1957.
2. *Unresting Cells,* by R. W. Gerard; New York, 1949.
3. *The Cell,* vol. 2, *Cells and Their Component Parts,* ed. by J. Brachet and A. E. Mirsky; New York and London, 1961.
4. *Cellular Physiology and Biochemistry,* by W. D. McElroy; Englewood Cliffs, N. J., 1961.

5-Enzymes: How Cells Promote Chemical Activities

IN PROTOPLASM many chemical reactions go forward with explosive speed. Yet if the reacting substances are removed from the cell and isolated in a test tube, they become very inert and no longer show much tendency to interact. Such puzzling behavior led a few biologists to postulate a "vital force" that activates the protoplasmic molecules. But others continued to search for missing factors, and during the past 35 years the problem has been greatly clarified.

A relatively simple protoplasmic reaction will serve to illustrate this problem more specifically. Many plant and animal tissues constantly produce hydrogen peroxide (H_2O_2). This fairly poisonous compound does not accumulate in toxic amounts because it decomposes almost as fast as it is formed. In decomposing, peroxide liberates free oxygen, as is shown in the equation at the top of the next column.

In protoplasm this peroxide reaction goes forward very rapidly. Yet a pure aqueous solution of H_2O_2, such as is commonly employed as a disinfectant, is relatively stable.

$$2H_2O_2 \rightleftarrows O_2 + 2H_2O$$

2 mol hydrogen peroxide — 1 mol oxygen — 2 mol water

In a stoppered bottle, peroxide keeps for months before it "goes flat," gradually freeing its content of O_2. Thus one phase of the problem is to ascertain why peroxide shows less reactivity in the test tube than in the protoplasm.

CATALYSIS

In many cases, the rate of chemical reaction is greatly changed by the presence of a **small amount** of some specific reagent in the reaction medium. In the case of peroxide, for example, a very faint trace of manganese dioxide (MnO_2), a black powder, will produce a thousandfold acceleration in the liberation of oxygen. If just a pinch of the powder is added to a test tube of peroxide solution, oxygen begins to come forth so rapidly

99

that the mixture froths like beer. Moreover, it can be determined that none of the manganese compound disappears from the test tube, and consequently the same small sample of MnO_2 can foster the decomposition of peroxide in a quantity that is virtually without limit.

In the foregoing reaction, manganese dioxide may be recognized as a **catalyst,** and its action upon the peroxide is a typical example of **catalysis.** A **catalyst** *is any reagent that accelerates a chemical reaction without affecting the end point, and without being destroyed when the end point is reached.* A wide variety of catalysts are known in inorganic chemistry, and there is an even greater number of **organic catalysts.**

ENZYMES: DEFINITION AND EXAMPLE

Enzymes *are organic (essentially protein) catalysts produced by living cells.* Typically each cell contains some 2 to 3 thousand different enzymes and these enable the protoplasm to carry on a very complex and vigorous traffic of chemical activity.

Many enzymes can be extracted from the protoplasm without impairing their activity. For example, **catalase,** the peroxide-activating enzyme, can be obtained in dry crystalline form practically devoid of contaminating impurities. Such a purified enzyme displays tremendous activity. A small fraction of a gram of catalase, dropped into a test tube containing peroxide solution, gives rise to a most vigorous evolution of oxygen. In fact, catalase accelerates the decomposition of peroxide much more effectively than manganese dioxide when equivalent concentrations of the two catalysts are employed in the reaction (p. 108).

Small amounts of catalase are present in a wide variety of animal and plant tissues, and catalase activity can be demonstrated in many crude preparations. Thus when peroxide is poured upon an open wound, the frothing of the solution indicates that catalase is present in the blood and serum that oozes from the wound. Also, one may add the scrapings from a raw potato to a peroxide solution and observe the bubbling, which results from catalase liberated by the damaged potato cells.

General Importance of Enzymes. Virtually all the many chemical reactions that sustain the life of the cell are activated by enzymes. Each different reaction generally depends upon a different enzyme. Most of these fulfill their duties inside the cell, speeding the reactions of **metabolism,** but some may be extruded from the protoplasm to foster the reactions of **digestion.** In other words, neither *metabolism* nor *digestion* could occur in the absence of the wide variety of enzymes that are produced by every living cell.

The Naming of Enzymes. Progress in the field of enzymology has been very rapid since 1926, when James B. Sumner of Cornell University first succeeded in isolating pure crystals of **urease,** the enzyme that catalyzes the hydrolytic breakdown of urea, $CO(NH_2)_2$, into carbon dioxide (CO_2) and ammonia (NH_3). This progress gave rise to the modern system of **enzyme nomenclature,** which is exemplified in Table 5-1. However, the names of some enzymes, especially those of the human digestive tract, do not conform to the system. These enzymes were very familiar before the modern terminology came into use and hence their old names have tended to persist (Table 5-1).

In modern enzyme nomenclature, the suffix *-ase* indicates the name of an enzyme or group of enzymes. Specific individual enzymes are usually named according to the principal substance, called the **substrate,** the chemical activity of which is being catalyzed. Thus the principal substrate of **urease** is urea, and that of starch (Latin = *amylum*) is **amylase.** However, not only the substrate but also the type of reaction may be indicated by the specific name, as in **lactic dehydrogenase,** which catalyzes the splitting off of hydrogen atoms from **lactic acid** (p. 101), and **fructokinase,** which catalyzes the phosphorylation of **fructose** (p. 101).

Groups of enzymes may also be specified by the system, according to: (1) the **class of substrate** involved—for example, **proteases,** which catalyze protein reactions, and **lipases,** for lipid reactions, etc.; or (2) the **type of reaction**—for example, **hydrolases,** for hydrolysis reactions; **oxidases,** for reactions in which oxygen has a *direct* involvement; and **dehydrogenases,** for the transfer of hydrogen (p. 145) from one organic substrate to another (an *indirect* type of oxidation). Metabolism, however, is exceedingly complex and enzyme nomenclature has developed certain other usages, which will be encountered later.

Table 5-1—Some Representative Enzymes

General Types; Specific Names	Catalytic Action	Comment
Metabolic Enzymes Dehydrogenases 1. Lactic dehydrogenase	1. Liberates 2 hydrogens from *lactic acid* $$CH_3\!-\!\underset{\underset{H}{\mid}}{\overset{\overset{OH}{\mid}}{C}}\!-\!COOH$$ and from other molecules having similar structure, namely $$-\underset{\underset{H}{\mid}}{\overset{\overset{OH}{\mid}}{C}}-$$	1. Hydrogen transferred to a hydrogen acceptor (p. 145); lactic acid *oxidized* to *pyruvic acid* $$CH_3\!\cdot\!\overset{\overset{O}{\parallel}}{C}\!-\!COOH$$ present in most, if not all, cells
2. Succinic dehydrogenase	2. Liberates 2 hydrogens from *succinic acid* $$HOOC\!-\!\underset{\underset{H}{\mid}}{\overset{\overset{H}{\mid}}{C}}\!-\!\underset{\underset{H}{\mid}}{\overset{\overset{H}{\mid}}{C}}\!-\!COOH$$ and from other molecules having $$-\underset{\underset{H}{\mid}}{\overset{\overset{H}{\mid}}{C}}\!-\!\underset{\underset{H}{\mid}}{\overset{\overset{H}{\mid}}{C}}-$$ in their structure	2. Hydrogen transferred to another type of hydrogen acceptor (p. 145); succinic acid oxidized to *fumaric acid* $$HOOC\!-\!\underset{\underset{H}{\mid}}{C}\!=\!\underset{\underset{H}{\mid}}{C}\!-\!COOH$$ also widely distributed in cells generally
Transphosphorylases 1. Glucokinase	1. Transfers phosphate ($H_2PO_4^-$) from ATP (p. 149) to *glucose*	1. *Activates* (p. 149) *glucose,* initiating its catabolic breakdown; widely distributed
2. Fructokinase	2. Transfers phosphate from ATP to fructose	2. Activates *fructose;* widely distributed

Table 5-1 (continued)

General Types; Specific Names	Catalytic Action	Comment
Aminases		
1. Pyruvic transaminase	1. Transfers the amino group ($-NH_2$) from certain amino acids to pyruvic acid $$CH_3 \cdot C{-}COOH$$ $$\parallel$$ $$O$$ forming alanine $$CH_3{-}C{-}COO$$ $$\mid$$ $$NH_2$$	1. Important in reference to the interconversion of amino acids (p. 156)
2. Alanine deaminase	2. Discharges the amino group ($-NH_2$) from alanine, forming pyruvic acid plus ammonia (NH_3) and hydrogen peroxide (H_2O_2)	2. Achieves deamination, an important process in protein catabolism (p. 156); accounts for presence of catalase in most cells
Digestive Enzymes (all hydrolases) Proteases		
1. Pepsin	1. An endopeptidase; breaks (hydrolysis) the peptide chain of a protein molecule at certain specific points, forming long-chain peptides	1. Present in the gastric juice of man and other animals; initiates the digestion (p. 129) of protein components of food; requires an acid medium for maximum activity
2. Trypsin	2. An endopeptidase; breaks certain internally placed peptide bonds of long-chain peptides, forming short-chain peptides	2. Present in pancreatic juices generally; very effective in the "middle range" of protein digestion; requires alkaline medium
3. Chymotrypsin	3. Also an endopeptidase; preferentially ruptures bonds bordering upon certain amino acids, namely tyrosine, phenylalanine, and tryptophan	3. Another pancreatic hydrolase; cooperates with trypsin in the intermediate range of protein digestion; requires alkaline medium
4. Carboxypeptidase	4. An exopeptidase; splits off terminal amino acids in which the carboxyl ($-COOH$) group is "exposed"	4. Present in pancreatic juice; accounts for appearance of single amino acids during pancreatic digestion; requires alkaline medium

Table 5-1 (continued)

General Types; Specific Names	Catalytic Action	Comment
5. Aminopeptidase	5. Another exopeptidase; specifically splits off amino acids at end of chain, if they possess an "exposed" amino ($-NH_2$) group	5. Present in the intestinal juice; trypsin, chymotrypsin, carboxypeptidase, and amino peptidase have been used to determine the order of different amino acids in the peptide chains of various proteins (Fig. 4-16)
Carbohydrases 1. Salivary and pancreatic amylases	1. Hydrolysis of polysaccharides (starches and glycogens) down to the disaccharide (maltose) stage	1. Present in saliva and pancreatic juices respectively, require neutral and alkaline media, respectively
2. Maltase	2,3, and 4. Each hydrolyzes its own specific disaccharide sugar, liberating appropriate monosaccharides	2. Liberates 2 molecules of glucose
3. Sucrase		3. Frees 1 mol glucose + 1 mol fructose
4. Lactase		4. Yields 1 mol glucose + 1 mol galactose
Lipases 1. Gastric lipase	1,2. Hydrolysis of fats, yielding glycerol and fatty acids	1. A relatively weak lipase; is acid stable, however, and may continue to act in alkaline chyme, following evacuation from stomach (p. 310).
2. Pancreatic lipase (Steapsin)		2. A potent lipase in pancreatic juice; requires alkaline medium

CHEMICAL NATURE OF ENZYMES

More than 300 enzymes, from a wide variety of cells and tissues, have now been obtained in *pure crystalline form* (Fig. 5-1). In every case an *essential part* of each enzyme has proved to be of **protein composition.** Moreover, all crude (that is, unpurified) enzyme extracts display protein characteristics. They tend to become denatured (p. 88) and inactive when exposed to: (1) *high temperature* (above 40° C, typically); (2) relatively high or low *pH conditions;* or (3) changes in the *ionic composition* of the medium. In short, the maintenance of catalytic activity in an enzyme preparation appears to depend upon the maintenance of the structural integrity of the protein component, especially with reference to the secondary and tertiary aspects of such structure (p. 87).

It is now generally accepted that every

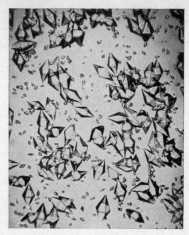

Fig. 5-1. Crystals of purified pepsin. (Courtesy of J. A. Northrop, Rockefeller Institute for Medical Research.)

enzyme has an essential protein component, without which the enzyme loses all catalytic power. Indeed, some enzymes (for example, pepsin and trypsin, Table 5-1) are solely protein. Many others, however, consist of a protein part, called the **apoenzyme,** and a nonprotein part, called a **cofactor.** Quite a few such cofactors have been identified. Each has proved to be a relatively simple phosphorylated substance, chemically united to some one or another of the **vitamin** compounds, such as **niacin, thiamine, riboflavin,** etc. (Chap. 18). In fact, recent developments indicate that the principal role of most vitamins is to act as cofactors in various metabolic enzyme systems—as will be discussed more fully in Chapters 8 and 18.

Coenzymes vs. Prosthetic Groups. The protein and nonprotein parts, in *some* enzymes (for example, succinic dehydrogenase, p. 108), are very firmly united, and a separation of the parts leads to an irreversible loss of catalytic activity. In such cases, the nonprotein cofactor is spoken of as a **prosthetic group,** and the total enzyme complex can be regarded as a **conjugated protein.** However, in other cases (for example, lactic dehydrogenase, p. 108), the affiliation is loose, and full activity can be restored after the parts have been separated and then brought together

again. Such readily separable cofactors, indeed, are called **coenzymes.** Moreover, several cases are known (for example, coenzyme A, p. 153) wherein the same coenzyme may team up with more than one apoenzyme, thus catalyzing several different metabolic reactions. This indicates that the **specificity** of enzyme action (p. 108) is determined mainly by the *structural configuration of the protein part* of each different enzyme complex.

HOW ENZYMES ACT

The precise mechanisms of enzyme catalysis are still not fully understood, although many investigators are concentrating on this area. The recent evidence indicates that frequently (perhaps always) the enzyme and substrate molecules combine together, rapidly and momentarily forming a highly unstable intermediary **enzyme-substrate compound** (Fig. 5-2). Almost instantaneously thereafter, however, the enzyme-substrate compound decomposes, restoring the free enzyme and liberating the end products of the reaction (Fig. 5-2). The evidence further indicates that energy is generated by the enzyme-substrate union. Presumably this energy serves to raise the energy level of the substrate molecule (Fig. 5-2), inducing what may be termed an **activated state,** in which certain of the bonds of its molecular structure are more susceptible to rupture. Moreover, union between enzyme and substrate molecules often seems to depend upon a mutual compatibility, or **reciprocal fit** between the molecular structure of the enzyme and that of the particular substrate. More specifically, the configuration of some particular part of the enzyme molecule, which is known as the **catalytic site,** must conform in some way to the configuration of some part of the substrate molecule —more or less in the fashion that a key must be fitted to its lock (Fig. 5-2).

Enzyme-Substrate Combinations. Almost 50 years ago Leonor Michaelis, of the Rockefeller Institute, first proposed that enzyme-substrate combinations are formed during

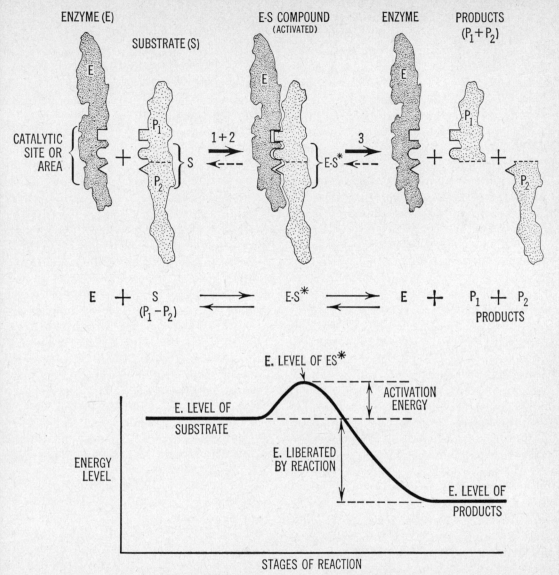

Fig. 5-2. The mechanisms of enzyme catalysis: (1) Formation of an enzyme-substrate compound. This requires a "molecular fit" between the enzyme and the substrate. (2) Energy, generated by union of E and S, activates the substrate. Activation weakens certain specific bonds. (3) Splitting of substrate molecule into end products. This generates the reaction energy.

enzyme catalysis. At this time, moreover, Michaelis formulated mathematical methods by which this hypothesis could be tested. Subsequently this brilliant theoretical analysis was borne out by many studies. These have shown conclusively that the speed of catalysis varies in predictable fashion when the concentrations of (1) the enzyme, or (2) the substrate, or (3) certain specific inhibiting substances (p. 106) are subjected to experimental variation.

Enzyme-substrate compounds are extremely unstable and short-lived, however. Consequently they are difficult to isolate. But some of them possess distinctive colors, and these can be identified when a tissue is examined with a **spectroscope**. Thus in 1943, Kurt G. Stern, working at Yale University, was able to demonstrate the formation of a *catalase-*H_2O_2 intermediary compound, even though the life of this unstable complex endures for only 1/85,000 of a second. Britton Chance, of the University of Pennsylvania, also found that peroxidase, a brown enzyme extracted from horse-radish, forms two successive intermediary complexes, one green and the other pale red, when H_2O_2 is added to the system; and subsequently a number of other enzyme-substrate intermediaries have been revealed.

Concept of Intermolecular Fit. The "lock and key concept" of enzyme-substrate fit was first proposed by the great German biochemist, Emil Fischer, almost 75 years ago. A detailed knowledge of the molecular structure of proteins has been difficult to gain, however, and evidence supporting this hypothesis, though very suggestive and intriguing, is not generally very specific. However, there are many cases where such an interpretation seems applicable. E. S. G. Barron at Chicago University, for example, studied the enzyme system that prepares acetic acid (CH_3COOH) for oxidation by the Krebs cycle enzymes (Fig. 8-5). Barron found that very small modifications in the configuration of the substrate molecule had a decisive influence in determining whether it could be handled by the enzyme. If, instead of acetic acid (CH_3COOH), fluoroacetic acid ($F-CH_2COOH$) was presented to the enzyme, a **stable** enzyme-substrate compound was formed, which blocked the catalytic focus of the enzyme. On the other hand, chloroacetic acid ($Cl-CH_2COOH$) had little or no effect. Barron concluded that probably the length of the interatomic bonds, namely carbon to hydrogen (1.09 Ångstroms), carbon to fluorine (1.41 Ångstroms), and carbon to chlorine 1.76 Ångstroms), played a decisive role in determining the fit—between the enzyme and substrate and between the enzyme and the inhibitor.

Many other examples can be given to illustrate the concept of fit, semifit, and misfit between specific enzymes, substrates, and inhibitors. The protein-hydrolyzing enzyme,

aminopeptidase (Table 5-1), fits only amino acids having an exposed amino (NH_2) group, and these must be situated at the end of a peptide chain; another pancreatic enzyme, carboxypeptidase, (Table 5-1), can only split off amino acids having an exposed carboxyl (—COOH) group, and these likewise must be terminal in the chain; trypsin (Table 5-1) splits protein chains only at certain specific linkage points, whereas chymotrypsin achieves rupture at other different points; and in each case the site of rupture appears to be determined by the configuration of the specific amino acids that adjoin the linkage. Moreover, cases of semifit, where a slightly modified substrate affixes itself firmly to the **catalytic area** of an enzyme and blocks off further catalytic activity (Fig. 5-3), have been studied in various ways. An outstanding example, in fact, is provided by the very useful drug, sulfanilamide. The molecular configurations of this compound and of an essential (vitamin) substance present in many cells (*para*-aminobenzoic acid) are very similar (Fig. 5-4). Thus it is not surprising to find that sulfanilamide kills bacteria by blocking off the enzyme system that normally would handle the synthesis of *para*-aminobenzoic acid in the bacterial cell.

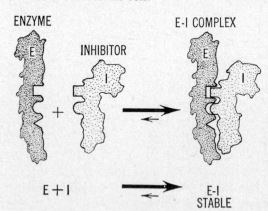

Fig. 5-3. Enzyme inhibition: concept of molecular fit. The inhibitor (I) unites very firmly with the enzyme, blocking off its catalytic site. When such union is relatively weak, and when the concentration of inhibitor is low, the inhibitor competes with the substrate for occupation of the catalytic site. This results in partial, or *competitive, inhibition.*

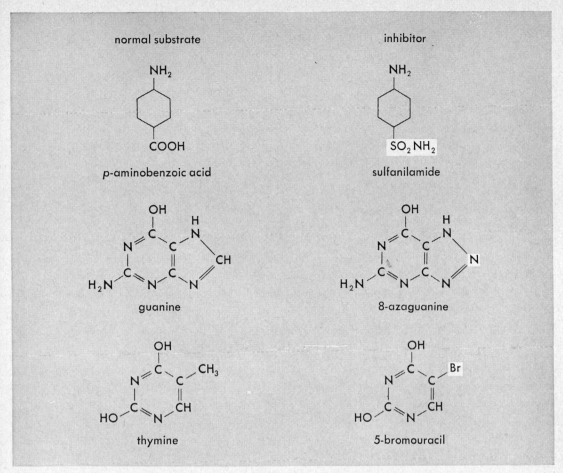

Fig. 5-4. The molecular configuration of an inhibitor substance tends to be similar to that of the normal substrate of the particular enzyme. Therefore the **inhibitor,** or **antagonist,** is able to compete with the substrate for occupation of the **catalytic site.**

Reversibility of Catalyzed Reactions. Theoretically the enzyme or inorganic catalyst does not determine the *direction* that a catalyzed reaction will take; that is, *the same enzyme is equally effective in accelerating a particular reaction in either direction.* In other words, the direction of a reaction is determined not by the catalyst, but by other factors. **Exothermic reactions,** which liberate energy, tend to occur spontaneously, although when the proper catalyst is present, such a reaction proceeds at infinitely greater speed. To drive an exothermic reaction in the *reverse* direction—or, to state the matter more directly, to force the occurrence of an endothermic reaction—*there must be some avail-*

able source of energy. Consequently an enzyme can accelerate an endothermic reaction only when a suitable source of energy is available.

Enzymes in Relation to Cell Structure; Coupled Reactions. Catabolic enzymes, which facilitate the exothermic reactions of the cell, tend to retain their activity after they are extracted from the protoplasm. But many anabolic reactions are difficult to duplicate outside the protoplasm.

Such endothermic reactions, which lead to synthesis in the cell, seem to require the cooperation of several enzymes acting as a team; and this degree of teamwork cannot be achieved unless the individual enzymes are properly localized in the protoplasmic structure—in the ribosomes or other parts of the endoplasmic reticulum, in the Golgi apparatus, in the mitochondria, or other specialized structures. Each endothermic reaction depends upon a simultaneous exothermic reaction, and these reactions must be *coupled* in such a way that energy is transferred from the exothermic to the endothermic process. Such an energy coupling between metabolic reactions depends in turn upon the integrity of the protoplasmic structure. The coupled reactions must occur synchronously and in close proximity to each other; and these conditions are usually realized only when the whole team of enzymes is suitably arranged in some specialized part of the intracellular structure. In muscle, for example, a continued resynthesis of adenosine triphosphate, an important organic component of the tissue, must go on if the muscle is to retain its contractile power; and this resynthesis is coupled with the decomposition of phosphocreatine, another component of the fibers (see Chap. 24). Likewise the resynthesis of phosphocreatine is coupled with the breakdown of glycogen in the muscle; and in turn, the restoration of glycogen is coupled with the oxidation of other substrates. In general, the exothermic processes of the muscle, such as glycolysis and oxidation, proceed readily after the protoplasmic structure has been disrupted, as by grinding the muscle; but the synthetic reactions are fully achieved only in the intact muscle. Despite the theoretical capacity of enzymes to act reversibly, the conditions necessary for reversal are not always available, and many enzymes exert their influence in one direction only. Moreover, even when a certain reaction is reversed in the protoplasm, the reversal does not necessarily involve the same enzyme that was utilized initially.

The importance of the fine structure of the cell in determining the behavior of associated enzymes is further emphasized by recent studies on mitochondria. Each mitochondrion represents a complex of six enzymes. This group as a whole accomplishes many reactions that cannot be duplicated after the mitochondria have been broken up completely, although some reactions may continue when the mitochondria are partially disrupted. As will be explained later, the mitochondrial enzymes, acting as a team, appear to play an important part in the oxidative metabolism of a variety of compounds derived not only from sugars, but also from amino acids and fatty acids (see Krebs cycle, p. 153).

OTHER CHARACTERISTIC OF ENZYMES

Enzymes tend to display a *greater specificity* than their inorganic counterparts. For example, three specifically *different* enzymes are necessary to hydrolyze the three common disaccharide sugars—sucrose, maltose, and lactose (Table 5-1). Frequently an enzyme acts only upon a single substrate, and even less specific enzymes act only on substrates with similar chemical structures.

Undoubtedly the specificity of enzyme action indicates that a molecular fit between the substrate and the active site of the enzyme is an essential prerequisite for catalysis. Several such cases already have been cited (*aminopeptidase, carboxypeptidase, trypsin,* and *chymotrypsin*) and two other examples will suffice: (1) *lactic dehydrogenase,* which acts upon only one type of molecular configuration $\left(\text{H}-\overset{|}{\underset{|}{\text{C}}}-\text{OH} \right)$; and (2) *succinic dehydrogenase,* which requires a different chemical structure $\left(-\overset{\text{H} \quad \text{H}}{\underset{\text{H} \quad \text{H}}{\overset{|}{\text{C}}-\overset{|}{\text{C}}}}- \right)$, as is shown in Table 5-1.

The **catalytic potency** of enzymes is *exceedingly great*. A single molecule or catalase, for example, proves able to handle the decomposition of about 5 million molecules of H_2O_2 per minute even at a low temperature (0° C), which is required to make such a measurement possible. This *turnover number* is unusually high, to be sure, but many enzymes can easily handle more than a million molecules of substrate per minute, under optimal conditions. Thus it is safe to say that enzymes are generally much more active than inorganic catalysts. The best calculations indicate, indeed, that often there may be only about 100 molecules of a particular enzyme in a given cell—which puts a heavy burden of activity upon each enzyme molecule.

Ptyalin, the amylase present in human saliva, is capable of activating the hydrolytic breakdown of more than a million times its weight of starch. Theoretically no potency should be lost, even with infinite activity. But enzymes, like other proteins, do not possess a very stable structure. Consequently some deterioration occurs even though the catalyst is not consumed in the reaction it catalyzes. Thus the maintenance of enzymic activity in the living cell depends upon a gradual replacement of its enzymes through the agency of constructive metabolism.

Sensitivity of Enzymes to Hydrogen and Other Ions. The activity of many enzymes is sensitive to the influence of various ions present in the reaction medium. This is particularly true as regards the hydrogen and hydroxyl ions. Each specific enzyme exhibits its most vigorous activity only when the acidity or alkalinity of the medium is adjusted to the proper level. Several examples of such sensitivity may be taken from the digestive enzymes of man. Pepsin, the powerful protease of the gastric juice, acts very sluggishly except when the medium is strongly acid; trypsin and the other enzymes of the pancreatic juice (Table 5-1) display full activity only when the medium is slightly alkaline. **Ptyalin,** the salivary amylase, requires a nearly neutral solution, and is quite *inactive* when chloride ion is absent from the medium. Most metabolic enzymes, which exert their influence in the protoplasm proper, attain greatest potency when the medium is approximately neutral.

Probably the unique sensitivity of enzymes to their ionic environment is related to changes in the secondary and tertiary structure of the protein component. Too great a degree of folding in the peptide chain (p. 87) may distort or block off the catalytic site, rendering it ineffective or only partially effective, and the same is true for any excessive unfolding. In other words, the stereochemical configuration of the active site cannot be changed unduly without destroying its catalytic potency.

Enzymes in Relation to Temperature. Heat accelerates the movements of molecules and ions, increasing the frequency of their contacts; consequently chemical reactions proceed more rapidly when the temperature of the medium is raised. As a general rule, each increase of 10° C doubles, or even trebles, the rate of most reactions.

The foregoing temperature rule applies equally for both catalyzed and uncatalyzed reactions; but enzyme systems constitute a very special case. Up to the point where the heat begins to unfold and denature the enzyme protein, warming the medium increases the reaction rate. But there is a critical temperature beyond which each enzyme cannot be carried. Above this point the enzyme becomes **denatured** (p. 88) and loses its catalytic power. Then the reaction rate drops quickly to the uncatalyzed level, which may be very slow, despite the elevated temperature.

The case of ptyalin will exemplify the thermal behavior of enzymes generally. If a small amount of saliva is mixed with a starch solution, the starch is hydrolyzed to maltose (Fig. 5-5). This reaction proceeds rather slowly at 0° C, but more and more rapidly as the temperature of the test tube is raised. Maximum rapidity is reached at about 40° C. If the temperature is then raised still further, chemical activity comes to a virtual standstill. Furthermore, if the damaging temperature is maintained for many minutes, no trace of amylase activity will persist after the system has been cooled again. In other words, an irreversible denaturation of the enzyme protein has occurred.

A

B

Fig. 5-5. Digestion of starch by saliva. A, two beakers were filled with an opaque suspension of starch in water. Some saliva (which contains ptyalin) was added to the left beaker only. B, later, the saliva has digested the starch, converting the large molecules into smaller molecules of sugar, rendering the solution transparent in the left beaker, while the solution in the right beaker remains unchanged. (From *Digestion of Foods*, Encyclopedia Britannica Films, Inc.)

The thermal behavior of enzymes imposes serious limitations upon organisms generally. Most cells lose their capacity to carry on metabolism at temperatures above 40° C. A few organisms possess enzymes that are especially resistant to heat, and only such organisms are able to survive in exceptionally hot places. In most cells, the rate of metabolism, and hence the intensity of the life processes, changes as the temperature varies from day to day, and from season to season. Thus the winter metabolism of most organisms subsides to a point where dormancy is inevitable. Only "warm-blooded" organisms, such as man and a few other vertebrates, have evolved a method of controlling their body temperature. In man, for example, the temperature seldom fluctuates more than a few degrees above or below 37.2° C. Accordingly

the numerous enzymes of our tissues operate at optimum efficiency, and our digestive and metabolic reactions proceed on schedule, despite fairly drastic changes in the environmental temperature.

ENZYMATIC NATURE OF GENES; AUTOCATALYSIS

Fundamentally the character of each cell must be determined, at least in large measure, by its metabolism; and the metabolism, in turn, must be determined by a particular set of enzymes, which are inherited by the cell. In some fashion, therefore, the genes of an organism must determine the nature of its intracellular enzymes. These considerations, of course, are tremendously important and they will be approached more closely later (Chap. 28).

It has been assumed for many years that genic substances possess a unique property, namely **autocatalysis.** This is the capacity of a substance to catalyze the production of itself. Such self-replication, it was thought, provided a basis for understanding how each cell, via the mechanisms of mitosis, could perpetuate its own characteristics. However, the mechanism of genic action—how a particular set of genes achieves the production of a particular set of enzymes—remained obscure.

Currently, however, much progress in this field is taking place. Now it is possible to identify the genes as DNA proteins, each characterized by a distinctive pattern in the arrangement of its nucleotide constituents (p. 134). When self-replication occurs, moreover, the pattern of each gene provides a template (p. 134) for the production of an equivalent unit. But in addition, each genic pattern provides a code for the production of similarly patterned RNA proteins, which have a site of action in the cytoplasm (p. 525). And finally, the pattern of each different RNA component carries the code for the synthesis of some one of the specific enzyme proteins in the cell (p. 529). The genes, accordingly, must be regarded as **master enzymes** in the cell. Not only do they perpetuate themselves by an intricate kind of autocatalysis, but also they govern the production of the enzyme proteins, utilizing the RNA constituents of the cell to transmit a precisely coded set of instructions (Chap. 27).

TEST QUESTIONS

1. Define the term catalyst and carefully describe any typical example of catalysis.
2. What is an enzyme? How and why are enzymes important in every cell and every organism?
3. Name any four enzymes and specify the chemical reaction that is catalyzed by each.
4. Distinguish between enzymes and inorganic catalysts, on the basis of:
    a. chemical composition
    b. stability at higher temperature
    c. specificity of action
    d. sensitivity to hydrogen and other ions
5. Is there any known relation between enzymes and vitamins? Explain.
6. Is there any known relation between enzymes and genes? Carefully explain.
7. Provide appropriate examples of:
    a. one or more enzymes that are *substrate specific*
    b. two enzymes that are specific in relation to some particular chemical configuration.
8. Summarize the evidence from which it may be concluded that all enzymes, in essential part, are of protein composition.
9. Define and explain:
    a. catalytic site
    b. catalytic fit
    c. enzyme-substrate compound
    d. energy of activation
    e. the mitochondrial enzyme team
    f. competitive inhibition of enzyme catalysis
10. Explain why certain enzymes lose their power of catalysis when they are extracted from the protoplasm.
11. Describe and explain the changes in the speed of reaction in the following cases:
    a. the decomposition of H_2O_2 in the presence of MnO_2 at 30°, 40°, and 50° C
    b. the decomposition of H_2O_2 in the presence of catalase at 30°, 40°, and 50° C
12. How might the oxygen consumption of a man be affected by (a) fever and (b) a subnormal temperature? Explain.

FURTHER READINGS

1. *Cellular Physiology and Biochemistry,* by William D. McElroy; Englewood Cliffs, N. J., 1961.
2. *Genes, Enzymes, and Inherited Diseases,* by H. E. Sutton; New York, 1961.
3. "Enzymes," by J. Pfeiffer, in *The Physics and Chemistry of Life,* a collection of articles from *Scientific American;* New York, 1955.
4. *Chemistry and Methods of Enzymes,* by J. B. Sumner and F. G. Somers; New York, 1953.

6 - Osmosis and Other Mechanisms by Which Cells Take In and Give Off Materials

THE METABOLISM of each living cell requires a ceaseless supply of new materials and produces a steady stream of waste products. These substances must be passed in and out between the protoplasm and the surrounding medium through the living cell surface, or **plasma membrane.** The metabolism itself may provide energy to keep the traffic moving, and extraneous cell coatings (p. 33) may influence the speed of flow, but the dominant role is played by the plasma membrane (Fig. 6-1).

PASSIVE vs. ACTIVE TRANSPORT MECHANISMS

In some respects the cell may be compared to a very small cellophane balloon, filled with a sugar solution and immersed in water. Owing to the tendency of various molecules and ions to disperse themselves evenly throughout any system (p. 113), water molecules would continue to enter the balloon and sugar molecules would leave it, until an equilibrium was reached. In like fashion water frequently tends to enter the cell and solute molecules tend to leave it. In such cases, however, the energy that drives the transport mechanism is not generated by the cell. It is the **kinetic** or **thermal movement** of molecules, which is characteristic of all matter—except when the temperature falls to **absolute zero** ($-273.2°$ C). No energy is expended by the cell in forcing the substances to enter or leave, and accordingly such exchanges are referred to as **passive transport.**

Frequently it is found, however, that the cell may accumulate a dissolved substance, so that the concentration is far greater inside the cell than outside; or the cell may exclude the entrance of a substance present in very high concentration in the outside medium. Generally speaking, for example, the

112

concentration of potassium ions (K+) in the protoplasm is often 30 times greater than in the medium surrounding the cell; and the level of sodium ions (Na+) outside may be 10 times greater than inside. Spontaneously, therefore, potassium ions are under pressure to leave the cell and sodium ions have a great tendency to enter. Under such circumstances the cell must generate energy to overcome the kinetic forces that are driving the substances to enter or leave. In short, whenever the cell expends energy to foster the entrance or exit of a substance, an **active transport** mechanism is involved. Much remains to be learned about the cellular mechanisms of active transport; they are very important in the life of the cell and currently they are a focal area of considerable research.

PASSIVE TRANSPORT: DIFFUSION AND OSMOSIS

The surrounding medium of the cell generally consists of some kind of aqueous solution. This solution may be the fresh or salt water in which the organism lives, or it may be a body fluid such as the blood and lymph of animals, or the tissue sap of plants. To enter the cell passively, the penetrating substance must display at least a minimum **solubility** in the fluid surrounding the cell and in the protoplasm of the cell itself. Ordinarily *only dissolved substances can pass* **spontaneously** *through the plasma membrane.*

Not all dissolved substances can penetrate the plasma membrane with equal facility. The molecules or ions may be too big, or they may encounter a variety of other interfering factors (p. 116). Thus the plasma membrane is a **semipermeable membrane**—permeable to some substances, but not to all.

Whenever *two different solutions* are *separated by a semipermeable membrane*, an **osmotic system** is established. Each typical cell, therefore, represents an osmotic unit, since the semipermeable plasma membrane always intervenes between the protoplasm, on the one hand, and the external solution on

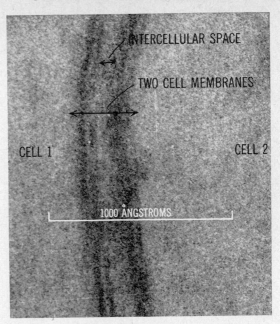

Fig. 6-1. Boundary membranes of two contiguous cells: electron micrograph of section of a nerve (mouse). The double membrane of each cell measures about 80 Ångstroms across; whereas the intercellular material is about twice as thick. Compare this photo with the Danielli diagram of the cell membrane (Fig. 6-5). (Photo courtesy of J. David Robertson, Department of Neuropathology, Harvard Medical School.)

the other. Large quantities of water and lesser amounts of dissolved substances are constantly passing into or out of the cell across the plasma membrane, and these exchanges are very important in the life of every cell.

Diffusion. The spontaneous migration of molecules and ions within the limits of a single solution must be considered before we deal with the more complex process of osmosis. If any dissolved substance is concentrated more heavily in one part of a solution, this substance will spread gradually until its molecules (or ions) are evenly distributed throughout the whole solution. This process is called **diffusion**. It is caused by the random movements of all the particles (solute as well as solvent) that make up the entire solution. Essentially these random movements are a manifestation of the molecular kinetic energy (heat).

The direction that a given particle will

take at any particular moment is entirely unpredictable. The particle may move in any direction, depending upon its chance collisions with other particles or with the wall of the containing vessel. Nevertheless the **mass movements** of each *kind* of particle present in a solution *can be predicted accurately* on a statistical basis. These mass movements are governed by the fundamental **law of diffusion.** The particles of *each different substance present in a solution will diffuse from a region where these particles are more concentrated toward a region where they are less concentrated.* Moreover, diffusion will continue until every component reaches equal concentration throughout the whole solution. In the sugar solution of Figure 6-2, for example, the mass movement of the water in a downward direction occurs simultaneously with the upward movement of the sugar

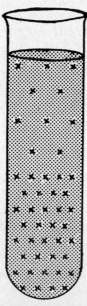

Fig. 6-2. Diagram of free diffusion. A weak sugar solution, layered on top of a stronger one. The attainment of equilibrium (equal distribution of all the molecules) depends upon *two* factors: (1) water molecules (the dots) diffuse downward from the upper solution where the water concentration is greater, and simultaneously, (2) sugar molecules (the crosses) diffuse upward from the region where the sugar concentration is greater. Each kind of molecule in a solution obeys the same law.

molecules, until complete equality in the distribution of both kinds of particles is finally reached.

The **concentration** of *each* different substance present in a solution is of critical importance in determining the *direction* of the diffusion of that substance. The concentration of a substance specifies the *number of its particles present in a unit volume of the solution.* No two molecules or ions can occupy the same space at the same time, and therefore it follows that the concentration of any one substance cannot be increased without displacing from each unit volume of the solution an equivalent number of the particles of all other components. Accordingly, whenever the total solute concentration is high, the concentration of solvent must be low; or whenever the concentration of one solute is increased, the concentration of the other solute and of the solvent must undergo a corresponding decrease.

The foregoing relationships may be seen in the sugar solution diagramed in Figure 6-2. The sugar and the water molecules reach equilibrium by diffusing in opposite directions. But each is obeying the same fundamental law: each is escaping from the region of its greater concentration toward the region of its lesser concentration. In the top part of the original solution, the higher concentration of water is determined by the lower concentration of sugar, and consequently the water diffuses downward. In the bottom of the test tube, the higher concentration of sugar corresponds to the lower concentration of water, and consequently the mass movement of the sugar molecules is in an upward direction.

The velocity of diffusion is determined by a number of factors. The whole process depends upon thermal energy, and consequently equilibrium is attained more quickly in warmer solutions. When the **concentration difference** (concentration gradient) is greater, the tendency of the particles to escape from the concentrated region is greater. Large particles diffuse more slowly than small ones

(p. 116), and the more viscous the medium the slower the diffusion. Equilibrium is reached very slowly when the distances involved are macroscopic; but within microscopic and ultramicroscopic limits, the equalization of concentrations may be almost instantaneous.

Osmosis. If a semipermeable membrane is placed between two different solutions, an osmotic system is established. In biology, however, only **aqueous** solutions are important. Therefore, from a biological viewpoint, osmosis may be defined as *the exchange of water between the protoplasm and any solution surrounding the cell*. Various other substances, *when able to penetrate the membrane*, may also enter or leave the cell, but these are diffusional exchanges that are superimposed upon the true osmotic exchanges.

In a simple osmotic system, such as is shown in Figure 6-3, both the solvent (water) and the solute (sugar) are under the same compulsion to diffuse, each from the region of its own higher concentration. But in such a perfect system only the water is able to penetrate the intervening membrane. Consequently the two solutions can reach equilibrium only by the transfer of water from one solution to the other. In Figure 6-3, for example, since sugar molecules are unable to penetrate the membrane, equilibrium will be reached solely by the passage of water from the upper solution (where the water concentration is greater) to the lower solution (where the water concentration is lesser). Eventually, however, an equal distribution of both water and sugar may be reached. As water is lost from the upper solution, the sugar concentration increases, and simultaneously, as water is gained by the lower solution, the sugar concentration decreases— until finally both solutions reach equality.

The Cell as an Imperfect Osmotic Unit. The cell, quite obviously, does not represent a perfect osmotic system. Not only water, but also many dissolved substances commonly present in and around the protoplasm are able to penetrate the plasma membrane in significant amounts. Therefore, the exchange of water between a cell and its surroundings (true osmosis) occurs simultaneously with the exchange (purely by diffusion) of other substances, such as oxygen and carbon dioxide, which experience no difficulty in passing into or out of the cell.

One set of purely diffusional exchanges between the cell and its surroundings is shown in Figure 6-4, which illustrates diagrammatically the process of respiration as it occurs in all typical animal cells. Both oxygen and carbon dioxide are freely soluble in the protoplasm as well as in the surrounding water; and both can pass very freely through the plasma membrane. Thus a steady supply of O_2 molecules streams into the living cell so long as the concentration of oxygen remains relatively high in the outside medium. Inside the cell the concentration of O_2 is low because free oxygen is used for oxidative metabolism as soon as it enters the protoplasm. The O_2 concentration in the surrounding water tends to remain relatively high, since

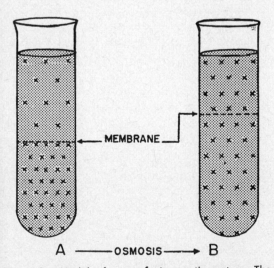

A ——— OSMOSIS ——➤ B

Fig. 6-3. Model of a **perfect** osmotic system. The membrane, which is free to shift position, is permeable to water (the dots) but not permeable to sugar molecules (crosses). Note that equilibrium is attained solely by the passage of water from the upper solution, where the original concentration of H_2O is higher, to the lower solution, where the concentration is lower. Finally both sugar and water are equally distributed.

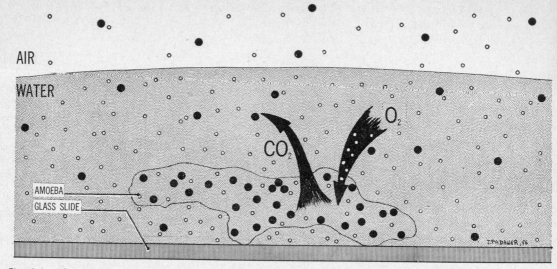

Fig. 6-4. The diffusional exchange of oxygen (the circles) and carbon dioxide (the dots) between the protoplasm of an amoeba and the surrounding water. Both substances obey the same law—passing toward the region of lowest concentration; i.e., into the protoplasm, in the case of the oxygen; and into the environment, in the case of the carbon dioxide.

this water remains at equilibrium with the 20 percent of oxygen in the supernatant air. Likewise carbon dioxide, in leaving the cell, follows a similar gradient. In the protoplasm, carbon dioxide is produced continuously by metabolism. Consequently CO_2 reaches a higher concentration relative to the outside water, which maintains equilibrium with the small amount (0.03 percent) of carbon dioxide in the atmosphere.

Passive Permeability of the Plasma Membrane. Nonprotoplasmic membranes such as the pellicle and cell wall are freely permeable to most of the substances that normally impinge upon the cell, and it is the plasma membrane that exerts a main control over all diffusional and osmotic processes. The permeability of the plasma membrane, which is very complex and variable, depends not only upon the nature of the impinging particles, but also upon the changing conditions inside and outside the cell. Permeability differs in different cells and sometimes on the different sides of the same cell. Nevertheless, certain generalizations can be made, and these are summarized in Table 6-1.

Table 6-1—Capacity of Various Substances to Penetrate (Passively) the Plasma Membrane

Very Rapid	Rapid	Slow	Very Slow	Virtually No Penetration
Gases	Water	Simple organic	Strong electrolytes	Complex (colloidal)
Carbon dioxide		substances	Inorganic salts	compounds
Oxygen		Glucose	Acids	Proteins
Nitrogen		Amino acids	Bases	Polysaccharides
Fat solvents		Glycerol	Disaccharides	Phospholipids, etc.
Alcohol		Fatty acids	Sucrose	
Ether			Maltose	
Chloroform			Lactose	

The factors that determine the capacity of a given substance to penetrate the cell are not completely understood, although the **size of the molecules** is certainly important. In general, larger molecules experience more difficulty in traversing the membrane, and **colloidal molecules** *generally display a negligible capacity to penetrate*. Such observations have led biologists to postulate the existence of *pores* in the structure of the plasma membrane (Fig. 6-5), the dimensions of which would prevent the passage of such larger molecules into or out of the cell.

Molecule size, however, is not the only factor; otherwise the inorganic electrolytes (salts, etc.) would enter the cell more rapidly than such substances as glucose and amino acids. In the case of electrolytes, the interfering factor appears to be the electric charge carried by the ions of these substances. The living membrane itself maintains an electric charge (usually negative in sign, p. 191), and this charge tends to repel ions of the same charge. And since one type of ion in a solution cannot abandon the oppositely charged ions, without setting up a counter electric force, blocking one type of ion is almost equivalent to blocking both.

The great freedom afforded to the passage of **fat solvents,** such as **alcohol** and **ether,** represents another problem in cell permeability. Fat solvents pass through the membrane even more rapidly than water, and this fact has led to a belief that fat solvents enter the cell by a special route: via lipoid phases in the membrane structure (Fig. 6-5). Under normal circumstances, however, very small quantities, if any, of fat solvents are present in the protoplasmic system or its surrounding media.

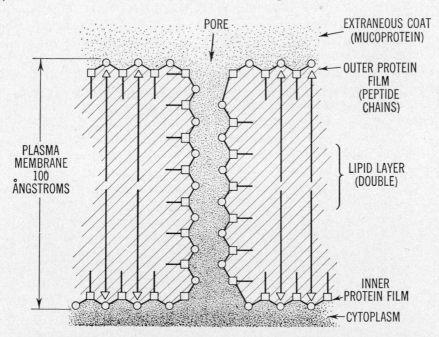

Fig. 6-5. Model of the molecular structure of a cell membrane, based on concepts of J. F. Danielli, Kings College, London. In the plasma membrane proper, note the peptide chains of the protein films, which consist of alternating C atoms (□) and N atoms (○), oriented tangentially; whereas the lipid molecules are arranged radially in a double layer, with the polar ends, or "heads" (△), directed toward the membrane surfaces, and the nonpolar hydrocarbon "tails" directed away from the membrane surfaces. The total thickness of such a molecular arrangement would be 80 to 100 Ångstroms, which closely agrees with electronmicrographs of the cell membrane (Fig. 6-1).

Water Equilibrium in the Cell: Osmosis.
The *bulk* of all solutes present in protoplasm
—and this includes proteins, most sugars,
and inorganic salts—are substances that
penetrate the plasma membrane very slowly,
if at all (see Table 6-1). The solvent, water,
on the other hand, can enter or leave the
cell quite quickly. Moreover, water is extremely abundant in all the media (fresh
water, sea water, blood, lymph, sap, etc.)
that normally surround the cell, *as well as
in the protoplasm itself*. These facts are of
great importance. They mean that the burden of establishing equilibrium between the
cell and a surrounding solution devolves
mainly upon the water. If a cell is placed in
an unbalanced solution in which the concentration of water is drastically different
compared with the protoplasm, so great a
quantity of water will enter or leave the cell
that the living structure will be destroyed.

Isotonic Solutions. In an **isotonic** solution,
the concentration of **water** is the same as in
the protoplasm. This condition is realized
only when the total concentration of solute[1]
(taken collectively) in the solution and the
protoplasm is likewise equal. In an isotonic
solution, the water exchange between the
cell and the solution is exactly balanced.
Owing to the random movement of molecules, water continues to escape across the
membrane, but the escaping water is exactly
balanced by an equivalent amount of water
that enters the cell simultaneously. As a general rule the **blood** and **lymph** of animals are
approximately **isotonic** *to the cells*. In the
blood stream, for example, the red blood cells
are in osmotic balance with the surrounding
plasma. Under these conditions no net gain
or loss of water occurs, and consequently the
cells are preserved from abnormal changes of
volume. But if red cells are studied in an
artificial medium such as a salt solution, abnormal changes are bound to occur unless
the artificial solution is made isotonic to the
protoplasm (for example, 0.9 percent NaCl).

[1] Disregarding the small amounts of rapidly penetrating solutes (for example, oxygen).

An isotonic solution contains a concentration of nonpenetrating (or very slowly penetrating) solute that approximates the total
concentration of nonpenetrating solutes (proteins, phospholipids, salts) in the protoplasm.
Otherwise an equality of the water concentrations inside and outside the cell is not possible. Various nonpenetrating solutes may be
used in the preparation of an isotonic solution, although the inorganic salts, especially
NaCl, are most frequently employed. Best
results are obtained from salt mixtures in
which Na^+, K^+, Ca^{2+}, and Mg^{2+} ions are
represented in the proper proportions, since
otherwise the normal semipermeability of
the plasma membrane gradually deteriorates.
In the various kinds of "Ringer's solution,"
as such balanced solutions are called, the
proper quantity and the proportions of inorganic salts vary considerably from one kind
of animal to another. In transfusion fluids,
which are used in emergencies to replace the
blood plasma, a considerable proportion of
protein is included with the salts. Various
foreign proteins have been tried as substitutes for the normal plasma proteins, but not
with much success. The main difficulty has
not been to obtain the proper osmotic conditions, but to find foreign proteins that will
remain in the blood stream and that are not
toxic to the organism.

Hypotonic Solutions. A hypotonic solution contains a relatively low concentration
of nonpenetrating solute (compared to the
protoplasm of the cell that it surrounds).
Because of the low concentration of solute,
the water concentration in a hypotonic solution is relatively high. Therefore, cells placed
in hypotonic solution tend to take in water
and to swell. The passage of water from the
external solution where the concentration is
higher into the cell where the concentration
is lower conforms, of course, with the fundamental law of osmosis and diffusion. If the
protoplasm can accommodate the extra water
and come into equilibrium with the surrounding solution, the swelling will stop.
Otherwise, the swelling continues until the

membranes around the cell are ruptured, and the cell as a whole is destroyed. When human red blood cells are put in a solution containing only 0.2 percent NaCl (instead of the 0.9 percent salt present in an isotonic solution), the corpuscles swell and burst so quickly that no opportunity is afforded for examining them with a microscope.

Plant and animal cells are very different in their capacity to tolerate submersion in hypotonic solutions. Pond water, since it contains only very small quantities of the inorganic salts and other nonpenetrating solutes, is extremely hypotonic to all cells. Nevertheless pond water is the normal habitat of a great variety of unicellular forms. In the case of aquatic *plants,* such as *Spirogyra,* the great strength of the cellulose wall prevents the cells from swelling unduly. As water enters by osmosis from the hypotonic medium, the protoplasm of the plant cell is forced outward against the unyielding cell wall. When a sufficiently high internal pressure is generated, the further entrance of water is prevented. This high internal pressure, which is called **turgor,** is characteristic of plant cells generally. The turgor pressure of a normal plant cell may rise to several atmospheres before a further influx of water is stopped. Typically the medium surrounding a plant cell remains hypotonic to the protoplasm, but turgor constitutes a counterforce that prevents more water from entering the cell.

If a plant is deprived of water, the individual cells lose turgor and the tissues become wilted. Such a wilted tissue (for example, a limp lettuce leaf) may regain its normal crispness and turgidity if it is returned soon enough to fresh water. But should the cells be killed from loss of water, the wilted tissue never regains turgor. At death, the plasma membrane becomes indiscriminately permeable to virtually all solutes, and consequently the normal osmotic behavior of the cells is lost.

Unlike plant cells, most animal cells cannot tolerate exposure to drastically hypotonic solutions. The pellicle is not sufficiently strong to generate much turgor. Consequently most animal cells continue to swell and will burst if the influx of water is excessive. This phenomenon is called **osmotic cytolysis.** Animal cells can withstand moderately hypotonic solutions, however, since the incoming water may dilute the protoplasm sufficiently to establish equilibrium. When the water concentration on either side of the membrane becomes equal, no further swelling will occur.

Many of the Protozoa constitute a special case. These animal cells have become adapted to live in fresh water. To counteract the constant influx of water into the protoplasm, these species have developed contractile vacuoles (Fig. 6-6). Such vacuoles prevent the cells from swelling by collecting water from the protoplasm and pumping it back into the environment. Just how the water is forced to move against its osmotic gradient in passing from the protoplasm into the vacuole is not clearly understood. But it is known that

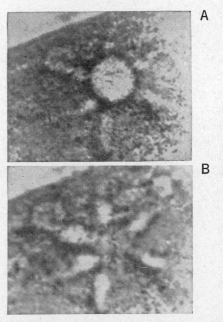

Fig. 6-6. Greatly magnified view of a contractile vacuole in a paramecium; A, filled to capacity; and B, just emptied. Note that the radiating canals, which conduct the fluid into the vacuole, can be seen more clearly when the vacuole is empty.

the cell must expend energy in performing this work. This energy comes from metabolism, and if a protozoan is treated with a metabolic poison, the contractile vacuole stops working. Then the cell begins to swell and eventually it will burst, unless the activity of the contracile vacuole is restored in time.

Hypertonic Solutions. A hypertonic solution, compared to the protoplasm of the cell that it surrounds, contains a relatively high concentration of nonpenetrating solute. Since the solute concentration is high, the concentration of water in a hypertonic solution is relatively low. Therefore cells placed in hypertonic solution tend to lose water and shrink.

Plant and animal cells behave differently when they undergo shrinkage in hypertonic solution. The pellicle of many animal cells, being flexible, becomes wrinkled as the cell loses volume. This wrinkled, shrunken appearance, which can be seen in the red blood cells of Figure 2-18, is described as **crenation.** The lesser volume of the crenated cells is due mainly to a loss of water. Water is by far the most prevalent of the substances capable of penetrating the membrane, and consequently equilibrium is established largely by the escape of water. The shrinking of the cell continues until finally the water concentration in the protoplasm is reduced to the level of the outside medium. In some cases, when the loss of water is not drastic enough to destroy the living structures, the cell may regain its original volume, if it is returned to an isotonic medium. But if the cells are severely damaged by the loss of water, hypertonic shrinkage is irreversible.

The appearance of plant cells in a hypertonic medium is quite different. The cell wall, being more rigid than the pellicle, maintains its original form, while the protoplasm continues to shrink. The resulting condition, which is shown in Figure 6-7, is called **plasmolysis.** The protoplasm of the plasmolyzed cell occupies only a part of the space enclosed by the cellulose wall. Plasmolysis is likewise reversible, provided that the plasma membrane is not damaged in the process.

Deplasmolysis. Instead of using a strong salt solution to plasmolyze a plant cell, one can use a hypertonic solution of glucose. Compared to the ions of a salt, glucose molecules can penetrate the cell more rapidly. Nevertheless the rate of penetration of the glucose is so slow compared to water that an initial plasmolysis occurs as soon as the cell is placed in the hypertonic solution. In a moderately hypertonic glucose solution, however, the plasmolysis does not endure indefinitely. Within about 10 minutes the protoplasm shows signs of swelling, and within half an hour the protoplasm again occupies all the space within the encompassing cell wall.

The original plasmolysis is due to a very rapid equalization of the water concentration inside and outside the plasma membrane; and as soon as the concentration of

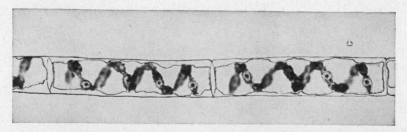

Fig. 6-7. Plasmolysis as seen in the cells of *Spirogyra*. Note that the cytoplasm (and chloroplast) has shrunk away, leaving a gap between the plasma membrane and the cell wall. Photograph retouched slightly to show outlines of the cytoplasm and cell walls more clearly. (Copyright, General Biological Supply House, Inc.)

water in the protoplasm is reduced to the level of the medium, the shrinking ceases. But later, the slow penetration of glucose begins to be significant. Glucose is the only solute present in the outside medium, and the concentration of glucose in the solution is greater than in the protoplasm. Consequently glucose slowly enters the cell. This disturbs the equilibrium that was reached when the plotoplasm stopped shrinking. As glucose enters, the water concentration increases in the outer solution and decreases in the protoplasm. Consequently, the entrance of glucose is continuously accompanied by an entrance of water. Gradually, therefore, deplasmolysis occurs, and finally the plant cell regains its normal turgor.

Animal cells, crenated in hypertonic solutions of slowly penetrating solutes, likewise do not remain crenated. Gradually such cells also regain their original volume. In fact, an animal cell, lacking the protection of a strong external wall, may continue swelling, and may undergo cytolysis in a solution that originally was distinctly hypertonic.

ACTIVE TRANSPORT MECHANISMS

Diffusion and osmosis do not by any means account for all exchanges between cells and their surrounding fluids. Many cells display a remarkable capacity to accumulate certain substances and to exclude other substances against the natural tides of diffusion. For example, many marine algae accumulate iodine up to a concentration that is more than a million times greater than that of the sea. Also, as was mentioned previously, the cytoplasm generally is exceedingly rich in potassium (K^+) and poor in sodium (Na^+), compared to the lymph, or sap, or other fluid around the cell; and fresh-water protozoan cells force water to pass into the contractile vacuole, from the cytoplasm, where the water concentration is considerably lower. Such phenomena do not "contradict" the laws of diffusion and osmosis any more than lifting a weight "contradicts" the law of gravity.

They merely mean that the cell is expending energy in forcing the molecules or ions of a particular substance to move against a concentration gradient. But when a substance is moved "against the diffusional tide," some other kind of energy, derived from metabolism, is being expended by the cell. Thus if metabolism is temporarily suspended or depressed, as by asphyxiation or by poisoning, the cell loses its capacity to work against the tide; and now the laws of simple diffusion and osmosis hold full sway.

Precisely how a cell manages to "pull in" some substances and to "push out" others represent questions that cannot be answered very precisely at present. However, intensive research is currently being devoted to these problems and some progress can be reported.

Pinocytosis and Phagocytosis. Pinocytosis and phagocytosis, the active processes of cellular ingestion, were described briefly in Chapter 2. Essentially they are similar, since each involves an inpocketing of the cell membrane and an internal pinching off of a fluid-filled vesicle, or **vacuole**, which may then be carried to other regions of the cytoplasm. However, phagocytic vacuoles are relatively larger and they always contain one or more microscopically visible particles, such as bacteria, coagulated organic matter, or other solid food materials. Phagocytosis represents the standard method by which protozoans and certain other cells ingest solid materials— as will be described more fully in Chapter 7.

Pinocytic vacuoles display no visible par-

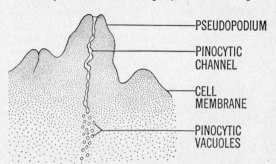

Fig. 6-8. Pinocytosis in a common *Amoeba*. Based on the observations and records of S. O. Mast and W. L. Doyle, at Johns Hopkins University in 1934.

ticles suspended in their fluid content. They are relatively small, ranging from 1 to 2 microns in the common amoebae (Fig. 6-8) down to 0.1 to 0.01 micron, in certain other cells (Fig. 6-9). Pinocytosis may represent an important mechanism by which cells actively take in dissolved substances, particularly macromolecular organic matter, from the external medium.

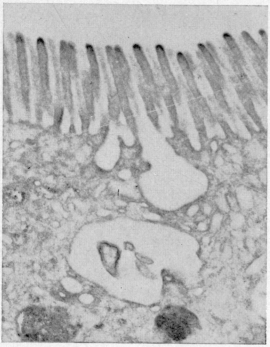

Fig. 6-9. Pinocytosis, observed by electron micrography, in an absorptive cell in the lining of the small intestine of a suckling mouse. Note that the cell membrane is deeply and complexly folded and that the pinocytic vacuoles appear to originate from the deep ends of the in-pocketings. The descriptive term "brush border cells" is often applied to cells of this type. (Courtesy of Sam. L. Clark, Jr., School of Medicine, Washington University, St. Louis. Total magnification, 18,000.)

The contents of a pinocytic or phagocytic vacuole cannot be considered as part of the protoplasm, however, since these materials are segregated within the vacuolar membrane. Moreover, it still is somewhat problematical as to how intravacuolar materials may be delivered into the protoplasm proper. Water and other relatively small molecules undoubtedly escape by diffusion and osmosis, since these vacuoles shrink and swell according to the tonicity of their fluid content (p. 131). Thus proteins and other macromolecular substances may escape from the vacuole after they have been digested, or hydrolyzed, into their micromolecular constituents (p. 129). In other cases, however, it seems probable that the macromolecules may be adsorbed upon the vacuolar membrane and that subsequently the membrane may fragment into pieces that become incorporated into the endoplasmic reticulum of the cell.

A close relationship between pinocytosis and phagocytosis has been demonstrated recently by studies on amoebae, made by Heinz Holter and collaborators of the Carlsberg Laboratory in Copenhagen. The amoebae were placed in a protein solution that induces very active pinocytosis for about 30 minutes, whereupon this activity comes to a halt. Such amoebae, now placed in a densely populated suspension of small ciliated protozoans, were able to phagocytize only a very few of these favorite food organisms, although ordinarily they would have ingested the ciliates in great numbers. Conversely, amoebae that had phagocytized to exhaustion in a dense suspension of ciliates showed little or no tendency to pinocytize when subsequently placed in protein solutions. In each case, apparently, the amoebae had used up almost all of their available supply of cell membrane materials during the period of very active pinocytosis or phagocytosis. Consequently scarcely any was left to be utilized for further activity.

The same Danish workers also observed that if glucose, as well as protein, is included in the solution being pinocytized, the protein is taken into the cell preferentially—to a tenfold extent. Such glucose as is taken in, however, freely diffuses forth from the pinocytic vacuoles into the surrounding cytoplasm, whereas the protein does not. The protein, in fact, appears to be adsorbed and bound to a mucoprotein component (p. 117) of the vacuolar membrane; subsequently this material sloughs off into the vacuolar cavity as a microscopically visible mass of coagulum (Fig. 6-9). It was possible to follow the translocation of the protein and glucose because, in each case, the molecules were radioactively labeled (p. 142). Thus when the amoebae, after proper fixation, were placed upon a sensitive, fine-grained photographic plate, a localization of the sites of radioactivity and an estimation of the intensity, or concentration, could be made.

Water Transport Mechanisms. Many cells are naturally exposed to a fresh-water environment from which, as a result of steepness of the concentration gradient, water tends to enter the protoplasm with considerable force. Plant cells, of course, possess very strong encasing walls and are able to develop a counteracting force, in the form of turgor pressure. But animal cells must expend energy, either to exclude the water or to pump it out after it has entered.

Very little is known about the mechanisms of water exclusion, although they must be important in certain cases—as in the skin cells of multicellular fresh water animals, particularly the fresh water fishes and amphibians. Unicellular animals, on the other hand, employ the contractile vacuole (Fig. 6-6) as a water-eliminating device.

The ability of a **contractile vacuole** to contract appears to depend upon the formation of a gelated photoplasmic layer immediately surrounding the vacuolar membrane and bordering the confluent channels leading into the vacuole (Fig. 6-6). Thus the pumping activity of the vacuole is abolished by agents, such as high hydrostatic pressure, that are known to cause a drastic solation of protoplasmic gels generally, as has been shown by D. A. Marsland, of New York University, in America and by J. A. Kitching, of the University of Bristol, in England. The formation of such contractile gel structures is an endothermic operation that cannot be performed unless the cell provides energy from its metabolism. Moreover, each potential bonding site in such a gel structure (Fig.

4-23) appears to be blocked off by a shell of densely packed, closely adsorbed water molecules, and this must be dispersed before the site becomes effective in forming a gelational bond. In short, these and other data led to the tentative conclusion that a gelational phenomenon underlies not only the mechanical pumping action of the contractile vacuole, but also its action in picking up water, during solation, and giving it up, during gelation, in a continued cycle of activity. But precisely how the gel delivers water into the vacuolar cavity remains an unsolved problem.

Ionic Transport Mechanisms. As previously stated, a relatively high concentration of certain ions, particularly potassium (K^+), is maintained within the cell, as compared to its surrounding medium; and a relatively low concentration of other ions, particularly sodium (Na^+), is likewise maintained. The maintenance of these differentials is very important in the life of the cell. They determine the electrical potential of the cell membrane (p. 191), which in turn determines cellular excitability (p. 190). But to create and preserve these important differences in ionic concentration, which usually are some 10- to 30-fold in magnitude, the cell must expend considerable metabolic energy in forcing or holding the appropriate ions against the steep diffusional gradients.

Despite intensive research upon ionic transport mechanisms, not much progress has been made. As a cloak for ignorance, one may speak of a "potassium pump" or a "sodium pump," but these terms merely designate rather than explain the basic phenomena. Among current theories, perhaps the most plausible postulates the existence of one or more "ion carrier molecules" that are energized by metabolism as they shuttle back and forth across the surface membrane. One such theory, proposed by T. J. Shaw, of Cambridge University, assumes that the same organic molecule carries both sodium and potassium ions. At the deep surface of the cell membrane, this carrier is assumed to pick up sodium ion (Na+) and to receive energy from the subjacent cytoplasm. Arriving at the external membrane surface, the carrier then discharges the sodium, along with the charge of energy, whereupon the carrier is free to pick up potassium (K+) and transport it back to the cytoplasm. But even though it is difficult to provide convincing experimental evidence in support of any particular ionic transport theory, the fact remains that cells cannot afford to lose their ionic differentials, particularly with reference to potassium and sodium ions. If metabolism is damped off, as by anaesthetics or by certain other drugs, the cell membrane potential gradually drops away and the capacity of the cell to respond to stimulation disappears (Chap. 11).

SUMMARY

Since a plasma membrane, which is semipermeable, intervenes between the protoplasm and surrounding solutions, each typical cell displays many of the attributes of an osmotic system. Any substance that can penetrate the membrane will tend to pass out of the cell if it is more concentrated inside than outside; it will tend to pass into the cell if the outside concentration is greater. The end products of **destructive metabolism,** such as carbon dioxide, water, and other simple substances, are all able to pass freely through the membrane. Due to their constant production, the concentrations of these substances inside the cell tend to be higher than outside and consequently they continuously tend to leave the protoplasm. Substances that are used up in metabolism, such as oxygen or glucose, tend to enter the cell from the surrounding solution. The very fact that these substances are consumed or converted into other substances as metabolism proceeds tends to keep their concentrations in the protoplasm generally lower than in the outside medium. The products of **constructive metabolism,** on the other hand, are mainly colloidal substances (proteins, polysaccharides, phospholipids, etc.) that cannot penetrate the membrane. Consequently these essential components of the protoplasm cannot escape despite their relatively high internal concentrations.

The water equilibrium between the cell and its environment assumes a very critical importance: first, because water is by far the most abundant substance both inside and outside the cell; and second, because water penetrates the cell membranes much more rapidly than most of the solutes present in the system. Plant cells frequently live in fresh water, but such cells are protected against a rapid and lethal influx of water from the surrounding hypotonic solution by the strength of the cell wall. This permits the development of a turgor pressure high enough to counteract the osmotic force under which the water continues to seek entrance into the cell. Animal cells, in contrast, cannot be maintained in a hypotonic medium unless some special mechanism like the contractile vacuole is present to deal with excess water as fast as it enters. In hypertonic solutions both plant and animal cells are equally vulnerable. No cell can lose too high a proportion of its water without suffering irreversible deterioration.

Ion transport mechanisms, by which a certain ion may be forced to move against an adverse diffusional gradient, enable cells to develop and maintain a high content of potassium and a low content of sodium ions, relative to surrounding media. Other active transport mechanisms, particularly pinocytosis and phagocytosis, permit individual cells to take in macromolecular types of organic substances that are not able to penetrate through the surface membranes.

TEST QUESTIONS

1. Define the term *osmosis*. What is the basis for describing the typical cell as a minute osmotic system?
2. What is diffusion; how is it energized?
3. State the general law that governs the *direction* of diffusion.
4. Explain why the solute and solvent (in the system shown in Fig. 6-2) continue to diffuse in *opposite* directions until equilibrium is reached.
5. Explain why the plasma membrane is typical of semipermeable membranes generally.
6. Arrange the following substances in an order that will designate their relative speeds in penetrating the plasma membrane: sucrose, oxygen, proteins, sodium chloride, glucose, starch, and ether.
7. Name three factors that have an important bearing on the capacity of a substance to pass through the plasma membrane.
8. Assuming that pure water is separated from a protein solution by a membrane that is permeable to water but not to protein, how would the system approach equilibrium?
9. Assuming that a cell is immersed in pure water, how would the system approach equilibrium?
10. In addition to the fact that water can traverse the plasma membrane more readily than most of the solutes ordinarily present inside and outside the cell, what other factor places the burden of attaining equilibrium mainly upon water?
11. Explain the respiration of an amoeba (Fig. 6-4) on the basis of diffusion. What is the common law that determines the movement of both the O_2 and the CO_2?
12. What is an isotonic solution? Give one specific example. What determines the balanced exchange of water between the cell and such a solution?
13. A solution that is isotonic to one cell is not necessarily isotonic to another. Explain.
14. Carefully identify each of the following terms: (a) cytolysis, (b) plasmolysis, (c) crenation, (d) deplasmolysis, (e) turgor.
15. In each of the following cases, what observable changes would be expected to occur when the cells are placed in the specified solutions:
    a. an amoeba in a very weak (hypotonic) salt solution
    b. a red blood cell in the same solution
    c. a plant cell in the same solution
    d. a plant cell in a strong (hypertonic) salt solution
    e. a plant cell in a hypertonic glucose solution
    f. a red cell in a hypertonic salt solution
    g. a red cell in a hypertonic glucose solution
    h. an amoeba in a hypertonic glucose solution
16. Carefully explain the effects described in parts a, b, c, d, e, and f of Question 15.
17. Distinguish between active and passive mechanisms of transport.
18. Specify three types of active transport mechanism. To what extent are these mechanisms understood? Explain.

FURTHER READINGS

1. "How Things Get into Cells," by H. Holter, in "The Living Cell," special issue of *Scientific American*, September 1961.
2. *Explorations into the Nature of the Living Cell*, by R. and E. L. Chambers; Cambridge, Mass., 1961.
3. *Life: an Introduction to Biology*, by G. G. Simpson, C. S. Pittendrigh, and L. H. Tiffany; New York, 1957.

7 – Animal Cells and Their Nutrition

NUTRITION includes all processes that have to do with obtaining and utilizing **food**—and obviously these matters are very important in every living thing. In animals, food furnishes the only source of energy; and in all organisms, food is the only source of matter for sustaining and increasing the living structure. Without food no plant or animal can maintain life, except during periods of virtual dormancy.

A **food** is *any substance that an organism obtains* **from its environment** *and utilizes, directly or indirectly, in its metabolism.* Some foods serve primarily as protoplasmic fuels whereas others serve as raw materials for the synthesis of essential protoplasmic compounds; but every food in one manner or another participates in the metabolism of the organism. Sometimes the food substance may pass without change directly into the cells, but often it must undergo chemical alteration (that is, digestion) before the derivatives may be absorbed. Moreover, it is necessary to realize that when we speak of a "food" in common language, we usually are referring to a **mixture** of many *food substances.* Steak, for example, consists of a high proportion of water, a variety of inorganic salts, considerable amounts of protein, fat, and carbohydrate, and a number of other individually distinct food substances. Only a few of the foods of man are highly purified single compounds, such as table salt and sugar. Moreover, what is a food for one organism is not necessarily a food for another (Table 7-1).

MODES OF NUTRITION; THE ANIMAL vs. THE PLANT

Typical animals and plants are distinguished by very fundamental differences in their nutrition. Green plants require only inorganic foods, but *animals must obtain at least a minium of organic foods,* in addition to their inorganic requirements. Water, carbon dioxide, an assortment of the inorganic salts, and sometimes oxygen are all that the green plant needs as raw materials for the

Table 7-1—Principal Food Substances—Sources and Uses in Organisms

Food Substances	Principal Uses in the Organism	Usual Source
Oxygen	Essential for oxidation of organic compounds in both plants and animals; oxidative metabolism important as a source of *energy*	Present in the atmosphere and (in solution) in the waters of the earth; liberated by green plants
Water	An essential structural component in all protoplasm and body fluids; participates in many metabolic reactions; used by green plants for the synthesis of glucose	Abundant in the environment as soil water, lake water, etc.; present in virtually all natural foods
Carbon dioxide..	Used mainly by green plants as a source of carbon in the synthesis of glucose and other organic compounds. Animals, however, possess a limited ability to "fix" CO_2 (p. 152)	Abundant in the environment as a component of the atmosphere and (dissolved) natural waters; plants diminish, animals replenish the carbon dioxide of the environment
Salts	Essential components in all protoplasm and body fluids. Take part in many metabolic reactions. Ions determine the electrical conductivity and membrane potential in cells generally	Abundant in the environment as components of the soil, and as solutes in natural waters; present in almost all natural foods
Proteins	Animals derive their essential amino acids from protein foods; whereas plants can synthesize all their amino acids. Animals also obtain some energy from protein foods	Protein parts and remnants of other organisms. Ultimate origin mainly from the plants
Carbohydrates ..	Animals utilize carbohydrates in synthesizing essential protoplasmic compounds; plants synthesize these compounds from CO_2 and H_2O. Carbohydrates yield energy on oxidation, in both plant and animal cells	Ultimate origin mainly from plants
Fats (lipids)	Animals require fatty foods for synthesis of essential compounds; plants derive these compounds indirectly from CO_2 and H_2O. Fats yield energy (on oxidation) in animals and (to a limited extent) in plants	Ultimate origin mainly from plants
Vitamins	Essential structural components in the protoplasm. Generally serve as coenzymes or prosthetic constituents in various intracellular enzymes	Synthesized by plants (see Chap 18)

synthesis of the various organic components of its protoplasm, and the typical plant can live and grow indefinitely so long as these simple foods are available. But an animal cannot do this; an animal's food requirements are on a higher level of complexity. Compared to plant cells, animal cells have more limited powers of synthesis, and animal metabolism cannot be maintained in the absence of organic foods such as preformed proteins (or amino acids), carbohydrates, lipids, and vitamins (Table 7-1).

Animals generally are quite similar as to their food requirements, and the same is true for green plants. Accordingly, the nutrition of the typical animal is referred to as **holozoic** nutrition in contrast to the **holophytic** nutrition of green plants.

The **holozoic** mode of nutrition is associated with the development among animals generally of many structures and activities not found among plants. The animal must obtain organic foods, and these compounds exist mainly in the bodies and remnants of other organisms. Therefore the animal is constantly faced with the necessity of finding and apprehending other organisms. This necessity has determined an evolution of highly developed sensory, nervous, and muscular structures, which are so characteristic of animals, but not of plants. The essential foods of a plant are all inorganic substances that are widely distributed in the environment. The plant does not have to seek them out. Rooted to a single locality, a typical plant remains constantly in direct contact with all its necessary foods.

Other structures generally present in animals, but absent in plants, are the organs of the digestive system. A digestive system is necessary in animals because most organic foods, such as proteins, are colloidal in their molecular dimensions. Such macromolecules cannot be absorbed into the cells of the animal until they have been digested into the micromolecular units of their structure. Therefore typical animals possess a digestive cavity wherein the colloidal components of the food are chemically broken up in preparation for absorption.

NUTRITION OF UNICELLULAR ANIMALS: HOLOZOIC NUTRITION

One-celled animals, such as *Amoeba,* sustain themselves in a fashion that is strikingly analogous to the nutrition of larger animals, including man. In obtaining and utilizing food, and in disposing of the waste products, all animals perform essentially the same processes and achieve essentially the same ends. Accordingly it is possible to describe the nutrition of *Amoeba,* man, or any other typical animal under the same eight headings: 1. **ingestion,** 2. **digestion,** 3. **absorption,** 4. **egestion,** 5. **distribution,** 6. **metabolism,** 7. **respiration,** and 8. **excretion.**

Ingestion. The amoeba, as seen in a drop of pond water, slowly approaches its living or nonliving food, engulfing the entire mass.

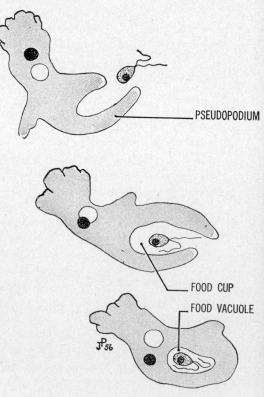

Fig. 7-1. *Amoeba* ingesting a flagellate.

Gradually the **pseudopodia** extend around the food, forming a **food cup** (Fig. 7-1), and finally, when the lip of the cup closes, a **food vacuole** is formed. This primitive digestive cavity now contains a quantity of pond water, together with the organic food, which is to be digested (Fig. 7-2). Essentially, in short, ingestion by the amoeba represents a type of phagocytosis, such as was described previously (p. 121).

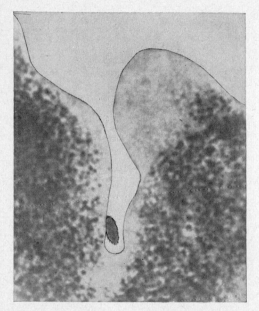

Fig. 7-2. *Amoeba* ingesting a living ciliate (dark oval body). The pseudopodia are about to close around the prey. The magnification is so great that only a small part of the amoeba can be seen. Photograph retouched to clarify the outlines. (Encyclopedia Britannica Films, Inc.)

Ingestion *is the process by which an animal takes food into its digestive cavity.* Although the method of ingestion varies in different animals, the end result is always the same. A paramecium (Fig. 7-3) swims about by means of its **cilia,** which also serve to sweep bacteria and other finely suspended particles of organic food along the **oral groove,** down the **gullet,** and into the **food vacuole** (Figs. 7-3 and 7-4). Or a frog catches a fly with a swift thrust of the tongue and carries its prey into the mouth for swallow-ing. Or a man manipulates his food with implements and introduces it into the upper part of the digestive tract. Whatever the method, the result is quite the same. Food is taken into some special cavity where digestion will begin.

Digestion. The crystalloidal components of the amoeba's food, such as water or salt, do not require digestion. Such foods are absorbed directly from the digestive cavity into the surrounding protoplasm, without preliminary preparation. But the colloidal molecules of proteins, polysaccharides, fats, etc., cannot penetrate the vacuolar membrane; and such molecules must be fragmented before they can be absorbed into the protoplasm. *In every typical animal, digestion is a series of* **hydrolytic decompositions,** *promoted by* **enzymes** *secreted into the digestive cavity, whereby the initially* **nonabsorbable (colloidal) components** *of the food are converted into* **absorbable (crystalloidal) end products.**

Digestion in the amoeba begins as soon as digestive enzymes are secreted by the protoplasm into the food vacuole. Only traces of these enzymes are necessary. The digestive enzymes of amoebae and other animals include several proteases. These proteases hydrolyze the proteins of the engulfed food, liberating amino acids that dissolve in the vacuolar water. Likewise there are carbohydrases, which act upon carbohydrates, digesting them mainly into glucose, and lipases, which convert the fats into glycerol and fatty acids. All these end products of digestion are quite soluble in the aqueous content of the vacuole and all are capable of penetrating the vacuole membrane.

The digestive enzymes of lower animals, such as the amoeba, and those of higher animals, including man, display many similarities. In the amoeba, during the first 10 minutes of digestion, the content of the food vacuole displays a distinctly acid reaction, indicating that some acid is secreted into the vacuole along with the enzymes. This acid phase of digestion in the amoeba has its

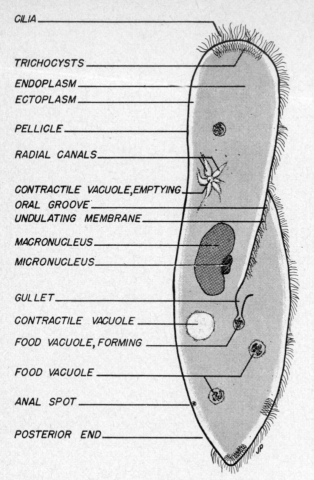

CILIA

TRICHOCYSTS

ENDOPLASM

ECTOPLASM

PELLICLE

RADIAL CANALS

CONTRACTILE VACUOLE,EMPTYING

ORAL GROOVE

UNDULATING MEMBRANE

MACRONUCLEUS

MICRONUCLEUS

GULLET

CONTRACTILE VACUOLE

FOOD VACUOLE, FORMING

FOOD VACUOLE

ANAL SPOT

POSTERIOR END

Fig. 7-3. *Paramecium,* a very familiar one-celled animal. Note that even a single cell can display a rather complex organization. Many of the trichocysts and cilia have been omitted, to simplify the drawing. Actually these structures are uniformly distributed throughout the whole surface.

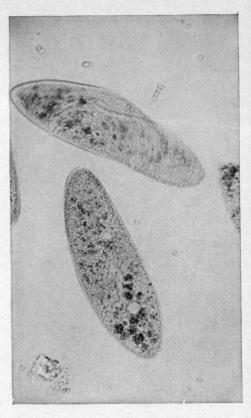

Fig. 7-4. Living paramecia, photographed at a magnification of about 250 diameters. In the posterior (broader) end of the lower specimen one can see several food vacuoles (grouped around the contractile vacuole) and trichocysts (along the posterior margin.) The upper specimen is in the act of turning and shows the oriented beating of the cilia, and the oral groove. (Bausch and Lomb Optical Co.)

counterpart in digestion as it occurs in the human **stomach.** In the human stomach food is subjected to the action of an acid **gastric juice,** which contains a very active **protease,** *pepsin.* Probably pepsin, or a pepsinlike protease, is also present in one-celled animals, although the specific digestive enzymes of the amoeba have not been isolated, due to the technical difficulties of handling such small organisms. During the later stages of digestion, the vacuolar content becomes distinctly alkaline. This indicates that the later-acting proteases, as well as the lipases and carbohydrases of the amoeba, are similar to the well-known intestinal enzymes of higher animals (Table 5-1).

Absorption. Absorption, in animals, *is the process by which food substances pass from the digestive cavity into the body proper.* In fact, the digestive cavity can be regarded as a portion of the environment that is encompassed by the animal. While the food remains in the digestive cavity, it does not subserve any useful function. Accordingly, digestion is merely a preliminary to absorption.

In the amoeba, as in organisms generally, diffusion and osmosis play an important role in absorption. After digestion, the content of the food vacuole consists of an aqueous solution of simple sugars, amino acids, glycerol, fatty acids, etc. These substances can penetrate the vacuole membrane, and as a result of digestion, each of the end products tends to reach a relatively high concentration in the vacuolar fluid. But these substances are constantly consumed or altered by metabolism, and therefore they remain at a relatively low level in the protoplasm surrounding the vacuole. Accordingly, each food substance tends to diffuse spontaneously from the vacuole into the cell. In some cases, however, absorption may be accelerated by active transport mechanisms.

The water and inorganic salts included in the vacuole at the time of its formation are also absorbed into the protoplasm, the former very rapidly and the latter very slowly. Initially the pond water that is engulfed along with the organic food is distinctly hypotonic. Thus a newly formed vacuole tends to shrink for several minutes, by losing water to the surrounding protoplasm. But later the vacuole enlarges, because the soluble end products of digestion accumulate, making the vacuolar fluid hypertonic to the protoplasm. Finally, however, the vacuole undergoes a permanent shrinkage, owing to the slow absorption of organic solutes together with a quantity of water sufficient to keep the vacuolar fluid isotonic with the protoplasm. Eventually just a small vestige of the vacuole remains, and such an "old" vacuole contains only a few residual granules of nondigestible material. These digestive wastes cannot be absorbed and must be ejected from the cell.

In higher animals, food substances are absorbed into the blood and lymph rather than directly into the protoplasm; and among animals generally, diffusion and osmosis are important in the absorption of substances from the digestive cavity, although other factors may modify the situation. In the higher animals also, there is always a residuum of nonabsorbable material that must be eliminated from the digestive cavity.

Egestion. **Egestion** *represents the elimination of nonabsorbable materials from the digestive cavity.* In the amoeba, egestion is essentially the reverse of ingestion. The nearly empty food vacuole comes into contact with the cell membrane at any point, and suddenly the vacuolar granules are spilled into the outside medium. In the paramecium, an old vacuole circulates in the cytoplasm until it reaches a fixed point, called the **anal spot** (Fig. 7-3). At the anal spot, which is situated near the posterior end of the paramecium, the pellicle is relatively weak, or perhaps absent; and egestion can occur as it does in the amoeba. Higher animals generally possess a tubular digestive passage, and egestion, or **defecation**, occurs through the **anal opening.**

The composition of the **egestive wastes,** or **feces,** varies according to the food habits of the particular animal. Herbivorous animals always have large remnants of cellulose from the woody parts of ingested plant tissues. This potential source of glucose (from the hydrolysis of cellulose) is partly lost, however, because **cellulase** is not included among the digestive enzymes of most animals. Carnivorous diets leave smaller residues of indigestible materials, such as bone and gristle; and in all animals small quantities of salts and water escape absorption.

Distribution. **Distribution** *represents the transportation of substances throughout the body of the organism.* In animals, absorbed foods must be carried from the digestive cavity to the other parts at a rate commensurate with the metabolic needs. Also, metabolic wastes must be transported to the site of elimination, and hormones and other substances must be carried from part to part in the body.

Distribution is not a very serious problem in one-celled animals, because diffusion is adequate to disseminate the foods and other substances within such narrow limits. But larger animals have developed circulating fluids, such as blood and lymph, which accelerate the distribution.

In the amoeba, absorbed foods can diffuse quite rapidly throughout the cytoplasm and nucleus. Moreover, the protoplasm constantly flows, as the amoeba moves in search of food, and the protoplasmic streaming tends to accelerate distribution.

Metabolism. Metabolism—*the sum total of all chemical processes* **occurring in the protoplasm** *of an organism*—represents the most essential phase of nutrition. All other nutritional processes are quite *accessory* to metabolism, since they merely provide the materials for metabolic activity, or remove the metabolic wastes.

Metabolism accomplishes two main objectives in every organism: (1) it liberates **energy,** which finds tangible expression in the movements and other activities of the organism; and (2) it achieves the **synthesis of new organic compounds,** which are necessary for the growth and maintenance of protoplasmic structure. On this basis, in fact, the metabolism of each organism is subdivided into two major parts: (1) **catabolism,** which includes all decomposition (exothermic) reactions and provides energy for the organism; and (2) **anabolism,** which embraces all synthetic (endothermic) reactions and creates new organic components in the protoplasm.

The metabolism of even the simplest cell involves a wide variety of chemical changes, catalyzed by a correspondingly wide variety of intracellular enzymes. And although quite a few matabolic reactions have been duplicated outside the cell, many details of intermediary metabolism, especially in lower animals, are still unknown.

Regardless of details, we do know that food substances in the protoplasm of an animal cell, such as the amoeba, are launched upon a series of chemical changes. In an anabolic direction, these reactions give rise to new proteins, lipids, carbohydrates, etc.; and these substances, together with absorbed water and salts, become organized into new protoplasm as the organism grows. Simultaneously, many organic foods are oxidized and decomposed in other ways. The **energy from catabolism** not only goes to sustain the mechanical and other work of the cell, but also **activates anabolism,** which as a whole is endothermic. Moreover, the metabolism of the amoeba produces a number of waste products, which are referred to collectively as the **metabolic** (or excretory) **wastes.**

The metabolic wastes of the amoeba and other animal cells include water, carbon dioxide, simple nitrogenous compounds such as ammonium salts, and a variety of other inorganic salts. Water and carbon dioxide are produced from the oxidation of all organic foods, since hydrogen and carbon are always present in these compounds. Nitrogenous wastes, however, are derived entirely from the decomposition of nitrogen-containing compounds, chiefly the amino acids. Other inorganic salts—such as sulfates and phosphates—result from the decomposition of compounds containing sulfur (for example, certain amino acids) and phosphorous (for example, phospholipids), etc.

Respiration. Without oxygen the metabolism of the amoeba and other animal cells may continue for a time, but without oxidative metabolism the intracellular reserves of ATP and other immediately available sources of energy (p. 143) are soon exhausted, and metabolism as a whole begins to falter. In addition, carbon dioxide must be disposed of before it accumulates to toxic levels. *This continuous exchange of gases, in which oxygen enters and carbon dioxide leaves the cell, constitutes the process of* **respiration.**[1] Unless respiration continues, aside from relatively short interruptions, most cells begin to die of **asphyxiation.**

Unicellular animals do not expend energy in obtaining oxygen or in disposing of carbon dioxide. In fact, among animals generally, respiration proceeds on a diffusional basis, although higher animals have circulatory fluids, such as blood, which carry O_2 and CO_2 between the cells and environment. In the

---

[1] Many biologists prefer to use the term respiration more broadly, to include what here is designated as *oxidative metabolism.*

amoeba, however, O_2 and CO_2 are exchanged directly between the protoplasm and the surrounding pond water (see Fig. 6-4).

Excretion. **Excretion** *is the process by which metabolic wastes* (excluding carbon dioxide) *are eliminated from the organism.* The excretory wastes (p. 138) are not very toxic, unless they accumulate in the protoplasm, but waste products are produced so constantly during metabolism that most animals can only survive a few hours if excretion fails to occur.

Except for water, the excretory wastes of amoeba and other one-celled animals are eliminated by **diffusion.** Owing to metabolism, such wastes as ammonium salts and other salts reach a higher concentration inside the cell than outside. Accordingly, these waste products pass out to the environment spontaneously. But the amoeba is forced to expend energy to eliminate water, since the surrounding pond water is distinctly hypotonic to the protoplasm. The total quantity of water eliminated by the contractile vacuole represents the sum of two parts: (1) the larger part, which constantly enters the cell by osmosis from the hypotonic outside medium, and (2) the smaller part, which is produced metabolically from the oxidation of hydrogen compounds in the protoplasm.

In higher animals the blood stream serves as an intermediary in excretion as well as in respiration. The metabolic wastes pass into the blood from the cells all over the body, and are carried to the kidneys, or other excretory organs, where excretion finally occurs.

METABOLISM, A DYNAMIC EQUILIBRIUM

Recent studies, stemming from the brilliant work of the late Rudolph Schoenheimer of Columbia University, have forced biochemists to the conclusion that the *organic components of an animal's body are in a dynamic state of flux*—to a most astonishing degree. Schoenheimer, in 1938, was among the first to use food substances labeled with tagged atoms (p. 142) as a means of following their metabolic fate. He fed his animals (rats) with amino acids labeled with heavy nitrogen (N^{15}) and fatty acids labeled with heavy hydrogen (H^2) and traced the rate at which these organic compounds became incorporated into the various tissues of the body. The amazing conclusion that must be drawn from this and many similar experiments is that the amino acids are rapidly incorporated into the proteins all over the body, even when no increase in total protein is occurring; and a similar incorporation of the fatty acids into the fat deposits also occurs. In fact, the calculations show that the whole protein content of the body, striking a general average, is broken down and rebuilt again about four times a year, although the proteins of some structures (for example, the liver) show a much more rapid turnover than those of others (for example, bone). In other words, each animal is not exactly the same individual from day to day, at least in a chemical sense; and what has been found true for man and other higher animals must certainly be even more applicable to one-celled animals, such as the amoeba and paramecium.

Metabolic Reactions of Animal Cells. Typical animals, regardless of their size and complexity, exhibit the same eight fundamental nutritive processes. In fact, the pattern of holozoic nutrition is coextensive with the animal kingdom, since it depends upon the *kind of metabolism* that characterizes animals. The metabolic enzymes of animals are generally similar, although many specific differences have arisen in the course of evolution. In short, similar enzymes and similar metabolic processes have been inherited by practically all members of the animal kingdom.

Constructive Metabolism: PROTEIN SYNTHESIS. A most vital problem faced by every cell is the necessity to synthesize its own unique protein structures—the protein components of its genes, ribosomes, enzymes, membrane systems, and so forth. In fact, the distinctive characteristics of each kind of cell are preserved and perpetuated mainly by the mechanism of protein synthesis. In these processes both DNA and RNA play roles of paramount importance.

How the cell achieves an exact replication of its DNA, or genic components, is a problem that will not be considered until later (Chap. 27). Here, however, it is important to know that such replication operates to preserve the *sequence of organic bases* (Fig. 7-5) in every part of every DNA unit. This means that the **adenine** (A), **cytosine** (C), **guanine** (G), and **thymine** (T) are arranged in a precisely determined, though widely varying, *order* along the sugar-phosphate skeleton in each segment of the elongate nucleic acid molecule.

The base sequence in the DNA of a cell likewise determines the sequence of bases in its RNA (Fig. 7-5). The RNA is synthesized—mainly, at least—in the nucleus, although later much of it is transported to the cytoplasm, where protein synthesis must also occur. In the nucleus, presumably, when a new RNA unit is formed, the basic constituents of a prospective RNA molecule are carefully lined up in relation to a master template, provided by some segment of the DNA (Fig. 7-5). This alignment determines the base sequence in the RNA product because it always follows a definite rule, namely the **base-pair rule.** According to this rule, only certain *pairs* of the purine (adenine and guanine) and pyrimidine (cytosine, thymine,

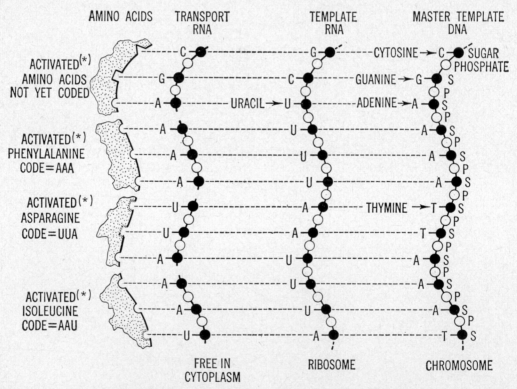

Fig. 7-5. Postulated mechanisms of protein synthesis. The sequence of organic bases in template RNA derives from that of the chromosomal DNA, in obedience to the **base-pair rule.** This rule states that only certain base-pairs can affiliate with one another: cytosine with guanine (C—G), adenine with thymine (A—T), and adenine with uracil (A—U). The pick-up of particular amino acids by transport RNA is determined by a partly known *triplet code*; e.g., AAA deals with phenylalanine; UUA with asparagine; AAU with isoleucine; etc. Thymine, although present in DNA, is absent in RNA; and uracil, present in RNA, is not present in DNA. Dotted lines indicate points of affinity among the specified constituents of the system.

and uracil) bases possess chemical affinity for one another: cytosine for guanine (C—G), adenine for thymine (A—T), and adenine for uracil (A—U)—as is shown in Figure 7-5. This important generalization was first predicted by F. H. C. Crick, of Cambridge University, in England, working in conjunction with J. D. Watson, now at Harvard University. From the base-pair rule it follows that the line-up of bases in a newly synthesized unit of RNA is predetermined by the line-up of bases in the DNA master template in a chromosome of the cell.

At this point it is not possible even to summarize the long trail of evidence that has led to two important conclusions: (1) that RNA plays a dominant role in the synthesis of enzymes and other protein components in the cell and (2) that the specificity of each protein produced is determined by the base sequence of the particular RNA unit that participates in the synthesis (Fig. 7-5). The *code* of this system—which popularly has been called the *code of life*—is currently in process of being solved, as will be explained more fully later (Chap. 27). It is, apparently, a fairly simple code, constituted of the four bases (A, C, G, and U) arranged in varying order in groups of three (Fig. 7-5). Each triplet—of which there are 64 ($4 \times 4 \times 4$) variations—appears to exert an attractive force upon a particular amino acid. However, some of the triplets may be neutral and some amino acids may display affinity for more than one triplet. Thus it has been found that triplet AAA is capable of picking up the amino acid *phenylalanine,* UUA picks up *asparagine,* and AAU picks up *isoleucine* —as is shown in Figure 7-5. At present the system has not been fully decoded, but intensive current research will doubtless soon yield more complete information. Already it is known, indeed, that the code is widely if not universally employed in nature and that it enables each cell to transmit its own genic instructions from the chromosomes to the sites where enzymes and other important protein components are being synthesized.

The processes of protein synthesis are not very simple, however. Undoubtedly, the *ribosomes* (Fig. 2-13) are very active and essential parts of the system. These particles, which are generally affiliated with the endoplasmic reticulum, display a very high (40 to 60 percent) content of RNA, and the ribosomal RNA is of very high molecular weight (3 to 4 million). There are, however, two other fractions of RNA in the cytoplasm, as will be explained more fully in Chapter 27. One of these, called *transport* RNA, is of low molecular weight (2 to 3 thousand) and this fraction can migrate freely throughout the cytoplasm. Moreover, much recent evidence indicates that this micromolecular fraction of RNA is first to affiliate with the separate amino acids, according to the triplet code. It seems highly probable that these freely diffusible RNA units serve to pick up and to transport the different amino acids to the ribosomal surface (Fig. 7-5). Coming to the surface of a ribosome, presumably, the transport RNA becomes aligned, according to the *base-pair rule,* with a template fraction of *RNA* (Chap. 27). Thus the template RNA serves to determine the amino acid sequence in the finished protein product, and this sequence in turn determines the specific nature of the final protein.

But many problems still remain. Energy must be provided for the synthesis, and this appears to be derived from the ATP reserves (p. 143) of the cell. In any case, protein synthesis does not occur in preparations of disintegrated cells, unless ATP is present. Moreover, the rate of protein synthesis falls off rapidly when *ribonuclease,* an enzyme that destroys RNA, is added to the medium. It is not known, however, how the serially aligned amino acids become linked together, forming an elongate peptide chain. It is, to be sure, essentially a process of dehydration synthesis; that is, a molecule of water is split away each time a peptide bond is formed. Furthermore, the efficiency of the process must be high, as has been demonstrated by the recent work of Richard Schweet, of the

Kentucky Medical School, working in conjunction with H. M. Dintzis, of the Massachusetts Institute of Technology. During the synthesis of the red blood-cell protein, *hemoglobin*, according to this study, about two amino acids per second are added to the growing peptide chain, so that a finished hemoglobin molecule, constituted of 150 amino acids, is produced within less than one and a half minutes.

Still another problem of protein synthesis must be mentioned. Before affiliation with a particular unit of transport RNA, each amino acid must be activated (Fig. 7-5), as first was shown by M. B. Hoagland, of Harvard University. A distinctively different activating enzyme appears to be required for each of the different amino acids being utilized for protein synthesis. But the coding instructions are carried by the RNA. Thus, for example, Severo Ochoa and co-workers at the New York University Medical School devised a method by which RNA of known composition can artificially be synthesized; and M. W. Nurenberg, working with J. H. Mathaei, of a National Institute of Health, in Bethesda, Md., utilized such a sample of RNA for protein synthesis. In this case, the artificial (template) RNA consisted entirely of —UUU— triplets and consequently only one amino acid, *phenylalanine,* became incorporated during the formation of the peptide chain. However, introducing a few —UUA— triplets into the template structure permitted the —AAU— units of the transfer system to bring a few molecules of another amino acid, *isoleucine,* into the peptide series (Fig. 7-5).

Undoubtedly the mechanisms of protein synthesis are generally similar in *plant* and *animal* cells, but there is *one important difference. Plant cells can synthesize all of the different amino acids,* starting entirely at the *inorganic* level—from water, carbon dioxide, and inorganic salts (particularly nitrates, sulfates, and phosphates). The animal cell, on the other hand, can utilize inorganic forms of nitrogen (ammonia and ammonium salts) only to a limited extent. Animal cells

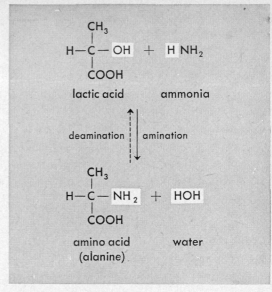

Fig. 7-6. The animal cell has the ability to utilize inorganic nitrogen (ammonia or ammonium salts) for the formation of a *limited number* of amino acids. The amino acids in this group, which can be synthesized and which, therefore, do not need to be acquired as preformed substances, are designated as the **nonessential amino acids.** The **essential amino acids** must be present as preformed substances, in the food or its derivatives (see Table 7-2).

can manufacture some kinds of amino acids in this manner (Fig. 7-6); and these kinds are called **nonessential.** The other kinds, in contrast, cannot be synthesized by animal cells. They *must be obtained by the animal as ready-made,* or *preformed substances,* and consequently they are referred to as the **essential amino acids** (Table 7-2). Moreover, since *all* of the different amino acids are needed for the synthesis of any complete protein molecule, every animal must include some protein food in its basic diet. Only by eating plants or other animals that have fed directly or indirectly upon plant proteins can the animal obtain, through the media of ingestion, digestion, and absorption, an adequate supply of the essential amino acids; these cannot be generated in the cells of its own body.

OTHER SYNTHETIC PROCESSES. Although the cells of animals, as compared to those of typical plants, have a relatively lower capa-

Table 7-2—Essential Amino Acids

These cannot be synthesized by animal cells and, therefore, must be included as preformed units in the protein foods of the animal.

$$R-\underset{\underset{NH_2}{|}}{\overset{\overset{H}{|}}{C}}-COOH$$

Amino acid	R
Threonine	CH_3CHOH-
Phenylalanine	$-CH_2-$ (benzene ring)
Lysine	$NH_2-(CH_2)_3-CH_2-$
Tryptophan	$-CH_2-$ (indole ring, N)
Valine	$(CH_3)_2-CH-$
Methionine	$CH_3-S-CH_2CH_2-$
Leucine	$(CH_3)_2-CH-CH_2-$
Isoleucine	$CH_3-CH_2-CH(CH_3)-$

city for organic synthesis, the synthetic capability of the animal is by no means negligible. The **purine** and **pyrimidine bases,** needed for the manufacture of **nucleic acids,** can be formed from catabolic fragments of the glucose molecule (**Fig.** 8-5) together with ammonia (or ammonium salts). Some preformed organic bases, particularly the pyrimidines, may also be utilized, if they are present in the food of the animal. Inorganic phosphate may be used in the synthesis of nucleic acids and **phospholipids.** Moreover, animal cells generally possess efficient enzyme systems for the manufacture of its various essential **sterol** compounds (p. 77).

Complex *carbohydrates,* particularly **glycogen,** which is a very common type of fuel stored in animal cells, can be derived by dehydration synthesis from absorbed glucose, of course, or from glucose generated from certain amino acids, subsequent to their deamination (Fig. 8-10). In man and other vertebrate animals, large reserves of glycogen may be found in the muscles and liver, deposited in the form of microscopic granules, and these reserves may be replenished if the animal eats adequate quantities of either carbohydrate or protein foods.

True fats can be *synthesized directly* from glycerol and fatty acids, absorbed from the digestive cavity. Or they may be manufactured *indirectly,* in which case the animal obtains the glycerol and fatty acids from metabolic fragments derived from glucose or from certain amino acids, subsequent to deamination (Fig. 8-10). Thus it is common knowledge that an animal can "get fat" by overeating not only fatty foods, but carbohydrate and protein foods as well.

Starting with organic precursors, animals generally can synthesize various other substances, including **hormones** (Chap. 22), which may be important in particular cases. *But no animal can synthesize its own vitamin requirements.* Consequently the vitamin compounds must be present, as such, in the daily diet (Chap. 18). The initial synthesis of vitamins occurs in plants, and this is another instance of the dependence of animals upon the synthetic capacities of plants.

The growth of protoplasm implies more than the synthesis or direct acquisition of essential component substances. The substances must be organized and oriented in relation to the protoplasmic structure—a process that is vaguely referred to as assimilation. Also there are **trace elements,** particularly copper, manganese, and cobalt, which must be present, even though in exceedingly small amounts. Apparently these metals serve as specific activators in certain of the enzyme systems of the cell.

Destructive Metabolism. The principal organic substances absorbed by animal cells are simple sugars, glycerol, fatty acids, and the amino acids. All these are high-potential compounds, capable of liberating considerable energy (p. 81). The decomposition of organic compounds in the protoplasm involves a variety of chemical processes as, step by step, energy is liberated for the use of the cell. Finally, when the catabolism of the organic compound is completed, it has been decomposed into simple, mainly inorganic, end products—and a certain quantity of energy has been made available to the protoplasm. Carbohydrates and fats, as previously stated, yield energy amounting to 4 and 9 Cal per gram, respectively, and the end products of carbohydrate and fat catabolism are solely carbon dioxide and water. Proteins (and amino acids), like carbohydrates, yield approximately 4 Cal per gram of energy, when completely catabolized. The end products of protein catabolism, however, in addition to carbon dioxide and water, include simple nitrogenous compounds, such as ammonium salts and urea (from the amino fractions, pp. 84 and 342), as well as sulfate and phosphate salts (from the sulfur- and phosphorus-containing proteins).

Many aspects of metabolism are similar in the cells of animals, plants, and other organisms generally, and these *basic patterns of* **cellular metabolism** will be considered separately, in Chapter 8. **Deamination reactions,** however, are particularly characteristic of animal cells, because these cells often absorb a greater quantity of amino acids than they need for protein synthesis.

Deamination. The most important usage of amino acids in each cell is for the synthesis of its own essential protein structures. But animals also derive energy from amino acids, if the quantity absorbed exceeds the constructive requirements.

This catabolism of amino acids in animal cells is achieved mainly by a series of oxidation reactions. Before oxidation occurs, however, the amino fraction is split off from each amino acid molecule. In man and certain other higher animals, such **deaminations** lead to the formation of **urea,** a very important **nitrogenous waste** (see p. 342). But in most lower animals, ammonia (or ammonium salts) results from deamination, and this inorganic end product becomes the chief nitrogenous waste.

The process of deamination is not identical in all cells, as is shown by the behavior of the enzymes (deaminases) extracted from different tissues. Frequently, however, deamination represents an oxidative reaction in which one molecule of water participates and one molecule each of ammonia (NH_3) and of hydrogen peroxide (H_2O_2) are formed as by-products. This may be shown in the following equation:

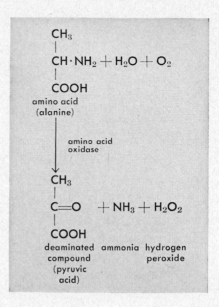

$$CH_3$$
$$|$$
$$CH \cdot NH_2 + H_2O + O_2$$
$$|$$
$$COOH$$

amino acid
(alanine)

amino acid oxidase

$$CH_3$$
$$|$$
$$C{=}O \quad + NH_3 + H_2O_2$$
$$|$$
$$COOH$$

deaminated   ammonia   hydrogen
compound   peroxide
(pyruvic
acid)

Neither the peroxide nor the ammonia produced in such deaminations ever accumulates to toxic levels in the protoplasm. The disposal of the peroxide as it forms is effected by **catalase,** which catalyzes the liberation of free oxygen (see p. 99). The ammonia quickly is bound, forming ammonium salts (for example, NH_4HCO_3), which are the chief nitrogenous wastes of lower organisms.

In man and other animals, another method of deamination (see p. 341) is employed, and the main nitrogenous waste resulting from the catabolism of the amino acids is **urea** (p. 342). This *odorless, white, crystalline* **solid** is very soluble in water, and may reach fairly high concentrations in the urine, especially when the diet is rich in protein foods.

Hydrolysis. **Hydrolytic reactions** (p. 89) occur frequently in catabolism. Hydrolyses are important in the mobilization of glucose from the glycogen reserves of the cell, and in the splitting of stored fat into glycerol and fatty acids, as a prelude to the oxidation of these products. Proteins, once formed in a cell, are seldom hydrolyzed; that is, animal cells normally sacrifice only *excesses* of *absorbed* amino acids to meet their energy requirements. But during **starvation,** when all reserves of carbohydrate and fat have been exhausted, cells may hydrolyze their structural proteins and use the resulting amino acids for energy. This, however, is only a stopgap procedure. If it continues very long the living structure will be destroyed beyond repair, and the cell is bound to die.

SUMMARY

The enzyme system evolved by typical animals is not capable of synthesizing proteins, carbohydrates, and the other organic components of protoplasm *solely* from inorganic substances. Therefore, animals must obtain a constant supply of preformed organic foods, particularly the essential amino acids, vitamins, and adequate amounts of organic fuel substances if they are to grow—or even if they are to maintain normal structure and activity. Such organic substances are abundant only in the bodies and remnants of other organisms, and therefore animals must resort to a predatory sort of life. An animal must possess well-developed sensory, nervous, and locomotor faculties, to find and apprehend its foods. And since the bulk of available organic foods exists in colloidal form (proteins, complex carbohydrates, and fats) the animal must have a digestive system in which to prepare the food compounds for absorption.

The *ultimate source of all energy in the animal body* is the potential *energy of organic compounds,* which are absorbed as such by the protoplasm. If destructive metabolism is suspended, all the more obvious movements and activities of the cells come to a halt, and all constructive metabolism also ceases. The various synthetic reactions in the animal cell, being all endothermic in nature, depend upon catabolic reactions for the energy that makes them proceed. As a whole, therefore, the *metabolism of the animal is destructive* in character. Inevitably *animal metabolism results in a diminution of the quantity of organic matter* available in the environment. Even the *growth* of an animal sacrifices part of the existing supply of organic matter. Preceding or accompanying each upward step there must be a slightly larger downward step. Part of the original quantity of organic matter must be degraded to the inorganic level in order to supply energy needed for raising the remaining part to a higher level of structural complexity. The few pounds or ounces gained by an animal in growing to maturity are obtained at the expense of a much greater quantity of organic matter. The smaller part of this material provides matter and energy for the synthesis of new components of the protoplasm as the body becomes larger; but the greater part is sacrificed in providing energy for finding, ingesting, digesting, absorbing, and distributing the foods, and for disposing of the waste products after they are formed within the cells.

The following chapters will show that the metabolism of animals is complementary in many ways to the metabolism of plants. As a whole the *metabolism of plants is constructive,* so that it *replenishes the organic matter of the earth.* This unique characteristic of plants depends upon their ability to draw upon the energy of sunlight in supporting their constructive metabolism. In short, it is the possession of a different set of enzymes, among which the green pigment **chlorophyll** is the keystone, that enables plants to base their metabolism entirely upon inorganic forms of matter.

140 - The Cell

TEST QUESTIONS

1. Define each term in such a way that it will apply to the nutrition of man *and* the amoeba: (a) ingestion; (b) digestion; (c) egestion; (d) absorption; (e) distribution; (f) metabolism; (g) excretion; (h) respiration.
2. Define the term "food"; explain why glucose is considered as a food among animals, but not among plants.
3. How would you account for the fact that a digestive system is generally found in animals, but not in plants?
4. Explain the similarities and differences between the amoeba and paramecium, in regard to: (a) ingestion; and (b) egestion.
5. Clearly distinguish between egestive and excretory wastes: (a) in animals generally; (b) in an amoeba; and (c) in man.
6. *Chemically* speaking, what is the nature of digestion? Specify the end products resulting from the digestion of: (a) starch; (b) protein; (c) fat; (d) sucrose; and (e) maltose.
7. The absorption of glucose (and the other end products of digestion) proceeds, partly at least, by diffusion. Carefully explain.
8. In the amoeba, respiration is a diffusional phenomenon. Explain in detail.
9. To what extent (if any) does the passage of substances into the contractile vacuole of an amoeba proceed on an osmotic basis? Explain carefully.
10. Distinguish between constructive and destructive metabolism, using the terms exothermic, endothermic, decomposition, and synthesis.
11. Discuss the role of DNA in relation to the synthesis of protein in the cell.
12. Explain the role of RNA in relation to protein synthesis.
13. Differentiate between transport and template RNA, on the basis of molecular weight, localization in the cytoplasm, and functional role.
14. Explain why protein specificity is of paramount importance in every cell.
15. Specify one source of energy utilized by cells for protein synthesis.
16. Define the term *amino acid activating enzyme*. How many such enzymes would you expect to find in any cell?
17. Specify the most direct method used by animals in synthesizing: (a) polysaccharides; (b) fats; and (c) proteins.
18. Are there any indirect methods by which an animal can synthesize: (a) polysaccharides; and (b) fats? Explain carefully.

FURTHER READINGS

1. "How Cells Make Molecules," by V. G. Allfrey and A. E. Mirsky, in "The Living Cell," special issue of *Scientific American,* September 1961.
2. *Molecular Basis of Evolution,* by C. B. Anfinsen; New York, 1959.
3. *Dynamic Aspects of Biochemistry,* 3d ed., by E. Baldwin; New York, 1957.
4. *Genes, Enzymes, and Inherited Diseases,* by H. E. Sutton; New York, 1961.

8—*Common Pathways of Cellular Metabolism*

SINCE World War II, when radioactive carbon (C^{14}), radioactive phosphorus (P^{32}), heavy oxygen (O^{18}), and other distinctively labeled atoms began to be available for "tagging" organic molecules, biochemists have succeeded more and more in unraveling the complexities of intermediary metabolism in many kinds of cells. Much was known previously about the initial and the final products of metabolism; but now many of the intermediary products are coming into focus. Intermediary metabolism, to be sure, is a difficult field, which extends beyond the scope of general biology. However, some general aspects of the field are very important and these must be considered.

One broad conclusion seems inescapable. Cells generally, regardless of type, display a number of basic patterns of metabolism that are common to them all. Bacteria, yeasts, and molds, and the cells of animals and plants —both simple and complex—all possess certain sets of enzymes, which determine the basic pathways of their metabolism. There are, of course, a number of metabolic differences, which distinctively characterize the cells of typical animals, plants, and other organisms, but these differences are superimposed upon a basic pattern that seems to be common to all protoplasm. Perhaps this indicates that organisms generally have had a common evolutionary origin. At least it seems unlikely that the same systems could have arisen independently in so many different types of living things.

ISOTOPE METHODS

Each of the isotopes of a particular atom possesses an identical system of planetary electrons but a different atomic center. Usually the isotopic center is heavier, owing to the presence of one or more supernumerary neutrons (Fig. 8-1). In the case of hydrogen, for example, the dominant form in nature, which may be specified as H^1, has a single proton and no neutrons in the center (Fig. 8-1). **Deuterium,** or heavy hydrogen (H^2), in contrast, has a neutron in addition to the proton; whereas **tritium** (H^3) has two neutrons, as is shown in Figure 8 1. But since the planetary system of the atom and its isotopes is identical, the chemical behavior is the same. Consequently, if heavy hydrogen (H^2), or radiocarbon (C^{14}), or any other isotope is built into the structure of an organic compound, the metabolic fate of the compound should not be changed; this prediction has been substantiated in a great many experiments, with very rare, not entirely unequivocal, exceptions.

Isotopes are most valuable for tagging and tracing molecules as they pass through the vortex of metabolic change within the cell. The isotopic compound and its derivatives can be identified and localized by a variety of physical methods. Some isotopes, such as H^3, C^{14}, and P^{32} (Table 8-1), are unstable and these emit radiation as the atomic centers disintegrate. Such isotopes and their derivatives, therefore, can be localized when a section of the cell containing them is brought into contact with a sensitive photographic plate, as was mentioned previously (p. 21); or they

may be followed by means of radiation meters, such as a **Geiger counter.** Stable, nonradioactive isotopes, such as O^{18} or N^{15} (Table 8-1), can also be traced by means of a **mass spectrometer,** owing to the fact that the atomic mass of the isotope differs from that of the common element. Regardless of detail, however, it is gratifying to know that part of the research in the field of atomic energy has been diverted into significant peace-time channels.

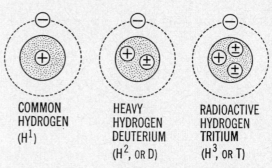

COMMON HYDROGEN (H^1) HEAVY HYDROGEN DEUTERIUM (H^2, OR D) RADIOACTIVE HYDROGEN TRITIUM (H^3, OR T)

Fig. 8-1. An atom and its isotopes possess identical planetary electron systems. Therefore they display an identical *chemical* behavior. Differences in the atomic centers, however, permit the element and its isotopes to be distinguished on the basis of weight, radioactivity, or other physical properties. Symbols: −, electron; +, proton; ±, neutron.

Table 8-1—Isotopes Useful as Metabolic Tracers

Symbol	Half-Life * (if radioactive)	Principal Field of Use
H^2	nonradioactive	Research on water exchanges; general metabolism
H^3	12.1 years	Localization of metabolic activity
C^{14}	5568 years	General metabolism
N^{15}	nonradioactive	Metabolism of proteins, nucleic acids, etc.
O^{18}	nonradioactive	Biological oxidations, photosynthesis, etc.
P^{32}	14.3 days	Metabolism of ATP, nucleic acids, carbohydrates, etc.
S^{35}	87.1 days	Coenzyme A activity; protein metabolism
Fe^{55}	2.9 years	Activity of cytochromes, hemoglobin, etc.
I^{131}	8 days	Functioning of thyroid gland and hormone
Ca^{45}	180 days	Calcification reactions; ionic activities of calcium
Na^{24}; K^{42}	14.8; 12.4 hours	Active transport mechanisms
Cl^{38}	37 minutes	Cell permeability, etc.

* As the name implies, the half-life of a radioactive isotope specifies the time required for half of the radioactivity of a given sample to be dissipated.

ENERGY TRANSFORMATIONS IN THE CELL

The cell, of course, must have a source of energy for supporting not only its movements, active transport processes, electrical activities, and so forth, but also the constructive phases of its metabolism. One major source, which is available to every cell, is the energy content of organic molecules present in the protoplasm. Generally speaking, the energy content of an organic molecule is much higher than that of the inorganic end products of its catabolism. Moreover, the larger and more complex the molecule, the greater is its fund of potentially available energy. All cells derive energy through catabolism. In addition, the cells of green plants and autotrophic (p. 182) organisms generally can utilize other forms of energy for the replenishment of their organic fuels; but even these cells depend upon organic molecules for current, moment to moment, expenditures. An important area of intermediary metabolism, therefore, deals with the step-by-step breakdown of organic molecules and the manner in which the cell derives energy at each step of this downward path. Some of the energy liberated in catabolism may be utilized for constructive purposes, however. In fact catabolism and anabolism in the cell are intricately interwoven and beautifully integrated.

It is important to realize that the same **thermodynamic laws** govern all chemical and physical reactions, whether they occur inside or outside of the cell. According to the **first law,** the sum of mass and energy remains constant as any reaction proceeds. Significant mass changes do not occur in biological systems, however, and therefore the first law, in essence, states that energy does not diminish or increase. But there are two general forms of energy; **free energy**—free in the sense that this energy is *available for* the performance of *work*—and dissipated energy, or **entropy,** which is not available for work. The **second law** of thermodynamics states that during any reaction in which energy is being trans-formed there is always some *loss of free energy*. In other words, *the entropy of a system tends to increase*. This means, of course, that no energy transaction can be 100 percent efficient—whether it is carried out by the cell for the performance of its work, or by an engineer in operating an engine. Some energy is dissipated, usually in the form of heat, which is lost to the environment. The cell, nevertheless, is a chemical machine that operates with remarkable efficiency. In transferring the energy liberated during the oxidation of carbohydrate fuel (glucose) to the **high-energy phosphate reserves** (p. 144) of the cell, more than 50 percent of the available free energy may be conserved. Yet engineers have not been able to devise a steam engine that can transform more than 30 percent of the combustion heat into useful mechanical work.

High-Energy Phosphate Compounds; Adenosine Triphosphate (ATP). Many cellular activities—the beating of cilia, the twitching of muscle, the electrical discharges at cell surfaces, and so forth—are very rapid. They require an almost instantaneous mobilization of energy. A natural question is therefore: how do cells develop energy so quickly?

Previously it was thought that cells get quick energy directly from the oxidation of glucose and other fuels. Now, however, it is known that oxidations are more concerned with storing energy in a form that is ready for instantaneous use. Certain compounds are used as repositories for this stored energy. Especially significant in this regard is a group of **high-energy phosphate molecules.** And chief among the high-energy phosphates is **adenosine triphosphate,** or **ATP** (see p. 90).

ATP and other high-energy phosphate compounds possess a unique distinction. All possess one or more special chemical structures, called **high-energy phosphate bonds.** Ordinary phosphate bonds, like that of glucose-phosphate, represent the binding of considerable energy (about 2 Cal per gram molecule). But high-energy phosphate bonds, for which a special symbol ($\sim$) has been devised, represent the binding of a *much greater amount*. In fact, the high-energy phosphate bond holds some *four times* more energy, or about 8 Cal per gram molecule.

Thus if we write:

Adenosine Monophosphate (AMP)
(Adenosine—Phosphate)

it indicates that the compound AMP possesses just an ordinary phosphate bond; whereas if we write:

Adenosine Diphosphate (ADP)
(Adenosine—Phosphate~Phosphate)

it indicates that ADP has *one energy-rich* bond, in addition to the ordinary one; and if we write:

Adenosine Triphosphate (ATP)
(Adenosine—Phosphate~Phosphate~Phosphate)

it shows that ATP has *two high-energy bonds,* as well as one ordinary linkage.

The ATP accumulations of a cell represent a very important fund of quickly available energy which can be used for a wide variety of purposes. When needed, the energy is liberated by the splitting of the high-energy bonds. This is a hydrolysis reaction. It requires an appropriate enzyme (an ATP-ase); and it produces one molecule of inorganic phosphate for each of the energy-rich bonds that is broken. It may be written:

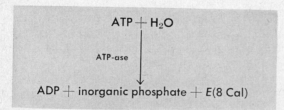

$$ATP + H_2O$$
$$\xrightarrow{\text{ATP-ase}}$$
$$ADP + \text{inorganic phosphate} + E(8\ Cal)$$

Fritz A. Lipmann, working at Harvard University, shared a Nobel Prize (1953) partly on the basis of his pioneer work on the energy-rich bonds of ATP; and since then the importance of the ATP system has been demonstrated in many kinds of cells. It now is known that ATP provides energy for such diverse cellular activities as muscle contraction, ciliary beating, amoeboid movement, bioluminescence, and cell division. But equally important, ATP provides energy for synthesizing complex organic compounds, and it serves to spark a number of important catabolic reactions. Moreover, many metabolic activities are mainly concerned with restoring, maintaining, and expanding the intracellular reserves of ATP.

Oxidative Metabolism. The over-all oxidation of an organic compound such as glucose may be stated very simply, by specifying the initial and end products of the reaction for example:

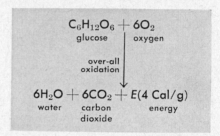

$$\underset{\text{glucose}}{C_6H_{12}O_6} + \underset{\text{oxygen}}{6O_2}$$
$$\xrightarrow{\text{over-all oxidation}}$$
$$\underset{\text{water}}{6H_2O} + \underset{\substack{\text{carbon}\\\text{dioxide}}}{6CO_2} + \underset{\text{energy}}{E(4\ Cal/g)}$$

But such an equation merely shows that, when the oxidation is complete, all the hydrogen of the original compound has united with oxygen, forming water, and all the carbon has been liberated as carbon dioxide. Nothing is shown of the complex intermediary stages. In the cell, however, these intermediary metabolic reactions are of great importance. Each step liberates a certain quantity of energy, which must not be wasted. Frequently these bursts of energy go into the formation of energy-rich phosphate bonds and thus they maintain the energy reserves of the cell; or they may assist in the synthesis of other compounds.

Biological Oxidation: an Oxidation-Reduction Series. Fundamentally, when a substance undergoes **oxidation**, it *loses one or more* of its *electrons*. Such electrons do not remain free, however. Instantaneously they are picked up, or *gained,* by some other substance; and this process of *gaining electrons* is called **reduction**. Consequently, each oxidation must occur concomitantly with an equivalent reduction. What we commonly call an oxidation is, therefore, essentially an **oxidation-reduction reaction.**

The oxidation of hydrogen (H_2) will serve as an example. In uniting with oxygen (O_2), each hydrogen atom loses one electron and each oxygen atom gains two, thus forming the compound H_2O. In essence, therefore, while the hydrogen is being oxidized, the oxygen is simultaneously being reduced.

Oxygen, however, is not the only substance in the cell that is able to accept, or gain, electrons—thus to act as an oxidizing agent. Eventually, the electrons given up while various organic substances are undergoing oxidative metabolism are delivered to oxygen. But meanwhile, the electrons are passed serially from one organic acceptor to another and the cell derives useful energy at virtually every step.

The tendency of a substance to be oxidized —that is, to yield up electrons—can be measured by bringing a solution of the substance into contact with an electrode that has a standardized potential for giving up or taking on electrons. By such measurements the oxidation-reduction potential of a particular substance may be specified. Thus it has been found that the total flow of electrons from compound to compound in the cell is always downhill—from compounds of higher to compounds of lower potential. There is an ever-flowing cascade of electrons that continues to liberate energy, and much of this energy goes to maintain and expand the high-energy phosphate reserves of the cell. Accordingly, oxidative metabolism, in large measure, may be described as **oxidative phosphorylation.**

It is important to realize that in giving up an electron an organic compound likewise tends to give up hydrogen: the hydrogen that previously was bonded to the molecule by the now missing electron. Thus biological oxidations usually involve **dehydrogenation.** Furthermore, the electron acceptor compound likewise serves, at least usually, as a **hydrogen acceptor,** and there are a number of important **acceptor compounds** in every cell (below). Many biological oxidations, accordingly, are dehydrogenation reactions, and a variety of specific enzymes, the **dehydrogenases,** are present in every cell. In accepting hydrogen, along with one or more electrons, the acceptor becomes reduced, as is shown in Figures 8-2 and 8-3.

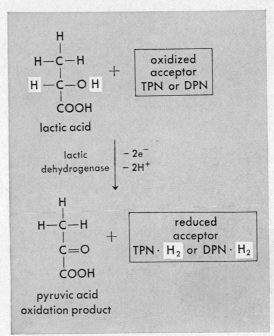

Fig. 8-2. Certain dehydrogenases (e.g., lactic dehydrogenase) act only upon substrates possessing a particular molecular configuration, namely H—C—OH. This group transmits electrons (and hydrogen) mainly to DPN or TPN (p. 145). **Pyruvic acid,** the oxidation product, is a very important intermediary metabolic derivative (see Figs. 8-5 and 8-7). Above reaction, in reverse, represents a reduction, rather than an oxidation.

Primary Acceptors of the Cell. The primary oxidizing agents in the cell—that is, substances that pick up electrons and hydrogen as these are discharged from various catabolizing substrates—are a group of four important nucleotides: (1) **Diphosphopyridine Nucleotide (DPN)**; (2) **Triphosphopyridine Nucleotide (TPN)**; (3) **Flavin Adenine Dinucleotide (FAD)**; and (4) **Flavin Mononu-**

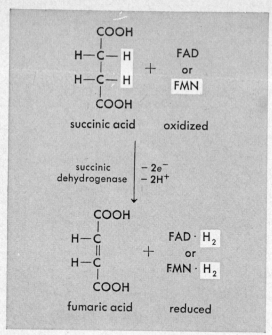

COOH
|
H—C—H
| + FAD or FMN
H—C—H
|
COOH

succinic acid   oxidized

succinic dehydrogenase   − 2e⁻
                          − 2H⁺

COOH
|
H—C
‖   + FAD · H₂ or FMN · H₂
H—C
|
COOH

fumaric acid   reduced

Fig. 8-3. Another group of dehydrogenases, here represented by succinic dehydrogenase, acts only upon substrates possessing the molecular configuration

$$H—\underset{|}{C}—H$$
$$H—\underset{|}{C}—H$$

This group performs most of its transactions with FAD or FMN (p. 147).

cleotide (FMN). In each of these molecules one of the B vitamins (p. 348) is represented: **niacin** (in DPN and TPN) and **riboflavin** (in FAD and FMN).

In essence, the acceptor nucleotides serve as **cofactors,** acting in conjunction with the dehydrogenase enzymes of the cell. Each fulfills its role by alternately undergoing reduction and oxidation in a continually repeating fashion. The electrons (and hydrogen) received from a substrate are continually passed on from one acceptor to another of lower potential, and the energy liberated by each transaction is conserved by the cell in the form of newly formed high-energy phosphate bonds (Fig. 8-4).

The dehydrogenases are quite specific—not only in reference to the molecular configuration of the substrate, but also in regard to the acceptor nucleotide to which a transfer of electrons and hydrogen can be made. Some (for example, *lactic dehydrogenase,* Fig. 8-2) require one type of configuration, namely

$$H—\underset{|}{C}—OH,$$ and this group of enzymes transacts business mainly with the pyridine nucleotides (DPN and TPN). But another group, represented by succinic dehydrogenase (Fig. 8-3), requires substrates of different configuration,

$$H—\underset{|}{C}—H$$
$$H—\underset{|}{C}—H$$

, and these enzymes generally employ one of the flavin nucleotides (FAD or FMN) as an electron-hydrogen accepting agency. Finally, it should be noted that the pyridine acceptors (DPN and TPN) generally transmit their electrons (and hydrogen) to the flavin acceptors (FAD and FMN)—as is shown in Figure 8-4.

The Cytochromes: a Secondary Electron-Hydrogen Transmitting System. To a very limited extent the flavin acceptors can transmit hydrogen directly to molecular oxygen.[1] This relatively unimportant pathway leads to the production of hydrogen peroxide (H_2O_2), which is catabolized through the agency of **catalase** (p. 100).

By far the greater flow electrons, however, passes into the **cytochrome system** (Fig. 8-4). This important electron-hydrogen transmitting mechanism, first studied by the great English biochemist, David Keilin, of Cambridge University, consists mainly of a series of hemoprotein (p. 321) enzymes, although one of the more recently identified components (ubiquinone) is not an iron (Fe) compound. Each successive member of the series (Fig. 8-4) displays a greater tendency to accept electrons. Thus, as electrons drop from level to level in this cascading system, energy is generated and utilized for building up the high-energy phosphate (ATP) reserves of the

[1] Enzymes that catalyze a direct transfer of electrons and hydrogen to oxygen are called **oxidases,** rather than dehydrogenases. Here, either FAD oxidase or FMN oxidase would be involved.

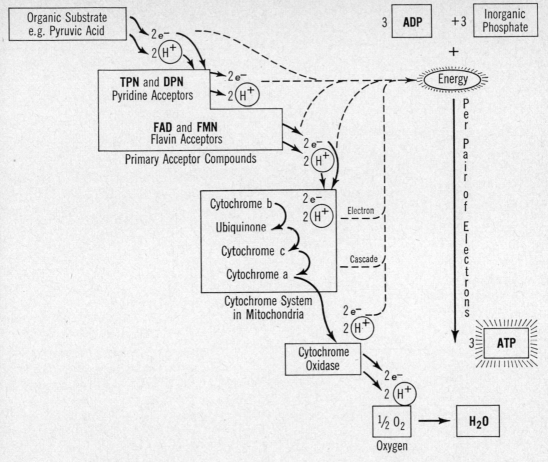

Fig. 8-4. Electron-hydrogen transmission during oxidative phosphorylation. Each time an electron (and hydrogen) passes from higher to lower level, the oxidation energy is conserved and stored—mainly in the form of high-energy phosphate (ATP).

cell (Fig. 8-4). At the very end, of course, the electron-hydrogen pairs are passed on to oxygen, forming water as the end product. This final direct oxidation cannot occur, however, in the absence of another enzyme,[2] **cytochrome oxidase** (Fig. 8-4).

It is difficult to see how such an orderly electron transmission system could operate unless the component enzymes were built into the structure of the cell in a very precisely patterned fashion. Therefore it is not

[2] Cytochrome oxidase is extremely sensitive to inactivation by *cyanide (CN)* compounds. This sensitivity accounts for the remarkable potency of cyanide poisons in inducing death by asphyxiation in cells and organisms generally.

surprising to find that the *cytochrome system* and some of the other enzymes are *localized in the mitochondria,* presumably at fixed positions in the internal membranes of these complex structures (p. 27). Mitochondria prepared from disrupted cells—or even fragments of mitochondria—can still carry on oxidative phosphorylation, under the proper conditions. Such a preparation will continue to utilize oxygen and to build up ATP if provided with $DPN \cdot H_2$ (as an electron-hydrogen source), plus ADP and inorganic phosphate.

In essence the nature of the electron transfer process can be understood when it is realized that the cytochrome enzymes are

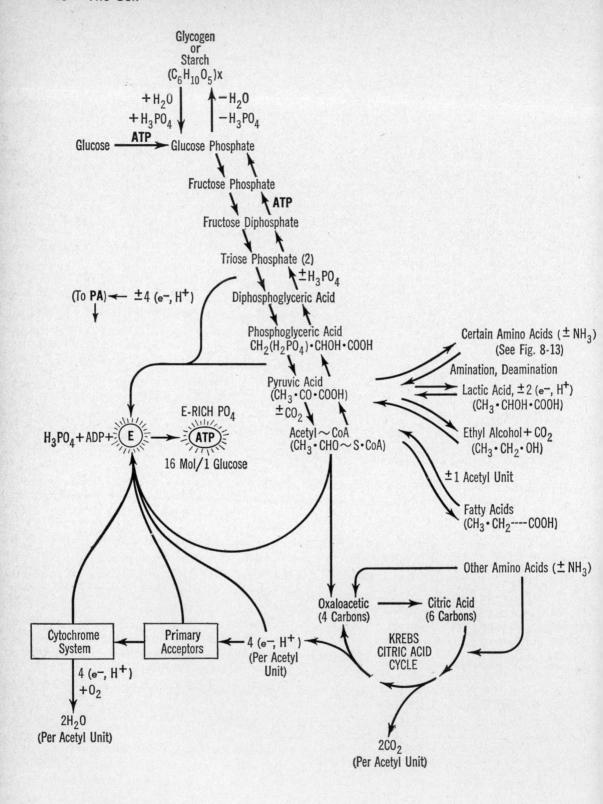

Glycogen
or
Starch
$(C_6H_{10}O_5)x$

$+H_2O$ $-H_2O$
$+H_3PO_4$ $-H_3PO_4$

Glucose —**ATP**→ Glucose Phosphate

Fructose Phosphate

ATP

Fructose Diphosphate

Triose Phosphate (2)

$\pm H_3PO_4$

(To **PA**) ← ± 4 (e−, H+)

Diphosphoglyceric Acid

Phosphoglyceric Acid
$CH_2(H_2PO_4) \cdot CHOH \cdot COOH$

Certain Amino Acids ($\pm NH_3$)
(See Fig. 8-13)

Amination, Deamination

Pyruvic Acid
$(CH_3 \cdot CO \cdot COOH)$
$\pm CO_2$

Lactic Acid, ± 2 (e−, H+)
$(CH_3 \cdot CHOH \cdot COOH)$

Ethyl Alcohol + CO_2
$(CH_3 \cdot CH_2 \cdot OH)$

E-RICH PO_4

$H_3PO_4 + ADP + $ (E) → (ATP)

16 Mol/1 Glucose

Acetyl ∼ CoA
$(CH_3 \cdot CHO \sim S \cdot CoA)$

± 1 Acetyl Unit

Fatty Acids
$(CH_3 \cdot CH_2 ---- COOH)$

Other Amino Acids ($\pm NH_3$)

Oxaloacetic
(4 Carbons) → Citric Acid
(6 Carbons)

Cytochrome
System ← Primary
Acceptors ← 4 (e−, H+)
(Per Acetyl
Unit)

KREBS
CITRIC ACID
CYCLE

4 (e−, H+)
$+O_2$

$2H_2O$
(Per Acetyl Unit)

$2CO_2$
(Per Acetyl Unit)

mainly heme compounds, in which an atom of iron (Fe) occupies an important position near the center of the molecule. In accepting an electron, the iron is shifted to the reduced (ferrous) state, Fe^{2+}; whereas in yielding up an electron it returns to the oxidized (ferric) state, Fe^{3+}. Thus we can represent the essential feature of these reversible oxidation-reduction reactions quite simply:

$$Fe^{3+} + 1e^- \rightleftarrows Fe^{2+}$$

The cytochromes change color as they alternately undergo reduction and oxidation. This is analogous to the darkening of the red blood pigment, **hemoglobin,** when it is reduced by lack of oxygen, as it is in venous blood. The intracellular color changes of the cytochromes are so faint, however, that their detection requires a **spectroscope.** If a spectroscope is directed upon a tissue that has been deprived of oxygen, the spectra of the reduced pigments are revealed. Then, when adequate oxygen is restored, the characteristic spectra of the oxidized cytochromes can be detected.

Although the quantity of primary acceptor compounds and cytochromes in a cell is small, the rapidity with which these agents keep shifting back and forth between the oxidized and reduced states provides for the delivery of considerable energy. An average man, for example, consumes about 260 cc of oxygen per minute, which represents the flow of some 2.8×10^{22} electrons in the given time. However, the voltage drop between the primary acceptors and oxygen is small (about 1.2 volts). Accordingly, it may be calculated that, on an average, the oxidative metabolism of a man generates energy at the rate of about 90 watts. This rate is roughly equivalent to the consumption of lamp bulbs commonly employed for household lighting.

OTHER METABOLIC PROCESSES

Oxidations and reductions, of course, do not by any means account for the complete metabolism of organic substrates in the cell. Now, therefore, we must consider some other important processes.

Phosphorylation and Related Processes. Although glucose is an excellent protoplasmic fuel, the glucose molecule must be activated before it is launched upon the metabolic stream. First it receives energy from ATP, undergoing **phosphorylation,** in the presence of the enzyme **glucokinase,** as may be indicated as follows:

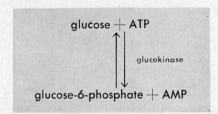

Fig. 8-5. *(facing).* Principal pathways of cellular metabolism. The path from glycogen (or glucose) to pyruvic acid (or lactic acid) is generally called **glycolysis;** whereas the similar route to ethyl alcohol is **fermentation—** both **anaerobic** processes. Note that the **acetyl CoA** complex stands at the crossroads where carbohydrate, protein, and fat metabolism interconnect with one another. Also note that free energy liberated by **oxidative metabolism,** mediated collectively by the enzymes of the Krebs cycle, the primary acceptors, and the cytochrome system, is conserved by a *build-up in the high energy phosphate* (ATP) *reserves of the cell.* In short, these phases of metabolism accomplish **oxidative phosphorylation.** Some intermediary steps, now well known, have been omitted from the diagram. Below the level of triose phosphate, only one of the two molecules derived from a glucose molecule has been followed. Actually, of course, two acetyl units are derived from each original molecule of glucose. Three formulas not given above are:

(1) Citric acid: $CH_2 \cdot COOH$
　　　|
　　$COH \cdot COOH$
　　　|
　　$CH_2 \cdot COOH$

(2) Oxaloacetic acid: $COH \cdot COOH$
　　　　　　　　‖
　　　　　　$CH \cdot COOH$

(3) Triose phosphate: $H_2C \cdot H_2PO_4$
　　　　　　　　|
　　　　　　$HCOH$
　　　　　　　　|
　　　　　　$HC{=}O$

But a second activation is also required. Quickly, in the presence of appropriate enzymes, the structural arrangement of glucose-6-phosphate changes to that of fructose-6-phosphate and a second phosphorylation, mediated by **fructokinase,** yields the very active compound **fructose diphosphate** (Fig. 8-5). Initially, therefore, the energy from 2 molecules of ATP is sacrificed for the initiation of carbohydrate catabolism. However, in the end, when this catabolism has run to completion, a generous recompense has occurred. In fact, the high-energy phosphate (ATP) reserves are considerably increased (Fig. 8-5).

In passing it should be noted that ATP also provides energy when the catabolism of fatty acids is initiated. In this case, however, the reactions are very complex. Suffice it to say that the long carbon chain of a fatty acid is made shorter and shorter by the breaking off of a series of 2-carbon (acetyl) units. These acetyl units are then passed on, one at a time, to the Krebs cycle (Fig. 8-5), for final oxidation.

Glycogen Synthesis and Glycolysis. In many cells, particularly in animals, some glucose is converted to glycogen, which represents a stable reserve of carbohydrate fuel. Each glycogen molecule is formed from many (up to 20,000) glucose units, which become chemically bonded into a single macromolecular structure, as is indicated in Figure 8-6.

In building glycogen, the cell starts with phosphorylated glucose. Many of the chemical bonds of the glycogen molecule (the 1-4 bonds of Fig. 8-6) are formed by dephosphorylation; the other (1-6) bonds are generated by the dehydration type of synthesis (p. 79).

Glycolysis may be defined as the partial catabolism of glycogen—down to the level of pyruvic acid or (in some cells) lactic acid (Fig. 8-5). This series of reactions generates only about 20 percent of the useful energy available from the total breakdown of carbohydrate. But no oxygen is required for gly-

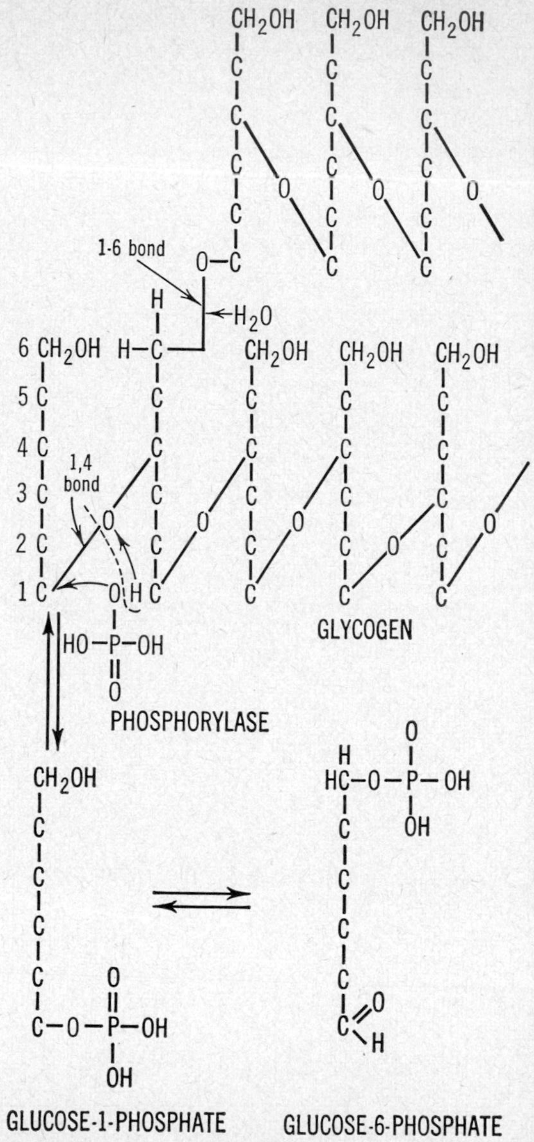

Fig. 8-6. Part of the macromolecular structure of **glycogen**; relation of glycogen to glucose phosphate. Note that the 1-4 bonds of glycogen are ruptured by **phosphorolysis**; whereas the 1-6 bonds are broken by **hydrolysis**.

colysis. Consequently cells can utilize this source of energy under **anaerobic** conditions, in which oxygen is scarce or lacking. A hard-working muscle, for example, expends its high-energy phosphate reserves at a very rapid rate. Eventually, if adequate oxygen is available, the muscle uses oxidative metabolism for rebuilding its high-energy reserves (p. 147). Meanwhile, however, glycolysis provides energy more quickly, and this helps to prevent any very rapid depletion of phosphate reserves.

The first step in glycolysis is the liberation of many glucose-phosphate units as the bonds of the huge glycogen molecule are ruptured. As may be seen in Figure 8-6, part of this initial breakdown is hydrolytic, but a larger part is **phosphorolytic.** For the rupture of the 1-4 bonds of the glycogen structure the cell employs inorganic phosphate (H_3PO_4), rather than water (Fig. 8-6).

The further steps of glycolysis are quite complex and hence will not be explained in full detail. It should be noted, however, that the pathway of glycolysis has been thoroughly explored by the intensive investigations of many biochemists, in many countries.

In brief summary, glucose phosphate undergoes rearrangement and phosphorylation, forming fructose diphosphate, at the expense of one molecule of ATP (Fig. 8-5). But now energy begins to appear on the positive side of the ledger. Each molecule of fructose diphosphate fragments into two molecules of **triose phosphate** (Fig. 8-5). Each triose phosphate undergoes oxidation, gaining energy as it passes hydrogen to a primary acceptor (DPN). This energy goes into the formation of diphosphoglyceric acid, to which inorganic phosphate has been bonded (Fig. 8-5). The newly formed phosphate bond (in the diphosphoglyceric acid) is of the **high-energy** type. It is destined to be transferred to ADP —in the reaction that converts diphosphoglyceric to monophosphoglyceric acid (Fig. 8-5)—thus generating a new molecule of ATP. If we remember that *two* triose diphosphates were formed from each original glucose molecule, it is plain that two new molecules of ATP have now been formed, at the expense of the one molecule originally sacrificed. In short, energy from oxidation has been used to achieve high-energy phosphorylation.

Two additional high-energy bonds are still to be gained before glycolysis reaches the end point (pyruvic acid; Fig. 8-5). By a complex set of reactions (Fig. 8-7) phosphoglyceric acid is transformed into pyruvic acid, generating energy for the conversion of one molecule of ADP to ATP for each of the two reacting molecules. Thus there has been a net gain of 3 molecules of ATP for each glucose-phosphate unit consumed in glycolytic catabolism.

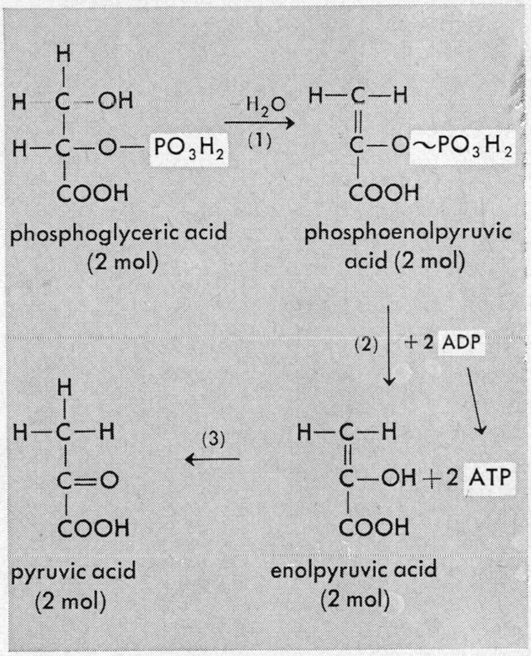

Fig. 8-7. Set of reactions that builds up the high-energy phosphate (ATP) reserves of the cell. Note that energy for building a new high energy bond ($\sim$) is provided by reaction 1 and that a transphosphorylation (reaction 2) shifts the high-energy phosphate to ADP, forming ATP. Enolpyruvic acid, being unstable, quickly passes to pyruvic (reaction 3).

The final end product of glycolysis as it occurs in a working muscle (p. 435) is lactic rather than pyruvic acid. The conversion of pyruvic to lactic acid, however, involves a relatively simple type of reaction, such as is shown by the equation on page 145.

Alcoholic Fermentation. Alcoholic fermentation is a process utilized by various yeast cells (p. 174) in obtaining energy under anaerobic conditions. Much of the pathway of fermentation—all the way down to pyruvic acid, in fact—is essentially the same as in glycolysis, except that fermentation ordinarily starts with glucose rather than with glycogen. Each molecule of the 3-carbon compound, pyruvic acid, then is degraded to the 2-carbon compound **ethyl alcohol**, by a complex **decarboxylation reaction**, which is shown in Figure 8-8. In fermentation, accordingly, each original glucose molecule gives rise to 2 molecules of alcohol ($CH_3 \cdot CH_2 \cdot OH$) and 2 molecules of carbon dioxide (CO_2); and in the process 2 molecules of ADP are transformed into ATP, at the expense of inorganic phosphate present in the cell.

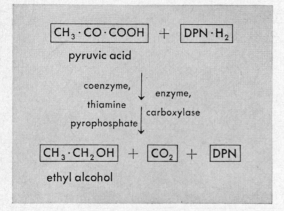

Fig. 8-8. Formation of *alcohol* from *pyruvic acid*, by decarboxylation. Double arrow indicates two-stage reaction; intermediary stages not shown. **Decarboxylation reactions** are very important in cellular metabolism generally.

Carboxylation and Decarboxylation. The complete catabolism of many organic substrates involves **decarboxylation** (Fig. 8-8). Thus the carbon chain of an organic molecule may be shortened not only by hydrolysis (or **phosphorolysis**) (Fig. 8-6) and by **fragmentation** (Fig. 8-5)—processes that break a molecule into fairly large pieces—but also by **decarboxylation** which shortens the chain just one carbon unit at a time. The cell contains a number of **carboxylases**, which catalyze the decarboxylation of various substrates. Also present are the necessary coenzymes,

especially **thiamine pyrophosphate**, which cooperate in such catalyses.

The importance of the carboxylases extends beyond catabolism, however, many of these enzymes can act *reversibly*. Thus they can bring about **carboxylation (carbon dioxide fixation)**, instead of decarboxylation (Fig. 8-9). Anabolically, therefore, the carboxylases enable the cell to lengthen the carbon chains of various organic substrates (Fig. 8-9).

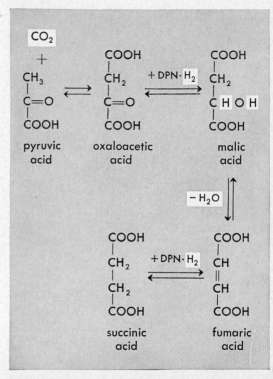

Fig. 8-9. Fixation of CO_2 **(carboxylation)**. Note that the 3-carbon compound, pyruvic acid, is converted into the 4-carbon compound, oxaloacetic acid. Reverse of this reaction, of course, is decarboxylation. Other reactions show interconversion of some common organic acids, by reduction (with $DPN \cdot H_2$) and by dehydration ($-H_2O$).

Amination and Deamination (Fig. 8–10). The primary and most important role fulfilled by amino acids is to provide components of protein structures (p. 134). However, some cells particularly animal cells, may absorb amino acids in excess of the requirements of protein synthesis. Such excesses may

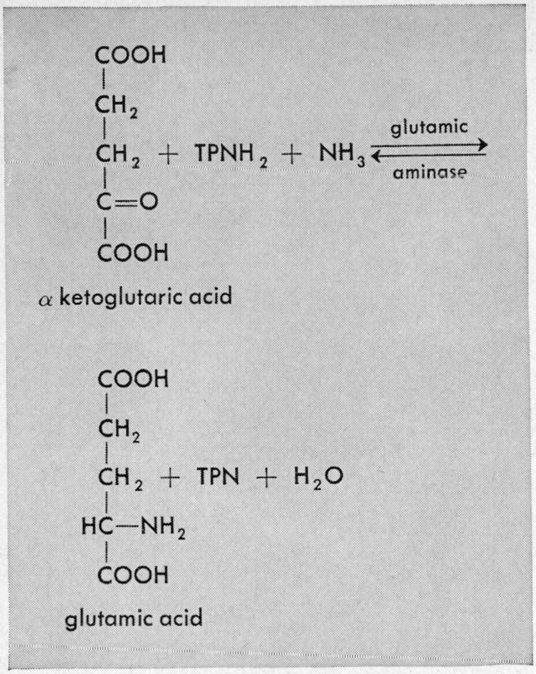

$$COOH$$
$$|$$
$$CH_2$$
$$|$$
$$CH_2 + TPNH_2 + NH_3 \underset{aminase}{\overset{glutamic}{\rightleftharpoons}}$$
$$|$$
$$C=O$$
$$|$$
$$COOH$$

α ketoglutaric acid

$$COOH$$
$$|$$
$$CH_2$$
$$|$$
$$CH_2 + TPN + H_2O$$
$$|$$
$$HC-NH_2$$
$$|$$
$$COOH$$

glutamic acid

Fig. 8-10. A typical **amination reaction.** The amino acid (glutamic acid) is formed from ammonia and an organic precursor (α-ketoglutaric acid). Plant cells can synthesize *all* the various amino acids in such fashion. Animal cells, however, can use this method only for the synthesis of the *"nonessential amino acids."*

be utilized as fuels. But as a prelude to such usage, the *amino group must be discharged* from the molecule (Fig. 8-10). The nonnitrogenous organic residuum of the molecule, possessing a carbon framework of varying length and structural complexity, is then launched upon metabolism. Either it may be catabolized, yielding a certain quantity of energy, or its molecular structure may be modified in such a way that it can be utilized by the cell for the synthesis of carbohydrate or lipid materials (Fig. 8-5).

Amination, the reverse of deamination (Fig. 8-10), is also very important. All cells can utilize inorganic nitrogen, in the form of ammonia (NH_3) or ammonium salts (for example, NH_4Cl), for the **amination** of certain organic derivatives of carbohydrate and lipid metabolism—as is indicated in Figure 8-5. Animal cells, however, are limited in

this regard. They are able to build up certain amino acids but not others. The amino acids of the latter group, which cannot be synthesized, are called the **essential amino acids** (p. 137). These units of protein structure must be obtained ready-made, or *preformed,* from the protein components of the animal's food.

The Krebs Cycle; Importance of Coenzyme A. A cycle of oxidation-reduction reactions, called the **Krebs cycle** (Fig. 8-5), occupies a very important central position in cellular metabolism. Another name for this cyclic series of reactions is the **citric acid cycle,** since citric acid, an important *6-carbon compound,* keeps appearing at the beginning and reappearing at the end of each complete "rotation" of the cycle. The Krebs cycle has also been called the *energy wheel of cellular metabolism.* It constantly generates new energy, conserved largely in the form of high-energy phosphate (ATP), so long as it keeps "turning." But equally important is the fact that the Krebs cycle deals not only with the metabolic derivatives of carbohydrate materials, but with the derivatives of proteins and lipids as well (Fig. 8-5). The separate parts of the cycle have been recognized for many years. However, in 1947, Hans A. Krebs, who later shared the 1953 Nobel Prize with Fritz Lipmann, first succeeded in demonstrating the nature and importance of the cycle as a whole.

Coenzyme A. This remarkably versatile cofactor (Fig. 8-11) plays a most important role. It serves to transmit a constant *flow of activated 2-carbon derivatives* (activated acetyl units) *into the Krebs cycle* (Fig. 8-5). The active 2-carbon derivative, transferred to the 4-carbon compound, **oxaloacetic acid,** produces the 6-carbon molecule, **citric acid—** which marks the beginning of a new cycle (Fig. 8-12).

A molecule of coenzyme A (Fig. 8-11) may be written, in abbreviation, as $CoA \cdot SH$, since it possesses a terminal sulfhydryl (—SH) group, in addition to its other constituents (adenine, pentose triphosphate,

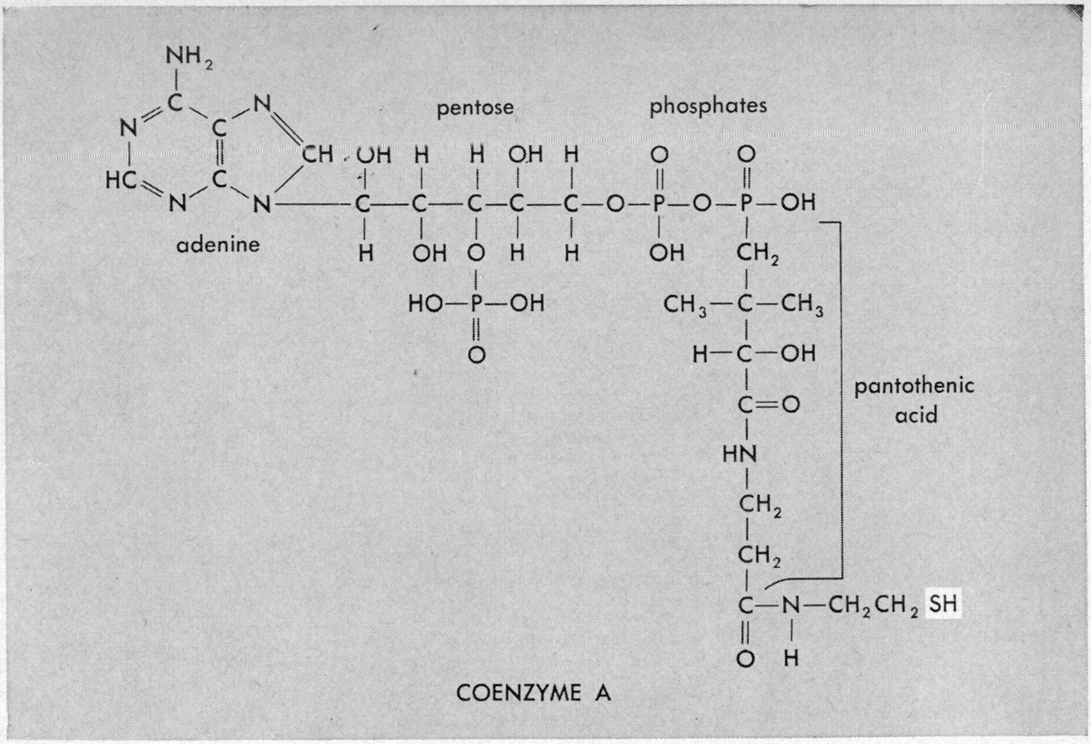

Fig. 8-11. Molecular structure of coenzyme A. Note the sulfhydryl (—SH) group and the vitamin (pantothenic acid), very important constituents of the CoA molecule.

and a vitamin, pantothenic acid). This terminal sulfur group is very active. In the series of reactions (Fig. 8-12) by which CoA·SH transmits 2-carbon acetyl units to the Krebs cycle, a **high-energy sulfur bond** is generated (Fig. 8-12). This bond conserves energy from the oxidative decarboxylation of pyruvic acid, and the energy is then utilized in launching activated acetyl units into the citric acid cycle. Moreover, CoA·SH is regenerated for further work each time such a transmission is completed (Fig. 8-12).

It should also be noted (Fig. 8-5) that the active acetyl units may originate not only from carbohydrate (via pyruvic acid) but also from the derivatives of fat and protein catabolism. Furthermore, since coenzyme A, under proper conditions, can act reversibly, it also can initiate the **synthesis** of protein, carbohydrate, and fatty compounds, from simpler intermediary metabolites (Fig. 8-5).

Essentially the Krebs cycle consists of a series of oxidation (dehydrogenation) and decarboxylation reactions by which the 6-carbon compound, *citric acid*, is *converted to* the 4-carbon compound, *oxaloacetic acid.* Then **acetylation** occurs and citric acid is regenerated once more. The intermediary compounds and reactions are now well known. They are very complex, however, and will not be considered in detail. For each acetyl unit ($CH_3·CHO$—), obviously, two decarboxylations must occur, and 2 pairs of electrons ($4e^- + 4H^+$) are passed over to the *primary acceptors* of the cell for final transmission through the *cytochrome system* (Figs. 8-4 and 8-5).

The quantity of useful energy generated by the Krebs cycle, working in conjunction with the primary acceptors and the cytochrome systems, is very impressive. Most of the energy is conserved by the cell in the form of high-energy phosphate (ATP), which stands ready for use when the cell must per-

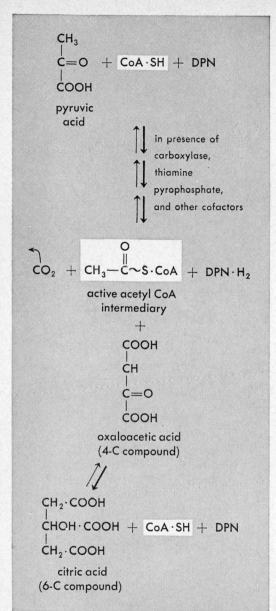

Fig. 8-12. Coenzyme A (CoA·SH) repeatedly transmits activated acetyl units to the Krebs cycle. This starts the cycle, converting oxaloacetic to citric acid (Fig. 8-5). As is shown in Figure 8-5, the acetyl constituent may come from the catabolism not only of carbohydrate, but also of protein and fat. Also note that there is a high-energy bond (~) in the acetyl-CoA complex and that CoA·SH keeps reappearing as the reaction continues.

form mechanical, osmotic, electrical, or other kinds of work, or when energy for

chemical synthesis is needed. Finally, when all the carbon of an original glucose molecule has been discharged as CO_2 and the hydrogen has been oxidized to H_2O, a total of 16 molecules of ADP have been charged with energy—that is, transformed into ATP.

Some of the Krebs cycle enzymes are localized in the mitochondrial membranes and others are associated with exceedingly fine particles, resolvable with the electron microscope, suspended in the mitochondrial cavities. Much remains to be learned, however, about the complex structural organization by which the intricately coupled reactions between the enzymes and coenzymes of the Krebs cycle and those of the primary acceptor and cytochrome systems are executed, integrated, and regulated, in subserving the needs of the cell.

SUMMARY

Catabolism provides the cell with energy as it follows a set of basic patterns that are generally similar in many (perhaps all) cells. Acetyl fragments and other units, derived from the breakdown of proteins, carbohydrates, and fats, are transmitted to the enzyme system of the Krebs cycle, mainly through the agency of coenzyme A (Fig. 8-13). In the Krebs cycle, a series of decarboxylation, oxidation, and acetylation reactions, operating in conjunction with the primary acceptors and cytochromes of the cell, gradually discharge the carbon of the original organic substrate in the form of CO_2 and the hydrogen in the form of H_2O. At almost every step of this delicately integrated series of reactions, energy is conserved by transmission to the high-energy phosphate (ATP) reserves of the cell.

This basic pattern is also very important from an anabolic point of view. High-energy phosphate reserves permit a cell to carry on energy-requiring (synthetic) reactions and thus to build up the macromolecular constituents of its structure. Many of the reactions of catabolism are reversible. The same

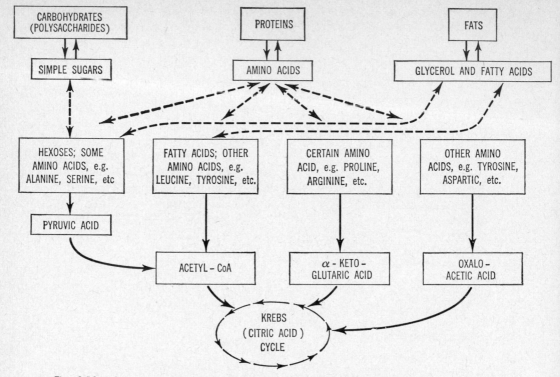

Fig. 8-13. Some major pathways of cellular metabolism. Schematic summary, after Krebs.

reactions, in reverse, can lead to synthesis, provided that a proper source of energy and precursory substances are on hand. The patterns of metabolism provide considerable facility for the interconversion of substrates —proteins into carbohydrates, carbohydrates into fats, and so forth. This is possible because the pathways of protein, carbohydrate, and fat metabolism join each other at a common cross road, provided by acetyl coenzyme A (Fig. 8-5). By **reverse pathways** material derived from one source (for example, protein) may be diverted into another (for example, carbohydrate), in such a manner that the cell has great flexibility in its utilization of different organic molecules.

TEST QUESTIONS

1. What important compounds are represented by the following symbols: ATP, ADP, and AMP? Specify the number (if any) of high-energy phosphate bonds that are present in each case.

2. How do high-energy phosphate bonds differ from ordinary phosphate linkages? What symbols are used to distinguish between the two types?

3. What type of chemical reaction is represented by the splitting of high-energy phosphate bonds? Give one such reaction.

4. Specify five different types of cellular activity that derive energy from the hydrolysis of ATP. What other cellular processes may be energized by ATP?

5. To what extent is it true that many catabolic reactions contribute energy toward maintaining the ATP reserves of the cell? Explain.

6. Differentiate between oxidation and reduction:
    a. in terms of the transfer of electrons
    b. in terms of hydrogen transfer

7. Provide an example to illustrate the fact that oxidations and reductions are inseparable, mutually dependent processes.

8. Under what circumstances will an oxidation-

reduction reaction occur spontaneously?

9. Give an example to illustrate the action of any dehydrogenase. Why are dehydrogenation reactions important in the cell?

10. Explain the term "primary acceptors." Specify four compounds in this category. Distinguish among these: (a) as to molecular structure; (b) as to vitamin constituents; and (c) as to recipients of their electron-hydrogen transmission.

11. Differentiate between oxidases and dehydrogenases.

12. Specify four components usually represented in the cytochrome system. Explain how the cytochrome system operates and why it is important in the cell.

13. Define the term "decarboxylation." Give a reaction that exemplifies this process. To what extent is decarboxylation involved in the catabolism of glucose?

14. Work out the reaction involved when lactic acid ($CH_3 \cdot CHOH \cdot COOH$) undergoes decarboxylation. Can you specify the organic compound produced by this reaction?

15. What is the opposite of decarboxylation? Explain the importance of carbon dioxide fixation.

16. Explain the term "glucose activation." What sort of reaction is involved in such activation? Does the cell gain or lose energy in such a transaction?

17. Differentiate among transphosphorylation, dephosphorylation and phosphorolysis. Give an example of each.

18. What is known about the chemical structure of coenzyme A? Evaluate the importance of coenzyme A in cellular metabolism generally.

19. Why is the Krebs cycle also designated: (a) as the citric acid cycle and (b) as the "energy wheel of cellular metabolism"?

20. What main types of metabolites are eventually catabolized in the Krebs cycle? What is the net result of this catabolism?

21. What are mitochondria and why are these cytoplasmic structures so important?

22. Sketch in the metabolic pathways by which many cells can convert:
    a. proteins (amino acids) into carbohydrates
    b. carbohydrates (glucose) into fats
    c. proteins into fats
    d. glucose into certain amino acids

23. Evaluate the contributions of Fritz Lipmann and Hans Krebs.

FURTHER READINGS

1. *Dynamic Aspects of Biochemistry*, 3d ed., by E. Baldwin; New York, 1957.

2. "The Metabolism of Fats," by D. E. Green, and "The Structure of Proteins," by Pauling, Corey, and Hayward, in *The Physics and Chemistry of Life*, a collection of articles from *Scientific American*; New York, 1955.

3. *Cellular Physiology and Biochemistry*, by W. D. McElroy; Englewood Cliffs, N. J., 1961.

4. "How Cells Transform Energy," by A. L. Lehninger, in "The Living Cell," special issue of *Scientific American*, September 1961.

9-*Nutrition of Green Plant Cells*

PHOTOSYNTHESIS is the cornerstone upon which green plants have built their mode of life. Possessing **chloroplasts,** typical plants are able to *use light energy* as a driving force for the *primary synthesis of organic matter.* Starting *entirely with inorganic materials*—water, carbon dioxide, and inorganic salts—green plants can synthesize all their needed carbohydrates, lipids, and proteins, as well as a rich variety of other organic compounds. In the last analysis photosynthesis accounts for the ultimate origin of virtually all organic matter. It is estimated, indeed, that the total synthesis of organic compounds by all the green plants of the world represents the utilization of more than a *billion tons of carbon every day.* These organic compounds, derived directly and indirectly from photosynthesis contain virtually all the energy that is available for the support of life upon this earth. This energy supports not only the life of the green plants themselves, but also that of animals and other organisms. Moreover,

photosynthesis maintains the free oxygen content of our atmosphere, which otherwise would tend to become exhausted.

MECHANISM OF PHOTOSYNTHESIS

Much of the **light energy** absorbed by the green parts of a plant is *utilized* for the **synthesis** of carbohydrate, particularly glucose. Thus the main pathway of photosynthesis, taken as an over-all process, can be stated very simply:

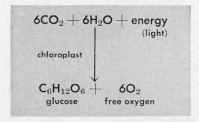

$$6CO_2 + 6H_2O + energy \text{ (light)}$$

chloroplast

$$C_6H_{12}O_6 + 6O_2$$
glucose   free oxygen

This equation, however, reveals almost nothing about the intrinsic mechanisms; nor does it show any of the very interesting inter-

158

mediary stages. Nevertheless it was many years before even this much information became available.

The first inkling that *photosynthesis liberates free oxygen* came in 1772, from the work of Priestley. Priestley showed that a mouse under a sealed bell jar can continue breathing more or less indefinitely, provided that a green plant is also placed under the jar. Within another ten years, Ingenhousz, a Dutch physician, had shown that *light must be available* if this experiment is to work, and that only the green parts of a plant are effective. In 1804 de Saussure found that the weight gained by a plant growing in a sealed atmosphere was distinctly greater than the weight of the carbon dioxide lost by the atmosphere. Thus de Saussure concluded that water (as well as carbon dioxide) must be an essential ingredient in the photosynthetic reaction. During the rest of the nineteenth century, the quantitative aspects of the overall reaction were established by the work of many investigators.

Chlorophyll and Chloroplasts. One of the most essential enzymes in photosynthesis is a **chlorophyll-protein** complex, which is often referred to, rather loosely, as **chlorophyll.** The nonprotein part, chlorophyll proper, which can be extracted from leaves by ether and similar solvents, proves to be a green pigment with a rather complicated molecular structure (Fig. 9-1). Structurally, the chlorophyll-protein complex tends to resemble hemoglobin, the red protein pigment of blood, except that a *magnesium,* rather than an iron, atom occupies a central position in the pigment part of the molecule; and attached peripherally there is a long-chain alcohol, **phytol.** In addition to chlorophyll, the cells of higher plants contain two other pigments: the deep orange **xanthophyll** (p. 596) and the bright yellow **carotene** (p. 350); and the cells of blue-green and red algae (p. 600) possess the accessory pigments **phycocyanin** and **phycoerythrin,** respectively. The accessory pigments of the algae probably participate directly in photo-

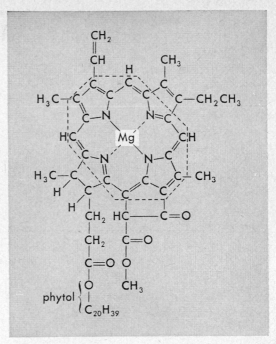

Fig. 9-1. Molecular structure of a chlorophyll (chlorophyll *a*). The "body" of this molecule (area enclosed by dotted line) is very similar to the heme part of a hemoglobin molecule. In hemoglobin, however, an atom of iron (Fe), rather than of magnesium (Mg), occupies the molecular center. Actually five kinds of chlorophyll, each differing slightly from the others, have been identified. These are specified as chlorophyll *a, b, c, d,* and *e,* respectively. Higher plants generally possess forms *a* and *b;* but lower plants often have the other forms.

synthesis, augmenting the activity of chlorophyll; but the role of such pigments in higher plants is not well understood.

The ordinary microscope shows that chlorophyll, in the typical plant cell, is not distributed evenly throughout the cytoplasm. Rather it is confined within one or more (usually about 30) rounded bodies, the **chloroplasts.** The electron microscope further shows that the chlorophyll is strictly localized even in the chloroplasts. All of it is contained within a number (usually about 50) of smaller bodies, called **grana,** which lie inside each chloroplast (Fig. 9-2). The chlorophyll is spread out into exceedingly thin, probably monomolecular, layers enclosed within the complexly folded membranes, or **lamellae,**

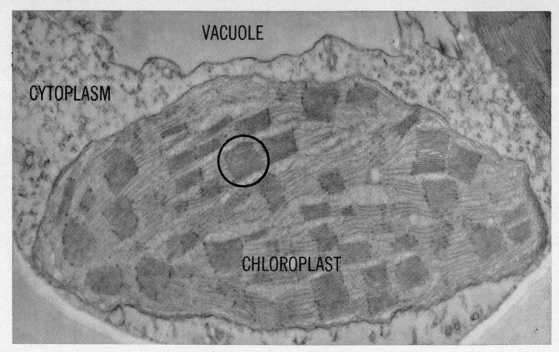

Fig. 9-2. Chloroplast of a corn plant: electronmicrograph with a total magnification of about 24,000. Chlorophyll is restricted to the **grana** (one granum encircled). The form of a granum, in three dimensions, is suggestive of a stack of coins. The several grana are suspended in the chloroplast by strands of material, called **stroma**. (Courtesy of A. E. Vatter, University of Colorado, Medical Center.)

of the granum (Fig. 9-3). Precise measurements of the thickness of each lamella and of the density of the components indicate that the layers of chlorophyll are regularly flanked

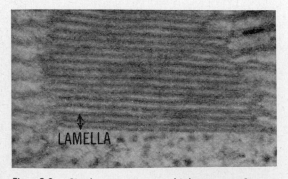

Fig. 9-3. Single granum at higher magnification (about 160,000). This reveals the **lamellar structure**. A thin layer of chlorophyll lies between the two membranes in each lamella, and the lamellar membranes appear to be made up of protein and lipid components. (Courtesy of A. E. Vatter, University of Colorado, Medical Center.)

by layers of protein and of a specialized lipid material. In any event, the fine structural organization of the grana and of the other parts of the chloroplast provides an amazingly effective molecular mechanism for utilizing light energy. This mechanism permits chlorophyll, working in partnership with various other enzymes and coenzymes, to transform and conserve light energy in the form of organic compounds newly synthesized from inorganic forms of matter.

Some Modern Developments. Since 1905, starting with the work of a British botanist, F. F. Blackman, it has been known that the synthesis of carbohydrates and other organic compounds by green plants must involve two separable kinds of reactions: (1) **light reactions,** an exceedingly rapid set of reactions that are *energized by light;* and (2) **dark reactions,** a series of slower reactions that can proceed in the absence of light. But truly impressive progress in the field of photosynthesis did not begin until about 1945, when two important isotopes, *heavy oxygen, O*^{18}, and *radioactive carbon,* C^{14}, had become available (Table 8-1). These tracer isotopes made it possible to discover the source of the oxygen that is liberated during photosynthesis and to follow the path of carbon, from the time it is absorbed in the form of CO$_2$, until it is incorporated into various organic compounds in the cell.

Much recent work has dealt with various unicellular green algae, which can be grown in test tubes under strictly controlled conditions; corroborative results have been obtained from higher plants. Moreover, Daniel Arnon, working at the University of California, has succeeded in observing photosynthesis in chloroplasts removed from the cells of macerated spinach leaves. Studies on such isolated chloroplasts have been very fruitful. The isolated chloroplasts carry on photosynthesis in a medium of known composition. Accordingly it is possible to vary the components of the medium in systematic fashion and thus to ascertain how each fulfills its role during the complex processes of photosynthesis.

The essence of photosynthesis, as deduced from the large body of recent evidence, is the conversion of radiant energy (light) into chemical energy. The conserved energy goes into the formation of: (1) ATP (from ADP and inorganic phosphate); and (2) **TPN·H$_2$**, FMN·H$_2$ and other *reduced* **primary acceptors** in the chloroplasts. Electrons, necessary for the reduction of the primary acceptors, are derived partly from chlorophyll and partly from water; and in each case the discharge of electrons is energized by light. Eventually many of the electrons flow back to the chlorophyll, restoring this unique molecule to its original uncharged state. But while the electrons are in flux, energy is generated and this is utilized for the build-up of the high-energy phosphate reserves of the cell. Equally important is the fact that H$_2$O, when it is forced to give off electrons, undergoes *photolysis.* This light-energized splitting of H$_2$O molecules liberates free O$_2$, while hydrogen (H$^+$) undergoes transmission to one of the primary acceptors of the cell (TPN $+ 2e^- + 2$H$^+ \rightarrow$ TPN·H$_2$). The net effect of light, accordingly, is to increase the reserves of chemical potential energy in the cell, mainly by the build-up of ATP and TPN·H$_2$.

The evidence that has led to this current view of how light energy is trapped and stored by the chloroplasts is very extensive. Outstanding contributions have been made by C. B. van Niel (Stanford University), S. Ruben, D. Arnon, and M. Calvin (University of California), H. Gaffron (University of Chicago), E. J. Rabinowitch (University of Illinois), S. Ochoa and W. Vishniac (New York University), and many others. This evidence will be presented in briefest outline only. But first it is necessary to consider some basic concept in **photochemistry.**

Photochemical reactions are those that are *energized by light.* To be effective, the light must be *absorbed* by one or more of the reacting substances; and, of course, chlorophyll is the principal light-absorbing molecule in the light-driven reactions of photosynthesis.

When light falls upon a metal, photons[1] (units of photoradiation) are absorbed and the electrons of the metal atoms, excited by the absorbed energy, tend to be ejected from the surface. The potential thus generated may be measured, as in a photographic light meter or other type of photoelectric cell. Likewise when photons are absorbed by a molecule, an electron in one or more of the constituent atoms, picking up energy, tends to shift outward from the atomic center into an orbit of higher potential. Such an excited electronic configuration is unstable, however. Within some fraction of a second, the electron either drops back into its original posi-

---

[1] A photon represents one quantum of light energy. Photons, however, vary in their energy content, according to the wavelength of the light. This is shown in the fundamental equation: $E = hc/\lambda$ in which $E =$ energy of the photon; $c =$ velocity of light in cm/sec; $\lambda =$ wavelength in millimicrons; and $h =$ the Planck energy frequency constant.

tion or *it may be transferred to an electron acceptor*—if such a molecule occupies a strategic position, in proximity to the locus of excitation. If no acceptor is present, the excitation energy returns to the environment, often in the form of re-emitted light, as in the case of substances that display fluorescence or phosphorescence subsequent to an exposure to light. But if an acceptor compound is on hand, the excitation energy is conserved as chemical energy.

The acceptor, after it has been reduced, possesses more energy than before. Chlorophyll, isolated from the cell in pure form, displays vigorous phosphorescence after it has been illuminated. But *in the chloroplast* the energy transformation is devoid of radiation and much of the energy is conserved as chemical potential energy for subsequent use by the cell.

As might be deduced from its color, chlorophyll displays a maximum absorption of light in the red-orange region of the spectrum. More specifically stated, the peak of absorption by chlorophyll is for photoradiations with wavelengths close to 660 millicrons ($m\mu$). The energy content of photons of this wavelength (43 Cal per mole of excited substrate) is not as great as for photons of shorter wavelength (for example, blue light: wavelength 440 $m\mu$; 64 Cal per mole of excited substrate). However, the photons absorbed by chlorophyll are exactly suited to the **excitation energy** requirements of this compound. Photons are units that must be used as a whole or not at all; and the photons absorbed by chlorophyll provide exactly the proper energy for the excitation of one electron per photon absorbed at the proper locus.

Photolysis of Water. A very important discovery was made by Samuel Ruben and co-workers at the University of California, in 1940, shortly after heavy oxygen (O^{18}) became available. Ruben showed that *all of the oxygen liberated in photosynthesis is derived from H_2O;* none of it from CO_2. Plant cells supplied with H_2O^{18} liberated O_2^{18}; but when the cells were supplied with CO_2^{18}, no heavy

oxygen was formed. Thus it can be said without equivocation that the **photochemical decomposition** of water (photolysis) accounts for the entire production of oxygen during photosynthesis. Part of the hydrogen, however, is transferred to a primary acceptor (TPN) during the process of photolysis, as is shown in Figure 9-4.

A major unsolved problem in photosynthesis is how light energizes the splitting of H_2O. Chlorophyll, TPN, and the cytochromes are essential components in the reaction, as has been shown by Arnon. But just how the photons absorbed by chlorophyll are employed to bring about a transfer of electrons from hydroxyl (OH^-) ions to the cytochrome system remains an open question (Fig. 9-4). It is plain, however, that four hydroxyl ions must be discharged of their electrons in the formation of each one molecule of oxygen: $[4(OH^-) - 4e^- \rightarrow O_2 + 2H_2O]$.

Photophosphorylation. As is clearly shown by the work of Arnon and his collaborators, chloroplasts can utilize light energy for the formation of ATP from ADP and inorganic phosphate. There are, however, two pathways. These are called **cyclic** and **noncyclic photophosphorylation,** respectively.

If isolated chloroplasts are provided with ample light, ADP, and inorganic phosphate, but no CO_2 and no TPN, they still are capable of generating ATP. Without CO_2 they cannot synthesize carbohydrates, of course, and without TPN (to accept hydrogen) they cannot split H_2O (and liberate O_2). But they can form ATP, in a manner indicated in Figure 9-4. The photon-excited electrons from chlorophyll are transmitted via FMN (or vitamin K) to the cytochrome system and thence they are *passed back to the chlorophyll.* The flow of each electron along this channel provides energy for charging up two molecules of ATP: one as electrons drop from FMN to the cytochromes, and the other as they flow through the cytochrome system, back to chlorophyll (Fig. 9-4). This pathway is referred as **cyclic** because the photon-

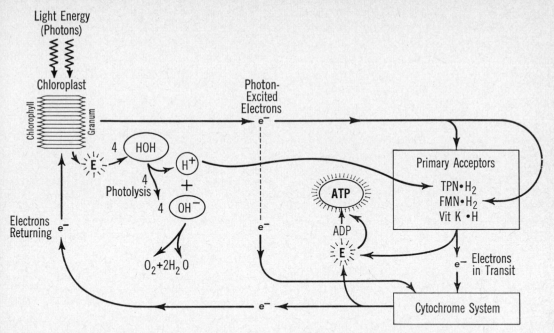

Fig. 9-4. In the chloroplasts, light energy is transformed into the chemical potential energy that is stored, mainly, as ATP, $TPN \cdot H_2$, and $FMN \cdot H_2$. Note that some of the electrons, after escaping from light-excited chlorophyll, finally return to chlorophyll, forming a cycle. Simplified schema, after Arnon.

excited electrons, ejected from chlorophyll, keep returning to the chlorophyll, having discharged their energy in the generating of two new high-energy phosphates (ATP).

For **noncyclic phosphorylation** to occur, in contrast, TPN must be added to the medium in which the isolated chloroplasts are operating. This compound, having received electrons from chlorophyll (Fig. 9-4), can now act as an acceptor of H^+ ion (from water), in which case $TPN \cdot H_2$ tends to accumulate in the medium. But the electrons that flow back to the chlorophyll via the cytochrome system are derived from OH^- ions, as is shown in Figure 9-4. Thus the flow of electrons is not cyclic. However, each electron, as it flows through the cytochrome system, generates energy for "charging up" one more molecule of ATP.

Certain bacteria, utilizing pigments other than chlorophyll, can draw upon light as the source for building up their reserves of chemical potential energy. These more primitive photochemical systems are important in rela-

tion to the evolution of plant life and they will be considered briefly later (p. 187) in that connection.

Dark Reactions: Assimilation CO_2. As currently conceived, the net effect of light energy, operating through mechanisms within the chloroplast, is to build up the cellular reserves of certain energy-rich molecules, particularly ATP and $TPN \cdot H_2$. Moreover, it is now known that even isolated chloroplasts can continue to utilize CO_2 for the synthesis of glucose and other compounds *in total darkness*, if adequate amounts of ATP and $TPN \cdot H_2$ are provided. Arnon in fact; has obtained similar results with chloroplasts from which all the chlorophyll had been removed.

The problem of tracing carbon from the time when it enters the green plant cell as CO_2 until it is built into the structure of glucose and other organic molecules represents a herculean project. The solution of this problem, which now appears to be almost complete, required the cooperation of many teams of workers, in many laboratories. But it is fair to say Melvin Calvin and collaborators at the Radiation Laboratory of the University of California have been outstanding leaders in this field—as was duly recognized by the Nobel Prize award in 1961.

Techniques. Two important technical developments contributed greatly to the prosecution of the carbon-tracing work. The discovery and preparation of radioactive carbon (C^{14}), by Samuel Ruben and Martin Kamen in 1940, provided an excellent tracer, because **radiocarbon** is very stable (its half-life is more than 5000 years) and because the radioactivity provides a means of localizing compounds in which C^{14} is a constituent. But almost equally important was the development of **paper chromatography**, initiated by two English workers, A. J. P. Martin and R. L. M. Synge.

Paper chromatography provides a method for achieving the separation and identification of unknown compounds, when these are dissolved in small amounts in an aqueous extract of cellular material. The separation results from small differentials in the solubilities of the compounds, as is indicated in Fig. 9-5. A drop of the *aqueous* solution of unknown compounds (X, Y, and Z) is placed on the filter paper, near the bottom, where the paper is in contact with a suitable organic solvent, saturated with water. As the organic solvent creeps by capillarity upward in the paper, it first will pick up compound X—if this displays the greatest degree of solubility in the particular organic solvent—and compound X will be carried the greatest distances from the locus of the original spot (Fig. 9-5). Likewise Y and Z, if this is the sequence of decreasing solubility, will not be picked up as quickly or carried as far by the upward-flowing solvent (Fig. 9-5). A further two-dimensional separation of the components can also be achieved by a second-stage treatment in which the position of the paper is changed, as is explained in the caption of Figure 9-5.

Identification of the separated compo-

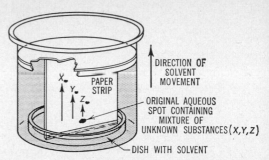

Fig. 9-5. One-dimensional (ascending) **paper chromatography.** The creeping solvent carries the substances at different rates, the final distances (note arrows) being *inversely* related to water solubility. Thus substance X (e.g., triose phosphate) would be carried further than Y (e.g., phosphoglyceric acid), which in turn would be carried further than Z (e.g., hexose diphosphate). Further separation of the substances can be effected by a second stage of treatment (two-dimensional chromatography) in which the position of the paper strip is changed. In the present case, for example, the left side of the paper might become the bottom, which is in contact with the solvent. Moreover, a different organic solvent may be used in the second stage.

nents requires further operations. Radioactive materials may be localized by plating the paper upon photographic film; but more specific detection requires that the paper be sprayed with reagents, which bring about some specific color reaction, or it may involve other analytical procedures.

Pathway of Carbon in Organic Synthesis: The Calvin Cycle. The pioneer experiments of the Calvin group regularly utilized a unicellular green alga *Chlorella* (Fig. 9-9) although confirmatory results have been derived from higher plants. All essential conditions in the experiments—intensity and duration of illumination, density of the cell population, temperature, concentration, and time of the exposure to radioactive carbon dioxide ($C^{14}O_2$), and so forth—were kept under strict control. Immediately after the experimental treatment, which sometimes lasted only a few seconds, the cells were quickly killed in alcohol, extracted, and analyzed by paper chromatography for their content of newly synthesized material.

It was surprising to find that even when

the light had acted for as little as one minute, radiocarbon could be detected in a variety of compounds—not only in sugars, but also in amino acids and other substances. However, when the illumination was cut to 5 seconds, or less, almost 80 percent of the fixed radiocarbon was found in just one compound, namely **phosphoglyceric acid** (Fig. 9-6). Apparently this 3-carbon compound is among the first to be formed during photosynthesis.

Naturally, the identification of phosphoglyceric acid (PGA) as an early product of CO_2 fixation led to the assumption that this compound must be a precursor of glucose (see Fig. 8-5). This assumption has proved correct. Essentially, *the build-up of glucose and other products represents a reversal of the steps by which these compounds are broken down* in cells generally. Energy and matter are required, however, for the climbing of this uphill path and these are provided by ATP and $TPN \cdot H_2$, previously generated by light. First the PGA molecule is energized by phosphorylation, forming diphosphoglyceric acid, at the expense of a molecule of ATP. This energized molecule undergoes reduction by $TPN \cdot H_2$, forming *triose phosphate* and releasing inorganic phosphate to the medium. The further steps, leading finally to starch, also follow the familiar pathway of cellular metabolism, as is shown in Figures 8-5 and 9-6. Moreover, the additional requirements of energy and of electron-hydrogen couplets are provided by ATP and $TPN \cdot H_2$, respectively.

It is important to realize that carbohydrates are not the only products formed during the dark period after a green plant cell has been illuminated—as is indicated in Figure 9-6. Radiocarbon soon finds its way into various amino acids and also into fatty acids. PGA appears to be an intermediary in these reactions. Moreover, the reducing potential of light-generated $TPN \cdot H_2$ is essential for the conversion of the oxidized (nitrate) form of nitrogen ($-NO_3$), which is absorbed by the plant, into the reduced (amino) form ($-NH_2$), which is found in the amino acids. In short, the energy stored as ATP and $TPN \cdot H_2$ by the photochemical mechanisms of the green plant, although mainly utilized for carbohydrate synthesis, is also employed for other syntheses.

The Calvin cycle of carbon dioxide assimilation is not very simple, however. It is so complex, in fact, that only a few highlights can be given in this brief account.

PGA proved *not to be the first compound* formed when carbon dioxide undergoes reduction $O{=}C{=}O + e^- + H^+ \rightarrow -C-OH$

$$\underset{O}{\overset{\parallel}{}}$$

which must occur when CO_2 is incorporated into an organic molecule. The CO_2 acceptor proved to be a doubly phosphorylated 5-carbon sugar, *ribulose diphosphate* (Fig. 9-6). When the green algae previously saturated with light and CO_2 were suddenly deprived of CO_2, there was an accumulation of ribulose diphosphate, but not of phosphoglyceric acid—as was first shown by Alex Wilson in the Calvin Laboratory. This result led to the proposal that the *first step in CO_2 fixation is by the carboxylation of* the very active compound, *ribulose diphosphate* (Fig. 9-6). As a result of carboxylation, apparently, a 6-carbon diphosphate intermediary is formed. This diphosphate intermediary appears to be exceedingly unstable, however, and it has not been isolated. It immediately breaks down, yielding two molecules of PGA. PGA, therefore, is not the first, but the second, product formed, subsequent to the primary fixation of CO_2.

Other phases of the complex Calvin cycle can only be mentioned here, although they have been worked out in considerable detail. Replenishment of the supply of ribulose diphosphate is achieved from part of the PGA, as this intermediary continues to be produced. In other words, not all of the PGA is utilized for the synthesis of glucose and other organic substances. A considerable part is returned to ribulose monophosphate, which then, at the expense of ATP, is converted to the active CO_2 fixer, ribulose diphosphate.

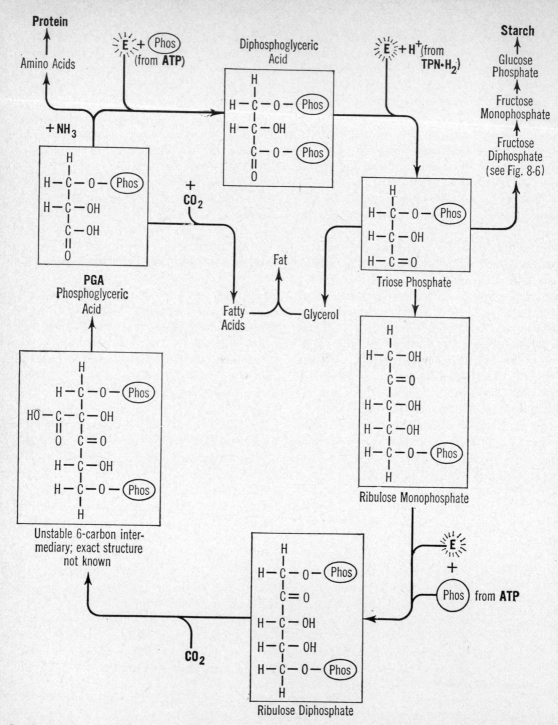

Fig. 9-6. Pathways of carbon assimilation in green plant cells; abbreviated version of the **Calvin cycle** (modified from Bassham). The major agency for the *fixation of CO_2* is *ribulose diphosphate* (lower right). Note that PGA the first stable product that accumulates subsequent to CO_2 fixation, is utilized in several ways. Part of it is recycled back to replenish ribulose diphosphate, the CO_2-fixation agency; but part provides material for the synthesis not only of carbohydrate (starch), but also of proteins and fats. Also note that the energy, which drives the cycle, comes from ATP and TPN·H_2, previously generated by means of light energy.

The route from the 3-carbon PGA to the 5-carbon ribulose phosphate is very indirect, however. It involves the formation of a number of interesting intermediaries, including 4-carbon (tetrose) and 7-carbon (heptose) sugars, as combinations and recombinations occur in the metabolic vortex. It is a cycle in the sense that the same intermediaries keep appearing over and over again. But only part of the PGA is cycled back to replenish the supplies of ribulose diphosphate. The rest goes into the building of glucose, amino acids, and other molecules essential to the life of the cell—as is shown in Figure 9-6.

As will be explained later (p. 181), a few bacteria can synthesize glucose from CO_2 and H_2O at the expense of energy, derived not from light, but from the oxidation of certain inorganic compounds. This process of **chemosynthesis** is of very limited occurrence, however. Almost all organic matter, which supports the life of this planet, comes into being as a result of the photosynthetic powers of the green plants. Considerably more than a billion tons a day of assorted carbohydrates, proteins, lipids, and other organic compounds are produced by green plants, although about 90 percent of this huge production comes from primitive, mainly unicellular algae in the sea.

OTHER ASPECTS OF PLANT NUTRITION

Nutrition among green plants is much simplified by the fact that a plant does not need to take in any *preformed* organic foods. All the foods are simple crystalloidal substances, present practically everywhere, and consequently they can be absorbed *directly from the environment.* Thus *plants generally do not possess any digestive system,* and the **holophytic mode of nutrition** *does not include* any processes **ingestion, digestion,** and **egestion.** Accordingly, nutrition in typical plants begins with the process of **absorption.**

Absorption in Unicellular and Colonial Plants. Virtually all simple **green** plants that lack roots, stems, and leaves are designated collectively as the **algae.** Many of the algae, such as *Closterium* and *Chlamydomonas* (Fig. 9-7), are unicellular; but some, such as *Spirogyra* (Fig. 9-8), are colonial, and others,

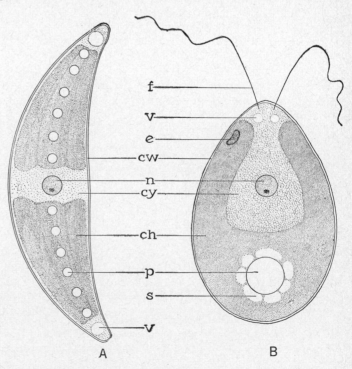

Fig. 9-7. Unicellular green algae; A, *Closterium;* B, *Chlamydomonas.* n, nucleus; cy, cytoplasm; ch, chloroplast; p, pyrenoid; s, starch grains; v, vacuole; cw, cell wall; f, flagellum; e, red pigmented "eye spot."

A   B

Fig. 9-8. One complete cell in a filament of the green alga, *Spirogyra*. The nucleus, with a distinct darkly stained nucleolus, lies at the center, suspended in place by delicate strands of cytoplasm. The chloroplast has the form of a spiral ribbon, on which numerous small stained bodies, the pyrenoids, are discernible in this retouched photograph. (Copyright, General Biological Supply House, Inc.)

such as *Nitella* (Fig. 13-2), are true multi-cellular organisms. Algae differ from the simple animals in that they all possess chlorophyll, and most have relatively thick, rigid **cell walls.** Usually the chlorophyll is localized within well-defined chloroplasts, of which one or more may be present in each cell. Sometimes the green color of the chlorophyll is masked by the presence of other pigments, as in the case of brown and red algae. Most algae differ from *protozoa* in having no means of locomotion, although some species possess one or more highly motile, whiplike **flagella** (Fig. 9-7B).

Algae, in contrast to most higher plants, are essentially **aquatic** plants. A few dwell in very moist places on the land, as for example, *Protococcus* (Fig. 9-9), which may be found on tree trunks, in the damp crevices of the bark. But most algae grow under water. *Closterium,* for example, is a unicellular form very commonly found in fresh-water ponds and lakes.

The problem of absorption in a submerged unicellular plant such as *Closterium* (Fig. 9-7A) is not very acute. All essential nutrients are right at hand, dissolved in the surrounding medium; and all the food substances can enter the cell through the plasma membrane by diffusion and osmosis. Fresh water, essentially, is a very hypotonic solution. The main solutes are inorganic salts—which dissolve in rain water as it seeps through the soil and collects in the pond—together with the atmospheric gases, carbon dioxide, and oxygen. These substances pass into the cell by diffusion, although active transport processes (p. 121) often intervene, increasing or decreasing the intracellular content of certain particular ions.

Distribution. In unicellular plants such as *Closterium,* the distribution of absorbed food substances throughout the protoplasm is just as simple as that in one-celled animals (p. 00). Once within the plasma membrane, the different nutrients diffuse freely throughout the

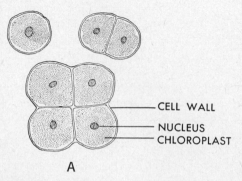
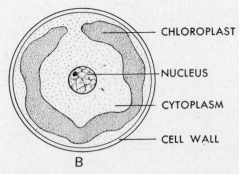

CELL WALL
NUCLEUS
CHLOROPLAST

A

CHLOROPLAST
NUCLEUS
CYTOPLASM
CELL WALL

B

Fig. 9-9. *Protococcus,* a unicellular green plant. A, temporary aggregates of cells, as they occur naturally. B, single cell, more highly magnified, stained and sectioned. *Chlorella* (see p. 164) has a structure similar, although not identical, to that of *Protococcus.*

cell. Also, many plant cells carry on a cyclic streaming (cyclosis, p. 198) of the protoplasm, and this assures a more rapid equilibration of absorbed substances.

The problem of absorption and distribution in the larger land plants is somewhat more difficult. In such forms, the root system accomplishes practically all absorption, since the roots are the only parts that lie in contact with the soil water. The water and salts absorbed by the roots are then carried in special vessels throughout the stem and leaf systems, which in some plants reach more than 100 feet above ground.

Constructive Metabolism in Green Plants. Green plant cells use glucose, after it is synthesized, as a source of energy and also as a source of matter for the synthesis of other organic compounds (proteins, carbohydrates, fats, etc.) that are needed for maintenance and growth. Frequently, however, the intermediaries of such constructive metabolism, particularly certain amino acids, glycerol, and fatty acids, are synthesized more directly as is shown in Figure 9-6.

Protein Synthesis. The formation of proteins in plant cells depends upon a preliminary synthesis of the various amino acids. All amino acids can be synthesized by plant cells, provided that glucose (or precursors of glucose) and inorganic salts are available. Glucose or its precursors (Fig. 9-6) provides the plant cell not only with energy for amino acid synthesis, but also with matter, to form the carbon-hydrogen parts of the molecules. The plant derives nitrogen, sulfur, and other constituents of the amino acids from the inorganic salts.

As a source of nitrogen, for the amino ($-NH_2$) portions of the amino acids, *typical plant cells cannot draw upon the free nitrogen* (N_2) of the atmosphere. But the plant does possess the proper catalytic equipment for using nitrogen in the form of **nitrate salts** ($NaNO_3$, KNO_3, etc.). Similarly the plant utilizes sulfur (for the synthesis of some of the amino acids) chiefly in the form of the sulfate ($-SO_4$) salts.

The reducing potential necessary for the conversion of the nitrate ($-NO_3$) to the amino ($-NH_2$) form of nitrogen and for the conversion of the sulfate ($-SO_4$) to the sulfhydryl ($-SH$) form of sulfur is provided by $TPN \cdot H_2$ and other reduced primary acceptors generated by photosynthesis. Precisely how the reduced nitrogen and sulfur radicals become affiliated with the carbon frameworks of the various precursors is not fully known, although it is plain that a number of amino acids begin to appear in the green plant cell within a few minutes subsequent to illumination. But given nitrates as a source of nitrogen and sulfates as a source of sulfur, green plants enjoy a full measure of growth. The nitrate content of the soil and of fertilizers is a prime consideration. If the nitrate supply is limited, the formation of amino acids within the plant is reduced; and since new proteins are formed solely by dehydration synthesis from previously formed amino acids the growth of the plant is likewise limited.

Carbohydrate Synthesis. During periods of abundant light, the plant cell produces glucose *in excess* of its current needs. This excess glucose is converted mainy into **starch** (Fig. 9-6). In many plant cells the enzymes responsible for starch synthesis are localized in small visible bodies, the **pyrenoids** (Figs. 9-7 and 9-8); and consequently starch grains first appear near this part of the cell. Starch represents a reserve of glucose; during periods of darkness starch may be hydrolyzed, yielding an immediate supply of glucose. Cellulose, for the cell walls and other structural parts, is also derived by dehydration synthesis from photosynthesized glucose.

Other Syntheses. Some complex proteins contain sulfur, phosphorus, and iron, which are derived from the inorganic salts of these elements absorbed by the plant. Like other cells, plant cells can form fats and other lipids from carbohydrates, and many of the intermediary stages of these transformations now are known (see Figs. 8-5 and 9-6).

In general, the synthetic powers in plants are greater and more varied than in animals. Besides synthesizing carbohydrates, fats, and all the various amino acids, plants can also synthesize a wide variety of other compounds that animals cannot. Such compounds include not only chlorophyll and other special pigments, but also all the vitamins (p. 346), and many other useful substances, such as drugs, perfumes, etc. Moreover, in producing this wide variety of organic compounds, green plants utilize nothing but inorganic substances that are absorbed from the environment.

Destructive Metabolism. As to destructive metabolism, plant and animal cells are essentially alike (see Fig. 8-5). But the metabolism of plants is simpler because plant cells depend almost solely upon **glucose** as a source of energy when light is not available. The supply of synthesized glucose is adequate to balance the energy expenditures of the plant, and consequently other fuels are seldom utilized. In particular, amino acids and proteins are not sacrificed for energy, except under conditions of starvation—as, for example, when a plant is deprived of light for a long period. The plant limits the synthesis of amino acids to its constructive needs, and thus no excesses are available for energy, and deamination seldom occurs.

The energy expended by a plant in destructive metabolism goes mainly to foster constructive metabolism. The plant does not have to move about in search of food and thus expends less total energy than the animal. In using a lesser proportion of its materials for destructive metabolism, the plant has more available for constructive purposes. Consequently plants in general grow more rapidly than animals.

Respiration in Plants. All plant cells constantly use oxygen and produce carbon dioxide, as a result of oxidative metabolism. But during periods when light is available, the green plant cell produces 15 to 30 times more oxygen than it uses, and consumes much more carbon dioxide than it produces. Conse-

quently in the daytime, respiration (taking in O_2 and giving off CO_2) is overbalanced by the gas exchange of photosynthesis (taking in CO_2 and giving off O_2), which is just the opposite. But in darkness, when photosynthesis is suspended, all plant cells carry on a small but measurable respiration.

Gas exchanges in a simple submerged plant such as *Closterium* (Fig. 9-7) proceed on a purely diffusional basis. While carbon dioxide is being used up faster than it is being produced, the CO_2 concentration in the cell remains lower than in the surrounding water; and while oxygen is being formed faster than it is consumed, the O_2 concentration in the cell remains relatively high. Consequently, during periods when light is available the gas exchange of photosynthesis predominates. But when photosynthesis ceases, the concentration of oxygen inside the cell sinks below the level of dissolved oxygen in the outside water, and the quantity of carbon dioxide rises above that of the environment. Under these circumstances, therefore, respiration holds sway.

Excretion in Plants. Very little excretion is necessary in green plants. Plants produce scarcely any metabolic wastes other than carbon dioxide and water—and these end products are reused during photosynthesis. Insofar as small quantities of other wastes are produced, these likewise may be consumed again in constructive metabolism. To a remarkable extent, therefore, it may be said that plant cells are able to "burn their own smoke." In a few cases, certain plant cells tend to accumulate special waste products, depositing them as insoluble crystals in the protoplasm or vacuoles.

When photosynthesis is in abeyance, carbon dioxide and water tend to accumulate. The carbon dioxide passes off in respiration, leaving water as the sole excretory waste produced in any abundance. In aquatic forms such as *Closterium*, this excess water also passes out into the environment. Despite the fact that the surrounding fresh water is very hypotonic, the high turgor of the cell establishes an equilibrium in which the inflow of water is balanced by the outflow. Therefore when additional water is formed by metabolism, the equilibrium is disturbed and the excess water passes to the outside.

GENERAL SIGNIFICANCE OF HOLOPHYTIC NUTRITION

The salient points of contrast between holophytic and holozoic nutrition are summarized in Table 9-1. The significance of small derive their energy from preformed organic foods, by feeding either directly upon the plants, or upon other organisms that directly or indirectly have obtained their organic matter from the plants. In addition to maintaining the supply of organic matter, light energy also maintains our oxygen supply, which would be exhausted in about 2000 years if photosynthesis did not occur. Only a small fraction of the sun's radiance happens to fall upon green plants, and only about 3 percent of this energy is claimed successfully

Table 9-1—Holophytic and Holozoic Nutritions Contrasted

Green Plant	*Animal*
1. Has chlorophyll; can synthesize glucose	1. Has no chlorophyll; cannot synthesize glucose
2. Can utilize nitrates and other inorganic salts to synthesize amino acids	2. Cannot utilize nitrates to synthesize amino acids
3. Can synthesize all amino acids	3. Cannot synthesize all amino acids
4. Independent of other organisms for organic compounds	4. Dependent on other organisms for organic compounds
5. Absorbs all food in solution	5. Ingests solid food
6. Does not move about for food; expends less energy; less catabolism	6. Moves about for food; expends more energy; more catabolism
7. Primary source of energy is light	7. Only source of energy is organic compounds
8. Metabolism as a whole *constructive;* that is, *increases available organic compounds* and increases the reserve of potential energy	8. Metabolism as a whole *destructive;* that is, *decreases available organic compounds* and decreases the reserve of potential energy

these points cannot be overemphasized. The holophytic system, with chlorophyll as a keystone, enables green plants to tap the tremendous fund of energy that radiates upon our earth from the distant sun. This kinetic energy, transformed into the potential energy of a great variety of organic compounds, represents almost the sole energy supply of all varieties of living things. Animals large and by photosynthesis. But this small fraction energizes virtually all the manifold processes of life, and this energy is not degraded into heat until it has found expression in the movements and other activities of many living things. Eventually, however, all the solar energy that strikes the earth becomes transformed to heat and is dissipated in the environment (Chap. 10).

TEST QUESTIONS

1. Most plants are nonmotile organisms. Explain this observation in terms of the food requirements of plants.

2. What is the basis for considering that *Closterium, Chlamydomonas,* and *Spirogyra* are all typical plants?

3. How do the algae differ from most higher plants: (a) as to habitat; and (b) as to general structure?

4. To what extent does absorption in *Closterium* and other algae depend upon diffusion and osmosis? Explain.

5. Define the term "photosynthesis," specifying precisely the kinds of matter and energy that are involved.

6. One plant is exposed to green light, and another to red light. Predict the relative rates of photosynthesis in the two plants. Explain.

7. In photosynthesis light energy is utilized, *not* to reduce CO_2 but to liberate oxygen from H_2O. Explain the experiments that substantiate this conclusion.

8. Can animals and plants utilize CO_2 in the formation of organic compounds? To what extent, if any, is light energy involved in such processes?

9. Is chlorophyll the only pigment capable of participating in photosynthesis? Explain.

10. What is a *granum?* Why is the fine structure of the granum important in relation to photosynthesis?

11. Explain the importance of heavy oxygen (O^{18}), radiocarbon (C^{14}), and paper chromatography, in relation to modern research on photosynthesis.

12. To what extent can isolated chloroplasts carry on photosynthesis? Explain.

13. Explain the importance of ATP and $TPN \cdot H_2$ in relation to photosynthesis.

14. Differentiate between "light reactions" and "dark reactions" in the metabolism of green plant cells.

15. What is a photon? How is the energy content of a photon related to the wavelength of light?

16. What are fluorescence and phosphorescence? Explain.

17. Differentiate between cyclic and noncyclic photophosphorylation. Explain the importance of these processes.

18. Briefly summarize the contributions of: (a) Ruben; (b) Arnon; (c) Priestley; and (d) Calvin to our understanding of photosynthesis.

19. Explain the importance of phosphoglyceric acid (PGA) in relation to CO_2 assimilation.

20. Explain the importance of ribulose diphosphate in relation to the fixation of CO_2.

21. Explain the general importance of photosynthesis:
    a. from the "viewpoint" of plants
    b. from the "viewpoint" of animals

22. State five ways in which glucose may be used in the cells of a typical plant, in each case specifying such chemical reactions as may be involved.

23. Compare animal and plant cells, as regards:
    a. the origin of amino acids utilized in metabolism
    b. ways in which amino acids are utilized in metabolism

24. Carefully explain why nitrate ($-NO_3$) salts are plant foods of great importance. Why are sulfates and phosphates likewise needed by green plants?

25. Account for the fact that considerable quantities of nitrogenous wastes are formed in the metabolism of animals, but not in the metabolism of plants.

26. Construct a table showing the main points of contrast between the holophytic and holozoic types of nutrition.

27. Point out five essential similarities between the holozoic and holophytic types of nutrition.

FURTHER READINGS

1. "The Role of Light in Photosynthesis," by D. I. Arnon, in *Scientific American,* November 1960.

2. "The Path of Carbon in Photosynthesis," by M. Calvin, in *Science,* vol. 135, March 16, 1962.

3. *Great Experiments in Biology,* ed. by M. Gabriel and S. Fogel; see sections on photosynthesis by Priestley, Ingenhousz, Ruben, and others; Englewood Cliffs, N. J., 1955.

4. *The Plant World,* 4th ed., by H. J. Fuller and Z. B. Carothers; New York, 1963.

10-*Other Modes of Nutrition;*
Conservation of Food
Elements

ALMOST all higher organisms are either typical animals or typical plants; but among lower organisms, the lines of distinction are somewhat blurred. Some lower organisms, are holophytic, some are holozoic, others are more or less intermediate between the plants and the animals, and still others are quite different, in their mode of nutrition, from either plants or animals.

THE FUNGI

The **fungi** are a large group (about 75,000 species) of relatively *simple plants that do not possess* **chlorophyll** and that lack a capacity to **ingest** food. Many fungi closely resemble the algae in general structure and reproductive habits, and consequently they are classified as plants, despite the lack of chlorophyll.

Many fungi, including the **bacteria** (Fig. 10-1) and **yeasts** (Fig. 10-2), are unicellular; but others, including the **molds, mildews, rusts, smuts, puffballs,** and **mushrooms,** are more complex in structure. The body, or **mycelium,** of a complex fungus consists of a mass of long, slender, much-branched threads, called **hyphae.** In some species the

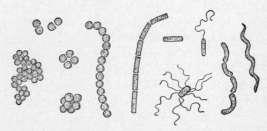

Fig. 10-1. The bacteria are extremely small fungus plants, which display three general forms. The spherical forms are **cocci;** the rod-shaped forms, **bacilli;** and the spiral forms, **spirilla.** Colonial aggregates of bacteria are designated by special names; e.g., staphylococcus, for irregular bunches of cocci, like those on the left; and streptococcus, and streptobacillus, for the chainlike colonies of cocci and bacilli (shown at the center).

mycelium displays a syncytial organization; in others it consists of distinct cells, individually separated by transverse cell walls (Fig. 10-3).

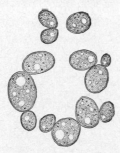

Fig. 10-2. Yeast cells, budding. The light spots are fat droplets and cell-sap vacuoles; the nuclei are not visible in living, unstained cells.

SAPROPHYTIC NUTRITION

The saprophytic mode of nutrition is displayed by most of the yeasts, molds, and bacteria. **Saprophytic organisms,** like animals, *require* at least *a minimum of preformed organic food;* but lacking a digestive cavity, **saprophytes** *must absorb their organic nutrients directly from the environment.* Therefore the localities favorable for the growth of saprophytes are very limited. Such forms are found only in places where considerable quantities of organic materials have accumulated, such as upon soil richly laden with humus (decomposing plant material), or directly upon the remnants of other organisms.

Nutrition of Yeasts. Many wild yeasts grow saprophytically upon sweet fruits that have been crushed in falling to the ground. The most important yeasts, however, are the kinds that are cultivated by man because of their usefulness in brewing and in bread-making (Fig. 10-1).

Yeast *cannot grow like a* **green** *plant* in a medium containing only inorganic substances. But yeast will thrive vigorously in a solution containing one or more sugars (glucose, fructose, mannose, sucrose, or maltose) oxygen, and a suitable variety of inorganic salts. Lacking chlorophyll, the yeast

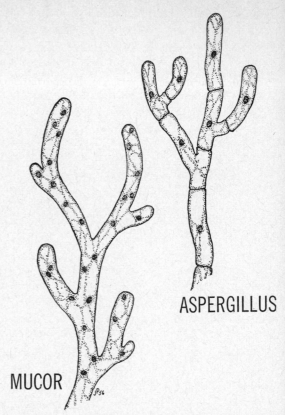

ASPERGILLUS

MUCOR

Fig. 10-3. Small portions of the mycelia of two common mold fungi. The black spots are nuclei. Note that *Mucor* is a syncytial organism, whereas *Aspergillus* is typically cellular.

cannot synthesize its own sugar; but given "ready-made" sugar as a source of energy and matter, it can carry on metabolism quite like a green plant. Like the green plant it can utilize inorganic nitrogen to synthesize all essential amino acids and proteins, although yeasts grow better when ammonium (NH_4^+) salts, rather than nitrates (NO_3^-), are available.

When glucose or some other monosaccharide is present in the surrounding medium, the yeast absorbs the sugar directly, without recourse to any sort of digestive process. But when the available sugar is a disaccharide, such as sucrose (or maltose), digestion must precede absorption. In this case, the enzyme **sucrase** (or **maltase**) is extruded from the yeast cells, and *digestion occurs externally,* in the surrounding medium. Starch cannot always be used as a source of glucose, because the **digestive enzymes** of the yeast do not include any of the **amylases.** However, ground malt (germinated barley) is usually added to a yeast brew, and the amylases from the barley cells serve to hydrolyze the starch to maltose.

Anaerobic Metabolism of Yeast. In the presence of adequate oxygen, yeast cells, like plants and animals generally, obtain energy by oxidizing carbohydrates and other compounds. But when free oxygen is scarce or lacking, the yeast replaces this **aerobic metabolism** by an **anaerobic metabolism.** Under these conditions the yeast obtains energy by **alcoholic fermentation** (Fig. 8-5). This decomposition of glucose into ethyl alcohol and carbon dioxide does not require the utilization of oxygen, as is shown in the following *over-all* reaction:

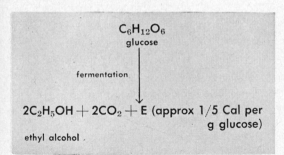

$$C_6H_{12}O_6$$
glucose

fermentation

$$2C_2H_5OH + 2CO_2 + E \text{ (approx 1/5 Cal per g glucose)}$$

ethyl alcohol

Because the nonoxidative metabolism of glucose yields only about $\frac{1}{20}$ as much energy as the oxidative metabolism (cf. Fig. 8-5), yeast grows much more slowly and less efficiently under anaerobic conditions. Moreover, the metabolic wastes, especially alcohol, tend to accumulate in the medium after escaping from the cells by diffusion; and the alcohol finally exerts a toxic effect, despite a unique tolerance that yeasts have developed to this compound.

The importance of yeast in human economy lies in the fact that fermentation constitutes the only practical source of alcoholic beverages, and of ethyl alcohol, which is widely used as a solvent and raw material in chemical industry. In the brew mashes of beers and wines, most of the alcohol is formed by the dense population of yeasts near the bottom of the brew tank. Near the top of the tank, which is more or less open to the atmosphere, there is ample oxygen, and the yeasts of this region produce little or no alcohol. But the oxygen is soon used up at the bottom of the tank, and new oxygen entering from the atmosphere is consumed by the upper layers of yeasts before it can diffuse to the bottom layers. The proportion of alcohol in a natural brew never exceeds about 14 percent, since this is the maximum tolerable to the yeasts themselves. However, by distillation the proportion of alcohol may be increased up to 95 percent. In bread making, the alcohol produced in dough is unimportant, since the relatively small quantity is dissipated during baking. But the carbon dioxide forms bubbles that are trapped in the thick dough mixture, and this "raises" the dough, giving a porous texture to the bread.

Nutrition in the Bread Mold. The spores of the bread mold (*Rhizopus nigricans*) are abundant in the atmosphere, especially in populated regions. Consequently an exposed piece of moist bread or other starchy food almost invariably becomes covered by the fuzzy white mycelium of the bread mold. Later this growth turns blackish gray, indicating that a new crop of spore capsules has become ripe (Fig. 12-10).

The **mycelium** of the bread mold (Fig. 12-10) is composed entirely of a mass of much-branched threads, or **hyphae,** which are of three types: (1) short, clustered **rhizoids,** which penetrate down into the substance of the bread; (2) long, stout **stolons,** which form an interlacing mass over the surface of the bread; and (3) long, slender **sporangiophores,** which extend vertically upward, each supporting a single **spore capsule** at its upper end (Fig. 12-10).

The bread mold, which is a typical saprophyte, uses starch as its main organic food. Starch cannot be absorbed as such, but the rhizoids of the mold secrete **amylase** (and maltase) into the surrounding bread or other food. Thus **digestion** occurs externally, and the resulting glucose is absorbed by the rhizoids. The rhizoids serve also for the **absorption** of the other essential nutrients, including water, salts, and oxygen. The **distribution** of the food substances proceeds by diffusion and protoplasmic streaming, via the rhizoids to the stolons, and via the stolons to the sporangiophores. The **metabolism** of the mold closely resembles that of the yeast, except that anaerobic growth does not occur. Also the mold (to a greater extent than yeast) utilizes nitrate ($—NO_3$) salts for the synthesis of amino acids and proteins. All energy is derived from preformed organic substances (chiefly carbohydrate) that are absorbed. Respiration and excretion are localized mainly in the rhizoids, because the upper parts of the mycelium are too dry to permit exchanges with the air. The only significant *excretory* waste is water, since carbohydrate is the main fuel.

Economic Importance of the Yeasts and Molds. A wide variety of yeasts and molds have been known to biologists for many years, and investigations on the metabolism of these organisms have gradually revealed a number of by-products that are very important in medicine and industry. More than 100,000 tons of yeasts are produced annually in the United States, and various kinds of fermentation are used in the production of citric acid, glycerol, acetone, purified fats, and a number of other valuable organic compounds. Likewise, yeasts are widely used in the production of vitamins, and massive yeast cultures are beginning to be used as direct sources of man's food.

Molds and bacteria are also very important as sources of **antibiotic compounds,** such as **penicillin, streptomycin,** and **aureomycin,** compounds that now are widely used as therapeutic agents in many serious infectious diseases (p. 580). Various molds are also useful in the curing of hides, tobacco, coffee, cocoa, paper pulp, etc.; and to some extent the yeasts and molds cooperate with the bacteria in achieving the decay of organic matter (see below).

Nutrition of the Saprophytic Bacteria: Decay and Putrefaction. Although bacteria are among the smallest and, from the viewpoint of visible structure, the simplest of organisms, they display a remarkable diversity in their nutritive processes. Among the saprophytic forms, which constitute a large majority of the bacteria, many variations exist as to the chemical nature of the organic substances required by the different species for the fulfillment of their metabolic needs.

Bacteria lack chlorophyll, although one small group, the purple bacteria, possesses a chlorophyll-like pigment, and can utilize light to energize some phases of their metabolism (p. 187). Bacteria possess relatively rigid cell walls, composed of organic substances other than cellulose. Accordingly, it is upon rather arbitrary grounds that the bacteria are classified among the plants.

Although the nutritional variation among bacteria is very great, the variation in form is generally limited to three common shapes. Among bacterial species there are: (1) spherical forms, called **cocci,** (2) rod-shaped forms, called **bacilli,** and (3) spiral forms, called **spirilla** (Fig. 10-1). Many bacteria are strictly unicellular, but others form colonial aggregates of greater or lesser permanence; and bacterial colonies are usually named according to the arrangement of the cells in the aggregate. Irregular clusters are designated by the prefix **staphylo-,** as in staphylococcus; chainlike forms are specified by the prefix **strepto-,** as in **streptococcus** or **streptobacillus.**

The great importance of saprophytic bacteria is that their digestive and metabolic processes effect the decomposition of a vast quantity and a rich variety of organic materials that otherwise would tend to accumulate on earth in a form not suitable for use by other organisms. Without the saprophytic bacteria all decay would be eliminated, except for that relatively small fraction which results from the nutrition of other saprophytes (e.g., yeasts and molds).

Decay and Putrefaction. The saprophytic bacteria are all spore formers (p. 56), and bacterial spores are abundant everywhere except in the purest atmospheres. Consequently whenever a mass of organic material, such as a dead body or other organic remnant, remains exposed, bacterial spores fall upon it and begin to grow. In their nutrition, the saprophytic bacteria utilize the various organic substances present in the original material, decomposing these compounds eventually into simple inorganic end products. This process, as a whole, is designated as **decay.**

Many different bacteria participate in decay, and each species is very specific as to the organic substances it utilizes as food. Some grow on carbohydrates; for example, the **cellulose bacteria,** which use the enzyme **cellulase** to digest woody materials and obtain glucose; the **milk-souring bacteria,** which absorb lactose and convert it (anaerobically) into **lactic acid** ($CH_3 \cdot CHOH \cdot COOH$); and the **vinegar bacteria,** which oxidize alcohol (present in hard ciders or wines) into **acetic acid** ($CH_3 \cdot COOH$). Other bacteria possess different enzymes, which enable them to grow on fatty substances. Thus, the smell of rancid butter is due mainly to **butyric acid** ($C_3H_7 \cdot COOH$), produced by the action of certain bacteria upon butter fat.

The total decay of **protein** material is designated by the special name of **putrefaction.** Putrefaction involves the growth of a variety of saprophytic bacteria, which act simultaneously and successively upon the protein, until nothing but inorganic end products remain. During the intervening stages, however, a number of foul-smelling and toxic substances (for example, various **organic amines**) are formed in the metabolism of some of the species, but these substances are finally absorbed and utilized by other species.

Return of Inorganic Nitrogen to the Soil and Air. The liberation of the inorganic compounds of nitrogen, which results from the bacterial decomposition of proteins and other organic nitrogen compounds, is very important in relation to soil fertility. Some saprophytic bacteria utilize urea $[CO(NH_2)_2]$, hydrolyzing this compound into ammonia (NH_3) and carbon dioxide (CO_2), which pass forth into the environment. The nitrogen of proteins and other complex nitrogenous compounds is likewise liberated by the putrefactive bacteria chiefly in the form of ammonia, although small quantities of free nitrogen (N_2) are produced by some species. Free nitrogen is also liberated by the burning (in fires) of organic nitrogen compounds, and in greater quantities by the **denitrifying bacteria.**

Denitrifying Bacteria. These soil saprophytes utilize carbohydrates present in decaying humus. When the soil is well aerated by cultivation, the denitrifying bacteria depend upon free oxygen for the oxidation of their carbohydrates. But when free oxygen is lacking, they decompose nitrate ($—NO_3$) salts, using this bound form of oxygen as an oxidizing agent. Under these circumstances the denitrifying bacteria liberate **free nitrogen.** The liberation of free nitrogen from various nitrogen compounds represents a definite loss of soil fertility, because green plants are not able to use free nitrogen to sustain their growth. Such a liberation of gaseous nitrogen has been designated rather loosely as *"a leak in the nitrogen cycle."*

Return of Elements to the Environment. In summary, the *complete* decay of any material involves a series of different bacteria acting successively upon the various organic substances as they appear in the decomposing mass. Some of the decomposition reactions are digestive, and others are metabolic in nature, but the final end products are all simple inorganic substances. The carbon of organic compounds emerges from the process mainly as CO_2, and the hydrogen mainly as H_2O. The nitrogen part of various organic compounds appears chiefly as NH_3, although small quantities of N_2 and of nitrate ($—NO_3$)

salts may be formed. Other elementary constituents (S, P, etc.) are also finally converted to inorganic form (chiefly —SO$_4$, —PO$_4$, etc.).

The processes of decay are very important in the general economy of life. Without decay including putrefaction, significant quantities of the inorganic substances necessary for the growth of green plants would not be returned to the soil and air. Man also makes use of a number of saprophytic bacteria: in tanning leather, curing tobacco, making cheese, and disposing of sewage. All in all, the benefits that accrue from the saprophytic bacteria far outweigh the harm done in the spoiling of foods and other valuable materials. Many methods have been developed to *preserve* foods from the action of bacteria; refrigeration retards their digestive and metabolic processes; salting plasmolyzes the cells; dehydration deprives them of adequate water; chemicals kill them; and above all, canning prevents the bacteria from regaining access to food after they have been killed by **heat sterilization.**

MIXOTROPHIC NUTRITION

Mixotrophic organisms are those that can carry on more than one mode of nutrition. For example, **Euglena** (Fig. 10-4) and many other **green flagellates** can live like typical plants when *light* is available; but these organisms can also grow saprophytically. Euglena resembles a one-celled animal—in having a mouth and gullet, in its ability to propel itself through the water, and in lacking a rigid cellulose cell wall. But Euglena also is like a plant, in that it possesses **chloroplasts** that enable it to carry on photosynthesis. Likewise Euglena stores its excess glucose in the form of starch and utilizes nitrate salts for the synthesis of amino acids, just like typically **holophytic** organisms. Euglena can live indefinitely without light, provided the surrounding medium contains adequate amounts of organic substances, especially carbohydrates. At the bottom of a

pond, where there is an abundance of decomposing organic material, Euglena carries on a **saprophytic** nutrition. Some other green flagellates can also grow **holozoically,** utilizing the mouth and gullet for the **ingestion** of organic foods. But the mouth and gullet of Euglena appear to be vestigial and are not capable of fulfilling these functions.

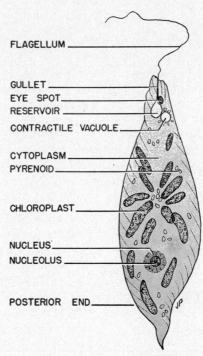

FLAGELLUM
GULLET
EYE SPOT
RESERVOIR
CONTRACTILE VACUOLE
CYTOPLASM
PYRENOID
CHLOROPLAST
NUCLEUS
NUCLEOLUS
POSTERIOR END

Fig. 10-4. Euglena, a green flagellate, displays a mixotrophic kind of nutrition.

PARASITIC NUTRITIONS

A parasitic organism lives on or in another organism, deriving food from the living **host.** Parasitic species are found among all kinds of plants and animals, although the parasitic habit tends to be more prevalent among lower organisms. Moreover, there is scarcely a single species of animal or plant that does not serve as host for one or more parasites. Some parasites, like lice, are **ectoparasites,** in that they never invade the interior of the host's body; but others, like the tapeworm, are **endoparasites,** which penetrate into some internal cavity, or into the tissues or cells of the host.

The kind of nutrition practiced by a parasite depends largely upon its evolutionary background. Many parasitic animals, for example, are essentially holozoic, in the sense that they ingest the blood or tissues of their hosts. But other parasites get their nourishment essentially like saprophytes, absorbing organic substances directly from the body fluids, tissues, or cells of their *living* hosts.

Many parasites do little or no harm to the hosts, aside from "stealing" a certain quantity of organic material. But many produce definite *diseases* in the hosts, either by direct injury to the cells and organs, or by producing toxic waste products. Among animal diseases, especially in man, many are caused by bacterial parasites (for example, diphtheria, pneumonia, tuberculosis, gonorrhea); others are caused by parasitic protozoans (for example, malaria, African sleeping sickness, syphilis); others by viruses (infantile paralysis, smallpox, mumps, etc.); and others by multicellular parasites (hookworm, trichinosis, etc.). Among plant diseases, most are caused by parasitic fungi (rusts, smuts, molds, mildews, etc.), although a few are caused by viruses.

Symbiosis. In certain cases not only the parasite but also the host derives benefit from their association. Such a mutually beneficial relation between parasite and host is called **symbiosis.** In this category there are many interesting cases. The **lichens,** for example, are essentially dual organisms, for among the cells of these multicellular fungi there are always a number of unicellular green algae (Fig. 10-5). The alga donates its extra carbohydrate to the fungus, and the fungus aids the alga by contributing water and salts, absorbed in excess through the hyphae. In this case the symbiotic organisms have become completely dependent upon each other, and neither is able to live very long in the absence of the other.

Some fungi live symbiotically on and in the roots of higher plants (for example, trees). These fungi aid the host plants in absorbing water and salts, through part of

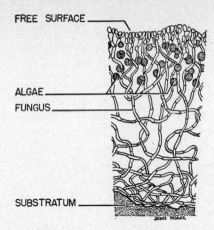

Fig. 10-5. The lichen is a dual organism, which provides a good example of symbiosis. Section of the mycelium showing the cells of a green alga nestled among the colorless hyphae of the fungus.

the mycelium that ramifies out among the soil particles; in return, the root of the host provides the fungus with the preformed carbohydrates. Many **herbivorous animals,** such as the cow, develop rich cultures of **cellulose bacteria** in the digestive tract. Here the bacteria convert considerable quantities of cellulose into glucose that is absorbed in part by the host and in part by the parasites. In return, the bacteria are afforded ideal conditions of warmth and darkness while they absorb their other essential nutrients (water, salts, etc.) from the digesting food mass as it passes through the alimentary canal of the contented host.

Neutral Parasites. In some cases, a parasite neither harms nor benefits the host in any tangible fashion. Such neutral parasites are, perhaps, even commoner than the harmful and beneficial types. For example, a number of species of bacteria inhabit the human digestive tract, especially in the region of the large intestine (p. 314). Aside from the fact that these bacteria appropriate small quantities of organic foodstuffs, no definite ill results from their presence in the gut. In fact, some of the intestinal bacteria of man are now known to benefit their host, by synthesizing several of the B vitamins, of which some may be absorbed by the host.

A parasite may be neutral with reference to one kind of host, but definitely pathogenic to another. Such a case is provided by Cryptocotyle, a parasitic flatworm. The usual host of Cryptocotyle is a seagull, and adult gulls are quite immune to the presence of the parasite in their intestine. But mammals, such as the dog and fox, may become seriously ill when they are infected with Cryptocotyle.

Natural immunity depends to a large extent upon the capacity of the host's tissues to form antibody substances (pp. 335 and 336). These **antibodies** counteract the toxic prod-ucts of the parasite; and the development of natural immunity indicates that an association between the parasite and host has existed for a comparatively long evolutionary period.

Nitrogen-fixing Bacteria. One case of symbiosis deserves special emphasis, because it plays an important role in the conservation of *soil fertility*. The **nitrogen-fixing bacteria** live *symbiotically* in the root tissues of several common species of higher plants (Fig. 10-6). These bacteria are the only organisms that are able to utilize free nitrogen (N_2) in their metabolism. Such a usage involves

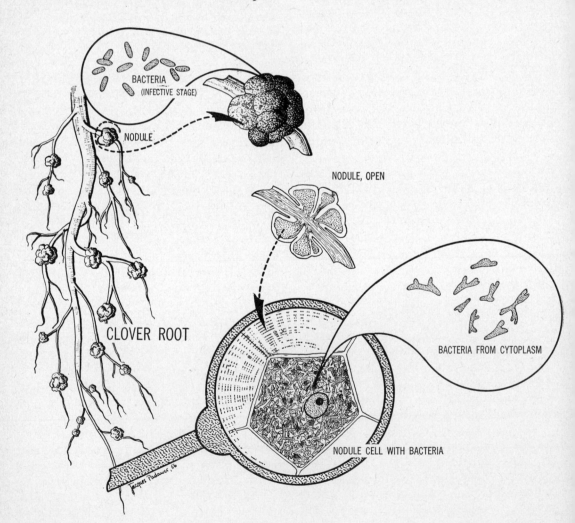

BACTERIA (INFECTIVE STAGE)

NODULE

NODULE, OPEN

CLOVER ROOT

BACTERIA FROM CYTOPLASM

NODULE CELL WITH BACTERIA

Fig. 10-6. Nitrogen-fixing bacteria. These symbiotic organisms live in the cytoplasm of cells of nodules found on the roots of clover and other leguminous plants.

the conversion of free nitrogen (N_2) into the nitrate ($-NO_3$) form of nitrogen, and this *fixation of nitrogen* is an uphill process. Unlike most oxidation reactions, the fixation of nitrogen requires the **absorption** of considerable energy. As a source for this energy, the nitrogen-fixing bacteria are dependent upon glucose (or other carbohydrate) provided by the root tissues of the host plant. In return, the host receives the excess quantities of nitrate compounds formed by the bacteria.

Rich cultures of the nitrogen-fixing bacteria *live in the* **cytoplasm** of the cells of nodulelike swellings that can be seen on the roots of the leguminous plants, such as beans and peas, and upon the roots of other plants, such as alfalfa and clover (Fig. 10-6). Frequently such crops are "rotated" with ordinary soil-depleting crops. The nitrate compounds formed by the bacteria, with the help of the host plant, may be returned to the soil directly, if the crop is plowed under; or the nitrates may be converted into proteins that return nitrogen to the soil indirectly, via the metabolism of animals that have eaten the protein, or of saprophytes that accomplish their decay. In any event the nitrogen-fixing bacteria accomplish the important function of reclaiming free nitrogen and restoring it to "circulation" in other forms of life.

CHEMOTROPHIC NUTRITION

The capacity of green plants to synthesize their organic essentials entirely from inorganic substances represents the primary source of organic foods utilized by other organisms. However, there are a few kinds of bacteria that also can grow in the complete absence of organic foods. These forms, lacking chlorophyll, cannot utilize the sun's energy to support their metabolism. Instead, they resort to the **oxidation** *of certain inorganic substances,* thus obtaining energy for synthesizing glucose; and this glucose then provides a source of matter and energy for the synthesis of the other organic compo-

nents of their protoplasm. This kind of nutrition, in which *metabolism is supported by energy derived from inorganic oxidations,* is called **chemotrophic nutrition.** Likewise, this kind of synthesis, which may be formulated as follows:

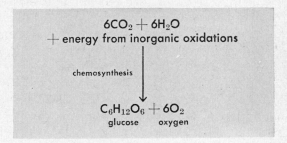

$$6CO_2 + 6H_2O$$
$$+ \text{energy from inorganic oxidations}$$

chemosynthesis

$$C_6H_{12}O_6 + 6O_2$$
glucose   oxygen

is sometimes referred to as **chemosynthesis** (in contrast to photosynthesis).

Inorganic substances capable of yielding energy through oxidation are not very abundant in the environment, and therefore chemotrophic modes of nutrition are restricted to a relatively small number of bacterial species.

The nutrition of the **sulfur bacteria** (Fig. 10-7) is typically chemotrophic. These bacteria oxidize hydrogen sulfide (H_2S), first into free sulfur (S) that is stored intracellularly (Fig. 10-7), and then into sulfate ($-SO_4$) compounds as further energy may be needed. Other **chemotrophic bacteria** oxidize free hydrogen (to water), carbon monoxide (to

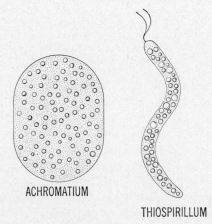

ACHROMATIUM

THIOSPIRILLUM

Fig. 10-7. Two kinds of sulfur bacteria. The spherical droplets are free sulfur.

carbon dioxide), iron salts (ferrous to ferric salts), and so on. These inorganic oxidations provide the energy by which all these species **synthesize carbohydrate** from CO_2 and H_2O. And since they can also utilize inorganic nitrogen compounds for the synthesis of amino acids and proteins, the **chemotrophic bacteria,** *like the green plants, are not directly dependent on other organisms* for their essential nutrients. In fact, both chemotrophic and holophytic organisms are said to be **autotrophic,** or literally "self-nourishing."

The Nitrite and the Nitrate Bacteria. These **autotrophic (chemotrophic)** bacteria are especially important in relation to soil fertility. Much of the nitrogen from decomposing remnants of plants and animals in the soil is liberated by the saprophytic bacteria in the form of ammonia (NH_3), or of ammonium (NH_4—) salts, which are not utilized very efficiently by most green plants. But **nitrate bacteria** (Fig. 10-8) are present in all rich soil, and these organisms get energy for growth by oxidizing **ammonia** (or ammonium salts) into **nitrite** (—NO_2) salts. **Nitrate bacteria** (Fig. 10-8), possessing a

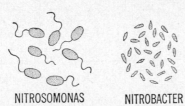

NITROSOMONAS   NITROBACTER

Fig. 10-8. Nitrite and nitrate bacteria. *Nitrosomonas* derives energy for chemosynthesis by oxidizing ammonia (NH_3), forming nitrites (—NO_2); *Nitrobacter* oxidizes nitrites, forming nitrates (—NO_3).

somewhat different set of enzymes, also obtain energy by oxidizing the **nitrite** (—NO_2) salts into **nitrates** (—NO_3). Consequently the reclamation of nitrate nitrogen from its various other combinations depends upon the nitrite and nitrate bacteria, as well as upon saprophytic organisms. In performing this function, the nitrite and nitrate bacteria gain energy with which to synthesize carbohydrates and the other organic components of their structure.

VARIOUS MODES OF NUTRITION: AN OUTLINE AND SUMMARY

According to their nutritional processes (Chaps. 7, 9, and 10), living organisms may be classified as follows:

I. *Autotrophic.* Can synthesize all essential organic components entirely from inorganic substances; therefore not directly dependent upon other organisms for foods.
   a. *Holophytic.* Utilize light (by photosynthesis) as a primary source of energy: **green plants.**
   b. *Chemotrophic.* Obtain energy by oxidizing inorganic substances: sulfur, nitrite, and nitrate bacteria, etc.

II. *Heterotrophic.* Require at least a minimum of **preformed organic compounds;** therefore dependent upon autotrophic organisms for food.
   a. *Holozoic.* Obtain organic foods by **ingestion, digestion,** etc.: *most animals.*
   b. *Saprophytic.* Absorb organic foods directly from the environment with or without external digestion: many **fungi,** including most **bacteria,** some **flagellates,** and a very few higher plants.
   c. *Parasitic.* Obtain food from the bodies of other *living* organisms, in or on which they live; some species in almost every category of plants and animals.

III. *Mixotrophic.* Combine autotrophic and heterotrophic nutritions in various ways: many flagellates and a few higher plants (for example, insectivorous species; see p. 261).

Holophytic and holozoic organisms have achieved great dominance, and practically all complex organisms are clearly divisible into two great groups: the plants and the animals. But among unicellular and simple colonial forms there are many borderline organisms and many radical departures from the main lines of evolution. In short, many methods of gaining matter and energy for growth and activity are found among simpler living bodies, but only the holophytic and holozoic modes of nutrition proved adequate for the sustenance of larger and more complex organisms.

CYCLIC USAGE OF THE FOOD ELEMENTS

Each organism, regardless of its mode of nutrition, grows at the expense of specific substances taken from the environment. Consequently, the life of a species cannot continue if any substance essential to its growth becomes exhausted. In the total economy of living things, however, the various food substances keep returning to the environment, ultimately in their original form and quantity. The earth is like a sealed but balanced aquarium. It receives no significant quantity of matter from other parts of the universe. But despite this material isolation, the earth can supply the material needs of all its inhabitants indefinitely—so long as light from the sun maintains its strength and continues to energize, directly or indirectly, the metabolic processes of existing organisms.

The simplest way to realize the inexhaustibility of the *material* requirements of life is to trace the cycle of chemical changes by which each *element* returns to the environment after participating in the metabolism of various organisms. Each element participates in the formation of many protoplasmic compounds, but finally each returns to the environment in its original form. Thus the **carbon cycle,** the **hydrogen cycle,** and the **nitrogen cycle** describe the specific series of chemical changes by which each of these elements is utilized by different organisms and finally restored to the environment in the original form. Each element exhibits a different cycle, but only the **carbon** and **nitrogen** cycles will be described.

The Carbon Cycle. The environmental source of carbon for all organic syntheses is the carbon dioxide present in the atmosphere and natural waters of the earth (Fig. 10-9). The green plants (by photosynthesis) and to a much smaller extent the autotrophic bacteria (by chemosynthesis) take this carbon and build it into the molecular structure of carbohydrates; and these carbohydrates furnish all the energy, and a large part of the matter needed by plants for the synthesis of proteins, lipids, and other organic compounds in the protoplasm. The potential energy stored by green plants in various organic compounds is derived initially from the sun, and this energy becomes the driving force in the metabolism of virtually all other organisms. Organic compounds, created by plants and appropriated by animals, saprophytes, and parasites, furnish energy and matter for the synthesis of all essential organic components in heterotrophic organisms. Eventually, however, all organic compounds suffer decomposition: sooner or later all organic carbon returns to the environment as carbon dioxide, via the respiration of the organisms wherein the energy is utilized (Fig. 10-9).

The Nitrogen Cycle. The main environmental source of nitrogen used by green plants for the synthesis of the amino acids and other essential nitrogen compounds is nitrate ($-NO_3$) nitrogen, in the soil and natural waters of the earth (Fig. 10-10). The organic nitrogen compounds formed by plants are used later by animals and other heterotrophic organisms for the synthesis of *their* proteins. In living animals, proteins and other complex nitrogen compounds may be catabolized—in which case the nitrogen is excreted as urea and other simple nitrogenous wastes; or such protein may pass to the environment as a remnant of some animal. In any event, organic nitrogen in the environment is utilized by the putrefactive bacteria (Fig. 10-10), which excrete the nitrogen mainly in the form of ammonia (NH_3) but partially in the form of free nitrogen (N_2). Ammonia and ammonium compounds in the soil are utilized as a source of energy

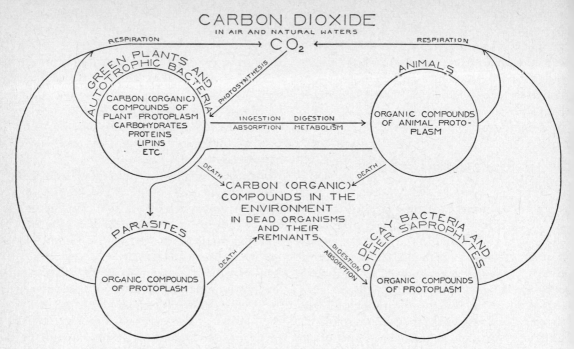

Fig. 10-9. The cyclic usage of carbon compounds in various organisms, i.e., the carbon cycle. Compounds not included in the circles are free in the environment.

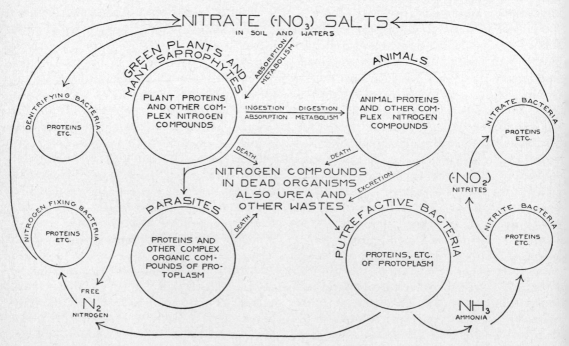

Fig. 10-10. The cyclic usage of nitrogen compounds in various organisms, i.e., the nitrogen cycle. Compounds not included in the circles are free in the environment.

and matter by the **nitrite bacteria,** which produce nitrites; and the nitrites are used by the **nitrate bacteria,** which finally restore the nitrogen to the environment in its original nitrate form. The small quanity of nitrogen that tends to "escape from the cycle" as free nitrogen (N_2) is reclaimed by the **nitrogen-fixing bacteria.** In the roots of leguminous plants, these symbiotic bacteria avail themselves of preformed carbohydrate for energy to oxidize free nitrogen to its nitrate form.

SOLAR ENERGY AND THE PERPETUATION OF LIFE

Each of the elements undergoes a **closed cycle** of chemical changes as it is utilized in the metabolism of various organisms. Consequently the material requirements of living things will never be exhausted so long as these cycles continue. To keep going, these cyclic changes do not require new matter, but they do require new energy, and this energy comes from the sun. Therefore the perpetuation of life as we know it depends upon the light of the sun.

The radiant energy absorbed by the chlorophyll of green plants is transformed into the potential energy of free oxygen and glucose—and indirectly into the potential energy of other organic compounds. All organisms get energy from organic substances and, in the process, eventually convert them back into their original form. The energy liberated by the complete oxidation of a given amount of carbohydrate is exactly equal to that previously absorbed in the photosynthesis of this carbohydrate. All energy transformations whether in animate or inanimate bodies, obey the **First Law of Energy.** Energy is conserved in that the total quantity of energy remains the same regardless of all transformations. But the energy released by the oxidation of carbohydrate does not appear in its original form. Much is liberated directly as **heat,** and only part is transformed into the chemical potential energy of other complex organic compounds, such as proteins and lipids. Eventually all the organic compounds in protoplasm are decomposed. In the catabolism of various cells, these decompositions give forth many kinds of energy, **mechanical, electrical, osmotic,** etc.—but eventually all energy liberated in organisms is transformed into **heat.** Therefore the net result of all activities in living organisms is the transformation of a certain quantity of energy from **light** finally into **heat.**

The sun is the source of practically all the available light energy on our earth. The sun liberates stupendous quantities of energy, probably by atomic fissions and fusions that occur spontaneously at high temperatures, but only a small fraction of the kinetic energy from the sun falls upon our earth. Of this small fraction the greater part strikes inanimate bodies (rocks, water, soil, etc.), which absorb the light and transform it *immediately* into heat. Only that minute fraction of solar energy that happens to fall upon the green plants escapes immediate degradation. But this fraction launches upon a peculiar and roundabout series of transformations that motivate the complex activities of living organisms. Then finally this energy likewise becomes converted entirely into heat.

Unlike matter, the **energy** utilized by living things *does not form a closed cycle.* This energy continuously runs "downhill"—from light to heat—turning the wheels of life as it flows. As it is formed, the heat is dissipated; it warms the water, the soil, the air, etc., and gradually it escapes into interstellar space. What eventually may become of this dissipated energy—whether it may be transformed back into some useful form in some unknown part of the universe—we do not know. So far as our earth is concerned, all processes, in living and in nonliving nature, conform with the **Second Law of Energy;** all forms of energy are continually degraded into heat and dissipated. Therefore the extinction of life on this planet must inevitably occur—if and when the radiant energy of the sun becomes too feeble to maintain a proper temperature in the environment and to support the metabolism of green plants and, indirectly, of other organisms.

ORIGIN OF LIVING MATTER

The origin of living organisms directly from nonliving matter, under present-day conditions in our environment, was a doctrine widely believed by scientists until about one hundred years ago. First it was thought that worms could come from mud, or maggots from meat, and so forth; later it was held that microorganisms, at least, could arise from the nonliving ingredients of decomposing beef broth. Finally, however, the classic experiments of Redi (1650), Spallanzani (1750), and Pasteur (1860) proved that this doctrine, called **spontaneous generation,** could not be substantiated. But what alternative was left to science?

Since the Pasteur experiments, the prevalent idea has been that some primitive form of protoplasm originated from nonliving matter during the Archeozoic Era (p. 563)—some two billion years ago—when conditions on this planet were quite different. Until recently, however, no definitive theory could be formulated, partly because speculations on the nature of the early environment were premature and misleading, and partly because scientists hesitated to theorize when so very few data were available. Gradually ideas on the nature of the early environment began to clarify, however, and in 1936, the Russian biochemist A. I. Oparin crystalized current thinking in his book, *The Origin of Life.* Since that time, the contributions of Harold Urey and Stanley Miller of California, and of George Wald of Harvard University have led to further advances. Finally, therefore, it now seems possible to reapproach the problem in a scientific manner and to ask such questions as: how did organic matter and primitive organisms come into being? and what was the nature of these first forms of life?

It is necessary to realize that the early atmosphere of the earth did not contain any gaseous oxygen (O_2) or nitrogen (N_2), but that other gases, particularly hydrogen (H_2), ammonia (NH_3), methane (CH_4), and water vapor (H_2O) were abundant. The temperature at the earth's surface was somewhat above the boiling point of water and there was considerable energy in the form of electrical discharges, from large cloud masses in the atmosphere, and from ultraviolet radiations from the sun, which could penetrate the clouds.

These conditions—a **reducing atmosphere,** suitable sources of carbon, hydrogen, and nitrogen, and abundant available energy—seem highly conducive to the formation and stabilization of organic molecules. Consequently, some recent experiments in which these conditions were duplicated as closely as possible are of tremendous interest. In 1953, Stanley Miller, working from suggestions by Harold Urey, arranged to circulate the gases of the early atmosphere through a closed system of vessels into which a continuous series of electric sparks was being discharged. At the end of only eight days, Miller found that significant quantities of at least three (probably five) different **amino acids** had accumulated in the water trap of the system, and there was evidence that other more complex unidentified organic compounds had come into being. In other words, it now seems probable that a variety of organic compounds could have been generated spontaneously in the ancient terrestrial environment and that these could have become well concentrated as the waters of the earth underwent condensation and evaporation. Granting the presence of such organic compounds in the early environment, the problem of how life may have arisen is greatly simplified—especially when one thinks of the infinity of time that has been available.

Certain molecules, especially amino acids and nucleic acids, by virtue of their intrinsic structure can form stable aggregates of considerable size. Moreover, such aggregates display a maximum stability when a certain size is reached. Consequently, larger particles that might arise would tend to split into smaller ones when the point of maximum stability was passed. Conceivably such phenomena might lead toward the more complex processes of growth and reproduction such as exist today, but nothing is known about the stages of transition. One cannot say how genes and enzymes first originated, nor how these remarkable entities gradually achieved some primitive form of protoplasmic organization.

Nature of the First Organisms. It was commonly believed for many years that the earliest organisms were very primitive green plants, similar perhaps to the blue-green algae (p. 594) of today. Considering what now seems true about the early environment, however, this theory must be abandoned. Carbon dioxide was not present in the early atmosphere and photosynthesis could not occur. It seems more probable, instead, that early primitive "organisms," generating in the rich organic brew that had accumulated in landlocked evaporating basins, derived their energy from fermentation or some other anaerobic kind of metabolism. In other words, the earliest organisms probably were saprophytes, which absorbed organic material from the environment and gained energy from anaerobic processes of metabolism. Such metabolism, to be sure, is relatively inefficient, but it does liberate energy when oxygen is lacking, and it does produce significant amounts of CO_2. Indeed, it seems quite likely that the carbon dioxide of our atmosphere originated completely from the metabolic activities of primitive organisms. This sounds incredible, at first. But when we consider that the green plants of today take up from the atmosphere the total supply of CO_2 once every three hundred years and that the Archeozoic Era endured at least two billion years, the credibility becomes apparent.

Evolution of Green Plants. Photosynthesis could not develop until an adequate supply of CO_2 became available in the environment, presumably as a result of fermentative processes in an ever-increasing population of saprophytic organisms. ATP, undoubtedly, assumed importance as an energy source very early in the evolution of protoplasmic systems; and presumably the cyclic type of photophosphorylation (p. 162), which does not generate free O_2, may be regarded as an early step in the direction of photosynthesis. With the advent of chlorophyll, however, photolysis and consequently the generation of free O_2 must have started, so that oxygen began to be an important component of the atmosphere. Accordingly, the greater efficiency of oxidative metabolism eventually could be extended from the green plants, where it must have originated, to the saprophytes, which previously had lived entirely by anaerobic means, and to new organisms that began to take on the habits of holozoic nutrition. Thus again we are forced to an unfamiliar conclusion. Not only have organisms been shaped in large measure by the changing environment, but also the environment itself has been fashioned and refashioned by organisms. Indeed, even today it is found that the *oxygen of our atmosphere is completely replaced every two thousand years* as a result of the metabolism of heterotrophic organisms and the photosynthetic activities of green plants.

Does Life Exist Elsewhere? Astronomical evidence indicates that planets similar to the earth in size, composition, and temperature occur quite rarely in the universe. But the universe is exceedingly large. In our own galaxy alone, there are thousands of earth-like planets; and at the present time almost a hundred million other galaxies have come into range of the most powerful telescopes. The inescapable conclusion is, therefore, that living things must have arisen and are arising in many places. We do not have to shoulder the whole burden of life's destiny. But we are isolated from other life-bearing planets by stupendous distances, and across such distances, probably, no signals will ever pass. We cannot know how life is faring elsewhere. We can only wish it well.

TEST QUESTIONS

1. Define the term "fungi." Name eight kinds of fungi.
2. Identify and exemplify each of the following terms: (a) mycelium; (b) hypha; (c) rhizoids; (d) sporangiophore.
3. Name at least three kinds of saprophytic organisms. What is distinctive about this mode of nutrition?
4. Discuss anaerobic metabolism in yeast. What is the significance of this type of metabolism (a) to the yeast? (b) to mankind?
5. How are the yeast and the bread mold different, as regards their capacity to utilize: (a) starch; and (b) nitrate salts, present in the culture medium?
6. Differentiate between *decay* and *putrefaction*. What mode of nutrition is exemplified by the organisms that are involved in these processes?
7. Name three kinds of bacteria that are important in the decomposition of carbohydrates and fats, specifying the product or products formed by each.
8. Specify the final end products of decay and putrefaction (taking these processes as a whole).
9. Explain the general importance of decay and putrefaction in relation to: (a) the kinds of matter that are disposed of; and (b) the kinds of matter that are liberated.
10. What is a parasite? Differentiate between harmful and neutral parasitism, citing two examples in each case.
11. Explain the nature of symbiosis, citing at least three specific examples.
12. Explain the phrase "cyclic usage of the food elements," using the *carbon* cycle to exemplify the discussion.
13. Name five different kinds of bacteria that play a significant role in the nitrogen cycle, and in each case specify: (a) the habitat of the species; (b) its mode of nutrition; and (c) the nitrogen compounds used and produced by the species (use equations, if possible).
14. Classify various organisms on the basis of their nutrition, naming at least one specific organism in every group.
15. Explain the relation of light energy to the other forms of energy expended by living organisms. How is this problem related to the eventual extinction of life upon this planet?
16. How was the early environment of the earth different from that of today?
17. What was the nature of the earliest organisms?
18. What is the basis for deciding that the first living things could not have been green plants?
19. Does life exist elsewhere in the universe? Explain.

FURTHER READINGS

1. *The Life of Bacteria,* by K. V. Thimann; New York, 1955.
2. *The Fitness of the Environment,* by L. J. Henderson; New York, 1913.
3. *The Microbial World,* rev. ed., by R. Y. Stanier; Englewood Cliffs, N. J., 1963.
4. *The Origin of Life,* by A. I. Oparin; New York, 1953.
5. *Great Experiments in Biology,* ed. by M. Gabriel and S. Fogel; sections by Redi, Spallanzani, and Pasteur; Englewood Cliffs, N. J., 1955.
6. *Chemical Evolution,* by Melvin Calvin; Condon Lectures, Oregon State University: 1. From Molecule to Microbe, and 2. The Origin of Life on Earth and Elsewhere.

11-*Responsiveness in Single Cells*

THE CHANGING conditions within and around each living body constantly act as stimuli that excite the organism to perform a variety of responses. The dog searches for food when stimulated by the hunger contractions of his empty stomach; if overheated by the sun he may lie down in a shady spot. **Responsiveness** includes the sum total of all an organism's reactions to stimuli. Our present aim is to analyze some of the factors that determine the responses of relatively simple organisms.

DISCONTINUOUS (ABRUPT) VS. CONTINUOUS (SLOW) RESPONSES

The most characteristic responses of organisms are of very short duration. They flare up and quickly subside after the stimulation ceases—as when one shies from a tossed stone or sneezes from some dust. The magnitude of such **discontinuous responses** is out of all proportion to the strength of the stimulation. Some very slight stimulus—of sight, touch, sound, etc.—precipitates a very energetic reaction.

In abrupt or discontinuous responses the stimulus does not provide the energy expended during the reaction. Like the pressure on the trigger of a rifle, the stimulus merely precipitates the liberation of a sudden burst of energy, and this burst subsides as soon as the responsive act has been performed. Accordingly, discontinuous responses are also called "explosive responses," and the stimulus is said to display a "trigger action."

In other cases, however, a very gradual and enduring change of condition (such as light, temperature, atmospheric pressure) leads to an equally gradual and enduring change in the general form and activity of the organism. A continuous exposure to the sun, for example, produces a gradual browning of the skin, or a lengthy sojourn at high altitude leads to a gradual enrichment of the hemoglobin of the blood. In such **continuous responses,** the quantity and quality of the bodily changes depend in large measure upon the quantity and quality of the stimulating factors. In the broadest sense such gradual changes in the organism may be called responses, and the environmental factors may be referred to as stimuli. But for the present, the discussion will include only responses of the discontinuous or "explosive" type, in which the stimulus exerts a "trigger-like" action.

SUCCESSFUL STIMULATION: THE STATE OF EXCITATION

Excitability is a universal protoplasmic characteristic. When successfully stimulated, every cell displays a wavelike change of structure and activity that originates at the point of stimulation, spreads throughout all parts of the protoplasm, and then subsides. This abrupt and strictly temporary disturbance of the ordinary resting condition of the protoplasm is designated as **excitation.** The **excited state** is invariably the forerunner of any definite cellular response, such as the contracting of a muscle or the secreting of a gland.

Some cells, like muscle cells, perform some visible action each time they are stimulated, and in such cases the visible action serves to indicate that a stimulation has been successful. But for cells like nerve cells, which are incapable of executing any visible act, several other criteria of successful excitation are available. Invariably there is a propagated change in the electrical potential of the cell membrane, and this **action potential** spreads in exact synchrony with the excitation. Excitation is also accompanied by the **liberation** of a small quantity of **heat**, and in most cases at least, excited cells display a temporary **increase** of permeability. Apparently excitation precipitates a temporary flare-up in the metabolism of the cell; and during excitation special enzymes and substrates, which are not used during periods of rest, are utilized by the excited cell.

The Action Potential. An action potential is an infallible sign of successful excitation. It has been measured accurately in many kinds of animal and plant tissues and in quite a number of individual cells. In the case of a single cell, difficulty is encountered unless the cell, like a nerve or muscle cell, is long enough to allow for the placement of electrodes leading to a **galvanometer** (Fig. 11-1), or to an **oscilloscope.**

The electrical potential, which gives rise

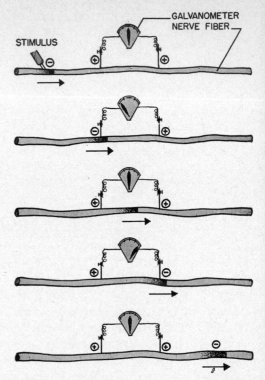

Fig. 11-1. Bioelectric potentials in the axon of a nerve cell. A nerve impulse (the arrow) traveling along a nerve fiber betrays its presence as a rapidly moving wave of negativity (as compared with the positivity of resting, inactive regions of the nerve fiber). Note how the needle of the galvanometer shifts as the impulse travels.

to an action current, varies between 0.01 and 0.1 volt (10 to 100 millivolts), although in animal cells it tends to approximate the higher value. The current generated in one cell, or group of cells, may be strong enough to spread to neighboring cells, thus relaying the excitation (Fig. 11-2). In the heart, for example, the excitation for each beat originates in a small mass of tissue in the wall of the right auricle. From this point the current travels along a highly specialized group of muscle fibers, reaching the other auricle and the ventricles in time to touch off their contractions just at the proper instant. In taking the **electrocardiogram,** the physician records the strength and pattern of the shifting action potential as it spreads throughout the

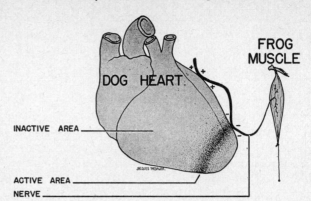

Fig. 11-2. The electric potentials developed in a beating heart are strong enough to stimulate a nerve, if it is brought into contact with the heart. In the experiment above, the frog muscle twitches with each beat of the dog's heart. Note the wave of electrical negativity that accompanies the wave of activity (contraction) in the heart tissue. (Redrawn from *The Machinery of the Body*, by Carlson and Johnson. University of Chicago Press.)

heart, and these measurements prove helpful in diagnosing cardiac function.

Bioelectric Potentials. Each cell, of course, is bounded by a plasma membrane that, in the living state, displays a very distinct **electrical polarization.** The outer surface is positive in relation to the negatively charged inner surface. In the **resting,** or unexcited, cell this difference of potential is called the **resting potential;** it usually amounts to some 50 to 100 millivolts (Fig. 11-3). When a cell is excited, however, a localized and momentary depolarization of the membrane occurs and, in fact, there is even a reversal of the normal polarity. This rapid shifting of the membrane potential is called the **action potential** (Fig. 11-3). The action potential is not static, however. It rapidly propagates itself over the entire cell surface, starting at the point of stimulation. Moreover, the

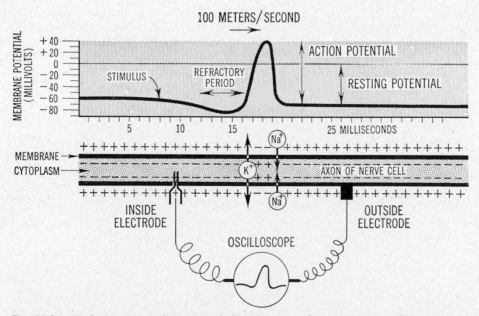

Fig. 11-3. Bioelectric potentials as recorded in the axon of a giant nerve cell (squid). The velocity of the **action potential,** as it speeds along the nerve fiber, is in exact synchrony with the transmission of the excitation, or **nerve impulse.** The velocity specified here, however, is derived from a mammalian nerve. (Modified from Bernhard Katz.)

propagation is synchronous with the spreading of the state of excitation.

Resting potentials and **action potentials** have been studied most extensively in nerve cells, particularly the giant nerve cells of the squid and other mollusks. These cells are large enough to permit one of the electrodes to the oscilloscope to be placed inside the cytoplasm, while the other is kept on the outer surface of the cell membrane (Fig. 11-3). Many other cells and tissues have also been studied, however, and it is safe to conclude that the propagation of a definitive action potential is a universal characteristic of cellular excitation.

The basic nature of these bioelectric potentials will be discussed more fully later, in a section dealing with the nervous system (Chap. 25). Here, however, a few important general factors will be considered.

The maintenance of an adequately high resting potential and the maintenance of excitability depend upon the active ion transport mechanisms of the cell (p. 121). These mechanisms build up the concentration of potassium ions (K^+) inside the membrane, frequently to a point where it is 30 times the outside concentration; and at the same time the "sodium pump" tends to keep the sodium (Na^+) concentration about 10 times lower inside than outside. But several other factors must also be kept in mind: (1) the cell membrane is distinctly more permeable to potassium (K^+) ions than to sodium (Na^+); (2) the mobility of K^+ is greater than that of Na^+; (3) most of the negatively charged ions inside the membrane are large organic anions, such as protein, which have very low mobility and virtually no penetrability; (4) most of the anions outside the membrane, among which chloride (Cl^-) is heavily represented, are small inorganic ions; and (5) the ion conductance of the **resting** membrane is very low.

Granting the foregoing conditions, which tend to be universally present, **a resting membrane potential** of the observed magnitude is inevitable. Perhaps the most important factor is the high concentration gradient of the K^+ ion. These mobile ions, driven by the high gradient, tend to escape through the membrane, but the large anions inside the cell are not able to follow. Thus a counter electrostatic force is built up, which holds a layer of K^+ ions hovering close to the outer surface of the membrane. Accordingly the outer surface is always positive in relation to the inner surface. Sodium ions, on the other hand, experience great difficulty in penetrating the resting membrane. Moreover, if such penetration should occur, chloride (Cl^-) ions would acompany the Na^+, canceling out the charge. Sooner or later, the sodium would be expelled by virtue of the active transport mechanisms.

The foregoing factors likewise play a dominant role in the generation of the **action potential,** which invariably accompanies successful excitation. A stimulus changes the membrane structure at the point of stimulation. In this small area, the membrane momentarily becomes much more permeable to ions, particularly sodium ions (Fig. 11-3). In this sharply localized region, therefore, sodium ions, driven by the high gradient and electrical potential, enter the cell very rapidly, canceling the negativity of the inner membrane surface and allowing potassium ions to escape from the outer surface. This rapid and momentary exchange of ions effects a localized depolarization of the membrane. Locally the outer surface in the excited area becomes distinctly negative with reference to surrounding unexcited areas. The influx of sodium is so vigorous, in fact, that a reversal of polarity occurs in the strictly localized excited area (Fig. 11-3). Within a few milliseconds, however, when the action potential is reaching its peak (Fig. 11-3), normal structure and resistance are regained by the membrane. Then quickly the membrane potential returns to normal sign and value. Meanwhile, however, the excitation keeps spreading. A wave of negativity travels over the cell surface. Apparently the changing potential in each localized area touches off excitation in neighboring areas and the excitation is propagated with undiminished vigor.

Apparently the maintenance of an electrically polarized membrane is an essential factor in maintaining reactivity in living cells. Whenever polarization is locally abolished, excitation occurs; conversely, whenever excitation occurs, the polarization is momentarily abolished. These changes are not necessarily confined to the plasma membrane. They may extend via the membranes of the endoplasmic reticulum to deeper parts of the cell.

Excitation Metabolism. An excited cell immediately begins to liberate extra heat, but it does *not* immediately begin to consume extra oxygen. In fact, many cells, such as muscle and nerve cells, can continue to respond to stimulation for quite a while after their oxygen has been used up. This **excitation metabolism** should not be confused with the **recovery metabolism,** which *follows* excitation. Recovery always involves an extra consumption of oxygen and an extra production of carbon dioxide. In short, the recovery reactions supply the energy required to restore the cell to its original condition (aside from the loss of a small quantity of oxidized fuel). When recovery metabolism is inhibited, as by lack of oxygen, the cell more quickly reaches a *state of total fatigue*—that is, a state in which it can no longer respond to stimulation. It may respond later, however, if it has been allowed to recover in the presence of an adequate supply of oxygen.

The precise nature and role of the excitation metabolism in relation to membrane structure and potential remains an open question. In nerve cells it has been proposed by David Nachmansohn of Columbia University that excitation involves the liberation of an excitatory substance, **acetylcholine** (p. 455), which then is hydrolyzed by a special enzyme, **cholinesterose,** as the excitation subsides. More evidence is needed, however, before the question can be resolved completely.

The Refractory Period. Immediately following excitation, before the membrane has returned to its original state, there is a brief **absolute refractory period,** during which the cell cannot be re-excited by any stimulus, however strong; and following this, there is a **relative refractory period,** during which an unusually strong stimulus is required to elicit excitation. The duration of the total refractory period differs in different cells, from less than 0.001 second (in nerve cells) to a number of seconds (in plant cells). Due to the refractory period, the state of excitation is self-limiting: a cell cannot remain continuously in the excited state.

The refractory period also has an important bearing on the rhythmicity of certain responses, such as the beating of heart muscle or of cilia, since the refractory period imposes a definite limit upon the frequency at which the responses are able to recur. Many responses that appear to endure for some time, like the prolonged contraction of a body muscle, actually represent a series of rapidly recurring responses. In the case of the muscle this can be seen in the electrical records, for the electromyogram always shows a series of action potentials occurring synchronously with the excitations.

STIMULI AND STIMULATION

Any physical or chemical *change* occurring within or around a living body may act as a stimulus, provided the quantity, quality, and rate of the change are properly adjusted to the sensitivities of the cell or cells that are to be excited. The various kinds of stimuli capable of exciting cells and organisms generally may be classified as follows:

Mechanical stimuli: Contact, pressure, sound.
Thermal stimuli: Changes of temperature.
Concentration stimuli: Changes in the concentration of substances.
Chemical stimuli: Changes in the kinds of substances present in or around the organism.

Electrical stimuli: Changes in strength or direction of electric currents.

Photic stimuli: Changes in the intensity, color, or direction of light.

Most cells *can* be excited by several kinds of stimuli, but usually each kind of cell is especially susceptible to a particular kind of stimulation. Successful stimulation of the retinal cells of the eye, for example, requires an unbelievably small quantity of light, whereas another kind of stimulus, such as a blow on the temple, can arouse sensations of light ("seeing stars") only if the intensity of the stimulus is relatively great. In the case of specialized cells, nonspecific stimuli are relatively ineffective; but there is one important exception to this general rule. All cells are easily excited by electrical stimulation, and this fact emphasizes the role of the action potential as a normal agency in propagating the excitation, once a cell has been aroused.

The *rate* of the stimulating change has a distinct influence upon its effectiveness, as can be demonstrated with light as an example. The rapid brightening or dimming of a light is always noticeable. But if the change develops slowly, it may fail to excite the cells of the retina, and consequently it is not perceived. Too short a change may also fail to excite the retina. An intermittently flashing light is perceived to be continuous if the individual flashes begin to follow one another at a rate exceeding about 14 per second.

Electrical stimulations will also illustrate the foregoing points. If a direct current is passed through a muscle, no contraction occurs except at the moment when the current is turned on or off—that is, while a *change* of current intensity is taking place. But the *rate* of the change must also be adjusted properly if the muscle is to be excited. Even with adequate voltage, no excitation occurs if the current rises or falls too slowly or too quickly.

Receptors, Conductors, and Effectors. In multicellular organisms a typical response involves not one, but a series of cells, each playing a specialized role. Let us take, for example, the closing of the pupil, which occurs when a bright light is directed into the eye. In this response the light does not act directly upon the muscle cells of the iris, which control the size of the pupil opening. Only the **cone and rod cells** of the retina, deep inside the eyeball, are excited by the light. Thus the retinal cells act as **receptors** when light is the stimulating agency. But after these cells receive the stimulus, they relay the excitation to a series of **nerve cells**, which serve as the **conductors** of the responsive system. The nerve cells conduct at high speed, and within about 0.01 second they transmit the excitation to the muscle cells of the iris. Thus the muscles are the **effectors** of this response, in that the muscles contract and close the pupil.

A **receptor** is any part of the organism that displays a special sensitivity to excitation, usually by a specific kind of stimulus. The main function of the receptor is to generate excitations and relay them to the conductor structures. A **conductor** is any specialized part of the organism that serves to propagate excitations toward an effector. And finally, an **effector** is a specialized part of the organism that executes the final or "active" phase of a response.

In the higher animals, including man, the receptors are mainly represented by the sensory cells and the sense organs; the conductors, by the cells of the nervous system; and the effectors, by the muscles and glands. But in many unicellular organisms there are receptor, conductor, and effector structures, differentiated within the single cell.

Responsive Mechanisms in One-celled Organisms. When the advancing pseudopodium of an amoeba is probed with a microinstrument, the amoeba withdraws the pseudopodium and starts retreating in the opposite direction (Fig. 11-4). Plainly the excitation does not remain localized at the point where the stimulus is *received*. It is *conducted* throughout the cell, or otherwise the several pseudopodia, which serve as **effectors,** could

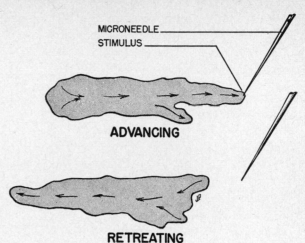

MICRONEEDLE
STIMULUS

ADVANCING

RETREATING

Fig. 11-4. Response of an amoeba, pricked by a microneedle. The specimen moves away in a coordinated manner, indicating that the excitation is **conducted** from the site of stimulation to all parts of the cell.

not act in a concerted fashion as the amoeba alters the direction of its locomotion. In the amoeba, apparently, any part of the cell may serve temporarily as receptor, conductor, or effector, and scarcely any definite differentiation of these parts can be recognized. In the amoeba, however, it has recently been shown that the tip of an advancing pseudopodium is consistently negative in relation to other parts of the cell surface, which indicates that the action potential has its origin here.

Perhaps the commonest **specialized receptors** in unicellular organisms are the red-colored **chromatophores,** or "eyespots," that are found in many green flagellates (Figs. 9-7 and 10-4). Each chromatophore is a small pigmented granule, which is generally regarded as a **photoreceptor.** Probably many of the light-seeking responses that are characteristic of the phytoflagellates are initiated in these receptor structures.

The **cilia** and **flagella** of the Protozoa and free-swimming algae serve as effectors of mechanical response, and probably also as receptors of tactile stimuli, since frequently these parts are first to make contact with external objects. Many protozoans, especially ciliates, also possess internally placed contractile fibrils, called **myonemes** (Figs. 11-5 and 11-6). These intracellular effectors act more or less like the muscle fibers of higher animals. By shortening quickly and forcibly, the myonemes enable a one-celled organism

to change its shape, sometimes in very drastic fashion.

Specialized conductors are relatively rare among unicellular organisms. The undifferentiated protoplasm of these cells propagates an excitation at a comparatively slow rate (see p. 447), but within the single cell this is fast enough. Certain large ciliated protozoans, however, display a delicate network of intracellular threads, called **neurofibrils.** The neurofibrillar network forms an interconnection between the cilia all over the body, and it is thought that the neurofibrils are a conductor system, which coordinates ciliary activity.

Ciliary Movement. Broadly speaking, the term **ciliary movement** includes the beating of flagella as well as of cilia, although cilia differ from flagella in being shorter, stouter, and more numerous. Flagella are characteristic of many protozoans and algae, and of the sperm cells of higher plants and animals generally. Cilia are found in a large group of the Protozoa (p. 625) and in the ciliated epithelia of the respiratory and genital tracts of higher animals.

In action, a cilium swings stiffly and rapidly in one direction, then limply and slowly returns to its original position (Fig. 11-7). In most ciliated epithelia the stiff **effective stroke** is always in one direction. For example, in man's bronchial passages, the ciliary beat is always upward, so that dust and other

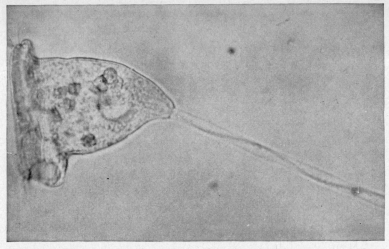

Fig. 11-5. A living *Vorticella*, expanded condition. Note the **myoneme** that extends along the stalk. (Bausch and Lomb Optical Co., Inc.)

foreign particles are carried from the lungs up through the trachea into the throat. In the Protozoa, however, the direction of the ciliary beat may be reversed temporarily, as when a paramecium backs away from an obstacle.

An active flagellum displays a whirling

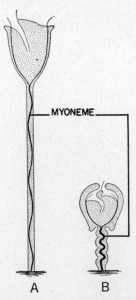

Fig. 11-6. *Vorticella*, a stalked ciliated protozoan; A, expanded; B, contracted. The contraction is effected by the shortening of the myoneme. (Other intracellular structures—nucleus, vacuole, etc.—are omitted from the figure.)

movement, especially at the free end, like the twirling of a whip. In some cases this action pulls the cell forward, as a propeller pulls an airplane, but in others it pushes the cell as a propeller pushes a steamship.

Recent electron microscope studies, initiated by Keith Porter of the Rockefeller Institute for Medical Research, show that the cilia and flagella from a wide variety of plants and animals display a uniform structure of considerable complexity. Always there seem to be *ten pairs* of **fibrillae** that extend lengthwise out into the cilium (or flagellum). The arrangement of these ten double filaments always conforms to a similar pattern, which is best shown in cross-sectional view (Fig. 11-8). Probably, these **ciliary fibrillae** are comparable to **myofibrillae** (p. 435), the **contractile elements of muscle fibers,** but experimental evidence is not available.

Amoeboid Movement. The amoeba moves by means of **pseudopodia,** which are *strictly temporary* protoplasmic extensions, projected from the surface of the cell. During locomotion, the protoplasm of the amoeba continues to flow forth into the leading pseudopodium, so that the cell moves as the pseudopodium extends. The pseudopodia also play a part in ingestion, when the amoeba engulfs small food particles from the surrounding medium.

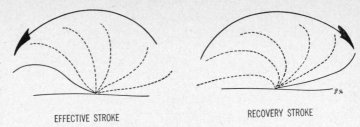

EFFECTIVE STROKE   RECOVERY STROKE

Fig. 11-7. Diagram illustrating movement of a cilium. The cilium appears to be relatively rigid during the effective stroke, but limp during the recovery.

Amoeboid movement is not restricted to the amoeba and other protozoans, but is also encountered in the white blood cells (leucocytes) and connective tissue cells (fibroblasts) of higher animals. Leucocytes migrate throughout the body by amoeboid movement, squeezing their way among the cells of other tissues, and engulfing particles of organic debris and bacteria, if the tissue is infected. This activity of leucocytes is called **phagocytosis,** although essentially phagocytosis resembles the process of ingestion in the amoeba and other free-living cells. In the human body there are also certain epithelial cells, located especially in the liver and spleen, which act as **stationary phagocytes.** Despite the fact that these cells are anchored in a fixed position in an epithelial surface, each is able to thrust forth pseudopodia from its free end and to engulf solid particles from the blood stream, upon which the epithelium borders.

By watching a pseudopodium as it extends from the surface of an amoeba, one can gain some concept of how the movement is effected. Not all the protoplasm flows as the pseudopodium extends. In fact, there is a semisolid layer of protoplasm—the **plasmagel**—which completely encases the fluid (flowing) protoplasm, or **plasmasol** (Fig. 11-9). Many experiments indicate that gelated protoplasm possesses a capacity to contract, and the plasmagel of the amoeba probably contracts, exerting a pressure upon the plasmasol and causing it to flow forward. At the tip of an advancing pseudopodium the plasmagel is virtually absent, so that the forward flow is impeded mainly by the elastic surface membrane. Moreover, the sol, upon reaching the tip of a pseudopodium, is diverted toward the side walls, where gelation occurs. Thus the plasmagel of the side walls is built up as a pseudopodium extends. Simultaneously, near the posterior extremity

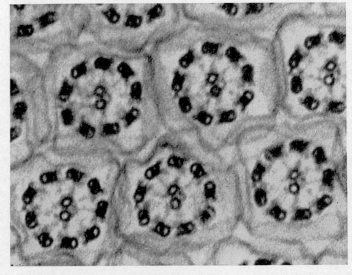

Fig. 11-8. Cross-sectional view of a group of cilia (six) from the lateral surface of the gill of a clam (*Anodonta cataracta*), photographed under the electron microscope at a magnification of 110,000 diameters. In each cilium, note the nine double filaments, in circular arrangement just inside the boundary membrane, and the one double filament, at the center of the cilium. (Courtesy of J. R. Gibbons, Harvard University.)

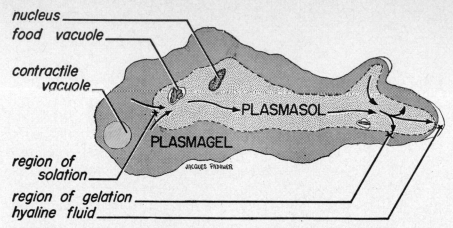

nucleus
food vacuole
contractile vacuole
PLASMASOL
PLASMAGEL
region of solation
region of gelation
hyaline fluid

JACQUES PADAWER

Fig. 11-9. Amoeboid movement involves a continuous series of gelation and solation reactions (see text).

of the amoeba, the plasmagel is solating forming new plasmasol that adds itself to the forward-flowing stream. There are, however, a number of unknown factors as to the mechanism of amoeboid movement. Virtually nothing is known about the metabolic reactions that determine the solling and gelling of the protoplasm, nor about how these processes are coordinated in the different parts of the cell.

Cyclosis. Quite a variety of plant and animal cells exhibit cyclosis, a rotational streaming of the protoplasm that does not effect any change in the external form of the cell. In certain plants, such as *Elodea* and *Nitella* (Fig. 13-2), the cells display an exceptionally rapid cyclosis, and these cells are favorable for a study of the movement.

Cyclosis, like amoeboid movement, seems to depend upon alternating processes of solation and gelation, but just how these reactions produce streaming is hard to understand. In *Nitella,* the streaming can be stopped and started by a variety of stimuli, and each successful stimulation produces a typical wave of excitation, attended by an action potential. Cyclosis serves to accelerate the distribution of substances from one part of the cell to another, or from one cell to neighboring cells—in multicellular organisms. In many cells, cyclosis goes on more or less continuously, even in the absence of any

apparent external stimulation. However, such a continuous cyclosis probably depends upon a series of internal stimuli, which arise from rhythmically recurring processes in the metabolism of the cell.

Cleavage. Cleavage is the pinching movement by which an animal cell cuts itself into daughter cells, and this movement has been studied most extensively in dividing eggs (Fig. 11-10). These large cells are very favorable because they cleave on a regular schedule, following the time when the sperm make contact with the eggs.

When a sperm comes into contact with an egg, a definite excitation arises at the contact point, and this excitation sweeps over the entire egg surface, visibly changing the protoplasmic structure. The original stimulus initiates a long series of responses that include the lifting of the fertilization membrane (p. 273), the penetration of the sperm head, the approach and fusion of the gamete nuclei, the divisions of the zygote nucleus, and the successive **cleavages** of the one cell into many (Fig. 11-10).

The cleavage **furrow** (Fig. 11-10), which cuts through the cell, first appears as a shallow groove encircling the egg. Then gradually the furrow deepens, and in a few minutes, it passes through the center of the egg and completes the division of the cytoplasm. Recent evidence (p. 48) provides several

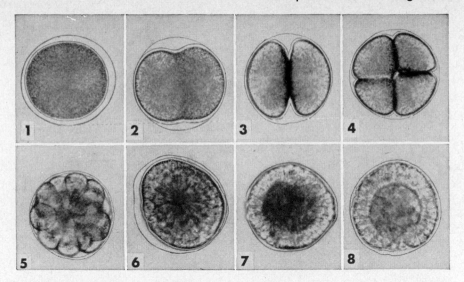

Fig. 11-10. Cleavage divisions, as seen in the egg of a sea urchin (*Arbacia punctulata*). 1, undivided egg; 2, egg dividing, furrow well started; 3 and 4, two-cell and four-cell stages; 5-8, progressively older blastula stages. Note that finally the cells are so small and numerous that it is difficult to distinguish them individually. (Courtesy of Ethel Browne Harvey.)

clues as to the nature of the force that enables the furrow to cleave the cell. Some minutes before the furrowing starts, a surface layer of protoplasm, where the furrow is about to form, suddenly solidifies into a very firm gel. This girdle of gelated protoplasm is only about 5 microns thick, but it appears to contract forcibly, pinching the egg in two. If the cleavage girdle is prevented from gelating—by mechanically agitating the protoplasm with a microneedle, or by a variety of other means—the furrow does not form. Or if a liquefication of the protoplasm of the cleavage girdle is induced after the furrowing has started, the furrow gradually recedes.

Secretion. Diffusional and osmotic exchanges between the cell and its environment occur on a spontaneous basis; that is, they do not require any expenditure of energy. But in some cases the cell *expends energy* in forcing substances to pass across its living membranes, and such responses are called **secretions.**

In **multicellular** organisms, the effectors of secretion are **glands.** Excitation of a salivary gland, for example, can be detected whenever its motor nerve is stimulated. Action currents from the secretory cells are discharged so long as the motor nerve is stimulated, and saliva continues to flow from the gland during the period of excitation.

Among **unicellular** organisms, the most familiar secretional effectors are the gastric and contractile vacuoles. Food in the gastric vacuole of an amoeba, for example, excites the cell to secrete digestive enzymes across the vacuole membrane, from the surrounding cytoplasm. This mobilization requires the cell to do work, since enzyme molecules are too large to penetrate the membrane spontaneously. In some way the cell manages to pass the enzymes into the digestive vacuoles, but exactly how this is done is problematical. In stained specimens the enzyme material appears to accumulate on the outer surface of the vacuolar membrane in the form of visible granules, and these granules seem to erupt through the membrane into the vacuole proper.

How the contractile vacuole functions is likewise not well understood. The content of the vacuole is mainly water and is distinctly hypotonic to the protoplasm. As a vacuole swells, therefore, water is forced to flow "uphill" from a region of lesser to a region of greater concentration. Accordingly, the cell must expend energy in forcing water to flow into the vacuole, and this energy must be derived ultimately from metabolism. Thus the contractile vacuole stops functioning when a cell is deprived of oxygen, or when its metabolism is depressed by narcotics; and in such cases the cell swells gradually until it reaches the bursting point.

Responses of Multicellular Organisms. It should be emphasized that the complicated behavior of higher organisms depends upon responses occurring in the individual cells. Receptivity, conductivity, and the capacity to execute effective responses are general attributes of all cells. However, considerable specialization has occurred among the cells of higher organisms, so that well-differentiated tissues and organs serve as the receptors, conductors, and effectors in the highly integrated responses of all higher forms.

TEST QUESTIONS

1. Define the term "stimulus." Differentiate between internal and external stimuli, citing an example of each.
2. Differentiate between continuous and discontinuous responses, citing two examples in each case.
3. Specify four criteria that distinguish the *state of excitation*—that is, four differences between an *excited* and an *unexcited cell.*
4. Discuss the *action potential* in relation to: (a) plant cells; (b) animal cells; (c) heart muscle; (d) the polarity of the plasma membrane.
5. Define the terms: (a) *resting potential* and (b) *action potential.*
6. Explain how these potentials are related to (a) membrane permeability; (b) ion transport mechanisms; and (c) ionic mobilities.
7. Classify the various kinds of stimuli.
8. Both the rate and the magnitude of a stimulating change are important in determining the effectiveness of a stimulus. Explain this statement in terms of the human retina.
9. Differentiate between receptors, conductors, and effectors, using (a) various unicellular organisms; and (b) man, to exemplify the discussion.
10. Differentiate between: (a) cilia and flagella; (b) the effective and the recovery strokes; (c) ciliary fibrillae and myofibrillae; (d) the plasmagel and the plasmasol; (e) amoeboid movement and cyclosis.
11. Both amoeboid movement and cleavage probably depend upon the capacity of protoplasm to undergo gelation. Explain and discuss this statement.
12. Secretion is an energy-expending process. Explain and discuss this statement.
13. Receptivity, conductivity, and the capacity to execute definite responses are general attributes of living cells. Explain and discuss this statement.
14. What new evidence is available in regard to the fine structure of cilia and flagella? Explain.

FURTHER READINGS

1. *Unresting Cells,* by Ralph W. Gerard; New York, 1961.
2. "How Cells Communicate," by Bernard Katz; in *Scientific American,* September 1961.
3. "How Cells Receive Stimuli," by W. H. Miller, F. Ratliff, and H. K. Hartline; in *Scientific American,* September 1961.
4. "Chemical Factors Controlling Nerve Activity," by David Nachmansohn; in *Science,* vol. 134, Dec. 15, 1961.

PART II-*Multicellular Plants*

12-*Reproduction in Multicellular Plants*

ALTERNATION OF GENERATIONS

Higher plants reproduce in two ways: (1) **sexually,** by forming gametes; and (2) **asexually,** by forming spores. The sexual stage of the plant alternates regularly with the asexual stage; and usually the sexual form differs so widely from the asexual form that it is difficult to recognize the two generations as stages in the life cycle of the same species. But the sexual generation always produces eggs, each of which (when fertilized) develops into an asexual plant; and the asexual plant always produces spores that give rise again to the original sexual plant. Accordingly the sexual generation, which produces gametes, is called the **gametophyte;** and the asexual generation, which produces spores, is called the **sporophyte.** Moreover, the cells of the gametophyte generation are always **haploid,** while the cells of the sporophyte are always **diploid.**

LIFE CYCLE OF A FERN

An alternation of generations is the common evolutionary heritage of all higher plants, although the character of the life cycle differs in detail in the different plant groups. First to be described will be the life cycle of a fern. All ferns (about 4000 species) display a similar cycle, and in a broad sense, the fern life cycle will serve as the prototype for higher plants generally.

The Sporophyte. The large, familiar fern plant (Fig. 12-1) represents the sporophyte generation—that is, the **diploid asexual** form of the fern. The green parts of the fern, which are seen above the ground level, consist entirely of the **leaves,** or **fronds.** Each complexly subdivided leaf arises from a horizontal **underground stem** (Fig. 12-1), and numerous fine **roots** grow downward from the stem into the soil. The sporophyte carries on an independent holophytic nutrition. It may live for a number of years, producing one crop of spores annually.

When the sporophyte of the fern reaches maturity a number of small, regularly arranged, dark-brown bodies (Fig. 12-2) appear on the undersurface of the leaves. Each brown "spot" as a whole is called a **sorus;** when magnified, each sorus is seen to be a

203

Fig. 12-1. The familiar fern plant is the sporophyte generation, consisting of exposed leaves (fronds), an underground stem (the rhizome), and the roots. (From *The Plant World*, by Fuller and Carothers. Holt, Rinehart and Winston, Inc.)

cluster of spore capsules, or **sporangia.** At higher magnification one can see that each **sporangium** is a hollow structure, containing numerous **spores** (Fig. 12-3). While a sporangium is ripening, the spores are produced from spore mother cells, or **sporocytes.** The spore mother cell undergoes meiosis, giving rise to four haploid **spores,** each covered by a thick cell wall. Finally when it is ripe, the sporangium bursts open, liberating the spores in large numbers (Fig. 12-4).

Usually the fern discharges its spores during dry weather, and the wind may carry the spores for considerable distances. The moisture-proof covering enables the spore to withstand exposure to dry air, which otherwise would be lethal. Eventually a spore must fall upon damp ground if it is to germinate successfully.

The Gametophyte. When a spore germinates (Fig. 12-4), it does *not* give rise to the familiar sporophyte from which it came, but grows into the **gametophyte** of the fern. The fern gametophyte is a *small*, flat, heart-shaped *green plant*, called a **prothallium** (Fig. 12-4).

A   B

Fig. 12-2. The regularly placed brown spots on the under surface of the fern leaf are **sori.** Each sorus consists of a covered cluster of spore capsules, or **sporangia** (not visible at this magnification). A, *Dryopteris marginalis*. B, *Polypodium scouleri*. (From *The Plant World*, by Fuller and Carothers. Holt, Rinehart and Winston, Inc.)

Fig. 12-3. Magnified vertical section of a fern leaf, passing through a **sorus.** Three of the clustered **sporangia** show quite clearly; and the ripening **spores** can be seen through the side walls of each sporangium. (From *The Plant World,* by Fuller and Carothers. Holt, Rinehart and Winston, Inc.)

The prothallia grow in moist shaded places on the ground, or on decaying logs; and these plants are not recognized as "ferns," except by those who have traced out their origin (Fig. 12-5).

The prothallium of a fern usually measures less than half an inch at the widest part. Nevertheless the prothallium grows independently like other green plants. All the cells of the prothallial *body* possess chloroplasts; but the numerous **rhizoids,** which grow down into the soil from the underside of the prothallium, are colorless. During growth, the rhizoids absorb water and mineral salts for the whole prothallium; and several weeks after a spore germinates, the prothallium is sexually mature.

When mature, the gametophyte of the fern produces gametes. Both male and female organs develop on the *undersurface* of each prothallium. Usually the egg-forming organs, called **archegonia,** lie near the indented margin **(apical notch)** of the prothallium (Fig. 12-4), and each archegonium contains a single egg. The egg lies in a hollow chamber, the **venter,** which communicates with the environment through a short tubular channel, the *neck*. The sperm-forming organs, called

antheridia, are usually situated among the rhizoids, nearer the other end and margins of the prothallium (Fig. 12-4). Each antheridium is a hollow structure from which a number of delicate flagellated sperm are finally liberated (Fig. 12-4).

The sperm are usually liberated in rainy weather, and they must *swim through water,* underneath the prothallium, in order to reach the archegonia. However, the archegonia and antheridia of any one prothallium do not reach maturity at the same time, and consequently the sperm that fertilize the eggs are derived from another nearby prothallium. In many cases, the archegonia produce secretions that attract the sperm toward the eggs; frequently a swarm of sperm will enter the neck of a single archegonium. However, only one sperm normally succeeds in penetrating the egg.

The fertilized egg marks the beginning of a new sporophyte generation. This single diploid cell, while it still lies in the archegonium of the parent gametophyte, divides repeatedly by **mitosis,** and gives rise eventually to all the cells of the new sporophyte (Fig. 12-6). During the early stages of this growth, the young sporophyte depends upon the parent gametophyte for its organic nutrients (Fig. 12-6). But soon the growing sporophyte develops its own root, stem, and leaf systems (Fig. 12-4), and thereafter the sporophyte carries on an independent holophytic nutrition. In about one year, the sporophyte reaches maturity and produces a new crop of spores—which completes the life cycle of the species.

HAPLOIDY AND DIPLOIDY IN HIGHER PLANTS

Generally speaking the foregoing life cycle is typical of *all* higher plants—as is shown diagrammatically in Figure 12-7. In all higher plants the diploid zygote marks the beginning of the sporophyte generation; and since the cells of the sporophyte are all derived by **mitosis** from this diploid cell, all the cells of

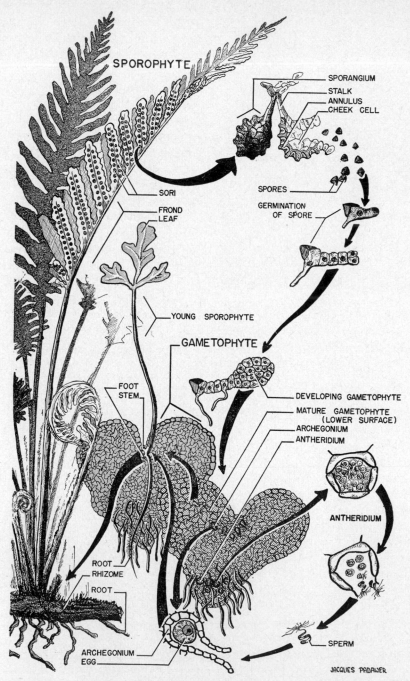

Fig. 12-4. Life cycle of a fern. The **gametophyte** generation starts with the germination of a spore (upper right), whereas the **sporophyte** generation starts with the fertilization of an egg (bottom center).

Fig. 12-5. Hundreds of fern gametophytes (prothallia) growing on the moist wall of a small flower pot. This photo shows the approximate actual size of the gametophytes. (Copyright, General Biological Supply House, Inc.)

the sporophyte generation are diploid. In the sporangia, however, the spores arise by **meiosis** from spore mother cells, and each haploid spore represents the beginning of the gametophyte generation. Each spore produces all the cells of the gametophyte by **mitosis,** and consequently all the cells of the gametophyte remain haploid. Higher plants, therefore, differ from higher animals in that the gametes of the plant arise by **mitosis** from the haploid cells of the gametophyte; or to state the matter differently, plants have developed a haploid generation that intervenes between meiosis and fertilization (Fig. 12-7).

TYPES OF LIFE CYCLES IN VARIOUS PLANTS

The main branches, or **phyla,** of the **plant kingdom** embrace a multitude of species; but all members of any one phylum have inherited a similar pattern of structure and function. Consequently it is possible to describe the *life cycles* of the different groups in fairly general terms.

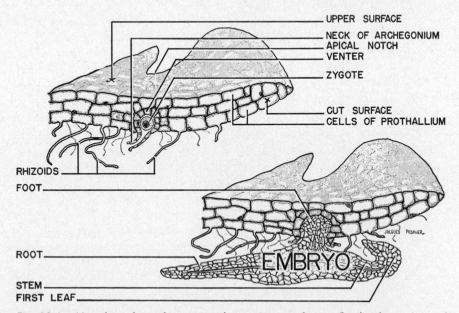

Fig. 12-6. Note how the embryo sporophyte originates from a fertilized egg (zygote) in the archegonium of the parent gametophyte (prothallium). The young sporophyte uses its foot for the absorption of organic nutrients from the parent—until its own root, stem, and leaf systems have developed adequately.

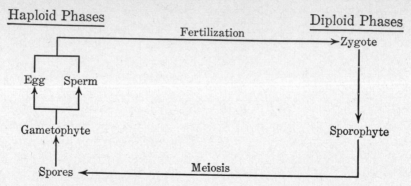

Fig. 12-7. Generalized life cycle of a typical higher plant.

The Cyanophytes (Blue-Green Algae). The blue-green algae (see p. 594) are very primitive plants that display *no clearly defined form of sexual reproduction.* Generally they reproduce by **binary fission** (p. 55), although quite a few species also form spores. None is truly multicellular; that is, all are either unicellular or colonial. Essentially these primitive forms are **aquatic** plants, although many species live in moist places, such as damp soil. No sharp distinction between nucleus and cytoplasm has been developed in the cells of a majority of these primitive organisms.

In the absence of sexual phenomenon, it is not possible to speak unequivocally about haploid and diploid stages, although by convention the blue-green algae are regarded as being haploid throughout their entire simple life cycle.

The Schizomycophytes, or Bacteria (Chapter 31). These colorless unicellular or colonial plants began to evolve even before the blue-green algae. Nevertheless some bacterial cells appear to possess one or more nuclei or at least masses of nuclear material that seem to be delimited within a membrane. Moreover, some bacteria display a primitive sort of sexual reproduction by which genic material may be passed from one individual to another, so that genic recombinations (p. 563) may occur. The sexual processes are somewhat ambiguous, however, and it is not possible to distinguish clearly between haploid and diploid phases of the life cycle.

Higher Thallophytes (Chapter 31). Many of the higher Thallophyta possess chlorophyll (green, red, brown, and other algae); but others (yeast, molds, rusts, smuts, mushrooms, and other fungi) lack this green pigment. Some are truly multicellular although many species remain unicellular or colonial. The cells of the higher Thallophyta display distinct nuclei; and practically all have developed *some form of sexual reproduction* that supplements the asexual methods. But a *regular alternation of sexual* (**gametophyte**) *and asexual* (**sporophyte**) generations is not generally characteristic of these plants. They have remained essentially aquatic, although many parasitic and saprophytic species have been evolved. The body structure is simple, without true roots, stems, or leaves (thallus type of body).

The Bryophytes (Chapter 31). The Bryophyta, which include the **mosses** and the **liverworts,** are among the simplest of the existing land plants. All the Bryophyta display a *regular alternation of sexual and asexual generations.* Among Bryophyta, however, the **gametophyte** *is the dominant form of the plant,* and the **sporophyte** is nutritively *dependent* upon the gametophyte (see later). Adaptation to the land is not very complete. The mosses have developed a very simple leaf and stem system, but possess rhizoids in place of *true roots.* The liverworts, most primitive of the Bryophyta, usually have a thalloid body, devoid of any root, stem, or leaf system (see Chap. 31).

The Filiceneae (Chapter 13). The **Fili-ceneae,** or ferns, are all fairly well adapted to land conditions. All have true root-stem-leaf systems, equipped with well-developed **vascular** (distributing) tissues (see later). Moreover, the filicenes have a *regular alternation of generations,* but the **sporophyte** is dominant relative to the **gametophyte.** Both the gametophyte and sporophyte grow independently in the holophytic manner.

The Gymnospermae and Angiospermae (Seed-bearing Plants, Chapter 31). The seed-bearing plants include a countless variety of **conifers, cycads,** and **flowering plants.** All these plants have a highly vascularized *root-stem-leaf* system, which gives an excellent adaptation to terrestrial conditions. The reproductive cycle is also very well adapted to the land habitat. In the *regular alternation of generations,* the sporophyte has become entirely dominant, and the gametophyte, which is reduced to microscopic dimensions, has become entirely dependent upon the parent sporophyte (see later).

THE LIFE CYCLE OF VARIOUS HIGHER THALLOPHYTES

Sexual reproduction appears first among the Thallophyta, but these primitive plants

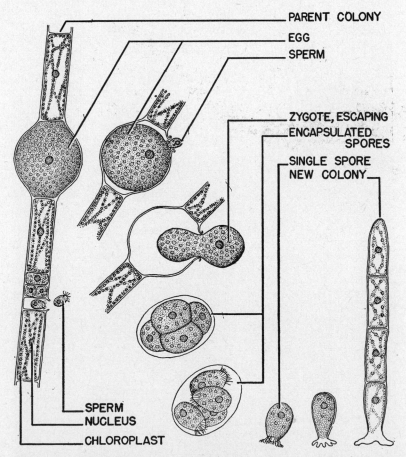

PARENT COLONY
EGG
SPERM
ZYGOTE, ESCAPING
ENCAPSULATED SPORES
SINGLE SPORE
NEW COLONY
SPERM
NUCLEUS
CHLOROPLAST

Fig. 12-8. Reproductive stages in *Oedogonium*, one of the green algae. From left to right: portion of the filament showing the large nonmotile egg and the small motile sperm; sperm entering egg, just prior to fertilization; the zygote, escaping through old cell wall; formation by meiosis of four **swarm spores;** development of one swarm spore into new filament.

do not adhere to any standard type of life cycle. The commonest type of cycle is exhibited by *Spirogyra* (p. 168), and *Oedogonium* (Fig. 12-8). In both these algae, the colony is composed of haploid cells; and any cell of the filament can give rise to one or more gametes. Accordingly, these plants are equivalent to the gametophyte generation in the higher plants. However, scarcely any sporophyte generation can be recognized, because the zygote divides **meiotically** as soon as it begins to germinate, and all the cells of the new filament are haploid (Fig. 12-8).

The opposite type of cycle is found in **Fucus** (Fig. 12-9) and some other **brown algae.** The body cells of this multicellular seaweed are all diploid, and only the gametes are haploid. The sperm and eggs respectively are formed by **meiosis** in hollow structures found at the ends of many of the branches of the sexually mature plants. After fertilization, which occurs when the gametes are extruded into the sea water, the diploid zygote multiplies **mitotically,** forming all the cells of the new individual.

An irregular alternation of generations, foreshadowing the reproductive habits of higher plants, occurs in a few Thallophyta—as in the bread mold, *Rhizopus* (p. 211). The spores of the mold are haploid, and in a suitable medium, such as moist bread, each haploid spore grows into a mycelium, called

Fig. 12-9. Rockweed (*Fucus*) growing on intertidal rocks along the California coast. (From *The Plant World*, by Fuller and Carothers. Holt, Rinehart and Winston, Inc.)

the **haplomycelium** (Fig. 12-10). In the sporangia of the haplomycelium, the spores are formed, *not* by **meiosis** as in most other plants, but by **mitosis**—and this asexual type of reproduction may continue for many generations. However, on rare occasions, *Rhizopus* also reproduces sexually. In this case, gametes are formed on two neighboring mycelia, and these fuse to form a diploid zygospore (Fig. 12-10). This zygote is very resistant to unfavorable conditions. But when a favorable environment is found, the zygospore gives rise by mitosis to a new mycelium, called the **diplomycelium**, because all the nuclei are diploid. The diplomycelium soon develops its sporangium, which contains diploid spore mother cells, or sporocytes. *In the* **sporangium** *of the* **diplomycelium** (Fig. 12-10), *the* spores *are formed by* **meiosis**, and after liberation, each haploid spore gives rise to a new haplomycelium.

The haplomycelium, since it is haploid and forms gametes, is equivalent to a gametophyte generation; and the diplomycelium, since it is diploid and reproduces by sporulation, represents the sporophyte. However, the cycle in *Rhizopus* is irregular, since fertilization occurs only rarely, and since the game-

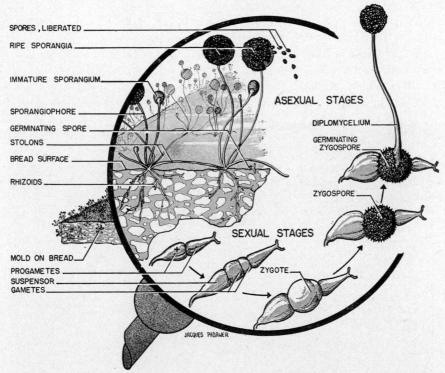

SPORES , LIBERATED

RIPE SPORANGIA

IMMATURE SPORANGIUM

SPORANGIOPHORE

GERMINATING SPORE

STOLONS

BREAD SURFACE

RHIZOIDS

ASEXUAL STAGES

DIPLOMYCELIUM

GERMINATING ZYGOSPORE

ZYGOSPORE

SEXUAL STAGES

MOLD ON BREAD

PROGAMETES

SUSPENSOR

GAMETES

ZYGOTE

JACQUES PADAWER

Fig. 12-10. Reproductive stages in the common **bread mold** (*Rhizopus nigricans*). The ordinary bread mold (left of figure) possesses haploid cells, and this **haplomycelium** perpetuates itself **asexually** by forming successive generations of haploid spores by **mitosis** from haploid spore mother cells in the **sporangia**. On rare occasions, however, two different (called plus and minus) strains of the mold participate in **sexual** reproduction. Then neighboring aerial hyphae develop gametes. These fuse to form a zygote, which soon metamorphoses into a heavily coated **zygospore**. The diploid stage of the bread mold is short-lived, however. The zygospore, when it germinates, gives rise to the highly simplified **diplomycelium,** consisting of a single sporangiophore, with just one sporangium at the apex. In this sporangium, the diploid spore mother cells undergo **meiosis**, giving rise to haploid spores, which initiate the haplomycelia of the next generation.

tophyte generation retains a capacity to reproduce by sporulation.

LIFE CYCLE OF THE MOSSES

Mosses, the most familiar of the Bryophyta, are small green *leafy* plants, which grow in densely crowded masses, on damp and shaded soils (Fig. 12-11). Mosses are *not well adapted to terrestrial conditions,* and most species cannot survive in dry localities. Most mosses are relatively short plants, with an average height of only about half an inch.

The small green leafy-stemmed moss plant is a gametophyte—that is, a haploid gamete-producing individual. The crowded *leaves* all originate from a single central stem, which cannot be seen unless the leaves are plucked away. Numerous **rhizoids** extend down into the soil from the lower end of the stem. The rhizoids absorb water and inorganic salts for the upper green parts of the

plant, which, in return, provide the rhizoids with glucose. Accordingly, the gametophyte of the moss is a small but independent plant, which displays a typically holophytic nutrition.

The **antheridia,** or **archegonia,** depending upon the sex of the gametophyte, develop at the top of the stem, hidden by the encircling upper leaves—Figure 12-12. In the mature female plants, a single large egg cell is found in the venter of each archegonium (Fig. 12-12). The sperm are liberated in swarms (Fig. 12-12) from the antheridia (Fig. 12-12) of the male plants during periods of rain or heavy dew. Each sperm (Fig. 12-12) is a delicate elongate cell possessing two flagella, which enable the sperm to swim through water to a neighboring female plant. Some sort of chemical attraction appears to emanate from the neck of the archegonium, and thousands of sperm may simultaneously attempt to swim down this narrow passage.

Fig. 12-11. A clump of moss plants (*Polytrichum*). The leafy (lower) part of each plant is a **gametophyte,** from the top of which grows the slender-stalked **sporophyte.** The conspicuous white spindle-shaped bodies are the **sporangia** of the sporophytes. (Photograph by L. W. Brownell, retouched.)

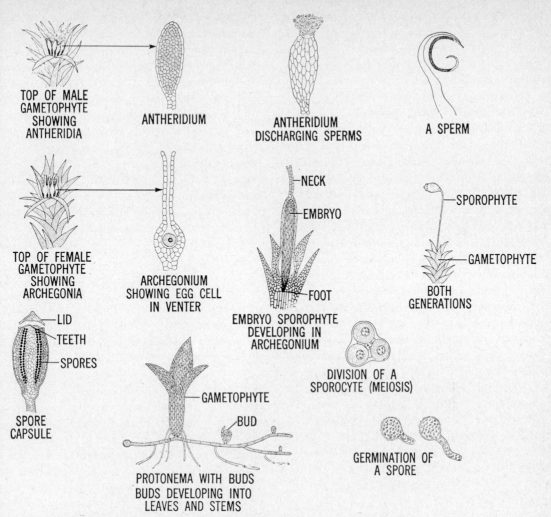

TOP OF MALE
GAMETOPHYTE
SHOWING
ANTHERIDIA

ANTHERIDIUM

ANTHERIDIUM
DISCHARGING SPERMS

A SPERM

NECK

EMBRYO

SPOROPHYTE

TOP OF FEMALE
GAMETOPHYTE
SHOWING
ARCHEGONIA

ARCHEGONIUM
SHOWING EGG CELL
IN VENTER

FOOT

GAMETOPHYTE

BOTH
GENERATIONS

EMBRYO SPOROPHYTE
DEVELOPING IN
ARCHEGONIUM

LID

TEETH

SPORES

DIVISION OF A
SPOROCYTE (MEIOSIS)

GAMETOPHYTE

BUD

SPORE
CAPSULE

GERMINATION OF
A SPORE

PROTONEMA WITH BUDS
BUDS DEVELOPING INTO
LEAVES AND STEMS

Fig. 12-12. Reproductive cycle of a moss plant, typical of bryophytes generally. Be sure to differentiate between the **haploid** and **diploid** stages.

However, only one sperm usually participates in fertilization, which occurs in the venter chamber.

The fertilized egg marks the inception of the sporophyte generation. Shortly after fertilization this diploid cell starts its development inside the archegonium of the female plant. A series of mitotic divisions leads to the formation of an elongate mass of cells (Fig. 12-12), which is the very young embryo sporophyte. The lower end of the embryo sporophyte, which is called the **foot**, grows downward into the stem of the parent gametophyte, where it becomes firmly at-

tached. The upper end of the embryo grows more or less vertically into a long slender **stalk**, at the top of which a hollow **sporangium** finally appears (Fig. 12-12). The early stages of this growth occur entirely within the archegonium, which enlarges accordingly (Fig. 12-12). But finally the stalk grows so rapidly that it tears the neck, which is carried aloft on the sporangium above the upper leaves of the female gametophyte.

The whole sporophyte—consisting of foot, stalk, and sporangium—remains permanently attached to the apex of the female gametophyte (Fig. 12-12). The exposed cells of the stalk and spore capsule may contain some chloroplasts and perform some photosynthesis; but the sporophyte obtains most of its nourishment from the gametophyte by absorption through the foot.

At maturity many spore mother cells, or sporocytes, are formed in the sporangium. Each of these diploid cells eventually produces four spores, by **meiosis;** and later, when the lid of the sporangium (Fig. 12-12) drops off, a multitude of tiny haploid spores are discharged into the dry atmosphere.

As in other higher plants, the spore represents the beginning of the gametophyte generation. In the mosses, however, more than one gametophyte may arise from one spore, if it happens to fall in a favorable locality. When the spore germinates, it bursts its protective cover and begins to divide rapidly by mitosis (Fig. 12-12). Initially this produces a branching filament that closely resembles some of the green algae, from which the mosses presumably have arisen. In the moss this young gametophyte is called a **protonema;** and each protonema may give rise to several erect leafy gametophytes by a process of budding (Fig. 12-12). Finally the protonema dies off, isolating the several erect leafy gametophytes, which soon mature and produce the gametes of the next generation.

SUMMARY: THE LIFE CYCLES OF THE MOSS AND FERN

In summary, the life cycle of the mosses displays a clear *general* resemblance to the cycle of the ferns. In both cases: (1) the haploid sexual gametophyte alternates regularly with the diploid asexual sporophyte; (2) the haploid spores are resistant to dryness, and are well adapted for dissemination through the atmosphere; and (3) the sperm require an abundance of water in order to reach the eggs. However, the gametophyte, which is dominant in the Bryophyta, is relatively inconspicuous in the Filiceneae, although the fern gametophyte still carries on an inde-

pendent nutrition. The sporophyte, on the other hand, which is relatively inconspicuous and dependent in Bryophyta, is the dominant independent generation in Filiceneae. These evolutionary tendencies continue, reaching a maximum in the seed plants. Among seed plants, the gametophyte generation is further reduced, to microscopic dimensions, and the gametophyte is completely dependent on the large dominant sporophyte. This development has enabled the seed plants to spread to much drier regions of the earth, since the sperm are free of the necessity of swimming through water on their journey toward the eggs (see later).

LIFE CYCLE OF SELAGINELLA

One of the club mosses (p. 613), *Selaginella* and a few related forms show transitional developments which foreshadow a further reduction of the gametophyte, such as occurs in all seed plants. The sporophyte of *Selaginella* (Fig. 12-13) has a profusely branched creeping stem, with short erect branches and small scalelike green leaves. The sporangia are borne in conelike structures at the tips of the erect branches (Fig. 12-13). But *Selaginella* has two kinds of sporangia: (1) **microsporangia,** in which the spores **(microspores)** are relatively small; and (2) **macrosporangia,** in which the spores are about a hundred times larger (Fig. 12-13).

When shed, each **microspore** develops into a very small (microscopic) *male* gametophyte, which lacks chlorophyll, and consists mainly of a single antheridium (Fig. 12-13). This growth occurs inside the protective cover of the microspore, at the expense of organic substances already present in the spore at the time of shedding. Meanwhile, the macrospore develops into a *female* gametophyte, which also lies mainly inside the old spore casing (Fig. 12-13). When mature, the female gametophyte displays several poorly differentiated archegonia, each containing a single egg cell. The female gametophyte has very

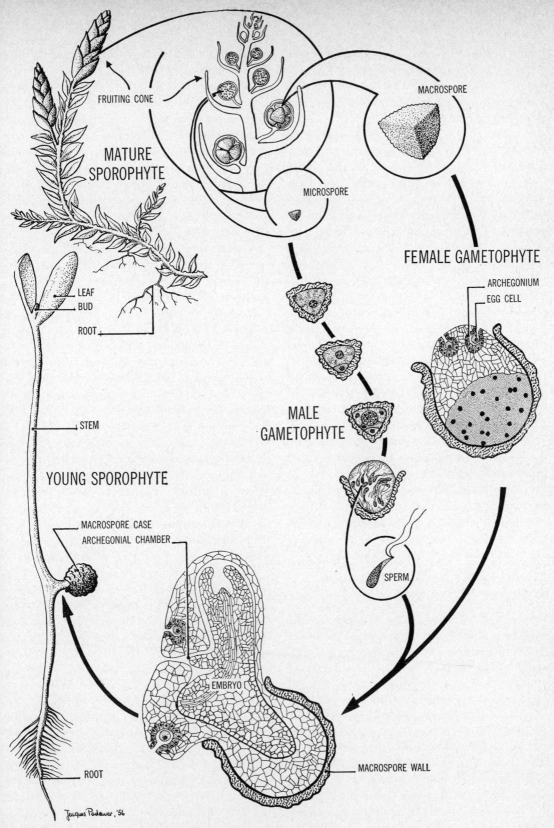

Fig. 12-13. Reproduction in *Selaginella*, one of the **club mosses.** Some of the club mosses are called creeping pines, and are often used for Christmas decoration (cf. Fig. 31-20).

little chlorophyll, and is dependent for its growth upon substances initially present in the macrospore.

The many sperm, which are liberated from the male gametophyte, swim in the soil water, and each may succeed in fertilizing an egg. The zygote gives rise to the young sporophyte, which at first grows inside the female gametophyte, at the expense of organic materials present in the gametophyte cells (Fig. 12-13). Finally, however, the sporophyte develops its own root-stem-leaf system and becomes an independent, self-sustaining plant (Fig. 12-13).

In *Selaginella* and other club mosses, the gametophyte has lost the status of an independent plant. It is reduced to a mere reproductive mechanism, which, however, assures the species of fertilization and biparental inheritance. The sturdy land-adapted sporophyte provides the gametophyte with a food supply adequate for the production of gametes, and thus the hazards experienced by a poorly adapted gametophyte are reduced. This eliminates one vulnerable feature of the cycle, which tended to prevent the spread of more primitive plants to drier regions of the earth. But only among the seed plants has another vulnerability of the cycle been eliminated, since *Selaginella* still requires a water-flooded soil at the time when the delicate sperm are swimming to the eggs.

LIFE CYCLE OF THE SEED PLANTS

The seed-bearing plants are by far the most successful groups in the plant kingdom. All common trees, shrubs, grasses, weeds, and "garden plants" are of this kind. In number of species, seed plants far exceed all other plants combined, even though their evolutionary history—as indicated by the absence of their fossils in all earlier geological formations—has been a comparatively short one. The seed plants are exceedingly well adapted to land conditions, and some species have spread to virtually all habitats.

A **seed,** essentially, is a dormant embryo

sporophyte, protected by several enveloping tissues. But the true nature of seeds, and the importance of seeds in the evolutionary success of the higher plants can be appreciated only in relation to the life cycle (see later).

Gymnosperms vs. Angiosperms. The Gymnospermae (literally, naked seeds) include the pines, spruces, hemlocks, ginkgoes, cycads, and all other plants having seeds that are formed in **cones** (rather than true flowers) and that are not contained within an ovule chamber (see below).

The Angiospermae (literally, covered seeds) include a wide variety of trees, shrubs, grasses, and all other plants possessing true flowers, and seeds that develop inside of the capsular **ovule chamber** of the flower.

The Gymnospermae, while less numerous in species than the Angiospermae, show more variability in the reproductive cycle (Chap. 31). The Gymnospermae exhibit many transitions between the rather primitive cycle of *Selaginella* (p. 214) and the well-established cycle of the Angiospermae. But it is necessary to pass over these transitional types and to deal mainly with the flowering plants (Angiospermae), which make up a great majority of familiar plants, especially in temperate zones.

The Sporophyte Generation. Among the Angiospermae the whole visible plant—consisting of roots, stem, leaves, and flowers—represents the sporophyte generation. The sporophyte varies in size in different species, from the tremendous bulk of larger trees to the inconspicuous size of many grasses. But both the male and the female gametophytes of the angiosperms are reduced to microscopic dimensions. In fact these *haploid sexual stages are only found by dissecting* into the tissues of the **flower.** In the flower the gametophytes receive protection and nourishment during the critical period when the eggs and sperm are formed, and while fertilization is occurring.

The Flower. A **flower** represents an organized group of modified leaves, which fulfills the reproductive functions of the plant. A *complete* flower displays four distinct kinds of modified leaves, arranged in concentric **whorls,** attached to a **receptacle,** which connects the flower with its stalk (Fig. 12-14). The outermost whorl, called the **calyx,** consists of separate parts, the **sepals** (Fig. 12-14), which are *usually* leaflike in form and color. Just inside the calyx lies the **corolla,** the separate parts of which are called the **petals** (Fig. 12-14). The petals also display a leaflike form, but often they are brightly colored, especially in insect-pollinated species. The petals and sepals are subject to endless variation in form, color, and number, and either or both may be entirely absent, since they play a very indirect role in reproduction.

Just inside the petals are the **microsporophylls,** which commonly are called the **stamens** (Fig. 12-14). Each stamen consists of a slender **filament** that bears an **anther** at the upper end. Essentially the anther is a group (usually of 2 or 4) of pollen capsules (**micro-**

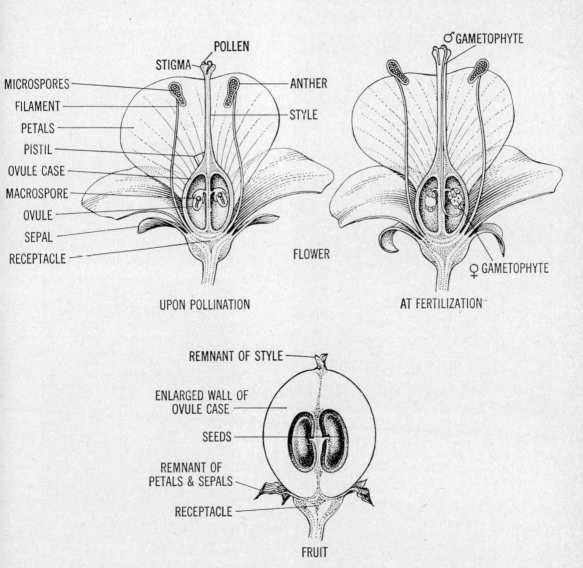

Fig. 12-14. Reproductive stages of flowering plants, showing relations between the flower, the fruit, and the seed (see text).

Fig. 12-15. Transition from petals to stamens in the white water lily. (Redrawn after Asa Gray. From *General Biology*, by Mavor. By permission of The Macmillan Co.)

In form, the anthers are so highly modified as to be quite unrecognizable as leaves (Fig. 12-15). This is also true of the **macrosporophylls** (commonly called the **carpels**) which make up the innermost whorl, at the very center of the flower. In most flowers the carpels are united, partially or completely, to form a single compound organ called the **pistil** (Fig. 12-14). Typically the pistil consists of an enlarged hollow basal part, the **ovule chamber,** surmounted by a slender cylinder, the **style,** which terminates in a moist

Fig. 12-16. The tulip is one of the Monocotyledoneae. The flower displays 3 sepals, 3 petals, 6 stamens, and a compound pistil with a 3-branched stigma. (From *College Botany*, by Fuller and Tippo. Holt, Rinehart and Winston, Inc.)

sporangia) in which the pollen grains[1] (**microspores**) are produced in great numbers.

[1] The terms "pollen grain" and "microspore" are almost, but not quite, synonymous, since the microspore nucleus usually divides once before the pollen is shed.

Fig. 12-17. Flowers of Amaryllis, one of the Monocotyledoneae. A, close-up of the stamens and stigmas; B, the whole flower. This flower has 3 sepals, 3 petals, 6 stamens, and 3 forked stigmas. (From *College Botany*, by Fuller and Tippo. Holt, Rinehart and Winston, Inc.)

sticky part, the **stigma.** Inside the ovule chamber are one or more ovules (**macrosporangia**), in which the macrospores are formed.

The flowers of different species exhibit many variations (Figs. 12-16 to 18). Usually both stamens and pistils are present, but some plants possess two kinds of incomplete flowers, one containing only stamens (**staminate flowers**), and the other containing only pistils (**pistillate flowers**). These kinds of flowers may be borne on the same, or upon separate individual plants. Plants bearing only staminate flowers may be referred to as male, and those with only pistillate flowers as female plants; but in either case, the sporophyte plant does not give rise directly to the sperm or eggs.

Essential Nature of the Floral Parts. The essential nature of the floral structures is difficult to comprehend, except in comparison with equivalent structures in the non-flowering plants. The **ovules**[2] that develop in the ovule chamber are equivalent to the

[2] Strictly speaking, only the inner part (**nucellus**) of the ovule is equivalent to the macrosporangium.

sporangia of other plants, or more specifically, to the **macrosporangium** of *Selaginella*. In seed plants, however, only one macrospore is formed in each **ovule** (macrosporangium). This single large haploid cell is formed by meiosis from a macrospore mother cell (**macrosporocyte**), and lies near the center of the ovule (Fig. 12-14). During the two divisions of meiosis most of the cytoplasm is retained by one of the four daughter cells, and this cell becomes the functional **macrospore.** The macrospore lies in direct contact with three smaller sister "spores" (Fig. 12-19), but the three smaller cells are sterile. Eventually they disintegrate and do not play any further part in reproduction.

The Gametophytes of the Angiosperm. Like the spores of other plants, the **macrospore** is a haploid cell that is destined to develop into a gametophyte—in this case the **female gametophyte** of the species. But the female gametophyte of the seed plant never attains anything but a microscopic size. At maturity it consists of only eight cells, including the **egg cell** and the two **endosperm nuclei** (Fig. 12-19). The diminutive female

Fig. 12-18. The flower of the peony is considered to be primitive, since it has numerous stamens and several separate, simple pistils (in the center of each flower). (From *College Botany*, by Fuller and Tippo. Holt, Rinehart and Winston, Inc.)

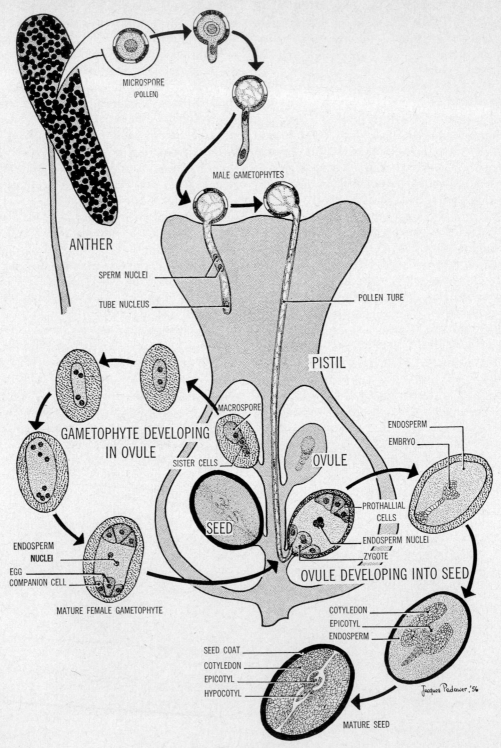

Fig. 12-19. Reproductive stages in an angiosperm.

gametophyte lies near the center of the ovule, protected and nourished by the surrounding nucellar tissues, and is not exposed to the hazards of an external environment (Fig. 12-14). Finally the single egg cell matures and must await fertilization before further development can occur.

Meanwhile the pollen grains (microspores), after liberation from the anthers, may light on the stigma (Fig. 12-14) of the same flower (**self-pollination**), or more frequently, they are carried by wind or insects to the stigma of another plant (**cross-pollination**). The pollen grains (microspores) are haploid cells, which are formed in the anthers as a result of meiosis, from diploid microspore mother cells (microsporocytes). Each pollen grain is destined to grow into a gametophyte—in this case, a **male** gametophyte. Such a development normally occurs only when the microspore falls into the sugary secretion of a stigma of the same species, although pollen grains can often be induced to germinate in artificial solutions. The male gametophyte, which is commonly called the **pollen tube,** now grows downward through the tissues of the stigma and style, deriving nourishment and protection from these tissues (Fig. 12-14). At maturity, when it penetrates an ovule and approaches the egg cell, the male gametophyte consists of only three cells—or rather consists of a trinucleate syncytium (Fig. 12-19). One of the three nuclei is the **tube nucleus,** which regulates the growth of the pollen tube; and the other two are sperm nuclei. One of these sperm nuclei unites with the egg, forming the zygote, while the other unites with both endosperm nuclei, forming a **triploid endosperm cell** (Fig. 12-19).

Significance of the Gametophytes. The intrinsic nature of the pollen tube could not be appreciated, were it not for the occurrence of equivalent stages in lower plants. The pollen tube must be regarded as a male gametophyte because (1) it arises from a spore, (2) consists of haploid cells, and (3) gives rise to sperm. On similar grounds, the

small female gametophyte of the seed plant is also identified as such. In seed plants, the vigorous land-adapted sporophyte harbors and nurtures the gametophytes inside the ovule and pistil), where they are protected from the hazards of independent life; and the gametophytes are reduced to the simplest condition, although they are still capable of fulfilling their essential functions. In this way the seed plants have adapted their life cycle to conditions as they exist in the land environment. The male and female gametophytes develop in close proximity to each other, protected by the flower tissues of the parent sporophyte. Under these conditions fertilization can occur even in very dry regions, where the water available in the external environment is so scant that free-swimming sperm would not be able to reach the eggs. Accordingly, seed plants have been able to spread to drier parts of the earth, where more primitive plants, handicapped by the aquatic type of fertilization, cannot survive. In the life cycle of the seed plants, the burden of carrying the paternal chromosomes to the egg is shifted from the sperm, which are ill adapted to land conditions, to the spores, which even in primitive plants are very resistant to the dry conditions of the atmosphere. The thick-walled pollen grains are produced in very large numbers, and this makes it likely that some will be carried, usually by air—but sometimes by insects or water—from an anther to the stigma of the same species.

The Embryo Sporophyte, the Seed, and the Fruit. Fertilization occurs when a sperm nucleus leaves the pollen tube (male gametophyte) and fuses with an egg nucleus (Fig. 12-19). The penetration of the sperm into the egg is facilitated by the fact that the intervening cell walls are "digested away" when the end of the pollen tube comes in contact with the egg cell. As in other plants, the zygote soon develops into a new sporophyte. The zygote multiplies by mitosis, and, growing at the expense of the surrounding endosperm tissue, it produces a mass of diploid cells that represents the embryo sporophyte (Fig. 12-19).

While the embryo is growing, many changes also occur in the several tissues surrounding the embryo: (1) the endosperm cell gives rise to a mass of endosperm tissue, which lies in direct contact with the embryo and provides it with organic food; (2) the ovule, taken as a whole, becomes the seed; and (3) the ovule chamber, also taken as a whole, enlarges and becomes the **fruit** (Fig. 12-14). Accordingly the **embryo sporophyte** (Fig. 12-19) lies near the center of the ripe seed, surrounded by an endosperm, unless this tissue is used up before the seed is ripe. In the seed, however, the only body of cells that arises from the fertilized egg is the embryo itself; and only these diploid cells are represented in the body of the mature sporophyte, which develops after the seed has sprouted.

The Seed. Seeds are uniquely distinctive of the Gymnospermae and Angiospermae. *A seed is a* **dormant embryo sporophyte,** *enclosed in a cover that is derived chiefly from the outer wall of the* **ovule.** In fact, the ovule as a whole gives rise to the seed as a whole. Some seeds contain gametophyte tissue (the endosperm), directly surrounding the embryo and separating the embryo from the seed cover (Fig. 12-19). But in many seeds, all the substance of the endosperm is absorbed by the growing embryo during the period of

ripening, leaving no trace of endosperm in the mature seed (Fig. 12-19).

Seeds have played an important role in permitting the seed plants to scatter themselves over wide areas of the earth. The dormant embryo within some seeds may survive for more than a hundred years, and is able to endure adverse conditions of dryness, temperature, etc. Many seeds are equipped with devices (wings, spines, etc.) that play a part in successfully dispersing the species. Moreover, because the embryo has reached a fairly advanced stage of development in the ripe seed, and because rapid growth is assured by organic food stored in the seed, the new sporophyte very quickly establishes itself as a sturdy independent plant soon after the seed falls upon new ground, where conditions are right for sprouting (Fig. 12-20).

Structure of the Embryo: the Cotyledons. When the protective coat of a bean seed is removed, the embryo as a whole is exposed. The main bulk of the embryo consists of the *two* **cotyledons**—that is, the two swollen fleshy "halves of the bean." But between the cotyledons, and not fully visible until one cotyledon is removed, lies the **body** of the embryo (Fig. 12-21).

The **cotyledons** are the **storage leaves** of the embryo. The swollen fleshiness of these embryonic leaves is due to large amounts of starch and other organic compounds contributed to the cotyledons by the endosperm

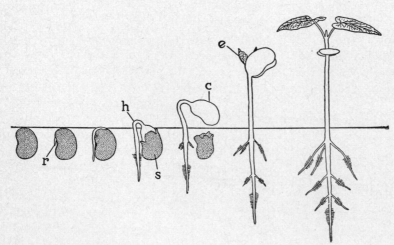

Fig. 12-20. Germination of a seed (bean). s, seed coats; r, radicle; h, hypocotyl; c, cotyledon; e, epicotyl.

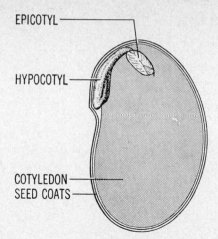

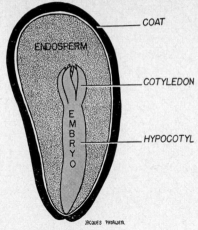

Fig. 12-21. An opened bean seed with one of the two cotyledons removed. This reveals the **body** of the embryo, which consists of the **hypocotyl** and the **epicotyl.**

Fig. 12-22. Longitudinal section of a pine seed.

and other surrounding tissues, while the seed is ripening. Such a reserve of organic matter is vitally important to the embryo when the seed begins to sprout. Until the young sporophyte develops a good root system and raises its stem and leaves above ground where light is available, it cannot synthesize its own organic materials and grow in a self-sufficient manner. During the first rapid growth of the young sporophyte, the cotyledons gradually give up their content of organic material, passing it to the growing body of the plant. Consequently the cotyledons keep shrinking as the seedling grows. In most seedlings the withered cotyledons finally drop off, but then the young sporophyte is no longer called a **seedling**—it is an independent plant.

The point of attachment between the cotyledons and the **body** of the embryo (Fig. 12-21) subdivides the body into two parts: (1) the **hypocotyl** (literally, below the cotyledons), a tapering, slightly curved, rodlike part; and (2) the **epicotyl** (literally, above the cotyledons), a small upper part, which must be dissected with needles before its full structure can be seen. Such a dissection reveals that the epicotyl of the bean consists of a pair of delicately folded **embryonic foliage leaves,** the **plumules,** and (hidden between the plumules) a small central conical mass, the **embryonic bud.**

Seed structure varies widely among different species, but three main types are generally recognized. In gymnosperm seeds, the embryo possesses 6 to 10 cotyledons, which are needlelike in form and not very conspicuously swollen (Fig. 12-22). And among angiosperm (p. 616) seeds the embryo possesses either *two* cotyledons, as in the Dicotyledoneae; or only *one* cotyledon, as in the Monocotyledoneae (see Fig. 12-23).

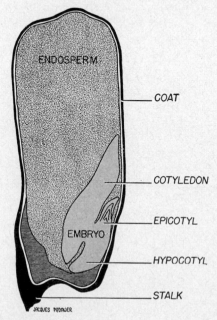

Fig. 12-23. Longitudinal section of a corn **grain,** a one-seeded fruit.

The developmental fate of the embryonic parts likewise varies in different seeds. In the pea and corn, for example, the cotyledons remain below the ground as the seedling develops, and thus the hypocotyl gives rise only to the root system, and the epicotyl produces all the stem and leaf systems (Figs. 12-24 and 12-25). But in the bean and pine, the cotyledons are lifted above ground, and thus the hypocotyl gives rise to part of the stem, as well as to the root system (Fig. 12-20). In the pines and many other plants, the cotyledons develop chlorophyll; and in some cases the cotyledons persist as foliage leaves, after their reserves of organic matter have been exhausted.

Variations of Floral Structure. Pollination has been a main factor in determining the evolution of the floral structure. Some species practice self-pollination, in which case the floral envelopes (calyx and corolla) tend to remain closed when the pollen is liberated. But a great majority of species depend upon cross-pollination, and the main **vectors** of pollen from plant to plant are the wind and animals, chiefly insects.

In general, bright and conspicuous petals (or sepals), distinct fragrances, and **nectar glands** represent adaptations that have arisen from a long evolutionary association between the angiosperms and insects. As is well known, many insects fly from flower to flower, seeking food (nectar and pollen), and incidentally carrying the pollen. In some cases, one finds a very specific relation between the form of the flower and that of the insect vector (Fig. 12-26).

Some plants possess modified leaves near the flower proper, and sometimes these **bracts** are bright and showy, usurping the insect-

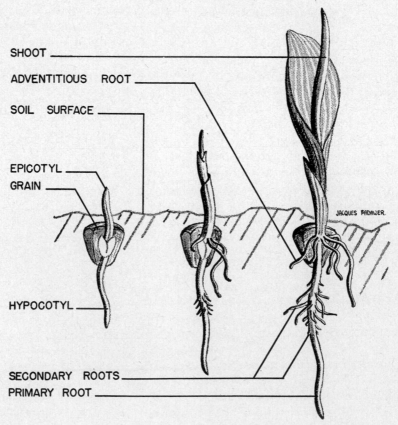

SHOOT

ADVENTITIOUS ROOT

SOIL SURFACE

EPICOTYL
GRAIN

JACQUES FADAWER.

HYPOCOTYL

SECONDARY ROOTS
PRIMARY ROOT

Fig. 12-24. Germination of corn grain. Compare with Fig. 12-23.

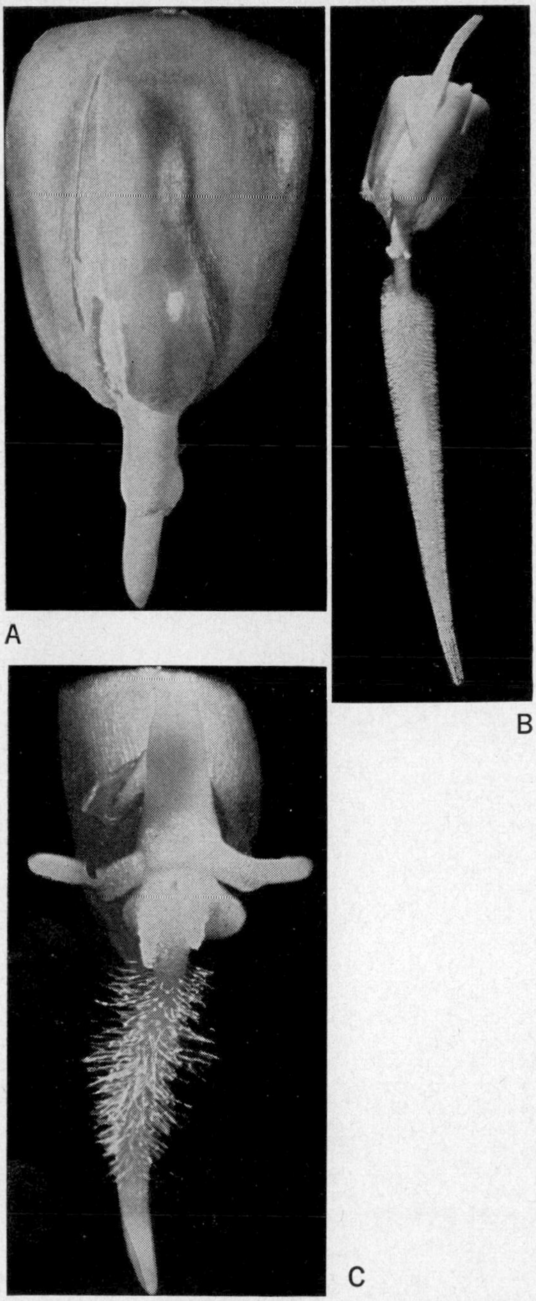

A

B

C

Fig. 12-25. Germinating grains. A, corn grain in early stage of germination. The primary root has penetrated the sheath and is emerging from the grain. B, a later stage in the germination of a corn grain. The primary root has numerous root hairs, and the plump epicotyl has emerged. C, a germinating wheat grain, showing the primary root with hairs, the short blunt epicotyl, and several young side roots. (From *College Botany,* by Fuller and Tippo. Holt, Rinehart and Winston, Inc.)

attracing function of the smaller true petals (for example, in poinsettia and dogwood, Fig. 12-27).

In wind-pollinated flowers (for example, the cottonwood, Fig. 12-28), petals and sepals are either lacking or inconspicuous, and usually the pistils and stamens occur in separate flowers. Such *incomplete* flowers are held aloft on the outermost branches of the plant, where there is a maximum exposure to the wind; and usually wind-pollinated flowers appear early in the spring, before the leaves come out to interfere with the transfer of the pollen, which is produced in very large amounts. Most of our common deciduous trees (maples, elms, willows, oaks, etc.) possess wind-pollinated flowers.

Frequently a multiple cluster of flowers is borne on one stalk (peduncle), which may or may not be branched (Figs. 12-27 and 12-28). Such floral clusters technically are called inflorescences, of which there is a wide variety of types. One very common type of inflorescence is possessed by the dandelions, daisies, sunflowers, dahlias, and the other members of a large family, the Compositae. The large "sunflower," for example, is an inflorescence composed of a multitude of very small individual flowers, which are of two sorts (Fig. 12-29). The sterile ray flowers, which lack both pistils and stamens, are arranged radially around the outer margin of the circular head. These ray flowers account for most of the showiness and color of the "sunflower." But the production of seeds is left entirely to the functional disc flowers, which are massed compactly in the central region of the head.

Variations of Fruit Structure. The *enlarged ripened* ovule chamber, *together with its content of* seeds, *is a* fruit, although in some cases (accessory fruits) other parts originally present in the flower may be incorporated in the fruit. For example, the apple (Fig. 12-30) is an accessory fruit of the pome type. In pomes, the receptacle of the flower surrounds the ovule chamber and gives rise to the skin and fleshy parts of the pome; and

Fig. 12-26. Bees entering snapdragon flowers, a feat possible only for large strong insects. The stigma of the snapdragon is so placed that it inevitably receives pollen from the hairy back of the bee, if the bee has previously visited another snapdragon. (From *The Plant World*, by Fuller and Carothers. Holt, Rinehart and Winston, Inc. Photo by C. F. Hottes.)

Fig. 12-27. Inflorescences of dogwood (*Cornus florida*). Each inflorescence consists of several very small flowers subtended by 4 large, white bracts. (From *The Plant World*, by Fuller and Carothers. Holt, Rinehart and Winston, Inc. Photo by C. F. Hottes.)

Fig. 12-28. Staminate (left) and pistillate (right) inflorescences of cottonwood (*Populus deltoides*). Cottonwoods are wind-pollinated. (From *the Plant World*, by Fuller, and Carothers. Holt, Rinehart and Winston, Inc.)

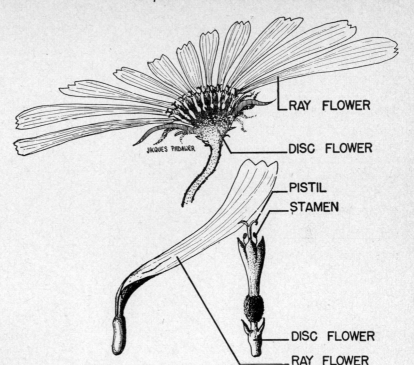

RAY FLOWER

DISC FLOWER

PISTIL
STAMEN

JACQUES PADAWER

DISC FLOWER
RAY FLOWER

Fig. 12-29. Diagram showing the individual flowers of the inflorescence of the sunflower.

only the "core" of the apple comes from the ovule chamber.

Fruits, like flowers, occur in almost endless variety; and frequently fruit structures are important to the dispersal of the seeds—by the wind, animals, or other agencies. This relation may be seen in the following classification, which includes many of the most common types of fruit.

A. Dry Fruits

1. **Winged fruits** or keys—as in maples, elms, and ashes (Fig. 12-31). The wings, which are outgrowths of the **pericarp** (wall of the ovule chamber), foster seed dispersal by wind.

2. **Plumed fruits,** as in dandelions, sycamores, and milkweeds (Fig. 12-31). The plumes are also pericarpal outgrowths that facilitate wind dispersal.

3. **Barbed fruits,** as in the burdock and wild carrot. These fruits are dispersed as "hitchhikers" on the fur or other skin covering of animals.

4. **Legumes,** as in peas and beans. The capsule of this podlike type of fruit is derived from a single ovule chamber. When ripe, the pod splits open along both seam-like margins, discharging the seeds.

5. **Grains,** as in corn and wheat. Only the very thin outer cover, which is closely adherent to the true seed coat of these single-seeded fruits, is derived from the pericarp (Fig. 12-23).

6. **Nuts,** such as hazel nuts and acorns. In these single-seeded fruits, the thick, hard outer shell is derived from the pericarp.

B. Fleshy Fruits

1. **Berries,** such as the grape and tomato (Fig. 12-32). The "skin" and all the flesh of the berry is derived from the wall of the ovule chamber, which may be monocarpellate (grape) or polycarpellate (tomato) in origin. Many berries are eaten by animals, and a dispersal of the species may result when the undigested seeds are voided in another locality.

2. **Drupes,** such as peaches and plums. Not only the skin and flesh of these one-seeded

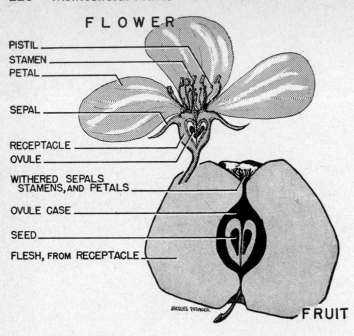

FLOWER

PISTIL
STAMEN
PETAL

SEPAL

RECEPTACLE
OVULE

WITHERED SEPALS
STAMENS, AND PETALS

OVULE CASE

SEED

FLESH, FROM RECEPTACLE

JACQUES PADAWER

FRUIT

Fig. 12-30. In **pome** fruits, such as the apple, the bulk of the fleshy part is derived from the receptable of the flower.

or two-seeded fruits but also the stony coat directly surrounding the seed proper are derived from the pericarp. The seeds of such fruits are also distributed by animals, which eat them.

Fruits are also classified as to the number of individual pistils that are originally represented in the flower. Accordingly:

A. A **simple fruit** is one that has developed from a single pistil, and all the fruits previously mentioned (except the burdock, tomato, and maple) are simple fruits.

B. An **aggregate fruit** is a cluster of ripened ovule chambers, the pistils of which were all borne in the same flower, for example, raspberries and blackberries.

C. A **multiple fruit** is a cluster of ripened ovule chambers, the pistils of which were borne in separate flowers, all having a common receptacle, for example, the pineapple.

GROWTH AND DEVELOPMENT IN PLANTS

In general, the development of plant structures is much simpler than that of animals. Most parts of the plant are essentially solid masses of cells, in contrast to the hollow or tubular nature of many animal organs. Ani-

mal development (see Chap. 15) involves a complex series of foldings, invaginations, and cell migrations; but plant development occurs mainly at localized **growing points,** where the cells **multiply, grow,** and **differentiate,** forming the **tissues** of the adult organs.

In thalloid plant bodies, the growing points are mainly localized at the apex of each filament, or lobe. At this point one usually finds a single large cell, the **apical cell,** which divides continually, producing all the cells of the thallus. The apical cell remains more or less permanently in an undifferentiated condition, and retains an unlimited capacity for multiplication and differentiation. But most of the other cells become differentiated sooner or later, forming the specialized tissues in the different parts of the thallus.

Among higher plants, which possess roots, stems, and leaves, cell division is largely restricted to growing points, which are localized masses of embryonic (**meristem**) tissue. The meristem cells remain in an undifferentiated state indefinitely, and retain their capacity for unlimited multiplication and differentiation. In the **root,** the growing point is located near the tip of each branch (Fig.

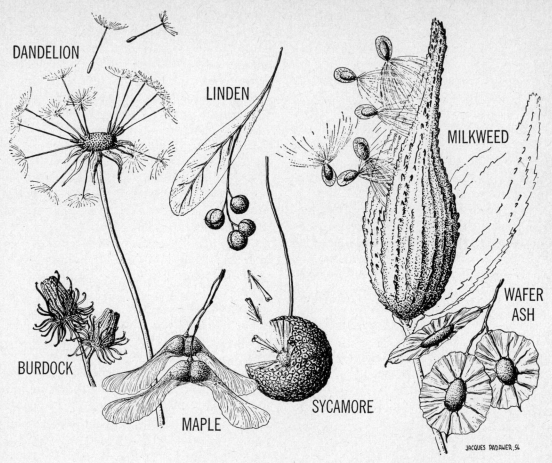

DANDELION

LINDEN

MILKWEED

WAFER ASH

BURDOCK

MAPLE

SYCAMORE

JACQUES PADAWER, 56

Fig. 12-31. (above). Types of seed-and-fruit-dispersal mechanisms.

Fig. 12-32. (right). Some common **berries**.

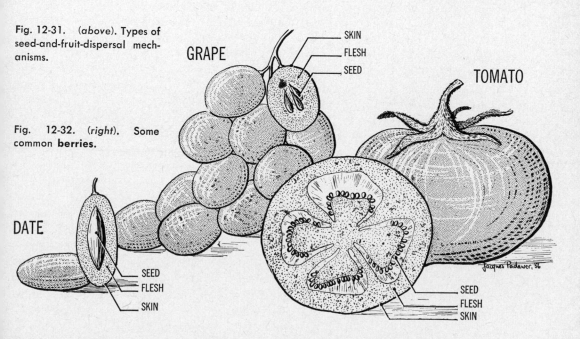

GRAPE

SKIN
FLESH
SEED

TOMATO

DATE

SEED
FLESH
SKIN

SEED
FLESH
SKIN

Jacques Padawer, 56

12-33); and in the stem, there is a growing point at the apex of each bud. However, many stems (Gymnospermae and dicotyledonous Angiospermae) possess a thin layer of meristem, the **cambium,** which encircles the trunk and its branches, underneath the bark. The cambium provides for increases in the **girth** of the stem. Also in most roots (Fig. 13-11) a layer of meristem, the **pericycle,** remains behind the growing point, providing for the origin of secondary offshoots from the primary root.

The nature of growth and development in plants is well illustrated by the case of a rootlet (Fig. 12-33). Virtually all new cells, both below and above the growing point, are formed by the multiplication of the meristem cells of the growing point. Below the growing point, the new cells become differentiated into the cells of the **root cap.** The

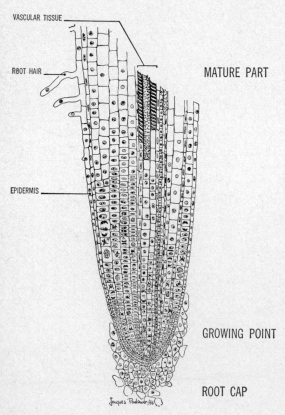

VASCULAR TISSUE

ROOT HAIR

EPIDERMIS

MATURE PART

GROWING POINT

ROOT CAP

Fig. 12-33. Longitudinal section of a young root of barley.

root cap never becomes very large, however, because the cells keep scuffing off as the root pushes down into the soil (Fig. 12-33). Above the growing point, the cells increase in size (particularly in length), and become differentiated into the several kinds of specialized tissues which make up the **body** of the root. Such mature differentiated cells develop thick woody walls and become incapable of further growth and division.

In plants, growth tends to be **localized** and potentially **unlimited;** while in animals, growth occurs throughout the body and is more limited in scope. Most animals stop growing when they achieve a certain size and form, but the size and form of a plant are limited mainly by external conditions.

Embryonic Development in a Dicotyledonous Seed Plant. After fertilization, the zygote begins development by a series of cell divisions. These first few divisions are all in one plane, producing a filament of cells, the **suspensor,** which pushes along the main axis toward the center of the endosperm tissue (Fig. 12-34). The end cell of the filament begins to divide in other planes, forming a rounded mass of cells (Fig. 12-34). The whole embryo is formed from this rounded mass of cells, and the suspensor degenerates before the seed is ripe. Growth and cell division now become most rapid at the sides of the embryo, near the free end. This results in two large outgrowths, which become the **cotyledons.** Meanwhile one end of the embryo elongates to form the **hypocotyl,** and the **epicotyl** begins to appear in the notch between the extended cotyledons. In some plants the embryo stops growing before it occupies the whole seed—in which case an endosperm persists around the embryo (Fig. 12-23). But in the bean (Fig. 12-21) and most other Dicotyledoneae, the cotyledons continue to grow, absorbing all the substance of the endosperm before the seed is ripe. In any event, the integuments of the ovule finally become thicker and tougher, forming the seed coats.

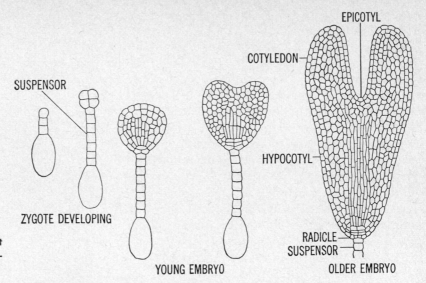

Fig. 12-34. Development of the embryo of a dicotyledonous plant.

Germination. When a seed is ripe, development stops temporarily. Under natural conditions most seeds remain in the dormant state throughout the winter or dry season; and some seeds cannot be forced to germinate without the intervention of a definite resting period. At the proper time, with the advent of warmth and moisture, the seed absorbs water, swells powerfully to burst the seed coats, and now the embryo resumes development.

The hypocotyl elongates rapidly, forming the primary root, which soon develops a zone of root hairs just above the tip (Fig. 12-20). The primary root is positively geotropic; that is, it grows downward, toward the earth, regardless of the position in which the seed may happen to lie (Fig. 12-35A). At the same time, or shortly later, the epicotyl, being negatively geotropic (Fig. 12-35B), begins to grow upward, forming the primary stem and the leaves. During these early stages of growth the young sporophyte draws upon the reserve organic nutrients stored in the cotyledons and endosperm (if present). This organic material is partly oxidized for energy and partly transformed into essential organic components in the growing cells. Despite the fact that the total amount of organic material is decreasing during this period, the actual size of the young plant increases greatly,

owing to the fact that a large amount of water is absorbed as the new protoplasm is formed. In some plants the cotyledons, after giving up their organic reserves, develop into ordinary foliage leaves, although more often the cotyledons shrivel and finally drop off. In either case, chlorophyll forms in the young leaves (and stem) shortly after they reach the light, and when the organic reserves originally present in the seed are

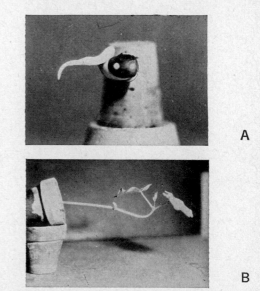

Fig. 12-35. A, positive geotropism in primary root of the bean. B, negative geotropism in young stem of bean plant.

exhausted, the young plant becomes entirely self-supporting.

Further Stages of Development. New branches and leaves originate from **buds,** which are generally situated at the apex and on the sides of the stem and its branches. The **terminal buds** provide for an elongation of the stem or branch; and the **lateral buds** give rise to more branches (Fig. 12-36). The lateral buds are also called **axillary buds** because each one lies in a leaf **axil**—that is, in the acute angle between the stem and the stalk, or **petiole,** of a leaf (Fig. 12-36). The immature bud is merely a conical mass of meristem tissue; but in mature buds (Fig. 12-37), partially developed leaves are present. The young leaves first appear as lateral outgrowths from the young bud; but gradually the young leaves overgrow and envelop the growing point of the bud (Fig. 12-37). Some buds remain in a dormant stage, without further development, for some time—as is true of the **winter buds** of trees. Such rest-

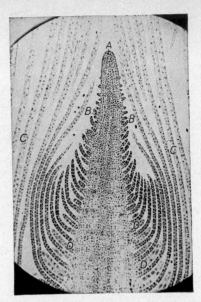

Fig. 12-37. Bud of *Elodea*, a naked bud. The growing point (A) lies at the top; and along the sides secondary buds (B and D) alternate with the leaves (C).

ing buds are usually of the **protected** type; that is, they possess an outer covering of horny modified leaves, called **scales,** which envelop the delicate embryonic leaves and the growing point of the bud (Fig. 12-36).

The growth of a leaf, unlike that of most stems and roots, is **limited;** that is, the leaf stops growing when it reaches a certain size and form. The short but rapid growth of a leaf subsides first in the basal portion, and only later does the apex of the leaf reach its maximum size.

In perennial plants, the **primary stem** may continue to elongate year after year as the terminal bud goes through its alternate periods of rest and growth. **Branches** of the stem originate from the axillary buds, but many axillary buds do not develop unless the terminal bud is cut off or otherwise destroyed. Accordingly, the general shape of many plants can be modified quite drastically by pruning.

The growth of roots differs somewhat from that of stems. Roots never give rise to buds or leaves, and the growing point is generally covered by a rootcap. Secondary branches of the root originate at various levels above the

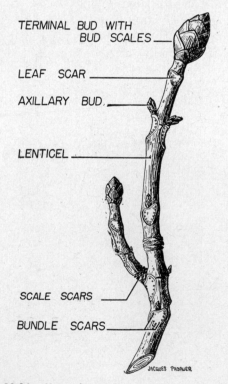

TERMINAL BUD WITH BUD SCALES

LEAF SCAR

AXILLARY BUD

LENTICEL

SCALE SCARS

BUNDLE SCARS

JACQUES PADAWER

Fig. 12-36. Horse-chestnut twig in winter condition.

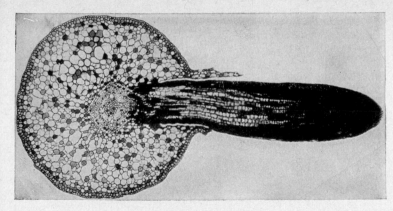

Fig. 12-38. A **secondary** root forces its way out through the cortex and epidermis of the **primary** root.

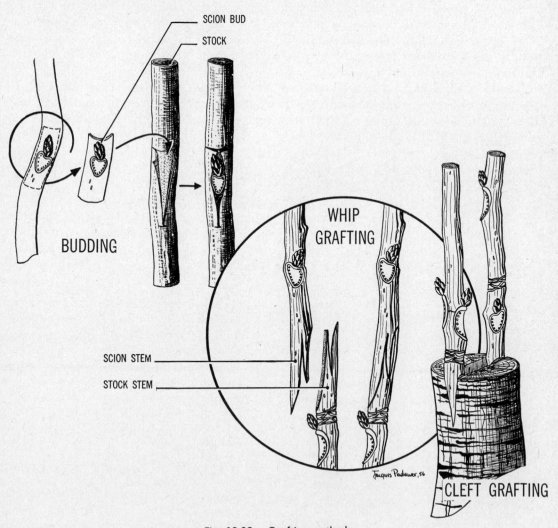

Fig. 12-39. Grafting methods.

growing point (Fig. 12-38), from the **peri-cycle,** a layer of meristem tissue that surrounds the core of the root. Accordingly, each new secondary root must break its way out through the cortical tissues of the old root. Some plants can form **adventitious roots** from the meristem tissue in any part of the stem, and in rare cases, even from leaf meristem.

Flowers develop at the ends of special stems, which are unable to grow beyond a fixed limit. Initially a **floral bud** looks much like a foliage bud, but later the terminal leaves modify their development and become the sepals, petals, stamens, and carpels. In the case of **mixed buds,** both foliage and floral branches originate from the same bud.

Vegetative Methods of Reproduction. Many plants exhibit a variety of reproductive processes that do not involve the production of either gametes or spores. In these **vegetative** methods of reproduction, the new plant usually arises from some multicellular part of the parent that contains some meristem tissue.

Many liverworts and ferns, and a few seed plants, form modified buds, called **bulbils** or **gemmae,** which develop into new plants after they become detached from the parent. Other plants—such as the strawberry—send out **runners,** or prostrate stems, producing offspring from the buds of the runners. New

plants may also arise from the buds, or **eyes,** of swollen underground stems, called **tubers** (for example, the potato). **Bulbs,** which are swollen underground buds, produce new bulbs in the axils of the scalelike leaves; and each new bulb can give rise to a separate plant.

In many plants, a slip, or **cutting**—that is, a piece cut from a stem—may send out adventitious roots and develop into a new plant; and in a few cases, a leaf, or even a portion of a leaf, may do the same thing. **Grafting,** on the other hand, involves the combining of portions of two plants, and grafting has become a valuable and widely practiced technique among fruitgrowers (Fig. 12-39). All vegetative methods of propagation provide a practical advantage to nurserymen. Vegetative reproduction never involves the processes of meiosis and fertilization, and therefore the new plant always **(barring mutation)** receives exactly the same set of chromosomes and hereditary characters as was possessed by the parent plant. Accordingly, the nurseryman is sure that the desirable qualities of a certain fruit tree, or potato, or other commercially valuable species are perpetuated in the new plants. A number of seed plants, including the banana, have lost their capacity for forming functional seeds, and are propagated solely by vegetative methods.

TEST QUESTIONS

1. Make labeled sketches showing the main features of: (a) the sporophyte; and (b) the gametophyte, of a fern.
2. What is the basis for recognizing the leafy fern plant as a sporophyte, and the prothallium as a gametophyte?
3. Specify five major groups in the plant kingdom and explain how the representatives of each group are to be distinguished on the basis of their life cycles.
4. A. Make labeled sketches to show the main stages in the life cycles of: (a) *Spirogyra,* and (b) the bread mold;
   B. Indicate the haploid and diploid stages

and specify the points where meiosis and fertilization occur.

5. Identify each of the following structures and give their localization in either the moss, or the fern, or both: (a) sporangia; (b) sporocytes; (c) spores; (d) sorus; (e) antheridia; (f) archegonia; (g) venter; (h) rhizoids; (i) fertilized egg; (j) foot; (k) protonema; (l) apical notch.
6. Describe the life cycle of *Selaginella*. Why is this cycle generally considered to represent a transition between the cycles of the ferns and seed plants?
7. Identify and locate each of the following

structures and wherever possible provide a synonym: (a) the pistil; (b) carpels; (c) the ovule; (d) the macrospore; (e) a stamen; (f) an anther; (g) a pollen grain; (h) the calyx; (i) the corolla; (j) the receptacle.

8. Make a labeled sketch to identify the female gametophyte of a seed plant. Where and when is this gametophyte to be found in a flower?

9. How does the female gametophyte of a seed plant either resemble or differ from the gametophytes of the fern and moss in regard to: (a) origin; (b) chromosome count of the component cells; (c) function; (d) mode of nutrition; (e) complexity of structure; (f) prospects of reaching maturity; (g) prospects of having the egg fertilized?

10. Carefully explain points (f) and (g) of the preceding question.

11. Differentiate between a seed and an ovule. What special features of seeds generally account for the success of the seed plants in spreading throughout the land areas of the earth?

12. Supply the missing parts of the following statements:
   a. all the cells of the embryo sporophyte, which occupies the center of a seed, are derived by mitosis from the ——— ———;
   b. each seed, as a whole, originates from an ———; whereas the fruit, as a whole, originates from the ———.

13. Identify and locate: (a) cotyledons; (b) the hypocotyl; (c) the epicotyl; (d) the plumule; (e) the embryonic bud; and (f) the suspensor.

14. In the bean and pea respectively, what parts (if any) of the adult sporophyte originate from: (a) the hypocotyl; (b) the epicotyl; and (c) the cotyledons?

15. In general, how are the parts of the flower modified in relation to the methods of pollination?

16. Enumerate five kinds of **dry fruits** and two kinds of **fleshy fruits,** giving the distinguishing features and an example of each type.

17. What is **cambium** and why is it important? What kinds of stems lack cambium?

18. What is a seedling? Explain the general importance of cotyledons (and endosperm, if present).

19. Identify each of the following: (a) lateral or axillary buds; (b) pericycle; (c) adventitious roots; (d) a bulbil; (e) a runner; (f) a tuber; (g) a bulb; (h) a cutting.

FURTHER READINGS

1. *The Plant World,* 4th ed., by Harry J. Fuller and Zane B. Carothers; New York, 1963.
2. *College Botany,* rev. ed., by Harry J. Fuller and Oswald Tippo; New York, 1954.
3. *Textbook of Botany,* by Transeau, Sampson, and Tiffany; New York, 1953.
4. *Botany,* by P. Weatherwax; Philadelphia, 1956.

13-*Nutrition of Multicellular Plants*

HOLOPHYTIC nutrition became dominant in the plant kingdom during an early evolutionary period, and as **multicellular** species developed they gained greater efficiency by a division of labor among the cells. Thus gradually the specialized tissues and organs of the modern higher plants came into being.

MULTICELLULAR ALGAE

All early primitive plants lived under water, and the aquatic environment puts little premium upon the development of specialized parts. Natural bodies of water contain adequate amounts of carbon dioxide, oxygen, and inorganic salts, so that every cell of a submerged plant can absorb these foods on an individual basis. Hence—as might be expected—the degree of differentiation among the cells of the green algae has not been very great.

Perhaps the commonest type of cell differentiation among nonmotile green algae is the modification of some of the cells to form organs of **attachment.** In some filamentous algae, a single cell at the basal end of the filament is specialized as a **rhizoid** (or holdfast) that attaches the filament to the soil or rock at the bottom of the water (Fig. 13-1). This specialized cell is modified in shape and

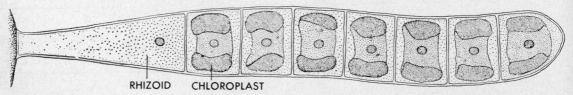

RHIZOID   CHLOROPLAST

Fig. 13-1.   Young filament of *Ulothrix*, a filamentous green alga, showing a slight degree of cellular differentiation. Normally this plant grows in a more or less vertical position attached to some object on the bottom of a pond or stream.

236

it lacks chlorophyll. The rhizoid cell is dependent on the other cells of the filament, and sugars produced by photosynthesis in the green cells are transferred to this colorless cell by diffusion through the intervening cell membranes.

Among the most highly differentiated of fresh-water algae is *Nitella* (Fig. 13-2). This relatively large green alga may measure almost a foot in length. *Nitella* exhibits a branching green "stem," which is attached to colorless rhizoids at the lower end, and which is surrounded above by whorls of

green "leaves." Superficially, *Nitella* resembles a higher plant; but microscopic study reveals that the alga has a relatively simple structure. The "stem" consists of a series of long **internodes,** alternating with short **nodes** (Fig. 13-2). Each node gives rise to a whorl of slender "leaves," which otherwise are similar to the main stem; and some nodes give off branches like the main stem. One or more of the lower nodes also sends off colorless rhizoids, which attach the plant to the soil or rock at the bottom of the pond. Except for the nodal cells, all parts of *Nitella*

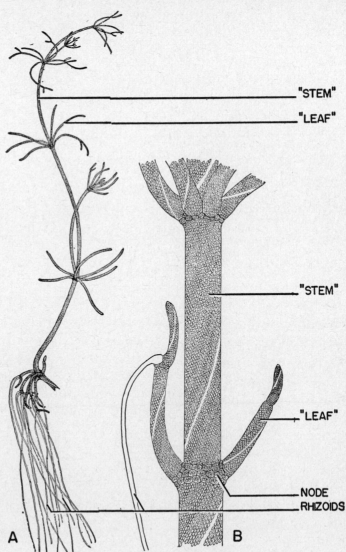

Fig. 13-2. The water plant, *Nitella*, exhibits some differentiation of its parts. A, whole plant, about natural size. B, a small portion, magnified.

are syncytial, with several nuclei enclosed within each wall; and except for the rhizoids, all parts of *Nitella* contain chloroplasts.

These structural differentiations in *Nitella* indicate a corresponding functional specialization, or division of labor, among the different parts of the plant. The rhizoids serve for **attachment,** and being incapable of photosynthesis, they depend upon the green parts for organic sustenance. The "leaves" are in a particularly favorable position for absorbing sunlight, and perform the major part of **photosynthesis.** The internodes, because of their elongate form and active protoplasmic streaming, specialize in the **distribution** of synthesized organic substances to the other parts of the plant. At the end of each stem and branch there is an **apical cell,** which continually divides to form the cells of a new node; and the nodal cells retain their capacity for dividing and differentiating into the various specialized parts of the *Nitella.* New "stem" and "leaves" originate as buds from the nodes in a manner that is characteristic of the growth of higher plants. However, "stems" and "leaves" of *Nitella* are syncytial, rather than multicellular structures.

Some larger marine algae (seaweeds) possess *multicellular* rhizoids, or "holdfasts," which are rootlike organs (Fig. 13-3). But rhizoids have a far simpler structure than true roots, being composed mainly of elongate cells twisted into stout strands, and the rhizoids serve only for attachment. A chief function of a true root is to absorb water and dissolved substances, but in the algae this function is performed by all the cells individually. Many large seaweeds also develop structures that *externally* resemble the true stems and leaves of higher plants, although *internally* these organs display only a small degree of cellular differentiation.

THE LAND AND ENVIRONMENT

To survive on land, plants have had to resolve a serious dilemma. *In the soil,* water, salts, carbon dioxide, and oxygen are available—but there is no light. And above the soil—that is, *in the air*—light is available, but the water supply is inadequate and inorganic salts are lacking. Therefore a truly successful land plant must possess parts that extend down into the soil and parts that reach up into the air. Accordingly, the conditions of the terrestrial habitat have determined the development of **roots, stems,** and **leaves,** which are the main **nutritive organs** of all well-adapted land plants. Typically, **roots** extend down into the soil to anchor the plant in an erect position and to *absorb* enough water and dissolved materials to meet the needs of the whole plant. The **leaves** are the specialized organs of photosynthesis, which pass on extra glucose and other organic compounds to the rest of the plant; and the **stem** supports the leaves and

Fig. 13-3. Holdfasts of a seaweed (*Macrocystis*) from the California coast.

transmits substances up and down between the leaves and roots.

NUTRITION OF THE BRYOPHYTES

The simplest and most primitive of **terrestrial** plants are the Bryophyta (p. 610). This phylum consists of two groups: (1) the **liverworts** (class Hepaticae, p. 611); and (2) the mosses (class Musci, Fig. 12-11). None of the Bryophyta is very well adapted to land conditions—the liverworts even less so than the mosses. In all the Bryophyta the main burden of nutrition falls upon the gametophyte generation—the sporophytes being relatively small and virtually dependent. Consequently the nutritive processes of only the gametophytes will be discussed.

The Liverworts. The liverworts are small semiterrestrial plants, unfamiliar to most people. The flat **thallus** body (Fig. 13-4), which seldom has an area of more than one or two square inches, grows in contact with the moist ground. Only the upper surface of

the thallus is exposed to light, and the lower surface, which lies in contact with the ground, sends numerous colorless rhizoids downward into the soil. Usually many plants lie crowded closely together, completely covering the moist ground in a region that is frequently flooded by a neighboring spring, or by seepage from a hillside.

These primitive land plants manage to survive even in the absence of true roots, stems, and leaves. The thallus displays a fairly complex internal structure, with considerable specialization among the cells (Fig. 13-5). To protect the thallus from the strong light and heat of the sun, and to prevent the plant from losing more water than it can absorb through the underlying rhizoids, the thallus is covered by a layer of **epidermoid tissue,** which is especially well developed on the upper surface. The outer walls of the epidermoid cells are thickened and cutinized (waxy), to prevent an indiscriminate evaporation of water from the delicate internal tissues as the sun beats down upon the plant.

Fig. 13-4. A group of liverworts (*Marchantia*) growing near a spring. Note how these primitive land plants crowd together, mutually protecting themselves from desiccation during dry weather. In the cuplike bodies (gemma cups), which can be seen on the upper surfaces of some of the thalli, budlike reproductive bodies (gemmae) are produced and liberated periodically. The background of this photograph was retouched to give more contrast.

Also the upper surface is equipped with clearly defined openings, the **pores,** each flanked by specialized **pore cells** (Fig. 13-5). The pore cells control the size of the numerous openings, tending to close them when the quantity of escaping water vapor becomes excessive. The pores lead into **air spaces,** inside the thallus, and these spaces permit carbon dioxide to diffuse from the outside air to the delicate green cells, or **chlorenchyma,** which border the air spaces. The remaining thickness of the thallus is composed mainly of larger cells with fewer chloroplasts. These cells serve chiefly as a **storage tissue,** in which extra quantities of photosynthesized glucose are deposited in the form of starch grains. In addition to the storage tissue, the cells in the central parts of the thallus, especially along the "midribs" (Fig. 13-5), are unusually long and display very active cyclosis. This **primitive vascular tissue** accelerates the *distribution* of substances from one part of the thallus to another.

The **rhizoids** (Fig. 13-5) are colorless elongate cells with delicate walls, adapted to the absorption of water and mineral salts. The rhizoids occur in clusters and each cluster is protected by one or more **scales,** which are multicellular extensions of the lower epidermoid layer. In dry weather, the scales tend to curl around the rhizoids, protecting them from desiccation.

Growth of the thallus is by the proliferation of **apical cells** at the end of each lobe. Frequently a growing point becomes divided into two masses of embryonic tissue, each of which generates a new lobe; and this method of growth accounts for the branching habit of the thallus.

The Mosses. The general form of the moss, with its small erect leaf-surrounded stem, was described previously (p. 208). Like the liverworts, typical mosses are only semiterrestrial. They grow in densely crowded clumps, protecting each other from desiccation; and except for a few highly developed species, the mosses are restricted to damp and shady localities.

The internal (microscopic) structure of a moss plant is shown diagrammatically in Figure 13-6. The **rhizoids,** which extend down

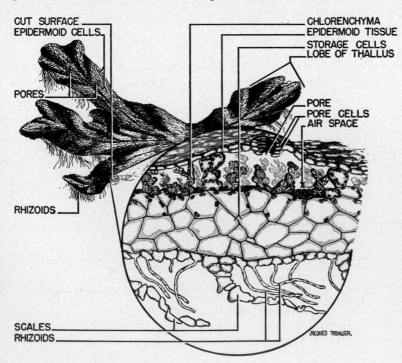

CUT SURFACE
EPIDERMOID CELLS
PORES
RHIZOIDS
SCALES
RHIZOIDS

CHLORENCHYMA
EPIDERMOID TISSUE
STORAGE CELLS
LOBE OF THALLUS
PORE
PORE CELLS
AIR SPACE

JACQUES PROANER

Fig. 13-5. A liverwort (*Marchantia*). This plant shows some very primitive adaptations that enable it to live on land, but only in places where water is abundant (see text).

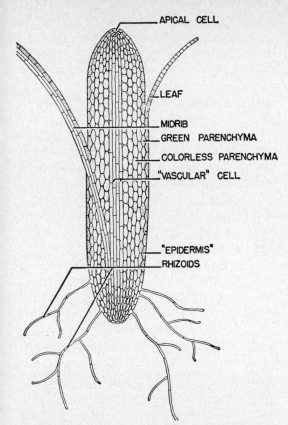

APICAL CELL

LEAF

MIDRIB

GREEN PARENCHYMA

COLORLESS PARENCHYMA

"VASCULAR" CELL

"EPIDERMIS"

RHIZOIDS

Fig. 13-6. Diagram of longitudinal section of moss plant.

into the soil from the lower end of the stem, are simple branched filaments of colorless elongate cells, often twisted into stout root-like strands. Like the true roots of higher plants, the rhizoids serve for both **absorption** and **attachment;** but structurally the rhizoids are much simpler than the true roots (p. 246). In most mosses, the blade of each **leaf** consists of a *single layer* of rather thick-walled cells, which contain numerous chloroplasts. During photosynthesis—and this is the special function of the leaf as a whole—each individual cell absorbs carbon dioxide directly from the air. But water, which is needed simultaneously in photosynthesis, is obtained from the rhizoids, via the stem and **midrib** of the leaf. The **midrib,** or central axis of the leaf, is somewhat thicker than the **blade,** due to the presence of several strands of elongate cells placed end to end along

the length of the leaf. This **primitive vascular tissue** serves not only to carry water and salts out into the leaf, but also to take glucose and other organic substances back from the leaf to the other parts of the plant.

The **stem** of a moss plant exhibits three fairly distinct concentric zones: (1) an outer zone made up of several layers of green cells; (2) an intermediate zone of larger more loosely packed colorless cells; and (3) an innermost core of elongate slender cells (Fig. 13-6). Some photosynthesis occurs in the green cells of the outer layers. However, these cells have thick cutinized walls, and their chief function is to waterproof the external surface of the stem—since very few mosses possess a distinct epidermal covering. The intermediate zone of thin-walled cells is for the storage of reserve organic substances, chiefly starch, although their loose arrangement provides air spaces to facilitate the **respiration** of the stem as a whole. The primitive vascular tissue in the central core of the moss stem serves for the *distribution* of inorganic materials *upward,* and of organic products *downward,* through the plant. In a few mosses the end walls of the vascular cells—where they make contact with each other end to end—are perforated, so that protoplasmic continuity exists from cell to cell, as in the **sieve tubes** of higher plants (p. 242). **Growth** occurs by the multiplication of an apical cell at the top of each stem. The leaves, and in a few species branches, originate as buds from this growing point.

Organs and Tissues of the Bryophytes. In summary, the specialized organs and tissues of higher land plants are foreshadowed only feebly in the Bryophyta. Without **true roots,** capable of absorbing water on a quantity basis, the bryophytes have not developed an extensive leaf surface, since such a surface would expose the plant to an excessive loss of water. Moreover, many of the Bryophyta —that is, the liverworts—have not developed even a primitive stem system.

Likewise the **tissues** of bryophytes are only partially differentiated. The **epidermoid** and storage tissue cells possess chloroplasts and continue to carry on photosynthesis as a secondary function; and the vascular tissue of bryophytes is of a very primitive type, which does not approach the efficiency of the **true vascular tissues** (p. 244) of the ferns and seed plants.

TRANSITIONAL DEVELOPMENTS: ASCENDANCE OF THE SPOROPHYTE GENERATION

Among the Bryophyta the **gametophyte generation** displays a limited fitness to cope with the land environment; and little evolutionary progress has been made by Bryophyta in recent geological times. Meanwhile the **sporophyte generation** of the higher plants evolved an efficient system of specialized organs and tissues; and the modern ferns and seed plants are well adapted to land conditions. In this evolution, however, the **gametophyte generation** of the higher plants has retrogressed and become relatively insignificant, from a nutritive point of view. Although the gametophyte (prothallium) of the fern is an independent plant, its nutritive processes are not any more complex than those of the liverwort; and the gametophytes of the **seed plants** are microscopic bodies, which are nourished entirely by the tissues of the sturdy land-adapted sporophytes (p. 219). In the following sections, therefore, the nutrition of the gametophyte generations will not be considered; and only the nutrition of the sporophytes of the higher plants will be discussed.

NUTRITIVE ORGANS AND TISSUES OF THE VASCULAR PLANTS

Collectively the *higher land plants,* which possess well-defined conducting (vascular) tissues (see below), constitute the **phylum Tracheophyta** (Chap. 31). These vascular plants, except for some virtually extinct groups (p. 613), are fairly similar as to their nutritive tissues and organs. The following discussion, however, deals mainly with the Angiospermae, which are the best adapted to land conditions and the most widely distributed of all tracheophytes.

Tissues of the Vascular Plants. The following tissues, classified according to function, are prseent in the vascular plants:

1. *Meristem Tissue* (also called **embryonic parenchyma**). Meristem tissue has an unlimited capacity for **multiplication** and **differentiation;** and all the specialized tissues (listed below) are derived from the meristem of the growing points of the plant. Typically the meristem consists of small thin-walled cells, which possess chloroplasts and which divide more or less continuously, forming more meristem.

2. *Epidermal Tissues.* Epidermal tissues provide a suitable covering for the various surfaces of the plant. Typical epidermal cells fit closely together with a minimum of inter-

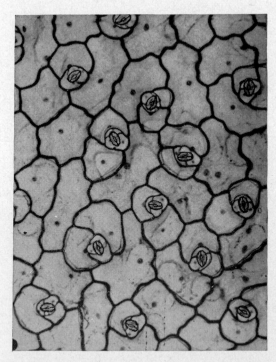

Fig. 13-7. Magnified surface view of a *Sedum* leaf. Each **stoma** is flanked by a pair of small sausage-shaped **guard cells**, which fit in among the large irregular **epidermal cells**. Photograph retouched to clarify outline of the guard cells.

cellular material or space—forming a layer that is only one cell deep. Epidermal cells vary in form in the different parts of the plant. In the leaf (Fig. 13-7), where the epidermis protects the internal tissues from losing too much water, the outer walls of the cells are thick and **cutinized.** Leaf epidermis is also unusually transparent, allowing light to pass through to the green tissue inside the leaf. Even in the leaf the epidermal cells do not possess chloroplasts. In the root, where the epidermis has an absorptive function, the cell walls are relatively delicate; and in the zone where absorption is most active, the epidermal cells of the root possess slender outgrowths, the **root hairs.**

3. *Green Parenchyma,* or *Chlorenchyma.* Parenchyma tissues are not highly specialized; that is, the cells resemble meristem cells in greater or lesser degree. Green parenchyma possesses chloroplasts (Fig. 13-16), and photo-synthesis is the main function. Green parenchyma cells are usually thin walled and loosely packed. This arrangement provides a continuous system of **intercellular spaces** and facilitates the exchange of gases during photosynthesis and respiration. Green parenchyma is localized mainly in the leaves, although some chlorenchyma is usually present near the surface in younger stems.

4. *Storage Parenchyma,* or *Colorless Parenchyma.* Storage parenchyma resembles green parenchyma, except that the cells are generally larger and lack chloroplasts. The main function of colorless parenchyma is to store organic substances (chiefly starch); but the loose arrangement of the cells facilitates respiration in the stem and roots (Fig. 13-8).

5. *Strengthening Tissues.* (a) *Sclerenchyma:* This loosely defined tissue consists of elongate cells with very thick cell walls. In some mature sclerenchyma all the protoplasm may

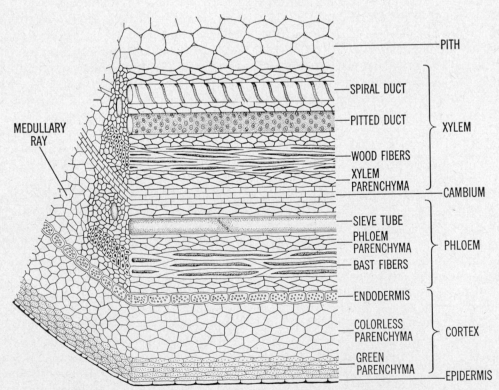

Fig. 13-8. Tissues of the higher plants as shown in a diagrammatic section of the stem of an angiosperm. For convenience of labeling, the stem has been placed horizontally rather than in the normal vertical position.

be replaced by the encroachment of the thick cell walls, which impart mechanical strength to the tissue. Sclerenchyma is present in many stems and roots, and in some leaves.

(b) *Bast.* This special type of sclerenchyma is found in the phloem (p. 243) of many stems (Fig. 13-8). Initially each bast fiber is a living cell, which develops an elongate spindlelike shape and very thick walls. A mature bast fiber finally displays a small central hollow, which is devoid of any protoplasm (Fig. 13-8). The pointed ends of the spindle-shaped bast fibers tend to overlap each other, imparting great flexibility and strength to the tissue as a whole.

(c) *Wood* likewise is a special type of sclerenchyma, which is found in the **xylem** (p. 243) of many stems (Fig. 13-8). Wood fibers resemble bast fibers in origin and form. However, in wood the cell walls are denser, and this imparts a "harder" quality to the tissue.

6. **Vascular Tissues.** (a) *Sieve tubes* are tubular units found in the **phloem** of stems (Fig. 13-8), roots, and leaves. Each sieve tube represents a column of elongate cylindrical cells, placed end to end. At maturity the end walls of these cells become perforated, forming the **sieve plates,** which give protoplasmic continuity between the successively placed cells in the column (Fig. 13-8). Moreover, the cytoplasm of a mature sieve tube unit appears to be somewhat modified and no nucleus is present. The protoplasm of the sieve tubes displays active **cyclosis,** which accelerates the distribution of substances lengthwise through the plant. The sieve tubes are concerned particularly with the transportation of sugars and other *organic* products, *downward* and *sideways* in the plant.

(b) *Ducts,* or *vessels,* are tubular units localized in the **xylem** regions of roots, stems, and leaves. The initial differentiation of a duct from embryonic parenchyma resembles that of a sieve tube, but later the side wall of the column of cells becomes much thicker, and gradually the end walls are *resorbed completely* (Fig. 13-8). Finally all the protoplasm disappears, leaving a free channel throughout

the length of each vessel. The ducts form continuous channels from the roots up through the stem and into the leaves. Ducts serve to transport substances—particularly water and inorganic salts—*upward* through the plant. Several kinds of ducts are distinguishable. In **pitted** ducts, the side walls are pocked with numerous round depressions (Fig. 13-8). These pits partially penetrate the cellulose and permit substances to escape from the ducts, supplying the surrounding tissues at various levels of the plant. In **spiral** (Fig. 13-8) and **annular** ducts, thickenings of the side walls can be seen, which give a "springlike" and a "ringlike" appearance to each respective type. The xylem of some vascular plants contains **tracheids,** which may replace the ducts, either partially or completely. Generally speaking, tracheids are like ducts, except that their conducting channels are interrupted periodically by diagonally placed perforated cell walls. In addition to the vascular function, ducts and tracheids augment the mechanical strength of the various parts, especially in the stem.

The Root and Its Functions. Aside from the fact that some roots serve as repositories for reserves of synthesized organic products, especially starch, the root system of a vascular plant has two main functions: (1) it **absorbs** water and salts for the plant as a whole; and (2) it **anchors** the plant in an upright position. Accordingly, the roots of a plant ramify extensively throughout the soil. In many trees the roots branch even more profusely than the stem; and frequently the total root *surface* is greater than that of the stem with all its branches (Fig. 13-9). The root system of a single rye plant, grown under ideal conditions, was found to measure more than 300 *miles* of branching length. These roots provide a surface area of more than 2500 square feet, not counting the area of the root hairs. However, the depth of roots seldom equals the height of the stem, although frequently the two systems have a corresponding lateral spread.

Not all parts of the root system are equally

Fig. 13-9. Roots of a white elm exposed by the encroachment of a stream. (Courtesy of the Missouri Botanical Garden.)

effective in the absorption of water and salts. In fact absorption is confined largely to the **root hair zone,** which lies above the growing point in each of the many young branches or **rootlets** (Fig. 13-10).

The root hair zone displays a highly organized structure, as may be seen in cross section (Fig. 13-11). At the center lies the **vascular cylinder,** sheathed by a thick cortex. The vascular cylinder is composed chiefly of **ducts** and **sieve tubes,** surrounded by a single layer of **growth tissue,** the **pericycle.** The thickness of the cortex is due to the several layers of **colorless parenchyma,** which is covered externally by a thin epidermis from which the root hairs are derived.

Absorption by the root is determined partly by osmosis, although active transport mechanisms (p. 121) serve to maintain a high concentration of certain ions in the tissues of the root. Water from the soil enters the root hairs and then passes across the cortex tissues, entering the **ducts** of the vascular cylinder (Fig. 13-11). The root hairs extend out from the epidermis and make contact with the film of water that wets the particles of moist soil

(Fig. 13-12). Although only 1 to 2 centimeters in length, each root hair zone displays a prodigious number of these tiny structures. The number of root hairs in a single rye plant, for example, has been carefully estimated at more than 14 million, adding some 4 thousand square feet of extra surface to the absorbing area of the root system. The root hairs, being very delicate, dry out and die within a few minutes if they are exposed to air. Consequently, if a plant is to be transplanted during the growing season, the soil around the roots must be disturbed as little as possible. This care avoids tearing the root hairs—which may be cemented to the soil particles—and protects them from being killed by drying. Without root hairs a plant usually wilts and dies before new root hairs can be regenerated, because the root hairs account for a high percentage of the absorbing surface of the root.

Soil water is a **hypotonic** solution of inorganic salts, which yields water to the root hair cells; and as these epidermal cells take in water, they become hypotonic to the cells

Fig. 13-10. Root hairs as seen on a seedling of the garden cress grown in moist air (× 4).

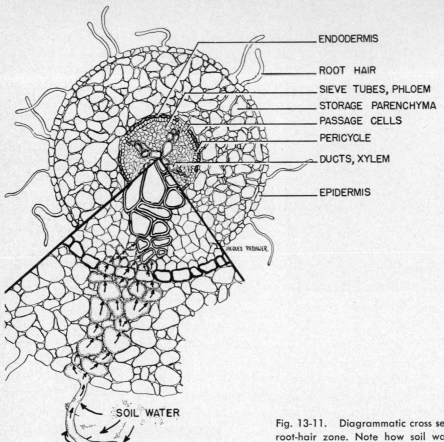

ENDODERMIS

ROOT HAIR

SIEVE TUBES, PHLOEM

STORAGE PARENCHYMA

PASSAGE CELLS

PERICYCLE

DUCTS, XYLEM

EPIDERMIS

SOIL WATER

Fig. 13-11.   Diagrammatic cross section of a root, in the root-hair zone. Note how soil water enters the xylem through the intervening tissues.

of the cortex. Thus water continues to pass inward through the root tissues, toward the **ducts** in the vascular cylinder. The ducts contain the **sap** of the plant. This solution, because of its content of sugars and salts, is distinctly hypertonic, and tends to absorb water from the surrounding tissues. The water entering the sap generates a pressure in the ducts; and this **root pressure** forces the sap to flow upward through the plant. At the top of the plant, much water constantly escapes from the leaves (p. 250), and in the leaves new sugars are being synthesized and sent downward to the roots. These processes are necessary to maintain the hypertonicity of the sap and to foster a further absorption of water (see p. 252).

The root also absorbs inorganic salts from the soil, although this is a relatively slow process. Probably roots are able to augment their salt absorption by energy-expending processes, but these processes are not well understood. Ordinarily, inorganic salts are absorbed in very small amounts, and consequently large volumes of sap must flow to the upper parts of the plant to supply the metabolic needs of the tissues (see later).

The Stem and Its Functions. The extensively branching **stem** system of the typical land plant has two primary functions: (1) it supports the leaves in a position that assures a maximum of photosynthesis, and (2) it conducts materials upward and downward between the leaves and the roots.

The vascular functions of the plant are performed mainly by the **ducts,** or **vessels,** and **sieve tubes.** These vascular elements always occur in the form of organized strands,

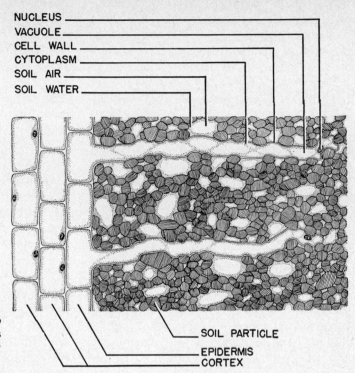

NUCLEUS
VACUOLE
CELL WALL
CYTOPLASM
SOIL AIR
SOIL WATER

SOIL PARTICLE
EPIDERMIS
CORTEX

Fig. 13-12. Relation of root hairs to the soil. Note particularly the air spaces in the soil, and the film of soil water that clings to the soil particles.

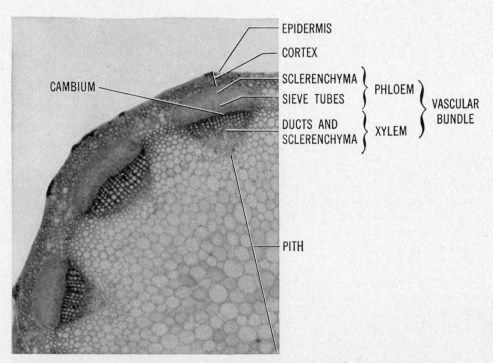

EPIDERMIS
CORTEX
CAMBIUM
SCLERENCHYMA } PHLEOM
SIEVE TUBES
DUCTS AND SCLERENCHYMA } XYLEM
VASCULAR BUNDLE
PITH

Fig. 13-13. Photomicrograph of one quadrant of a cross section of stem of a dicotyledonous plant (clover). Note particularly the circular arrangement of the **vascular bundles** and the disposition of the **cambium.**

called **vascular bundles.** The vascular bundles of the stem extend downward into the root and upward into the leaves, forming a continuous system of channels throughout the plant. In addition to vessels and sieve tubes, most vascular bundles contain considerable strengthening tissue, sclerenchyma tissue. However, much of the strength and flexibility of the stem and its branches is due to the mechanical properties of the vascular bundles (Fig. 13-13).

Microscopic Structure of a Stem. The tissues of the stem are organized around the vascular bundles, although the arrangement of the bundles differs considerably in different plants. Main attention will be given to the stem of a clover plant, which is quite typical of the *young* stems of dicotyledonous plants generally.

In cross section, the clover stem displays a circular arrangement of the **vascular bundles** (Fig. 13-13). Accordingly, it is possible to subdivide the stem into three concentric regions: (1) the **pith,** a central core of colorless parenchyma; (2) the **vascular region,** comprised by the ring of bundles, taken collectively; and (3) the **cortex,** the tissues that surround the ring of bundles.

Figure 13-13 shows that each vascular bundle is subdivided into an inner part, the **xylem,** and an outer part, the **phloem,** by the **cambium,** a layer of meristem tissue. All growth in the girth of the stem results from the activity of the cambium cells, which keep multiplying and differentiating to form the other tissues. New phloem—which consists mainly of sieve tubes—is formed along the *outer* margin of the cambium; and new xylem—mainly ducts—is formed by the cambium along its *inner margin.*

Surrounding the vascular region lie the tissues of the **cortex,** which commonly is called the bark; and between the bundles lie the **rays,** the strands of tissue that extend radially from the pith to the cortex (Fig. 13-8). The cortex, together with its superficial layer of **epidermis,** serves chiefly as a protective cover, although in young stems the cortex may contain chlorenchyma and perform a limited amount of photosynthesis. The **pith** consists of colorless parenchyma, in which the large thin-walled cells serve as storage centers, chiefly of starch grains. In older stems, which, unlike the clover stem, continue to grow from year to year, the cells of the rays become elongate in a horizontal direction. This growth indicates that the rays act as channels for the radial distribution of substances, from the vascular tissues outward into the cortex and inward into the pith.

During the first year of growth, **woody stems** such as are characteristic of most trees and shrubs closely resemble the clover stem. But in *woody stems,* the cambium gives rise *each year* to *an additional layer of* **xylem** on the inside, and another (much thinner) layer of **phloem** on the outside. These yearly deposits of xylem in woody stems are clearly differentiated as the **annual rings** (Fig. 13-14). The annual rings are distinguishable because the ducts that are formed in the spring of each year are larger than those that are formed in summer; and because fewer wood fibers (p. 243) are formed during the spring growth of the xylem (Fig. 13-15). Only the outermost, or youngest, layer of the xylem continues to carry sap upward through the plant, but the older xylem keeps augmenting the strength of the stem as the load of foliage

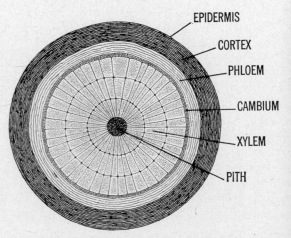

Fig. 13-14. Diagram showing cross-sectional structure of a 3-year-old pine stem.

becomes greater. Woody stems also tend to develop a "corky" layer outside the cortex proper, and this cork replaces the epidermis (Fig. 13-14). Moreover, the thickness of the bark does not increase indefinitely because the outer layers are continually worn away by the action of the elements.

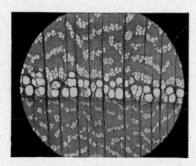

Fig. 13-15. Photomicrograph of a cross section of the wood of elm (*Ulmus americana*). The light circles, both large and small, are ducts, between which lie chiefly wood fibers; and the vertical streaks are rays.

Conduction in the Stem. The upward flow of sap in the **xylem,** which carries water and salts to the higher parts of the plant, can be demonstrated by *girdling experiments.* If a cut is made through the cortex and phloem, encircling the stem just to the depth of the cambium, the leaves of the plant remain turgid and do not wilt for a number of days. This shows that water passes the girdled region and reaches the foliage in adequate amounts. However, growth in the stem and roots *below* the cut stops as soon as the local stores of organic substances are exhausted. Finally the roots begin to die, and then the whole plant dies, indicating that the roots and other nonleafy parts of the plant depend upon synthesized organic substances brought *downward* from the leaves via the **sieve tubes** of the phloem.

Internal girdling, which is the opposite experiment, involves cutting the xylem of a stem without disturbing the phloem. This operation is difficult, but it can be done in small stems, by means of special instruments. The leaves of such a girdled plant begin to wilt and die immediately after the operation, because water cannot get to the leaves to replace the evaporative losses. And without leaves the whole plant will die, unless it can put forth new foliage from the stem below the level of the operation.

The Leaf and Its Function. The broad bladelike form of typical leaves is well adapted to their main function, which is to carry on photosynthesis for the plant as a whole. To fulfill this function the leaf must possess an adequate surface that is exposed as directly as possible to sunlight.

The leaf in dicotyledonous plants consists of a stalk, called the **petiole,** and a broad part, the **blade,** which may be either simple or subdivided into leaflets. In structure the petiole closely resembles the stem; and the vascular bundles of the petiole extend out into the blade, forming the **midrib** of the leaf. In the blade the vascular bundles of the midrib "fan out," forming a network of **veins** throughout all the blade. Essentially each vein is a small vascular bundle, surrounded by a sheath of parenchyma cells.

Microscopic Structure of a Leaf. The internal structure of the leaf is seen more clearly in *cross section* (Figs. 13-16 and 13-17). The colorless cells of the upper and lower epidermis possess relatively thick, thoroughly cutinized outer cell walls. This epidermal layer protects the more delicate internal cells from drying and from mechanical injuries and infections. The epidermis, especially on the lower side of the leaf, is characterized by the presence of numerous small pores, the **stomata.** Each stoma is flanked by a pair of **guard cells** (Figs. 13-16 and 13-17), which control the escape of water vapor, and regulate the exchange of CO_2 and O_2 between the internal tissues and the atmosphere. Unlike epidermal cells, the guard cells possess chloroplasts.

Most of the space between the upper and lower epidermis is filled with chlorenchyma tissue, but these green cells are loosely arranged, especially in the lower layers (Fig. 13-16). Accordingly there is an extensive system of intercellular air spaces inside the leaf,

EPIDERMIS
ENDODERMIS
XYLEM
PHLOEM

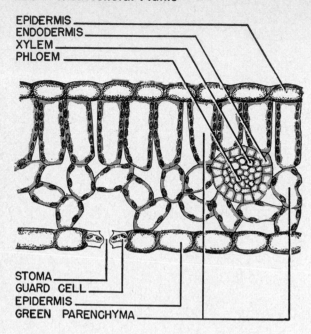

STOMA
GUARD CELL
EPIDERMIS
GREEN PARENCHYMA

Fig. 13-16. Cross section of portion of the blade of a leaf, including a single vein.

and these internal air spaces communicate with the outside air through the stomata.

The network of veins, or vascular bundles, in the leaf is so extensive that one or more bundles is likely to be present in any section of the leaf, however small. The xylem of each vein occupies an upper position relative to the phloem, and the smaller veins may consist of only a few ducts and a corresponding number of sieve tubes. The very smallest veins—out near the margin of the blade—lack sieve tubes and consist of only one or two ducts, which end blindly among

the chlorenchyma cells. As in the stem, the vascular bundles of the leaf are chiefly channels of distribution. Water and salts are brought to the chlorenchyma cells by the ducts, and organic substances are carried out of the leaf by the sieve tubes.

Transpiration. On sunny days the leaves give off large amounts of water vapor, provided the plant is able to absorb a compensating quantity of water from the soil. This loss of water vapor from the leaves, which is controlled by the guard cells, is called **transpiration**. The heat of the sun keeps vaporiz-

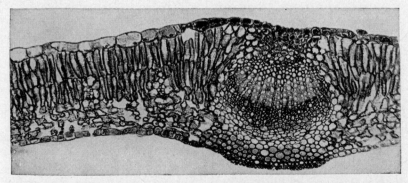

Fig. 13-17. Photograph of a cross section of a lilac leaf. One large vein lies in the thick part of the section, and two very small veins are present in the thinner part to the left.

ing water from the surface of the thin-walled chlorenchyma cells inside the leaf, and the resulting vapor passes out of the leaf by way of the stomatal openings.

In most leaves the stomata occur chiefly or entirely on the lower surface; and the number of stomata varies between 50 and 500 per square millimeter of the surface (Fig. 13-7). The average size at maximal opening is about 6×18 microns, so that about $\frac{1}{20}$ of the leaf surface may be occupied by stomata. The transmission of gases through such a perforated membrane is almost as rapid as in free diffusion. However, the size of the stomata is regulated strictly by the guard cells. When plenty of water comes up to the leaf from the soil, the guard cells remain turgid; and when turgid, the guard cells spring apart, opening the stomata (Fig. 13-18). But when the loss of water by transpiration exceeds the gain of water from the soil, the guard cells wilt, and the wilted guard cells change shape in such a fashion that they block the stomatal openings. The guard cells possess chloroplasts, which enable them to regulate their own turgor according to current conditions. By synthesizing sugar, the cells may increase their turgor, or by converting sugar into starch, the cells may lose turgor. Accordingly the stomata tend to remain open in the daytime—provided the water supply is adequate—but at night they tend to be partially closed.

The quantity of water transpired by an average plant in sunlight is about 50 grams per square meter of leaf surface per hour. Thus a single corn plant puts forth more than 50 gallons of water in the course of one summer; or an acre of corn transpires about 300,000 gallons of water in the same time. An average tree transpires more than 1500 gallons annually, and the total quantity of water vaporized from the vegetation of a forested region has a significant influence upon the rainfall, humidity, and temperature of that region.

As the sun beats down, the leaf absorbs about 75 percent of the impinging light. However, roughly only 3 percent of this energy is utilized in photosynthesis. The rest is transformed into heat—the heat that vaporizes water and leads to transpiration. This vaporization is most important, not only because it dissipates the heat that otherwise would kill the tissues of the leaf, but also because it generates an osmotic force that evacuates the ducts of the leaf and brings about a further flow of sap upward from the roots.

Transpiration and the Flow of Sap. Transpiration motivates the upward flow of sap by altering osmotic conditions in the leaves. When the chlorenchyma tissues lose water, the cells become hypertonic to the sap in the veins, which lie in close contact with the chlorenchyma (Fig. 13-16). During transpiration, consequently, water tends to be drawn from the ducts into the chlorenchyma tissues. Such a forceful evacuation of the ducts of the leaf creates a lifting force that helps to elevate the whole column of sap in its ascent from the roots. At certain times, in fact, when the solute content of the root sap is low, **transpirational lift** represents the principal, or even the only, force that maintains an upward flow of sap. Transpirational lift could not be effective, however, were it not for the high **cohesive strength** of the aqueous

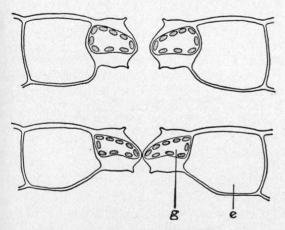

Fig. 13-18. The action of guard cells. Above, the guard cells are turgid, leaving the stoma open; below, the guard cells are wilted (i.e., less turgid), closing the stoma.

sap, which prevents the column from breaking as it is pulled upward in the vessels. The tensile strength of a column of water, which is almost equivalent to that of a sap column, has been measured in several ways. These measurements yield values that are equal to or greater than 60 kilograms per square centimeter, or 60 atmospheres. Such a force would be adequate to lift sap to the tallest tree-top, even considering the high resistance encountered by the sap as it flows through the very fine vessels of the plant. Also this force would account for the rapidity of sap ascent, which reaches a maximum of some 200 feet per hour in some hardwood trees such as the oak. A large flow of sap is essential to the plant, but not because a great quantity of water is needed for photosynthesis. Actually only about 1 percent of the water reaching the leaf is used this way. A very copious flow is necessary if the leaf cells are to receive adequate quantities of salts (for protein synthesis), since only very small amounts of inorganic salts are present in the sap. Moreover, large quantities of water must be vaporized from the leaf to prevent an overheating of the tissues.

Elevation of Sap in Tall Trees. The rise of sap in tall trees—which may grow to heights of more than 300 feet—may involve mechanisms that are not yet fully understood, although certainly both **transpiration** and **root pressure** must act in cooperation with one another. Root pressure is the positive pressure of the sap in the ducts at the point where these vessels emerge from the root to enter the stem. A rough measurement of root pressure may be obtained by cutting off the stem close to the root and joining the base of the stem to a pressure gauge, which records the force built up by the exuding sap (Fig. 13-19). Technical difficulty is encountered in making a junction that is both leakproof and noninjurious to the tissues in the region of the joint; and on this account early investigators failed to record pressures that were adequate to lift the sap to any significant height. However, recent experiments

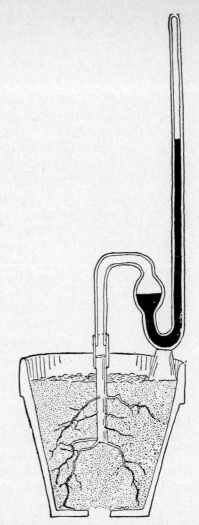

Fig. 13-19. A rough method of measuring root pressure. The stem of a potted plant is cut off and replaced by a closed tube containing water and mercury. As water is absorbed, sap exudes from the cut stem, forcing the mercury upward.

prove that even a small plant, such as the tomato, can generate a root pressure amounting to at least 2 to 3 atmospheres.

Root pressure results from the hypertonicity of the root sap, relative to the soil water that surrounds the root. A 10 percent glucose solution separated from soil water by a membrane that is permeable to water but not to the sugar will continue to absorb water until a pressure of more than 12 atmospheres has been developed. This would be adequate to elevate water to a height of some 380 feet, although it is doubtful that root pressures of this magnitude are actually generated. In the root, the semipermeable membrane is provided, not by the walls of the ducts—since these vessels are nonliving —but by the layers of living cells that intervene between the sap in the ducts and the soil water, at the external surface of the root (Fig. 13-11).

In the intact plant, transpiration, of course, participates in the lifting of the sap. The constant evaporation of water from the leaves—and the fact that the leaves produce considerable sugar—keep the chlorenchyma cells distinctly hypertonic to the sap in the veins. Consequently the chlorenchyma continually draws water from the upper parts of the ducts, and this evacuation tends to *lift* the column of sap upward in each duct. This lifting power of transpiration can be observed in a leafy branch that has been cut from a plant and placed in water. In such a branch, the leaves continue to transpire, and can draw up enough water to maintain a normal turgor in the tissues for several days.

In the springtime, before leaves have developed on the branches, a tree is much more dependent upon root pressure for the large amounts of water needed by the sprouting buds. At this time the sugar content—and hence the hypertonicity of the root sap— reaches a maximum, because the winter stores of starch in the root parenchyma are converted in the spring to sugar, which passes into the ducts. It may be, however, that other forces, still unknown, may operate to energize the upsurging of sap in the springtime.

In summer the solute content of the root sap tends to drop away, because now the root depends mainly upon the amount of sugar that gradually comes down to the roots from the leaves. Consequently, in summer root pressure is relatively low, and the plant depends upon the lifting power of transpiration.

DISTRIBUTION OF ORGANIC SUBSTANCES IN PLANTS

Part of the sugars and other organic substances synthesized in the leaf is utilized in the metabolism of the cells of the leaf itself. But a greater part passes from the leaves to the lower parts of the plant, mainly via the sieve tubes of phloem.

The sieve tubes convey organic products at a relatively slow rate—depending partly upon the rate of passage of materials through the sieve plates that interrupt the columns (p. 243); partly upon the rate of streaming in the sieve tube cells; and partly, perhaps, upon other factors, such as electro-osmosis. The rate of downward flow has been measured in various ways that yield equivalent values of some 20 to 40 *inches* per hour. But as the sugars and other soluble products pass downward through the stem, some diffuse radially, supplying the tissues at each level. The rays in thicker stems facilitate this radial distribution to the cells of the pith, which tend to accumulate reserves of starch. The remaining organic products eventually reach the root parenchyma, which also stores considerable quantities of starch, especially in the case of perennial plants.

Just before leaf fall, in hardy deciduous plants, much organic content (aside from cellulose) is salvaged from the leaves and carried, via the sieve tube elements, to parts that will survive through the winter. When such transportation is completed, however, the pores of the sieve plates are closed off by deposition of a special high-polymer sugar, called **callose**. Then in the following spring a new set of sieve tubes, as well as a new set of xylem vessels, must be formed from the cambium and other meristemic tissues.

METABOLISM IN HIGHER PLANTS

Metabolism goes on in all the living cells of the plant, producing new organic substances needed for the growth and maintenance of the tissues, and providing energy, without which the synthetic and responsive activities of the plant could not proceed.

The mainspring of **constructive** metabolism is photosynthesis, which is effected chiefly in the leaves. Light energy provides for the synthesis of various organic molecules (p. 164), among which glucose is very important. This sugar (or its derivatives) provides a source of matter and energy in the cells throughout the whole plant.

Under average conditions the amount of glucose produced in a leaf is about 1 gram per square meter of surface per hour of daylight. In the present period of geological time one limiting factor imposed upon the rate of photosynthesis is the relatively small concentration (about 0.03 percent) of CO_2 in the atmosphere; if a greater amount (up to 10 percent) of CO_2 be provided artificially (as is done in some modern greenhouses) the rate of photosynthesis can be accelerated considerably. This, in fact, is part of the evidence indicating that the tremendous growth of vegetation that occurred during the era when our coal deposits were formed resulted from a higher content of CO_2 in the terrestrial atmosphere.

In daylight, the production of glucose exceeds the rate at which sugar can be evacuated from the leaf, and the excess is converted into starch in the chlorenchyma cells. At sunset, accordingly, the leaf contains an abundance of starch—as can be demonstrated by the iodine test. But at sunrise the test is apt to be negative. During the night the temporary deposits of starch are reconverted to glucose, which gradually passes from the leaf to other parts of the plant.

Aside from photosynthesis, constructive metabolism is essentially similar in the different tissues of the plant. Given glucose, together with nitrates, sulfates, phosphates, and other inorganic salts, plant cells can synthesize all the different amino acids; and from the amino acids, by dehydration synthesis, each cell forms the specific proteins essential to its protoplasmic structure. Although all the cells of a plant can synthesize amino acids, the chlorenchyma cells—having a direct supply of light energy—are in a specially favorable position. Accordingly the green tissues of the plant tend to produce extra amino acids and to transmit the extra amounts to the lower parts of the plant via the sieve tubes.

Plant cells also can convert glucose into fats and steroids; and if phosphates and other salts are available, glucose can be converted into phospholipids. Thus it may be said that *plants use glucose* as a source of carbon, hydrogen, and oxygen *in synthesizing all their organic requirements,* including such *other compounds as vitamins, special drugs, perfumes,* etc.

Destructive metabolism in plants is not quite as complex as in animals, because plants derive most of their energy from the catabolism of glucose. Except in seeds and certain other regions where reserve supplies are necessary, plants tend to limit their synthesis of proteins, lipids, and other structural components of the protoplasm to such amounts as are needed for growth and maintenance. Consequently plants do not usually possess excesses of these structural compounds for use as fuel. During periods of malnutrition, especially when light is lacking or inadequate, plants may sacrifice some of their proteins and other essential compounds in order to obtain energy for maintaining the protoplasmic structure—but this last resort postpones death only for a short while. Ordinarily plants derive virtually all energy from carbohydrates, and consequently the end products of plant catabolism are mainly CO_2 and H_2O.

Because of photosynthesis, the constructive metabolism of plants greatly exceeds destructive metabolism. In growing, an average plant oxidizes only about 15 percent of its photosynthesized glucose. This oxidized glucose liberates enough energy to convert the remaining glucose into starch (about 50 percent); into cellulose and related compounds (about 25 percent); and into the carbon-hydrogen-oxygen parts of proteins and other essential compounds (about 10 percent). Inevitably, therefore, plant growth represents a net increase of organic matter in which the stores of useful energy are derived entirely from the sun.

Again it must be emphasized that the synthetic powers of plants are amazingly complex and that plant metabolism is still a very active field of research. For example, the role of the trace elements (boron, manganese, zinc, etc.), which are needed in extremely small amounts to maintain the growth of many plants, is now receiving an intensive investigation (see Fig. 13-20), and the relation between these elements and spe-

cific metabolic enzymes is undergoing clarification.

RESPIRATION[1] IN HIGHER PLANTS

Each organ of the plant takes in oxygen and gives off carbon dioxide mainly on a local basis. All the cells use oxygen and produce carbon dioxide as oxidative metabolism proceeds, and consequently respiration must occur in all the organs.

The leaves differ from the stem and roots

[1] In a broader sense the term "respiration" embraces all processes of oxidative metabolism. Here, however, it merely designates the taking in of oxygen and the giving off of carbon dioxide by the organism.

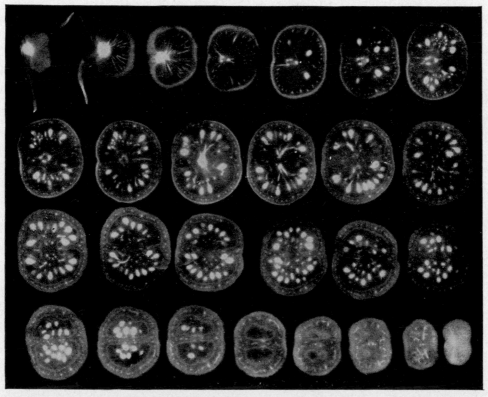

Fig. 13-20. Radioactive zinc (Zn^{65}) accumulated in the seeds of the fruit of a tomato plant grown in a culture solution containing only 0.1 part of radioactive zinc per million parts of solution. Although the amount of zinc present in one seed is only three-billionths of one gram, without this small amount no seed would be formed. This photograph, called a radioautograph, was made by placing thin slices of the young fruit in contact with a photographic plate. Thus an exposure of the film is effected only in local areas where the radiations from the accumulated Zn^{65} are sufficiently intense. Such experiments show that small amounts of zinc are essential to many plants, and that the plant does not differentiate between ordinary zinc and the radioactive isotope (Zn^{65}). (Courtesy of Perry R. Stout, Division of Plant Nutrition, University of California.)

in that, during photosynthesis, the leaves produce more oxygen than they use in oxidative metabolism. Likewise leaves in daylight consume more carbon dioxide than they form. Consequently the gas exchange of photosynthesis overrides that of respiration in the leaves of the plant during the daylight hours. However, the stem and root, and the leaves at night, must obtain oxygen from the outside, and must get rid of carbon dioxide; and this respiratory gas exchange takes place through air spaces in the loosely packed parenchyma tissues (Fig. 13-21). These air spaces form a continuous system throughout the plant, and in the leaves and stem, the air spaces communicate with the outside

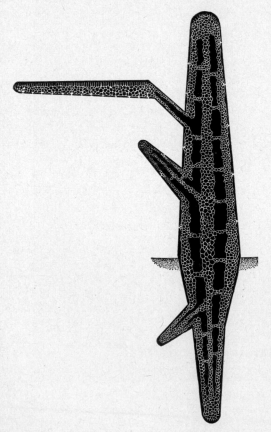

Fig. 13-21. Diagram of the aeration system of a vascular plant. The white lines represent intercellular air spaces, opening to the outside through stomata.

atmosphere through stomata. Roots have no stomata, but the respiratory gases are exchanged by diffusion between the root tissues and the soil water. Well-aerated soil contains 20 to 40 percent (by volume) of air, and this air maintains equilibrium with the soil water, which clings to the loosely packed soil particles. Closely packed soils—or swampy soils in which the air spaces are filled with water—are ill suited to most plants, because these conditions tend to asphyxiate the roots, eventually killing the whole plant. Likewise a heaping of soil around the lower parts of the stem may cause asphyxiation. Each part of the plant must breathe for itself, and the movements of the respiratory gases depend entirely upon diffusion. However, the oxygen requirements of plants are compartively modest, and each plant, as a whole, produces more oxygen than it uses.

EXCRETION

Aside from oxygen, the metabolic end products of plants are chiefly water and carbon dioxide—the very substances that serve as raw materials for photosynthesis. To a large extent the plant utilizes its own products of combustion; and there is relatively little excretion. The small amount of metabolically formed water may remain in the plant until it is utilized, or it may be passed off by osmosis or transpiration.

In plants, it is difficult to define the metabolic wastes and to differentiate between excretion and secretion. Many flowers and certain leaves give off sweet and fragrant fluids in the form of **nectar,** which may be partially excretory in nature. Some plant cells tend to accumulate organic acids, especially oxalic acid, which may precipitate in the vacuoles as crystals of the calcium salt. Such crystals usually are formed in the leaves or bark, where disposal occurs—by the shedding of the leaves or the wearing of the bark.

STORAGE PROBLEMS AMONG THE PLANTS

The storage of reserve organic products is largely a matter of self-preservation for the individual plant, although if plants had not developed this capacity, much of the food that supports the animal kingdom—including mankind—would not be produced. The individual plant accumulates organic reserves to tide it over periods when photosynthesis cannot be carried on. Among seed plants, for example, the embryo cannot grow independently until the seed has sprouted and the new sporophyte has developed a functional root, stem, and leaf system. Accordingly the parent plant deposits a reserve of organic substances in the seed and frequently in the surrounding fruit structures as well. Deciduous plants, which shed their leaves each season, also depend upon organic reserves laid down during the previous year in the stems or roots or both. In the spring, deciduous plants use these organic reserves for the matter and energy without which a growth of the new foliage could not occur.

The most abundant organic reserve in the plant kingdom is starch, and the starch grains of different plants display many characteristic variations of size and form (Fig. 4-9). Given starch—or glucose derived from starch—plants can synthesize all their growth requirements, provided inorganic salts and oxygen are also available. In addition to starch, some seeds contain fat globules and crystals of reserve proteins in the cells of the cotyledons. Reserve proteins permit the embryo to grow more extensively prior to the time when the roots develop a capacity to absorb an adequate quantity of nitrates and other inorganic salts. In perennial plants, reserve starch is deposited mainly in the colorless parenchyma: more or less equally in the stem and root; or predominantly in the stem, or root, depending on the species.

ECONOMIC IMPORTANCE OF PLANT PRODUCTS

The *importance* of plant products, as direct sources of man's food, and in the sustenance of animals which in turn become man's food, is altogether *inestimable*. Plant **seeds** (corn, wheat, oats, barley, rye, rice, and a wide variety of nuts) and fruits (apples, oranges, eggplant, squash, pumpkin, etc.) have a world-wide cultivation and give tremendous yields. **Roots** (beets, carrots, parsnips, radishes, turnips, sweet potato, tapioca, etc.) and **stems** (sugar cane, sugar maple, white potato, onion, etc.), and finally **leaves** (lettuce, spinach, artichoke, cabbage, etc.) also provide a considerable quantity of man's needs. Moreover, leaves, especially of the grasses, provide the staple food of all man's grazing livestock.

Many other economic values of plant products can also be enumerated: (1) **lumber,** for construction and other purposes; (2) **drugs,** such as aconite, asafetida, and valerian (from roots); quinine, cascara, and ephedrine (from stems); belladonna, cocaine, and digitalis (from leaves); and castor and chalmoogra oils (from seeds); (3) **spices** and **flavors,** such as horse-radish, sarsaparilla, and sassafras (from roots); garlic and ginger (from stems); sage, wintergreen, and thyme (from leaves); and anise, nutmeg, and mustard (from seeds); and (4) miscellaneous other products, such as latex for rubber; oils, gums, resins, and turpentine for paints, varnishes, and soaps; cork for stoppers; fibers for ropes and fabrics; and many other items. Man has been very prodigal in his expenditure of *wild* plant resources, especially in the ravaging of forests. Only in the cultivation of many selected plant species has man given a fair degree of reciprocity. Under cultivation a plant is assured of perpetuation, and man takes only the excess of the synthesized products.

TEST QUESTIONS

1. How do the "holdfasts" of the algae differ in structure and function from the true roots of higher plants?
2. What factors help to explain the fact that the algae have remained in a relatively undifferentiated state as compared to most terrestrial plants?
3. Compare the tissues of the Bryophyta with the corresponding tissues of the vascular plants. To what extent do these differences account for the greater "success" of the higher plants? Explain.
4. Identify: (a) meristem tissue; (b) epidermis; (c) chlorenchyma; (d) storage parenchyma; (e) bast fibers; (f) wood fibers; (g) sieve tubes; (h) ducts; (i) xylem; (j) phloem.
5. Specify the major nutritive organs of the vascular plants and explain the main functions of each.
6. Differentiate between woody and herbaceous stems.
7. A. Make labeled diagrams showing the essential features of:
   a. the one-year-old stem of a dicotyledonous plant, as seen in cross section;
   b. a rootlet (long section);
   c. a typical leaf (cross section).
   B. State the function or functions of each labeled part.

8. Define and discuss transpiration, emphasizing:
   a. how it is energized
   b. its magnitude and how it is controlled
   c. its effect upon the rise of sap
   d. its relation to the leaf temperature
9. Define and discuss root pressure, emphasizing:
   a. the fundamental nature of the phenomenon
   b. how it is measured
   c. how it is maintained
   d. its effectiveness in elevating the sap
10. Assuming that a plant has synthesized 100 grams of glucose, about how much of this matter would be:
    a. oxidized to provide energy for constructive metabolism
    b. transformed into starch
    c. transformed into cellulose
    d. transformed (together with inorganic salts) into proteins and other structural components of the protoplasm?
11. Explain the importance of starch storage:
    a. from the plant "viewpoint"
    b. from the viewpoint of mankind
12. Explain how respiration occurs in the leaves, stem, and roots of a seed plant. Specify two conditions that frequently cause an asphyxiation of roots.

FURTHER READINGS

1. *Translocation in Plants,* by A. S. Crafts; New York, 1961.
2. *Plant Physiology,* by B. M. Duggar; New York, 1927.
3. *Botany,* by P. Weatherwax; Philadelphia, 1956.
4. *College Botany,* rev. ed., by Harry J. Fuller and Oswald Tippo; New York, 1954.
5. *The World of Plant Life,* by C. J. Hylander; New York, 1956.
6. *Botany,* 3d ed., by C. L. Wilson and W. E. Loomis; New York, 1962.
7. *The Living Plant,* by Peter M. Ray; New York, 1963.

14-*The Responses of Higher Plants*

THE responses of higher plants are generally slow, subtle, and varied. Nonetheless they are most important to the survival of the species. Plant responses include not only growth and turgor movements (see below), but also flowering and fruiting responses, the germination of seeds and pollen, and a number of other less obvious responses to the changing conditions of the environment.

TURGOR MOVEMENTS VS. GROWTH MOVEMENTS

Among higher plants two general types of movement can be distinguished. **Growth movements**—such as the bending of stems toward light—are so slow that an hour or more is required to perceive a change, and once a growth movement has occurred, it usually is not reversed. **Turgor movements**, in contrast, are relatively rapid and reversible—like the drooping of leaves during a rainfall. Such a difference in tempo and reversibility indicates a difference in the basic mechanism of these responses. Growth movements, in fact, depend upon an unequal rate of growth in the cells on opposite sides of the bending part; but turgor movements are effected by osmotic changes occurring in specialized effector cells (see below).

TURGOR MOVEMENT

The rapid drooping of the leaves of the sensitive plant (*Mimosa pudica*) is an outstanding example of a turgor movement (Fig. 14-1). The normal position of the leaves of the plant is more or less horizontal; but if one of the leaves is touched, even lightly, all the leaflets begin to fold up, and within 2 or 3 *seconds* the whole leaf droops to a marked degree. Or if a leaf is struck less gently, not only does the stimulated leaf fold and droop, but a wave of folding and drooping spreads from the stimulated leaf to all neighboring leaves (Fig. 14-1). This response of the mimosa is strictly reversible, and after about a

259

Fig. 14-1. Response of the "sensitive plant," *Mimosa pudica:* A, before being touched; B, five seconds after being touched (E. H. Runyon).

minute, the plant slowly regains its original posture.

The receptors, conductors, and effectors of this response of Mimosa are strictly localized. The **excitation** (p. 190) originates in the epidermal cells of the leaf, which possess numerous tactile hairs projecting from the surface; and the excitation spreads, mainly along the sieve tubes. The excitation, as indicated by the **action potential,** follows the course of the vascular bundles through the petiole to the point where the petiole joins the stem. Here lies the **pulvinus,** a cushion of cells that normally supports the leaf in a horizontal position. When an excitation reaches the pulvinus, the pulvinus cells become more permeable, and losing turgor they relax their support of the leaf. Thus the pulvinus is the effector of the drooping response, and the sieve tubes and epidermal cells, respectively, are the conductors and receptors.

Specialized receptor - conductor - effector structures in plants are less clearly defined than in animals, and consequently the responses of plants are less rapid and precise. The drooping of the mimosa leaf is very rapid compared to most other plant responses, but even in this case the propagated excitation—as timed by the spread of the action potential—is transmitted at a rate of only about 5 centimeters per second (compared to 120 meters per second along the nerves of man). Nevertheless the basic nature of excitation and conduction appears to be similar in plants and animals. In both cases, the excitation may be blocked by narcotic agents, and in both plants and animals excitation appears to be accompanied by a bioelectric discharge, increased permeability of the excited cells, and a temporary alteration of the local metabolism.

Other Turgor Movements. Although the evidence is somewhat scanty, it seems probable that other rapid and reversible responses in plants are turgor movements involving receptor-conductor-effector structures similar to those of *Mimosa*. Accordingly, (1) the drooping of leaves during rainfall, (2) the movements by which leaves and flowers follow the course of the sun, (3) the leaf-closing movements by which **insectivorous plants** trap their living prey (Fig. 14-2), and (4) the sleep movements of many plants (Fig. 14-3) are all considered as typical turgor movements.

GROWTH MOVEMENTS

An example of growth movement is the bending of young stems toward a source of light (Fig. 14-4). Such growth movements proceed so slowly that about an hour is required to appreciate the change. Growth movements tend to be irreversible. The bending depends upon a faster *lengthwise* growth of the cells on one side of the stem, and the convexity of the curvature always lies on the side of faster growth (Fig. 14-4).

The fundamental difference between growth and turgor movements was not clarified until 1910, when evidence began to accumulate proving the existence of **growth substances,** which regulate the growth of cells in different parts of the plant. Previously it was known that cutting off the meristem tissue at the tip of a stem *stops growth* in the cells of the stump, where normally the cells continue to *elongate* until they become fully differentiated. The situation remained obscure, however, until about 1930. Then as a result of the researches of Boysen-Jensen, in Denmark, and Frits Went, in

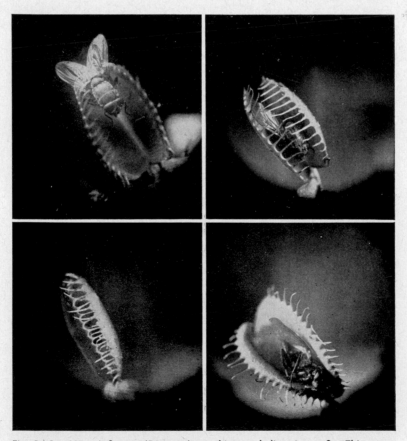

Fig. 14-2. Venus's-flytrap (*Dionaea*), catching and digesting a fly. This movement is a turgor movement. (Copyright, General Biological Supply House, Inc.)

Fig. 14-3. Sleep movements in *Oxalis stricta*. Left, day position of leaflets; right, night position of leaflets. Another example of turgor movement.

Holland and the United States, the nature growth substances began to become clearer. The early experiments showed that replacing the decapitated tip of meristem tissue restores the growth of the cells of the stump. Moreover, Went found that this effect was still obtained even when a fairly thick (2 mm) layer of agar was interposed between the cut surfaces, which proved that some diffusible substance—rather than a wave of excitation—is responsible for the growth effect.

Phytohormones, Especially the Auxins. Since these early experiments, three natural **growth substances**, or **auxins**, have been identified; and a variety of synthetic prod-

Fig. 14-4. Positive phototropism of the stem of a bean seedling. Successive photographic exposures taken at 40-minute intervals.

ucts have been found that exert analogous effects. The three natural auxins—auxin *a* ($C_{18}H_{32}O_5$), auxin *b* ($C_{18}H_{30}O_4$), and heteroauxin ($C_{10}H_{15}NO_2$)—are all relatively simple, readily diffusible organic compounds, although heteroauxin has been obtained mainly from animal sources. All the natural auxins have been prepared in pure form, and all have been synthesized artificially. Virtually no specificity is found in the action of the different compounds; that is, all have similar effects when applied to corresponding parts of different plants. *The* **auxins** *are produced primarily by* **meristem tissue** *in the growing points of the plant,* whence they are transported to the nearby regions, where cell differentiation is occurring. The auxins exert various effects on the metabolism and rate of multiplication of plant cells (see below). But one outstanding function of the auxins is to regulate—by *accelerating* or *retarding*—the *lengthwise growth* of individual cells in the growing parts of the plant.

It is important to realize that the action of the auxins upon the growth of stem and root cells is exactly opposite: Lengthwise growth is *accelerated* in the stem but *retarded* in the root. When extra auxin is available—either under experimental or natural conditions—the stem elongates with unusual rapidity, whereas the root lengthens at a reduced rate. Thus if a poultice containing an auxin is applied to *one side* of a stem, faster growth occurs on that side, causing the stem to bend *away from* the site of application; but under similar treatment, the root bends *toward* the side where the extra auxin has been applied.

Tropisms. In both plants and animals the *direction* of many movements is determined by the *direction* from which the stimulus impinges upon the body. Stems generally bend toward a steady source of light, but roots turn away, and oppositely directly reactions are obtained when gravity is the stimulus (Figs. 12-35 and 14-5). Regardless of how these responses are effected, *oriented movements, in which the direction is determined by the orientation of the stimulus, are called* **tropisms.**

Fig. 14-5. Negative geotropism of a bean stem; successive photographs made on same plate at intervals of 45 minutes.

Movements directed toward or away from the source of stimulation are designated, respectively, as positive or negative tropisms. Accordingly, one speaks of the positive **phototropism** of leaves and stems, the positive **geotropism** and **hydrotropism** of roots, the negative geotropism of stems, and the negative phototropism of roots.

In plants most tropisms are growth movements, in which the curvature results from an unequal distribution of auxins to the sides of the growing part. For example, when a primary root is placed in a horizontal position (Fig. 14-6), gradually a curvature develops as the rootlet grows longer, and finally the tip turns straight downward, toward the gravitational center of the earth. In this response it can be proved that more auxin is conveyed to the cells on the *lower* side of the root, and that the curvature is

due to an inhibiting action of auxin upon the growth of the cells on this side of the root. Just how an unequal distribution of the growth substances occurs has not been demonstrated, but without auxin no curvature takes place. If the meristem of the growing point is removed by decapitating the rootlet about 1 millimeter above the tip, the responsiveness of the root to gravity is abolished.

The negative geotropism of the *stem* is also effected on a similar basis. In the case of the stem, however, auxin *stimulates* growth. Greater concentrations of auxin are conveyed to the lower side of the stem, and consequently the stem bends upward rather than downward (Fig. 14-6).

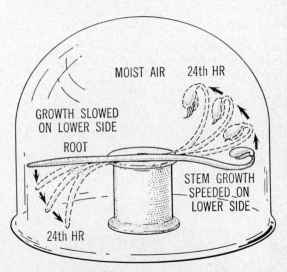

MOIST AIR   24th HR

GROWTH SLOWED
ON LOWER SIDE
ROOT

STEM GROWTH
SPEEDED ON
LOWER SIDE

24th HR

Fig. 14-6. These tropisms, both the positive geotropism of the root and the negative geotropism of the stem, are **growth movements**, determined by **auxin**. Note, however, that a higher concentration on the lower side of the *root retards* local growth; whereas the same condition in the *stem accelerates* growth.

Likewise the positive phototropism of the stem and the negative phototropism of the root are explained by the effects of light upon the auxin distribution in the plant. The growing point sends more auxin to the darker side of the stem or root, although *why* this occurs has not been demonstrated. In the stem, the stimulating effect of the

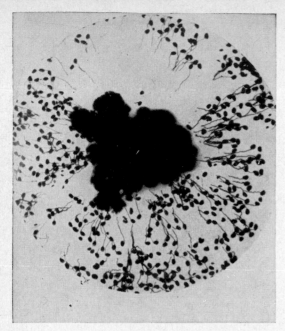

Fig. 14-7. Positive chemotropism of pollen tubes, which are growing toward a crushed stigma (central dark area).

auxin produces a curvature toward the source of light; whereas in the root, the inhibiting effect gives a bending in the opposite direction.

Many other tropisms also depend upon the auxins. **Chemotropisms,** such as the growth of pollen tubes through the style (Fig. 14-7), or the growth of roots toward water (Fig. 14-8); and **thigmotropisms,** such as the twining of the tendrils of climbing plants around solid supporting objects—all appear to be typical growth movements, although these reactions have not been studied very intensively. However, some plant tropisms—such as the turning of leaves in following the course of the sun—appear to be turgor movements, involving receptor-conductor-effector structures that are generally similar to those of *Mimosa.*

Characteristics of the Auxins. In distinct contrast to the hormones of higher animals (Chap. 22), the auxins do not display a very high degree of specificity. Under proper conditions, in fact, very similar effects are observed when one auxin is substituted for another. Each single compound, on the other hand, displays a surprising *versatility of action* when applied in *different concentrations* and *to different parts* of the same plant. In the stem, for example, the same concentration of an auxin may stimulate growth in the cells directly behind the main terminal bud, but inhibit the development of the

Fig. 14-8. Positive hydrotropism. These roots entered cracks in the drain pipes and stopped them up. (Courtesy of Missouri Botanical Garden.)

nearby lateral buds. Or a low concentration of an auxin may merely accelerate the elongation of the cells of a growing stem, whereas a higher concentration stimulates cell multiplication and leads to the putting forth of roots from the stimulated section of the stem. As yet, no precise information is available in regard to how the auxins produce their action. A promising hypotheses is, however, that auxins exert their influence through certain metabolic enzymes—which would account for the fact that a very minute quantity of each compound suffices to give a very large effect.

Other Phytohormones. Gibberellic acid $(C_{19}H_{22}O_6)$ and several other closely related compounds constitute another very interesting group of plant hormones. These, collectively, are designated as the **gibberellins**. The gibberellins began to be recognized by Japanese workers as early as 1926. These workers studied a disease of rice, called the "foolish seedling disease," so named because it causes young rice plants to grow too rapidly and to assume grotesquely tall, abnormal forms. The disease is caused by a fungus (*Gibberella fujikuoi*) infection. This fungus, in fact, provides a source from which several active compounds have been extracted and identified.

The gibberellins not only stimulate very rapid growth in young stems, but they also induce the development of flowers in a number of plants, even when normal flower-inducing stimuli (p. 266) are withheld. It seems likely, therefore, that further study will show that gibberellins may play an important and interesting role in plant development and physiology.

Some other substances that appear to be important as plant hormones are: (1) **diphenylurea** and other factors extractible from *coconut milk;* and (2) **kinetin,** and other **adenine derivatives**, which have been extracted from yeasts and other plant materials. The coconut milk factors stimulate cell growth and cell division in many plant embryos. Kinetin, on the other hand, appears to influence bud development. Plant shoots, grown in culture medium, respond by putting forth more and more roots as kinetin is replaced by auxin.

Plant Inhibitors. A relatively recent field in plant physiology was opened up by the discovery of certain very potent inhibiting substances. These provide a system of checks and balances in the operation of the phytohormone system. Particularly promising in this regard is a group of **unsaturated lactone compounds,** for example, **coumarin** and **parascorbic acid.** Root growth, seed germination, and floral development have all proved susceptible to inhibition by one or another of these substances. In fact, a fuller understanding of the mode of action of plant hormones probably will involve further knowledge about inhibitors.

Photoperiodism and Other Responses to Light. A currently active field of research deals with the triggering of plant responses by seasonal changes in their exposure alternately to daylight and darkness. The flowering response has been studied most intensively. However, considerable attention has also been given to the germination of seeds and to early embryonic growth.

The regularity with which various plants produce their flowers on a well-regulated seasonal schedule is familiar to everyone. However, only recently, starting in 1920 with the work of Garner and Allard of the U.S. Department of Agriculture, has it been realized that this nicely timed schedule of flowering is governed, in a majority of cases, by seasonal changes in the length of the nights and days.

This work has made it possible to classify flowering plants in three categories: (1) *short-day species,* such as asters, chrysanthemums, and soybeans, which normally bloom at a specific time in the late summer or fall, when the nights are growing longer; (2) *long-day species,* such as clover, beets, and delphinium, which bloom in spring or early summer, when the period of darkness is growing shorter; and (3) *indeterminate species,* such as carnations, dandelions, and tomatoes, which are relatively insensitive to dark-light alternations, but are sensitive to other seasonal changes, particularly temperature.

The experimental evidence upon which this classification is based is very extensive. Here it will be sampled only sparsely, with mere mention of a few pioneer workers, namely J. A. D. Leevaart, James Bonner, and H. A. Borthwick.

If a short-day plant, grown under experimentally controlled lighting conditions, is exposed to less than a certain span of darkness (usually about 12 hours), it will not produce any floral buds. If, on the other hand, it is exposed to three or four long nights, it will initiate flowering, provided the dark periods are not interrupted. Even a very brief exposure to light, interrupting the dark period for only 2 to 3 minutes, suffices to abolish the flowering reaction. The leaves, apparently, serve as the site of induction, since only the leaves—in some cases only a single leaf—need be exposed to the appropriate period of darkness. Long-day species, on the other hand, display an opposite behavior. To flower, these plants must be provided with a relatively short night, and the flowering tendency is damped off if the dark period is interrupted by just a few minutes of exposure to light.

An analysis of the wavelength of light utilized in these experiments led to the conclusion that certain wavelengths are critical. Red light of 660 mμ wavelength was most effective in damping off the flowering reaction when used to interrupt the periods of darkness. Moreover, it was found that infrared light, of wavelength 730 mμ, was exceedingly effective in canceling out the effects of a previous illumination with red (660 mμ) light.

Wavelength studies also indicate that a **receptor pigment,** with an absorption maximum in the red range (660 mμ), is important and that a **reversible photochemical reaction** serves as a trigger for the photoperiodic responses. Recently, this pigment has been identified and named **phytochrome,** although

it has not yet been obtained in fully purified form. Phytochrome is a photosensitive protein compound. It can be shifted back and forth between two forms, phytochrome 660 (P_{660}) and phytochrome 730 (P_{730}), according to the wavelength of the light to which it is exposed. Exposure to red light shifts it from P_{660} to P_{730}; whereas exposure to infrared has the opposite effect. The *physiologically active form* appears to be **phytochrome 730.** The concentration of this form, maintained throughout a critical period, serves as a trigger for the various photosensitive responses of the plant. At the end of a day, all the phytochrome of the leaves has been converted to the P_{730} form; but gradually during the darkness P_{730} reverts spontaneously to P_{660}. Whether or not a response is triggered depends, apparently, upon *how much of and how long* the active (P_{730}) form of phytochrome is present at the site of stimulation.

Although many unresolved areas remain in our understanding of photoperiodic phenomena, one current working hypothesis may be presented as follows:

Phytochrome 660

Spontaneous reversal in dark.	↑	Red component of white light.
Photochemical reversal by infrared.	↓	Photochemical reaction.

Phytochrome 730

Active form; stimulates in long-day plants; inhibits in short-day species.

Precisely how the flowering stimulus is transmitted from the leaves, where the photochemical timing device is localized, to the growing points of the stem, where the floral buds are formed, is still not known. Undoubtedly one or more substances, perhaps hormones of the gibberellin type, are liberated when the photochemical mechanism is tripped, and these substances are conveyed by the vascular elements from the leaves to the buds. In any event, flower induction can be observed in a plant that has not received any inducing treatment, when leaves from a plant that has received such treatment are transplanted to it. Moreover, the spreading of induction follows along the sieve tube elements of the phloem.

The phytochrome system is important not only in relation to the photoperiodic responses of the plant, but also in relation to other responses. Certain seeds, for example, will not germinate unless first exposed to light, particularly red light, and this light-induced activation can be abolished by a subsequent illumination with infrared light. Moreover, red-infrared reversals of growth rate and curvature in developing plant embryos have been observed. It seems probable, therefore, that the phytochrome system triggers most of the photic responses of plants, including positive and negative phototropic growth movements.

Practical Importance of Auxins and Other Growth Substances. Auxins are now being used to initiate the development of roots in plants and now many commercially valuable plants are being grown from auxin-treated cuttings. Promising results are also being obtained in other directions. Auxins are used to foster the "taking" of grafts, and auxin-treated seeds (in certain species) germinate more successfully than untreated ones. With sugar beets, for example, the yield has been increased by about 60 percent, although this effect is probably due to a stimulation of the growth of the seedlings rather than to a direct action on germination. Auxins may also prove to be important in the development of fruits. In most species, the fruit fails to develop properly unless pollination has occurred; but in the tomato at least, the application of auxins has yielded well-developed seedless fruits from unpollinated flowers.

Another economically important use of auxin preparations is to prevent the premature dropping of fruit in apple and pear orchards; and more recently, a new synthetic auxinlike compound (2,4-dichlorophenoxyacetic acid, or 2,4-D) has been employed quite widely as a "weed killer" on lawns and golf courses. In proper concentrations, apparently, 2,4-D has litle effect upon the grasses, but it exerts a lethal action on broad-leaved plants (for example dandelions) by over-stimulating oxidative metabolism in leaves contacted by the spray.

TEST QUESTIONS

1. Explain two essential differences between growth movements and turgor movements.
2. Analyze the mechanical response of the sensitive plant in terms of the receptors, conductors, and effectors of the system. Why is this movement called a turgor movement?
3. Describe and explain the experiments that first demonstrated the existence of a *growth substance,* or *auxin.*
4. How do roots and stems differ in regard to their responses to the auxins?
5. A. What is a tropism?
   B. Describe precisely how the behavior of auxin helps to explain: (a) the positive phototropisms of stems; (b) the negative phototropisms of roots; (c) the positive geotropisms of roots; (d) the negative geotropisms of stems; (e) other tropisms.
6. Specify four practical uses of auxins and related compounds. In each case explain the basic action.
7. Identify and briefly discuss: (a) gibberellins; (b) coconut milk factors; (c) kinetin; (d) unsaturated lactones.
8. Define the terms: (a) photoperiodism; (b) short-day plants; (c) indeterminate plants.
9. Summarize the evidence that indicates that photoperiodism is controlled by a reversible photochemical reaction.
10. Identify phytochromes P660 and P730.
11. Explain how the phytochromes are affected by: (a) white light; (b) red light; (c) infrared light; (d) darkness.
12. Explain how short-day and long-day plants differ in relation to the operation of the phytochrome system.

FURTHER READINGS

1. *Phytohormones,* by F. W. Went and K. V. Thimann; New York, 1937.
2. "On Growth-accelerating Substances in the Coleoptile of *Avena sativa,*" by F. W. Went; in *Great Experiments in Biology,* ed by M. Gabriel and S. Fogel; Englewood Cliffs, N. J., 1955.
3. *The Living Plant,* by Peter M. Ray; New York, 1963.
3. "Plant Photoperiods," by H. A. Borthwick; Chapter 9 in *Frontiers of Modern Biology,* G. B. Moment, coordinator; Boston, Mass., 1963.
4. "Plant Growth Substances," by F. B. Salisbury; in *Scientific American,* November 1960.
5. "Physiology of Flowering," by J. A. D. Zeevaart; in *Science,* September 7, 1962.

PART III-*Multicellular Animals, Especially Man*

15-*Embryonic Development;*
Differentiation of the Tissues

AT CONCEPTION, each animal, whether starfish, frog, or man, begins life as a single cell. The **fertilized egg,** or **zygote,** soon divides, however, and it continues to divide, forming the many cells of the developing embryo. The cells become arranged and differentiated according to a precise and intricate pattern in each particular species; and a study of these beautifully integrated processes constitutes a fascinating area in biology. The events of embryonic development sometimes can be observed under the microscope, because the embryos of many marine animals are small and transparent. A fertilized egg placed in a drop of sea water on a microscopic slide continues to cleave. One can watch as the cells become regimented and differentiated in the various developing organs and tissues.

First to be considered here are the morphological aspects of development, which constitute **descriptive embryology.** In Chapter 27, an analysis of some of the problems of **experimental embryology** will be undertaken.

Each parent contributes just one haploid cell, or **gamete,** to the constitution of the zygote and embryo. Also, in a vast majority of cases, the female gamete is quite different from the male. Each has specialized functions and each has developed a specialized form (p. 59).

The Egg Cell, or Ovum. Typically the egg is a large, nonmotile, haploid cell. The size, however, varies greatly depending upon how much yolk material is present. Eggs may be classified, in fact, on the basis of amount and distribution of this material (Fig. 15-1). Essentially the yolk represents a stored reserve of organic matter. This is utilized during the very active processes of embryonic development.

The haploidy, of course, results from the formation of the **polar bodies** (Figs. 15-2 and 26-3). These meiotic divisions provide for the selection of a full haploid set of chromosomes for transmission to the incipient new generation, without sacrificing much of the organic reserves that have been built up by the maturing oöcyte (p. 53). At the same

271

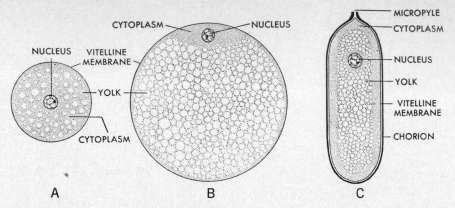

Fig. 15-1.   Types of egg cells: A, homolecithal egg; B, telolecithal egg; C, centrolecithal egg (of an insect).

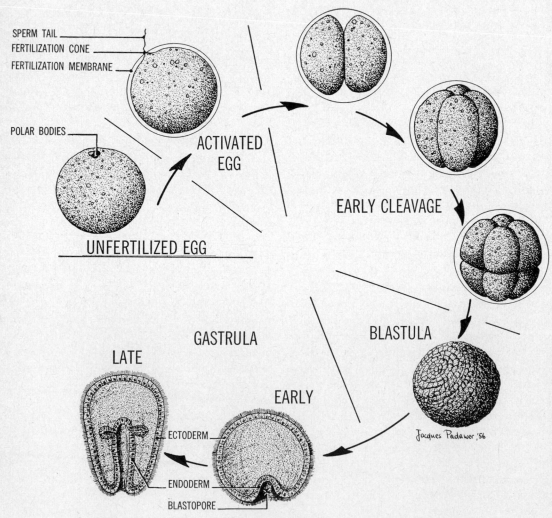

Fig. 15-2.   Fertilization and early development of a homolecithal egg (starfish).

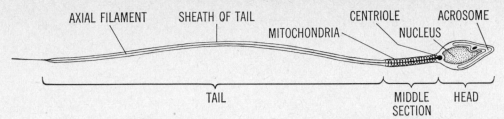

AXIAL FILAMENT   SHEATH OF TAIL   MITOCHONDRIA   CENTRIOLE   ACROSOME   NUCLEUS

TAIL   MIDDLE SECTION   HEAD

Fig.15-3. Typically the **sperm,** or male gamete, is a highly specialized, exceedingly motile, haploid cell.

time, the **locus of polar body formation** constitutes an important determinant of future development. The egg is a **polarized cell.** One pole, designated as the **animal pole,** is marked by the point of appearance of the polar bodies, while the other, called the **vegetal pole,** lies at dead center in the opposite hemisphere of the egg (see p. 277). Thus an **anterior-posterior axis** of development is provided along the line that extends from pole to pole—even before the egg cell has been fertilized.

The outermost membrane of the **unfertilized** egg, a specialized sort of pellicle, is called the **vitelline membrane** (Fig. 15-1). Upon **activation** (p. 274) this membrane becomes lifted away from the cytoplasmic surface of the egg, giving rise to what now is called the **fertilization membrane** (Fig. 15-2).

The Sperm Cell. Typically the sperm is an extremely small, highly motile, haploid cell. It consists of three differentiated parts, namely, **head, middle piece,** and **tail** (Fig. 15-3).

Perhaps the most essential feature of the head is the highly condensed haploid nucleus. Each of the many primary spermatocytes produced in a testis gives rise to four sperm, as a result of the **meiotic divisions.** A haploid set of chromosomes, brought into the egg by a sperm, participates in the formation of the zygote nucleus (Fig. 15-4), and this constitutes the essence of fertilization.

At the tip of the head of a sperm, at least in many cases, is a highly specialized structure, called the **acrosome** (Fig. 15-3). For some years it was thought that the acrosome facilitates penetration of the sperm into the egg, but evidence was lacking until recently. Now, however, the work of Dan and Wada in Japan and Colwin and Colwin in the United States has demonstrated that the acrosome has two functions. First, it discharges an exceedingly fine thread, the **acrosome filament.** This maintains a connection between the sperm head and the surface of the egg. Then an amoeboid protrusion from the egg surface, the **fertilization cone,**

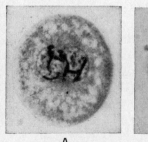
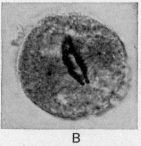
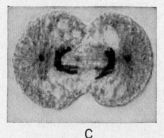

A   B   C   D

Fig. 15-4. Fertilization and cleavage of the egg of a roundworm (*Ascaris*). A, fertilization proper: the egg and the sperm nuclei are fusing to form the diploid zygote nucleus, which (in this case) bears two chromosomes from the female parent and two from the male parent. B, early anaphase, first cleavage. C, telophase, first cleavage. D, polar view of the metaphase of the first division, showing the two pairs of chromosomes of the zygote. (Photo D, slightly retouched. Copyright, General Biological Supply House, Inc.)

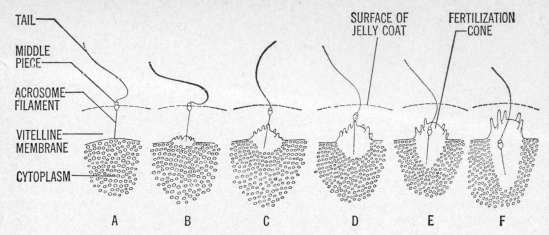

Fig. 15-5. Entry of sperm into an egg (*Holothuria atra*). Note pseudopodial activity at apex of cone, by which the acrosome filament and other parts of sperm appear to be engulfed. (Diagram based on observations of Colwin and Colwin, Queens College, New York.)

engulfs both filament and sperm (Fig. 15-5). And second, the acrosome secretes an enzyme. This digests part of the surface membrane and makes a tiny hole for entrance of the sperm.

The middle piece of the sperm is also important. It carries a **pair of centrioles** (p. 45), which act as division centers in the cleavage divisions, and it also contains a neatly packaged group of mitochondria that participate in the metabolism of the developing egg.

The movements of the sperm are effected, of course, by the tail. This is a typical flagellum. The **axial filament** (Fig. 15-3) displays the same pattern of fibrillar structure (10 pairs: 1 central and 9 in a peripheral circle) as is seen in electronmicrographs of cross sections of other flagella and cilia (Fig. 11-8).

Insemination. Most **aquatic** animals discharge their eggs and sperm into the surrounding water, and the gametes come together more or less by chance. Such animals produce thousands or even millions of eggs and many times as many sperm. The sperm are usually discharged in the general vicinity of where the eggs are laid, and the tremendous number of sperm assures the fertilization of a high percentage of the eggs. Aqua-

tic embryos, developing in an unprotected environment, are exposed to many hazards, so that only a small proportion of the offspring are likely to reach maturity.

Most **terrestrial** animals discharge sperm directly into the reproductive tract of the female, during **copulation.** In such cases, the number of eggs is sharply reduced, although a multitude of sperm is still the rule. The sperm are extremely small and fragile cells, and even when fertilization occurs within the relatively narrow limits of the female reproductive tract, the distance traveled by a sperm is very great in terms of its own size. Consequently, many sperm are required if a few are to succeed in reaching the eggs.

Activation vs. Fertilization. Contact of a sperm with an egg of the same species stimulates the egg to respond almost instantaneously. Upon such **activation,** the cytoplasm forms a **fertilization cone,** from which pseudopodia reach out along the acrosome filament, engulfing the relatively passive sperm. Sometimes, however, the sperm continues lashing its flagellum until the penetration is complete. Simultaneously the **vitelline membrane** lifts off from the egg cytoplasm, forming the **fertilization membrane** (Fig. 15-6). In most species the fertilization membrane persists, enveloping and protecting the em-

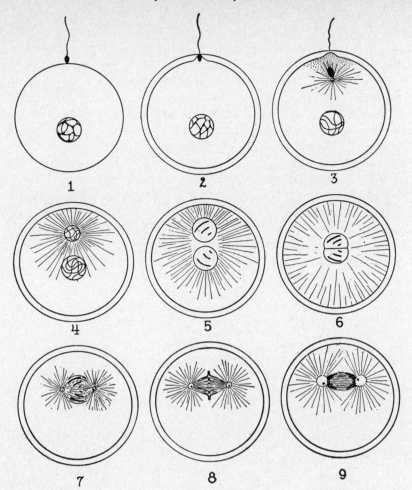

Fig. 15-6. Diagram of fertilization. 1, contact of sperm with surface of egg. 2, response of the egg: formation of the fertilization cone, which engulfs the sperm, and of the fertilization membrane. 3, sperm head drawn into the egg; appearance of aster. 4, 5, enlargement of sperm nucleus and approach of the two gamete nuclei; appearance of the haploid number of chromosomes (here three) in each gamete nucleus. 6, union of the two gamete nuclei. 7-9, first division of the zygote nucleus; each daughter nucleus receiving a replica of each chromosome present in the zygote nucleus.

bryo while further development proceeds (Fig. 11-10).

Usually, only the head and middle piece of the sperm enter the egg; and even when the whole sperm becomes engulfed, the flagellum soon disintegrates. The sperm head consists mainly of nucleus, and from this nucleus half the chromosomes in all of the cells of the new individual will be derived.

The sperm nucleus swells gradually as it moves toward the center of the egg where it is to join the egg nucleus (Fig. 15-6). Simul-

taneously a large single aster forms in the surrounding cytoplasm; and the aster appears to be concerned with bringing the gamete nuclei together. Finally the **gamete nuclei** *fuse to form the* **zygote nucleus.** This event, strictly speaking, is fertilization. At this stage, the chromosomes of both nuclei are individually visible (Figs. 15-4D and 15-6); and it is entirely certain that the chromosomes of the diploid zygote represent a combination of the chromosomes of the haploid gametes. Half the chromosomes of the zygote are derived from the paternal parent, and half from the maternal parent.

Shortly after the zygote nucleus is formed, the egg begins a long series of divisions, giving rise to the many cells of the embryo and adult of the next generation (Fig. 15-2). All these divisions are mitotic, and consequently every cell of the embryo and adult receives a diploid set of chromosomes equally derived from the two parents.

Parthenogenesis. Having contacted an egg, the sperm performs two other functions: (1) it contributes its chromosomes to the zygote nucleus, and (2) it activates the development of the egg. These two functions are separable, to some extent, as is demonstrated by the fact that if a sperm is removed just after it has made contact with an egg, fertilization proper cannot occur. Nevertheless such an egg may develop, at least partially, even in the absence of the paternal chromosomes. The contact of the sperm initiates a visible reaction that sweeps over the surface of the egg. This **activation** reaction involves the discharge of a bioelectric current, which precedes the lifting of the fertilization membrane. As a result of activation, the egg becomes nonreceptive to other sperm; and the metabolism of the egg is changed and accelerated. In due time the activated unfertilized egg begins to divide; in some cases it may continue development, forming an embryo, or even an adult—although such individuals are not entirely normal in appearance and vitality.

Activation represents the normal **response** of a ripe egg to stimulation. In fact, a variety of stimuli are now known that can substitute for the contacting sperm. Some eggs can be activated by mechanical pricking, or by drastic temperature changes, or by chemicals, or by sudden changes of the osmotic conditions in the surrounding medium. Apparently the unfertilized egg is all "set" and ready to develop. Normally, the stimulus for starting development is provided by the sperm that first succeeds in contacting the egg surface; but a variety of other strong stimuli may inadvertently "jolt the mechanism" into activity.

The development of an egg, in the absence of fertilization, is called **parthenogenesis.** Parthenogenesis may be artificial—that is, induced experimentally; or it may be **natural,** in that it occurs normally in the reproduction of some species. An organism produced by artificial parthenogenesis is haploid, at least in the sense that it lacks paternal chromosomes. Moreover, the development of such organisms tends to be abortive. A few animals (for example, frogs) have been reared into adults by careful nursing; but such adults are small and delicate, and they are never able to reproduce.

Natural parthenogenesis is regularly encountered in certain worms, insects, and crustaceans; they may be either haploid or diploid in nature. **Haploid parthenogenesis** is common to the ants, bees, and wasps (p. 659). The **unfertilized** eggs of these animals always develop into **males,** which, being haploid, produce sperm, not in the usual fashion, but by **mitosis.** The **fertilized** eggs of these species always develop into **females,** and these diploid females finally produce haploid eggs by meiosis, as in other animals.

Diploid parthenogenesis is exemplified by the aphids, or plant lice. Commonly the female aphid produces diploid reproductive cells by **mitosis.** These diploid cells are called **parthenogonidia,** rather than eggs. During the spring and summer months, the parthenogonidia develop into other parthenogenetic females; and in this way a number of asexual generations may be produced. In the fall, however, the parthenogonidia develop into **males** and **sexual females;** and these forms of the organism produce haploid gametes, by meiosis, in the usual fashion. Further development cannot occur until fertilization takes place. If aphids are raised in a greenhouse, under uniform conditions throughout the year, the sexual generation may never appear; and in certain species, males are unknown even under natural conditions. Thus parthenogenesis, although technically an asexual process, bears a very close relationship to the sexual modes of reproduction.

DEVELOPMENT—THE EMBRYONIC PERIOD

During development, the fertilized egg undergoes many changes. The original cell multiplies, and the many resulting cells arrange themselves and undergo differentiation—forming the tissues and organs of the growing body. Collectively these complex transformations make up development. Until the time of hatching, or birth—that is, until the offspring emerges from the egg or from the uterus—the developing individual is called an **embryo.** In *detail,* embryonic development varies widely in different species; but certain broad fundamental resemblances can be observed in the *early* development of practically all multicellular animals.

Cleavage—Formation of the Blastula. Soon after fertilization the zygote divides by repeated mitosis, forming a group of smaller cells. These early divisions, which lead to the formation of a multicellular embryo, are referred to collectively as **cleavage.**

Homolecithal eggs (Fig. 15-1A), which display a homogeneous cytoplasm and relatively little yolk, nevertheless possess a distinct **polarity.** The animal pole is marked by the point where the **polar bodies** were formed (Fig. 15-2); and the opposite pole is referred to as the **vegetal pole.** The first and second cleavages pass through the poles, giving rise to a four-celled embryo (Fig. 15-2). The third cleavage passes at right angles to the first two, at or near the equator, and now the embryo consists of eight fairly equal-sized cells—four in the animal hemisphere and four in the vegetal hemisphere. The further cleavages are usually synchronous so that the number of cells increases in geometrical progression —8, 16, 32, 64, etc. When several hundred cells are formed, the embryo typically has the form of a hollow sphere. This is the **blastula** stage; and the cavity within the blastula is called the **blastocoel** (Fig. 15-7).

Telolecithal eggs (Fig. 15-1B) have an abundance of yolk, especially in the vegetal hemisphere, and the cleavage divisions of the telolecithal egg are not equal. The first *horizontal* cleavage passes above the equator; consequently, the cells in the animal hemisphere are distinctly smaller than those in the vegetal region. The lower cells contain a larger amount of yolk and divide less rapidly than the upper cells. Accordingly, when the blastula is formed, the cells in the vegetal hemisphere are larger and less numerous (Fig. 15-7). Also the blastocoel is small and lies eccentrically, nearer the animal pole (Fig. 15-7). In very heavily yolked eggs, such as the eggs of birds and reptiles, the vegetal cytoplasm may not cleave at all; and in such cases the blastula consists of a small disc of cells, roofing over a narrow blastocoel, in the region of the animal pole (Fig. 15-7).

Gastrulation—Formation of Endoderm. A few simple colonial organisms do not progress beyond the blastula stage. In *Volvox,* for example, the adult colony consists merely of a hollow sphere of cells, among which very little differentiation has occurred.

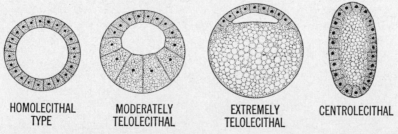

HOMOLECITHAL TYPE   MODERATELY TELOLECITHAL   EXTREMELY TELOLECITHAL   CENTROLECITHAL

Fig. 15-7. Blastulas derived from different types of egg. Compare with Figure 15-1.

But in higher animals, as cleavage continues, the cells in the vegetal region appear to be crowded inward, so that they encroach upon the blastocoel (Fig. 15-2). This inpocketing, or **invagination,** continues until a tubular pouch, the **archenteron,** is formed (Fig. 15-2). The archenteron is the embryonic forerunner of the **digestive tract.** The cells forming the wall of the archenteron are specified as the **endoderm;** and the cells remaining at the surface of the embryo are called the **ectoderm.** Such a two-layered embryo is a **gastrula;** and the orifice leading into the archenteron is the **blastopore.**

In heavily yolked eggs **gastrulation** is modified considerably (Fig. 15-8A,B); but it is always possible to recognize a gastrula. This two-layered embryo possesses a saccular archenteron, which communicates with the exterior through a blastopore.

The Mesoderm and the Coelom. Very primitive animals, such as *Hydra* and other Coelenterata (p. 630), do not progress further than the gastrula stage. The adult body of such animals is two-layered, consisting entirely of ectoderm and endoderm. In all higher animals, however, a third layer of cells, the **mesoderm,** is formed between the ectoderm and endoderm. These three embryonic layers—the **ectoderm, endoderm,** and **mesoderm**—are called the **primary germ layers** of the embryo. The ectoderm is destined to give rise to all epithelial layers on the external surface of the body, and also to the sensory and nervous tissues of the animal. The endoderm provides a glandular

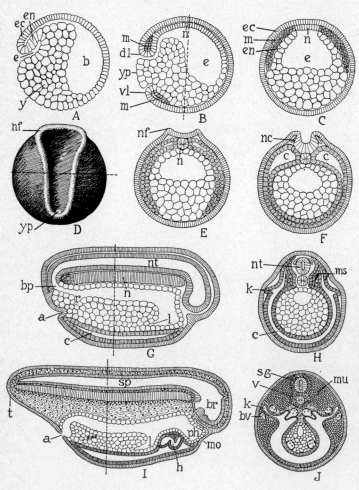

Fig. 15-8. Amphibian embryos, showing development of typical vertebrate structures. A, median longitudinal section of early gastrula; B, similar section of late gastrula; C, cross section of same stage; D, dorsal view of slightly later stage, showing neural folds; E, cross section of same stage; F, similar section of later stage; G, median longitudinal section of embryo after closing of neural tube; H, cross section of the same stage; I, longitudinal section of embryo at time of hatching; J, cross section of same stage. ec, ectoderm; en, endoderm; y, yolk cells; b, blastocoel; e, archenteron; m, mesoderm; dl, dorsal lip of blastopore; vl, ventral lip of blastopore; yp, yolk plug; n, notochord; nf, neural fold; nc, neural crest (which develops into sensory ganglia); c, coelom; nt, neural tube; bp, blastopore; a, anus; r, rectum; l, liver; k, embryonic kidney tubule; br, brain; sp, spinal cord; t, tail; h, heart; ph, pharynx; mo, mouth; mu, muscle; sg, sensory ganglion; v, vertebra; bv, blood vessel; ms, mesodermal somite.

lining throughout the **digestive tract** and all of its branches, and the mesoderm give rise to all other body structures—such as the muscle, bone, and connective tissues of the animal. Animals possessing only ectoderm and endoderm are said to be **diploblastic,** whereas those having all three germ layers are said to be **triploblastic.**

The mesoderm arises differently in different embryos. In the earthworm and many other invertebrates, the mesoderm derives chiefly from a pair of large cells, the **pole cells,** which are pushed into the blastocoel at or about the time of gastrulation (Fig. 15-9). These mesoderm cells multiply rapidly, forming two strands of tissue that crowd forward on either side of the archenteron, between the ectoderm and the endoderm (Fig. 15-9). As the mesoderm proliferates, it tends to fill and obliterate the blastocoel, encroaching above and below the archenteron (Fig. 15-9). Then a new cavity develops in the mesoderm itself; and this **coelom,** or **body cavity,** is found in all higher animals. The coelom enlarges and encircles the archenteron completely, separating the mesoderm into

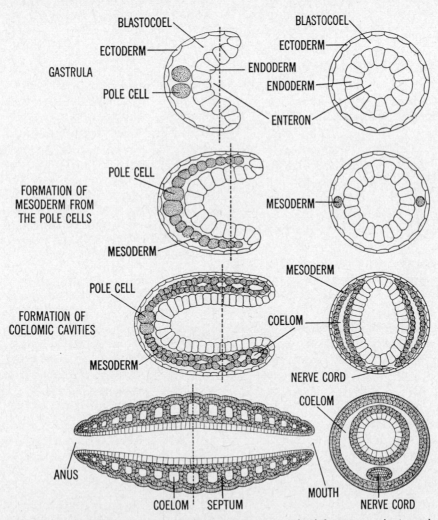

Fig. 15-9. Development in the **earthworm.** Figures on the left represent horizontal longitudinal sections, those on the right cross sections through the points indicated by the dotted lines.

two distinct layers (Fig. 15-9). The outer layer, or **somatic mesoderm,** together with the ectoderm around it, becomes the **body wall** of the adult; and the inner layer, or **visceral mesoderm,** together with the endoderm, becomes the **gut wall** of the adult.

All triploblastic animals except the flatworms possess a coelom, although the coelom does not always rise in the same manner. The coelom surrounds the digestive tract and separates it from the body wall. This arrangement permits the digestive tract to move freely—independently of the movement of the body as a whole. Generally the archenteron continues to invaginate, until it establishes communication with the exterior at the opposite end of the embryo. In this way the digestive tract becomes a tubular passage, leading from the *mouth* to the *anus.* Accordingly, the body structure of most higher animals can be described as that of a "tube within a tube." The inner tube, which is the **enteron,** or digestive tract, is separated from the outer tube, or **body wall,** by the **coelom,** which extends throughout most of the length of the body.

In many invertebrates, such as starfish and other Echinodermata (p. 660), the mesoderm and coelom arise from a pair of hollow evaginations, the **enterocoelic pouches** (Fig. 15-2). These outpocketings pinch off from the archenteron and grow larger until they obliterate the blastocoel. Meanwhile the cavity of each pouch encircles the enteron, forming the definitive coelom.

A similar method of mesoderm formation is also found in *Amphioxus* (p. 665) and some other primitive Chordata (p. 664); but the mesoderm arises in a different way, in embryos of true vertebrates. In the frog, for example, most of the mesoderm is formed by a proliferation of the cells of the **rim** *of the* **blastopore**—that is, at the junction between the ectoderm and endoderm (Fig. 15-8B,C). However, some mesoderm seems to bud off from the sides of the archenteron.

Regardless of origin, the mesoderm grows, crowding forward in the embryo and insinuating itself between the ectoderm and endoderm along both sides of the archenteron. Then the **coelomic** cavity appears (Fig. 15-8E) and enlarges (Fig. 15-8F), finally encircling (Fig. 15-8H) the enteron, except in the mid-dorsal region. Thus the coelom comes to separate the **visceral** and **somatic layers** of the mesoderm; and the body wall becomes differentiated from the gut wall. In the **dorsal** region, however, the opposite parts of the developing coelom fail to meet each other above the enteron, although ventrally the coelom completely encircles the gut (Fig. 15-8J). Owing to this failure of the coelom to encircle the gut in the dorsal region of the vertebrate embryo, the gut wall remains in continuity with the body wall—by way of a sheetlike connection of mesoderm tissue (Fig. 15-8J). This connecting sheet of mesoderm becomes the **mesentery,** which suspends the digestive tract in the coelomic cavity of the adult. Also the mesentery provides a connection through which nerves and blood vessels pass between the body wall and the gut wall, which otherwise are isolated throughout the length of the body.

FURTHER DEVELOPMENT— VERTEBRATE ANIMALS

All vertebrates (fish, amphibians, reptiles, birds, and mammals) resemble each other as to many characteristics of development and structure (p. 668); but *three* vertebrate characteristics are of primary importance. All vertebrates possess: (1) a **segmented vertebral column** (also called the "backbone"); (2) a **dorsally placed tubular nervous system** (that is, a tubular brain and spinal cord that are enveloped by the vertebral column); and (3) **gill clefts** (several, usually five, pairs of slitlike channels, leading from the digestive tract to the exterior, in the region of the pharynx).

Among the fish, the gill arches bear functional gills, which serve as respiratory organs. But in higher vertebrates, including man, the gill clefts appear only transiently during embryonic development—although modified remnants of the gill slits persist in the adult body (p. 283).

Despite the large number of species, the Vertebrata are classified as a subphylum in the **phylum Chordata** (p. 664). In addition to the vertebrates, the phylum Chordata includes a number of less familiar animals, which possess gill clefts and a dorsal hollow nerve cord, *but no true* **vertebral column.** In place of a vertebral column, primitive chordates possess an unsegmented flexible rodlike supporting structure, the **notochord,** which occupies an equivalent position in the body (Fig. 15-10). Vertebrate animals develop

neural groove (Fig. 15-11, A,B), which runs lengthwise of the embryo and is broader at the anterior end (Fig. 15-8D). The neural groove is bounded laterally by the **neural folds,** which rise slightly from the surface of the embryo. Posteriorly the neural folds encircle the **blastopore** (Fig. 15-8D), which is called the **yolk plug** because it is blocked by yolk cells.

As development proceeds, the neural groove sinks below the surface of the embryo, and the neural folds come together along the mid-dorsal line (Fig. 15-11B,C). This invagination forms the **neural tube,** which will

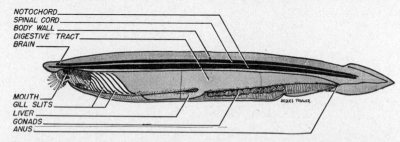

Fig. 15-10. *Amphioxus,* a primitive chordate, sectioned longitudinally. Note especially: 1, the notochord; 2, the **dorsal** nervous system (brain and spinal cord; and 3, the gill slits. This animal cannot be classed as a vertebrate since it lacks a segmented vertebral column.

a notochord, but only transiently, during the embryonic period, prior to the appearance of the segmented vertebral column. In fact, it is the possession of a notochord, as well as of gill clefts and a dorsal nervous system, that confirms the relationship between the vertebrates and more primitive chordate forms, and justifies placing all these animals in the same phylum.

Origin of the Nerve Cord and Notochord. The nerve cord and notochord arise almost simultaneously in the late gastrula period (Fig. 15-11A-D). The nerve cord comes from ectoderm, as will be described presently, whereas the notochord, at least in some forms, arises from a strand of endoderm that buds off from the archenteron (Fig. 15-11, B-D).

The nerve cord first appears on the dorsal surface of the gastrula. In the beginning it is merely a shallow depression, called the

give rise to the brain and spinal cord (Fig. 15-11F). The neural tube continues to sink below the surface of the embryo, and soon it becomes roofed over by surface ectoderm that encroaches from the sides. At an early stage (Fig. 15-11F), the cavity within the neural tube establishes continuity with the enteron cavity, although later this **neurenteric canal** becomes obliterated and the enteron breaks through more ventrally to join an invagination from the exterior, forming a new opening, the **anus** (Fig. 15-8I).

The **neural tube** gives rise to: (1) the entire **nervous system,** including the brain, spinal cord, and nerves; and (2) the special **sensory epithelia,** such as the retina of the eye. The **brain** develops from the anterior portion of the neural tube (Fig. 15-11F). This anterior part is larger initially and grows faster than the long narrow posterior portion, which becomes the **spinal cord.** The

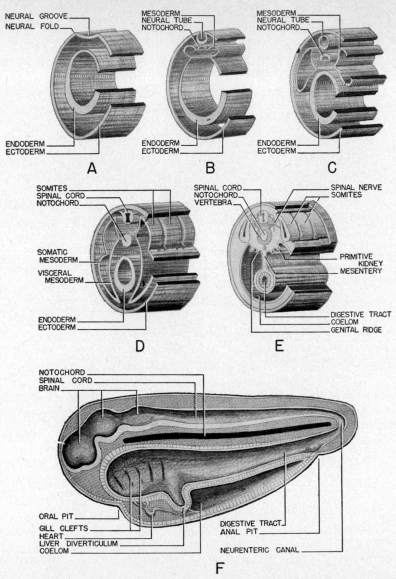

NEURAL GROOVE
NEURAL FOLD

ENDODERM
ECTODERM

A

MESODERM
NEURAL TUBE
NOTOCHORD

ENDODERM
ECTODERM

B

MESODERM
NEURAL TUBE
NOTOCHORD

ENDODERM
ECTODERM

C

SOMITES
SPINAL CORD
NOTOCHORD

SOMATIC
MESODERM

VISCERAL
MESODERM

ENDODERM
ECTODERM

D

SPINAL CORD
NOTOCHORD
VERTEBRA

SPINAL NERVE
SOMITES

PRIMITIVE
KIDNEY
MESENTERY

DIGESTIVE TRACT
COELOM
GENITAL RIDGE

E

NOTOCHORD
SPINAL CORD
BRAIN

ORAL PIT
GILL CLEFTS
HEART
LIVER DIVERTICULUM
COELOM

DIGESTIVE TRACT
ANAL PIT

NEURENTERIC CANAL

F

Fig. 15-11. Some generalized stages in the development of a primitive verte-brate. Stages A to E are cross sections cut from the mid-body region; whereas F is a longitudinal section.

nerves of the body represent outgrowths from the neural tube. Each nerve consists of a bundle of fibers that originate from nerve cells as soon as these begin to differentiate in the developing brain and spinal cord.

The flexible unsegmented **notochord** is a skeletal rod that is found in all vertebrate embryos, extending lengthwise through the embryo—between the neural tube and the archenteron (Fig. 15-11 D,F). In vertebrates, however, the notochord is a short-lived, vestigial structure. In most cases it is totally replaced by the segmented vertebral column; but among primitive vertebrates (for example, lampreys, sharks, and frogs), remnants of the notochord can be found between the vertebrae, even in the adult animals.

Origin of the Skeleton and Musculature. Except for certain parts of the skull—which arise from the ectoderm overlying the developing brain—the **skeleton** arises from mesoderm. Initially the skeletal material is **cartilage;** but this cartilage tissue (p. 289) is almost completely replaced by bone during later embryonic development—except in the lower cartilaginous fishes (p. 669). However, the form and pattern of the skeletal parts remain essentially the same during the period when the cartilage is resorbed and replaced by bone.

In vertebrate embryos (at the stage shown in Fig. 15-11D,E) one can identify a dorsal mass of mesoderm, which lies on either side of the notochord and neural tube. As development proceeds, this dorsal mesoderm becomes subdivided by a number of transverse creases into a series of blocklike segments, called **somites.** The mesodermal somites (Fig. 15-11E) give rise to the skeletal and muscular structures in the several segments of the body. Each vertebra is blocked off by the mesoderm surrounding the notochord and neural tube, as this tissue differentiates into cartilage. The cartilage grows dorsally around the neural tube, forming a **neural arch** (Fig. 15-11E); and ventrally, the cartilage first surrounds (Fig. 15-11E), and then **invades** the notochord. Gradually all the notochordal tissue is resorbed, leaving the segments of cartilage, which become the **centra** of the vertebrae. Accordingly, the vertebral column is made up of a series of segments, or **vertebrae,** linked together end to end. Collectively the vertebrae form a flexible skeleton —the vertebral column—that lies embedded in the dorsal body wall. The neural arch of each vertebra surrounds one portion of the spinal cord, so that the column as a whole provides a protective tunnel, which houses the spinal cord throughout its length. This protective housing becomes even more effective when the cartilage is later replaced by bone (in all except the lower vertebrates).

Virtually all of the muscle in each body segment arises from the lateral part of the mesodermal somites. Some of these mesoderm cells remain *in situ,* giving rise to the massive muscles of the back, but others migrate ventrally—through the mesentery into the gut wall—and into the lateral and ventral parts of the body wall. In the gut wall this mesoderm differentiates into **visceral** (nonstriated) **muscle** (p. 286); but in the body wall it gives rise to **skeletal** (striated) muscle (p. 286). Most of the **connective tissues** (p. 288) also arise from cells that migrate out from the mesodermal somites.

Further Development of the Digestive Tract and Its Outgrowths. The **mouth,** in vertebrates, arises as a shallow invagination, the **oral pit,** which pushes inward and joins the archenteron near the anterior extremity of the embryo (Fig. 15-11F); the **anus** arises similarly at the posterior end of the enteron, just ventral to the blastopore. Thus part of the lining of both the mouth and the anus is derived from ectoderm, and both these passages display a line of junction between the ectodermal and endodermal tissues. Among invertebrates, the blastopore persists, becoming the mouth, as in the earthworm (Fig. 15-9).

The **gill slits** originate as a series of outpocketings (Fig. 15-11F), which push laterally from the endoderm to join a corresponding set of inpocketings from the surface ectoderm. In higher vertebrates the penetration of the gill passages is usually incomplete— although one pair of clefts forms a passage that persists and gives rise to the **Eustachian tubes** (p. 425) and **middle ear chambers** of the adult.

The **lungs, liver, pancreas,** and **urinary bladder** all originate as tubular *outgrowths from the developing* **enteron.** Accordingly all these structures possess an **internal lining** derived from endoderm. However, visceral mesoderm always envelops these outgrowths at the time when they originate from the enteron, and this mesoderm gives rise to the muscle, connective tissue, blood and lymph vessels, and the *external* epithelia of all the organs that grow out from the gut. In fact, the endoderm provides only the internal epithelium of the digestive tract and its branches. This epithelium is particularly important in the case of the liver, pancreas, and other digestive glands, because only these endoderm cells are destined to give rise to glandular tissues.

Origin of Some Other Structures. The blood and lymph vessels originate as fissures, called **sinuses,** in the mesoderm (Fig. 15-8,J), and these sinuses eventually become interconnected, forming a continuous system of tubes. At first, the **heart** appears as a simple tube formed by the coalescence of two of the larger vessels in the anterior ventral region of the embryo (Fig. 17-8). This primitive heart soon becomes muscular and begins to beat regularly, and thereafter the heart continues to perform its ceaseless work while further development goes on. The initially straight tube becomes twisted rather complexly (Fig. 17-8), and meanwhile partitions are formed, first between the auricles, and then between the ventricles. In the embryonic mammalian heart, therefore, it is possible to recognize stages that are equivalent to the two-chambered heart of the fishes and the three-chambered heart of the amphibians, before finally the four-chambered heart of the adult mammal comes into being.

In the early embryo the blood plasma appears to be secreted into the sinuses by the surrounding epithelial cells, and both red and white corpuscles arise from cells that detach themselves from the sinus epithelium. Later, however, the formation of new corpuscles becomes delegated to other tissues, particularly the bone marrow (p. 322).

The **kidneys** and the **gonads** (ovaries or testes) originate from mesodermal foldings along the dorsal wall of the coelom, on either side of the mesentery (Fig. 15-11E). In the embryo of reptiles, birds and mammals, moreover, three stages may be recognized during the development of the kidneys. The earliest embryonic kidney, called the **pronephros,** occupies a relatively anterior position in the embryo. In structure this primi-

tive kidney resembles the adult kidneys of present-day fishes. In higher vertebrates the pronephros never becomes functional and is soon replaced by a functional **mesonephros,** which is situated more posteriorly and plainly displays a structural resemblance to the adult amphibian kidney. Finally, the mesonephros is likewise replaced by the adult type of kidney, the **metanephros,** which develops near the posterior extremity of the coelomic cavity.

Contributions of the Primary Germ Layers. In summary, the eventual contribution of each germ layer, especially in vertebrate animals, can be given as follows:

The **ectoderm** gives rise to: (1) the entire nervous system—including the brain, spinal cord, ganglia, nerves, and the receptor cells of the sense organs; (2) the outer, or **epidermal layers** of the skin, and skin structures—including hair, nails, the superficial parts of scales and feathers, and the secretory cells of skin glands (for example, sweat glands); (3) the lens of the eye; and (4) part of the **lining** of the mouth, nostrils, and anus, including the enamel layer of the **teeth.**

The **endoderm** provides the **lining** of the enteron (excluding part of the mouth and anus) and all its offshoots. These offshoots include not only the digestive glands such as the liver and pancreas, but also the lungs and other parts of the respiratory tract, the thyroid and thymus glands, and most of the urinary bladder and the urethra.

Finally, the **mesoderm** gives rise to all other body structures. These include (1) the deeper (dermal) layers of the skin and associated structures; (2) the gut wall, except for its endodermal lining; (3) the mesenteries and other parts of the epithelial lining of the coelom and its derivatives; (4) the kidneys and most of the reproductive system; (5) the vascular system, including the heart, blood vessels, and lymphatics; (6) the muscles; and (7) the various connective and supporting tissues, including almost all the bones, and the deeper (dentine) layers of the teeth.

HISTOLOGY: ORIGIN AND NATURE OF THE BODY TISSUES

All the cells of the developing embryo possess equivalent chromosomes, derived by mitosis from the zygote, and in young embryos, the cells display little or no obvious differentiation. But sooner or later the cells in different regions of the embryo become different; some become muscles, some nerve, etc., until finally all the **tissues** of the adult become recognizable.

Initially, the particular destiny of an embryonic cell is not determined, and many factors, both physical and chemical, cooperate in determining the eventual fate. In the frog embryo, for example, the ectoderm cells that lie in the **mid-dorsal** region of the embryo would normally give rise to nerve cells. But these same cells can be transplanted to the side of another embryo—and in this case they become skin cells. In other words, the cells develop differently according to their respective positions in the embryonic body. The physical and chemical forces that act upon the surface cells of an embryo differ from those that play upon the deeper cells; and there are many less obvious differences that affect development in the different embryonic regions. Moreover, cells that have become differentiated sometimes exert a differentiating influence upon other cells, especially in nearby regions of the embryo (p. 534). But the problems of differentiation will be considered later (Chap. 27), and at present we will be concerned only with the end results of differentiation—the **tissues of the adult animal.**

Many *specific* differences are found among the tissues of various animals, although the same four general types can always be recognized. These **fundamental tissues** are: (1) *epithelium,* (2) *muscle,* (3) *nerve,* and (4) *connective (sustentive) tissue.* Each of these fundamental tissues will be described in terms of the vertebrate animal.

Epithelial Tissues. The epithelial tissues, which cover the various external and internal *surfaces* of the body, are composed of closely fitting cells, with only a minimum of intercellular material binding the tissue into a continuous membrane.

Epithelial cells are variously modified at different surfaces, and accordingly, several kinds of epithelia can be recognized. In **squamous** epithelium (Fig. 2-8) the cells are flat and scalelike; whereas in **columnar** epithelium the cells are cylinders, or bricks, of greater or lesser depth (Fig. 2-8). In **simple** epithelia there is only a single tier of cells, but in **stratified** epithelia there are several or many tiers. Moreover, some epithelia are **ciliated** (Fig. 15-12), but others are **nonciliated.**

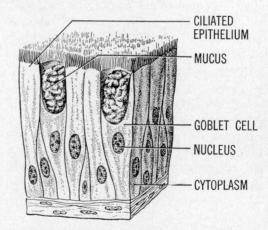

CILIATED EPITHELIUM

MUCUS

GOBLET CELL

NUCLEUS

CYTOPLASM

Fig. 15-12. Epithelial cells in the mucosal lining of the human trachea.

Some epithelia are composed entirely of **glandular cells,** which secrete their products at the epithelial surface. This is true of the lining of the coelomic cavity and all its derivatives. In the abdominal cavity, where the epithelium is called the **peritoneum;** in the thoracic cavity, where it is called the **pleura;** and in the pericardial cavity, where it is called the **pericardium**—all the cells produce a watery, or **serous,** fluid, which lubricates the internal surfaces of the body. But in the **mucosa,** which lines the digestive tract and most of its offshoots, only some of the cells are gland cells (Fig. 15-12). All multicellular glands in the body are derived from

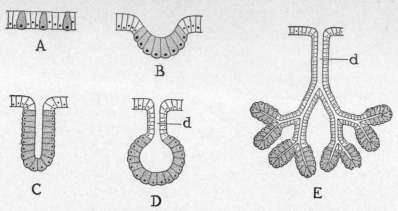

Fig. 15-13. Structure of glands; the actual gland cells are shaded in each figure. A, single gland cells scattered among ordinary epithelial cells; B, simple multicellular gland, consisting of a group of gland cells lining a slight invagination of the epithelium; C, simple tubular gland; D, simple alveolar gland; E, compound tubular gland (large glands, such as the liver and pancreas, are of this type, with thousands of secreting alveoli); d, duct.

epithelial outpocketings (Fig. 15-13). Some multicellular glands are **simple glands,** like the gastric glands of the stomach, being composed of epithelial cells (Fig. 15-13C); but others are **compound glands** (Fig. 15-13E), which contain a significant amount of connective tissue between the epithelial channels. Likewise compound glands are independently supplied with nerves and blood vessels, and each is covered by an epithelial membrane.

Muscle Tissues. The three kinds of muscle tissue of vertebrate animals are: (1) *visceral muscle,* which is found in most of the internal organs, or **viscera;** (2) *skeletal muscle,* which occurs mainly in the body wall, connected to the bones and other skeletal parts; and (3) *cardiac muscle,* which is found only in the heart. All muscle tissues are characterized by **elongate** cells or fibers, which generate movement by shortening, or contracting, in a forcible manner. No force is developed during the **relaxation** of a muscle fiber; in other words, muscle fibers work, not by pushing, but by pulling. All muscle tissues appear to generate a contractile force by the shortening of numerous delicate protoplasmic fibrils, the **myofibrils,** which are present in the fibers. The myofibrils run lengthwise through

the fluid protoplasm, or **sarcoplasm,** of the fibers, as can be demonstrated by proper staining, in all varieties of muscle tissue.

In **visceral muscle,** each fiber is a single spindle-shaped cell (Fig. 15-14), but the individual fibers of **skeletal muscle** are syncytia, containing many nuclei (Fig. 15-14). In skeletal muscle, the nuclei are found at regular intervals near the surface of the fiber, just subjacent to a well-marked membrane, the **sarcolemma.** In skeletal and cardiac muscle, but not in visceral muscle, one can see a number of transverse **striations** (Fig. 15-14). These striations look like a series of parallel bands, passing across the fibers, but they are not actual partitions subdividing the fiber into discrete sections. The nature and fine structure of the striations will be discussed in Chapter 24.

Cardiac muscle is found only in the vertebrate heart. The general structure of the tissue is like that of skeletal muscle, except that the fibers of cardiac muscle are interrupted periodically along the length by zigzag cross membranes, called *intercalated discs* (Fig. 15-14), and the nuclei are deeply embedded near the central axis of the fiber.

Functionally, the three types of muscle are also quite different. The action of skeletal

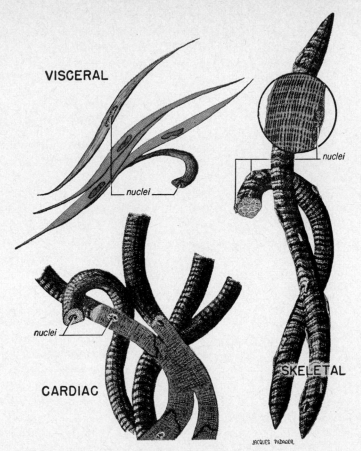

VISCERAL

nuclei

nuclei

nuclei

CARDIAC

SKELETAL

JACQUES PADAWER

Fig. 15-14.   The three kinds of muscle tissue.

muscle is very rapid—such that contraction and relaxation are completed in less than 0.1 second, compared to an average of 1 and 10 seconds, respectively, for cardiac and visceral muscles. Also the contractions of skeletal muscle are finely graded and precisely controlled as to their force and amplitude. Essentially, each separate skeletal muscle is a bundle containing thousands of parallel fibers stretching between two parts of the skeleton. Each fiber receives an individual nerve supply. Accordingly the demands of the nervous system can be varied in such a way that all or only some of the fibers contract, adding their strength to the whole contraction. Cardiac muscle, in contrast, tends to contract in an **all-or-none** fashion, and a single excitation tends to spread throughout the whole syncytium. In lesser degree such

generalized contractions also occur in visceral muscle; but in this tissue the excitation seems to be passed from cell to cell.

Nerve Tissue. The cells of the nervous system are called **neurons** (Fig. 15-15). Each neuron consists of a cell body, or **centron**—that is, the nucleus and the cytoplasm immediately surrounding the nucleus—and of delicate threadlike **nerve fibers,** which extend out from the cell body. Some of these fibers normally conduct impulses toward the centron, and these fibers are called **dendrons;** but other fibers, the **axons,** normally convey impulses away from the centron. The many neurons that compose the nervous system form a coordinating system of fibers connecting the many sensory and motor structures of the body.

The centron part of a nerve cell maintains the nutrition of its own outlying fibers. Thus an axon or dendron that is cut off from continuity with its centron undergoes degeneration, although a replacement of the fiber may be effected by a new outgrowth from the cut end. The centrons of the nervous system are aggregated in small masses, called **ganglia,** and—to a much greater extent—in the brain and spinal cord. **Nerves**— which lead to and away from the ganglia, brain, and spinal cord—are made up of axons, dendrons, or both, running together in a common bundle. In many nerves, each fiber is insulated from its neighbors by an individual sheath (Fig. 15-15) of fatty material,

which is called the **myelin** or **medullary sheath.** However, some nerves, particularly in the autonomic system (p. 465), are **nonmyelinated.**

Connective (Sustentive) Tissues. The connective tissues bind the other tissues together, giving substantial form to each organ, and connecting and supporting the various organs. In all connective tissues, the **intercellular matrix** is far more conspicuous than the cells by which this matrix is secreted. In fact, the character of the matrix mainly determines the properties of the particular kind of connective tissue in question—as may be noted in the following description.

1. *Fibrillar Connective Tissues.* The matrix of the fibrillar tissues is characterized by the presence of numerous nonliving fibers, which form dense interlacing networks or thick parallel strands. The **fibroblasts,** or cells that form the matrix, are usually difficult to see among the fibers. They are inconspicuous amoeboid cells, capable of migrating to the various parts of the tissue. The chemical nature of the fibers differs in different connective tissues. In general, two main types are recognized: (a) **white fibers,** which are relatively delicate and inelastic, and (b) **yellow fibers,** which are stouter and more elastic. White fibrous connective tissue is widely dis-

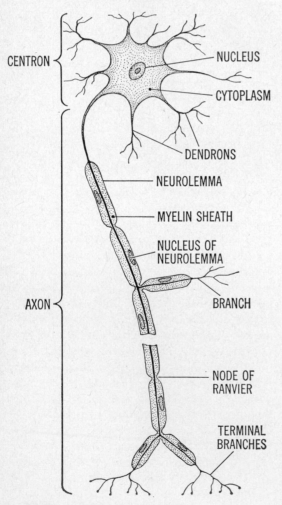

CENTRON
NUCLEUS
CYTOPLASM
DENDRONS
NEUROLEMMA
MYELIN SHEATH
NUCLEUS OF NEUROLEMMA
AXON
BRANCH
NODE OF RANVIER
TERMINAL BRANCHES

Fig. 15-15.   A neuron, or nerve cell.

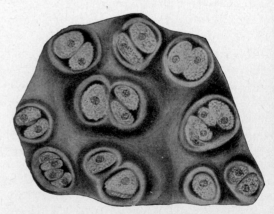

Fig. 15-16.   Hyaline cartilage. One to several cartilage-producing cells (chondroblasts) occupy each of the spaces (lacunae) in the chondrin matrix. (From *The Living Body,* by Best and Taylor. Holt, Rinehart and Winston, Inc.)

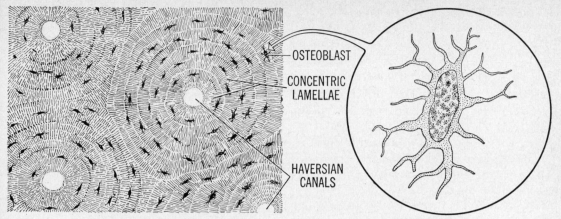

Fig. 15-17. Compact bone: cross section, with detail of an osteoblast.

tributed throughout the body; the yellow type of connective tissue is encountered mainly in the **ligaments** of the skeletal joints of the body.

2. *Cartilage* (Fig. 15-16). The matrix of cartilage is composed mainly of a protein substance, **chondrin.** The chondrin appears as a homogeneous mass between the cells, or **chondroblasts,** that secrete it. Cartilage has a flexible, resilient consistency. In lower vertebrates cartilage forms the entire skeleton, but in higher vertebrates, cartilage supplements bone; that is, cartilage is used as a padding between the bones, and as the skeleton of parts of the body, such as the nose and ears, where flexibility is a desirable characteristic. All kinds of cartilage display fibers, like those of fibrillar connective tissue, embedded in the chondrin matrix.

3. *Bone* (Fig. 15-17). Bone is the characteristic skeletal material of most vertebrate animals. The matrix of bone is hard and rigid, being composed largely of phosphate and carbonate compounds of calcium. The bone cells, or **osteoblasts,** which deposit the bony matrix, are small cells with numerous fine cytoplasmic branches (Fig. 15-17). Usually the osteoblasts are arranged in concentric

circles around tubular channels, called **Haversian canals.** These canals penetrate through the bone, allowing for the passage of nerves and blood vessels (Fig. 15-17).

4. *Blood and Lymph.* Blood (Fig. 15-18) has a fluid matrix, called the **plasma.** This complex aqueous solution (p. 321) serves as the chief medium of transportation throughout the body. In the plasma, the several different kinds of blood cells are suspended (see p. 321).

The **blood cells** of vertebrates are of three types. (1) The **erythrocytes,** or *red corpuscles,* contain large quantities of **hemoglobin,** the red pigment that facilitates the transportation of oxygen. (2) The **leucocytes,** or *white corpuscles,* are amoeboid cells, which in some cases can ingest bacteria and other foreign particles, thus counteracting infections, and preventing the blood vessels from clogging. (3) The **blood platelets,** or *thrombocytes,* are fragile colorless corpuscles, which initiate a clotting of the plasma—by disintegrating as soon as blood is shed (see p. 323).

Invertebrate bloods do not contain erythrocytes, although hemoglobin (or allied respiratory pigments) may be present—dissolved directly in the plasma. The erythro-

Fig. 15-18. Red and white blood corpuscles of man, all drawn to the same scale. A, red blood corpuscle, flat and edgewise; B, lymphocyte; C, mononuclear leucocyte; D, polymorphonuclear leucocyte (granulocyte).

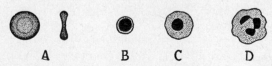

A   B   C   D

cytes of vertebrates, except for the mammals, possess nuclei.

Leucocytes are of various kinds according to their form and origin (p. 322); and not all leucocytes are able to migrate through the walls of the capillary blood vessels into the tissue spaces. The lymph—or body fluid, as it is more frequently called in lower animals—resembles blood, except that lymph contains less protein and no erythrocytes. Lymph fills the tissue spaces; and in a majority of animals, the lymph circulates slowly through these tissue spaces (p. 334).

TEST QUESTIONS

1. Distinguish carefully between:
    a. the vitelline membrane and the fertilization membrane
    b. activation and fertilization
    c. activation and parthenogenesis
    d. natural and artificial parthenogenesis
    e. haploid and diploid parthenogenesis
2. Describe an experiment proving that activation and fertilization are separate functions of the sperm.
3. Distinguish between the acrosome filament and the fertilization cone. Explain the function of each.
4. Is there any relation between the quantity of yolk in an egg and the length of the embryonic period? Explain.
5. Explain the significance of polarity in the egg.
6. Why is the middle piece of the sperm important?
7. What is a blastula? How does the blastula derived from a homolecithal egg differ from one derived from a telolecithal egg (for example, a frog's egg)?
8. What is a gastrula and how does it arise? Identify: (a) the archenteron; (b) the ectoderm and endoderm; and (c) the blastopore and blastocoel.
9. Explain three ways in which mesoderm may arise in various embryos.
10. Differentiate between diploblastic and triploblastic animals, citing an example of each.
11. Enumerate the adult structures (in vertebrate animals) that are derived from: (a) the ectoderm; (b) the endoderm; (c) the mesoderm.
12. A. Describe the origin of the coelom and explain how the coelom is related to the somatic and visceral layers of mesoderm, and to the mesentery.
    B. Explain the importance of the coelom in higher animals generally.
13. Explain the distinctive features that differentiate:
    a. vertebrates from invertebrate animals
    b. vertebrates from other chordate animals
14. Identify, locate, and explain the origin of:
    a. the neural groove, the neural folds, and the neural tube
    b. the brain and spinal cord
    c. the notochord
    d. the vertebrae, including the neural arches and centra
    e. visceral and skeletal muscle
    f. the gill slits and the Eustachian tubes
    g. the lungs, liver, and pancreas
    h. the blood and lymph vessels
15. Trace the development of the digestive tract (in vertebrates) from the time of invagination until the saccular enteron becomes tubular.
16. What are the *fundamental tissues* and how are they differentiated one from another?
17. Specify four kinds of epithelia and explain the distinctive features of each.
18. Specify the three kinds of muscle tissue and describe the distinctive features of each kind. In what ways are all kinds of muscle similar to each other.
19. Identify: (a) yellow fibrous connective tissue; (b) fibroblasts; (c) chondrin; (d) chondroblasts; (e) Haversian canals; and (f) lacunae.

FURTHER READINGS

1. *Ourselves Unborn,* by George W. Corner; New Haven, 1944.
2. *Embryos and Ancestors,* by G. R. DeBeer; Oxford, 1958.
3. *Human Embryology,* by B. M. Patten; Philadelphia, 1953.
4. *Developmental Anatomy,* by L. B. Arey; Philadelphia, 1954.

16-*The Digestive System in Man and Other Multicellular Animals*

THE SIMPLEST animals carry on ingestion, digestion, and the other processes of nutrition entirely within the limits of the single cell. But higher animals have developed specialized multicellular organs that display various degrees of complexity and efficiency. Moreover, these organs are subordinated into definite organ systems; well-defined **digestive, circulatory, respiratory,** and **excretory systems** are recognizable in all higher animals. First to be considered will be the **digestive system,** which fulfills the functions of **ingestion, digestion, absorption,** and **egestion,** in multicellular animals generally.

THE GASTRIC VACUOLES OF PRIMITIVE METAZOA

The earliest multicellular animals did not develop a new type of digestive cavity. They depended upon gastric vacuoles essentially similar to those found among the Protozoa. This is particularly true of the **Porifera,** a primitive phylum of animals commonly called the **sponges** (Chap. 32).

The cells of a sponge are aggregated in the form of a porous tube, which may or may not be complexly branched (Fig. 16-1). The tube is closed at the lower end, but communicates with the outside water through

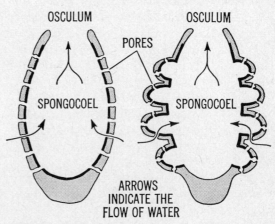

Fig. 16-1. The canal systems of two relatively simple sponges.

the **osculum**, a large opening at the upper extremity, and also there are many small **pores** in the side walls of the sponge. The entire tube is lined internally with flagellated cells (Fig. 16-2). These set up a stream of water that enters through the pores and leaves through the osculum (Fig. 16-1). Some of the cells, which are aggregated around pit-like chambers, possess collars encircling the flagella (Fig. 16-2). The flagella of these cells serve to waft small particles of food into the collars, whence the food passes into gastric vacuoles in the individual cells. Here the colloidal foods are digested. Part of the glucose, amino acids, and other products of digestion are utilized by the cells in which they are liberated, but part diffuses to the neighboring cells. No parts of the body are very remote from the source of absorption. The wall of the sponge is composed of only two cell layers, although some sponges have a large amount of relatively inert material, the **mesoglea,** interposed between the outer and inner cell layers. In commercially valuable sponges (Fig. 16-3), the mesoglea is composed of a silklike protein substance (**spongen**); but in others the skeletal material is calcareous or silicaceous, according to the species.

THE SACCULAR DIGESTIVE SYSTEMS OF HYDRA AND PLANARIA

In simplest form, the saccular type of digestive cavity is found in the fresh water polyp, **Hydra.** Essentially this small familiar aquarium animal has the form of a sac, in which one opening, the **mouth,** communicates with the surrounding water (Fig. 16-4). The **body wall** of *Hydra* is composed of only two cell layers; but between the outer **ectodermal epithelium** and inner **endodermal epithelium,** there is a thin layer of nonliving matrix. the **mesoglea.**

Hydra captures a variety of small free-swimming animals by means of **tentacles,** a group of slender, mobile, threadlike organs that originate from the body in the region surrounding the mouth (Fig. 3-12). Each ten-

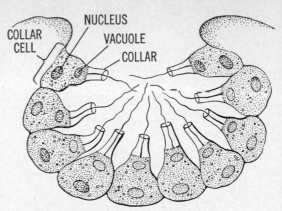

Fig. 16-2. Section of a flagellated chamber of a sponge.

tacle is armed with numerous evenly arranged batteries of **stinging cells** (Fig. 16-4). When the stinging cells discharge, they inject a paralyzing fluid into such victims as may

Fig. 16-3. Yellow sponge. The skeletal material of this sponge is **spongin,** a silklike compound. (The asculum is at the top.) (Courtesy of the Fish and Wildlife Service, U.S. Department of the Interior.)

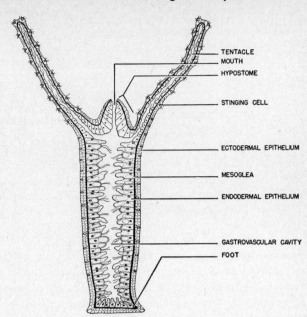

TENTACLE
MOUTH
HYPOSTOME

STINGING CELL

ECTODERMAL EPITHELIUM

MESOGLEA

ENDODERMAL EPITHELIUM

GASTROVASCULAR CAVITY
FOOT

Fig. 16-4. *Hydra,* longitudinal section.

happen to swim into contact with one of the waving tentacles. Then the tentacles push the immobile prey into the mouth, which can be opened very wide when necessary.

The **ingested** food of *Hydra* tends to accumulate in the saccular enteron, which is also called the **gastrovascular cavity.** *Digestion* begins in the gastrovascular cavity, but is completed in the separate cells that line the cavity and form gastric vacuoles on an individual basis. Some of the cells of the endermal epithelium are unicellular glands, which secrete enzymes into the gastrovascular cavity. These enzymes appear to act primarily upon the connective tissues of the ingested organism, and gradually the body of the prey disintegrates into many small pieces. Then the epithelial cells, which are flagellated, begin to form food vacuoles, and the fragments of the food organism are ingested for a second time. In the individual food vacuoles, digestion is completed. The complex protein, carbohydrate, and lipid components of the food are hydrolyzed, forming absorbable end products, which diffuse to the neighboring cells of the hydra. Nondigestible remnants of the food mass are passed from the vacuoles back into the gastro-

vascular cavity and out into the environment via the mouth.

The saccular type of enteron, in which the mouth opening serves for both ingestion and egestion, has a fairly wide distribution among primitive kinds of animals. It is possessed not only by *Hydra* and other Coelenterata (p. 630), but also by the flatworms or Platyhelminthes (p. 635). Among flatworms, however, the gastrovascular cavity is not a simple sac, but a branched system of blind pockets all connected by main channels which lead inward from the mouth (Fig. 16-5).

The branched type of gastrovascular cavity is well exemplified by Planaria, one of the commonest of the free-living flatworms. These graceful little animals (Fig. 16-6) have a flexible ribbonlike form. The ciliated **epithelium,** which covers the undersurface of the body externally, enables the flatworm to glide through the water, with the flat ventral surface in contact with rocks and other objects on the bottom of the pond. The anterior end, or head, is broader than the tapered tail and the dorsal surface has a darker color than the ventral. A pair of light-sensitive **eyespots** is located on the dorsal surface near the anterior end of the head; and on each

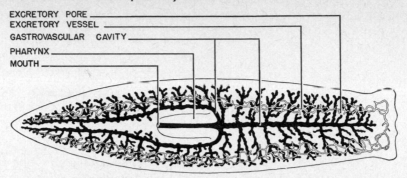

EXCRETORY PORE
EXCRETORY VESSEL
GASTROVASCULAR CAVITY
PHARYNX
MOUTH

Fig. 16-5. *Planaria,* a common flatworm. Diagram of a specimen with digestive system injected with India ink. Note that the ink flows into all branches of the **gastrovascular cavity.**

side of the head there is a small blunt-pointed lateral projection, the **auricle,** which is thought to be a receptor of tactile stimuli.

The **mouth** of *Planaria* is found at the tip of a hoselike muscular organ, the **pharynx** (Fig. 16-7). The pharynx protrudes out from the ventral surface only when the planarian is feeding; and at all other times it is withdrawn into the **pharyngeal pouch** (Fig. 16-7).

Planaria feeds upon minute organisms and particles of organic matter on the bottom of the pond. The food passes through the mouth and pharynx into the branches of the gastrovascular cavity. The full extent of this branching system can be demonstrated by injecting an ink suspension through the mouth and pharynx by means of a hypodermic syringe. Then it can be seen that the many branches of the digestive cavity penetrate to all parts of the body (Fig. 16-5).

Fig. 16-6. This free-living flatworm (*Dugesia dorotocephala*) is closely related to *Planaria.* It lives in fresh-water ponds and brooks, where it glides through the crevices between the stones, using its cilia, which cover the underside of the body. At the head end (right) note the light-sensitive "eye spots" and the touch-sensitive "auricles." Also note that the protrusible pharynx can be seen (vaguely) enclosed in a pocket near the center of the body. (Courtesy of J. A. Miller, Emory University.)

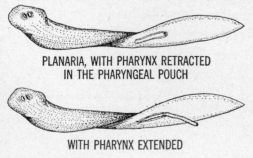

PLANARIA, WITH PHARYNX RETRACTED
IN THE PHARYNGEAL POUCH

WITH PHARYNX EXTENDED

Fig. 16-7. *Planaria.*

The branching of the gastrovascular system facilitates the distribution of the absorbed foods to the outlying cells of the animal. The body of the flatworm, compared to *Hydra,* is considerably thicker because a layer of **mesoderm** develops between the ectoderm and endoderm (Fig. 16-8). In *Planaria,* the mesoderm consists mainly of loosely arranged **parenchyma** tissue, which surrounds the various structures of the muscular, nervous, reproductive, and excretory

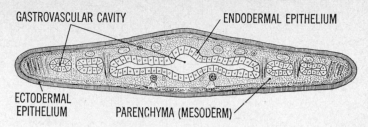

Fig. 16-8. *Planaria,* diagrammatic cross section.

GASTROVASCULAR CAVITY   ENDODERMAL EPITHELIUM

ECTODERMAL EPITHELIUM   PARENCHYMA (MESODERM)

systems. The intercellular spaces of the meso-derm are filled with a body fluid, which distributes food substances absorbed from the numerous branches of the gastrovascular cavity. Distribution is accelerated by the movements of the body, which set up haphazard currents in the body fluid; but there is not any very definite or sustained circulation of the body fluid of *Planaria.*

THE TUBULAR DIGESTIVE TRACT OF THE EARTHWORM

All animals above the evolutionary level of the flatworms possess a tubular type of enteron, generally similar to the digestive tract of man. Such tubular systems allow for a one-way passage of food materials from the mouth to the anal opening. Food ingested through the mouth undergoes digestion and absorption as it moves along the length of the enteron, and finally the remnants of the food are egested through the anus.

The earthworm and other Annelida (p. 647) possess a tubular enteron (Fig. 16-9)

which illustrates the advantages of such a system. Annelida, like higher forms generally, have developed a sharply defined **coelomic cavity,** which intervenes between the wall of the digestive tract and the body wall (Fig. 16-10). Moreover, the gut wall has developed a separate musculature, so that the digestive movements of the animal are independent of its external movements. The gut musculature takes care of churning, mixing, and moving the food mass in the digestive tract, while simultaneously the muscles of the body wall are executing the various external responses of the animal.

Tubular enterons are variously modified in different higher animals. In the earthworm, the **pharynx** lies directly behind the mouth and displays a relatively thick muscular wall (Fig. 16-9). The pharynx acts as a sort of suction pump that expands and contracts, sucking in small masses of moist earth as the worm burrows into the soil. The ingested earth, which contains considerable rotting plant material, mixed with the hard soil particles, then passes through the straight cylindrical **esophagus** (segments 6 to 14) to a

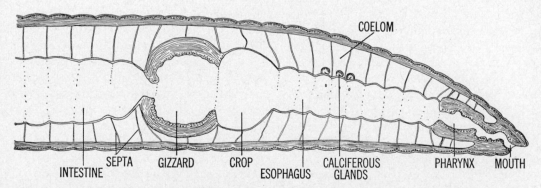

COELOM

INTESTINE   SEPTA   GIZZARD   CROP   ESOPHAGUS   CALCIFEROUS GLANDS   PHARYNX   MOUTH

Fig. 16-9. Tubular digestive tract of the earthworm (diagrammatic). Note the differentiation of the successive parts.

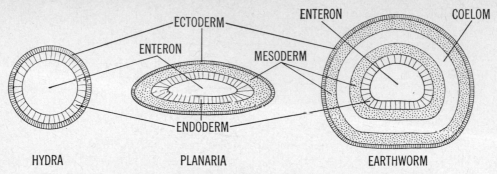

Fig. 16-10. Diagrams of cross sections of *Hydra, Planaria,* and earthworm.

thin-walled distensible chamber, the **crop.** While passing through the esophagus the food mass is mixed with the juices from three pairs of **multicellular glands,** the **calciferous glands** (Fig. 16-9). These secretions are rich in calcium carbonate, which may influence the digestive reactions. When the crop accumulates sufficient food, it passes the mass on to the thick-walled **gizzard** (segments 17 and 18), which is a grinding organ. The grinding action of the gizzard results from the strong rhythmic contractions of its thick muscular walls. Bits of leaves and other small masses of organic material are cut into smaller and smaller pieces, as they are repeatedly compressed between the sharp particles of the soil. This grinding action is important because it increases the exposed surface of the food mass and permits the digestive enzymes to act more effectively.

The **intestine** of the earthworm is the last and longest part of the digestive tract (Fig. 16-9). This thin-walled tube extends straight back from the gizzard to the anal opening, at the posterior extremity of the worm. While the food mass moves slowly along the intestine, digestion and absorption are completed. Many **unicellular digestive glands** are present in the epithelial lining of the intestine, and these glands secrete carbohydrases, proteases, and lipases upon the passing food. The sugars, amino acids, glycerol, and other relatively simple end products derived from the hydrolysis of the organic foods dissolve in the water fraction of the moist food mass; and as these end products accumulate, they tend to be absorbed by diffusion, through the endoderm into the blood, which flows continuously through the capillaries in the wall of the intestine.

THE DIGESTIVE SYSTEM OF MAN

The human digestive tract, like that of Vertebrata generally, is a tubular system, possessing a characteristic number and arrangement of the several parts (Fig. 16-11). Food is ingested through the mouth into the **oral cavity,** where it is chewed and mixed with saliva (Fig. 16-11). Then the food is swallowed and passes quickly through the short **pharynx** and the long **esophagus** to the **stomach.** The stomach is a thick-walled, muscular, saclike portion of the enteron, which churns the food mass sometimes for as long as 3 to 5 hours, while the food is acted upon by the **gastric juice.** This juice pours into the stomach cavity from thousands of microscopic glands, the **gastric glands,** present in the lining of the stomach wall (p. 299). When the food has been reduced to fluid form, it is passed on into the **small intestine** (Fig. 16-11). This long (23 ft) and relatively narrow part of the digestive tract is highly coiled, and the many coils of the small intestine are all crowded together in the abdominal cavity. The small intestine receives the food mixture from the stomach and, in the course of about 10 hours, transmits the remnants of the food to the **large intestine** (Fig. 16-11). Meanwhile, **pancreatic juice** from the **pancreas** and **bile** from the **liver** (Fig. 16-11)

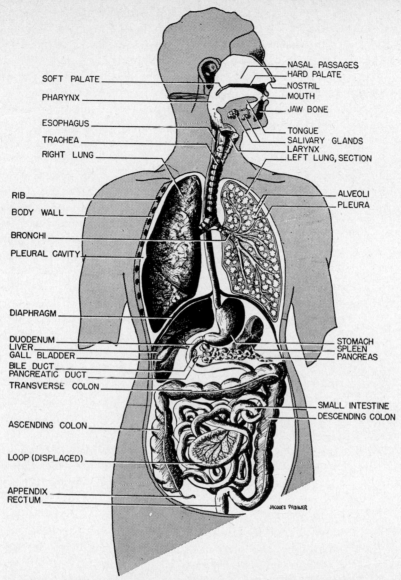

SOFT PALATE
PHARYNX
ESOPHAGUS
TRACHEA
RIGHT LUNG

NASAL PASSAGES
HARD PALATE
NOSTRIL
MOUTH
JAW BONE
TONGUE
SALIVARY GLANDS
LARYNX
LEFT LUNG, SECTION

RIB
BODY WALL
BRONCHI
PLEURAL CAVITY

ALVEOLI
PLEURA

DIAPHRAGM

DUODENUM
LIVER
GALL BLADDER
BILE DUCT
PANCREATIC DUCT
TRANSVERSE COLON

STOMACH
SPLEEN
PANCREAS

ASCENDING COLON

SMALL INTESTINE
DESCENDING COLON

LOOP (DISPLACED)

APPENDIX
RECTUM

JACQUES PRIGAUER

Fig. 16-11. Internal organs of man, with emphasis on the digestive and respiratory systems (semidiagrammatic).

are poured upon the food while it passes through the very first part of the small intestine, and the **intestinal juice,** from the numerous microscopic **intestinal glands** in the intestinal wall, is added further along in the tract. When the food mixture reaches the large intestine, digestion has been completed and most of the end products of **digestion** have been **absorbed.** But while the remnants of the food pass through the large intestine to the **rectum** (Fig. 16-11), much of the residual water is absorbed. Accordingly, when the mass is **egested** through the **anus,** it usually displays a semisolid consistency.

Microscopic Structure of the Digestive Tract. Although the various parts of the digestive tract are superficially quite different, all parts display a similar histological structure. In fact the enteron wall is formed throughout by four concentric layers, which are named from within outward: (1) the **mucosa,** (2) the **submucosa,** (3) the **muscularis,** and (4) the **serosa.** In the frog's intestine, for example, one finds the same four layers as in the human digestive tract, although the intestinal wall of the frog (Fig. 16-12) is relatively simple, compared to that of man. The **mucosa,** or innermost layer of the enteron wall, comes into direct contact with the food in the digestive tract, and in the frog the mucosa is represented mainly by a single layer of glandular epithelium, which is derived entirely from the endoderm (Fig. 16-12).

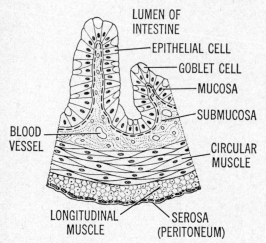

LUMEN OF INTESTINE

EPITHELIAL CELL

GOBLET CELL

MUCOSA

SUBMUCOSA

BLOOD VESSEL

CIRCULAR MUSCLE

LONGITUDINAL MUSCLE

SEROSA (PERITONEUM)

Fig. 16-12.   Simplified cross section of a frog's intestine.

The other three layers of the enteron wall are all derived embryologically from mesoderm. The **submucosa** consists mainly of fibrous connective tissues, although it is abundantly supplied with blood capillaries and lymph vessels, into which the digested foods are finally absorbed. The **muscularis** (Fig. 16-12) consists of two sheets of visceral muscle, which effect the movements of the bowel. The inner part of the muscularis is called the **transverse** layer, because its fibers tend to encircle the enteron; but the fibers of the outer part run lengthwise of the intestine, and these make up the **longitudinal layer** of the muscularis. The **serosa,** essentially, is a single tier of flattened epithelial cells, which provides a smooth external lining for the enteron. A serious fluid is secreted by the serosa, and this fluid lubricates the abdominal surfaces, reducing the frictional irritation as the coils of the intestine rub against each other and against the other organs of the abdominal cavity.

Glands of the Digestive Tract. Many of the cells of the mucosa are **goblet cells** (Fig. 15-12), which, essentially, are **unicellular mucous glands.** Each goblet cell produces a small globule of mucous periodically and extrudes this secretion upon the food mass. Collectively the mucosa produces considerable quantities of mucus, which serves as a lubricant, facilitating the passage of food through the digestive tract.

The other digestive glands represent multicellular outfoldings of the endodermal epithelium. The **gastric glands** (Fig. 16-13) and the **intestinal glands** are **simple** glands, in that they are microscopic and lie entirely in the wall of the digestive tract, but the salivary glands, liver, and pancreas are **compound** glands, and these large separate organs are connected to the digestive tract only by their ducts (Fig. 16-11).

The Oral Cavity. The main structures of man's oral cavity are quite familiar. The **palate,** or "roof of the mouth," is a partition that separates the oral cavity from the **nasal passages** (Fig. 16-11). The anterior bony part of this partition is the **hard palate,** and the posterior nonbony part is the **soft palate,** which terminates as a fleshy projection, the **uvula.** The oral cavity is guarded in front by the **lips,** and flanked at the sides and in front by the upper and lower sets of **teeth.** The **tongue,** which is a flexible muscular organ, arises from the floor of the mouth, and the **mucosa** lines the oral cavity throughout, except in the region of the gums and lips, where the lining represents a sort of modified skin. The oral mucosa is continuously moistened by the mucous secretions of its own goblet cells and by **saliva,** which drains into the mouth from the **salivary glands** (Fig. 16-11).

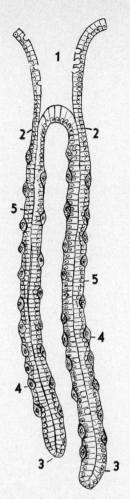

Fig. 16-13. Gastric glands, fundus region of stomach. 1, pit on mucous surface of stomach; 2, neck of gland; 3, deep end of gland; 4, cells that produce HCl; 5, enzyme-producing cells. (From *The Living Body*, by Best and Taylor. Holt, Rinehart and Winston, Inc.)

The Teeth. The teeth of different vertebrates are adapted to the food habits of the individual species, but vertebrate teeth generally conform to a common structural pattern. The **crown,** which is the part that projects above the gum level (Fig. 16-14), is made up of three layers: (1) the **enamel,** an external covering of exceedingly dense hard material; (2) the **dentine,** an intermediate layer of bonelike matter, not quite so hard as the enamel; and (3) the **pulp,** a soft tissue (including the nerves and blood vessels of the tooth) that fills the central **pulp cavity.** The

part of a tooth that is encircled by the fleshy **gum** tissues is called the **neck;** and below the neck lies the **root,** which fits snugly into a **socket,** provided by the jawbone. In composition the root resembles the crown, but the enamel is replaced by **cement,** a material that binds the dentine to the bone of the jaw.

Vertebrate teeth arose among primitive fish, from scalelike structures called **placoid scales** (p. 669). Such scales are found in the modern sharks and other cartilaginous fishes, but not in the bony fishes. The sharks have many rows of teeth, which rim the mouth in the region where the skin folds inward into the oral cavity; and these teeth are replicas of the smaller placoid scales that cover the entire body surface. The shark's teeth display the same structural layers as other vertebrate teeth, but in higher vertebrates the teeth have become modified in form to fit the food habits of the particular species.

The *permanent* teeth of adult *man* are normally 32 in number; there are 8 teeth on each side of both the upper and lower jaws (Fig. 16-15). Each group of eight consists of: (1) two **incisors,** the chisellike **cutting teeth,** in the front of the jaw; (2) one **canine,** the blunt-pointed tearing tooth at the side of the incisors; (3) two **premolars,** the **simple** grinding teeth behind the canines; and (4) three **molars,** the **complex**

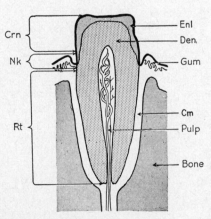

Fig. 16-14. Structure of a human tooth, diagrammatic Enl, enamel; Den, dentine; Cm, cement; Crn, crown; Nk, neck; Rt, root.

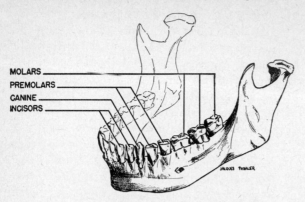

MOLARS
PREMOLARS
CANINE
INCISORS

Fig. 16-15. The dentition of man. The same kinds of teeth are duplicated in the upper jaw.

grinding teeth behind the premolars (Fig. 16-15). However, the third molars, or wisdom teeth, sometimes fail to erupt beyond the gum level. In man and other mammals (p. 673), the permanent teeth are preceded by the **milk teeth,** which resemble the adult teeth, except that the molars are not represented.

The dentition of man is generally similar to that of the other Mammalia; but in different mammals the dentition is variously modified according to the food habits of the species. In Rodentia (squirrels, mice, etc.), for example, the incisors, or gnawing teeth, are very prominent. Herbivorous animals (horses, cows, etc.) also have well-developed incisors with which to crop the vegetation; even more particularly, herbivorous animals have very conspicuous molar teeth, to grind and pulp the vegetation in preparation for swallowing. Carnivorous animals (such as wolves and tigers) have very prominent canine teeth, which serve for tearing flesh from the victim, as well as for offensive and defensive purposes. Man, however, is quite omnivorous in his food habits, and the dentition of man is very conservatively balanced.

As it is chewed, the food is cut and ground thoroughly, which increases the surface exposed to the action of the saliva and other digestive juices. Chewing also mixes the food with the saliva and converts the whole food mass into a pulp that can be swallowed without difficulty.

The Tongue. The tongue, essentially, is a mucosa-covered mass of intricately arranged muscle fibers, which can be shaped and moved in a very agile manner. The role of the tongue in shaping our speech—especially when we ask for food—is related indirectly to nutrition, but the tongue also has three direct nutritional functions: (1) the tongue manipulates the food during chewing, so that each morsel is kept in range of the proper teeth; (2) the tongue shapes the chewed food into a pulpy mass, the **bolus,** and squeezes the bolus into the pharynx, when it is time for swallowing; and (3) the mucosa of the tongue provides a housing for a majority of the **taste buds** (p. 421).

The Salivary Glands. Man and most other mammals possess three pairs of **salivary glands,** which secrete the **saliva** and send it into the oral cavity. The salivary glands of man include: (1) the **parotid** glands, which lie embedded in the soft tissues of the cheeks. just below and behind the cheek bones; (2) the **submaxillary** glands, which are embedded in the floor of the mouth immediately in front of the angles of the lower jaws; and (3) the **sublingual** glands, which also lie in the floor of the mouth along the sides of the tongue (Fig. 16-16). Each gland is a lobulated mass of glandular tissue, weighing about one ounce; but the salivary glands jointly produce about two quarts of saliva daily. The saliva drains from the glands via ducts. A single duct from each parotid opens upon the inner surface of the cheek opposite the second upper molar; whereas the duct from each submaxillary, and the several ducts from each sublingual, drain upon the floor of the mouth near the roots of the lower canine teeth (Fig. 16-16).

COMPOSITION AND FUNCTIONS OF THE SA-LIVA. The composition of human saliva, based on an analysis of the mixed juices of all the glands, is given in Table 16-1. This shows that saliva, like all other digestive juices, contains a large proportion of water, which serves as a solvent for all other components of the juice.

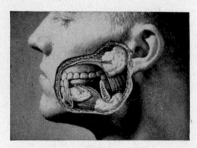

Fig. 16-16. Drawing of the salivary glands superimposed upon a photograph. The sublingual gland, lower front; the submaxillary gland, lower back; the parotid gland, above. (From *The Digestion of Foods.* Encyclopedia Britannica Films, Inc.)

The functions of saliva are partly chemical and partly mechanical. Among the chemical reagents in saliva, the enzyme **ptyalin** is a very active amylase. Thus if a suspension of boiled starch is incubated at body temperature with a few drops of saliva, a hydrolysis of the starch to **maltose** is completed within about 20 minutes (see Fig. 5-5). The opaque starch suspension gradually becomes first translucent and then transparent, which indicates that the large starch molecules are decomposing into smaller and smaller fragments. Finally all the starch is converted into maltose. Moreover, some of the maltose is converted to glucose, since human saliva contains small amounts of the enzyme **maltase**.

As to its mechanical functions, saliva facilitates swallowing by *softening* and *lubricating* the food, and by *binding* the separate food particles into a plastic mass, the **bolus,** which can be swallowed as a whole. Thus when the flow of saliva is inhibited—as by fright—a cracker or other *dry* food can scarcely be swallowed. Saliva also augments

taste. The taste buds are sensitive only to dissolved substances; and by dissolving the dry components of the food, the saliva brings out their taste.

A small flow of saliva continues even between meals. This flow is important because it *cleanses* the mouth, preventing an encrustation of the teeth and tongue with food particles, bacteria, scuffed-off epithelial cells, and

Table 16-1—Human Saliva; Average Composition

Components	Percent by Weight
Water	99.5
Inorganic salts (mainly chlorides, bicarbonates, and phosphates of sodium, potassium, and calcium)	0.2
Inorganic gases: oxygen and carbon dioxide	Traces
Organic substances	
Enzymes: *ptyalin* and *maltase*	Traces
Other proteins: mucin, globulin, albumen	0.2
Wastes: urea, etc.	Traces
Reaction: slightly acid (pH 6.5-6.8)	

other detritus of the oral cavity. Thus if salivation is inhibited for a long period, as occurs in certain fevers, the mouth tends to foul, unless it is washed at frequent intervals. The continuous flow of saliva also lubricates the tongue during speech; if the saliva does not flow properly the tongue is apt to "cling to the roof of the mouth."

THE SALIVATION REFLEX. The main flow of saliva occurs at mealtimes; and the activity of the salivary glands is controlled entirely by the nervous system. Other digestive glands (see p. 306) are also activated by **hormones**, which exert a slower and more sustained effect. But the flow of saliva must occur very rapidly, while the food is in the mouth. Accordingly, salivation is entirely a **reflex** act, which is effected through the nervous system.

The main receptor-conductor-effector pathway of a **salivation reflex** is shown in Figure 16-17. All flow of saliva is abolished if the motor nerves to the glands are severed or if the brain is damaged in the region of the salivation centers. This experiment proves that the entire output of the glands is controlled by the nervous system; that is, *no hormone is involved.*

The salivation reflex was used by the well-known Russian physiologist, Pavlov, in his early studies on reflexes generally. Pavlov worked on dogs in which the ducts of the salivary glands were brought to the outer surface of the cheeks, thus permitting him to observe the flow of saliva whenever a suitable stimulus was applied. These studies led Pavlov to draw a distinction between the two main kinds of reflexes: (1) **conditioned reflexes** and (2) **unconditioned reflexes.**

If food, or anything associated with food, is shown to a very young puppy, or child, no salivation occurs, but the saliva promptly flows if anything—even a tasteless object—is placed directly in the mouth. This shows that the **primary receptors** of the salivation reflex are localized *in the mouth.* These primary receptors are mainly the **taste buds** (p. 421), although the tactile receptors of the oral mucosa play a minor role. This type of reflex, which can be elicited in the absence of any previous training or conditioning, is called an **unconditioned reflex.** But Pavlov showed that in trained, or conditioned, animals, other types of stimulation—or more precisely other receptors—can be substituted for the primary receptors. Thus in older dogs or children, the sight or smell of food—or sounds associated with food—will cause the "mouth to water." These **conditioned reflexes** result from a frequent association between stimuli affecting the primary receptors and stimuli acting upon other (**secondary**) receptors of the body. After a period of conditioning, salivation is obtained merely by sounding a bell that previously was rung each time a puppy was fed, or by showing any object that has been displayed at each feeding during the conditioning period. Thus in man and other animals, the salivation of an older individual represents a dual reflex. It is partly an unconditioned reflex, elicited by the food that is actually in the mouth; and partly a conditioned reflex, resulting

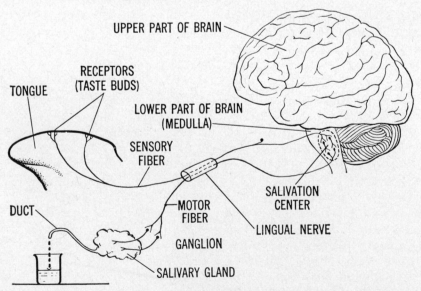

Fig. 16-17. Diagram showing one of the pathways of the salivation reflex. Such a typical reflex involves a series of nerve cells, which convey impulses from the receptors, via the central nervous system, to the effectors.

from the sounds, sights, and smells that are regularly associated with eating.

The Pharynx and Esophagus. Most of man's digestive organs lie in the abdominal cavity, that is, below the diaphragm; and the pharynx and esophagus carry the food quickly through the neck and thorax to the stomach (Fig. 16-11).

The **pharynx** is a very complex portion of the digestive tract, which conducts not only food from the mouth to the esophagus, but also air from the nasal passages to the **trachea** (Fig. 16-11). The pharynx originates immediately behind the palate, where the nasal passages join the digestive tract, and terminates in the upper part of the neck, where the trachea forks off from the food passage (Fig. 16-11). Moreover, the pharynx communicates with the **middle ear** chamber via the paired **Eustachian tubes.** The upper part of the trachea, where the wall is reinforced by a conspicuous housing of cartilage, is called the **larynx,** or Adam's apple"—in which lie the vocal cords. The opening that conducts air from the pharynx to the larynx is a narrow channel, the **glottis** (Fig. 16-11), above which lies a valvelike flap, the **epiglottis.**

The **esophagus,** or gullet, is a thick-walled muscular tube that leads straight downward through the neck and thorax, from the pharynx to the stomach. The muscular layers of the esophagus are well developed—being composed of **skeletal** muscle, in the upper third of the tube, and of **visceral** muscle, in the lower two-thirds of the length.

Swallowing is a complex series of unconditioned reflexes that sweep the bolus of food rapidly from the mouth to the stomach. The tongue initiates swallowing by molding the food mass into a bolus and projecting the bolus from the mouth into the pharynx. This part of the reflex is under voluntary control, but the succeeding events, once started, cannot be stopped at will.

When a bolus comes in contact with the wall of the pharynx, it initiates a series of reflex movements that (1) closes off the air passages and (2) propels the bolus into the esophagus. The soft palate is elevated, closing off the nasal passages, and the larynx is raised, bringing the glottis under cover of the epiglottis and posterior part of the tongue. Then, while the tongue is pressed firmly against the roof of the mouth, the whole pharyngeal wall constricts, forcing the bolus into the esophagus.

In the esophagus the bolus is seized by a wave of muscular movement, which sweeps downward toward the stomach. This wave-like type of movement is called a **peristaltic wave,** and is a characteristic movement in most parts of the digestive tract. Each typical peristaltic wave represents a slowly moving wave of **constriction,** involving only a short length of the wall of the digestive tract; but a similar wave of **dilatation** runs along the tract, immediately in front of the wave of constriction (Fig. 16-18). The constriction represents a contraction of the circular layer of the muscularis, which squeezes the bolus before it; and the dilatation, which chiefly involves the longitudinal muscle, paces along ahead of the bolus, opening the tube at each moment to receive the moving food. In the esophagus the waves are unusually rapid, so that the food takes only about 6 seconds in passing through the esophagus to the stomach. Liquids are swallowed even more quickly, because the esophagus tends to remain dilated while liquids are being swallowed, allowing them to flow mainly under gravity.

The Stomach. The **stomach** is a thick-walled muscular sac, which plays a very important role in digestion. The **muscularis** of the stomach contains a layer of **diagonal fibers,** in addition to the circular and longitudinal layers, and the gastric **mucosa** is pitted with a great number of simple glandular outpocketings, the **gastric glands.** While the food remains in the stomach it is churned and mixed with the **gastric juice,** and the stomach does not pass its contents on to the small intestine until the meal has been thoroughly liquefied as a result of many

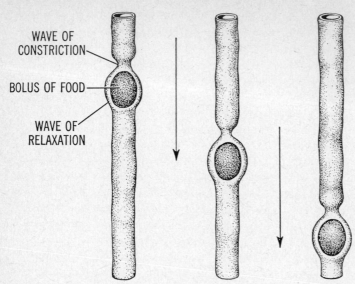

WAVE OF CONSTRICTION

BOLUS OF FOOD

WAVE OF RELAXATION

Fig. 16-18. Peristalsis in the esophagus. Three stages in the downward movement of a semisolid bolus of food are shown.

changes. The emptying of the stomach is relatively rapid (about 10 minutes) in the case of a drink of plain water; but some meals may take 3 to 4 hours in passing through the stomach, depending on the quality and quantity of the food.

The Size and Shape of the Stomach. The capacity of the stomach varies according to its contents, and during the ingestion of a meal the muscular wall is capable of expanding to a maximum capacity of about 3 quarts, in an average individual. Then during the digestion of the meal, the stomach gradually shrinks, as the semidigested food is passed, little by little, into the small intestine. Finally the gastric cavity is practically obliterated, whereupon further peristaltic waves, in which the stomach merely squeezes down upon itself, give rise to "hunger pangs," and it is time to eat again.

The anatomy of the stomach is best described in terms of the half-filled organ such as is outlined in Figure 16-19. Such a stomach is distinctly J-shaped, and permits one to identify the *three main parts* of the stomach. (1) The **fundus** is a small, bulbous, gas-filled chamber, which occupies the vertical limb of the J, above the opening from the esophagus; (2) the **cardiac** region consists of the remainder of the vertical limb; (3) the **pyloric** region extends from the "bend of the J" to the point where the stomach joins the **duodenum,** or first part of the small intestine. Guarding the entrance and exit channels of the stomach are ringlike bands of muscle: (1) the **cardiac valve,** which encircles the esophageal opening and prevents a regurgitation of food into the esophagus; and (2) the **pyloric valve,** which prevents food from passing out of the stomach into the duodenum, until the proper time. Both of these valves are typical **sphincter valves,** such as are found

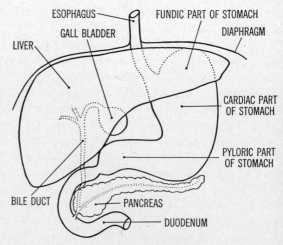

ESOPHAGUS

GALL BLADDER

LIVER

FUNDIC PART OF STOMACH

DIAPHRAGM

CARDIAC PART OF STOMACH

PYLORIC PART OF STOMACH

BILE DUCT

PANCREAS

DUODENUM

Fig. 16-19. The stomach and duodenum in relation to the liver and pancreas in man.

in other regions of the digestive tract—namely, at the point where the small intestine leads into the large intestine, and at the anus. Essentially, a sphincter represents a local thickening of the circular layer of the muscularis, which contracts and closes the passage, except at certain times, when the valve relaxes and allows the food mass to pass.

Nerve Supply of the Stomach. Like all the other **viscera,** or internal organs of the body, the stomach is supplied by two sets of nerves, both belonging to the **autonomic nervous system** (Chap. 25). These two sets of autonomic nerves have an antagonistic effect upon the gastric musculature and upon the secretion of the gastric glands. The **parasympathetic fibers** (p. 465) are carried to the stomach by the **vagus nerves,** which originate from the brain stem and pass along the sides of the esophagus to the stomach and small intestine. Impulses from these parasympathetic fibers augment—that is, strengthen and accelerate—the gastric movements and increase the secretion of the gastric glands. But in addition, the stomach receives a number of delicate **sympathetic nerves** from the spinal cord (p. 465); and these sympathetic fibers depress the mobility of the gastric musculature and reduce the flow of gastric juice.

The Gastric Juice. The gastric juice is a powerful digestive fluid secreted by the gastric glands, of which there are about 35,000,-000 in the human stomach. Each gastric gland is a minute tubular outfolding of the mucosa, although several glands may be associated with each of the small pits that can be observed with a hand lens, when the inner lining of the stomach is inspected (Fig. 16-13).

Two early studies on human gastric juice deserve to be mentioned specifically. In 1776 Spallanzani demonstrated the **chemical** potency of the juice; this was important because previously the action of the stomach upon the food was thought to be entirely mechanical. Spallanzani swallowed porous wooden capsules filled with meat and other protein foods; and when the capsules were reclaimed and examined, it was found that the proteins gradually had dissolved and escaped from the capsule—despite the fact that the food was entirely protected from mechanical influences by the rigidity of the capsule walls. Then in 1819 William Beaumont, an American Army surgeon, began a long series of studies on a patient with an unusual gastric fistula. A fistula is an artificial channel communicating between a part of the digestive tract and the exterior of the body. In the present case, the patient was a Canadian trapper named Alexis St. Martin, who had exploded a shotgun into the pit of his stomach. The charge penetrated not only the body wall, but also the stomach wall; and when the wound healed, the stomach and body walls adhered together, leaving a permanent fistula that led directly into the gastric cavity. A flaplike overgrowth of the body wall covered the external opening so that food could be retained in the stomach and normal gastric digestion could proceed. At any given time, however, the valvelike flap could be lifted, permitting Beaumont to obtain a sample of the semidigested food mass or to collect pure gastric juice—uncontaminated with food.

Composition of Gastric Juice. The collection of gastric juice by means of a stomach tube is now a routine procedure, carried out by the physician in the clinic or by the medical student in the physiology laboratory. An out-

Table 16-2—Composition of Gastric Juice

Components	Percent by Weight
Inorganic	
Water	98.02
Hydrochloric acid (HCl)	0.50
Salts	1.03
Organic	
Mucin	
Enzymes (pepsin, rennin, lipase)	0.45
Other proteins	
	100.00

standing characteristic of the gastric juice is its extreme acidity (pH = 1.2 to 0.3); and a complete analysis of the juice shows the average composition given in Table 16-2.

Functions of the Gastric Juice. The **digestive** functions of the gastric juice are all related to its enzymes, of which **pepsin** is the most important. This very potent **protease** is especially active in the initial stages of the hydrolysis of proteins. Pepsin hydrolyzes each large protein molecule into a number of smaller molecules, mainly **long-chain peptides;** and this reaction, as catalyzed by pepsin, may be written:

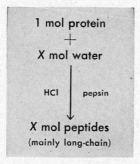

1 mol protein
+
X mol water

HCl | pepsin

X mol peptides
(mainly long-chain)

Specifically, pepsin is a powerful **endopeptidase,** which achieves a rupturing of peptide bonds, not at the ends of the protein chain, but at definite points along its length. In fact, it is only the linkages adjacent to two specific amino acids, namely, **tyrosine** and **phenylalanine** (p. 102), which are susceptible to the hydrolytic action of pepsin. But the net result of the action of pepsin in the stomach is the conversion of the various complex and frequently insoluble protein components of the ingested food into much simpler **soluble** compounds. Thus when a mass of coagulated egg albumen is incubated at body temperature in a test tube containing gastric juice, the material dissolves within about half an hour, and suitable tests prove that each of the large molecules of albumen has decomposed into about 100 smaller molecules, which can be identified mainly as long-chain peptides.

The presence of the acid is essential to the activity of pepsin; neutralized gastric juice displays very little peptic activity. The enzyme pepsin, as secreted by the cells of the gastric glands, is in an inactive form, called **pepsinogen;** but pepsinogen is converted into pepsin when it comes into contact with an acid medium. The hydrochloric acid also augments the activity of the other enzymes of the gastric juice; and perhaps the germicidal properties of this acid are important in counteracting infective bacteria ingested with the food.

In Mammalia, the gastric juice contains an enzyme, **rennin,** which acts solely upon caseinogen, the main protein present in milk. When milk, which is the main diet of all *young* mammals, comes into contact with the gastric juice, the milk is **curded** immediately. Essentially curding represents a chemical reaction whereby the soluble protein **caseinogen** is converted to an insoluble protein, **casein,** which comes out of solution as a fine flocculent precipitate. This action is important, because curding delays the passage of the milk through the stomach, allowing time for pepsin to digest the casein to the same extent as other proteins. Were the milk to remain in its native fluid state, it would be evacuated too quickly from the stomach, since fluids such as water are passed on to the small intestine within a few minutes after they are drunk. Since ancient times, rennin extracts from calves' stomachs have been used in making certain cheeses; and the active component of modern "junket" preparations is rennin.

The presence of lipase in the gastric juice is debatable; at best the **gastric lipase** has a very weak fat-splitting action, effective mainly upon finely emulsified fats, such as milk and cream. In adults, if adequate precautions are taken against a contamination of the gastric juice by juices regurgitated into the stomach from the small intestine, little if any lipase activity can be detected in the gastric juice.

Control of the Flow of Gastric Juice. The total quantity of gastric juice produced during the digestion of an average meal ranges usually between 400 and 800 cc. This copious flow is induced partly by a series of well-defined **reflexes** and partly by a **hormone** called **gastrin.** The flow of gastric juice commences at the very beginning of a meal, and this early secretion of juice is mainly of reflex nature. But the gastric juice continues to flow until shortly after the stomach is emptied, and this late sustained secretion is effected mainly by the gastric hormone.

Pavlov was one of the first investigators to study the secretion of the gastric juice, and he devised the experimental techniques that are shown in Figures 16-20 and 16-21. If a dog with an esophageal fistula (Fig. 16-20) is fed, the food of such a "sham feeding" never reaches the stomach. Nevertheless about one quarter of the normal flow of gastric juice takes place. This fraction of the total gastric juice is entirely reflex in origin, since it is abolished when the gastric nerves are cut. Like salivation, this gastric reflex is partly unconditioned, involving the taste buds as primary receptors, and partly conditioned,

Fig. 16-20. Showing an esophageal fistula, used in "sham feeding" experiments. (From *The Living Body,* by Best and Taylor. Holt, Rinehart and Winston, Inc.)

involving other receptors of smell and sight, etc., as substitutes for the taste buds.

Isolating a small part of the stomach, called the Pavlov pouch (Fig. 16-21), and leading this pouch to the external surface of the abdominal wall permitted Pavlov to observe the flow of gastric juice under a variety of conditions. Introducing food directly into the stomach—without allowing the animal to taste, smell, or see the food—calls forth almost three-quarters of the total normal production of the juice. This flow, which results from the mere presence of food in the stom-

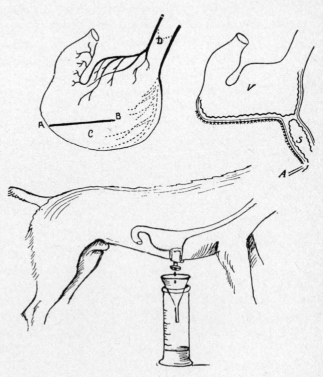

Fig. 16-21. Upper drawings show Pavlov's method of fashioning a gastric pouch, or miniature stomach. A horizontal incision (A-B) is made, which causes minimal injury to the gastric nerve and blood supply. (D) vagus nerves. The flap (C) is turned down and the pouch (S) isolated (by sutures) from the main cavity of the stomach (V) as shown in the right-hand sketch. (A) abdominal wall. The lower drawing illustrates the manner in which pure gastric juice can be collected from the miniature stomach while digestion is proceeding in the main part of the stomach. (From *The Living Body,* by Best and Taylor. Holt, Rinehart and Winston, Inc.)

ach, is controlled only in small part by a reflex mechanism, since cutting all the gastric nerves merely reduces this fraction. Accordingly, it may be concluded that a large part of the production of the gastric juice is controlled by some other mechanism, and this proved to be the hormone **gastrin**.

Gastrin is formed in the mucosa of the pyloric part of the stomach, and is discharged into the blood stream whenever the semi-digested food mass comes into contact with this mucosa. If an extract of the pyloric mucosa is prepared and injected into the blood, the gastric glands begin to secrete shortly after the injection. Complete proof of a hormonal agency in normal gastric secretion depends, however, upon cross-circulation experiments. The Pavlov pouch remains in continuity with the other parts of the stomach, and so it is not certain that all the nerves to the pouch can be cut. But if the blood streams of two dogs (A and B) are connected artificially, by mutual junction established between the major arteries (Fig. 16-22), any substance present in the blood of dog A must sooner or later be carried over into the blood of dog B. In this case there

is no possibility that nerve connections exist between the organs of the two animals. Nevertheless, when food is placed in the pyloric stomach of dog A, the gastric glands of dog B—as well as those of A—begin to secrete, after a short lag. This secretion must be effected by some substance carried by the blood, and this is the hormone called **gastrin**.

Some flow of gastric juice continues after the stomach is emptied—that is, while the digesting food is passing through the first part of the small intestine—but this activity of the gastric glands has not been studied adequately. Possibly amino acids, sugars, and other products of digestion, which begin to be absorbed into the blood from the small intestine, exert an influence upon the gastric glands; or perhaps this final flow depends upon a reflex or a hormone that has not yet been recognized.

The Churning Movements of the Stomach. Each meal remains in the stomach until it has been thoroughly **liquefied** and converted into a smooth thick fluid called **chyme**. Chyme has the consistency of a heavy cream soup. The transformation of the ingested food mass into chyme depends partly upon

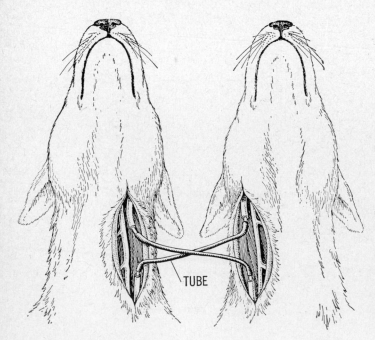

TUBE

Fig. 16-22. By connecting the neck arteries (carotids) of two dogs with rubber tubing, as shown, the blood flows through both animals alike in the course of its travels. Such "cross-circulation" experiments are especially useful in demonstrating control of body activity by chemicals circulating in the blood stream.

the chemical properties of the gastric juice and partly upon mechanical changes induced by the churning action of the gastric musculature.

The churning movements are confined mainly to the pyloric part of the stomach, as is shown in x-ray photographs of the stomach during the digestion of a **barium meal.** The barium compounds mixed with such a meal are opaque to x-rays, and the barium-laden chyme throws a shadow, outlining the stomach contents on the photographic plate (Fig. 16-23). Thus it may be seen that during active digestion the pyloric mill is very active,

while the *body* of the stomach remains more or less passive. As digestion proceeds, however, the body gradually shrinks as it slowly passes its contents into the actively churning "pyloric mill."

Essentially, the churning of the pylorus represents a series of regularly recurrent peristaltic waves that sweep toward the pyloric valve. However, this valve remains tightly closed until the chyme is thoroughly liquid, and consequently the waves merely sweep the food mass back and forth in the "pyloric mill," until the valve begins to open. When the chyme is thoroughly liquefied, the

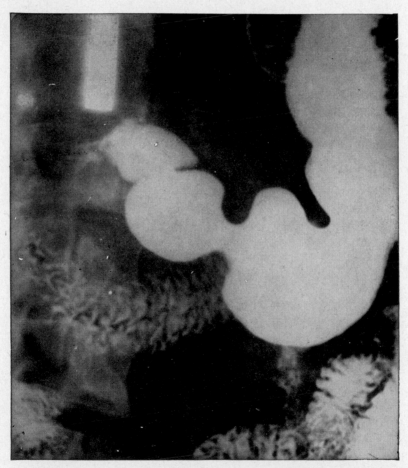

Fig. 16-23. X-ray photograph showing contraction waves in the human stomach. Barium sulfate taken recently in some milk has made the stomach contents visible in the photograph. Note that the peristaltic waves that churn the food mass are most vigorous in the pyloric part of the stomach. A metal rod marks the position of the backbone. (Couresty Roentgenology Staff, Billings Hospital.)

pyloric valve begins to open periodically (p. 311), allowing small quantities of the chyme to squeeze through. When this occurs, a new sample of less thoroughly liquefied food is passed on to the pylorus by the body of the stomach, which thus acts as a reservoir for the "pyloric mill."

The movements of the stomach are coordinated by nerve impulses from the autonomic nervous system. Parasympathetic impulses accelerate and strengthen the gastric contractions, whereas sympathetic excitations retard and weaken the motility. The latter action delays digestion and prolongs the time required for the stomach to empty itself. Consequently emotional states, such as fear and worry, which involve a generalized excitation of the sympathetic system, are to be avoided, particularly during and after a heavy meal. For some reason, fat-rich meals are emptied from the stomach very slowly, whereas meals especially rich in carbohydrates are evacuated more rapidly than usual.

Factors Involved in the Liquefaction of the Meal. A number of factors tend to liquefy the food mass and convert it into chyme while a meal remains in the stomach. Insoluble compounds in the food are transformed to soluble compounds; the ptyalin of the saliva continues to hydrolize starch into maltose, especially in the interior of each bolus, before the HCl of the gastric juice permeates the mass; and pepsin begins to convert the proteins to freely soluble peptides as soon as the food mass is thoroughly acidified. Moreover, considerable water, in the form of saliva and gastric juice, is added to the meal, and this water increases the general fluidity, in addition to exerting a solvent action upon soluble compounds as they are produced during digestion. Also the gastric contents are gradually warmed by body heat, which accelerates all chemical reactions and promotes solution. Moreover, this heat melts the fatty components of the food, permitting them to be emulsified more thoroughly, as the chyme is churned in the "pyloric mill."

Emptying of the Stomach. When the strongly acid gastric chyme is thoroughly liquid, it is squirted, about a teaspoonful at a time, through the pyloric valve into the first part of the small intestine. In fact, the pyloric valve begins to relax, allowing some of the chyme to pass as soon as the content of the mill reaches the proper consistency. The relaxing of the valve appears to be under reflex control, but the receptors and the nervous pathway of this reflex have been difficult to determine precisely.

The Small Intestine. The great length of the small intestine (Fig. 16-24) is an index of its importance; and in fact the small intestine completes the **digestion** of every type of food, and is the site of the **absorption** of all the end products of digestion.

All types of glands pour their juices into the small intestine. The intestinal mucosa is dotted throughout with numerous **unicellular** mucous glands, and there is a prodigious number of **simple** tubular glands, the **intestinal glands,** present in the wall of the intestine. But even more important are two large compound glands, the **liver** and the **pancreas,** which send their juices into the first part of the small intestine, near its origin from the stomach.

The great absorptive capacity of the small intestine depends partly upon the fact that it is more than 23 feet long, and partly upon the fact that its internal surface is greatly augmented by the presence of a large number of hairlike structures, the intestinal **villi.** In fact, the internal lining of some parts of the intestine has the appearance of velvet, and each hair, or villus, of this lining extends inward, making contact with the chyme as it passes along the tube (Fig. 16-25).

On the basis of small differences of structure the small intestine is subdivided into three parts. The first part, the **duodenum,** is only about 10 inches long; but the duodenum is important because it receives the **bile** from the liver, and the **pancreatic juice** from the pancreas (Fig. 16-24). Unlike the other coils of the small intestine, the duo-

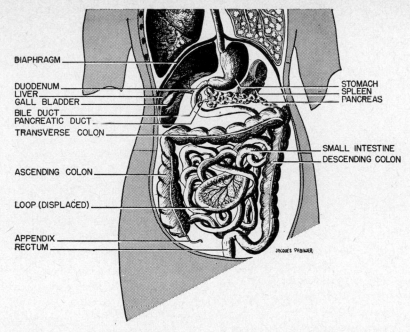

DIAPHRAGM

DUODENUM
LIVER
GALL BLADDER
BILE DUCT
PANCREATIC DUCT
TRANSVERSE COLON

ASCENDING COLON

LOOP (DISPLACED)

APPENDIX
RECTUM

STOMACH
SPLEEN
PANCREAS

SMALL INTESTINE
DESCENDING COLON

JACQUES PRBAWER

Fig. 16-24. Abdominal part of the human digestive tract (semidiagrammatic).

denum occupies a fixed position in the abdominal cavity, because it is attached directly to the dorsal body wall. All other parts of the small gut, in contrast, enjoy some freedom of movement, because they are suspended to the dorsal body wall by a thin, transparent, sheetlike membrane, the **mesentery.** This mesentery also provides a connection between the intestine and the body wall, through which nerves and blood vessels pass to and from these otherwise isolated parts.

Fig. 16-25. Magnified view of the inside surface of the small intestine showing the numerous villi.

The second and third parts of the small intestine are, respectively, the **jejunum** and the **ileum.** The jejunum is about 10 feet in length, and displays a greater number of the intestinal glands and a lesser number of villi than the ileum. The ileum terminates abruptly in the lower right region of the abdominal cavity, at which point it joins the **colon,** or **large intestine** (Fig. 16-24).

Relations of the Duodenum to the Liver and Pancreas. Each small sample of the chyme passes from the stomach into the duodenum, whereupon it immediately encounters a copious flow of both the pancreatic juice and the bile. These two juices flow into the duodenum together, because the bile duct and pancreatic duct join each other, forming a short common duct that penetrates the duodenal wall (Fig. 16-24).

The Pancreatic Juice. The inorganic components of the pancreatic juice are mainly water (about 98 percent by weight), and various inorganic salts. Among these salts there is an unusually high concentration of the alkaline salt, **sodium bicarbonate,** which serves to neutralize the strongly acid chyme as soon as it leaves the stomach:

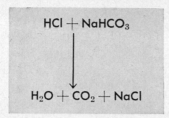

$$HCl + NaHCO_3$$

$$\downarrow$$

$$H_2O + CO_2 + NaCl$$

This function is important because all the digestive enzymes that act upon foods in the small intestine require a neutral or slightly alkaline medium for optimal activity.

Four enzymes are present in the pancreatic juice: two proteases, namely, **trypsin** and **chymotrypsin;** one **pancreatic amylase** (also called *amylopsin*); and one **pancreatic lipase** (also called *steapsin*).

The two pancreatic proteases are endopeptidases: trypsin and chymotrypsin. These enzymes are particularly effective in the "middle range" of protein digestion; that is, in the hydrolytic splitting of long-chain peptides into short-chain fragments. Both, however, can act on full-fledged proteins, such as may have escaped peptic digestion. The specific lytic action of **trypsin** is upon peptide bonds bordering on the amino acids **lysine** and **arginine** (p. 342); whereas the action of **chymotrypsin,** like that of pepsin, is upon linkages next to **tyrosine** and **phenylalanine.** The main net effect of the pancreatic proteases, working together, may thus be written:

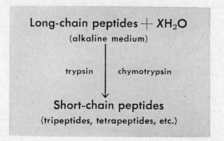

$$\text{Long-chain peptides} + XH_2O$$
(alkaline medium)

trypsin | chymotrypsin
$$\downarrow$$

Short-chain peptides
(tripeptides, tetrapeptides, etc.)

As collected directly from the pancreatic duct, the pancreatic juice contains an inactive form of trypsin, called **trypsinogen.**

The trypsinogen is tranformed into trypsin, however, as soon as the pancreatic juice begins to mix with the intestinal juice, which contains a specific *activating enzyme,* **enterokinase.**

Pancreatic amylase (amylopsin) plays a very significant role in the digestion of the starchy components of our foods, namely, the various kinds of starch and glycogen (p. 80). Amylopsin is afforded more time than ptyalin to act upon these compounds, and amylopsin works more rapidly than ptyalin. As in the case of ptyalin, the end product of this digestion by amylopsin is maltose.

Steapsin, or **pancreatic lipase,** is the only truly active lipase in the whole gastrointestinal tract, and in the absence of a proper flow of pancreatic juice, much of the fat in a meal remains undigested and is egested with the feces. The hydrolysis of fat, which may be written:

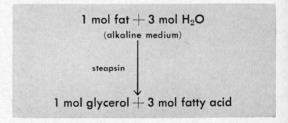

$$\text{1 mol fat} + \text{3 mol } H_2O$$
(alkaline medium)

steapsin
$$\downarrow$$

$$\text{1 mol glycerol} + \text{3 mol fatty acid}$$

is essential if the fatty components of our food are to be properly absorbed and distributed throughout the body.

The Liver. In vertebrates generally, the **liver** is a comparatively huge organ, and in man the liver occupies the whole upper part of the abdominal cavity, just below the **diaphragm** (Fig. 16-24). In fact the dome-shaped diaphragm, which separates the abdominal and thoracic cavities, arches directly over the liver, coming into contact with a considerable area on the upper hepatic surface.

The formation of bile is only one of the many functions of the liver (see p. 313). The bile is formed in all parts of the liver, and is drained into a system of fine ducts that permeate the whole organ. These hepatic ducts lead the bile to a main duct, but instead of flowing directly to the duodenum, the bile flows back into the **gall bladder,** where it is stored until needed (Fig. 16-24). Then later, during the digestion of a meal, the muscular wall of the gall bladder contracts, forcing a stream of bile down the **bile duct,** through which the bile enters the small intestine, together with the pancreatic juice. While the bile is stored in the gall bladder, however, part of its water content is absorbed by the walls of the bladder, so that bile collected from the bladder is more concentrated compared to the bile that comes directly from the liver.

The Bile. Although it contains *no* enzymes, bile plays a very important role in normal digestion. The inorganic components are relatively unimportant, although the sodium bicarbonate of the bile augments the neutralizing capacity of the pancreatic juice. Among the main organic components of bile, which include (1) the **bile salts,** (2) the **bile pigments,** and (3) **cholesterol,** only the bile salts are related to digestion.

The bile of man has a deep yellow-orange color; but the bile of other vertebrates is colored various shades of green, yellow, orange, or red, depending upon the proportion of **bile pigments** represented in each case. The main bile pigments are a red compound, **bilirubin,** and a green one, **biliverdin.** Both of these bile pigments are decomposition products derived from **hemoglobin.** As the red blood cells of the body gradually disintegrate and are replaced by new ones, the hemoglobin of the disrupted corpuscles, after its iron (Fe) content has been salvaged, decomposes further, forming the bile pigments. These pigments are then carried in the blood stream to the liver, where they are **excreted** via the bile into the intestine. In the digestive tract, the bile pigments suffer further chemical change whereby the color darkens to brown or black, and the color of the normal stools, or feces, is derived mainly from the bile pigments. Thus when the flow of bile is stopped, as by a gallstone or a catarrhal condition in the bile duct, the con-

dition is indicated by the occurrence of a whitish, or "clay-colored" stool. Moreover, if the bile pigments accumulate sufficiently in the blood and tissues, the skin of the patient shows a yellowish or **jaundiced** appearance, which confirms the diagnosis that bile pigments are not being excreted properly.

The importance of the **bile salts** is related mainly to the **digestion** *and* **absorption** *of fats*. The bile salts serve mainly as emulsifying agents, so that the churning movements of the intestine are more effective in producing a fine emulsion from the fatty components of the chyme. In such an emulsified state, the fats expose a maximum surface on which the pancreatic lipase can act with high efficiency. Moreover, the bile salts appear to serve as **specific activators** of steapsin.

In the absence of bile salts—that is, when the flow of bile is stopped—the **absorption,** as well as the digestion, of fatty foods is seriously impaired, and a considerable proportion of fatty foods is lost to the body in the feces. In fact, the bile salts act as very effective **detergents,** in that they augment the solubility of the fatty acids in the chyme, and this greatly increases the absorbability of the fatty acids. Moreover, the bile salts are carefully conserved by the body. In fact, the bile salts themselves are absorbed in the lower parts of the small intestine, and are carried back to the liver, which resecretes them into the bile. This regular *circulation of the bile salts* has been known for many years, although its significance was realized only in comparatively recent times.

The presence of **cholesterol** in bile is important from a clinical point of view. In certain cases, cholesterol precipitates from the bile, forming the commonest type of **gallstones.** The precipitation of such a "stone" occurs in the gall bladder while the bile is undergoing concentration, although stoppage of the bile flow occurs only when a stone finds its way into the bile duct. One factor conducive to such gallstones appears to be a lowered reserve of bile salts, since these compounds also exert a detergent action upon cholesterol and help to keep it in solution.

The Flow of Bile and Pancreatic Juice. Cutting the nerves to the gall bladder and pancreas results in only a small reduction in the flow of bile and pancreatic juice. Moreover, intravenous injections of extracts of the duodenal mucosa are followed by a copious flow of these juices, even after all nerves to the glands are cut. These and other experiments indicate that a hormonal control predominates for both the gall bladder and the pancreas; and in fact, two distinct hormones are involved: (1) **cholecystokinin,** for the gall bladder; and (2) **secretin** for the pancreas.

In the normal course of events, both secretin and cholecystokinin are liberated by the mucosa cells of the duodenum as soon as chyme flows from the stomach into the duodenum. The hormones pass in the blood stream to all parts of the body; but only the gall bladder is stimulated by cholecystokinin; and only the pancreas is activated by secretin.

The Intestinal Juice. The final stages of digestion proceed in the jejunum and upper coils of the ileum under the auspices of the enzymes of the intestinal juice, of which there are at least five: **two peptidases** and **three disaccharases.** Together the two peptidases, formerly designated as **erepsin,** complete the digestion of protein foods by splitting off individual amino acids from the *end position* of the peptide chains. On this account they are called **exopeptidases** (Table 5-1). Each is very specific, however. **Carboxypeptidase** splits off amino acids at one end of the chain, where a carboxyl (—COOH) group is exposed; whereas **aminopeptidase** acts at the other end, where an amino (—NH_2) group is free.

As to the disaccharases, **maltase, sucrase,** and **lactase** act respectively on maltose, sucrose, and lactose, hydrolyzing these disaccharides into their monosaccharide constituents (p. 80). Recent reports indicate some lipase activity in the intestinal juice; but the potency is not very significant. The intestinal juice also contains sodium bicarbonate, which maintains a slightly alkaline reaction in the intestinal chyme, fostering a maximal activity of the intestinal enzymes.

By the time the chyme reaches the lower coils of the small intestine, practically all digestion is finished and absorption is proceeding apace. At the end point of digestion the various foodstuffs are entirely converted to readily absorbable compounds; the proteins to amino acids; the carbohydrates to monosaccharides; and the fats to glycerol and fatty acids.

Movements of the Small Intestine. Some 5 to 10 hours are usually required for the transmission of a meal through the small intestine. During this time the chyme is gently churned and gradually moved from coil to coil along the length of the small gut.

The *churning* movements of the small intestine, as revealed by x-ray studies, are mainly of a type called **pendular** movements. These, essentially, are gentle peristaltic waves which sweep *back and forth* without progressing beyond the limits of a single loop of the bowel. Pendular movements assure a complete mixing of the intestinal chyme with the digestive juices.

To *move* the chyme forward toward the large intestine, there are two kinds of peristaltic movements: (1) ordinary **peristaltic waves** (p. 303); and (2) **peristaltic rushes.** The waves are relatively slow (about 1 cm per sec), and transient, since they tend to fade away after traveling a meter along the bowel; but peristaltic rushes are faster (about 12 cm per sec), and they sweep the bowel for considerable distances, sometimes all the way from the duodenum to the colon.

The Colon, Rectum, and Anus. The relations of the **colon,** or **large intestine,** to the other parts of the digestive tract are shown in Figure 16-24. This figure also shows the positions of the subsidiary parts of the colon, which are: (1) the **caecum,** a large blind pocket, which hangs down below the point where the small bowel enters the large one; (2) the **vermiform appendix,** a small finger-like outpocketing of the caecum; (3) the

ascending colon, which passes upward on the right side of the abdominal cavity; (4) the **transverse colon,** which slants diagonally across the abdomen, from the right to left; and (5) the **descending colon,** which passes downward toward the rectum, on the left side of the body. Just prior to the point where the large intestine joins the **rectum,** the descending colon displays a marked bend, the **sigmoid flexure.** One muscular valve, the **ileocaecal sphincter,** guards the opening of the ileum into the caecal portion of the large intestine; and two valves, the **anal sphincters,** close off the anal passage except when egestion is about to occur.

When the residual food mass reaches the colon, most organic compounds, as well as considerable quantities of water, have been absorbed (p. 310). However, the mass is still very fluid when it reaches the ileocaecal valve —where it tends to accumulate, pending one of the periodic peristaltic rushes that sweep the material into the colon. This fluidity is not surprising when it is realized that the quantity of water absorbed from the food mass, while it passes through the small intestine, is just about counterbalanced by the water content of the digestive juices that are secreted into the small intestine.

The main function of the colon, aside from conducting the residual food mass to the rectum and anus, is to *absorb water* from the mass, conserving this water for the use of the body. Aquatic vertebrates, in which water conservation is not a serious problem, do not possess a very well-developed colon, but in terrestrial forms the colon is usually more conspicuous. The contents of the large bowel move very slowly, and usually about 12 to 14 hours are required for a given sample of the food mass to traverse the colon. Thus time is allowed for water absorption; and usually the fecal mass, when it reaches the descending colon, displays a plastic semisolid consistency.

This lag in the passage of the food residues through the colon accounts, at least partially, for the very large growth of bacteria that are always found in the large intestine. In fact, these bacteria represent as much as 50 percent of the dry weight of the normal feces. The colonic bacteria thrive— under ideal conditions of warmth, moisture, and darkness—upon such remnants of proteins, carbohydrates, and fats as may escape absorption in the small intestine. Ordinarily the bacteria inhabiting the colon are non-pathogenic; that is, these bacteria are neutral parasites for which man has been a host for many centuries.

The proteolytic, or putrefactive, bacteria of the colon produce a variety of nitrogenous compounds in the course of their digestive and metabolic activities, and some of these products are highly toxic and odoriferous. Formerly it was thought that these nitrogenous compounds might be responsible for the unpleasant symptoms of "autointoxication"; but more recent studies indicate that these substances never reach toxic concentrations in the general circulation (see p. 343).

Movements of the Large Intestine. Two types of colonic movement have been described: (1) feeble, sluggish, **peristaltic waves,** which gradually advance the food residue through the ascending and transverse loops; and (2) vigorous **peristaltic rushes,** which periodically evacuate the contents of the whole colon into the rectum. Ordinarily the rectum remains empty of feces until a few moments before **defecation** is to occur.

The various movements of the large and small bowels are coordinated by autonomic reflexes (p. 465). Peristaltic waves may be initiated by any local distention of the gut— as by an accumulation of the digesting food mass, or by artificially stretching the wall by the inflation of a rubber balloon placed in the lumen. A particularly vigorous peristaltic rush, involving a large part of the small intestine, as well as the transverse and descending loops of the large intestine, frequently accompanies the ingestion of a new meal. This reflex, which is called the **gastrocolic reflex,** sweeps the food remnants from the colon into the rectum. In fact, this filling of the rectum normally generates the "desire to defecate," which tends to follow certain meals, according to the habits of the individual. The headache and other discomfitures of "constipation" appear to be associated with a prolonged and unnatural distention of the rectum by packed feces, when defecation fails to occur at proper intervals. All the symptoms of the condition can be duplicated in man by merely packing the rectum with an inert mass, such as sterile cotton. This indicates that the discomfiture arises not from toxins absorbed from the gut, but from a reflex irritation of the nervous system.

Different cathartics initiate mass movements—that is, vigorous and enduring peristaltic rushes in the small and large intestines—in various ways. Certain drugs (for example, castor oil) strongly irritate the nerve endings in the mucosa of the tract, and these nerve endings are the receptors of the powerful reflex movements that follow. Salts (for example, magnesium sulfate) have a double action. In the high concentrations used, they irritate the gastrointestinal receptors; but more important still, a **hypertonic** solution of such a relatively nonabsorbable salt tends to hold water in the digestive tract, keeping the food mass abnormally fluid even after it passes through the colon. The third type of cathartic (for example, drugs such as cascara) acts upon the reflex centers in the central nervous system (medulla), sensitizing these centers to discharge motor impulses to the musculature of the intestinal tract.

Regular use of any type of cathartic is to be avoided, because all types are to some extent habit forming and at least slightly deleterious to the normal digestive and absorptive functions. In almost all cases constipation can be avoided by regularizing the defecation habit, bringing it into synchrony with the normal autonomic reflexes of the gastrointestinal tract; and in rare cases when this procedure is ineffective, a qualified physician should be consulted.

TEST QUESTIONS

1. Gastric vacuoles, which are characteristic of unicellular animals generally, have persisted among primitive multicellular animals. Explain, citing at least two specific examples.
2. Describe the processes of ingestion and digestion as they occur in *Hydra*.
3. Tubular digestive tracts tend to display more differentiation than saccular tracts. Explain this statement, basing the discussion on the digestive tracts of *Hydra* and the earthworm.
4. Explain the importance of the coelomic cavity in relation to the "digestive movements" of an animal.
5. Diagram the digestive tract of man, showing the connections of the various digestive glands.
6. Describe the general similarity of histological structure that is found in different parts of man's digestive tract.
7. Identify and locate: (a) the hard palate; (b) the uvula; (c) goblet cells; (d) the gastric glands; (e) the intestinal glands; (f) placoid scales; and (g) the parotid glands.
8. Briefly discuss man's dentition in relation to the teeth of other mammals, especially the rodents, herbivores, and carnivores.
9. Briefly explain the functions of each juice in terms of its **composition**: (a) the saliva; (b) the gastric juice; (c) the pancreatic juice; (d) the bile; (e) the intestinal juice.
10. Assume that a man has eaten a bowl of rice, served with sugar and milk. Make a table to show the complete digestion of the **carbohydrate** components of this meal. Be sure to specify:
    a. all the different carbohydrates present in the meal
    b. the enzyme or enzymes involved in the digestion of each compound
    c. the glandular source of each enzyme
    d. the end products produced by digestion
    e. the part of the digestive tract in which the digestion occurs
11. Make similar tables assuming that the man has eaten:
    a. some olive oil.
    b. some boiled egg albumen (**protein**)

12. Make a labeled diagram showing the connections of the human pharynx; discuss these connections in relation to the swallowing reflexes.

13. Explain how the mechanisms controlling the flow of saliva and pancreatic juice are different.

14. Name three hormones that are important in controlling the flow of the digestive juices, and in each case specify:
    a. the site of production of the hormone
    b. the gland (or other part) which is specifically activated by the hormone
    c. the manner in which the hormone reaches the effector organ

15. Plan an experiment that would prove that the pancreas is activated by a substance (or substances) that is carried in the blood stream.

16. Discuss the innervation of the stomach in relation to the gastric movements.

17. What is a sphincter valve? Specify four sphincters present in the gastrointestinal tract of man; explain the different functions of these valves.

18. Describe the movements of the stomach in relation to:
    a. the churning of the chyme
    b. the evacuation of the chyme from the stomach

19. Explain how the early work of Spallanzani and Beaumont contributed to an understanding of the composition and functions of the gastric juice.

20. How did Pavlov prove that seeing, smelling, and tasting food elicit a flow of gastric juice even when the food doesn't reach the stomach? How is this part of the secretion effected?

21. What is rennin? What important role is played by rennin in the digestive processes of man and other mammals?

22. Make a labeled diagram to show the essential relations of the duodenum to the stomach, pancreas, and liver.

23. The gastric chyme is highly acid, whereas the intestinal chyme is definitely alkaline. Explain precisely where and how this transition is effected, and why it is important.

24. Explain the relation between:
    a. the blood pigments, bile pigments, and fecal pigments
    b. the bile pigments and jaundice
    c. the "concentrating function" of the gall bladder and gallstones
    d. gallstones and the bile salts

25. Describe and explain the *circulation of bile salts*.

26. Describe the movements of the small intestine and explain their significance.

27. Differentiate between: (a) trypsin and chymotrypsin; (b) trypsin and trypsinogen; (c) casein and caseinogen; (d) endopeptidases and exopeptidases.

28. For each of the enzyme groups mentioned in Question 27, give an example and specify the catalyzed reaction.

29. Compare the movements of the small and large intestines.

30. Make a carefully labeled diagram showing the relations of the colon to the ileum, caecum, appendix, rectum, and anus.

31. Briefly discuss: (a) the functions of the colon; (b) the importance of the colonic bacteria.

32. What is the gastrocolic reflex and how is it related: (a) to defecation; (b) to the symptoms of "autointoxication"?

33. Specify three different kinds of cathartics and explain the mode of action of each.

FURTHER READINGS

1. *The Living Body,* 4th ed., by C. H. Best and N. B. Taylor; New York, 1958.
2. *The Body Functions,* by R. W. Gerard; New York, 1941.
3. *The Machinery of the Body,* by A. J. Carlson and V. Johnson; Chicago, 1953.

17-*The Circulatory System*

LARGE animals could not exist without an effective circulation. Foods from the digestive tract must be carried to all the cells of the body, and the respiratory gases must be transported between the various tissues and the breathing organs. Metabolic wastes have to be collected and brought to the excretory organs; and hormones and other special substances must be distributed throughout the body without delay. Diffusion and osmosis alone are much too slow to fulfill these needs, except in very small and simple animals such as *Hydra*. Accordingly, all larger animals have developed one or more circulatory fluids, which are forcefully pumped throughout the body for the transportation of necessary substances.

DIRECT CIRCULATIONS; HEMOLYMPH

Some lower animals possess only one circulatory fluid, the **hemolymph,** which performs the functions of both the blood and the lymph of higher forms. Hemolymph fills the tissue spaces, coming into contact with the cells; and thus the hemolymph carries materials *directly* to the cells.

Planaria and the other flatworms (p. 635)

possess a very simple hemolymph system. The hemolymph of *Planaria* flows through the intercellular spaces that permeate the loosely packed mesodermal tissues. No heart is present to pump the body fluid; but the hemolymph flows irregularly back and forth throughout the body, as a result of the muscular movements of the worm. Such a slow and irregular flow suffices to distribute foods to the various tissues, because the gastrovascular cavity of this animal sends branches to all parts. Branches of the excretory system also reach all the tissues, so that the metabolic wastes are not carried very far before they are eliminated. Nor is the hemolymph very important in the respiration of *Planaria*. The animal is relatively small, and an exchange of gases between the cells and the surrounding water takes place quite rapidly.

The hemolymph system of the lobster (p. 318) and other Arthropoda (p. 654) is somewhat more complex. The heart of the lobster is a hollow muscular sac, which lies in a **pericardial cavity** that is filled with hemolymph (Fig. 17-1). When the heart expands, it sucks in hemolymph through valved openings, the **ostia,** which penetrate the cardiac wall. Then, when the heart contracts, the

318

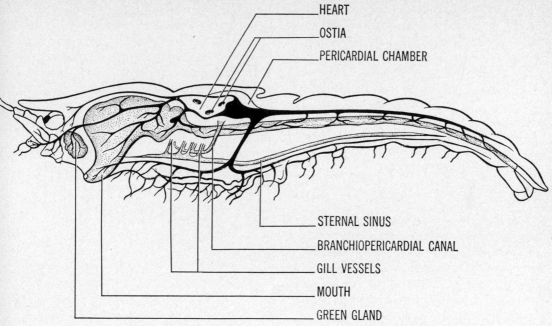

HEART
OSTIA
PERICARDIAL CHAMBER

STERNAL SINUS
BRANCHIOPERICARDIAL CANAL
GILL VESSELS
MOUTH
GREEN GLAND

Fig. 17-1.   Hemolymph circulation of the lobster, as shown in a diagrammatic longitudinal section.

ostial valves close, and the hemolymph is forced out through the arteries to the various parts of the body (Fig. 17-1). The arteries convey the hemolymph directly to the tissue spaces in each organ of the body. Some arteries go to the enteron and here the hemolymph passes through the channels in the gut wall, absorbing food substances as it flows. Large arteries also go to the excretory organs (**green glands**), and while the hemolymph filters through these organs, it gives up excretory wastes collected in other parts of the body. In the muscles and other tissues of the body, the arteries bring the hemolymph directly to the tissues, where it flows out into the tissue spaces and so comes into direct contact with the cells. The hemolymph provides the cells with food and oxygen and carries away the waste products of metabolism.

In returning to the heart the hemolymph of the lobster drains from the tissue spaces into the **sternal sinus** (Fig. 17-1), a large channel that leads to the gills. Then, in flowing through the gills, the hemolymph takes on oxygen from the water bathing the gills,

and gives up carbon dioxide. Finally, the hemolymph passes via six pairs of broad channels, the **branchiopericardial** canals, back to the pericardial cavity, completing the circuit.

INDIRECT (BLOOD-LYMPH) CIRCULATIONS

The disadvantage of such *direct* types of circulation is the relatively *slow rate of flow*. Inevitably the flow is slow because the hemolymph must be forced through irregular tissue spaces, where it encounters large resistance. This difficulty has been circumvented in higher animals by the evolution of two circulatory fluids: the **blood** and the **lymph.** In vertebrates, for example, the lymph flows slowly through the tissue spaces; but the blood flows at high speed through well-defined pipelike blood vessels.

In such *indirect* types of circulation, substances in the blood can reach a tissue cell only indirectly, by diffusing through the wall of a capillary and diffusing through the lymph to the cell in question. However, each tissue of the body is very thoroughly permeated by blood capillaries to such an extent that the total area of the capillaries in our muscles alone measures more than 5000 square meters. The very rapid flow of blood and the almost instantaneous equilibrium that takes place between the blood and lymph in the capillaries all over the body enables the **vertebrate circulatory system** to cope with the distribution problems of the largest and most active animals in existence.

BLOOD

If mammalian blood is prevented from clotting, it will settle on standing, forming two main layers. The upper straw-colored layer is the fluid **plasma,** which accounts for about 55 percent of the blood volume; and the dark-red lower layer is a densely packed mass of cells—the **corpuscles.**

The Plasma. The plasma not only serves as a vehicle for the blood corpuscles, but it also transports a wide variety of substances in solution (see Table 17-1). Some of these substances—for example, foods and metabolic wastes—enter and leave the blood stream in the different parts of the system; but others—such as proteins—remain in the plasma quite indefinitely. Some of the proteins, particularly **fibrinogen,** play an essential role in the clotting of blood (p. 323); and all the blood proteins probably help to maintain the osmotic properties of the plasma (p. 334).

Owing to the presence of **antibodies,** blood plasma is frequently able to neutralize specific poisons, such as the toxins produced by infecting bacteria and other parasites. If a small dose of rattlesnake venom is injected into a horse, for example, the plasma of the horse—after several days—is found to contain a specific antibody capable of neutralizing a much larger dose of this venom. Consequently serum from the treated horse can be used to save the life of human snake-bite victims. In general, the toxic product that elicits the production of an antibody is called an **antigen;** and virtually all **protein** compounds, provided they are foreign to the organism producing the antibody, are capable of acting as antigens. Antibodies are produced in various tissues of the body, but they are carried mainly in the blood plasma. A significant part of the organism's resistance to infectious diseases depends upon the production of specific antibodies, and a lasting immunity to certain diseases indicates that some antibodies, once they have been formed, remain in the blood stream more or less indefinitely.

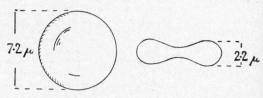

Fig. 17-2. Showing the diameter and thickness of a red blood cell.

The Red Corpuscles. There are from four to six million red cells per cubic millimeter in the blood of normal human adults, although in males the count tends to run about a million higher than in females. Each individual erythrocyte is an extremely small biconcave disc with a pale pink color (Figs. 17-2 and 17-3); but collectively they account for the deep red color of the blood.

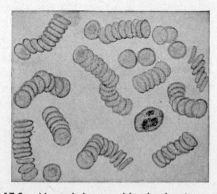

Fig. 17-3. Normal human blood, showing relative numbers of red and white cells. A field as large again as that shown would probably contain no other white cell. (From *The Living Body,* by Best and Taylor. Holt, Rinehart and Winston, Inc.)

Table 17-1—Main Components of Human Blood

A. **Corpuscles**
   1. Red corpuscles, or **erythrocytes**
   2. White corpuscles, or **leucocytes**
   3. Platelets, or **thrombocytes**

B. **Plasma**
   1. Water (90 percent, by weight)
   2. Inorganic salts (1 percent)
   3. Major proteins, 7 percent: serum albumin (4 percent), serum globulin (2.7 percent), fibrinogen (0.3 percent)
   4. Other substances, 2 percent
      a. Absorbed foods (glucose, amino acids, glycerol, fatty acids, neutral fats, other lipids, and vitamins)
      b. Collected wastes (urea, uric acid, and other compounds)
      c. Hormones, enzymes, and antibodies
      d. Respiratory gases (oxygen and carbon dioxide)

The chief function of the erythrocytes is to augment the oxygen-carrying capacity of the blood. About 50 percent of the weight of an erythrocyte represents **hemoglobin,** an iron-containing protein compound. The hemoglobin molecule is a fairly large one, having a molecular weight of 68,000 and consisting of a complex of four **heme** units (p. 364). Each heme unit possesses a single centrally localized iron (Fe) atom and can combine chemically with one molecule of oxygen (O_2). Thus the whole hemoglobin molecule when fully saturated (at high partial pressure of O_2) can carry four molecules of oxygen. For the sake of simplicity, however, the equilibrium between oxygen and hemoglobin is often written: hemoglobin + oxygen $\rightleftarrows$ oxyhemoglobin, or: $Hb + O_2 \rightleftarrows HbO_2$.

In any event, hemoglobin greatly augments the oxygen-carrying capacity of the blood. In addition to a small quantity of oxygen carried in solution in the plasma there is always the much larger quantity that is chemically united with hemoglobin in the erythrocytes.

A majority of vertebrates (fish, amphibians, reptiles, and birds) possess erythrocytes with typical nuclei. But in man and other **mammals,** the nuclei are lost by the cells before the erythrocytes are launched into the blood stream. Mammalian erythrocytes survive in the circulation for an average of only 125 days, whereupon the aging corpuscles are phagocytized by certain tissues, particularly in the spleen (p. 335). Accordingly a constant replacement of red cells must go on, if **anemia** is to be avoided, and, in fact, several million new red cells are launched into the circulation during every *second* of man's life. In adult man the formation of new red cells occurs in the **hemopoietic tissues** of **red bone marrow;** but in the embryo—and in lower vertebrates generally—erythrocytes are formed in the liver, spleen, and lymph nodes (p. 334). A lowered content of hemoglobin in the blood—whether due to an abnormally rapid loss of erythrocytes, or to a defective formation of the red cells—is called **anemia.** The anemia may be due to a variety of causes, such as hemorrhage, metal poisoning, hereditary fragility of the corpuscles, or inadequate iron in the diet. Inadequate dietary iron does not reduce the number of erythrocytes; but the individual red cells are small and pale, due to a paucity of hemoglobin.

In pernicious anemia, the body lacks a specific compound that is closely related to (perhaps identical with) vitamin B_{12}, the antipernicious anemia factor (APA). Normally this bone-marrow stimulant is stored in the liver, and the feeding or injecting of beef liver concentrates (or of the purified vitamin) brings most cases of pernicious anemia under control (see p. 353).

Leucocytes. The white cells of the blood (Fig. 17-3) are far less numerous than the reds, and they normally total to only about 6000 to 10,000 per cubic millimeter. All leucocytes have a colorless cytoplasm and definite nuclei. Leucocytes are of various kinds, as is shown in Table 17-2, and some kinds are able to leave the blood stream through the capillary walls.

Phagocytosis: Another Defense against Infection. Some leucocytes, particularly the neutrophils and monocytes, carry on an active defense against pathogenic bacteria

bacteria in large numbers (Fig. 17-4). Also the leucocytes tend to surround the infected region and to prevent the bacteria from spreading. Many white cells succumb to toxins produced by the bacteria; and these dead leucocytes make up the chief compo-

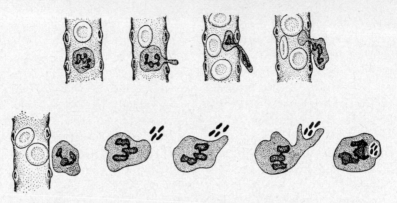

Fig. 17-4. Leucocyte performing **diapedesis,** by which it actively penetrates the wall of a capillary blood vessel, and **phagocytosis,** by which it engulfs bacteria in the tissue spaces. Semidiagrammatic.

when these parasites manage to enter the tissues through an open wound. The leucocytes migrate toward the wound, passing out through the walls of the capillaries in the infected area by a process called **diapedesis** (Fig. 17-4). The white cells arrive in force at the site of infection, and begin ingesting the

nent of **pus,** as it accumulates at the infection. Besides being able to digest the bacteria and other foreign particles they have phagocytized, the leucocytes secrete enzymes extracellularly. These enzymes digest away the dead or dying (necrotic) tissues, especially near the external surface of the infection.

Table 17-2—The Kinds of Leucocytes in Man

A. **Granulocytes (polymorphonuclear leucocytes);** with distinct granules in the cytoplasm; nuclei conspicuously irregular and lobose, or even subdivided; originate from bone marrow:

    1. *Neutrophils:* granules stain with neutral dyes, or with mixtures of acid and basic dyes; nucleus, with many lobes, highly motile and phagocytic; very numerous, making up about 67 percent of the total white cell count.

    2. *Basophils:* granules stain with basic dyes (e.g., methylene blue); nucleus usually with two lobes; about 0.5 percent of total whites: nonphagocytic.

    3. *Eosinophils:* granules stain with acid dyes (e.g., eosin); bilobed nucleus; 3 percent of total white cell count; nonphagocytic.

B. **Agranulocytes (lymphocytes):** cytoplasm, without granules; nucleus rounded; originate from lymphoid tissues (lymph glands, spleen, etc.):

    1. *Small lymphocytes:* about 8 microns diameter; 25 percent of total whites.

    2. *Large lymphocytes:* about 11 microns: 3 percent of total whites.

    3. *Monocytes:* about 15 microns; actively amoeboid and **phagocytic;** 1.5 percent of total whites.

Thus the leucocytes clear a channel to the exterior; and through this channel the pus and other contents of the **abcess** may finally be discharged.

The functions of the other leucocytes (small and large lymphocytes, basophils, and eosinophils) are not clearly understood although probably they have some relationship to disease resistance. In different infections different kinds of leucocytes tend to accumulate in the blood, and consequently the physician must obtain a *differential white cell count,* in seeking the diagnosis of an unknown infection.

PLATELETS

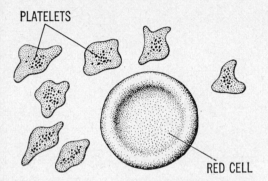

RED CELL

Fig. 17-5. Human blood platelets, or **thrombocytes.** A red blood cell is shown for comparison.

Thrombocytes. The **thrombocytes,** or **blood platelets** (Fig. 17-5), are smaller and less regularly shaped than erythrocytes, although they resemble erythrocytes in that they are abundant (about 250 thousand per cu mm) and they lack nuclei. The thrombocytes are formed from the cytoplasm of certain very large cells in the bone marrow, by a process of fragmentation. Platelets cannot be seen in ordinary *shed* blood because they disintegrate immediately, liberating a substance that participates in clotting.

Blood Coagulation. Victims of **hemophilia** —a rare hereditary defect of the blood— bleed very profusely even from the slightest wound. Hemophilic blood fails to clot in the normal time (6 to 8 min), but takes an hour or more to coagulate. In the absence of a normal clot to stop the bleeding, blood continues to flow from any ruptured vessel, and

the life of the "bleeder" may be endangered.

The clotting of a sample of normal blood involves a series of chemical reactions that starts as soon as the blood comes into contact with a damaged tissue or with some other foreign surface. The main reaction involves the conversion of the soluble protein, **fibrinogen,** into the insoluble protein, **fibrin.** The fibrin precipitates in the form of a submicroscopic network of interlacing fibrils, which holds the other blood components within a colloidal mesh (Fig. 17-6). At first the clot, or **thrombus,** is a semisolid mass with a gelatinous consistency. But in time the fibrin framework shrinks, squeezing a straw-colored fluid, the **serum,** to the surface of the clot, which now becomes hard and tough. The serum is almost totally lacking in fibrinogen and displays no further tendency to clot.

The fibrinogen → fibrin reaction depends upon a specific enzyme, **thrombase,** which is also called thrombin. Thrombase itself is not present in the circulating blood, but blood contains an inactive precursor of the enzyme, which is called **prothrombase** (prothrombin). Prothrombase must be converted into thrombase before the blood can clot. In the absence of ionic calcium, prothrombase cannot be activated (except very slowly); and this accounts for the fact that coagulation does not occur when calcium-precipitating reagents (for example, oxalate compounds) are added to the blood.

The conversion of prothrombase to thrombase occurs only when another substance, **thromboplastin,** is available. Thromboplastin is not present in circulating blood, but the precursory protein, **thromboplastinogen,** has been identified recently as one of the normal **globulin** components of plasma. Clotting does not begin, therefore, until thromboplastinogen has been transformed into thromboplastin. This reaction requires the presence of another enzyme (**thromboplastinogenase**) which is liberated, in shed blood, by the disintegration of the platelets. Thus, the platelets, which disintegrate when blood escapes from a vessel and makes con-

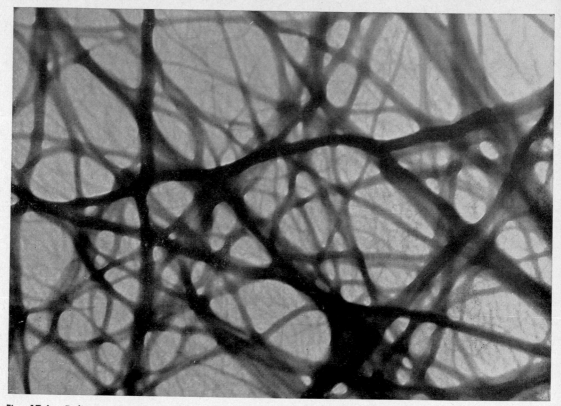

Fig. 17-6. Delicate network of fibrin fibers deposited after thrombin (thrombase) has been added to a fibrinogen solution. A similar network, formed in normally coagulating whole blood, enmeshes the corpuscles and fluid components and provides the thrombus, or clot, with a considerable degree of solidity. The magnification in this electronmicrograph is 30,000 diameters. (Courtesy of Clinton Van Zandt Hawn, Keith R. Porter, and the Rockefeller Institute for Medical Research.)

tact with a damaged tissue, liberate the enzyme that initiates the whole series of clotting reactions. First, thromboplastin is produced and this (together with ionic calcium) leads to the production of thrombase. Then, finally, thrombase catalyzes the production of the thrombin clot.

Recent studies on hemophilic blood have revealed a very specific defect. Such blood contains little, if any, of the normal plasma globulin component, thromboplastinogen. Now, in fact, the control of hemophilia can be achieved by periodic injections of concentrates of the missing protein, which also has been called the **antihemophilic globulin.**

Although some factors still remain unknown, the foregoing account of coagulation is substantiated by a large accumulation of evidence. The synthesis of prothrombase is a well-recognized function of the liver, and both prothrombase and thrombase have been extracted from blood in highly active, dry form. Like other enzymes, thrombase is readily destroyed by heat (50° C), although the precursory protein, prothrombase, is much more heat stable. Thromboplastinogenase, which normally initiates the clotting reactions, appears to come in small part from the cells of the damaged tissues; but mainly it comes from the blood platelets, which disintegrate whenever blood comes into contact with a foreign surface—except when such a surface is exceedingly smooth. Thus if blood is drawn directly from a vein into a test tube that has been coated internally with a film of oil, coagulation is delayed for an hour or more. In this case no contact with the damaged tissues has been allowed, and the platelets fail to disintegrate as quickly when they come into contact with an oiled surface.

Anticoagulants. Anticoagulants are compounds that prevent, or definitely inhibit, blood clotting. Citrate, fluoride, and oxalate salts all have the common property of removing ionic calcium from the blood; and these anticoagulants are used very commonly in handling blood for routine analysis. Bloodsucking creatures, such as leeches, produce organic anticoagulants. Typically these reagents interfere with the formation or activity of thrombase, as is the case for **hirudin,** the anticoagulant of the leech. In normal circulating blood there appears to be an unidentified anticoagulant, but this is neutralized by thromboplastin when coagulation occurs. Also a very powerful anticoagulant, **heparin,** can be extracted from liver and muscle tissues.

Blood Types in Relation to Transfusion. Transfusions have saved many lives in cases of severe hemorrhage, and in other cases where the blood volume falls so low that the heart no longer can maintain the circulation. But the early history of blood transfusion was beset with many tragedies, until 1900, when Landsteiner developed an understanding of the **blood types** of man. Previously the many deaths had resulted from the mixing of *incompatible* bloods, which leads to a clumping (**agglutination**) of the red corpuscles and consequently to a blocking of the capillary circulation.

The agglutination of blood corpuscles represents a typical antigen-antibody reaction.

However, in the case of blood, the reacting components are called **agglutinogens** and **agglutinins,** the agglutinogens being present in (or on) the red cells and the agglutinins in the plasma. In man's blood there are two agglutinogens, namely A and B, and two agglutinins, a and b; and the four main blood groups of man are determined by the presence or absence of these components, as is shown in Table 17-3.

Table 17-3—Blood Types in Man

Blood Groups	Agglutinogens (in corpuscles)	Agglutinins (in plasma)	Can Donate to	Can Receive from
A	A	b	A, AB	O, A
B	B	a	B, AB	O, B
AB	A and B	none	AB	O, A, B, AB
O	none	a and b	O, A, B, AB	O

When a transfusion is necessary every effort is made to find a donor belonging to the same group as the recipient. Also, whenever possible, a test of compatibility is performed before the transfusion is started. However, if such a donor is not available, the other combinations shown in Table 17-3 may be employed. For example, type O, which is called a **universal donor,** may give blood to a type A recipient. In this case, the donor corpuscles, lacking any agglutinogen, are not clumped by the recipient's plasma, and the recipient's corpuscles escape agglutination because the agglutinins of the donor plasma become so diluted by the plasma of the recipient that they do not retain much, if any, activity.

The blood types of man and other mammals are inherited in Mendelian fashion (p. 481) and do not change during the lifetime of the individual. Also, there is another heritable agglutinogen, the **Rh factor,**[1] although the importance of this antigen was not appreciated until recently. Among white people, about 85 percent of the population are Rh

[1] So named because it was first identified in the rhesus monkey.

positive and complications involving the Rh factor do not arise from intermarriages within this majority group. After the first child, however, the offspring of an Rh positive father and an Rh negative mother are endangered by the possibility that a reaction will occur between the blood of the mother and that of the fetus. In this case, the fetus always inherits an Rh positive blood, and during the first pregnancy the fetal antigen stimulates the production of Rh antibody in the maternal plasma. The production of Rh antibody by the mother is not rapid enough to produce much reaction in the first child, but during another pregnancy a widespread agglutination and subsequent destruction of the red cells may occur in the fetal blood. This condition is recognized as **erythroblastosis fetalis,** a drastic type of anemia that may be fatal to the embryo before delivery or to the child soon after.

THE VERTEBRATE HEART

Embryologically the vertebrate heart represents a highly modified blood vessel with thick contractile walls. In man and other vertebrates, this special vessel develops in the mid-ventral region of the embryo, just behind the gill slits. The embryonic heart soon differentiates into two muscular chambers—the **auricle** and **ventricle**—which then begin to pulsate rhythmically (Fig. 17-7).

The auricle has a thinner wall than the ventricle. Each time it relaxes the auricle collects blood from the **sinus venosus** (Fig. 17-7); when it is filled, the auricle contracts, forcing the blood into the ventricle. Then the thick-walled ventricle contracts, forcing the blood to flow at high pressure, out into the arteries of the body. Valves, situated at the entrance and exit points of the auricle and ventricle, prevent any appreciable backflow; practically all the force of the contracting heart goes to the propulsion of the blood in a forward direction.

The simple **two-chambered** heart of the early **embryo** is essentially similar to the fully developed heart of **lower** (fishlike) **vertebrates,** in which **gills** serve as the respiratory organs. Lung-breathing vertebrates, however, except for the Amphibia, have developed a **four-chambered heart,** with a separate auricle and ventricle to pump blood through the lungs (Figs. 17-8). Regardless of type, however, the heart is essentially a hollow muscular chamber that contracts repeatedly, forcing the blood to circulate.

Primitive organisms may lack a definite heart, or strictly localized pumping organ. The earthworm, for example, possesses a **dorsal blood vessel,** which is contractile all throughout the length of the body (Fig. 17-9). This elongate blood vessel, together with the five pairs of vessels that encircle the esophagus of the earthworm (Fig. 17-9), maintains a steady series of contractions that propel the blood. The flow is entirely in one

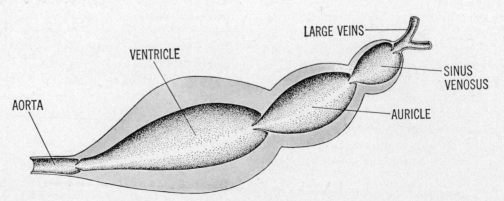

Fig. 17-7.   An early stage in the development of the heart.

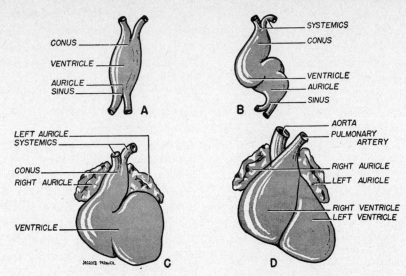

CONUS
VENTRICLE
AURICLE
SINUS
A

SYSTEMICS
CONUS
VENTRICLE
AURICLE
SINUS
B

LEFT AURICLE
SYSTEMICS
CONUS
RIGHT AURICLE
VENTRICLE
C

AORTA
PULMONARY ARTERY
RIGHT AURICLE
LEFT AURICLE
RIGHT VENTRICLE
LEFT VENTRICLE
D

Fig. 17-8.   Stages in the development of the mammalian heart (ventral view). Note the resemblance of stages B and C to the fish and amphibian hearts, respectively. Also see page 284, embryonic development of the heart.

direction, due to the presence of numerous valves in the blood vessels.

The Blood Vessels. The blood vessels of an adult vertebrate are defined in relation to the heart: **arteries** lead *away* from the heart; **veins** lead *toward* the heart; and **capillary networks** connect the arteries with the veins.

In man there are two arterial systems: (1) the **pulmonary system,** which carries blood from the **right ventricle** to the **lungs;** and (2) the **systemic system,** which leads from the **left ventricle** to all other organs in the body. The main trunk of the pulmonary system is the pulmonary artery (Fig. 17-10), which sends a branch directly to each lung;

and the main trunk of the systemic circuit is a very large artery, the **aorta,** which sends smaller branches to every part of the body, except the lungs (Fig. 17-10). The artery to each organ ends in a capillary network that permeates all the tissues of that organ. The venous system begins as many small tributaries from the capillaries in the various organs, and terminates in the large veins, which enter the auricles (Fig. 17-10). In general, the artery to a particular organ runs side by side with the vein from the same organ, so that the artery and vein are given corresponding names (for example, renal arteries and renal veins; see Fig. 17-10). How-

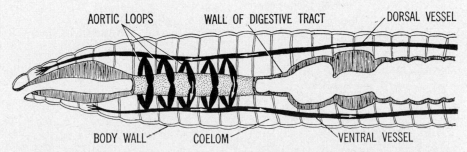

AORTIC LOOPS   WALL OF DIGESTIVE TRACT   DORSAL VESSEL

BODY WALL   COELOM   VENTRAL VESSEL

Fig. 17-9.   The main blood vessels of the earthworm. The dorsal vessel runs above the digestive tract and conducts the blood forward (*left*); the ventral vessel is below the digestive tract and conducts the blood backward (*right*); and the five pairs of aortic loops encircle the esophagus.

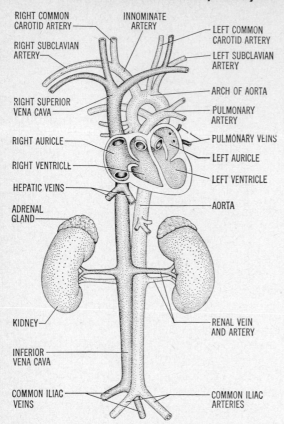

RIGHT COMMON CAROTID ARTERY

INNOMINATE ARTERY

LEFT COMMON CAROTID ARTERY

RIGHT SUBCLAVIAN ARTERY

LEFT SUBCLAVIAN ARTERY

ARCH OF AORTA

RIGHT SUPERIOR VENA CAVA

PULMONARY ARTERY

PULMONARY VEINS

RIGHT AURICLE

LEFT AURICLE

RIGHT VENTRICLE

LEFT VENTRICLE

HEPATIC VEINS

AORTA

ADRENAL GLAND

KIDNEY

RENAL VEIN AND ARTERY

INFERIOR VENA CAVA

COMMON ILIAC VEINS

COMMON ILIAC ARTERIES

Fig. 17-10. Principal blood vessels of man and their connections with the heart chambers. Ventral view. Be sure to differentiate between the *systemic* and the *pulmonary* circuits (see text, p. 327).

ever, there are many exceptions to this general rule (see later).

Structure of the Blood Vessels. Arteries and veins display a similar structure, although the arterial wall is thicker and stronger (Fig. 17-11). Blood pressure is at a maximum as the blood is forced from the heart; and the pressure remains relatively high throughout the whole arterial system. Consequently if any artery is cut, the blood tends to spurt out. As blood passes through the capillary network, however, much of its pressure is dissipated, owing to the frictional resistance offered by these microscopic channels. Consequently blood reaching the venous system is under a relatively low pressure, and if a vein is cut, the bleeding is less forceful. Valves, which prevent a backflow of blood, are found at

fairly frequent intervals within the veins, but not within the arteries.

The same *three layers of tissue* are present in the walls of an artery and vein, although these layers are thicker and more clearly defined in the artery. The *inner layer* (Fig. 17-11) is the **endothelium,** a smooth lining of squamous epithelial cells, arranged more or less like the stones of a pavement. This smooth endothelial lining offers a minimal resistance to the flow of blood through the vessels. The *middle layer* is a sheath of **visceral muscle,** flanked both inside and out by **elastic connective tissue;** and the *outer layer* is composed of loose connective tissue. The fibers of the muscle sheath tend to encircle the artery, permitting the artery to change its caliber according to the needs of the tissues at the particular time. During exercise, for example, the arteries to the muscles and lungs dilate, thus providing a more abundant blood supply to these parts during the period of extra activity.

Unless the arterial walls were elastic, the circulation could not be maintained on an efficient basis. Each time the ventricle contracts, it quickly empties its full content of blood into the arterial system. This blood cannot flow instantaneously through the very

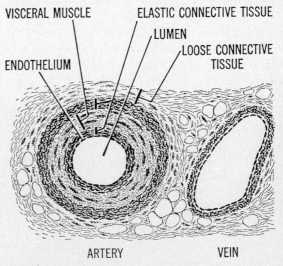

VISCERAL MUSCLE

ELASTIC CONNECTIVE TISSUE

LUMEN

LOOSE CONNECTIVE TISSUE

ENDOTHELIUM

ARTERY

VEIN

Fig. 17-11. Microscopic structure of a small artery and vein. Cross-sectional view, semidiagrammatic.

fine capillary networks, and consequently the walls throughout the whole arterial system must stretch to accommodate each output from the ventricle. Then, in the short intervals between the beats of the heart, the elastic recoil of the stretched arterial walls tends to maintain the blood pressure, assuring a continuous flow in the capillary system. In feeling one's pulse, accordingly, one is detecting the rapidly alternating stretching and recoiling of the walls of one of the larger arteries.

Both the visceral muscle and the yellow connective tissue of the wall contribute to the elasticity of the arteries. With increasing age, however, the arteries tend to lose their natural resilience, partially because of a progressive hardening in the older tissues. When this occurs the blood pressure rises, since the heart works harder to maintain the circulation. Such a combination of rising blood pressure and more brittle arteries has serious consequences if an artery breaks and deprives a vital organ of its circulation.

The Capillary Circulation. The **aorta** sends branches to all parts of the body (except the lungs), and each organ receives at least one larger or smaller branch depending on its size and activity. *In the organ,* a profuse branching occurs, and this branching permeates all the tissues. The initial branches, or **arterioles,** are like the main artery, except that they are smaller and have thinner walls. Gradually, however, the outer and middle tissue layers of the arteriole become thinner and thinner, until finally only the naked endothelium remains—and this is the wall of a **capillary** (Fig. 17-12). The diameter of some of the capillaries is so small that the blood corpuscles must pass through in single file (Fig. 17-13). Also the capillary network is so extensive in every part of the body that one can scarcely suffer the slightest cut without drawing blood from the severed capillaries.

Eventually the capillaries throughout an organ begin to join each other, forming larger vessels, called **venules.** The venules, in turn, become the tributaries of the one or

Fig. 17-12. A capillary. Note that the wall consists merely of a simple **endothelium.**

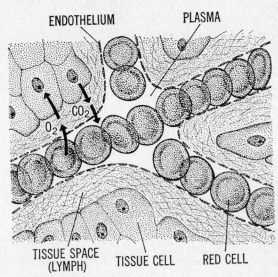

Fig. 17-13. Internal respiration: diffusional exchange of gases between tissue cells and blood.

more **veins,** which drain blood from the organ and return it toward the heart.

RELATIONSHIP BETWEEN THE BLOOD, LYMPH, AND TISSUE CELLS

As may be seen in Figure 17-13, the blood in an organ does not come into direct contact with the tissue cells. Consequently material exchanges between the blood and the cells must involve a passage of substances through the capillary walls and across the lymph in the tissue spaces. Such exchanges go on rapidly and continuously only in the capillary parts of the blood system, where the walls are sufficiently thin.

The exchanges between capillary blood and the surrounding tissues of a working muscle are typical of such exchanges generally. Blood entering the muscle is well supplied with oxygen absorbed from the lungs, and with food compounds absorbed from the gastrointestinal tract. The muscle fibers, however, contain very little of these substances, which are continually consumed in metabolism. Consequently oxygen, glucose, and the other nutrients keep passing from the blood across the lymph and into the muscle fibers. Conversely carbon dioxide and the other metabolic wastes tend to reach a relatively high concentration in the fibers, where they are produced, and so the metabolic wastes keep passing from the fibers, through the lymph, and into the capillaries.

SINGLE vs. DOUBLE CIRCULATIONS

The circulatory system of man and other higher vertebrates is a highly modified and improved version of the circulation of the lower vertebrates. The general pattern of the circulation in primitive vertebrates is well illustrated by the dogfish (Fig. 17-14). This typical form possesses a relatively simple **two-chambered heart** that pumps the blood through just a *single* cir-cuit; and in passing through this one circuit the blood performs all necessary functions.

As may be seen in Figure 17-14, the **unaerated** (unshaded) blood leaves the **ventricle** via a large arterial trunk, the **ventral aorta;** and there are five pairs of branches, the **aortic arches,** which surround the gill clefts and carry the blood to the **dorsal aorta.** Before reaching the dorsal aorta, however, the blood must flow through the capillaries of the **gills,** where the blood becomes aerated (shaded).

The branches of the **dorsal aorta** extend to all other parts of the body, carrying aerated blood: to the kidneys, digestive tract, and all structures in head, trunk, and tail (Fig. 17-14). In all these regions the blood must flow through a second network of capillaries, and as it flows through the various organs, the blood returns to an **unaerated** condition (unshaded in Fig. 17-14). The many smaller veins, which collect unaerated blood from all parts of the body, empty mainly into four large veins: the two **precardinal** veins, which drain the two sides of the head, and the two **postcardinal** veins, which drain the kidneys, gonads, and the body wall musculature in the tail and trunk. These four major veins then empty, via the **sinus venosus,** into the

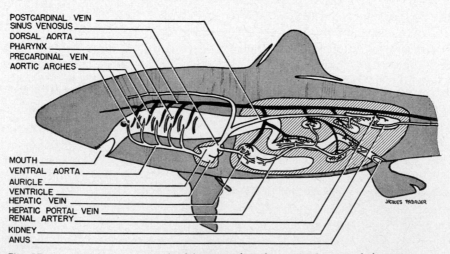

POSTCARDINAL VEIN
SINUS VENOSUS
DORSAL AORTA
PHARYNX
PRECARDINAL VEIN
AORTIC ARCHES

MOUTH
VENTRAL AORTA
AURICLE
VENTRICLE
HEPATIC VEIN
HEPATIC PORTAL VEIN
RENAL ARTERY
KIDNEY
ANUS

JACQUES FRADAUER

Fig. 17-14. Circulation of the dogfish. Note that the aerated parts of the system are shaded, whereas unaerated parts are unshaded.

auricle of the heart, thus completing the circuit.

The *single circulation* of the gill-breathing vertebrates—which *collects* and *distributes* oxygen in one and the same circuit—suffices to supply the relatively modest requirements of these cold-blooded creatures. However, the fact that the heart must force the blood against the high resistance of at least two networks of capillaries, before the blood returns to the heart, has tended to limit the efficiency of such a system.

In the higher (lung-breathing) vertebrates, the single circulation has been replaced by a *double circulation*. The birds, mammals, and many of the reptiles have developed a respiratory (pulmonary) circuit that is quite separate from the general (systemic) circuit of the blood. Such forms possess a four-chambered heart. In man, for example, the unaerated blood is collected by the *right* auricle and pumped through the lung capillaries by the *right* ventricle. Then the aerated blood returns from the pulmonary circuit to the left auricle and is pumped by the *left* ventricle out into the systemic circuit. Thus the four-chambered heart (Fig. 17-8) has separate ventricles for pumping blood through the pulmonary and systemic circuits, and such a heart is able to maintain a more rapid circulation. The blood first *collects* oxygen, in passing through the pulmonary capillaries, and then it returns to the heart for a new impetus, before passing to the capillaries of the systemic circuit, where the oxygen is *distributed*.

The three-chambered heart of the Amphibia (Fig. 17-8) and the incomplete four-chambered heart of some of the reptiles represent transitional developments, more or less intermediate between the lower and higher vertebrates. In the amphibian circulation, the single ventricle pumps blood through both the pulmonary and systematic circuits. The unaerated and aerated kinds of blood are received by the right and left auricles respectively, and sent to the ventricle. To a large extent the ventricle keeps the two types of blood separate, sending most of the unaerated through the pulmonary, and most of the aerated through the systemic circuits. However, there is some mixing; and consequently this kind of system is called an incomplete double circulation.

MAJOR ARTERIES AND VEINS OF THE HUMAN BODY

In the circulation of man, the main arteries and veins of the systemic circuit and some of the vessels of the pulmonary circuit are presented in Figure 17-10. This figure shows the postcaval and precaval veins entering the right auricle, and the pulmonary artery emerging from the right ventricle. Also, the figure shows the pulmonary veins returning to the left auricle, although this chamber lies in front of the pulmonary veins. The ventral aorta, and the aortic arch—which loops around the pulmonary artery to reach the dorsal aorta—can be seen clearly, as is also true of the lower part of the dorsal aorta. This large artery passes through the diaphragm—near the lower margin of the heart—and continues downward in the abdominal cavity, sending branches to all the lower parts of the body.

The aorta serves as the trunk line of the systemic circulation; and the major branches of the aorta display essentially the same arrangement in all Mammalia. The innominate artery (Fig. 17-10), or first large branch, forks almost immediately into (1) the right subclavian, which supplies the right shoulder and arm regions; and (2) the right common carotid, which supplies the right side of the head as a whole. The second and third large branches of the aorta are, respectively, the left common carotid and left subclavian. These arteries supply: (1) the left side of the head; (2) the left shoulder and arm.

In the thorax (dorsal to the heart) the aorta gives off a number of small intercostal arteries (not shown in Fig. 17-10), which supply the thoracic body wall. In the abdomen, the aorta sends branches to the digestive tract, kidneys, and abdominal body wall. Finally, the aorta terminates in the lower extremity of the abdominal region, by forking into the **iliac arteries,** which carry blood to the legs.

DEVELOPMENT OF THE CIRCULATORY SYSTEM

At an early stage of development, the embryonic circulation of man and other mammals is distinctly similar to the circulation of the dogfish and other primitive vertebrates. In the embryo, there are five pairs of gill clefts, and the six aortic arches branch off from the ventral aorta (Fig. 17-15). However, this arrangement does not persist as development proceeds. Arches I, II and V are destined to disappear. Arch IV, on the left side, becomes the adult aortic arch; and on the right arch IV becomes the right subclavian artery. Of the other arteries associated with the human heart, the carotids (Fig. 17-10) are derived partly from arch III; and the pulmonary arteries come from arch VI.

THE HEPATIC PORTAL SYSTEM

The vertebrate circulation displays still another distinctive feature. Blood from the gastrointestinal tract does not return directly to the heart, but first passes through the capillaries of the **liver** (Fig. 17-16). This part of the circulation is called the **hepatic portal system,** and it has an important bearing upon the metabolism of vertebrate animals generally. Blood in the gastrointestinal capillaries becomes laden with a wide variety of absorbed products. However, many of these compounds never reach the *general* circulation—because the liver intervenes between the intestinal tract and all other parts of the circulation (p. 333).

The **hepatic portal system** of man is shown in Figure 17-16. The **hepatic portal vein** is formed by the confluence of three tributaries: (1) the **gastrosplenic** vein, from the stomach and spleen; (2) the **superior mesenteric vein,** from the upper parts of the small intestine, and (3) the **inferior mesenteric vein,** from the lower small intestine and colon. The portal vein passes directly to the liver and, upon entering it, gives rise to a set of capillaries that extend throughout the liver tissue. Eventually blood drains from the liver by way of the **hepatic veins,** which join the postcava. Accordingly it is important to distinguish clearly between the hepatic **portal** vein, which brings blood *to* the liver, and

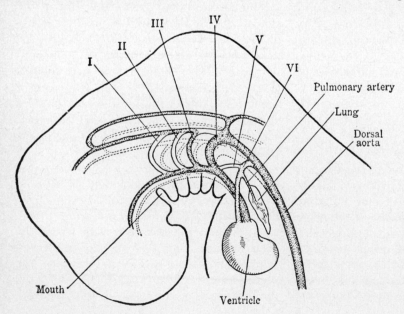

Fig. 17-15. Head of a human embryo, side view, showing the development of the arterial system. I, II, III, IV, V, VI, aortic arches. I, II, and V do not persist, while III forms the internal carotid arteries, IV forms a portion of the aorta, and VI forms the pulmonary arteries of the adult. (From *General Biology,* by James W. Mavor. The Macmillan Co.)

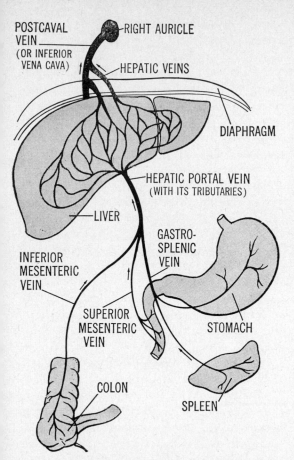

POSTCAVAL VEIN (OR INFERIOR VENA CAVA)

RIGHT AURICLE

HEPATIC VEINS

DIAPHRAGM

HEPATIC PORTAL VEIN (WITH ITS TRIBUTARIES)

LIVER

GASTRO-SPLENIC VEIN

INFERIOR MESENTERIC VEIN

SUPERIOR MESENTERIC VEIN

STOMACH

COLON

SPLEEN

Fig. 17-16. The **hepatic portal** circulation of man. Note that blood, after absorbing food substances from the gastrointestinal tract, passes directly to the capillary system of the **liver**. A portal vein always originates from and terminates in a **capillary network**.

the **hepatic** veins, which carry blood *away from* the liver. In vertebrate animals, it is generally not difficult to identify the portal vein, because this large vein always originates near the duodenum and runs to the base of the liver, closely accompanied by the **bile duct.**

A portal vein not only originates from capillaries but also terminates in capillaries; whereas other veins originate from capillaries but terminate either by joining some other vein, or by emptying into an auricle. In man and other mammals, the hepatic portal vein is the only large portal vein of the body, but many lower vertebrates also

possess a renal portal vein, which brings blood to the kidney (Fig. 17-14).

THE LYMPH AND ITS ORIGIN

Blood in all capillaries continually loses a small proportion of its fluid volume by seepage through the capillary walls. This fluid is the lymph, which filters from the capillaries into the tissue spaces (Fig. 17-13).

The formation of lymph is not an osmotic process. It is a kind of *forced filtration,* which is energized by blood pressure. Normal blood is slightly hypertonic to the lymph, but the osmotic tendency for water to return to the blood is counterbalanced by blood pressure.

At the arterial end of a capillary, blood pressure is highest—being equivalent, on the average, to a pressure of about 30 mm of mercury. This pressure exceeds the lymph pressure by about 22 mm, and since the hypertonicity of the blood is only 15 mm, the effective force that accounts for the formation of new lymph is about 7 mm of mercury. Near the venous end of the capillaries, where the blood pressure has dissipated somewhat, there is a definite tendency for fluid to re-enter the blood from the lymph. However, the re-entering fluid is of a smaller volume than that which filtered out at the arterial end of the network.

The Composition of Lymph. The lymph is a *force filtrate* of the blood and consequently lymph has a composition that is closely related to the composition of the plasma. However, the capillary walls tend to hold back the colloidal components of the blood. Accordingly, lymph contains all the crystalloid components (water, salts, glucose, amino acids, urea, etc.) of the plasma, in amounts that very closely approximate those in the plasma. But the plasma proteins, being colloidal in their molecular dimensions, are present in the lymph in much lesser amounts than in the plasma. In fact the protein content of lymph is only about one third that of plasma.

The Lymphatic Circulation. In the body it is difficult to find the **lymph vessels,** or **lymphatics,** because they are so delicate. However, the network of lymph vessels (Fig. 17-17) is very extensive and reaches all parts of the body. The lymphatics drain lymph directly

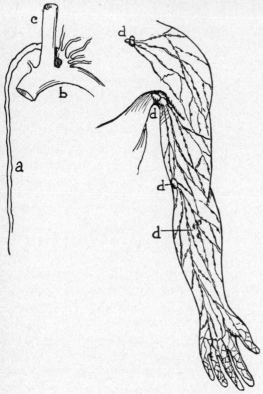

Fig. 17-17. Part of the lymphatic system of man. On left, thoracic duct (a) opening into left subclavian vein (b); c, internal jugular vein. On right, lymphatics of hand and forearm; d, lymph nodes. (From *The Living Body*, by Best and Taylor. Holt, Rinehart and Winston, Inc.)

from the tissue spaces, and carry the lymph slowly from the outlying parts toward the thorax.

In the thorax the lymphatic network drains into the two main lymph vessels of the body: (1) the **thoracic duct** and (2) the **right lymphatic duct.** The thoracic duct is the largest lymph vessel in the body, since it drains lymph not only from the digestive tract, but also from the *whole left side* of the body and from the right *leg* and *trunk.* The lymph

vessels of the digestive tract pass into the mesentery where they form larger vessels, called the **lacteals.** The lacteals converge toward the root of the mesentery, just below the diaphragm, where they flow together into the **thoracic duct.** This large vessel passes upward through the thorax, where it finally terminates by emptying into the **left subclavian vein** (Fig. 17-17). Meanwhile the thoracic duct receives tributaries from *all* of the left and *part* of the right sides of the body. The smaller **right lymphatic duct** has an equivalent course and position on the right side of the thorax. It collects lymph from the lymphatic network of the right arm, the right sides of the head, neck, and thorax, and delivers this lymph into the **right subclavian vein.** Thus the lymph, which filters from the blood in all the capillaries of the body, returns to the blood via the subclavian veins.

The Flow of Lymph. Lymph flows very slowly, as compared to blood. A given sample of blood returns to the heart within less than a minute after it is pumped forth from the heart. But an hour or more elapses before a sample of lymph, formed in the leg, finds its way back into the blood stream. Lymph pressure, which sustains this sluggish flow, originates from the fact that new lymph is continually forced from the capillaries into the already filled tissue spaces. Lymph pressure amounts to only about 8 mm of mercury; but there are many valves in the lymphatics, and these valves prevent any backflow. Moreover many parts of the lymphatic network lie between the muscles of the body, and thus whenever a muscle contracts and presses against its neighbors, the lymph is driven forward in a considerable part of the local network.

The Lymph Nodes (Glands). These oval masses of **lymphoid tissue** are situated in strategic positions in the lymphatic network, especially at points where the smaller lymph vessels converge to form larger ones (Fig. 17-17). There are several groups of unusually large nodes: in the knee and elbow joints;

in the groin and armpits; and along the sides of the neck.

The lymph nodes constitute a reserve line of defense against bacterial infection. The lymphoid tissues in the nodes (and in the tonsils, spleen, and intestinal wall) give rise to the lymphocytes (p. 322); and the nodes also tend to "strain" the lymph as it passes through. If bacteria from the site of an infection manage to elude the locally mobilized phagocytes, they are carried in the lymph stream toward the more vital centers of the body. But in passing through the lymph glands, most if not all of these bacteria are likely to be destroyed by the phagocytes in the nodes. Accordingly, lymph glands are frequently swollen during any infection; and the position of the swollen glands provides an index of the site of the infection: a swelling of the nodes of the groin indicates a leg infection; swellings in the armpit indicate an infection in the arm.

Edema. Any part of the body tends to swell if lymph accumulates in the tissue spaces. Such a condition, which is called **edema,** may result from a variety of factors, such as: (1) high blood pressure, as in certain kinds of heart disease; (2) low plasma tonicity due to an excessive loss of plasma proteins, as in chronic kidney disease; (3) abnormally permeable capillaries, due to a severe local damage of the tissues (for example, spraining an ankle); or (4) obstruction of the lymphatics draining the particular part. In edema, the skin and other tissues become very puffy; and if pressed, edematous tissue remains indented much longer than is normal.

The Spleen. The spleen is a large reddish-brown organ (Fig. 17-16) occupying a dorsal position in the upper part of the abdominal cavity, where it comes in contact with the dorsal surface of the stomach and the upper extremity of the left kidney. Structurally the spleen resembles a lymph node, except for its size, which is somewhat larger than the kidney. Also the spleen possesses considerable muscle tissue in its capsule and internal framework. This permits the organ to expand and contract, increasing or decreasing the quantity of blood contained within its spongy structure.

For many years the function of this vascular organ remained obscure, but now it is clear that the spleen serves mainly as a sort of blood bank from which reserves of blood, and particularly of red cells, may be mobilized when needed in the circulation. In the cat, for example, it is estimated that as much as one quarter of the erythrocytes and one sixth of the plasma may be present in the expanded spleen; and most of these reserves can be launched into circulation when the spleen contracts completely, as it does during heavy muscular activity, or after severe hemorrhage. In addition, the spleen has several minor functions. It cooperates with the other lymphoid tissues of the body in the production of lymphocytes and in the phagocytosis of effete erythrocytes. In the embryo, moreover, the spleen takes part in the production of new erythrocytes.

Antibody Production; Role of the Thymus Glands. It has long been accepted that lymphoid cells contribute heavily to the production of antibodies in the body. However, no involvement of the thymus gland was suspected until some recent thymectomy (surgical removal of the thymus) experiments were reported by Jacques F. A. P. Miller, an Australian investigator, working at the Chester Beatty Research Institute in London. In fact, the functional importance of the thymus, a gland that lies subjacent to the upper part of the breast bone, has long remained a mystery, despite the fact that in prepubertal mammals the thymus constitutes a conspicuous mass of lymphoid tissue, accounting for almost 1 percent of the body weight. In postpubertal individuals, however, the thymus tissue atrophies and finally it is scarcely distinguishable from the surrounding adipose tissue.

Miller used mice in his experiments and other workers have obtained confirmatory evidence with the same animal. But in addition, Sir Macfarland Burnet, another Australian worker, has reported analogous evidence in birds. In the bird, however, another enigmatic lymphoid organ, the bursa of Fabricius, collaborates with the thymus in influencing antibody production.

Thymectomy in an adolescent or an adult mouse has very little, if any, physiological effect. But if the thymus is removed at birth —and it requires great skill to excise this pinhead-sized body from a newly delivered mouseling—the consequences are remarkable. The mouselings develop quite normally for some 3 weeks, but soon thereafter they are prone to sicken and die; and the cause of death is usually some common infection. Moreover, further tests reveal that the anti-body, or gamma globulin, fraction (p. 505) is virtually absent from the plasma of such thymectomized individuals.

Another important observation is that such thymectomized individuals are able to accept skin grafts, not only from themselves, but also from unrelated strains of mice and even from a rat (Fig. 17-18). Such successful **heterotransplants** are most unusual. Ordinarily the antibody mechanisms of the animal lead to a rejection of the foreign tissue shortly after it has started to grow, although **homotransplants** from one site to another in the same individual (or transplants from an identical twin) are generally successful. Thus again the conclusion seems to be that the immuno-

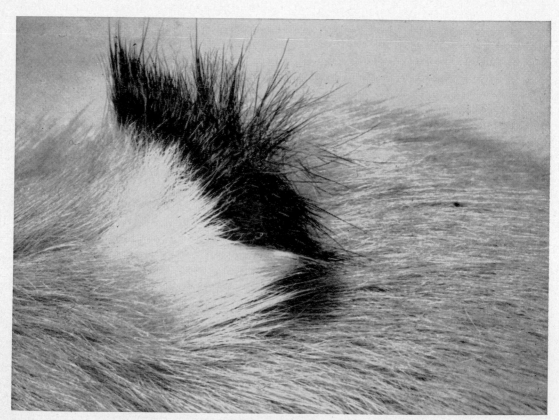

Fig. 17-18. Removal of the **thymus gland** from a mouse 1 to 3 days after birth leads to a severe impairment of the immunity responses. This postnatally thymectomized mouse, tested at the age of 5 weeks, accepted and maintained two foreign skin grafts: (1) from an **unrelated mouse** (strain C3H), as is shown by the patch of black hair, which grew in quickly; and (2) from a white **rat** (Wistar strain), as is shown by the white patch. Normally, of course, in a nonoperated animal, vigorous immune reactions would have led to a rejection of these **heterografts**. (Courtesy of Jacques F. A. P. Miller, The Chester Beatty Research Institute and the New York Academy of Sciences.)

logical defenses of the thymectomized animal do not function properly when a thymectomy is performed during the first few days of postnatal life.

Miller and others have postulated that the thymus represents the *primary source* of immunologically active lymphoid cells in the young mammal. Mitotic activity in the fetal and early postnatal thymus is very high. It is presumed that many of the lymphoid cells produced are soon despatched from the thymus to the other lymphoid stations of the body—particularly to the lymph nodes and spleen—where multiplication continues. The importance of the primary source, accordingly, diminishes with age. Eventually, therefore, the thymus tends to atrophy. The actual production of antibody proteins occurs mainly in the lymph nodes, particularly in masses of special cells, called **plasma cells.** These are derived from the primary lymphoid cells. In any event, the masses of plasma cells become exceptionally conspicuous in lymph nodes when these are located near an infected area (p. 335).

There are many unsolved problems in immunology, however: Are there many kinds of plasma cells, each responsible for the production of a particular antibody protein; or can one kind produce a variety of antibodies, when stimulated by the presence of the corresponding antigens? How is the very precise specificity of the antigen-antibody relationship determined? Does the antigen provide a template (p. 134) for the synthesis of a corresponding antibody—and if so, how? Considerable progress has been made recently in analyzing the structure of the antibody proteins in the gamma globulin (p. 505) fraction of the plasma. Thus it seems likely that some of these questions will, in the near future, receive definitive answers.

TEST QUESTIONS

1. Why is a circulatory system essential in all larger animals? What are the general functions of the circulatory system?
2. Specify two kinds of animals possessing direct (hemolymph) circulations, and two kinds of animals possessing indirect (blood-lymph) circulations; explain the essential differences between these types of circulation, and relate these differences to the question of "efficiency."
3. Exchanges between the blood and the cells of an organ cannot occur in the arteries and veins, but only in the capillaries. Is this statement true, and if so, why (at least two reasons)?
4. Differentiate between erythrocytes, leucocytes, and thrombocytes on the basis of: (a) size and form; (b) abundance in the blood; (c) general functions; (d) origin.
5. Differentiate between diapedesis and phagocytosis; explain the importance of these processes in relation to the body's defenses against bacterial infection.
6. What other defense mechanisms are localized: (a) in the plasma; and (b) in the lymph glands?
7. Without vitamin K the body is unable to synthesize prothrombase. Predict the effects of a diet that is very low in K, explaining your answer fully.
8. Propose three different methods by which you might prevent a sample of blood from clotting while you were withdrawing it into a test tube. Carefully explain the basis of each method in relation to the clotting mechanisms.
9. Differentiate between arteries, veins, and capillaries as to: (a) structure; (b) function; (c) the relative pressure of the conducted blood.
10. Explain the physiological basis for the adage "a man is as young as his arteries," stressing the importance of the "elasticity factor."
11. Make a labeled diagram to show the relations of a capillary to the lymph and the surrounding tissue cells.
12. Assuming that the foregoing tissue is a muscle, explain how and why:
    a. glucose passes from the blood into the cells
    b. oxygen passes from the blood into the cells
    c. carbon dioxide passes from the cells into the blood

d. other metabolic wastes pass from the cells into the blood

13. Why is the formation of lymph described as a *force* filtration?

14. Why is this process also called a *colloidal* filtration?

15. Compare the compositions of the plasma and lymph in regard to: (a) protein content; (b) content of glucose and amino acids; (c) content of urea and inorganic salts; (d) relative tonicity.

16. Carefully explain the balance of forces that accounts for:
    a. the escape of lymph from the plasma
    b. the backflow of some lymph into the plasma
    c. the flow of lymph from the tissue spaces into the lymphatics

17. Trace the general course followed by the lymphatics which drain the tissue spaces of each of the following regions: (a) wall of the small intestine; (b) left side of trunk and head; (c) left leg; (d) right leg; (e) right side of the thorax and head.

18. Is there any relation between the position of a "swollen gland" (lymph node) and the site of a particular infection? Explain.

19. Explain the relation between muscular activity and the flowing of the lymph. Of what importance are the lymphatic valves?

20. Differentiate between a single and a double type of circulation; and between a two-chambered and a four-chambered heart.

21. On what grounds is the circulation of man and other mammals regarded as "more efficient" than the circulation of the primitive vertebrates (fish)?

22. In man and other mammals, all the blood that returns from the systemic circuit via the postcaval or precaval veins must pass through the pulmonary circuit before reaching the aorta and starting anew on the systemic circuit (Fig. 17-10). Demonstrate the truth of this statement by listing in proper sequence the heart chambers, arteries, and veins through which a certain sample of the blood would have to pass in flowing from the postcaval, or one of the precaval veins, to the aorta.

23. List in proper sequence the main branches of the aorta (trunk line of the systemic circuit) and specify the parts or organs supplied by each main branch. What three main veins return the systemic blood to the right auricle?

24. As to the composition (aerated vs. unaerated) of the blood conveyed:
    (a) how does the pulmonary artery differ from all other arteries;
    (b) how does the pulmonary vein differ from other veins?

25. Make a labeled diagram to show how the aorta, the carotids, the subclavian, and the pulmonary arteries were evolved from the gill arches of primitive vertebrates.

26. Make a labeled diagram showing the relations of the hepatic portal vein to the gastrointestinal tract, the liver, and the postcaval vein.

27. On the basis of the foregoing diagram, explain why it is impossible for substances absorbed from the gastrointestinal tract to reach the general circulation without first coming under the influence of the liver tissues.

28. Summarize what is known about the spleen and its functions.

29. Discuss the nature and significance of the Rh factor.

30. Explain the nature and significance of the blood groups in man.

31. Discuss the functions of the thymus gland. Give experimental evidence.

FURTHER READINGS

1. *The Living Body*, by C. H. Best and N. B. Taylor; New York, 1958.
2. *The Machinery of the Body*, by A. J. Carlson and V. Johnson; Chicago, 1953.
3. *Textbook of Anatomy and Physiology*, by Kimber, Gray, and Stackpole; New York, 1955.
4. *Blood Groups and Transfusions*, by A. S. Weiner; Springfield (Ill.), 1943.
5. *Biology*, by C. A. Villee; Philadelphia, 1962.

18-*Absorption, Metabolism, and the Diet*

ABSORPTION

The major burden of absorption falls upon the small intestine, and all organic and inorganic food compounds, except water, enter the circulation mainly through the wall of this part of the gut.

The large absorbing capacity of the small bowel depends upon its very great surface. The intestinal mucosa comes into contact with the chyme throughout a length of 23 feet, and throughout this distance the intestinal wall is richly supplied with blood capillaries and lymph channels. Consequently ample opportunity is afforded for the blood and lymph in the intestinal wall to come into equilibrium with the chyme. Moreover, the intestinal mucosa does not have a flat surface. In fact, as mentioned earlier, this surface resembles velvet, in that it is studded with numerous hairlike **villi,** which provide at least a tenfold increase of the absorbing area (Fig. 16-25).

As may be seen in Figure 18-1, each **villus**

is well designed to perform the function of absorption. A network of blood capillaries extends out into the villus, and there is a **central lymph vessel** at the core. The wall of this lymph vessel, unlike the capillary wall, is perforated by definite flaps, which communicate with the tissue spaces. The blood flows very rapidly through the capillaries of the villus, but the lymph moves very slowly through its channels. Slowly the lymph filters from the capillaries, seeping through the tissue spaces. Then the lymph enters the central lymph vessel and drains away to the network of lymphatics in the wall of the intestine. (Fig. 18-1).

The transfer of food compounds from the chyme into the blood and lymph is greatly influenced by the structure of the villi. Essentially the chyme is an aqueous solution containing the various digested food products, and these compounds are all able to pass into either the blood or the lymph. But a large part of the **sugars** and **amino acids** are picked up by the blood stream, because the

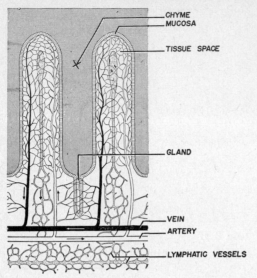

CHYME
MUCOSA
TISSUE SPACE
GLAND
VEIN
ARTERY
LYMPHATIC VESSELS

Fig. 18-1. Diagrammatic section of two villi, showing the blood and lymphatic vessels. Note that the wall of the **central lymph vessel** in each villus is imperfect, i.e., perforated by gaps. The interstices among the blood and lymph vessels are occupied by connective tissue, in which the tissue spaces are filled with lymph.

blood keeps changing rapidly in the capillaries. Time is not afforded for the blood to become fully saturated with the food products as they are absorbed. But the lymph flows so slowly that the concentration of each foodstup soon becomes approximately the same in the lymph as in the chyme. Then there is little or no tendency for the food molecules to enter the lymph, except in very small quantities, as the old lymph is replaced by new.

The absorption of **fatty materials** (glycerol and fatty acids) is quite different. The glycerol and fatty acids recombine into fats as they pass through the mucosa of the villus; and this resynthesized fat appears in the form of fine globules in the lymph of the tissue spaces—just subjacent to the mucosa. Such fat globules are not able to enter the blood through the capillary walls. Accordingly, the fat globules are slowly carried into the central lymph vessel, which conveys them to the lymphatic network. After a fat-rich meal, the **lacteals** (p. 334), pasing through the mesentery toward the **thoracic duct,** dis-

play a conspicuously white, milky hue, indicating that the lymph at this time is essentially a fatty emulsion.

Water and inorganic salts—as well as sugars and amino acids—are absorbed primarily into the blood stream. But the quantity of water leaving the small intestine is more or less counterbalanced by the water entering via the digestive juices. The absorption of salts, to some extent, appears to involve active transport processes. In any event, certain salts are absorbed preferentially—to an extent that is difficult to explain in terms of differences in the permeability of the various ions. Also the absorption of glucose and amino acids is definitely augmented by active transport processes, requiring the expenditure of energy by the cells of the intestinal mucosa.

In summary, the nonfatty food components are absorbed chiefly into the blood of the hepatic portal system, whereas the fatty foods are taken mostly into the lymph. But since the lymph gradually drains into the blood stream via the thoracic duct, the eventual distribution of all the food components is effected by the blood.

THE LIVER AND ITS SPECIAL METABOLIC FUNCTIONS

The liver occupies a strategic position in the vertebrate circulation (Fig. 17-16), and on this account the vertebrate liver has assumed several important metabolic functions. Probably the liver originated as an ordinary digestive gland, but in modern vertebrates it is an exceptionally large mass of tissue, possessing a wide variety of enzymes. All the blood from the digestive tract passes to the liver capillaries via the hepatic portal system. Accordingly, the cells of the liver are in position to extract various absorbed products from the blood and chemically to alter these compounds before allowing them to pass on into the general circulation.

Conversion of Other Sugars to Glucose. Although carbohydrates are absorbed into the blood stream mainly in the form of glucose, small quantities of other monosaccharides (fructose and galactose) also get into the portal circulation. On reaching the liver, these other sugars are converted into glucose, which is the kind of sugar best suited to the needs of the tissues generally.

Regulation of the Blood Glucose Level. During the absorption of a carbohydrate-rich meal, the glucose concentration in the portal blood may rise considerably. But if simultaneously a sample of blood from the general circulation is analyzed, there is not a corresponding rise in the sugar content. The excess sugar has been removed from the portal blood as it flows through the hepatic capillaries. The liver cells convert the extra glucose into glycogen, storing this stable reserve of carbohydrate for the future needs of the body. Thus, the liver of a well-nourished dog or man may contain as much as 20 percent (by dry weight) of glycogen.

Conversely, after fasting, the portal blood contains very little glucose. Nonetheless, a sample of blood from the general circulation displays a normal sugar content. The difference has been made up in the liver by a hydrolysis of part of the glycogen reserves into glucose.

The liver, therefore, has the important function of maintaining a constant supply of glucose in the circulation. Normally the blood glucose level remains at about 0.1 percent; and this amount is just adequate to supply the needs of the tissues. When the glucose absorbed into the portal blood goes higher, the liver stores glucose as glycogen; but when the blood sugar tends to fall below normal, glucose is mobilized from liver glycogen.

This blood-sugar control is of great importance in the economy of the body. **Hyperglycemia,** or excess blood sugar, is wasteful, since the kidneys begin to excrete glucose under this circumstance—and "sugar in the urine" (**glycosuria**) results. Conversely, a gravely lowered blood sugar (**hypoglycemia**) is dangerous. Lacking an adequate sugar supply, the tissues cannot function properly.

The patient sinks into a state of **hypoglycemic shock,** which may prove fatal unless glucose is provided quickly—usually by intravenous injection.

Some glycogen is stored in the muscles, and a small amount of this **muscle glycogen** may be drawn upon to maintain the blood sugar. However, muscle glycogen acts mainly as a local fuel deposit, available for muscular work (p. 435).

The endocrine glands (Chap. 22) cooperate with the liver in maintaining the blood sugar level. **Adrenalin** (p. 406) stimulates the liver to convert glycogen to glucose; whereas **insulin** (p. 408) prevents a too rapid breakdown of glycogen. A diabetic patient, lacking insulin, fails to store glycogen in normal fashion; in addition, the tissues of a diabetic partly lose their capacity to utilize glucose. In diabetes, consequently, sugar accumulates in the blood and drains off in the urine. A suitable injection of insulin removes both of these impairments, and the blood sugar comes back to normal. Such injections must be calibrated with the utmost care, however. If the injection is too large, the patient may be thrown into "insulin shock" from the resulting hypoglycemia.

After a meal containing large amounts of sugar, a *normal* individual may temporarily display hyperglycemia and glycosuria; but this merely indicates that the liver is not able to cope completely with such a sudden flood of glucose, absorbed from the digestive tract.

Deamination and Urea Formation. The primary function of the **amino acids** is to enable the tissues to synthesize their essential protein components. An ample protein diet, however, provides the body with an excess of amino acids; and under these circumstances the *extra* amino acids are used as fuel.

Deamination (p. 138) must occur before an amino acid can be fully oxidized; and in mammals, this important catabolic function is delegated very largely to the cells of the liver. During the absorption of a protein-rich meal, a superabundance of amino acids is found in the portal blood. But in the liver, these *excess* amino acids are **deaminated.** Deamination liberates the carbon-hydrogen oxygen residues (CHO residues) of the molecules for oxidation by the body tissues; simultaneously the amino parts of the molecules go into the formation of **urea,** the main nitrogenous waste in man and other *mammals.*

Deamination, as it is accomplished in the mammalian liver, does not occur by the direct process that was described previously (p. 138). In the liver, in fact, the amino fractions that are discharged from the various amino acids do not appear as free ammonia (NH_3), but are *transferred* to one particular amino acid, namely **ornithine,** which is thus transformed to **arginine:**

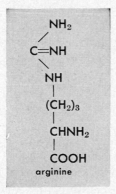

Then arginine decomposes, liberating **urea.** The importance of arginine, therefore, is that it acts as an intermediary in the formation of urea. Arginine receives amino nitrogen from the various other amino acids and transfers this nitrogen to urea, a relatively nontoxic waste product (see column 2, top).

To a small extent the mammalian kidney also engages in the deamination of amino acids. The kidney deaminations are *direct,* however, and lead to the production of NH_3 (p. 378). In fact, the kidney utilizes this ammonia in neutralizing various acid metabolites, which otherwise would tend to acidify the system unduly (see column 2, bottom).

Urea is not eliminated by the liver, but passes through the blood stream to the kidneys. Accordingly, a considerable quantity

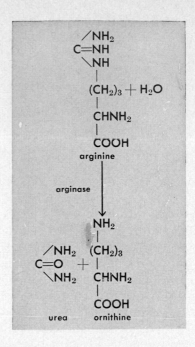

of this crystalline end product of amino acid catabolism is present in the urine of man and other mammals. In birds and reptiles, however, much of the urea is converted, also in the liver, into a more complex nitrogen compound, **uric acid,** and uric acid is the chief nitrogenous waste excreted by these other vertebrates. Some uric acid is also excreted by man and other mammals; but *in mammals uric acid is derived from the catabolism of nucleic acids.*

The nonnitrogenous compounds produced by the deamination of the amino acids are all relatively simple organic acids (p. 138). These CHO residues may be sent to other tissues in the body; or they may be retained by the liver for conversion into glucose and

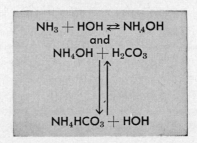

glycogen. In short, the organic acids liberated by deamination are utilized by the body in one manner or another.

Action of the Liver on Fats. True fats are absorbed mainly in an emulsified form and cannot pass directly into the cells of most of the tissues. But certain cells, especially in the liver, are able to engulf fat globules—by a process that resembles phagocytosis. In the liver these special cells are called **Kupffer cells.** The Kupffer cells project partially into the capillaries, and in this strategic position they take in fat globules and other granular material from the passing blood stream.

The fats are partially catabolized in the liver before passing to the other body tissues. The liver chemically alters the fatty materials, increasing their capacity to be absorbed and oxidized by other tissues. A partial **desaturation** of the fat molecules results from the action of liver dehydrogenases; and the double bonds thus introduced into the carbon chains make the fats more susceptible to further oxidation. Moreover, the partially oxidized intermediary products of fat catabolism are more soluble in the blood and lymph and more easily distributed throughout the body.

Other Functions of the Liver. The liver has a number of other special functions. Organic toxins (p. 315), produced by bacteria in the large intestine, are absorbed into the portal blood. But the liver prevents these compounds from reaching toxic levels in the general circulation. A variety of special enzymes are present in the liver cells, and these convert the toxic products into nontoxic compounds. In some cases the toxin is merely combined with some other substance (for example, benzoic acid is combined with an amino acid, glycine) to form a nontoxic compound, which later is eliminated by the kidneys. However, the **detoxifying** reactions in the liver are very complex and varied.

Other hepatic functions, such as the **synthesis of prothrombase** and the **secretion of bile** (p. 323), have been mentioned previously; still other functions, such as the **storage of vitamins A, D, and B_{12} (APA),** will be mentioned later.

GENERAL METABOLISM: A BALANCED DIET

On any long-term basis, the daily intake of food must be sufficient (1) to provide the *energy* expended by the body; (2) to provide the *proper kinds of matter* from which the body assembles and synthesizes its essential components. The first of these objectives is fulfilled by catabolism, and the second, by anabolism—each taken as a whole.

The Energy Requirement: Destructive Metabolism. The only source of energy available to the human body is the decomposition of organic compounds, such as proteins, carbohydrates, and fats, and the derivatives of these substances. Carbohydrates and proteins each yield about 4 Calories of energy, and fats 9 Calories, per gram utilized in metabolism. Provided the final products of decomposition are the same, these energy quantities are constant, regardless of the intermediary course of metabolism, and regardless of whether the reactions occur inside or outside the living body.

The most direct method of determining the energy expenditure of an individual is to measure the total *heat* output of the body. All other forms of energy (movement, electricity, etc.) that are generated during metabolism are finally and totally converted to heat, which is given off to the environment.

Measuring the heat output of the human body—a procedure called **direct calorimetry** —is very difficult. The subject must be confined for a long period in a heat-insulated chamber, which is equipped with complicated devices for collecting and measuring the total heat given off by the body. Such experiments have been done, and they prove conclusively that (1) if the caloric content of the utilized foods is just equal to the energy expended, the body weight remains unchanged; (2) if the calories of the food are less than the expended energy, the body weight decreases; and (3) if the energy of the absorbed food is more than that expended, the body weight increases.

In recent times, **metabolism tests** involving a direct measurement of the heat output have been supplanted by **indirect calorimetry.** When this method is employed, the patient's consumption of oxygen and production of carbon dioxide are accurately tallied for a given length of time. These figures provide a basis for calculating not only how much total food has been oxidized, but also the proportions of the carbohydrates, fats, and proteins that have been utilized. However, in addition to the oxygen and carbon dioxide data, the output of urea and other nitrogenous end products must be considered if an accurate diagnosis of the patient's metabolism is to be obtained.

The Basal Metabolic Rate. The daily energy expenditure varies widely, depending on the general activity of a person, as well as upon a variety of other factors. To obtain the **basal metabolism** it is necessary to standardize conditions very strictly. The subject must fast overnight before the test, and must recline in a completely relaxed condition during the test. Also the *age, weight,* and *bodily proportions* must be considered in establishing the normal standards.

For a *man* of average weight and proportions (150 pounds, 5 feet, 8 inches, the **normal basal metabolism** is about 1600 Calories *daily.* More than half of this energy goes toward maintaining the body temperature, which is considerably above the usual environmental level. The main loss of heat is from the body *surface,* and consequently the bodily proportions are very important in determining the proper standard. For short stout individuals, the proportion of surface to weight is at a minimum. Consequently such a person has a normal basal metabolism somewhat lower than 1600 Calories.

The remainder of the basal energy expenditure represents the work done by the vital organs in the maintenance of life. The heart must work ceaselessly, and this is also true of the muscles of breathing. Under basal conditions not much work is done by the musculature of the digestive tract, or of the body wall, since the subject has been fasting and is not maintaining an upright posture.

In recent years measurements of the basal metabolism are frequently used in medical diagnosis. Abnormally high basal metabolisms are encountered in patients with an overactive **thyroid gland** (hyperthyroidism) and in fevers. A low metabolism, on the other hand, may indicate hypothyroidism; a deficiency of the **adrenal** or **pituitary glands;** or just plain undernutrition.

Metabolic Rates under Other Conditions. If the subject is allowed to eat, but remains in bed, the metabolism rises to 1800 Calories. The extra energy (200 Calories) goes mainly into the secretory work of the digestive glands, and to the muscular movements of the digestive tract. However, the taking of food, especially proteins, has a stimulating effect upon general metabolism. When sedentary work as well as food is allowed, the metabolism will average about 2400 Calories. This additional energy (600 Calories) goes mainly to the work of the body muscles in maintaining posture and in performing daily routine movements. Under these circumstances, however, the work of the heart is also greater, since a more active circulation through the brain, muscles, and digestive tract is required. A manual laborer will usually expend from 3000 to 5000 Calories, depending on the intensity and duration of the work.

Availability of Energy from Different Foods. Disregarding the structural needs of the body and reckoning only in terms of *energy* requirements, one type of food may substitute quite equally for another. A very high protein diet increases the daily output of nitrogenous wastes and puts extra work upon the kidneys; but the kidneys can safely handle the extra load if they are in good condition. Too high a proportion of fat (more than 40 percent of all the Caloric expenditure) is to be avoided, however. Fatty substances do not "burn" very completely when the tissues lack carbohydrates to oxidize simultaneously.

In the body considerable interconversion takes place among the foodstuffs (p. 156). Many amino acids can be converted to glucose; and carbohydrates can be converted to fat. However, there is only a very limited conversion of fatty materials into carbohydrate, and only the nonessential amino acids (p. 136) can be derived from nonprotein foods. Most natural foods are mixtures containing some of each kind of the main organic nutrients (Table 18-1). Consequently the problem of meeting the *energy* requirements of the body is largely a matter of getting a sufficient *quantity* of food.

inorganic foods were not considered, simply because these substances do not supply energy to the body. But there are a number of essential inorganic compounds in the protoplasm; and unless the intake and output of these substances are balanced, the body cannot maintain its normal functions.

Inorganic Requirements. The *water* balance of the body is very important. Each day an average individual loses about 2000 cc of water via the urine, sweat, feces, and expired air. These losses must be restored very regularly, or else the tissues become seriously dehydrated. The body dies of "thirst" more quickly than from starvation in the ordinary sense.

Table 18-1—Analysis of Some Common Foods
(Percentage by Weight)

	Water	*Protein*	*Fat*	*Carbo-hydrates*	*Inorganic Matter*
Meat	76.6	20.6	1.4	0.2	1.2
Eggs	73.8	12.8	12.2	....	1.2
Milk	87.8	3.4	3.2	4.8	0.8
White bread	35.7	7.3	0.2	55.6	1.2
Potatoes	75.6	2.2	0.3	20.8	1.1
Fruit	86.0	1.5	....	10.0	2.5

Starvation. When the total consumption of food is inadequate to meet the energy expenditure, the body begins to sacrifice its existing fund of organic materials. First to go are the carbohydrate stores, mainly the glycogen of the liver and muscles. Simultaneously fat is gradually withdrawn from the adipose tissues. When the fat and carbohydrate reserves have been exhausted, the body begins to consume its own essential structural components—the proteins, phospholipids, etc., in the tissues of the less essential organs of the body. Finally the protoplasmic constituents of the essential organs (brain, spinal cord, and heart) are drawn upon; but when this occurs, death rapidly becomes inevitable.

Constructive Metabolism: Essential Kinds of Foods. From an *energy* point of view the

The replenishment of salts is also important. The body loses about 30 grams of assorted minerals each day via the urine, sweat, and feces. Most natural foods contain approximately the proper proportions of the protoplasmic salts (p. 75), although plant foods are generally low in NaCl. Consequently man has learned to use the crystalline form of this salt to supplement his own diet and the diets of his domestic animals.

Severe muscular work carried on in a hot environment induces a very large loss of salts (and water) via the perspiration. When this condition is carried to an extreme, the worker develops "miner's cramp," a painful spasm involving a large part of the musculature. Such workers are rabidly thirsty, but to drink water only aggravates the condition by increasing the flow of sweat and accelerating the loss of salt. Finally it was learned that salt water should be provided, and during hot heavy work, salt solutions can be drunk without distaste.

Certain *specific* minerals are regularly needed by the body for the synthesis of its essential components. The minerals most likely to be deficient in the diet are iron, calcium, and iodine. Without a source of iron, from the organic and inorganic components of our food, the body cannot continue to synthesize hemoglobin, and anemia must result. However, most meats (especially liver), eggs, and many fruits and vegetables provide an adequate source of iron. Calcium compounds are necessary for the formation of bone and teeth: about 1.0 gram for children; 2.0 grams for women during pregnancy and nursing; and 0.8 gram for other adults—computed on a daily basis, in terms of the calcium content. The best source of this mineral is milk, although cereals and such vegetables as beans and peas are also rich in calcium. Most meats provide a good source of phosphorus, which is essential for the synthesis of ATP, nucleic acids, etc., as well as for a proper formation of bones and teeth.

Without iodine the body cannot synthesize **thyroxin,** the essential hormone of the thyroid gland; and the resulting **hypothyroidism** (p. 403) represents a very serious and, in former times, fairly prevalent disease. Iodine is especially abundant in the sea and in seafoods. Formerly, iodine deficiencies were encountered mainly in populations living in inland regions that never were inundated by the ocean during any geological period. Nowadays, however, dietary hypothyroidism (including **cretinism**) is seldom found, due mainly to the fact that commercial salts are artificially fortified by the addition of small amounts of potassium iodide (KI).

Recent investigations indicate that health-maintaining diets must contain zinc, copper, manganese, cobalt, and perhaps one or two other metals. But only the merest traces of these substances are sufficient. These **trace metals** appear to be needed for the activation of some of the metabolic enzymes, and most natural diets contain more than adequate amounts of the trace elements.

Organic Requirements. In addition to the fuel foods, 50 grams of protein, at the very least, must be included in the diet of an adult, and more protein is needed in growing individuals. Such a quantity of protein provides only the minimal amount and variety of the amino acids needed by the tissues for the synthesis of essential proteins. As in animals generally, the cells of the human body cannot synthesize all of the amino acids from simpler substances. Consequently the body depends upon a ready-made supply of these nonsynthesizable (**essential**) amino acids. Not all protein foods are equally valuable in contributing these **essential amino acids,** as may be seen in Table 18-2.

Some natural fat must also be included in a balanced diet. The body is able to synthesize all except a few of the fatty acids, but these specific exceptions are essential. Also, natural fats are our main source of some of the vitamins, without which the body cannot grow or function properly.

The Vitamins. In 1912 it was definitely proved that *animals* cannot survive on diets in which the organic food is provided entirely by *purified* proteins, carbohydrates, and lipids. This result indicated that the natural sources of organic food must contain small amounts of then unknown essential substances, which were named the vitamins. Since 1912, many experiments have been performed, using all kinds of controlled diets; and these experiments have amply substantiated the **vitamin hypothesis.** At the present time, therefore, it is possible to define the missing factors very precisely. Each vitamin is a simple specific organic food compound, regularly needed by an animal in very small amounts for the maintenance of health, growth, and even of life itself. Almost all the vitamins have now been identified as essential **coenzymes** without which a number of important steps in cellular metabolism cannot proceed (see Table 18-3). Thus if any

Table 18-2*—Character of Proteins in Some Common Foods

Food	Chief Proteins Present	Amino Acid Constitution
Milk and cheese	Casein Lactalbumin	Complete, but low in cystine Complete
Corn (maize)	Zein	Lacks *lysine* and *tryptophan,* and is low in cystine
Eggs	Ovalbumin Ovovitelline	Complete Complete
Meat	Albumin Myosin	Complete Complete
Peas	Legumin Gliadin	Incomplete, low in cystine Incomplete, lacks *lysine*
Wheat	Glutenin	Complete
Gelatin	Gelatin	Incomplete, lacking *tryptophan* and tyrosine; very low in cystine

Italicized amino acids are **essential.**
* From Best and Taylor, *The Living Body,* 4th Ed., 1963.

vitamin necessary to the species is regularly absent from the diet, the animal begins to show specific symptoms, which can be recognized as one of the **deficiency diseases,** or **avitaminoses,** and eventually the animal dies unless the deficiency is corrected.

Because of its historic interest, vitamin C will be used to exemplify the vitamins generally. Scurvy, the **avitaminosis** which develops when vitamin C is absent from the diet, was described very accurately by Richard Hawkins, more than 350 years ago. Hawkins, a captain in the English navy, observed the bleeding gums, bruised skin, anemia, and general weakness that developed in the crew when a sailing vessel had been at sea for many months and all supplies of fresh fruits and vegetables had been exhausted. Hawkins also observed that a small amount of lime juice, added to the daily menu of the crew, was completely effective in preventing the development of the **scorbutic symptoms.**

In 1933, Albert Szent-Gyorgyi, the well-known Hungarian biochemist and Nobel laureate, now working in the United States, first succeeded in isolating and purifying vitamin C—which proved to be **ascorbic acid** ($C_6H_8O_6$). Meanwhile, many other vitamins have now been identified (Table 18-3), and all have been found to be relatively simple organic compounds that can be absorbed without digestion—if they are present in the foods of the animal. Moreover, each vitamin is specific in relieving the particular symptoms caused by its deficiency. Only ascorbic acid (or compounds from which the body can derive ascorbic acid) is effective in preventing or relieving the specific symptoms of scurvy (Fig. 18-2).

In scurvy, the main symptoms are generally attributed to a weakening of the walls of the arterioles and capillaries. The scorbutic animal displays spontaneous bleeding —in the gums and joints, and beneath the skin—and this may account for the fact that scorbutic individuals are very susceptible to bruises. Probably the anemia is likewise a result of internal bleeding, although some re-

Table 18-3—Principal Vitamins

Names and Chemical Nature	Specific Metabolic or Physiological Role, If Known	Deficiency Symptoms	Good Natural (Food) Sources
Vitamin A, $C_{20}H_{30}O$; provitamin = **carotene**, $C_{40}H_{56}$, a yellow plant pigment	Precursor in the synthesis of **rhodopsin**, the photosensitive pigment of the **rods** of the retina (p. 423)	**Night blindness**, in mild cases; **xerophthalmia**, in severe deficiency; abnormal changes in various epithelial membranes; retarded growth	Animal oils, especially the liver oils of certain fish; egg yolk; yellow and green vegetables
Vitamin B_1; **thiamine**, $C_{12}H_{16}N_4SO$	Provides for the synthesis of **thiamine pyrophosphate**, coenzyme active in metabolism of **pyruvic acid** (see p. 155)	**Beriberi**, **polyneuritis**: loss of appetite, weight and vigor; progressive paralysis, retarded growth	Cereal grains, especially the outer seed coats; meats, especially pork; yeast
Vitamin B_2; **riboflavin**, $C_{17}H_{20}N_4O_6$	Necessary for the formation of **flavin adenine dinucleotide** (FAD), coenzyme important in metabolism of glucose and some amino acids (p. 145)	Predisposition to cataract; defective skin patches around mouth and ears; deranged metabolism and retarded growth	Associated with B_1 and other members of the B-complex
Vitamin B_6; **pyridoxine**	A constituent of **pyridoxal phosphate**, coenzyme in metabolism of various amino acids	Mild anemia; atrophied lymph tissues; inadequate white cells and antibodies; lowered resistance to infection	Meat, eggs, nuts, and cereals (whole grain)
Vitamin P-P; **niacin**, $C_6H_5NO_2$, pellagra-preventing vitamin	A component of two important metabolic coenzymes, DPN and TPN (p. 145); serve as H acceptors in various reactions	Uncomplicated **pellagra**; retarded growth	Part of the B-complex

Vitamin	Function	Deficiency	Source
Vitamin B_{12}, the anti-pernicious anemia (APA) factor, **cobalamin**	Coenzyme; participates in synthesis of certain amino acids and of **thymidine** (p. 146)	Pernicious anemia	Liver
Vitamin C; **ascorbic acid**, $C_6H_8O_6$	Participates in oxidative metabolism particularly of the amino acid, tyrosine	Scurvy, retarded growth	Juices of the citrus fruits (lemons, limes, oranges, etc.); many vegetables
Vitamin D; **calciferol**, $C_{28}H_{44}O$, formed by U-V radiation from ergosterol	Promotes proper absorption of calcium and phosphorus salts by the small intestine	Rickets: faulty bones and teeth; deranged calcium metabolism; retarded growth	Animal oils, such as butter, milk, and the liver oils of fish
Vitamin E; **α-tocopherol**, $C_{29}H_{50}O_2$	Still not specifically known	Sterility in rats, but perhaps not in man; females fail to retain embryos; males fail to form functional sperm; muscular paralysis (in advanced stage)	Vegetable and animal oils; wheat germ oil, particularly
Vitamin K; $C_{31}H_{46}O_2$	Stimulates or participates in the synthesis of prothrombase in cells of the liver. Other compounds likewise are probably involved	Improper coagulation of blood; improper growth	Leafy vegetables; alfalfa

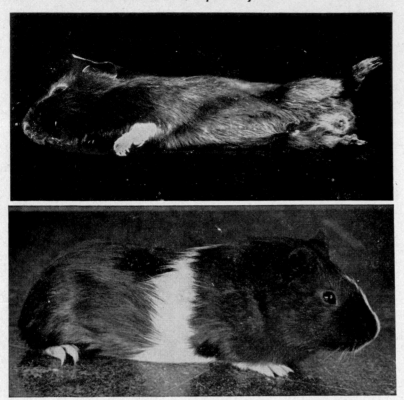

Fig. 18-2. *Upper photograph:* Drastic scurvy in a guinea pig. *Lower photograph:* Restoration with pure ascorbic acid (crystalline vitamin C.) (Courtesy E. R. Squibb and Sons.)

cent work indicates that the fragility of the capillaries may be due partly to a deficiency of an unidentified factor, which is closely associated with ascorbic acid in many foods.

The minimum daily requirement of each vitamin is very small. Ten milligrams (.01 g) of ascorbic acid, and considerably less of most of the other vitamins, are entirely adequate in preventing a deficiency. Consequently it is plain that the vitamins are not important as sources of energy for the body. Rather the vitamins represent important structural components in the protoplasm.

FACTS ABOUT SOME OTHER VITAMINS. Vitamin research has advanced very rapidly in recent years, and only a brief description of the firmly established results can be presented in this account.

Vitamin A is a colorless compound ($C_{20}H_{30}O$), but the body can derive vitamin A from **carotene** ($C_{40}H_{56}$), an orange pigment present in many green and yellow vegetables. Accordingly, carotene may be specified as a **provitamin.** Mild deficiencies of vitamin A result in **night blindness** (p. 423), whereas drastic deficiency leads to a serious eye defect, called **xerophthalmia,** in which the cornea becomes very dry and ulcerated (Fig. 18-3 and Table 18-3).

Recently it has been shown that vitamin A plays an important role in vision. It is a component needed by our retinal **rod cells** for the synthesis of **rhodopsin,** the photosensitive pigment concerned with black-white vision (p. 423). Night blindness—that is, an inability to see properly in dim light—results, therefore, when the pigment content of rods of the retina becomes depleted.

Vitamin A is one of the group of the **fat-soluble** vitamins (A, D, and E), which are stored to some extent in the liver; and this accounts for the fact that liver oils, derived from fish such as the cod, halibut, and shark, are excellent natural sources of these vitamins.

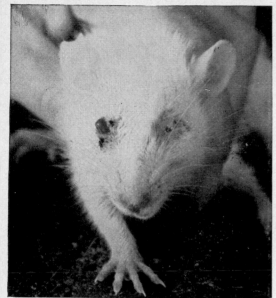

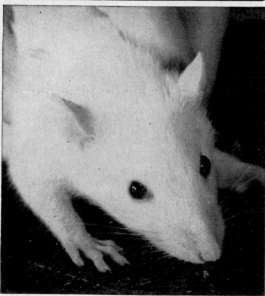

malfunction. Moreover, two of the fat-soluble group, namely A and D, are the only vitamins that are known to have deleterious effects when taken in *great* excess.

Previously the **B-complex** of vitamins was thought to be a single compound. Now, however, *at least ten* separate B vitamins have been identified, although not all of these will be discussed.

A deficiency of **thiamine,** or vitamin B_1, gives rise to **polyneuritis,** or **beriberi,** as it is usually called in man. Drastic polyneuritis involves degenerative changes in the nerves and a severe progressive paralysis. The paralysis disappears very rapidly, however, when thiamine is given. A polyneuritic animal frequently regains normal muscular

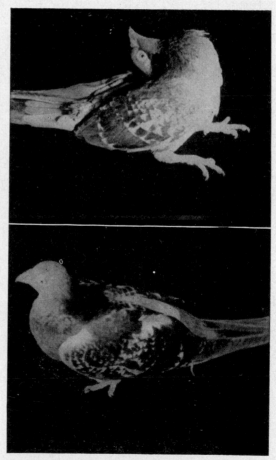

Fig. 18-3. *Upper photograph:* Drastic vitamin A deficiency in a white rat, showing blindness as a result of an ulceration of the cornea. *Lower photograph:* Restoration of the eyes after feeding adequate quantities of vitamin A.

In some cases a deficiency of the fat-soluble vitamins may result, not so much from their lack in the diet, but more from a failure in their absorption. Because bile salts are necessary for this absorption, deficiencies may arise in cases of gall bladder or other liver

Fig. 18-4. *Upper photograph:* Pigeon suffering from polyneuritis. *Lower photograph:* Same bird less than 3 hours after treatment with thiamine (vitamin B_1).

movement in one hour, after the vitamin is injected intravenously (Fig. 18-4). Drastic beriberi became prevalent for a time among rice-eating populations when modern methods of polishing the grain began to be adopted. The outer seed coats of the cereal grains are excellent sources of thiamine and the other vitamins of the B-complex, and consequently highly refined grain is a poor substitute for whole grain (Table 18-3).

A deficiency of vitamin B_2 (**riboflavin**) leads to various symptoms, including (1) loss of weight; (2) a scaliness of the skin around the mouth and ears; and (3) a predisposition to cataract (Fig. 18-5). Riboflavin, thiamine, niacin, pyridoxin, and cobalamin (see Table 18-3) all serve as **coenzymes** in various reactions in cellular metabolism (p. 104).

Pellagra is still a fairly prevalent deficiency disease. This is especially true in some districts of the South Atlantic states, where the traditional diet is restricted mainly to maize, molasses, and meat. The main symptoms of pellagra are dermatitis and diarrhea, although severe pellagra may terminate finally in prostration and death. The main pellagra-preventing (P-P) factor is **niacin**, which also has been called nicotinic acid, although many cases of pellagra are complicated by an absence of other B-complex vitamins. Niacin has become available—since the vitamin has been isolated and synthesized artificially—but traditions of diets are hard to eradicate, and pellagra still remains somewhat of a problem. Vitamin B_6 (**pyridoxin**)—the antidermatitis factor—is frequently absent from

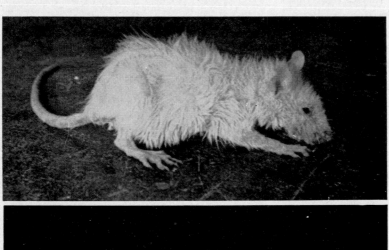

Fig. 18-5. *Upper photograph:* Deficency of riboflavin retards growth and induces certain changes in the skin. *Lower photograph:* Same animal, restored to normal by riboflavin feeding.

the pellagra diet, and this vitamin may be responsible for the skin complications that are almost always observed in clinical pellagra.

Six other B-complex vitamins can only be mentioned. Vitamin B_{12} (APA), the antipernicious anemia factor, has recently been crystallized from liver concentrates, and this crystalline product displays great potency in maintaining the activity of the erythrocyte-forming tissues of the body. Likewise **folic acid** is now recognized as an important factor in normal red-cell formation, and most cases of pernicious anemia respond completely to the administration of APA in combination with folic acid. Inositol and para-aminobenzoic acid, respectively, are reported to prevent the falling and the graying of the hair of rats; and a deficiency of **pantothenic acid** is associated with certain nerve and skin disorders. However, deficiencies of these last three vitamins have not been demonstrated in man, perhaps because the very small requirements are almost inevitably provided in almost any diet—or because inositol and para-aminobenzoic acid, at least, like certain other B-complex components are synthesized in significant quantities by the bacteria of the intestinal tract. Finally there is **biotin,** a vitamin that initially was shown to be essential for the growth of yeast. This compound also seems necessary, in very minute amounts, in many mammals, including man. Biotin is widely distributed in natural foods, although molasses, egg *yolk,* and liver have an especially high content. *Raw* egg white, on the other hand, contains a specific protein, **avidin,** which interferes with the absorption of biotin. One of the few human cases in which a biotin deficiency has been demonstrated was that of a man whose diet consisted almost entirely of raw eggs and wine.

Both biotin and pantothenic acid are now known to serve as coenzymes in cellular metabolism. Biotin is active in reactions leading to the synthesis of certain **purines** (p. 89) and in reactions involving the fixation or transfer of CO_2; whereas pantothenic acid is a constituent of the very important **coenzyme A** (p. 154).

Rickets—which is caused by a deficiency of vitamin D—was fairly prevalent some fifty years ago, but the spindly, crooked legs of the rachitic child are seldom seen today. In rickets, the deposition of calcium and phosphorus compounds in the growing bones is faulty; and consequently the bones are weak and malformed.

Vitamin D, or **calciferol,** is derived from ergosterol—a closely related steroid compound—when the latter is irradiated by ultraviolet light. The body accomplishes this transformation in the skin, provided there is an adequate exposure to direct sunlight, or to some other source of ultraviolet radiation. Ergosterol, which is called the **provitamin,** is present in many animal fats such as butter; and in summer vitamin D deficiencies are relatively rare. But in winter—and under other conditions of reduced sunlight—supplementary concentrates of vitamin D should be added to the diet of children and of women during pregnancy and lactation. Great excesses of vitamin D are to be avoided, however, since they may lead to malformations of the limbs.

Vitamins E and K have been identified also. A deficiency of vitamin E (α-tocopherol) induces sterility, at least in some animals, such as the rat. Female rats abort their young long before the normal time of birth; and males become sterile, due to degenerative changes in the testes. At present it has not been shown that a vitamin E deficiency is responsible for any kind of sterility in man, although this possibility has not been ruled out completely. Certain types of muscular paralysis and of heart disease, on the other hand, have responded well to the administration of vitamin E, although the relation between these diseases and a lack of α-tocopherol remains obscure.

With a deficiency of vitamin K, the liver fails to synthesize adequate quantities of **prothrombase;** and consequently the coagulating capacity of the blood becomes impaired.[1] Significant amounts of vitamin K are synthesized by the bacteria in man's colon so that human deficiencies of this vitamin are quite rare—except under certain circumstances. In new-born infants, a deficiency may arise before the bacterial flora in the large intestine has reached full development, and in adults it may arise in cases of bile duct obstruction—since the bile salts are necessary for a proper absorption of the fat-soluble vitamins (A, D, E, and K). Thus many hospitals now give fortifying doses of vitamin K as a precaution against hemorrhage in obstetrical cases, and in operations involving the liver or the biliary tract.

ORIGIN AND NATURE OF VITAMINS. Modern studies have made it clear that most, if not all, of the compounds designated as vitamins in animal nutrition are essential components of protoplasm generally—in plants as well as animals. In fact most of these compounds play similar roles—as essential coenzyme components of metabolic enzymes—in plant and animal cells generally. However, typical *plants* are able to synthesize their own essential compounds entirely from inorganic matter—and therefore vitamins are not listed among the *food* requirements of the plant.

Among saprophytic forms the power of synthesizing essential protoplasmic compounds varies widely, and there is good evidence to indicate that a loss of synthesizing power has played a significant role in the evolution of different species. The ordinary "wild" variety of the red baker's mold, **Neurospora,** for example, displays maximum growth on a medium that contains only one of the generally recognized vitamins (biotin). But if this mold is subjected to a suitable dosage of x-ray—a treatment that induces genic mutations (p. 510)—new varieties are obtained that cannot grow unless the medium contains one or more other vitamins, or even the full assortment of vitamins necessary in animals generally. In many cases,

[1] Several different compounds having an action similar to that of vitamin K have been discovered, and it is possible that vitamin K is not a single substance.

moreover, the experiments demonstrate a definite relation between the mutation of a single gene and the inability of the mold to synthesize some one particular compound.

It is early to generalize from such experiments, even though considerable data are beginning to accumulate. It seems likely, however, that primitive organisms, much earlier in geological time, generally possessed more extensive synthetic powers. In plants such powers of synthesis were completely essential to survive, because plants take in no organic foods, and such syntheses were not eliminated by natural selection (p. 158). Animals, on the other hand, feed extensively upon the products of other organisms, and consequently the capacity to synthesize organic compounds is less essential. Among animals, therefore, the capacity to synthesize many compounds was susceptible to elimination through natural selection. And even today, although the vitamin requirements of different animals are generally alike, what is the vitamin in one animal is not necessarily the vitamin of another. In the case of ascorbic acid, for example, this vitamin is essential only in man and a few other species—such as apes, monkeys, and guinea pigs. In other words, scurvy, or its equivalent, is never encountered in a majority of species, because most animals have not lost the metabolic enzymes by which ascorbic acid can be synthesized in the cells.

SUMMARY

Only a carefully balanced diet will sustain growth and health in man and other animals. The daily energy expenditure must be balanced by an adequate caloric content in food; and the food must provide adequate amounts of all substances needed in constructive metabolism. These structural requirements include water, various essential inorganic salts, at least a minimum of proteins and natural fats, and a full assortment of such vitamins as are essential in the particular species.

TEST QUESTIONS

1. Specify three factors that account for the fact that a large proportion of our organic food can be *absorbed* from the small intestine.

2. Make a labeled diagram of one of the intestinal villi, showing its relations to the blood vessels and lymphatics of the intestinal wall.

3. What factors help to explain the fact that fatty components of our foods are absorbed mainly into the lymph stream rather than into the blood stream?

4. What factors account for the fact that the end products of the digestion of our nonfatty foods are absorbed mainly into the blood stream rather than into the lymph stream?

5. Specify at least five metabolic functions performed by the liver. How can you account for the fact that the vertebrate liver has assumed so many important functions?

6. Under what circumstances would you expect to find:
   a. galactose and benzoic acid in all parts of the blood stream
   b. that blood entering the liver (portal blood) contains more glucose than blood leaving the liver (hepatic blood)
   c. that the hepatic blood contains more glucose than the portal blood?

7. How are (b) and (c) of the previous question related to glycogen storage and the maintenance of a steady blood-sugar level?

8. What are the symptoms of hypoglycemia and hyperglycemia, and how are these conditions related to insulin and adrenalin?

9. When the diet is very low in protein foods, scarcely any of the absorbed amino acids are deaminated in the body and very little urea appears in the urine. Explain fully.

10. A high protein diet is accompanied by a large urea production. Explain.

11. In man's liver and kidney the deamination reactions are quite different. Explain fully.

12. Explain why the total energy expenditures of the body are measured in terms of Calories (heat units).

13. What is meant by the basal metabolism of an individual; how is the B.M. usually measured; and why is this basic energy expenditure essential for the maintenance of life?

14. Assuming that the energy deficit is made up partly ($\frac{2}{3}$) by sacrificing the glycogen reserves and partly ($\frac{1}{3}$) by oxidizing reserve fat, how much weight will a man lose in one week if his daily food provides only 2000 Calories while his daily work demands an expenditure of 2500 Calories?

15. During starvation, the organic components of the body are sacrificed in such a way that a maximum time of survival is assured. Explain fully.

16. The daily diets of four college students are given below. Appraise each diet and explain the consequences of the deficiencies (if any):

    Diet A:
    Water, salts, and vitamins, adequate
    Fats, 100 grams
    Starch, 100 grams
    Protein, 50 grams

    Diet B:
    Water, adequate
    Salts, adequate quantity but lacking in iodides
    Vitamins, adequate
    Carbohydrates, 500 grams
    Fats, 50 grams
    Proteins, 25 grams

    Diet C:
    Water, salts, and vitamins, adequate
    Proteins, 600 grams
    Fats, 50 grams
    Carbohydrates, virtually none

    Diet D:
    Water, salts, and vitamins, adequate
    Carbohydrates, 400 grams
    Fats, 50 grams
    Proteins (all from corn and gelatin), 200 grams

17. Select any one of the known vitamins and explain how and why it is typical of the vitamins generally.

18. The physiological roles of some of the vitamins are now partially understood. Explain this statement carefully, citing at least six specific examples.

19. A doctor's new patient is observed to have bow legs and poor teeth, and he stumbles over a footstool in the dimly lighted office. Prescribe:

(a) the proper purified vitamins (if the patient can afford this), or

(b) a fortification of the diet by appropriate foods

20. Prescribe, as above, in the following cases:

    a. the patient complains of a lack of "pep" and appetite and a thorough examination fails to reveal any tangible pathology

    b. the youngster is "small for his age," has scaly patches around the mouth and ears, and doesn't see very well

FURTHER READINGS

1. *Chemistry of Food and Nutrition,* by H. C. Sherman; New York, 1946.

2. *Vitamins,* by Henry Borsook; New York, 1941.

3. *Nutritional Deficiencies,* by J. B. Youmans; Philadelphia, 1943.

4. *Great Experiments in Biology,* sections on vitamins, by C. Eijkman, B. C. Jansen, W. F. Donath, K. Lohmann, and P. Schuster, ed. by M. Gabriel and S. Fogel; Englewood Cliffs, N. J., 1955.

19-*Respiration*

WITHOUT oxygen the cells of the body deteriorate quite rapidly. Certain parts of the brain, indeed, may be damaged irreparably by less than five minutes of *complete* asphyxiation. This probably represents an extreme of vulnerability, but the fact remains that the cells of most animals need a fairly constant supply of oxygen. Also, the carbon dioxide produced by the body must constantly be removed if the cells are to maintain their living structure and activity.

The problem of respiration is not very acute among small aquatic animals, like *Paramecium* or *Hydra*. The respiratory gases have relatively high diffusion rates. Oxygen from the surrounding water enters the protoplasm of such small organisms as fast as it is consumed, and carbon dioxide passes out to the environment before it accumulates unduly in the protoplasm. Therefore no specialized respiratory structures are necessary among such small aquatic forms.

With larger animals, the deeper-lying tissues would soon be asphyxiated if they depended solely upon diffusion in obtaining their oxygen and disposing of their carbon dioxide. Oxygen from the environment would be used up by the superficial cells before it could reach the deeper ones; and the super-ficial tissues would be called upon to eliminate not only their own carbon dioxide, but also that produced by the deeper cells. Accordingly, the problem of respiration becomes more acute as the mass of the animal body becomes greater, and in all larger animals the **circulatory system** takes over the function of transporting the respiratory gases between the deep-lying tissues and a **respiratory surface.**

With the intervention of the circulatory system, the processes of respiration become more complicated. In fact, the respiration of higher animals involves three processes: (1) **external respiration**—the exchange of oxygen and carbon dioxide between the blood and the environment; (2) the **transportation** of oxygen and carbon dioxide in the blood stream to and from the various tissues; and (3) **internal respiration**—the exchange of oxygen and carbon dioxide between the blood and the tissues of the body.

EXTERNAL RESPIRATION

Each animal is equipped with some sort of moist surface at which the blood undergoes **aeration.** Typically the **respiratory surface** comes into direct contact with the environ-

357

ing air or water, and the respiratory surface is provided with an extensive network of capillaries immediately beneath the surface. At such a richly capillaried surface, equilibrium occurs very quickly between the blood and the environment; that is, oxygen quickly enters and saturates the blood, whereas carbon dioxide leaves the blood, entering the environment.

In animals like the earthworm, the entire body surface takes part in external respiration, but this is not a very efficient arrangement. To facilitate a rapid aeration of the blood, the respiratory surface must be moist and delicate, and this makes it susceptible to external injury. The earthworm, for example, cannot leave the protection of its bur-

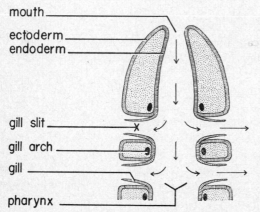

mouth
ectoderm
endoderm
gill slit
gill arch
gill
pharynx

Fig. 19-1. Diagram of the gills of a fish (shark). Arrows indicate the direction of *flow of water.*

row, except for relatively short periods. Exposure to sunlight shrivels and hardens the delicate skin of the earthworm—and when this occurs, respiration becomes inadequate.

Gills. Most aquatic animals have developed **gills** (Fig. 19-1), which serve as specialized organs of external respiration. Typical fish, for example, possess a hard scaly surface covering most of the body. Such a surface protects the individual from injurious contacts, but it is not a suitable surface for aeration. But the delicate gills of the fish provide an excellent surface for the aeration of the blood. The gills lie in a protected position in the **gill clefts,** which lead from the pharynx to the exterior of the body. The fish takes in a continuous stream of water, which passes through the mouth and out through the gill clefts, bathing the soft fleshy gills. Typically each gill is a lobulated mass, which is well supplied with blood capillaries (Fig. 19-2). This arrangement provides an adequate surface across which oxygen and carbon dioxide are exchanged between the blood passing *through* the gill and the water passing *over* the gill.

Lungs. Gills are not well suited to terrestrial conditions because they are too exposed and vulnerable to the drying effects of the atmosphere. Instead of gills, many land animals have developed **lungs.** Essentially a lung is a deeply inpocketed respiratory surface, which is not exposed directly to the external

EYE
GILLS

Fig. 19-2. The larva of an amphibian (*Amblystoma punctatum*) showing external gills. Each gill is a fleshy outgrowth richly permeated by capillaries, in which the blood very quickly undergoes aeration. (Courtesy of Roberts Rugh, Columbia University.)

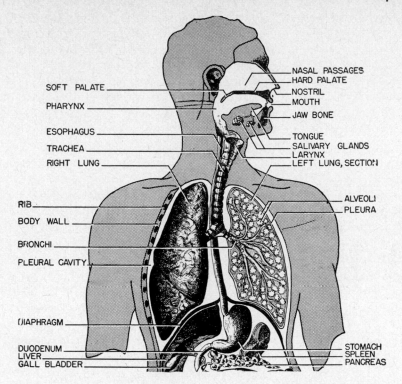

SOFT PALATE

PHARYNX

ESOPHAGUS

TRACHEA

RIGHT LUNG

RIB

BODY WALL

BRONCHI

PLEURAL CAVITY

DIAPHRAGM

DUODENUM
LIVER
GALL BLADDER

NASAL PASSAGES
HARD PALATE
NOSTRIL
MOUTH
JAW BONE

TONGUE
SALIVARY GLANDS
LARYNX
LEFT LUNG, SECTION

ALVEOLI
PLEURA

STOMACH
SPLEEN
PANCREAS

Fig. 19-3. The human respiratory system, semidiagrammatic.

atmosphere. Accordingly lung-breathing animals have developed methods of ventilating the recesses of the lungs. Unless air in the lung sac is changed from moment to moment, oxygen is soon depleted from the pulmonary air, and carbon dioxide accumulates to toxic levels.

In higher vertebrates the lungs arise as a simple tubular outgrowth from the floor of the pharynx. This **lung bud** pushes posteriorly—parallel and ventral to the esophagus —until it reaches the thorax. Here the tube forks, sending a branch to each side of the thorax. Each branch gives rise to a lung, which eventually occupies almost all the corresponding side of the thoracic cavity.

The unbranched portion of the air passage (Fig. 19-3) becomes the **larynx** and **trachea,** and the two main forks become the **bronchi.** On entering the lung each bronchus gives rise to many branches, which form the smaller **bronchioles** in all parts of the lung. Eventually each bronchiole terminates

blindly, by leading into a cluster of tiny air chambers, the **aeveoli** (Fig. 19-4) Each alveolus lies in intimate contact with a network of capillaries; in the human lung, there is an alveolar surface of more than 1000 square feet across which an aeration of the blood occurs. All the many branches of the "bronchial tree" are held in place by elastic connective tissue that fills in the interalveolar spaces; and each lung is covered as a whole by its own external epithelium, called the **pleura.**

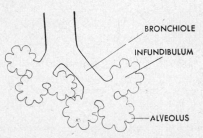

BRONCHIOLE

INFUNDIBULUM

ALVEOLUS

Fig. 19-4. Structure of a small portion of the human lung.

If removed from the body, the lung shrinks down into a relatively small spongy mass. Such a deflated lung may be reinflated through the trachea—in which case the walls become stretched like those of a toy balloon. But if the inflation pressure is released, the elasticity of the stretched pulmonary walls again deflates the lung, expelling most of its content of air.

The free transit of air to and from the lungs is assured by the fact that the walls of the larynx, trachea, bronchi, and larger bronchioles are reinforced with cartilage, which prevents the passages from collapsing (Fig. 19-3). In the trachea and bronchi the cartilaginous reinforcements take the form of a series of incomplete rings, or bands. But the larynx, which houses the **vocal cords,** is strengthened by a larger single encasement of cartilage (Fig. 19-3).

Each lung is covered externally by a smooth epithelium, which is called the **pleura;** and there is also a pleural lining on the inner surface of the thorax wall (Fig. 19-3). Thus between the two layers of the pleura there exists, at least potentially, a cavity, called the **pleural cavity.** Normally the pleural cavity is practically obliterated by the fact that the outer surface of the lung lies in intimate contact with the inner surface of the thoracic wall. However, if the pleural linings become inflamed, as in pleurisy, fluid tends to accumulate in the pleural cavity.

The pleural cavity has no communication with the outside atmosphere. Above and to the sides it is bounded by the body wall, and below, the pleural cavity is walled off from the abdominal cavity by the **diaphragm,** a strong dome-shaped sheet of muscle tissue (Fig. 19-3). Pressure in the pleural cavity is generally negative (that is, less than the pressure of the outside atmosphere), because the

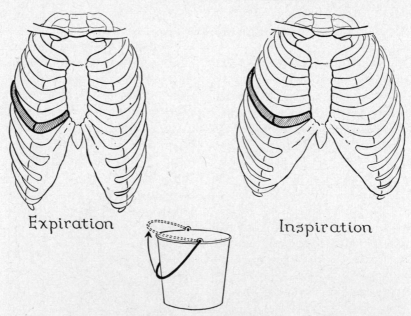

Expiration Inspiration

Fig. 19-5. Manner in which the volume of the chest cavity is increased during an inspiration. Each rib is attached to the vertebral column behind, and to the breastbone in front, and, like the handle of a bucket, moves outward as it is pulled up. In addition, the whole breastbone moves up slightly during an inspiration, so that the distance from vertebral column to breastbone is also increased. Finally, the downward movement of the diaphragm increases the third (vertical) dimension of the chest. (Drawn by E. M. From Gerard, *The Body Functions.* Permission of John Wiley and Sons, Inc.)

elasticity of the inflated lung tends to pull the lung away from the thoracic wall, generating a partial vacuum in the pleural cavity. Thus to collapse a lung while it is still in the body—and this is sometimes necessary in severe tuberculosis—the surgeon merely punctures the thoracic wall. This operation permits air to flow directly into the pleural cavity, destroying the partial vacuum and allowing the lung to deflate itself as a result of its own elasticity.

Breathing Movements. Adequate aeration of the blood in the lungs depends upon an efficient ventilation of the alveolar air spaces; and in most animals the breathing movements go on continuously. Each **inspiration** is quickly followed by an **expiration,** and in man, these respiratory movements recur about 18 times per minute from birth to death.

Inspiration involves a coordinated contraction of a number of muscles; and expiration follows when the same muscles relax. The muscles most important in breathing are the diaphragm and the intercostal muscles. The action of the rib muscles is to broaden and deepen the thorax, increasing its cubic capacity (Figs. 19-5 and 19-6). The intercostal muscles raise the ribs and swing them later-

ally, more or less like the handle of a bucket (Fig. 19-5); and simultaneously the dome-shaped diaphragm contracts, lowering the floor of the thorax (Fig. 19-6). Such an enlargement of the thorax increases the partial vacuum in the pleural cavity, and this suction is transmitted through the lungs to the outside air. Thus, as soon as the intrapulmonary pressure falls below that of the outside atmosphere, air passes into the lungs via the trachea and other passages.

Expiration usually involves a simple reversal of these movements. The relaxing intercostal muscles allow the ribs to spring back to their former position; the diaphragm encroaches upon the thorax from below; and both these processes allow the lungs to expel the air that previously was inhaled.

Extra deep, or forced, breathing requires the cooperation of the abdominal muscles. At the apex of the fullest inspiration the diaphragm is greatly depressed. Thus considerable pressure would be exerted upon the abdominal organs, were it not for the fact that simultaneously there is a relaxation of the muscles of the abdominal wall. Conversely, at the extremity of a forced expiration, the muscular abdominal wall clamps down, forcing the viscera to push the dia-

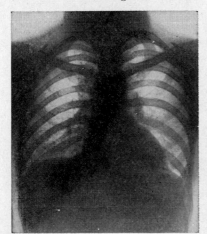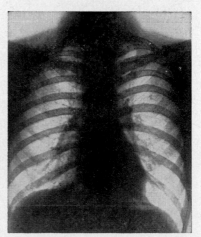

Fig. 19-6. Normal chest, at end of expiration (*left*); and at end of inspiration (*right*). Note that during inspiration (1) the ribs and breastbone are elevated, and (2) the diaphragm and heart are depressed. (Courtesy, Roentgenology Staff, Billings Hospital. From Gerard, *The Body Functions.* Permission of John Wiley and Sons, Inc.)

phragm as far as possible upward into the thoracic cavity. Likewise, coughing and sneezing represent forced expirations that involve a vigorous contraction of the abdominal muscles. The resulting wave of pressure in the abdominal cavity is transmitted across the diaphragm to the lungs, and a draft of air is forced upward through the respiratory passages, clearing the trachea, pharynx, and, perhaps, the nasal passages of irritating matter.

Volume Intake and Output of the Lungs. The lungs of man have large reserves to meet the demands of work and exercise. During sedentary activity, only about 500 cc of air are swept into and out of the lungs each time we breathe. But with the deepest inhalation it is possible to encompass an extra 2500 cc, and the strongest exhalation can put forth an additional 1000 cc of air. Thus a maximum exhalation following a maximum inhalation may deliver about 4000 cc; this total represents the **vital capacity** of an individual. A trained athlete usually displays a relatively high vital capacity, although the physical stature and build of the individual must be taken into consideration. Certain diseases of the lungs and heart, on the other hand, may reduce the vital capacity below the standard of the age-sex-stature group to which the individual belongs.

About 1000 cc of air remain in the lungs at the end of the strongest exhalation. The trachea, bronchi, and bronchioles contain about 150 cc of this **residual air,** and the remainder lies in the alveolar spaces. Even a collapsed lung, completely removed from the body, contains some air. Accordingly such a lung is sufficiently buoyant to float in water. This is not true, however, of the lung of a fetus, or of a stillborn child, which never has been inflated with air. Consequently the floating test is commonly employed by the medical examiner in cases of suspected infanticide.

Composition of the Alveolar Air. The aeration of the blood occurs almost entirely in the alveoli, and not in the larger air passages (trachea, bronchi, and larger bronchi-

oles). Consequently it is most important to determine the composition of the inspired air that reaches the alveolar chambers. Owing to the incompleteness of the ventilation of the deeper recesses of the lungs, the composition of alveolar air is somewhat different from that of the outside atmosphere. Inevitably there is some depletion of oxygen and accumulation of carbon dioxide in the alveolar air.

Of the 500 cc of fresh air inhaled at each breath, about 150 cc never reach the aveoli but remain in the so-called "dead space" of the trachea, bronchi, and larger bronchioles. Thus only 350 cc reach the alveolar chambers. Accordingly the new air is diluted by (1) the air that previously occupied the dead space and (2) the residual alveolar air. Thus the alveolar air is a mixture of "new" and "old" air in which the "old" predominates. An air sample collected at the end of a maximum forced expiration closely approximates the alveolar air; the composition of alveolar air, compared with atmospheric air, is given in Table 19-1.

Table 19-1—Comparison between Atmospheric and Alveolar Air

	Percent by Volume	
	Atmos-pheric Air (Dried)	Alveolar Air (Dried)
Oxygen	20.96	14.2
Carbon dioxide	0.04	5.5
Nitrogen (with argon)	79.00	80.3
Totals	100.00	100.0

Even though alveolar air is relatively poor in oxygen and rich in carbon dioxide, aeration of the blood in the alveolar capillaries proceeds on *a strictly diffusional basis.* If venous blood, such as passes to the lungs, is exposed directly to alveolar air, the blood absorbs oxygen and gives off carbon dioxide. In the lung the alveolar air is separated from the blood merely by the exquisitely thin

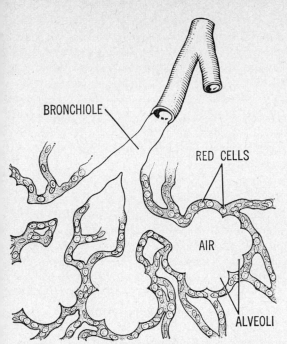

BRONCHIOLE

RED CELLS

AIR

ALVEOLI

Fig. 19-7. Close relation between the alveolar air sacs and the blood in the lung capillaries.

walls of the alveolus and capillaries (Fig. 19.7), and these membranes are so freely permeable to the respiratory gases that they cause little delay in the attainment of equilibrium.

Many early students of respiration believed that the alveolar walls could force oxygen into the blood, especially when the concentration of oxygen in the alveolar air is abnormally low. However, no convincing evidence for this view has been obtained. At high altitudes—where the air is rarefied— the oxygen concentration in the alveolar air falls off despite the fact that the breathing becomes deeper and faster. At sea level the total atmospheric pressure approximates 760 mm of mercury, of which about 150 mm represents the **partial pressure** of the oxygen. In the alveoli, where the proportion of oxygen is only two thirds that of the outside atmosphere, the oxygen pressure is therefore only about 100 mm of Hg. Acute respiratory embarrassment begins to appear at about 14,000 feet. Here the outside atmospheric pressure falls to about 450 mm of Hg

and the oxygen pressure in the alveoli is reduced to about 55 mm of Hg. Now the blood passing through the lungs fails to absorb enough oxygen to supply the body's needs. The venous blood as it comes to the lungs from the tissues still has an oxygen content equivalent to 40 mm of Hg. Thus the concentration gradient between the alveolar air and blood has been reduced to 15 mm (55 mm in alveolar air at 14,000 feet elevation minus 40 mm in the alveolar blood); and at this gradient the diffusional force that drives O_2 into the blood begins to be dangerously close to inadequate.

The symptoms of **mountain sickness,** including severe headache, nausea, and emotional instability, indicate that the body, and especially the brain cells, are suffering from partial asphyxia, although some of the symtoms of high altitude distress originate from an excess outpouring of CO_2 from the blood stream. Gradually an individual can become acclimated to high altitude, because altitude stimulates the bone marrow to mobilize a much greater abundance of red cells; and these of course augment the oxygen-carrying capacity of the blood. However, no person can live at altitudes very much higher than 14,000 feet, unless equipped with an artificial oxygen supply. When the alveolar oxygen tension drops significantly below 50 mm of Hg, the quantity of oxygen that can reach the blood is insufficient, and the blood is unable to carry enough oxygen to supply the minimum demands of the body.

THE OXYGEN-CARRYING CAPACITY OF BLOOD

Blood is able to absorb and carry large quantities of oxygen—about 50 times more than an equivalent volume of plasma. If blood is exposed to a sea level atmosphere containing 14 percent of oxygen (alveolar air), it continues to absorb oxygen until it contains about 20 cc of pure oxygen per 100 cc of blood. This high oxygen-carrying capacity of blood is mainly due to its content of

hemoglobin, which is a very efficient respiratory pigment.

Only a small fraction (about 2 percent) of the oxygen load of the blood remains freely dissolved in the plasma and in the protoplasm of the corpuscles. Most of the oxygen unites chemically with the hemoglobin in the erythrocytes. As fast as it diffuses into the corpuscles from the plasma, free oxygen continues to unite with hemoglobin until all of this pigment has become oxygenated. Consequently the plasma does not reach equilibrium with the alveolar air until the hemoglobin becomes saturated.

Hemoglobin vs. Oxyhemoglobin. About 90 percent of the dry weight of each red corpuscle represents the complex iron-containing protein pigment, **hemoglobin.** The chemical properties of this compound are admirably adapted to the role it plays as an oxygen carrier. Hemoglobin combines with oxygen on a 1:4 molecular basis, forming **oxyhemoglobin** (p. 321). Oxyhemoglobin displays a bright scarlet color—in contrast to the dull purplish red of **reduced hemoglobin.** Consequently, the color of whole blood alters considerably while it flows through the lungs and changes from an unaerated (venous) to an aerated (arterial) condition.

As a carrier of oxygen, oxyhemoglobin must be an unstable compound, capable of liberating free oxygen when the blood reaches the various tissues of the body. In other words, the oxygenation of hemoglobin is a delicately poised *reversible* reaction. It shifts in either direction, depending upon small changes that occur in the chemical composition of the blood in the different parts of the circulation. This reaction, expressed in simplified equational form, may be written as follows:

$$Hb + (4)O_2 \underset{\substack{\text{at the tissues} \\ \text{low } O_2;\ \text{high } CO_2}}{\overset{\substack{\text{high } O_2;\ \text{low } CO_2 \\ \text{at the lungs}}}{\rightleftarrows}} Hb(O_2)_4$$

reduced hemoglobin   oxyhemoglobin

The binding and freeing of oxygen in the blood is mainly controlled by the quantities of oxygen and carbon dioxide present in the different parts of the circulatory system—a conclusion (see Fig. 19-8) based on many experiments. In leaving the lungs, arterial blood remains isolated in the pulmonary veins and in the various arteries, until it reaches the capillaries in some other part of the body. Here the HbO_2 is exposed to an environment in which there is relatively little free oxygen—since the tissue cells consume oxygen—and here also carbon dioxide is abundant due to the continuous production of CO_2 by the tissues. Under these conditions (Fig. 19-8) HbO_2 liberates free oxygen, which then diffuses from the corpuscles, across the plasma and intervening membranes, into the tissue cells. Carbon dioxide, in contrast, continually diffuses in the opposite direction. Carbon dioxide passes from the cells, where its concentration is maximum, into the blood. This gas exchange between the blood and the tissues is specified as **internal respiration,** and internal respiration proceeds *spontaneously on a diffusional basis.*

Venous blood, on leaving the tissues, likewise remains isolated in the veins and in the pulmonary arteries until it reaches the lung capillaries. Here the reduced Hb is exposed to the relatively abundant oxygen of the alveolar air, and here also carbon dioxide begins to leave the blood by diffusing into the alveolar air spaces. Both these factors, namely high O_2 and low CO_2, favor the formation of HbO_2; and in the few seconds required for the corpuscles to file through the capillaries bordering the alveoli, practically all the hemoglobin is transformed to oxyhemoglobin.

CARBON DIOXIDE-CARRYING CAPACITY OF BLOOD

Whole blood will absorb and carry more than 50 cc of CO_2, which is some 10 times greater than the amount that can be dissolved in an equivalent amount of plain

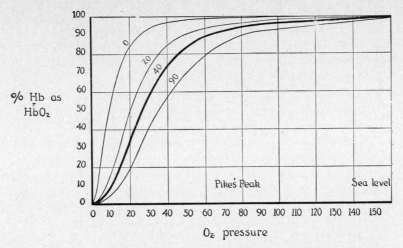

Fig. 19-8. The "oxygen dissociation curves" of hemoglobin are shown at four different carbon dioxide pressures, indicated above each curve. Carbon dioxide has a marked influence on the amount of oxygen with which hemoglobin will combine at any particular oxygen pressure, and this action of carbon dioxide is very important in the normal functioning of hemoglobin. The normal carbon dioxide pressure in arterial blood is slightly over 40 millimeters, so that the heavy curve shows approximately the physiological condition. (Drawn by E. M. From Gerard, *The Body Functions*. Permission of John Wiley and Sons, Inc.)

plasma. Moreover, there is scarcely any shift in the pH of the blood, despite the fact that CO_2, dissolved in aqueous media, gives rise to carbonic acid (H_2CO_3). The normal range, pH 7.3 to 7.5, outside of which the cells of the blood fail to maintain normal structure and activity, is not disturbed by the influx of CO_2 into whole blood; whereas plain plasma, saturated with CO_2, displays a distinctly acidic reaction (less than pH 6).

The hemoglobin of the red cells plays an important role in the transport not only of O_2 but also of CO_2. To be sure, only a small fraction (perhaps 10 percent) of the CO_2 actually unites with hemoglobin, forming a loose combination called **carbamino hemoglobin,** which liberates CO_2 when the blood reaches the lung. But changes in the dissociation tendencies of hemoglobin when it is oxygenated to oxyhemoglobin are intimately associated with the binding and freeing of carbon dioxide and with the stabilization of blood pH during these transactions. Both forms of hemoglobin, at the pH of blood, are in the acid range of their dissociation. Thus

we may write $H \cdot Hb \rightleftarrows H^+ + Hb^-$ and $H \cdot HbO_2 \rightleftarrows H^+ + HbO_2^-$. Moreover it is important to realize that $H \cdot HbO_2$ displays a stronger tendency to dissociate, yielding a greater concentration of H^+ ion, than does $H \cdot Hb$.

The relationship between the equilibrium, $H \cdot Hb + O_2 \rightleftarrows H \cdot HbO_2$, and the binding and freeing of CO_2 is very complex. Therefore it can be presented in boldest outline only, with particular reference to what goes on in the corpuscles.

Aside from the small amount transported as carbamino hemoglobin, CO_2 is carried in the blood in the form of **bicarbonates,** partly in the corpuscles as $KHCO_3$ and partly in the plasma as $NaHCO_3$. In the lung capillaries, $H \cdot Hb$ is converted to $H \cdot HbO_2$ and this conversion yields extra hydrogen ion (H^+) needed for the liberation of CO_2 from the bicarbonates. Simultaneously, however, $H \cdot HbO_2$ is converted to $K \cdot HbO_2$, a relatively stable form of oxyhemoglobin, which serves as the actual oxygen transport agency. Thus we may write: $H \cdot HbO_2 + K \cdot HCO_3 \rightleftarrows$

$K \cdot HbO_2 + H \cdot HCO_3$, and $H \cdot HCO_3 \rightleftarrows H_2O + CO_2$—to indicate the stabilization of the O_2 carrier and the simultaneous freeing of CO_2 for diffusion into the alveoli of the lung.

At the tissues, however, another trigger is provided by the coming in of CO_2 and the concurrent formation of carbonic acid, $H \cdot HCO_3$. This provides extra H+ ion for the conversion of $K \cdot HbO_2$ to the less stable form, $H \cdot HbO_2$, which then liberates free O_2. Simultaneously, however, CO_2 is bound as bicarbonate. Thus we may write: $CO_2 + H_2O \rightleftarrows H \cdot HCO_3$ and $H \cdot HCO_3 + K \cdot HbO_2 \rightleftarrows K \cdot HCO_3 + H \cdot HbO_2$ and $H \cdot HbO_2 \rightleftarrows H \cdot Hb + O_2$—to indicate the whole series of reactions. The net effect, however, is to bind CO_2 and to liberate O_2 at the proper moment. Meanwhile, however, the pH situation is stabilized by rapid exchanges of the H+ ion. Truly the hemoglobin molecule has been cunningly evolved to subserve the essential functions of respiration, both external and internal. Moreover, a special enzyme, **carbonic anhydrase,** has been evolved to speed up, by a factor of some 1300, the $CO_2 + H_2O \rightleftarrows H \cdot HCO_3$ reaction.

In summary, the chemical reactions which liberate CO_2 from the bicarbonates are coupled with the oxygenation of hemoglobin. Just as the pouring in of CO_2 at the tissues favors the liberation of O_2 at the proper time, so the coming in of O_2 fosters the freeing of CO_2 at the lungs. Another main factor in the decomposition of the bicarbonates in the lungs, of course, is the reduction of the CO_2 concentration as this gas escapes into the avleolar spaces. Very small changes in the concentration of the gases in the blood in the different capillary regions act upon these chemical equilibria and determine the binding or freeing of each gas at the proper time and in the proper place.

ASPHYXIA

Any failure in the delivery of oxygen to the tissues, or in the usage of oxygen by the tissues, produces **asphyxia** in greater or lesser degree. Accordingly the causes of asphyxia may reside in the lungs, in the circulatory system, or in the tissue cells.

Pulmonary asphyxia may result from a blocking of the bronchial passages, by water, as in drowning, or by an exudate of tissue fluid, as in pneumonia. When air cannot reach a large proportion of the alveoli, the quantity of oxygen absorbed and distributed by the blood is correspondingly restricted. Giving the patient pure oxygen helps—by augmenting the oxygen absorbed by the functioning alveoli; and in drowning, of course, an artificial ventilation of the lungs should be used if the asphyxia has abolished the normal respiratory movements. In asthma, there is a spasmic contraction of the muscles in the walls of the bronchi and bronchioles, which narrows these passages so drastically that they cannot conduct adequate air to the lungs.

Curtailment of the circulation—due to disorders of the heart or blood vessels—likewise curtails the delivery of oxygen to the tissues. **Carbon monoxide** (CO), however, acts upon the circulation in a different way. Carbon monoxide, which is present in illuminating gas and in the exhaust fumes of gasoline motors, acts by blocking the capacity of hemoglobin to combine with oxygen. Hemoglobin unites with CO much more readily than with O_2; and the resulting cherry-red compound, HbCO, has no affinity for oxygen. In carbon monoxide asphyxia, therefore, the victim does not "turn blue," but appears "flushed" due to the color of carbon-monoxyl hemoglobin. Resuscitation from CO asphyxia may be effected by artificial respiration, using an augmented oxygen supply—if available. Free Hb begins to be restored as soon as CO is removed from the alveolar air; and this restoration occurs more readily when the O_2 pressure of the alveolar air is increased. In **anemia,** all the available hemoglobin may be oxygenated, but the amount of hemoglobin is so low that the blood does not carry enough oxygen to the tissues.

Respiratory poisons, such as cyanide, act

primarily upon the tissues, rather than upon the blood. Cyanide, for example, blocks cytochrome oxidase (p. 147) and perhaps others of the oxidizing enzymes of the cells, thus preventing a proper usage of oxygen in the tissues.

CONTROL OF BREATHING

Active work may double or even treble the oxygen consumption of the muscles and other tissues, and this extra demand evokes a large increase in the depth and frequency of breathing, as well as an acceleration of the circulation. The **breathing reflexes** are integrated in the **respiratory center,** which is a specialized group of nerve cells situated in the **medulla** part of the brain (p. 459). The respiratory center is particularly responsive to **chemical conditions** in the blood that flows to this part of the brain, and these conditions may greatly modify both the rate and the intensity of the motor discharges of the respiratory center, which are sent to the diaphragm via the **phrenic nerves.**

Chemical Control of Breathing. The chief chemical factor controlling the activity of the respiratory center is the quantity of carbon dioxide present in the blood, and the respiratory center is extremely sensitive to changes in the CO_2 content of the blood. If, for example, the breathing is not fast and deep enough to prevent an accumulation of CO_2 in the alveolar air, CO_2 tends to accumulate in the blood. This stimulates the respiratory center, increasing the rate and depth of the breathing until the excess of CO_2 has been "blown off" from the lungs. Such an automatic control is very effective. An increase in the alveolar CO_2 from 5.5 to 5.7 percent is enough to double the breathing rate; and a decrease to 5.3 percent results in a temporary cessation of breathing. Thus after a series of very deep voluntary inhalations and exhalations, the alveolar CO_2 concentration is significantly reduced, and the subsequent breathing of the individual is usually suspended for about half a minute.

Also the efficacy of 10 percent CO_2, used to initiate the breathing of newborn infants, depends upon the stimulating effect of CO_2 upon the respiratory center.

The respiratory center is also sensitive, at least indirectly, to a diminution in the oxygen concentration of the blood. Thus breathing becomes faster and deeper whenever the aeration of the blood becomes inadequate. For the most part this oxygen control is indirect, however. Lack of oxygen leads to an accumulation of incompletely oxidized products such as lactic acid, and a very slight increase of hydrogen ion concentration in the blood strongly stimulates the respiratory center.

A person cannot "hold the breath" beyond a certain relatively safe limit, because inhibitory impulses from the **cerebrum** (p. 464) are quenched at the respiratory center as soon as the chemical influences become strong enough to revive the rhythmic discharges of this center.

Nervous Control of Breathing. Sensory impulses from various receptors also modify the rhythmic motor discharges of the respiratory center. At the crest of an inspiration, the stretching of the pulmonary wall excites the pressure receptors in the wall of the lung, and these receptors discharge a series of **inhibitory** impulses, which reach the medulla by way of the sensory fibers of the vagus nerves (p. 467). Conversely, at the depth of an expiration, other receptors in the pulmonary wall may send **excitatory** impulses, also via the vagus, to the central nervous system. Severe pain in any region of the body may act reflexly through the respiratory center, and the breath begins to "come faster." In swallowing, impulses from the pharyngeal receptors inhibit breathing for a moment—while food passes the glottis—and this prevents food from being sucked into the trachea and lungs. The gasp evoked by a plunge into icy water is also mediated through the respiratory center, as is likewise true of the coughing and sneezing reflexes. And last but not least, there is an additional mechanism for the control of respiration (and heart rate). This is provided by a special chemoreceptor, the **carotid sinus,** imbedded in the wall of each internal carotid artery near the point of origin. The cells of this receptor are excited by increases in either CO_2 or hydrogen ion in the blood that is flowing through the artery. The nerve impulses thus generated are carried via the sensory branches of the vagus nerve (p. 467) to the respiratory and cardiac centers, increasing the intensity and frequency of the motor discharges from these vital reflex centers. All in all, therefore, the body has developed a number of checks and balances upon the breathing mechanism—for this mechanism must be relied upon constantly from the instant of birth to the time of death.

TEST QUESTIONS

1. Differentiate between external and internal respiration. Why is it not possible to make such a distinction in very small organisms, like *Hydra?*
2. What is a specialized respiratory surface, and what advantages are provided by such a surface?
3. Differentiate between lungs and gills. Explain why gills are poorly suited to terrestrial conditions.
4. Explain the part played by the diaphragm and intercostal muscles in inspiration and expiration. How does a forced expiration differ from the expiration of ordinary breathing?
5. What is alveolar air? Explain how and why it differs from the external air.
6. Explain the term "partial pressure" of oxygen. Specify the partial pressure of oxygen: (a) in the outside atmosphere at sea level; (b) in the alveolar air at sea level; (c) in the outside air at 14,000 ft elevation; and (d) in the alveolar air at 14,000 feet.
7. What are the symptoms of "mountain silkness"? What is the cause of this condition?
8. Compare the oxygen-carrying capacity of whole blood with that of (a) plasma and (b) salt solution. How is this difference to be accounted for?
9. Describe and explain the difference of color between venous (unaerated) and arterial (aerated) blood.
10. The binding and freeing of oxygen by hemoglobin is determined by the following equilibrium:

$$H \cdot Hb + O_2 \rightleftharpoons H \cdot HbO_2$$

   Explain how and why this equilibrium is shifted: (a) while the blood flows through the capillaries of the lung; and (b) while the blood flows through the capillaries of the other parts of the body.
11. Carefully explain how the mechanisms of O_2 and CO_2 transport are intimately interrelated.
12. Explain the mechanism of carbon monoxide asphyxia, specifying the best method of resuscitation.
13. Describe two other types of asphyxia, citing an example of each type.
14. Carefully explain how our breathing movements are modified by (a) chemical and (b) nervous factors.

FURTHER READINGS

1. *Lessons from High Altitude,* by Joseph Barcroft; Cambridge, Eng., 1925.
2. *Respiration,* by J. S. Haldane; New Haven, 1927.
3. *The Wisdom of the Body,* by Walter B. Cannon; New York, 1939.

20-Excretion

THE MAIN excretory organs of man and other vertebrates are the kidneys (Fig. 20-1). This pair of large bean-shaped organs is copiously supplied with blood, via the stout renal arteries. Night and day the kidneys work to rid the blood of metabolic wastes. Urea and other excretory wastes, which enter the blood in the different parts of the body, are eliminated as fast as they are formed; and normally these wastes never accumulate to toxic levels in the blood stream. Even with a single kidney, a man may get along quite safely; but if both kidneys are lost, the individual will then succumb to uremic poisoning within a very few hours.

But the work of the kidneys involves much more than the elimination of metabolic wastes. The renal organs stabilize and regulate the composition of the blood. They keep the concentration of water, inorganic salts, glucose, and other essential blood components at proper levels with an amazing degree of constancy and efficiency. And since the lymph is derived directly from blood plasma, the kidneys also maintain **homeostatic control** over this intercellular fluid. In short, control of the **internal environment** of the

body cells is assumed in large measure by the kidneys. Each day of man's life more than 1500 liters of blood are pumped through the renal organs, and from this blood excesses of each component are removed and eliminated in the form of about 1.5 liters of urine.

EXCRETORY PROCESSES IN LOWER ANIMALS

Small and relatively simple animals, such as the Protozoa and the Coelenterata, eliminate their excretory wastes mainly by diffusion. As soon as any metabolic end product is produced in significant quantities in the cells it begins to diffuse from this locus of higher concentration out into the environment, where the concentration is lower.

Water, however, presents a special problem (p. 133). Water is always an end product of oxidative metabolism, and in fresh-water animals, water cannot diffuse out into the **hypotonic** environment. Consequently small fresh-water animals possess **contractile vacuoles,** or other mechanisms capable of performing work in forcing water out into the hypotonic environment.

The diffusional escape of excretory wastes

369

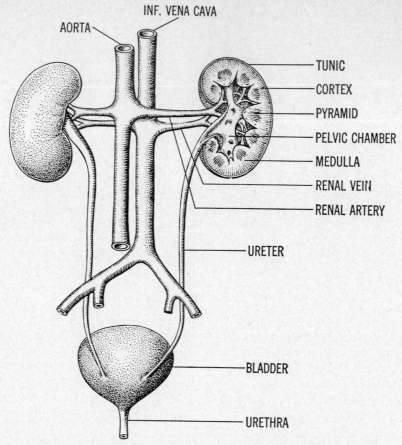

AORTA
INF. VENA CAVA
TUNIC
CORTEX
PYRAMID
PELVIC CHAMBER
MEDULLA
RENAL VEIN
RENAL ARTERY
URETER
BLADDER
URETHRA

Fig. 20-1.   Diagram of the human urinary system, **posterior view.**

becomes less and less adequate as the mass of an animal increases. In flatworms, such as *Planaria,* the body encompasses a considerable mass of mesodermal tissues, intervening between the ectoderm and endoderm. Such an increase in the mass of the body requires the development of specialized excretory organs, and planarians possess a large number of **flame cells** (Fig. 20-2), scattered throughout the mesoderm. Each flame cell is a hollow structure with a tuft of active cilia in the central cavity; and the beating of these accounts for the "flickering" that can be seen in a flame cell when it is viewed with a microscope. The many flame cells on each side of the planarian are connected by a branching system of fine tubes to main **excretory ducts.** The excretory ducts run anteriorly on either side of the mid-line of the body, emptying

through a series of **excretory pores,** on the dorsal surface of the animal.

Precisely how the flame cells function is not well understood. Apparently these cells extract water and other excretory wastes from the body fluid—which fills the tissue

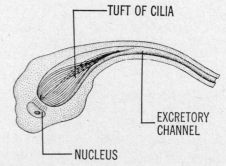

TUFT OF CILIA
EXCRETORY CHANNEL
NUCLEUS

Fig. 20-2.   A flame cell. Such primitive excretory units are characteristic of flatworms.

spaces of the mesoderm—and drive the resulting solution of wastes out of the body, via the excretory ducts.

In Annelida, such as the earthworm, the mesodermal tissues are much more abundant and highly differentiated; also there is a well-developed blood system. The *excretory organs* of the earthworm and other Annelida are the **nephridia,** of which there are usually two in each *segment* of the body (Fig. 20-3). Each nephridium is a long, highly coiled tube, which leads from the body cavity of one segment to the external surface of the succeeding segment of the body. At the coelolic end of the nephridium there is a cilated funnel-shaped opening, the **nephrostome.** The lumen of the nephridium—throughout most of its length—is also lined with cilia. Moreover, there is a network of capillaries (not shown in the figure) that comes into intimate contact with the glandular walls of the nephridium.

The functioning of the nephridial tubules has not been studied very adequately. However, the nephridia tend to resemble the kidney tubules of higher animals (p. 372); and it may be supposed that they function in a somewhat similar fashion. The cilia maintain a flow of the body fluid—from the coelomic cavity, through the tubule, toward the external opening. The coelomic fluid contains glucose and other useful substances, as well as metabolic wastes, and probably the glandular cells in the wall of the nephridium —like the cells in the wall of a **kidney tubule** —extract glucose, water, and other useful substances from the fluid while it passes toward the outside. In this way useful components of the body fluid are returned to the blood in the capillaries of the tubule; and waste products, *due to a reabsorption of water,* are more concentrated by the time the excretory fluid is voided at the surface of the body.

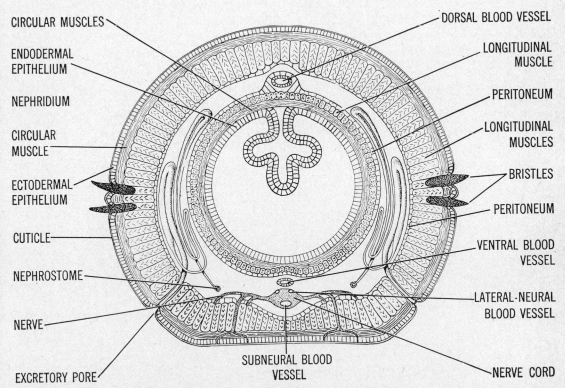

CIRCULAR MUSCLES
ENDODERMAL EPITHELIUM
NEPHRIDIUM
CIRCULAR MUSCLE
ECTODERMAL EPITHELIUM
CUTICLE
NEPHROSTOME
NERVE
EXCRETORY PORE

DORSAL BLOOD VESSEL
LONGITUDINAL MUSCLE
PERITONEUM
LONGITUDINAL MUSCLES
BRISTLES
PERITONEUM
VENTRAL BLOOD VESSEL
LATERAL-NEURAL BLOOD VESSEL
NERVE CORD

SUBNEURAL BLOOD VESSEL

Fig. 20-3. Diagrammatic cross section of an **earthworm**. Note particularly the **nephridium,** an excretory tubule that originates at the **nephrostome** and terminates at the **excretory pore.**

STRUCTURE AND FUNCTIONS OF THE KIDNEY

The work of the kidney is to separate urine from the blood that flows through it; and by extracting excess wastes and other substances from the plasma and delivering these compounds into the urine, the kidney plays a major role in regulating the composition of the plasma and the lymph.

Each kidney (Fig. 20-1) receives a major artery—the **renal artery**—directly from the **dorsal aorta;** and the kidneys are drained by large veins—the **renal veins**—that pass to the **postcaval vein.** While it is being formed, urine collects in a small chamber—the **pelvic chamber**—situated along the medial border of the kidney (Fig. 20-1); and from the pelvic chamber the urine drains into the **urinary bladder,** via each of the two **ureters.** The urinary bladder distends its muscular walls to receive the urine; but finally—when a critical pressure is reached—the urination reflex is generated. Then the bladder contracts—voiding the urine through the **urethra,** a single duct leading to the outside (Fig. 20-1).

The Nephrons, or Functional Units of the Kidney. The human kidney represents an aggregation of about one million excretory tubules—called the **nephrons** (Fig. 20-4). Each nephron is a highly coiled microscopic tubule that is responsible for forming a small part of the total quantity of urine produced by the kidney as a whole. Thus the functioning of the whole kidney can be determined by studying the structure and activity of the single nephron.

The first part of a kidney tubule is a double-walled capsule, that surrounds a compact cluster of blood capillaries (Fig. 20-4). This peculiar tuft of capillary coils is called a **glomerulus;** and the surrounding double-walled chamber is called **Bowman's capsule,** first observed in 1842 by a young English anatomist, William Bowman. Both the outer and inner walls of Bowman's capsule consist of a single layer of flattened epithelial cells; and the inner wall adheres very intimately to the tufted glomerular capillaries.

The cavity of Bowman's capsule leads directly into the long lumen of the nephron that eventually leads into a **collecting tubule** (Fig. 20-4). To reach a collecting tubule, however, fluid in Bowman's capsule must flow consecutively through (1) the **proximal convoluted tubule,** (2) the hairpin-shaped **loop of Henle,** and (3) the **distal convoluted**

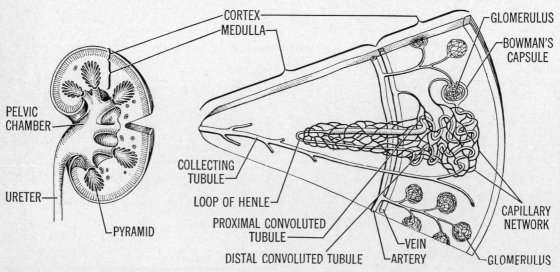

Fig. 20-4. Structure of the human kidney. Note particularly the blood supply of the **nephron.** About a million of these excretory units are present in each kidney.

tubule. The walls of the kidney tubules are made up of a single layer of **glandular** epithelium; and the different parts of the nephrons occupy characteristic positions in the kidney (Fig. 20-4). The collecting tubules serve merely to drain the urine from the nephrons proper into the pelvic chamber of the kidney.

The blood supply of the nephron is very important in determining kidney function. As may be seen in Figure 20-4, each glomerulus is supplied by an **afferent vessel,** which is a branch of the renal artery, and each glomerulus is drained by an **efferent vessel.** The efferent vessels, however, return to the renal vein by a very indirect route—through a network of capillaries that enmeshes all the tubular parts of the nephron. Thus a given sample of blood in passing from the renal artery to the renal vein must flow through two sets of capillaries: (1) the capillary coils of the glomerulus itself and (2) the capillary network that lies in intimate contact with the tubular parts of the nephron (Fig. 20-5).

The Formation of Urine. Kidney function has been studied intensively for many years, and today, although some problems remain unsolved, the main issues have been defined quite clearly.

The work of the kidney involves three processes:

1. The glomerulus and capsule, working together, subject each sample of blood to a process of pressure **filtration.** This process forms a fluid, the **nephric filtrate,** that passes into Bowman's capsule while a given part of the blood flows through the glomerulus.

2. The tubular parts of the nephron salvage very large quantities of water (which accounts, mainly, for a concentration of the waste products) and smaller quantities of glucose and other useful compounds—by *reabsorbing* these substances from the nephric filtrate while it passes through the tubules toward the pelvic chamber. This process of **selective reabsorption** demands that the gland cells in the tubule wall transfer the reabsorbed compounds back into the blood in the capillaries surrounding the tubule.

3. The glandular walls of the nephric tubules *secrete* additional quantities of metabolic wastes into the nephric filtrate, extracting these wastes from the capillaries around the tubule and passing them into the lumen of the nephron.

Reabsorption and *secretion* greatly change the composition of the **nephric filtrate** as this fluid drains through the nephron toward the collecting tubules. In fact, the fluid as it reaches the collecting tubule can no longer be called the filtrate—it is the **urine.**

Filtration: Nature of the Nephric Filtrate. The glomerulus and Bowman's capsule together form a very effective **force filter.** In filtering the blood the glomerular and capsu-

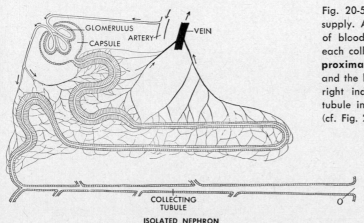

GLOMERULUS
CAPSULE
ARTERY
VEIN
COLLECTING
TUBULE
ISOLATED NEPHRON

Fig. 20-5. A single nephron, with its blood supply. Arrows indicate direction of the flow of blood. A number of nephrons drain into each collecting tubule. Be sure to identify the **proximal** and **distal convoluted tubules** and the **loop of Henle.** The letter O at lower right indicates the opening of a collecting tubule into the pelvic chamber of the kidney (cf. Fig. 20-4).

lar walls allow considerable quantities of water, glucose, urea, and all other of the crystalloidal components of the plasma to escape from the blood into the capsule. However, all the more complex components of the blood, particularly the plasma proteins and other **colloids** (and, of course, the corpuscles), cannot pass through the glomerular walls, and do not appear in the filtrate. These colloids remain in the blood as it leaves the glomerulus via the efferent vessel. Each sample of blood passes rapidly through a glomerulus; and while it is passing, it loses only a fraction (5 to 10 percent) of its volume. This fraction becomes the filtrate, which is sidetracked into the nephric tubule; but simultaneously the main flow of blood continues through the glomerulus and efferent vessel, and finally through the capillaries surrounding the other parts of the nephron (see Fig. 20-5).

Determining the composition of the nephric filtrate is a very difficult task. The kidney of a frog, for example, can be exposed; and a special microscope is then used to examine the glomeruli while the nephric filtrate pours into the capsules of the nephrons. A very delicate glass syringe is required to withdraw samples of the filtrate from the capsules; and new microchemical methods were devised to analyze the extremely small samples of filtrate obtained. In fact, the collection and analysis of nephric filtrate by A. N. Richards and co-workers at the University of Pennsylvania represented one of the most important achievements in physiology of the decade 1921 to 1930.

Analysis of the capsular fluid (Table 20-1) revealed essentially that *the* **nephric filtrate** *is a* **colloid-free filtrate** *of the* **blood plasma.** The filtrate contains all the plasma crystalloids, including water, glucose, amino acids, and salts, as well as purely waste substances, such as urea and uric acid. Moreover the concentration of these crystalloids *is the same in the* **filtrate** *as it is in the* **plasma** (see Table 20-1). But the colloids of the plasma, mainly the proteins and lipoids, are held back.

Under normal conditions no colloids are present in the filtrate as it enters Bowman's capsule.

The work of forcing filtrate from the blood into the capsule is done, not by the kidney, but by the heart. Blood pressure in the glomerulus must be maintained at a level above 30 mm of mercury if any filtrate is to be formed; and other factors being equal, the quantity of filtrate and urine formed in a given time tends to parallel the blood pressure.

The filtrate contains the same solutes as the plasma, except that the colloids of the plasma are lacking in the filtrate—and consequently filtrate is hypotonic to the plasma. Normally the glomerular blood pressure amounts to about 70 mm of mercury. About 30 mm of this pressure is expended in overcoming back-pressure—due to the hypotonicity of the filtrate—and only 40 mm is the *effective pressure,* which drives more filtrate into the nephric capsule. If the blood pressure in the glomeruli rises or falls, the effective filtration pressure follows, and the quantity of filtrate varies accordingly.

Reabsorption. Normal urine (Table 20-1) contains virtually no glucose or amino acids, because the convoluted tubules extract these useful compounds from the filtrate and return them to the blood that flows through surrounding capillaries.

TABLE 20-1—The Nephric Filtrate As Compared to the Plasma and Urine

Main Components	Grams per 100 cc of Fluid		
	Plasma	Nephric Filtrate	Urine
Urea	0.03	0.03	2.0
Uric acid	0.004	0.004	0.05
Glucose	0.10	0.10	Trace
Amino acids	0.05	0.05	Trace
Total inorganic salts	0.72	0.72	1.50
Proteins and other colloids	8.00	0.000	0.00

Often the reabsorption of useful substances is not complete, however, since always it is a **selective process.** During hyperglycemia, for example, the excess of glucose is left in the filtrate and appears in the urine. In other words, the tubule tends to stop reabsorbing a substance when a proper amount has been put back into circulation. Thus many substances do not appear in the urine unless their concentration in the blood exceeds a certain **threshold** value. Such so-called **threshold substances** include many of the inorganic salts, which thus are retained in proper amounts in the blood stream. In fact, the selective nature of the reabsorptive processes in large measure accounts for the ability of the renal organs to maintain a beautifully regulated homeostatic control of the body fluids.

In salvaging glucose, amino acids, and other substances from the filtrate, the tubules must expend energy. Initially the concentration of glucose, for example, is equal in the filtrate and in the blood. Consequently there is no tendency for glucose to be reabsorbed spontaneously, except to a small extent, by virtue of the fact that glucose in the filtrate may become more concentrated as the reabsorption of water proceeds (see below). The kidney cells derive the energy for this work from their oxidative metabolism; and if a kidney is deprived of oxygen (for example, by treatment with cyanide), reabsorption quickly ceases. Such a kidney still forms urine, but the urine is extremely copious and dilute, possessing practically the same composition as the filtrate.

Reabsorption of Water. The salvaging of water from the nephric filtrate is a major kidney function. In fact, the human kidney produces about 100 liters of filtrate while it is forming just one liter of urine. In other words, the kidney usually reabsorbs about 99 liters of water in the process of forming one liter of urine; and if the kidneys lose their capacity to reabsorb water, they put forth very large volumes of highly dilute urine (p. 412).

In order to calculate the filtrate/urine volume ratio and thus to determine the true extent of water reabsorption by the kidney, it was necessary to find a substance capable of meeting four precise specifications: (1) The substance must be nontoxic when measurable amounts are injected into the blood stream. (2) It must be completely impervious to any reabsorption by the tubules. (3) It must be altogether nonsusceptible to **secretional activity** (see below) in the tubules. (4) It must be freely filtered into Bowman's capsule. Such a substance was finally found in the form of **inulin,** a relatively short-chain polysaccharide compound; and the studies of Homer W. Smith and co-workers at New York University, dealing with the excretion of inulin, contributed greatly to the progress of renal physiology during the second quarter of the present century. The heavy reabsorption of water accounts mainly for the high concentrations of **urea** and other wastes that are found in the urine. In fact, any solute originally present in the filtrate becomes highly concentrated in the urine, unless this solute is reabsorbed while water is being reabsorbed. In the human urine, urea usually reaches a concentration about 60 times greater than in the blood plasma, and were it not for the fact that small quantities of urea are reabsorbed along with the larger quantities of water, this difference of concentration would be even greater.

The quantity of water reabsorbed by the human kidney varies quite widely, depending on the needs of the body. When large quantities of water are drunk, and while the blood tends to be diluted, the reabsorption of water remains at a minimum and a large volume of dilute urine is formed by the kidney. But if the water intake is restricted, reabsorption reaches a maximum, so that the kidney conserves a maximum of water for the body.

The water-reabsorbing capacity of the kidney is a good measure of an animal's capacity to conserve water. In aquatic and semiaquatic vertebrates, especially fresh-water fish and

Amphibia, water absorption is not conspicuous, and such animals form large quantities of hypotonic urine. But in terrestrial vertebrates, the average quantity of urine is much reduced, and in mammals the urine often is distinctly hypertonic compared to plasma. In producing such a hypertonic urine the kidney performs definite *work,* which requires that the tubules must be supplied with adequate oxygen. When deprived of oxygen, the kidney loses its capacity to reabsorb water and produces a very large volume of highly dilute urine, regardless of the needs of the body.

Secretion. Certain drugs, dyestuffs, and perhaps some natural wastes seem to be transmitted from the blood in the capillaries surrounding the nephric tubule into the nephric fluid. Therefore, the total quantity of such substances in the urine represents the sum of two quantities: (1) the portion that filters into Bowman's capsule, and (2) the portion that is **secreted** into the tubule by the glandular walls. In the case of phenol red—the dye used by E. K. Marshall, Jr., in 1924, when he and co-workers at Johns Hopkins University first demonstrated secretional activity in the kidney—the concentration of the dye in the urine was more than 200 times greater than in the blood; and this degree of concentration cannot be accounted for by water reabsorption alone.

Secretional activity, however, probably plays a relatively minor role in the functioning of a normal *human* kidney. The evidence shows that a large proportion of the water that is filtered into Bowman's capsule is reabsorbed before the filtrate reaches the collecting tubule, and this mainly accounts for the high concentration of wastes in human urine.

However, the nephrons of certain fish *do not possess* **glomeruli,** and in such **aglomerular kidneys** secretional activity assumes a very important part in the formation of the urine.

Renal Impairments. Ordinary kidney dissease, or **nephritis,** involves primarily the glomeruli. The diseased glomeruli become more freely permeable than normally, and in severe cases the glomeruli show signs of disintegration. Normally the filtrate and urine are free of proteins; but in nephritis, first the plasma albumins, and then the more complex globulins, appear in the urine—depending on the serevity of the case. In the severest cases, even intact erythrocytes are found in the urine. Owing to a continued loss of proteins, the capacity of the plasma to reabsorb fluid from the tissue spaces becomes impaired, and consequently edema develops (p. 335). In the terminal stages of nephritis the glomeruli cease to conduct blood and the filtration volume drops drastically. Then both water and excretory wastes accumulate in the body, and death from uremic poisoning becomes inevitable in about 24 hours, unless curative measures can be taken.

In **diabetes insipidus,** the patient's daily output of urine is 30 to 40 liters, instead of the normal average of about 1.5 liters. This condition represents a grave impairment of the water-reabsorbing capacity of the tubules. The primary cause of diabetes insipidus is not localized in the kidney, however. The disease represents a failure of the pituitary gland to produce the antidiuretic hormone, **vasopressin** (p. 412). Normally this hormone stimulates and controls the water-reabsorbing activities of the tubules.

Chronic **hypertension,** or high blood pressure, is very frequently associated with nephritic impairments. The high pressure produces a very high filtration volume and injures the glomeruli. The kidney is not necessarily a passive factor in hypertensive cases. Recent work indicates that a normal function of the kidney is to produce one or more vasodilator substances, which tend to counteract high blood pressure. A kidney with restricted circulation seems to produce also a vasoconstrictor substance—called **renin**—which may aggravate the hypertension.

Evolution of the Vertebrate Kidney. The earliest chordate animals (p. 664) appear to have arisen in the dilutely brackish waters of river estuaries, although the ancestral stock originated in salt water. An early problem in chordate development was, accordingly, an adequate elimination of water since water kept seeping into the salt-rich body fluids from the surrounding hypotonic medium. In these early chordates the glomerulus appears to have arisen as a water-eliminating device. At first, however, the filtrate was passed into the coelomic fluid, which was drained off by the nephric tubules. But later the glomerulus became surrounded by the end of the tubule, forming Bowman's capsule, and this arrangement became very well developed in the truly fresh-water fishes and in the amphibians.

Some of the evolving fishes returned to the sea, however, and now the problem was to hold water in the body fluids. Among such marine fishes two lines of evolution came into being. One group, which led to the modern sharks and other cartilaginous fish, returned to the ocean very early in Silurian (p. 563) times. This group developed a system of maintaining a high osmotic pressure in the blood and lymph by virtue of a very heavy reabsorption of urea. Accordingly, the plasma of these fish today contains a truly astonishing quantity of this nitrogenous waste—up to some 25 grams per liter. The other group, which led to the bony fishes of contemporary times, did not go back to the sea until the end of the Mesozoic era (p. 565), and this group adopted another procedure. They developed a means of eliminating excess salts from the blood through an active transport, or secretory, mechanism localized in the membranes of the gills. The glomerulus of these marine fish also came to be reduced or even absent, as in the modern goose-fish and allied forms.

Land vertebrates, particularly reptiles and birds, likewise faced a problem of water conservation, owing to evaporative losses suffered by exposure to the atmosphere. In these groups, however, a biochemical adjustment occurred. Instead of forming urea as an end product of the catabolism of proteins and other nitrogenous compounds, the reptiles and birds produce uric acid. This compound, which is only sparingly soluble in aqueous media, precipitates out in the cloacal cavity of the animals and does not require much water for its elimination, in the form of guano. Likewise, the glomeruli of reptiles and birds are considerably reduced.

Mammals arrived rather late upon the evolutionary scene. Accordingly, the expedient evolved for the mammalian kidney is different. Mainly the mammalian kidney has resorted to an acceleration of its water-reabsorbing mechanisms. To this end a special hormone, the antidiuretic hormone, **vasopressin,** has developed (p. 412). When a dilution of the blood results from drinking excess water, a more copious secretion of this posterior pituitary hormone is triggered; the converse occurs when insufficient water is imbibed and absorbed into the blood. The dehydrating effects of high alcohol consumption appear to be related to the fact that ethyl alcohol tends to suppress the production or liberation of the antidiuretic hormone.

SUMMARY

The function of the kidney is to maintain a normal blood composition by removing excesses of the various blood components and passing these substances into the urine. The kidneys differ from the lungs in that not all the blood of the body passes through the renal vessels during each circuit. However, the renal blood flow is very copious. Indeed it may be calculated that all the body fluid, including the volume of both lymph and blood, is subjected to filtration and reabsorption some 15 times in the course of every day.

The important units of renal function are the nephrons, of which there are about a million in each kidney. The nephrons form the urine *mainly* by two processes—filtration and reabsorption. Each hour an average of about 6000 cc of colloid-free filtrate is forced into the capsular parts of the nephrons from the glomeruli, but only about 60 cc of this fluid reaches the collecting tubules as urine. Meanwhile the volume is reduced, mainly by the reabsorption of water, but partly by the reabsorption of glucose, amino acids, and various inorganic salts. In many cases reabsorption acts in opposition to the normal processes of osmosis, and in performing this definite work, the tubules expend energy and utilize oxygen. Precisely how the cells of a tubule are able to force substances to move against a concentration gradient is still an unsolved problem. A considerable amount of water is reabsorbed by the distal tubules, which are subject to control by the pituitary hormone, vasopressin. The distal tubules likewise are dominant in the reabsorption of salts, and in regulating the hydrogen ion concentration of the plasma and urine. In contrast, glucose is reclaimed mainly in the proximal tubules, but the other functional differentiations of the various parts of the nephron are not entirely clear.

The urine is a remnant of the nephric filtrate, which retains most of the metabolic wastes as well as *excesses* of the other plasma components, such as inorganic salts and glucose. To a small extent, the initial quantity of certain wastes in the filtrate may be augmented by further quantities derived from the capillaries surrounding the tubule walls, but this *secretional* activity does not appear to be very important in the human kidney.

The kidney also has an important influence on the acid-base balance of the blood and other body fluids. By excreting extra quantities of acidic or basic compounds, the kidney can shift the equilibrium in either an alkaline or acid direction—although the magnitude of these changes in hydrogen ion concentration is very small, by virtue of the excellent buffering capacity of the body fluids. Moreover, the kidney exerts a further effect on the acid-base balance of the body through the medium of ammonia (NH_3), since this alkaline compound is liberated when the kidney participates in the deamination of amino acids (p. 342). All in all it may be said that the renal organs serve to maintain a high degree of constancy in the internal environment of the body cells.

TEST QUESTIONS

1. Specify the major metabolic wastes of man. What organs cooperate with the kidneys in eliminating these products? Explain.
2. Make a labeled diagram to show the human kidneys, the renal blood vessels, and the connections of the kidneys with the other parts of the excretory tract.
3. Make a labeled diagram to show all parts of a nephric tubule and the relations of the tubule to the capillary circulation.
4. What is the "nephric filtrate"? How is it formed?
5. Carefully explain why the nephric filtrate is called (a) a forced filtrate; (b) a colloid filtrate.
6. To what extent is glucose present (a) in the filtrate and (b) in the urine? Carefully explain this difference.
7. To what extent is urea present (a) in the nephric filtrate and (b) in the urine? Carefully explain this difference.

8. Why is reabsorption described as a *selective* process? Explain carefully, using (a) glucose, and (b) water to exemplify the discussion.
9. In achieving reabsorption, the tubule cells perform work. Carefully explain the statement in terms of: (a) the reabsorption of glucose; (b) the reabsorption of water.
10. Assuming that the kidneys of a normal individual produce 100 cc of urine per hour, approximately what would be: (a) the hourly filtration volume; (b) the quantity of glucose reabsorbed each hour; (c) the quantity of urea present in an hourly sample of the urine?
11. Trace a given molecule of water through the kidney, assuming:
    a. it does not enter the filtrate
    b. it enters the filtrate and is reabsorbed
    c. it enters the filtrate and is not reabsorbed
12. After the injection of a certain dye into the

blood stream of a dog, the concentration of the dye in the urine is found to be 125 times greater than in the filtrate. How might this observation be explained, knowing that the filtrate/urine ratio of the dog is 100/1?

13. Explain why the plasma/urine concentration ratio for inulin may be 100/1 while simultaneously the ratio for urea may be 60/1.

14. Carefully explain each of the following conditions in terms of kidney structure and function: (a) albumin in the urine; (b) red corpuscles in the urine; (c) glucose in the urine; (d) an extremely copious dilute urine; (e) virtually no urine.

15. Briefly explain how the kidney may participate in controlling the acid-base balance of the body.

16. Briefly explain some of the evolutionary history of the vertebrate kidney.

FURTHER READINGS

1. *The Physiology of the Kidney,* by Homer Smith; New York, 1937.

2. *The Living Body,* by C. H. Best and N. B. Taylor; New York, 1958.

3. "The Kidney," by Homer W. Smith; in *Scientific American,* January 1953.

21-*Reproduction in*
Multicellular Animals

EACH KIND of animal and plant must reproduce rapidly enough to compensate for the death rate of its population; failing this, extinction is inevitable. Accordingly, the trail of evolution is strewn with thousands of extinct species, known today only by the fossilized remnants of their former being.

With few exceptions, multicellular animals reproduce sexually, although quite a few can also multiply asexually. Primary attention will be given to the sexual methods, with only a brief discussion of the asexual processes.

REPRODUCTIVE ORGANS

Most multicellular animals possess well-developed **gonads.** These *essential reproductive organs* produce the **gamete cells,** which are destined to convey part of the protoplasm of each parent to the zygote and other cells of the next generation.

Typically the **testes,** or sperm-producing gonads, are distinct from the **ovaries,** which

produce the eggs. However, in rare cases (for example, certain mollusks), eggs and sperm are generated within the same gonad, although not usually at the same time.

One very simple type of gonad is possessed by *Hydra* (Fig. 21-1). During the sexual period this primitive animal develops both testes and ovaries, which, however, are merely *temporary* organs. The gonads first appear as small swellings at the surface of the body, the testes near the upper end, and the ovaries nearer the foot. Each gonad represents a local accumulation of **germ cells** (p. 476), covered externally by an ectodermal epithelium. In the testes (Fig. 21-1) the germ cells divide repeatedly, forming a large number of very small flagellated sperm. Eventually these sperm escape into the surrounding water when the epithelial wall of the ripe testes begins to disintegrate.

In the ovary (Fig. 21-1) the germ cells also divide several times, but in this case the resulting cells are actively amoeboid and begin devouring each other in cannibalistic fashion.

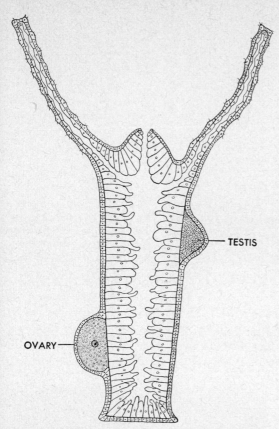

Fig. 21-1. Sexually mature *Hydra*, showing the temporary gonads.

TESTIS

OVARY

Finally only one hugely swollen cell remains, and this is the egg. Fertilization occurs after the epithelial wall of the ovary has disintegrated and one of the free-swimming sperm chances to make contact with an exposed egg. Cross-fertilization is assured by the fact that the eggs and sperm of any one individual do not reach maturity simultaneously. Temporarily, while the egg is cleaving to form the blastula, the embryo remains attached to the body of the parent; but at about the time of gastrulation, the offspring develops cilia and swims away as an independent **larva.**

The **monoecious (hermaphroditic)** condition, in which *both testes and ovaries are possessed by one individual,* is not uncommon, especially among invertebrate animals; but on the whole, **dioecious** species, in which the *sexes are clearly separate,* greatly predominate. Also a vast majority of animals possess truly permanent gonads of greater or lesser complexity.

In addition to the gonads most animals possess various *accessory reproductive structures.* Usually there are two or more **sperm ducts,** through which the sperm are conducted from the testes, and **oviducts,** which convey the eggs from the ovaries. Also one may find a variety of glands and other special structures, closely associated with either or both of the **gonoducts.**

EXTERNAL VS. INTERNAL FERTILIZATION

As a general rule *aquatic* animals merely liberate the gametes into the surrounding water and the coming together of the sperm and eggs is more or less a matter of chance. However, in many cases the males are attracted to the vicinity of where the females are discharging the eggs and are excited to discharge the sperm simultaneously. Usually such *externally fertilized* eggs receive little or no parental care during development, but in some cases (Fig. 21-2) either or both parents may stand guard over the eggs. In some cases also the fertilized eggs become cemented to the body of one of the parents, which carries and protects the embryos during development.

Some essentially nonaquatic animals—such as many amphibians and insects—return to the water to lay their eggs, which may be fertilized either before or after discharge. Most terrestrial forms, however, ejaculate the sperm directly into the reproductive tract of the female, and thus fertilization occurs *internally.* Typically this process involves **copulation** between the sexes, and frequently the male is equipped with a **penis,** or some other type of **intromittent organ.** The **ejaculate,** or **semen,** includes not only the sperm, but also a greater or lesser amount of aqueous fluid secreted by the sperm ducts and associated glands. This fluid provides a suitable medium for the sperm to swim in, and also

Fig 21-2. Male brook stickleback, guarding nest. (Courtesy the New York Conservation Department.)

contains nutrient substances to sustain the sperm until they make contact with the eggs.

In most cases a single copulation serves to fertilize only such eggs as happen to be mature at that time. However, the female reproductive tracts of some animals (for example, many birds and insects) display one or more blind outpocketings, the **seminal receptacles**, in which the sperm collect and remain active for considerable periods after copulation. Thus the queen bee receives just a single visitation of the drone, and yet continues to deposit fertilized eggs for the rest of her reproductive life. Also the domestic hen may lay fertile eggs for a number of months after one contact with a rooster.

In some hermaphroditic animals, the copulating partners may mutually inseminate each other. For example, when earthworms copulate (Fig. 21-3), both individuals extrude semen from the sperm duct openings (segment 15). In each case the semen of one worm is guided into the other's seminal receptacles, two pair of blind pockets that extend inward from the ventral body wall in the ninth and tenth segments. Thus the net result of copulation is that the seminal receptacles of each worm become filled with the semen of the other, and actual fertilization of the eggs does not occur until after the partners have separated. Then each worm

secretes a broad beltlike cocoon around its **clitellum,** and starts wriggling backward to escape from the encircling girdle. The eggs of the worm are extruded into the cocoon when this girdle has been displaced forward

Fig. 21-3. Earthworms, copulating. (Copyright, General Biological Supply House, Inc.)

as far as the oviduct openings in the fourteenth segment; and the sperm (of the other worm) from the receptacles pass into the cocoon as soon as it reaches the ninth and tenth segments. Finally, the worm wriggles entirely free of the cocoon, slipping it off over its tapered "head." Then the cocoon, which now contains fertilized eggs, seals itself by drying and twisting at the ends.

THE MALE REPRODUCTIVE TRACT OF MAN

In man and other vertebrates the reproductive tract, especially in the male, develops in close association with the excretory system. Therefore the two systems together may be called the **urogenital system.** This association is mainly anatomical, however. Functionally the two sets of organs are quite separate, except that some of the ducts serve to transmit both genital and excretory products.

In vertebrates generally, the testes *originate* in the coelom just ventral to the embryonic kidneys, and in lower vertebrates, such as the frog, the adult gonads remain in this position (Fig. 21-4). But in man and many other mammals the testes *descend* shortly before or after birth, taking up a permanent position in the **scrotum** (Fig. 21-5). The scrotum, essentially, is an outpocketing of the body wall, which encloses a small portion of the original coelom. However, the **inguinal canal,** which initially is a free channel connecting the scrotal and abdominal cavities, becomes blocked off by connective tissues. Thus in adults the scrotal and abdominal cavities are separate, except in cases of **inguinal hernia.** When herniation occurs, the original channel reopens and in severe cases a loop of the intestine may be extruded into the scrotal sac. Rarely one or both testes may fail to descend into the scrotum, resulting in unilateral or bilateral **cryptorchy.** Moreover, such undescended testes fail to produce any functional sperm (p. 400).

Primarily the testis is a mass of highly coiled tubules, the **seminiferous tubules** (Fig. 21-6). These generate the sperm by a multiplication of the germinal epithelial cells lining the walls (Fig. 21-7). Secondarily, however, the testis is an **endocrine gland.** Packed into the spaces between the tubules there is a considerable mass of **interstitial cells** (Fig. 21-7). This interstitial tissue produces the male sex hormone, **testosterone,** which is concerned with the development of the **second-**

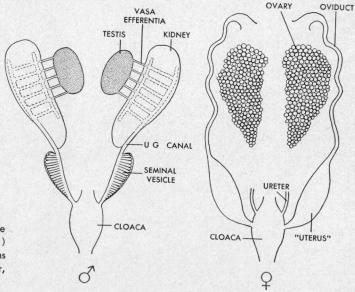

Fig. 21-4. Diagrams of reproductive organs of male (♂) and female (♀) frog. Dotted lines show the connections of the spermiducts with the ureter, within the kidney.

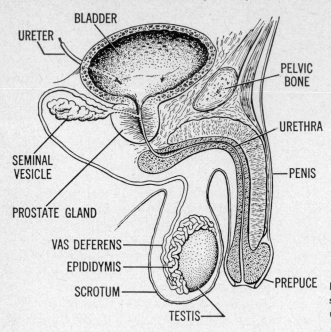

Fig. 21-5. Genital organs of human male, semidiagrammatic. Note connection with the urinary tract, near origin of urethra.

ary sexual characteristics of the male (p. 399).

In the frog and most other lower vertebrates, the sperm pass through the kidney before they reach the main gonoduct (Fig. 21-4). A number of fine ducts, the **vasa efferentia,** lead from the testis to some of the **nephric tubules** in the kidney, and these nephric tubules drain into the **urogenital canal.** Moreover, the urogenital canal does not lead to the exterior, but drains into the **cloaca.** This terminal portion of the digestive tract transmits the sperm, through the external opening to the environment.

In man the sperm tract is very complex. There are a number of **vasa efferentia,** which

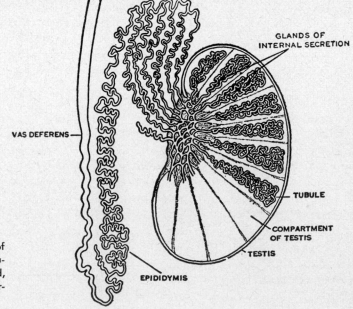

Fig. 21-6. Human testis. Relations of the epididymis to the seminiferous tubules and vas deferens. (From Haggard, *The Science of Health and Disease.* Permission of Harper and Row.)

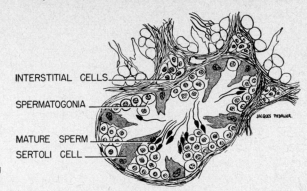

INTERSTITIAL CELLS

SPERMATOGONIA

MATURE SPERM
SERTOLI CELL

Fig. 21-7. Cross section of a sperm-forming tubule of the human testis (semidiagrammatic).

carry the sperm into the **epididymis** (Fig. 21-6), a part of the genital tract that is derived from an embryonic kidney. The epididymis in man has the appearance of a compact mass that half encircles the testis (Fig. 21-5), but actually the epididymis is a very long (about 20 feet), much-coiled tube that leads finally into the **vas deferens,** or sperm duct proper. The vas deferens is a relatively simple tube, with a thick muscular wall, that leaves the scrotum and passes into the abdominal cavity, through the inguinal canal. In the abdominal cavity, the vas deferens ends by joining the **urethra,** a short stout tube that originates from the **urinary bladder.** Thus the urethra fulfills a double duty, in that it conveys both urine and semen to the extremity of the **penis** (Fig. 21-5).

In addition to the sperm tract proper, the male reproductive system includes three pairs of glands. A large **seminal vesicle** drains into the vas deferens on each side, near the point where the sperm duct joins the urethra (Fig. 21-5), and the **prostate glands** empty into the urethra. In many mammals, the **prostate** is plainly a double gland; but in man it appears as a single mass encompassing the root of the urethra (Fig. 21-5). The prostate secretion enters the urethra by two sets of fine ducts that come in from either side of the mass. And finally there are **Cowper's glands,** a pair of glands that empty into the urethra more distally (these small glands are not shown in Figure 21-5).

The composition of the **semen** is very complex. In addition to the sperm, semen con-

tains numerous glandular secretions, but the precise origin of these secetions is somewhat obscure. Probably some components of the semen are derived from the epithelium of the epididymis, and until the sperm have passed through the epididymis they never become motile. In fact the sperm do not gain full motility until they make contact with the secretions of the seminal vesicles; and the sperm tend to be swept through the vas deferens by peristaltic waves occurring in the wall of this muscular duct. The sperm tend to accumulate in the **ampulla,** a swollen part of the vas deferens, near the point where it receives the secretions of the seminal vesicle. The vesicular secretion provides an ideal medium for exciting and sustaining the swimming activity of the sperm. This fluid is well buffered with inorganic salts, and contains an unusually high concentration of *fructose,* which the sperm utilize in their metabolism. However, the metabolism of the sperm appears to be largely anaerobic. Sperm decompose the sugar only as far as lactic acid and thus they utilize only a small fraction of the potentially available energy.

The secretions of the prostate and Cowper's glands are less clearly understood. During sexual excitement these fluids appear to precede the sperm through the urethra, and possibly the secretions are purely lubricatory in function.

As it traverses the penis, the **urethra** is flanked on all sides by **erectile tissue,** disposed in stout columns, called the **corpora cavernosa** (Fig. 21-5). This spongy tissue is permeated with blood sinuses, and ordinarily, when the sinuses are not distended with blood, the tissue is flaccid. But one of the reflexes in the pattern of sexual excitation leads to a constriction of the vessels that drain the sinuses. At this time, therefore, the erectile tissue becomes turgid and distended with blood; and temporarily the penis becomes an effective intromittent organ. When ejaculation occurs, the urethra is swept by a short but powerful series of peristaltic contractions.

THE FEMALE REPRODUCTIVE ORGANS

The **ovaries,** in vertebrate animals, are not connected directly with the oviducts. In the frog, for example, each large ovary or **egg mass,** lies in the body cavity, ventral to the corresponding kidney (Fig. 21-4). The **ostium,** or dilated mouth of the oviduct, opens directly into the body cavity in a region somewhat anterior to the ovary (Fig. 21-4). To be liberated, therefore, the eggs must break through the wall of the ovary and pass through the body cavity to the ostium. This rupturing of the ovarian wall is referred to as **ovulation,** and after ovulation the eggs are carried to the mouth of the oviduct by the activity of the ciliated epithelium that lines the peritoneal cavity.

The eggs of the frog do not possess any external coating of "jelly" before they enter the oviduct; but while an egg is passing through the oviduct it receives its "jelly coat" from gland cells lining the wall. Like the sperm duct, the oviduct of the frog leads to the cloaca rather than to the exterior, and the eggs are finally voided through the cloacal opening. Just before joining the cloaca, the oviduct shows a slightly expanded section, called the "uterus" (Fig. 21-4). However, no development occurs while the eggs remain in this part of the oviduct, and consequently the term uterus is not a very apt one.

True copulation does not occur in the frog, but an analogous reaction, called **amplexus** (Fig. 21-8), takes place about 24 hours before the female starts to shed the eggs. Amplexus continues until all the eggs have been extruded into the water; and simultaneously the male continues to liberate a stream of sperm while the eggs are issuing forth.

The Human Ovary and Its Functions. In the human female, as in other vertebrates, the ovaries have no direct connection with the oviducts, or **Fallopian tubes.** The human

Fig. 21-8.　Amplexus, in toads. (Courtesy of Roberts Rugh, Columbia University.)

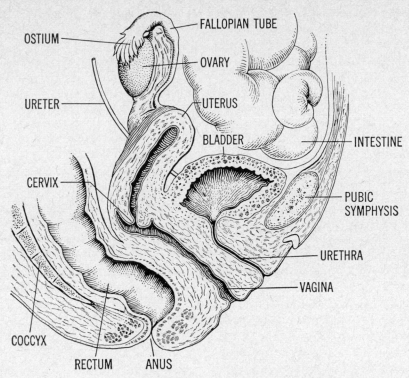

Fig. 21-9. Genital tract of human female.

ovary—in size and shape—resembles a shelled almond (Fig. 21-9), although in older individuals the ovarian surface is roughened and pocketed with numerous scars. These scars result from a repeated rupturing of the ovarian wall during successive ovulations.

The human ovaries usually produce only one egg during each 28-day cycle of activity. The egg cell arises from the germinal epithelium of the ovary (Fig. 21-10). This epithelium proliferates periodically, forming a group of cells that is pushed inward from the surface of the ovary and finally pinched off as a separate mass (Fig. 21-10). This mass represents an incipient **Graafian follicle,** which soon becomes organized into a vesicle, enclosing the maturing egg (Fig. 21-10). The Graafian follicle continues to enlarge until it protrudes slightly from the surface of the ovary. Then, finally, when the egg is ripe, the follicle ruptures, discharging an egg near the mouth of the Fallopian tube. This process of **ovulation** occurs periodically in the

human female, usually at a fixed time in relation to the menstrual cycle (p. 401).

The ovary has also developed two important endocrine functions, which are associated mainly with the Graafian follicles. As each follicle ripens, it becomes filled with a **follicular fluid,** which contains the "female sex hormone," **estrogen** (p. 400). Estrogen has

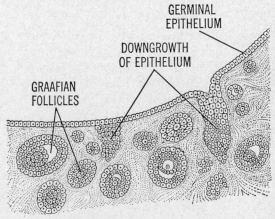

Fig. 21-10. Section of ovary.

a profound effect upon bodily development, especially in regard to the **secondary sexual characteristics** of the female (p. 400). Before the time of **puberty,** none of the follicles develops, and the features peculiar to womanhood are not very clearly differentiated.

The other endocrine function of the ovary is likewise associated with the Graafian follicles. *Subsequent* to ovulation, each follicle undergoes a considerable change of structure. The cavity of the follicle first becomes filled with a small clot of blood, the **blutpunkt,** but the blood is soon replaced by a mass of **yellow tissue,** derived from the inner lining of the follicle. This yellow body is the **corpus luteum,** an endocrine gland that produces **progesterone,** the so-called pregnancy hormone (p. 401).

The Oviducts, Uterus, and Vagina. The anatomical features of the other parts of the female reproductive tract are shown in Figure 21-9. The **uterus** is a pear-shaped thick-walled muscular chamber, lined internally with a richly vascular mucous membrane. On each side of the upper margin, the uterus receives a Fallopian tube, and below and centrally the uterus communicates with the **vagina.** The **cervix,** or lower tapered portion of the uterus, protrudes somewhat into the vaginal canal, which, like the uterus, has a muscular wall lined internally by a well-defined mucosa. Except in pregnancy, the uterus is scarcely larger than a closed fist, but during pregnancy the uterus enlarges to accommodate the growing **fetus.**

Fertilization; Implantation of the Embryo. Shortly after ovulation, the egg finds its way into the ostium of the Fallopian tube, which bears a fringe of ciliated outgrowths, surrounding the mouth of the oviduct (Fig. 21-9). Meanwhile, if copulation has occurred recently, sperm will probably have succeeded in leaving the vagina, traversing the uterine cavity, and reaching the lumen of the Fallopian tube. Unless fertilization occurs before the egg leaves the oviduct, **pregnancy** rarely, if ever, takes place.

Granting fertilization, the first cleavages of the egg occur in the oviduct, but soon the young embryo descends into the uterus. Here the embryo stimulates the uterine wall, and the maternal tissues begin to surround and embed the embryo. As a result of this **decidual** reaction, the embryo becomes firmly **implanted.** After successful implantation, development continues at the expense of substances absorbed from the maternal blood stream. At the end of about 6 weeks the embryo measures almost an inch in length; and thereafter it may be called a **fetus.** The fetus grows gradually, attaining a length of about 3 inches at 3 months; 10 inches at 5 months; and 20 inches at 9 months. The **gestation period** in man is about 10 lunar months (approximately 9 calendar months), whereupon the fetus is delivered through the vaginal passage.

NUTRITION OF THE EMBRYO

Lower Vertebrates. The problem of sustaining the metabolism of the embryo during the developmental period is relatively simple in the case of the lower vertebrates (for example, fish and amphibians) that deposit their eggs in *water*. Such eggs invariably contain a large amount of yolk materials, including protein, lipid, and carbohydrate reserves, and these substances are gradually mobilized and used by the cells of the embryo as they multiply, grow, and differentiate. Before it is used up, most of the yolk comes to lie in the **yolk sac,** a pouchlike extension of the embryonic enteron (Fig. 21-11). The walls of this embryonic nutritive organ become highly vascularized at an early developmental stage, and the stored food materials begin to be absorbed and distributed as soon as circulation is established. The embryo is surrounded by an aerated aqueous fluid, from which the blood absorbs oxygen, and to which it gives off carbon dioxide and other waste products of metabolism.

Land-Dwelling Vertebrates. The reptiles and birds were among the earliest terrestrial vertebrates, and these animals retained the

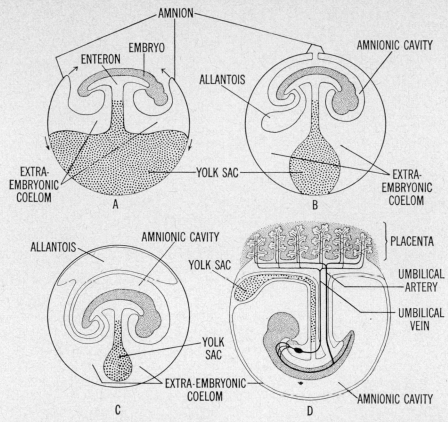

Fig. 21-11. Development of the embryonic membranes and the placenta in man and higher mammals generally. Compare with membranes of the bird's egg (Fig. 21—12), noting differences in the amnion, allantois, and yolk sac.

oviparous (egg-laying) habits of their aquatic ancestors. Eggs laid on land, however, are always covered by a shell and other protective **membranes,** for otherwise the developing embryos could not survive the drying effects of the atmosphere. Moreover, the embryos of land animals reach a relatively high state of development before they are able to face the hazards of the land environment. Accordingly, the egg cells of birds and reptiles, besides containing relatively large amounts of yolk, are surrounded by an "egg-white." This albuminous fluid provides the developing embryo with an extra reserve of water and additional protein reserves. Both the "egg-white" and the calcareous shell are secreted by the glandular walls of the oviducts, after ovulation has occurred, while the egg is passing through the oviduct.

The Embryonic Membranes. In reptiles, birds, and mammals, embryonic development proceeds in the absence of the age-old aquatic environment, and such development involved the evolution of a highly specialized system of **embryonic membranes.** These arose in the form of the **amnion** and the **allantois,** a pair of living membranes that grow out from the embryo, enveloping it completely. Jointly these membranes, together with the yolk sac (Fig. 21-12), protect the embryo and sustain it by absorbing oxygen and foods and by eliminating metabolic wastes during the extended period of development.

The Amnion. The amnion, as it first appears, is an outfolding of the **body wall** of the embryo, which carries with it an extension of the **coelomic cavity** (Fig. 21-11A). This double membranous fold continues to grow until it envelops the embryo completely (Fig. 21-11B). Then the amniotic folds *meet* and *fuse* above the embryo, forming a new cavity, which is called the **amniotic cavity.** This amniotic cavity lies between the embryo and the inner layer of the amniotic fold, and is not to be confused with **extraembryonic coelom,** which lies between the inner and outer folds of the original outgrowth. After the amniotic folds meet and fuse above the embryo, the inner layer of the outgrowth is called the **amniotic membrane,** and the outer layer is called the **chorion** (Fig. 21-11C).

The amniotic cavity is filled with an aqueous fluid secreted by the amniotic membrane. Accordingly the embryo continues development suspended in a watery medium, which duplicates many of the conditions of a truly aquatic environment. In eggs of the birds and reptiles, the chorionic layer of the amniotic fold comes to lie in contact with the inner surface of the egg shell (Fig. 21-12). But in higher mammals, the chorion comes into direct contact with the uterine wall, which, after implantation, envelops the whole embryo.

The Allantois. The **allantois,** or second embryonic membrane, arises as an outpocketing from the **enteron.** As it grows, the allantois continues to push out into the extraem-bryonic coelom, especially in a posterior direction (Fig. 21-11B, C). Then the outer layer of the allantois fuses intimately with the chorion, forming a single highly vascular membrane that lies immediately subjacent to the egg shell (Fig. 21-12).

The allantois is an embryonic organ that fulfills the absorptive, respiratory, and excretory needs of the developing embryo. Shortly after its formation, the allantois becomes permeated with blood capillaries that are supplied and drained by major vessels from the embryo proper. In the bird and reptile, the allantoic capillaries serve not only to take in oxygen and give off carbon dioxide through the porous shells, but also to absorb the material of the egg white. Moreover, the allantois is a repository for the nongaseous metabolic wastes that are formed during embryonic development. At the time of hatching, most of the allantois is discarded, together with all of the amnion. But the root of the allantois, at its junction with the enteron, is retained in mammals, being converted into part of the **urinary bladder** of the adult.

The Uterus and Placenta. The **monotremes,** an almost extinct group of very primitive mammals, have retained the oviparous habit (Fig. 21-13), but a great ma-

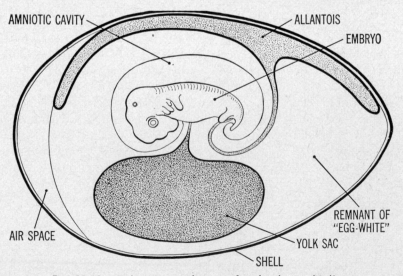

Fig. 21-12. Embryonic membranes of a developing bird's egg.

Fig. 21-13. The duckbill, one of the few surviving species of monotremes, which do not develop any placenta. This primitive egg-laying **mammal** has a birdlike bill and webbed feet. (Courtesy of the American Museum of Natural History, New York.)

jority of present-day mammals are **viviparous.** In such mammals the developing offspring are retained within the uterus of the female until the end of the embryonic period, and the embryos are nourished during the developmental period by food substances derived from the maternal blood stream. Essentially the uterus is a specialized portion of the oviducts (Fig. 21-14), which in some mammals, like the rabbit, remains **duplex,** but in others, like man, becomes **simplex.**

The efficiency of the uterus as an abode for the developing embryo hinges upon the development of another structure, the **pla-**

centa. This important nutritive organ is derived partly from maternal tissues that grow around the embryo when it becomes implanted in the uterine wall, and partly from certain of the tissues of the embryonic membranes.

In higher mammals, the chorion and allantois arise in much the same fashion as in reptiles and in birds; but in mammals the chorion comes into contact with the tissues of the uterine wall (Fig. 21-11D), rather than with the inner surface of the egg shell. Moreover, the chorion sends out a large number of fingerlike outgrowths, the **chorionic villi,**

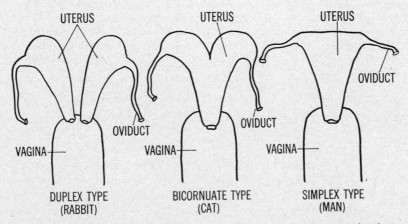

Fig 21-14. Types of uteri in various mammals. Note that the uterus develops as a specialized part of the oviduct.

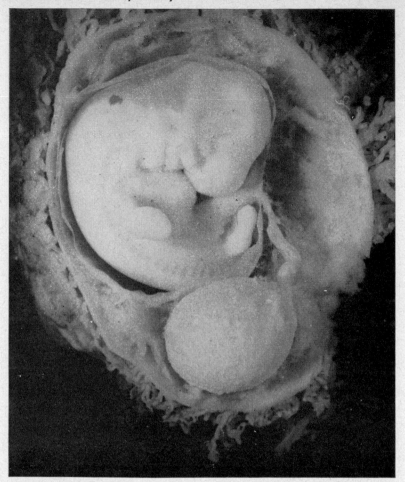

Fig. 21-15. Human embryo (7.1 mm long) enclosed in the embryonic membranes. The yolk sac lies below, connected with the embryo by the umbilical cord. The embryo almost completely fills the amniotic cavity, which is bounded by the plainly visible amniotic membrane. The outermost membrane is the chorion, from which the tufted **chorionic villi** (embryonic part of the placenta) protrude. Gill slits appear on the side of the neck, and the mesodermal somites show along the dorsal margin of the trunk. The limbs are present, but no fingers or toes have yet been formed. (Courtesy of W. Chesterman, Oxford University.)

which penetrate deeply into the uterine wall (Fig. 21-15). This region, where the tissues of the chorion and uterus are intermingled, is the **placenta**, which permits exchanges to occur between the blood of the fetus and that of the mother. The **chorionic villi** are richly supplied with blood capillaries, derived from the **umbilical artery**. This large artery extends out from the embryo along the stalk of the allantois, and the chorionic capillaries are drained by the **umbilical vein**, which returns to the embryo parallel to the umbilical artery (Fig. 21-16). The uterine wall, in the region of the chorionic villi, is also highly **vascularized**, and this tissue constitutes the maternal part of the **placenta**. The central part of the placenta has the form of a circular disc, embedded in the uterine wall at the site of implantation (Fig. 21-16), but some placental tissue tends to

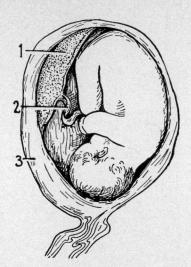

Fig. 21-16. Usual position of the fetus shortly before birth. 1, placenta; 2, umbilical cord; 3, uterus. (From *The Living Body*, by Best and Taylor. Holt, Rinehart and Winston, Inc.)

grow out and surround the fetus almost completely (Fig. 21-15).

In the placenta the maternal and embryonic bloods do not intermingle, but they come into equilibrium with each other, because the two separate sets of capillaries lie very close together over an extensive area. Oxygen and other food substances are transmitted from the maternal to the embryonic blood, thus compensating for the fact that mammalian eggs contain a very small supply of yolk. Moreover, metabolic wastes, such as urea and carbon dioxide, pass into the maternal blood and do not accumulate in the blood of the embryo.

At the end of the gestation period, **delivery** is initiated by the rupture of the embryonic membranes, in the region near the cervix. This first liberates the amniotic fluid; and shortly thereafter the fetus is forced through the vaginal passage by a rhythmic series of massive contractions of the uterine wall (Fig. 21-17). After the umbilical cord is tied and cut, the infant must depend upon its own nutritive organs. The **afterbirth,** which is delivered shortly after the fetus, represents a part or all of the placenta. In man and some other mammals, the whole placenta, including the maternal part, is expelled, but in other mammals, the maternal tissues of the placenta are retained within the womb.

All mammals, except the **monotremes** and **marsupials,** are called **placentates,** owing to their common possession of the placenta (see Chap. 32). The monotremes are oviparous and display an essentially reptilian embryogeny. The marsupials, which include the kangaroo and other *pouched* mammals, have a fairly well-developed uterus, but *no placenta.* Lacking adequate facilities for sustaining the fetus until development is complete, the marsupials deliver their young "prematurely." When born, the young marsupial is deposited in a pouch that is an infolding of the body wall. This pouch also surrounds the mammary glands, so that the young are suckled and protected until a fuller development is reached (Fig. 32-42).

As is shown by the fossil record, monotremes and marsupials were much more prevalent in an earlier evolutionary era, but a retrogression of the nonplacentates occurred shortly after the placentates began to offer serious competition. However, in Australia, which was isolated from the mainland before the placentates became numerous, the nonplacentates, especially the marsupials, continue to prosper in considerable numbers and varieties.

ASEXUAL MULTIPLICATION IN MULTICELLULAR ANIMALS

Sexual reproduction is virtually universal among multicellular animals, but many species, especialy among the invertebrates, also reproduce asexually—by methods that do not involve fertilization. These asexual processes include parthenogenesis—which was discussed previously (p. 276)—as well as **fission** and **budding.**

Fission and Budding. The direct splitting of an organism into two more or less *equal* parts is called **binary fission.** However, sometimes a new individual arises from a relatively small piece of the parent, and this

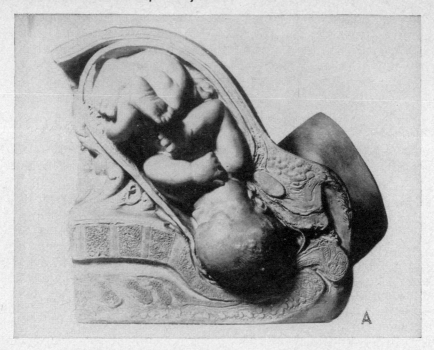

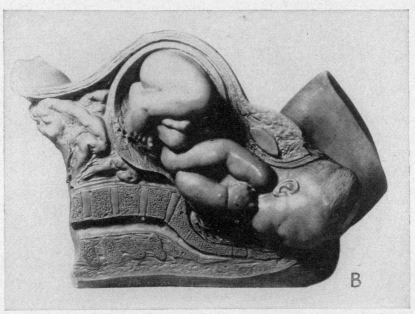

Fig. 21-17.   Two stages in the delivery of the human child. In A, the head is in the process of passing through the dilated cervix into the vagina. In B, the head is passing through the external orifice of the vagina. Note the thick part of the placenta near the right foot of the infant. (Courtesy of the Cleveland Health Museum.)

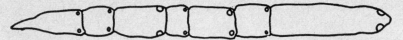

Fig. 21-18. Colony formation due to fission, in a flatworm (*Stenostomum grande*). The eyespots of the members of the colony are shown as small circles. Semidiagrammatic. (After Child.)

asexual method of reproduction is called **budding.** Among multicellular organisms the equal or unequal fragments that generate such new individuals consist of several or many cells.

Some coelenterates, flatworms, and annelids regularly multiply by fission. Among the flatworms the division is always transverse, forming two elongate pieces, which separate and regenerate the missing organs. In some worms, however, the separation is delayed until several other fissions begin to cut across the serially arranged pieces (Fig. 21-18). Such a process of fission gives rise to a chainlike colony, which persists until the individuals separate. From an evolutionary viewpoint, this type of fission may be important, because it may provide a clue as to how **segmented** animals may have arisen. In fact it is considered possible that the **segmented** type of body, which occurs in many higher animals, arose from a permanent association of such colonial individuals.

In some animals the young embryo undergoes fission, and this process of **polyembryony** gives rise to two or more embryos derived from a single egg. Certain parasitic "bees" and "wasps" produce hundreds of offspring from each egg; and one mammal, the nine-handed armadillo, regularly produces four young, by two fissions of each early embryo. Likewise polyembryony sometimes occurs in man and other mammals. In man, the result is usually **identical twins**—although multiple fissions, resulting in identical triplets, quadruplets, and even quintuplets, have been recorded. These offspring bear a very close resemblance one to another, because they all arise from the same zygote, and all receive an identical set of genes and chromosomes. Ordinary **fraternal** twins, unlike identical twins, arise from separate zygotes, and conse-

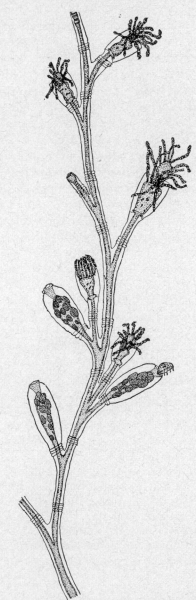

Fig. 21-19. Considerable structural and functional differentiation may occur between members of a colony —as is shown by **Obelia**, one of the coelenterates. The upper (four) members are nutritive zooids, which ingest and digest food for the colony as a whole, whereas the lower members are reproductive zooids, which are responsible for reproduction.

quently fraternal twins do not tend to resemble each other any more than other brothers and sisters. On rare occasions, in man and other mammals, incomplete embryonic fission may occur, producing grossly abnormal offspring, such as "Siamese twins," or individuals with a supernumerary head or limbs.

Budding, which occurs in some flatworms and Annelida, and in many sponges, Coelenterata, and Tunicata, is well exemplified by the case of *Hydra*. In *Hydra* the bud originates as a local accumulation of germ cells. These cells soon develop into a small but perfect offspring, which sooner or later becomes detached from the parent (Fig. 3-12). In many other Coelenterata, however, the developing buds remain attached to the parent, forming colonies in which considerable differentiation occurs among the associated individuals (Fig. 21-19).

Regeneration. In many *primitive* animals such as *Hydra,* even a small piece of the body can regenerate into a whole animal, and some lower forms fragment so readily that it is difficult to draw a sharp line between accidental regeneration and normal reproduction by multiple fission.

In higher animals, such as Mollusca, Arthropoda, and Vertebrata, the power of regeneration is more limited. Many of these animals can regenerate parts of the body, such as a limb that has been lost or injured; but the limb cannot regenerate a whole animal. Moreover, if the whole body be divided into two or more parts, all the parts will die. Among vertebrates, fish can regenerate fins and tails; and salamanders may regenerate tails, legs, and jaws. An adult frog cannot restore a lost leg, but a metamorphosing tadpole can. Adult reptiles, birds, and mammals cannot replace lost limbs, although lizards (but not other reptiles) can regenerate the tail. In mammals, the regeneration of external parts is limited to the growth of skin and connective tissue over wounds; but some of the internal organs—especially the liver and some other glands—have considerable powers of regeneration.

TEST QUESTIONS

1. Provide an example in each case: (a) temporary gonads; (b) a monoecious animal; (c) external fertilization; (d) mutual insemination.
2. Some animals produce many eggs, others very few. Explain.
3. Identify, locate, and give the connections of: (a) seminiferous tubules; (b) interstitial tissue; (c) inguinal canal; (d) epididymis; (e) vas deferens; (f) urethra.
4. Make a labeled diagram to show all the parts and connections of the human male reproductive tract.
5. Discuss the functions of the seminal vesicles, the prostate, and the glands of Cowper.
6. Make a labeled diagram to show the parts and connections of the human female reproductive tract. Specify the function or functions of each part.
7. Distinguish between amplexus and copulation.
8. Identify, locate, and state the functions of: (a) the Graafian follicles; (b) the corpus luteum; (c) the ostium.
9. Identify and describe in terms of the human species: (a) ovulation; (b) fertilization; (c) implantation; (d) the decidual reaction; (e) the growth of the fetus; (f) delivery.
10. Distinguish between ovipary and vivipary. Which is more prevalent among vetrebrates? Explain.
11. How does the amnion differ from the allantois as to its origin in the embryo?
12. What is the amniotic fluid and why is it important?
13. Explain the functional importance of the allantois: (a) in reptiles and birds; (b) in mammals.
14. What is the placenta?
15. How is the placenta related to: (a) the chorionic layer of the amniotic fold; (b) the allantois; (c) the tissues of the uterus?
16. What are the chorionic villi and why are they important?

17. Adrenalin injected into the maternal blood stream accelerates the heartbeat of the fetus as well as of the mother. Explain.
18. Trace a sample of blood from the umbilical artery to the umbilical vein (Fig. 21-11D).
19. For each of the following substances, state whether it tends to pass (a) from the maternal to the embryonic blood, or (b) from the embryonic to the maternal blood, in the capillary system of the placenta: (1) glucose; (2) CO_2; (3) urea; (4) O_2.
20. What is the afterbirth? How does it differ in different mammals?
21. Specify two kinds of nonplacentate mammals. Explain why such creatures undoubtedly found difficulty in competing with the modern mammals.
22. Distinguish between: (a) budding and fission; (b) identical and fraternal twins; (c) complete and incomplete embryonic fission.
23. Discuss the possible relation between fission and segmentation.

FURTHER READINGS

1. *Ourselves Unborn,* by George W. Corner; New Haven, 1944.
2. *Atlas of Human Anatomy,* by Frohse, Broedel, and Schlossberg; New York, 1950.
3. *The Living Body,* by C. H. Best and N. B. Taylor; New York, 1958.
4. *The Science of Human Reproduction,* by H. M. Parshley; New York, 1933.

22-*The Endocrine Glands*

THE MANIFOLD functions of the body are integrated partly by the **nervous system** and partly by the **endocrine glands.** Each endocrine gland secretes one or more highly active organic compounds directly into the blood stream, and these **hormones** control activity in many parts of the body. Compared to the rapidly executed commands of the nervous system, hormonal control is more deliberate and sustained. Consequently the endocrine glands are especially important in determining the slower and more enduring adjustments by which each organ keeps pace with the changing activities of the other body parts.

The principal glands of the endocrine system are shown diagrammatically in Figure 22-1. Some of these glands—that is, the **thyroids, parathyroids, pituitary,** and **adrenals**—are purely endocrine in function, and these glands *possess no ducts.* Such ductless glands send *all* their secretions into the blood stream; in other words, the ductless glands secrete *internally,* into the blood, rather than externally, into a duct. However, the endocrine system also includes such duct-possessing glands as the **pancreas, ovaries,** and **testes,** which secrete both internally and ex-

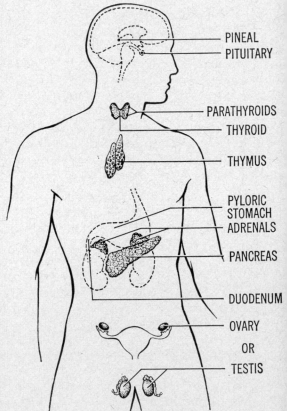

Fig. 22-1. Location of the endocrine organs in the human body.

- PINEAL
- PITUITARY
- PARATHYROIDS
- THYROID
- THYMUS
- PYLORIC STOMACH
- ADRENALS
- PANCREAS
- DUODENUM
- OVARY
- OR
- TESTIS

398

ternally; and there are some organs, such as the stomach, intestine, and perhaps the kidney, which produce hormones as a minor, or incidental, sideline to their regular activity (p. 307).

METHODS OF ENDOCRINE RESEARCH

Deficiency and *replacement* experiments are widely used in endocrinology. If a gland is removed from an animal, and the animal develops drastic dysfunctions as a result of the deficiency, there is no justification for believing that the excised organ is an endocrine gland—unless the impaired functions can be restored by replacing the gland, either by grafting it in another part of the body or by injecting extracts prepared from the excised tissue. Replacement by glandular extracts is a particularly valuable technique, because the method of extraction provides a good index of the chemical nature of the hormone and ultimately may lead to the isolation, identification, and synthesis of the active compound. Moreover, if more than one hormone is present in the excised gland, these hormones can be separated by preparing different extracts. In this way, for example, several distinct hormones have been obtained from the pituitary gland; and each separate hormone restores some but not all of the dysfunctions associated with the removal of the whole pituitary gland.

Overdosage methods are also quite useful in endocrinology. Grafting extra gland tissue, or injecting extracts—without first removing the gland in question—may give symptoms more or less opposite to the deficiency effects; in clinical cases, hyperactivity of a diseased gland may provide some clue as to the normal functions.

In the final analysis, however, a hormone is not established until it has been *isolated* and *identified* as a pure substance. In recent years this goal has been reached in the case of almost all of the principal hormones (see below). Moreover, many of these compounds have now been *artificially synthesized.*

THE TESTIS AS AN ENDOCRINE GLAND

In addition to its sperm-forming function, the testis produces **testosterone,** a very active hormone that stimulates the development of the *secondary sexual characteristics of maleness* in all vertebrate species.

The drastic results of **castration,** over and above the mere development of sterility, have been recognized since ancient times, and several classical accounts describe the characteristics of the **eunuch,** especially emphasizing the high-pitched voice, the hairless face, obesity, and mental inertia. In fact, several ancient peoples resorted to castration, employing the eunuchs as safe keepers of the harem.

The castration of any vertebrate tends to suppress the *secondary sexual characteristics* of the species. The **capon,** for example, lacks the large comb of the **cock,** and the body of a capon becomes unusually plump. The **gelding** also becomes heavier and more docile than the **stallion,** and hence the gelding is more useful as a beast of burden.

The secondary characteristics of the male can be restored to the castrate by grafting or injecting testicular material, and this fact provided the first evidence that the testis is an endocrine gland. In the capon, for example, the characteristics of the cock—aside from fertility—can be restored by a suitable regime of testicular injections; in fact even a young **hen** will take on the bodily features and habits of a rooster if subjected to a similar treatment.

Testosterone is produced by the **interstitial tissue** of the testis, which occupies the space between the sperm-forming tubules (p. 385). This fact was first suspected from clinical evidence. In cases of cryptorchy (p. 383), the **undescended testis** displays an almost normal amount of interstitial tissue, but the sperm-forming tubules are degenerate. Thus a bilateral cryptorchid, although completely sterile, largely retains the secondary attributes of masculinity. The temperature in the abdominal cavity is higher than in the exposed scrotal sac, and such a temperature damages the sperm-forming tissues but does not greatly harm interstitial cells. Thus if a testis is transplanted from the scrotum into the body cavity, the interstitial tissues persist but the tubules degenerate. Moreover, the importance of the interstitial tissue is borne out by x-ray experiments. A suitable dosage of x-radiation virtually destroys the tubules of the testis, without much impairment of the interstitial cells. Subsequently the treated individual is sterile but still retains the secondary characteristics of the male.

Isolation of Testosterone. In 1932, testosterone, $C_{19}H_{30}O_2$, was isolated from a massive extract of sheep testes; and this *steroid compound* is generally acknowledged to be the main testicular hormone. This crystalline compound is so potent that just one hundredth of a milligram (.00001 g) will produce a measurable enlargement of the comb of a capon; in other words, one gram —the quantity extractable from about a ton of fresh testes—will give an appreciable effect in 100,000 birds.

In addition to testosterone, several other steroid compounds, having a distinctly similar though usually less potent action, have been identified. Some of these **androgenic compounds** are probably metabolic derivatives or precursors of testosterone, since they can be extracted from some tissues and from the urine. Others, however, are purely synthetic products that derive their androgenic potency from the similarity of their chemical structure to the natural androgens.

Puberty. Except for the primary difference in the sex organs proper, there is scarcely any sex differentiation in newborn children; and this lack of differentiation between the sexes persists until the time of puberty. At puberty, however, the interstitial tissues of the testes becomes active, and soon the newly mobilized testosterone begins to take effect. Now the boy becomes broader shouldered and more muscular; the voice deepens and the beard begins to grow; also there is a characteristic growth of hair in the axillary and pubic regions; and finally the genitalia proper take on the proportions of an adult.

THE OVARY AS AN ENDOCRINE ORGAN

In the female, the counterpart to testosterone is an ovarian hormone, **estrogen,**[1] which is produced by the Graafian follicles (p. 387). These follicles lie relatively dormant in the ovary until the time of puberty and then they ripen and begin to secrete estrogen.

The puberty changes of the female body are initiated by the liberation of estrogen from the newly developing follicles. Gradually the body contours lose their angularity, and the pelvis becomes somewhat broader; the breasts begin to develop, and there is an appreciable growth of the uterus and the vagina. But the complete development of the reproductive structures, and the establishment of a menstrual cycle, necessitates the intervention of a *second* ovarian hormone. This is the hormone **progesterone,** which is produced by the **corpus luteum.**[2]

Isolation of the **ovarian hormones** entailed the cooperation of biochemists and physiologists in several nations; and all the ovarian hormones (except for relaxin) prove to be *steroid componds,* somewhat similar in chemical structure to testosterone.

The Ovarian Hormones and the Estrous Cycle. Among most mammals, the female of the species displays a distinct and periodic rhythm of sexual activity; and this so-called **estrous cycle** is dominated by the ovarian hormones. A dog or cat, for example, comes into "heat," or **estrus,** only about twice yearly; but such species as rats and mice have a cycle that recurs much more frequently. Usually the female is receptive to the male only at the time of estrus; and regularly the Graafian follicles reach maturity and **ovulation** occurs at a definite time in the estrous period.

[1] **Estrogen:** the one or more hormones produced by the follicles.
[2] Small quantities of progesterone are also secreted by the Graafian follicles; and some estrogen may be secreted by the corpus luteum.

The Menstrual Cycle. In man and the anthropoid apes, the period of estrus is not distinct, and the situation is complicated by the occurrence of **menstruation.** However, the menstrual cycle is likewise dominated partly by the follicular hormone, estrogen, and partly by the luteal hormone, progesterone.

The average menstrual cycle endures for a total period of 28 days during which only one Graafian follicle, usually, ripens and ovulates. Starting at the time when the menstrual flow has just begun, a new follicle commences to develop. This new follicle reaches maturity usually on the twelfth to sixteenth day, and this is the time when ovulation normally occurs (Fig. 22-2).

The follicle continues to increase its production of estrogen as it matures, passing the increased amounts of the hormones into the blood stream from the accumulating follicular fluid, until the follicle ruptures and liberates the egg.

In addition to stimulating the growth of the mammary glands, uterus, and vagina at the time of puberty, estrogen exerts a cyclic (monthly) influence upon the growth of the mucosal lining of the uterus. Each month as a result of menstruation, the uterine mucosa is virtually destroyed; and in fact, the menstrual discharge consists of mucosal debris, together with some blood that escapes from the subjacent capillaries in the uterine wall. Thus an important function of estrogen is to stimulate the initial stages of regeneration and reconstruction in the internal lining *immediately after menstruation.* However, estrogen alone is inadequate to complete the reconstruction of the uterine mucosa; without the subsequent action of progesterone, an implantation of the embryo cannot occur, and pregnancy cannot take place.

Following ovulation (Fig. 22-2), the **corpus luteum** develops, usurping the region formerly occupied by the follicle, and from about the sixteenth to the twenty-third day of the menstrual cycle, the luteal hormone, **progesterone,** is produced in increasing amounts.

Progesterone exerts a very important influence upon the structure and activity of the female reproductive organs: (1) it inhibits the ripening of new Graafian follicles, and consequently further ovulations do not occur while the corpus luteum is active; (2) it stimulates a continued growth of the uterus and perfects the reconstruction of the uterine mucosa, which now becomes highly vascular and capable of effecting an implantation of the embryo; (3) it inhibits muscular contractions in the uterine wall; and (4) it augments the growth of the mammary glands.

Obviously all these effects of progesterone are preparations for the event of pregnancy; and in fact, if pregnancy does occur, the corpus luteum persists during the first five months of the gestational period. However, if the egg is not fertilized, the corpus luteum

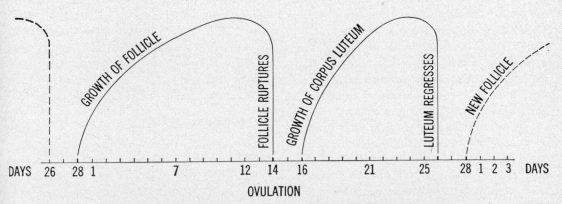

Fig. 22-2. The menstrual cycle in relation to the ovarian hormones.

suddenly retrogresses—on the twenty-fifth to twenty-seventh day of the menstrual cycle. This sudden withdrawal of progesterone precipitates a breakdown of the uterine mucosa, and leads to the menstrual flow. Moreover, when the corpus luteum subsides, another Graafian follicle—freed from the inhibiting effects of progesterone—begins to ripen; and this marks the beginning of the next menstrual cycle (Fig. 22-2).

The human ovum, subsequent to the time of ovulation, remains fertile for a very limited time. Ordinarily the egg is capable of being fertilized for only about 24 hours, although some three days are usually spent by the ovum in passing through the Fallopian tube, en route to the uterine cavity. Likewise, sperm remain viable in the female reproductive tract for only about 2 days. In view of these factors the period of maximum fertility is closely associated with the time of ovulation, which *usually* occurs from the twelfth to the sixteenth day of the cycle. However, extremely early and extremely late ovulations are known to occur in some cases.

Progesterone as a Factor in Pregnancy. Without progesterone, the **decidual reaction** (p. 388) cannot be elicited in the uterine mucosa; consequently an implantation of the embryo cannot occur. Normally, however, the corpus luteum is well developed at the time when the embryo descends into the uterus, and at this time the decidual reaction (p. 389) occurs very readily. Now, in fact, the uterine wall is so receptive that it can be induced to envelop almost any small object, however inert and foreign it may be.

If the corpus luteum is destroyed very early in pregnancy, the uterine mucosa retrogresses and **abortion** follows. But in a normal pregnancy the corpus luteum continues to be active for about five months, and by then the placenta is producing adequate quantities of progesterone and gonadotropic hormone (p. 411). Accordingly, the uterus continues to enlarge; the uterine contractions are held in check; the mucosa is maintained; and the mammary glands continue to

develop. Then near the end of the pregnancy, the corpus luteum involutes, and the placenta becomes less active. Deprived of progesterone, the uterine mucosa retrogresses and loses its capacity to nurture the fetus. Then the musculature of the womb becomes active, and the fetus is forcibly delivered through the dilated vaginal canal.

Hormonal Control of Lactation. All mammals suckle their young with milk from the mammary glands. The breasts undergo an initial devlopment at the time of puberty, and further development occurs during pregnancy. However, it is only after **parturition** (delivery of the fetus) that the mammary glands are stimulated to produce milk.

At least three hormones, namely estrogen, progesterone, and luteotrophin (lactogen), must act successively in preparing the mammary glands for secretion (p. 411). At puberty, estrogen produces an initial growth of the glands, but this growth soon reaches a maximum. During the menstrual cycle there is a slight waxing and waning of the mammary tissue, following the rise and fall of progesterone, but during pregnancy progesterone has time to produce a much larger effect. However, the actual production of milk can only be elicited after parturition, when the pituitary gland begins to liberate larger quantities of the lactogenic hormone, luteotrophin (p. 411).

The rudimentary mammary glands of a male dog or other laboratory animal are sometimes used to test the potency of the lactation hormones. By suitably timed injections of estrogen, progesterone, and luteotrophin, the mammary glands of the male can be developed quite completely, and milk can be obtained.

THE THYROID GLAND

The human thyroid is a small bilobed gland that lies in the neck, along the sides of the trachea. The two lobes are connected by the **isthmus,** a narrow strand of tissue that passes across the front of the trachea, just below the larynx (Fig. 22-3). The entire thyroid weighs only about an ounce; and the gland is purely endocrine in function.

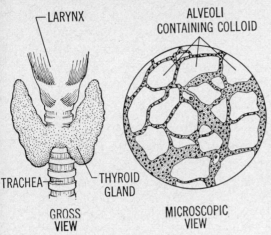

Fig. 22-3.   Thyroid gland: structure and position.

The thyroid arises in all vertebrate embryos as an outgrowth from the floor of the pharynx. All vertebrates also possess **parathyroid** glands (p. 405), which arise from the wall of the pharynx. In many species the parathyroids lie some distance from the thyroid, but in man the parathyroids are four small bean-shaped bodies, embedded in the thyroid tissue.

The importance of the thyroid was suspected even in ancient times; but in 1885 replacement experiments gave definite proof of a thyroid hormone; and in 1916 **thyroxin** ($C_{15}H_{11}O_4NI_4$) was isolated for the first time. Thyroxin successfully counteracts the effects of thyroidectomy, although the hormone appears to be carried in the blood stream as a thyroxin-protein compound.[3]

The *primary* effect of the thyroid hormone is upon the rate of **metabolism** in the body tissues. With inadequate thyroxin, the body consumes less oxygen and produces less metabolic wastes; and in extreme cases the **basal metabolism** falls to less than 30 percent of

[3] Recently a series of compounds, closely related to thyroxin, have been isolated from thyroid tissues; among these, tri-iodothyronine (T_3) is about five times more active than thyroxin.

normal. Conversely, an excess of thyroxin elevates the metabolic rate considerably above normal levels.

Many of the severe symptoms that accompany thyroid derangement probably represent secondary effects, resulting from the drastic metabolic changes in the various organs. Also the net results are different, depending upon whether the thyroid deficiency (or excess) is experienced before or after the animal reaches maturity.

Hypothyroidism in young animals retards development very profoundly (Fig. 22-4). In

Fig. 22-4.   Thyroidectomized cretin lamb about 14 months old and a normal sheep of the same age. The thyroids had been removed from the cretin about 12 months previously. (After Sutherland Simpson. From *The Living Body*, by Best and Taylor. Holt, Rinehart and Winston, Inc.)

tadpoles, for example, metamorphosis into adult frogs does not occur if the thyroid is destroyed at an early stage. This situation has a parallel in the **axolotl,** a kind of salamander which inhabits the highlands of Mexico. This species possesses a hereditary defect of the thyroid and does not develop beyond the gill-bearing "tadpole stage." However, if thyroxin is administered, the axolotl completes development like other salamanders. Soon it loses its gills and becomes a true land animal—a sort of "new species," produced artificially (Fig. 22-5).

Overdosage experiments also give striking

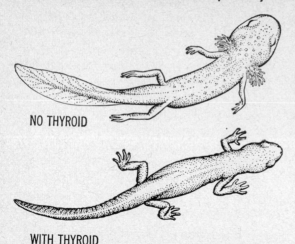

NO THYROID

WITH THYROID

Fig. 22-5. Mexican axolotls. In nature this amphibian, which congenitally lacks a thyroid gland, fails to undergo metamorphosis; that is, it retains its larval form (above). Below, metamorphosis, induced by thyroid treatment.

results as to the role of the thyroid in development. If tadpoles are continually fed with minced sheep thyroid, they develop with astonishing rapidity. In fact, such a tadpole becomes a full-fledged frog long before it has a chance to grow to a suitable size; and in some experiments these miniature adults were scarcely larger than houseflies.

In a newborn child a seriously *underactive* thyroid leads to **cretinism.** This condition is now quite rate, but formerly cretins were often encountered in the Alps and certain other districts where the iodine content of the soil—and consequently of the local produce—is exceptionally low. Lacking iodine, the thyroid is unable to synthesize thyroxin, and gradually the thyroid tissues lose their normal structural characteristics. Typically the cretinous child is very small and malformed, with swollen tongue and puffy skin; and physical and mental development are scarcely perceptible even after years. The disease gives a very dramatic response to thyroxin, however, if the hormone is given in the early stages.

In adults the commonest forms of **hypothyroidism** are **myxedema** and **endemic goiter.** Both of these conditions may arise from inadequate iodine in the diet, although probably there are other contributing factors, including hereditary susceptibility.

In myxedema the thyroid deficiency is relatively great, but there is no appreciable swelling of the thyroid tissue—which, in fact, may become degenerate. Usually the myxedematous patient displays a basal metabolism which is at least 25 percent below normal. The subject complains of cold, and, indeed, with the metabolism at so low an ebb, the body temperature may fall as much as 4 degrees. Extreme physical and mental lethargy are common, and sometimes there is a tendency toward obesity. Also the skin becomes puffy and doughy, due to a deposit of mucoid material in the deeper layers. In some cases, myxedema responds to the addition of iodine to the diet; but more generally it is necessary to give the thyroid hormone.

In **endemic goiter** the deficiency is relatively mild, so that the fall in basal metabolism is usually not more than 15 to 20 percent. A swelling of the thyroid tissue forms the goiter, which usually protrudes from the neck. The swelling is due to the accumulation of a colloid fluid in the thyroid tissue, and consequently this type of goiter is also called **colloid goiter.** The colloid in such cases, however, is very low in its content of thyroxin.

Typically endemic goiter results from a deficiency of iodine, and the swelling may represent an attempt by the gland to compensate for the lack of iodine. Endemic goiter tends to be localized in certain regions. Detroit, for example, occupies a locality where the soil lacks iodine; and in 1924, 36 percent of the school children of this city displayed endemic goiter—at least in the incipient stages. Seven years later, however, subsequent to the compulsory addition of small quantities of potassium iodide (KI) to the table salt of the region, the incidence of goiter in the school population of Detroit had dropped to less than 3 percent.

A swelling of the thyroid does not invariably indicate that the gland is underactive.

In fact the commonest form of **hyperthyroidism** is found in **exophthalmic goiter,** or Graves' disease. In this condition the swelling is apt to be moderate, although the degree of hyperactivity may be very great.

The basal metabolism of a hyperthyroid patient may be more than doubled, and such an acceleration of the metabolism of the tissues has drastic consequences. The nervous and muscular systems become hyperirritable; and there is profuse sweating, insomnia, and muscular tremors. The subject eats more food, yet loses weight. The blood pressure rises and the heart may be overworked to a serious degree. Moreover this type of goiter is usually marked by a protrusion of the eyeballs (exophthalmos), although the underlying cause of this peculiar symptom probably lies in the pituitary gland, rather than in the thyroid. In fact, the factor that induces the goiter and drives the gland to such extremes of activity seems to be an overproduction of the **thyrotrophic hormone** (p. 411) by the pituitary gland. To alleviate the condition, however, the surgeon usually removes a certain proportion of the thyroid, guiding his judgment by preliminary measurements of the metabolic rate. Also x-rays and radium may be used to destroy some of the thyroid tissue. More recently also, radioactive iodine,[4] which accumulates sufficiently in the thyroid gland to dampen the activity of the secretory cells, and certain drugs that inhibit thyroxin synthesis, have yielded promising results.

THE PARATHYROID GLANDS

In 1957, Howard Rasmussen and co-workers at The Rockefeller Institute in New York, first succeeded in isolating and identifying the **parathyroid hormone.** Like insulin (p. 408), this hormone proved to be a relatively simple protein-type compound—a polypeptide chain, consisting of 83 amino

[4] Perhaps an even more important recent use of radioactive iodine has been to arrest the growth of malignant tumors of the thyroid gland.

acid units. The isolation was an exceedingly difficult task, however, and required more than five years of very intensive work. It involved extraction of the protein components of the parathyroid glands from more than 300 head of cattle, separating these components on the basis of their differential solubility in various organic media.

The parathyroids are essential to life, and without replacement therapy the animal dies in about three weeks after the parathyroids are removed. This result is amply substantiated in a variety of species, including man. In surgical history there are records of several cases in which the parathyroids were sacrificed inadvertently, during operations on the thyroid (see Fig. 22-1).

Usually within two to three days after the removal of *all* the parathyroid tissue, an animal displays severe muscular tremulations and then violent cramps and convulsions. Such a condition of **tetany** gradually progresses to the point of exhaustion, and the victim dies in a comatose state. Rarely, the tetanic phase of the disorder does not appear, in which case there are only muscular weakness and a very slow wasting of the tissues.

The parathyroids appear to have a critical effect upon the metabolism of calcium and phosphorus in the tissues. Following the removal of the glands, the blood calcium level falls, and the severity of the symptoms runs parallel, at least roughly, to the degree of calcium depletion. Moreover, the symptoms of parathyroid insufficiency are held in abeyance quite indefinitely by injections either of parathyroid concentrates or of calcium solutions—although best results are obtained when both are used. With overdoses of parathyroid concentrates, the level of calcium in the blood becomes too high, but the blood content of phosphorus tends to fall away. Also there is a marked depletion of both calcium and phosphorus compound in the tissues, especially in the bones.

Recent studies, utilizing newly available purified parathyroid hormone, have yielded a clearer picture of the physiological role of the parathyroid glands. They exert homeostatic control over the Ca^{2+} ion content of the body fluids, both blood and lymph. The parathyroid glands, in fact, have been called the **calciostats** of the body. This is a very important role, since cells in general—but nerve and muscle tissues in particular—are very sensitive to the Ca^{2+} ion level of the internal environment. Also a proper Ca^{2+} ion level is essential to the maintenance of the mineral content of bone, which is mainly a calcium-phosphate complex, called **hydroxyapatite.**

The primary target organs of the parathyroid hormone are the intestines, the kidneys, and certain of the cells in bone tissue. Moreover, a release of hormone by the glands is triggered when a drop occurs in the level of Ca^{2+} ion in the circulating fluids. Stimulated by the parathyroid secretion, the intestinal mucosa absorbs more calcium, the kidney tubules reabsorb more calcium but *less phosphate,* and the bone-eroding cells, or **osteoclasts,** become more numerous and more active in decomposing the mineral deposits of the bone, thus liberating calcium and phosphate into the circulation. The main effect, accordingly, is to raise the circulating Ca^{2+} ion level, although simultaneously the phosphate level tends to fall because of the extra phosphate excretion by the kidney. This, in fact, more than compensates for the influx of phosphate from the bone.

A direct **feed-back control** (p. 412) of activity in the parathyroid glands appears to be operative. An excess of Ca^{2+} ion in the body fluids tends to suppress the mobilization of parathyroid hormone by the gland. Moreover, it has been found that the parathyroid hormone fails to function effectively in cases of vitamin D deficiency.

THE ADRENAL GLANDS

In man, each adrenal gland perches like a small cap on the upper end of the corresponding kidney (Fig. 22-6). Both glands

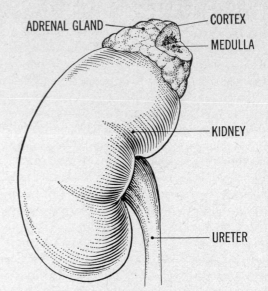

Fig. 22-6. The adrenal gland, perched atop the kidney, produces an assortment of important hormones in its **cortex** and adrenalin in its **medulla.**

together weigh less than one ounce, but the adrenal blood supply is very copious.

Each adrenal is a duplex gland that in section displays a dark-brown central core, the **medulla,** surrounded by a paler shell of tissue, the **cortex** (Fig. 22-6). These two distinct parts of the adrenal arise separately in the embryo: the cortex from the mesodermal lining of the coelom; and the medulla from an ectodermal outgrowth of the neural tube. Likewise the cortex and medulla have distinctly different functions in the adult body, and, in fact, an animal survives quite well without any adrenal medulla, but cannot live in the absence of all cortical tissue.

The Adrenal Medulla. Adrenalin,[5] or **epinephrin** ($C_9H_{13}O_3N$), was isolated quite early (1904). Adrenalin has been synthesized artificially, and chemists have likewise produced several other drugs, such as **ephedrin,** that exert a comparable action in the body.

The physiological effects of an adrenalin injection are widespread and potent. The

---

[5] In addition to adrenalin, the adrenal medulla produces smaller quantities of a related compound, **noradrenalin,** which lacks a terminal $\cdot CH_3$ radical and has slightly different physiological effects.

heart action becomes stronger and quicker; but the digestive tract becomes quiescent. The skin pales, the pupils dilate, and the hair erects. Moreover, adrenalin produces a marked effect upon the arteries. The arteries supplying the viscera and skin become constricted—which shunts most of the circulation into the lungs, muscles, and brain. The spleen contracts, augmenting the total quantity of circulating blood, and the liver draws upon its glycogen reserves to mobilize additional blood sugar. The coagulation reactions of the blood are also speeded up considerably.

In sum total, adrenalin simulates a generalized excitation of the whole **sympathetic** nervous system (p. 465). The body displays a similar picture under stress of fear and anger, which likewise calls forth a widespread hyperactivity of the sympathetic nerves. These observations form a basis for the **emergency theory of adrenal function.** According to this view, the sudden release of extra adrenalin in times of stress is instrumental in transforming the body into a more effective "fighting machine."

The Adrenal Cortex. An absence of the cortex accounts for the prostration and early death that follows a total extirpation of the adrenal glands; adrenalectomized animals remain alive and free of drastic symptoms if about one fifth of the cortical tissue remains intact—irrespective of the presence or absence of any medullary tissue.

The symptoms of adrenal cortical insufficiency, which culminate in death, are numerous and obscure. Apparently there is a generalized derangement of carbohydrate metabolism. The tissues display an impaired capacity for deriving glucose from protein sources, and the blood glucose is apt to fall to a dangerous level. The osmotic characteristics of the blood are also seriously altered. The kidneys fail to reabsorb adequate quantities of inorganic salts, especially NaCl. Under these circumstances of lowered osmotic pressure, fluid tends to escape too rapidly from the capillaries, the blood plasma fails to maintain its normal volume, the blood pressure falls drastically, and the animal goes into a state of **"shock."** During a protracted cortical insufficiency, the sex functions also fail—although this failure probably represents an indirect effect resulting from the metabolic derangement that accompanies the deficiency. In males the seminiferous tubules degenerate; and in females, the Graafian follicles stop developing—or if pregnancy has started, abortion follows. Moreover, mothers with recently delivered offspring fail in the secretion of milk.

The first life-sustaining extract of the adrenal cortex, obtained in 1930, was named **cortin.** Subsequently many efforts have been made to isolate, purify, and identify the individual active components of the extract; and these efforts have been fairly successful. In fact, some 20 compounds have been obtained, among which **cortisol** ($C_{21}H_{30}O_5$), **deoxycorticosterone** ($C_{21}H_{30}O_3$), and **aldosterone** ($C_{21}H_{28}O_5$) are perhaps the most important. All the isolated substances are steroid compounds, and all bear a close chemical relationship to the hormones produced by the testes and ovaries. Probably some of these compounds are merely derivatives of the hormones naturally present in the intact cortex.

In 1948 one of the adrenocortical hormones, namely **cortisol** was synthesized artificially, and this compound relieves many of the symptoms of adrenocortical insufficiency. It also possesses astonishing alleviative values when used in the treatment of rheumatoid arthritis and certain other diseases in man. However, cortisol must be administered with caution because of its great potency and many side effects.

Recently **aldosterone** has also been isolated and synthesized artificially. Aldosterone is very effective in regulating the osmotic balance between the blood and the tissues and seems to provide a valuable treatment for cases of surgical, or traumatic shock.

There are still a number of unsolved problems as to the functions of the adrenal cortex. The total potency of cortin (the unfractionated extract of the tissue) seems to exceed the combined potencies of all the individual substances that have been isolated from the extract. Also the whole cortin extract, prepared according to the best known methods, shows very little influence upon the sexual functions of the animal.

In man, the commonest type of adrenal cortex insufficiency is encountered in Addison's disease, a tubercular infection localized *mainly* in the cortex portion of the gland. A hyperactivity of the cortex is encountered in some cases of adrenal tumor. Such tumors, although very rare, especially in males, are apt to give rise to a condition known as **adrenal virilism,** which can appear at any age. In boys the sex organs, *except for the testes,* may approximate full size and maturity at an age of 1 or 2 years, and simultaneously the hair, voice, and body musculature take on the characteristics of an adult man. But even greater is the misfortune of a girl or woman who develops adrenal virilism. In this case, the bodily development is all in a masculine direction, producing a bearded face, deepened voice, and considerable muscularity. Simultaneously the ovaries, uterus, and vagina begin to atrophy; but the clitoris enlarges, assuming the proportion of a penis. Such changes, in both male and female subjects, are somewhat difficult to interpret, although they may be due to a great overproduction of cortical hormones, some of which have distinct androgenic properties. All in all, therefore, many more data are needed before the problem of adrenal virilism can be clarified and brought under control.

THE ENDOCRINE FUNCTION OF THE PANCREAS

An endocrine function of the pancreas was first suspected in 1892, when it was observed that depancreatized dogs quickly develop severe symptoms of a fairly common human ailment, **diabetes mellitus.** However, no hormonal activity could be found in the pancreas until 1922. Then an extract capable of alleviating diabetes was prepared from pancreatic tissue, and in 1927, purified crystalline **insulin** was finally isolated. Insulin proved to be a protein compound that is digested by the **trypsin** of the pancreas; and unless precautions are taken to inactivate the enzyme before extracting the hormone, insulin cannot be obtained from the pancreatic tissues.

The main part of the pancreas consists of the digestive tubules that form the pancreatic juice, but there are considerable masses of endocrine tissue occupying the spaces between the tubules (Fig. 22-7). This tissue makes up the **islands of Langerhans,** which secrete insulin directly into the blood stream. In the embryo, the endocrine tissue of the pancreas buds off from the digestive tubules and loses all connection with the duct system of the gland.

Hypoinsulinism. Diabetes mellitus is a severe and fairly prevalent malady that has been recognized since antiquity. Without treatment, the diabetic displays great thirst, excessive urination, a steady and unchecked loss of weight, weakness, prostration, coma,

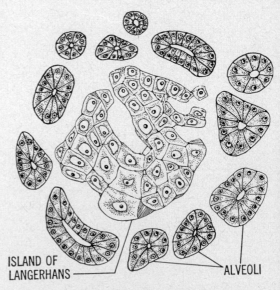

ISLAND OF LANGERHANS   ALVEOLI

Fig. 22-7. The pancreas is both an endocrine and an exocrine gland. It internally secretes **insulin** from the islands of Langerhans tissue and it externally secretes **pancreatic juice** from the alveoli.

and finally death. Clinically the picture includes a very high blood sugar level; persistent glucose in the urine (sometimes approaching 8 percent); depletion of the glycogen stores of the liver; and—when the comatose stage is reached—a distinct acidosis, with detectable amounts of acetone and related compounds in the blood and urine.

All these symptoms point to a generalized impairment of carbohydrate metabolism in the body. In the absence of insulin the tissues of the body seem to lose their capacity to metabolize glucose effectively, and the liver fails to store glycogen adequately. Accordingly, glucose accumulates in the blood and drains forth in the urine. Even if carbohydrates are withheld from a diabetic, glucose continues to be formed and excreted. Despite the fact that the tissues cannot use it, glucose continues to be mobilized by an excessive deamination of absorbed amino acids; and even the tissue proteins are sacrificed to the same quite useless end. Fats are also oxidized to an excessive degree. This leads to a piling up of certain acidic compounds—formed as intermediary products during the excessive oxidation of the fat—at the terminal stages of acidosis.

Injection of insulin alleviates the diabetic symptoms, but the action only persists for several hours. Consequently diabetics require a daily regime of insulin injections, and the maintenance of health depends upon a me-thodical adherence to the treatment—although rarely the endocrine tissues of the pancreas may recover their normal function.

Hyperinsulinism. Unless accurately calibrated, an injection of insulin may overshoot its mark. In this case the blood sugar level sinks drastically and *hypoglycemic* **shock** (p. 341) ensues. Therefore, most patients take precaution to have sweet drinks on hand—to be taken at first sign of "postinjection shakiness." If shock ensues and the individual becomes unconscious, the attending physician may have difficulty in deciding quickly whether to give sugar for shock or insulin for diabetic coma.

Insulin has proved most effective in the treatment of diabetes mellitus, but there are still several unsolved aspects of the problem. In rare cases, for example, no appreciable degeneration of the endocrine tissues of the pancreas can be found at autopsy even when diabetes seems to have been the cause of death. Also some evidence indicates that abnormalities of anterior pituitary and the adrenal cortex, as well as of the pancreas, may sometimes be involved in the disease.

THE PITUITARY

The **hypophysis,** or pituitary gland, is scarcely larger than a pea, and yet this gland is one of the most important in the whole endocrine system. The pituitary lies approxi-

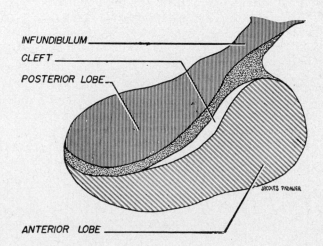

INFUNDIBULUM

CLEFT

POSTERIOR LOBE

ANTERIOR LOBE

Fig. 22-8. The pituitary gland of man. Note the *intermediate part* (stippled area, just posterior to the cleft) between the principal tissues of the anterior and posterior lobes.

mately at the center of the head, attached to the base of the brain by a stalk, the **infundibulum** (Fig. 22-8). Moreover, the pituitary is a double gland, consisting of two main parts —the **anterior lobe** and **posterior lobe**—although part of the posterior lobe appears to be different from the main mass, constituting what is called the **intermediary tissue** (Fig. 22-8). The anterior lobe arises in the embryo as a pouchlike upgrowth from the roof of the pharynx; whereas the posterior lobe is a solid downgrowth from the floor of the brain. These parts of the embryonic pituitary make contact, but the anterior lobe grows more rapidly, partially encompassing the posterior lobe. In the adult, all connection between the anterior lobe and the oral cavity is lost, except in rare anomalous cases, but the connection of the posterior lobe with the brain persists as the infundibulum.

Pituitary research has been very active for many years, but it still presents a number of unsolved problems. The work is very difficult, because the gland lies in a relatively inaccessible position and because most, if not all, of the pituitary hormones are protein compounds, which are difficult to isolate and identify.

Deficiency and Overdosage Experiments. Rats are excellent specimens for pituitary research, because the pituitary of the rat is relatively easy to remove by operating through the roof of the mouth. When this operation is successful, no damage is done to the overlying brain; and there is seldom any infection even in the absence of aseptic precautions.

Deprived of the pituitary, the animal displays a number of characteristic symptoms. Young specimens stop growing and never reach sexual maturity. In adults, the males suffer a distinct retrogression of the testes and accessory reproductive structures, and females display a degeneration of the ovaries, uterus and vagina. Both sexes are prone to show an atrophy of the adrenal cortex and of the thyroid glands.

Consistent results are also obtained by overdosage with pituitary material, either in the form of injected extracts, or from the implantation of extra glands. Characteristically young animals grow prodigiously, reaching a state of gigantism, with a very early onset of sexual maturity. Also adult specimens display hypertrophy and hyperactivity of the primary and secondary sex organs, as well as of the thyroid and adrenal cortex.

Hormones of the Anterior Pituitary. On the basis of these and many other experiments, several separate anterior lobe hormones have now been demonstrated. These include **somatotrophin,** which is better known as the **growth hormone;** the **gonadotrophins,** a group of hormones that act primarily on the sex organs; and also **thyrotrophin** and **corticotrophin,** which act respectively on the thyroid and adrenal cortex. Other anterior pituitary hormones are also indicated, but these will not be included in the present account.

The Growth Hormone. Human cases of **gigantism,** with statures greater than 9 feet, were recorded by the Greeks and Romans, but it was not until about 1860 that the condition was related to an overactive pituitary. More recently, the work of separating the growth-promoting substance from crude pituitary extracts finally culminated in 1944 with the isolation of a simple protein, **somatotrophin.** This hormone is exceedingly potent in restoring growth to hypophysectomized animals.

The **pituitary giant** is a well-proportioned individual, although the overgrowth of the limbs exceeds that of the other body parts. Likewise the **pituitary midget** may be quite normal, except for extremely diminutive legs and arms. Apparently hyperactivity or hypoactivity of the pituitary *may* be restricted largely to the tissue that secretes the growth hormone.

Acromegaly is another human ailment in which an excess of somatrophin appears to be the major factor. In acromegaly the hyperactivity of the pituitary is usually due to a tumorous condition, which develops after an individual reaches maturity. By this time the capacity for skeletal growth is largely restricted to the hands, feet, and facial regions; and if acromegaly persists, the jaws become abnormally long and broad, and the brows enlarge to beetling proportions. Also the bones of the hands and feet become abnormally thickened, especially at the joints of the fingers and toes.

The Gonadotrophic Hormones. Three gonadstimulating fractions have now been identified. These are called FSH (follicle-stimulating hormone), LH (luteinizing hormone), and LT (luteotrophin). All are protein compounds, the first two being glycoproteins.

In males and females, both FSH and LH are necessary, for puberty to be established in younger animals and for the sexual functions to be maintained in older individuals. Without FSH, the Graafian follicles fail to develop, or, if the animal is male, the seminiferous tubules remain inactive. Without LH, on the other hand, ovulation does not occur; that is, the ripe eggs are retained within the follicles, or in male specimens, the interstitial tissue of the testis remains dormant and fails to produce testosterone. FSH accordingly serves to stimulate growth in the Graafian follicles and seminiferous tubules, whereas LH induces ovulation and activates the corpus luteum (in the female) and enhances the activity of the interstitial tissue (in the male).

The third gonadotrophin of the anterior pituitary, **luteotrophin,** serves primarily to sustain the corpus luteum during the early part of pregnancy. Luteotrophin also has an important secondary action—on the mammary glands. It is responsible for inducing an active secretion of milk. However, luteotrophin can do this only after the glands have been stimulated previously by estrogen and progesterone—and possibly also by another unidentified pituitary hormone. Formerly it was thought that the luteotrophin and the lactogenic hormone were separate entities, but now it seems evident that they are a single compound. Moreover, this same compound exerts a distinct influence on *maternal behavior,* at least in many species.

Thyrotrophic and Corticotrophic Hormones. The consistent regression of both the thyroid and adrenal cortex in animals deprived of the pituitary soon indicated that probably the pituitary produces two other hormones; and recently **thyrotrophin,** which is also called the thyroid-stimulating hormone (TSH), and the **adrenocorticotrophic hormone** (ACTH) have been identified.

The thyroid gland is exceedingly sensitive to stimulation by TSH and, in fact, the primary disturbance in exophthalmic goiter appears to be an overproduction of this hormone by the anterior pituitary.

A triumph of biochemical research was consummated recently with the synthesis in 1961 of a very active part of the ACTH molecule. This work was done by K. Hofmann and collaborators at the University of Pittsburgh. A previous analysis of purified extracted hormone had revealed it to be a peptide chain, consisting of some 39 amino acid units. However, the part synthesized, in which 23 amino acids are united in proper sequence, displays almost as much activity as the total molecule. Then finally, in 1963, the total synthesis of ACTH was achieved by Schwyzer and Sieber in the Ciba laboratory, Switzerland.

As the name implies, ACTH stimulates the production or release of the adrenocortical hormones, particularly cortisol. Like cortisol, therefore, ACTH is effective in alleviating the symptoms of a number of diseases, including rheumatoid arthritis, asthma, and allergies generally. A study of ACTH and of the corticosteroids has led to a general theory, called the **stress theory,** as to the basic nature of the sustained reactions of the body to stress, including particularly the stress imposed by disease-producing agents. As greater quantities of these synthesized hormones become available, it will probably be possible to evaluate their physiological activity more precisely. Meanwhile, because of their great potency and because of inadequately studied side effects, medical usage must be conducted with great caution and under rigorous supervision.

Hormones of the Posterior Lobe. Damage to the posterior lobe, or to its controlling center in the brain (see below), gives rise to **diabetes insipidus,** a drastic condition in which the kidney fails to concentrate the urine (p. 376). The water reabsorption of the nephric tubules is greatly impaired; and such diabetics void as much as 3 to 10 gallons of urine daily and must drink corresponding quantities of water to avoid insufferable thirst. Under this condition the urine is quite devoid of sugar and low in salts (or, in other words, insipid).

For some years it has been known that crude extracts of the posterior pituitary could be separated into two potent fractions, called **oxytocin** and **vasopressin.** Oxytocin was found to augment the rhythmic contractions of the uterus and hence proved useful in some obstetrical cases. Vasopressin, on the other hand, produced a marked rise in blood pressure—by constricting the smaller arterioles throughout the body. Moreover, vasopressin was found to be very effective in relieving the symptoms of diabetes insipidus.

No purified posterior pituitary hormones were isolated, however, until 1954. Then Vincent du Vigneaud and co-workers at Cornell University Medical College succeeded not only in obtaining *pure preparations* of **oxytocin** and **vasopressin,** but also in *artificially synthesizing both compounds.* Both compounds proved to be relatively simple **polypeptides,** with eight amino acids represented in the chainlike molecules, although the amino acids are slightly different in each case. The action of pure oxytocin and vasopressin is essentially similar to that of the extracts of the same name. However, the pure compounds display a much greater potency. Extremely small doses of oxytocin, injected intravenously, produce strong contractions of the uterine wall. Hence oxytocin is proving to be useful in initiating childbirth when abnormal delays are encountered; and vaso-

pressin has proved to be very effective in controlling diabetes insipidus.

Another pituitary hormone, the **melanocyte-stimulating hormone** (MSH), is produced by the intermediate part (Fig. 22-8) of the gland. This hormone helps to control skin color, particularly in amphibians, although the pigmentation of other vertebrates, including man, may also be susceptible to its influence. MSH stimulates the melanocytes of the amphibian, causing them to disperse the pigment granules; and as the pigment extends out into the extensively ramifying branches of these cells, the skin color of the whole animal grows darker (p. 444). The evidence indicates that MSH acts in opposition to another hormone, **melatonin,** produced by the **pineal gland** (see below). Melatonin causes the skin to become much lighter, because it stimulates the melanocytes to mobilize the pigment into a small area deeply hidden at the cell center (Fig. 24-13). Both of these hormones have recently been isolated and identified by A. B. Lerner and co-workers at the University of Oregon; and MSH was recently synthesized by Schwyzer and Sieber. MSH, formerly called *intermedin,* is a terminally acetylated polypeptide, consisting of 13 amino acid units; whereas melatonin is a smaller molecule of cyclic structure.

Control of Pituitary Secretion. A number of different cell types are observed in microscopic sections of the pituitary, and presumably each type secretes one or more of the pituitary hormones. Each appears to be separately susceptible to control.

Control of the *trophic* hormones of the pituitary represents a direct **feed-back** type.

The production or release of TSH and ACTH respectively is controlled by the levels of thyroxin and cortisol present in the circulation. If the level falls off, the production of the particular trophic hormone is stimulated. Then, as the level rises, production is inhibited. In other words, a balance, or **homeostasis,** is maintained by direct interaction between the product of the target gland and the particular group of pituitary cells responsible for producing and releasing the particular trophic hormone of that gland.

Control of the other pituitary products is more obscure. The **hypothalamus**—that part of the brain to which the pituitary is connected (Fig. 22-8)—appears to be important. But whether control is mediated by nerve impulses, by neurosecretions (see below), or by both, remains an open question. The pituitary receives a small portal vein (p. 333) directly from the capillary bed of the hypothalamus and therefore it seems likely that neurosecretions are at least partially involved. Moreover there is good evidence to indicate that vasopressin and oxytocin are synthesized in the hypothalamus and merely accumulated and released by the posterior lobe of the pituitary gland.

OTHER ENDOCRINE ACTIVITIES

The **placenta** augments the hormonal output of the ovaries, and in addition, produces a potent gonadotrophic hormone, which simulates the action of the luteinizing hormone (LH) of the pituitary. During pregnancy large amounts of this placental hormone are present in the urine, and this fact forms the basis for a widely used **pregnancy test.** Pregnancy urine, injected into a mature but virgin rabbit, stimulates ovulation. A **blutpunkt** on the rabbit's ovary indicates the ovulation, and the female urine usually shows a positive reaction by the end of the sixth week of pregnancy.

A recently recognized hormone of the mammalian endocrine system is **relaxin.** Relaxin acts upon the pubic symphysis by loosening this ligamentous connection and allowing the pelvic bones to separate slightly during childbirth (Fig. 21-17). The hormone appears to be a complex polypeptide produced partly by the ovary and uterus and partly by the placenta. Injections of relaxin extracts cause a swelling of the cartilage of the pubic symphysis and a softening of the fibrous elements. However, these changes do not occur unless the animal first has been primed by a series of estrogen treatments.

Erythropoietin. Erythropoietin, a powerful stimulant to the production of erythrocytes by the red bone marrow, represents another hormone that is beginning to receive widespread recognition. This substance, apparently a glycoprotein of low molecular weight, has been extracted from the plasma and urine of anemic animals (including man) and studied intensively by A. S. Gordon and co-workers at New York University. The stimulus for the production of erythropoietin, probably by the kidney, is any form of oxygen deficiency—imposed by high altitude, excessive loss of blood, or other condition of anemia. Extra red cell production at high altitude or after hemorrhage has been observed for many years, but the basic mechanism for the response remained obscure prior to these recent studies.

The Pineal Body. The pineal body (Fig. 22-1) arises as an outgrowth from the roof of the forebrain, although later the pineal becomes flanked by overgrowth of the cerebral hemispheres. In the ancient reptiles, the pineal was associated with the development of a median sense organ, situated on the roof of the skull, but in modern vertebrates the pineal body has until recently been regarded as a vestigial structure. Now, however, it is known that the pineal produces at least one hormone, namely, melatonin.

The work of Lerner, referred to previously (p. 412), definitely establishes **melatonin,** the melanocyte pigment-concentrating factor, as an important neurohormone, at least among fish, reptiles, and amphibians. Moreover, recent studies, utilizing the isolated product, indicate that melatonin may also be important in determining pigmentation processes in mammals, including man.

Search for a *thymus* hormone was negative for many years, but evidence now indicates the young gland produces a substance that stimulates the production of small lymphocytes.

Neurosecretion.[6] Nerve cells release hormonelike compounds at the distal extremities of their axons, and these potent excitatory substances play a key role in the transmission of nerve impulses across the synaptic gaps of the nervous system (p. 453). **Acetylcholine,** the excitatory agent of the parasympathetic nervous system (p. 465), and **noradrenalin,** of the sympathetic system (p. 467), are excellent examples of neurosecretions. A more detailed consideration of these important compounds will be undertaken later, in connection with a discussion of the nervous system (Chap. 25).

Specialized nerve cells and glandular derivatives of nerve tissues are known to produce neurohormones. The hypothalamus and the posterior lobe of the pituitary gland (which is an embryonic outgrowth from the brain) provide good examples, as does the pineal gland (see above). Among insects, one finds a group of specialized neurosecretory cells in the brain (cerebral ganglia). These cells transmit excitatory substances to associated glands (the **corpora cardiaca**), and jointly these structures exert an important influence upon development and metamorphosis (p. 415).

There are some cases in which the hormonal product appears to be synthesized in the centron of the nerve cell and then to be conducted along the axon toward the tip. It is interesting to note, therefore, that a wavelike sort of "peristaltic flow" has been observed

[6] The line of distinction between a *neurohumor* and a *neurohormone* is not very sharp. However, generally the term neurohumor (for example, acetylcholine) is used to designate a neurosecretion that has a restricted local action upon certain synaptic membranes, whereas a neurohormone (for example, noradrenalin) in addition to such local action can, as a result of being carried in the blood stream, exert widespread effects throughout the body.

in the axon fibers of many living nerves—as is shown in the beautiful time-lapse cinematic records of Paul Weiss at the Rockefeller Institute in New York and of Cecil Taylor at New York University.

Hormones of Invertebrate Animals. Studies on the endocrine systems of insects, pioneered by V. B. Wigglesworth in England and Carroll M. Williams in the United States, have shown that the complex cycle of development in these animals is definitely controlled by hormones. Some work has also been done on other arthropods, but generally speaking **invertebrate endocrinology** has not yet received an adequate share of attention.

Differences are found in the endocrine systems of various insects, especially when there are differences in the life cycles. Many insects, such as moths and butterflies, undergo **complete metamorphosis,** in which case distinct **larval, pupal,** and **adult** stages can be recognized (Fig. 22-9). But others, such as bugs and grasshoppers, display **incomplete metamorphosis.** In this case, the larval, or rather the **nymphal stages,** gradually merge from molt to molt until finally, at the last molt, a winged adult emerges. Only one of the insect systems will be discussed, however. This deals mainly with the life cycle of the Cecropia moth (Fig. 22-10), which exemplifies the complete type of metamorphosis.

An important component in insect systems is the **juvenile hormone.** The juvenile hormone is produced by a small pair of glands, the **corpora allata,** which lie in the head, behind the cerebral ganglion, or brain (Fig. 22-11). The juvenile hormone inhibits development in the tissues, while other hormones (see below) continue to induce molting. The larva grows and molts through several stages and pupation is not initiated. But if the corpora allata are removed prematurely, pupation and metamorphosis soon begin. In some insects (e.g., silkworms) this results in the formation of a very small, though perfectly formed adult. Conversely, if extra glands are implanted, pupation is delayed until the larva has grown enormously,

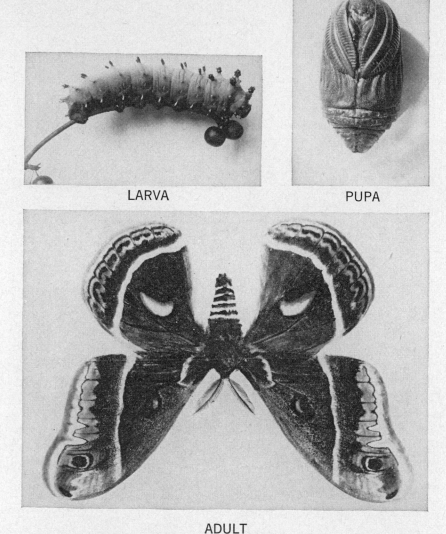

LARVA   PUPA

ADULT

Fig. 22-9.   Stages in life history of a Cecropia moth. See Figures 22-10 and 22-11, and consult text (p. 414) in reference to the hormones that control these developments.

so that finally a giant pupa and adult may be produced. In the normal course of events, the corpora allata temporarily become inactive, soon after the last larval molt, whereupon a normal sized pupa and adult comes into being.

In the pupa the complex reactions of metamorphosis are sustained by another important hormone, the **growth and differentiation hormone** (GDH). Recently this hormone has been isolated in pure form from silkworms by two German workers, Karlson and Butenandt, although they have named it **ecdysone,** since it also induces molting. GDH is produced by a pair of star-shaped masses of glandular tissue, the **prothoracic glands,** which lie in the anterior part of the thorax. The prothoracic glands lie dormant until they become activated by a trophic hormone. This **brain hormone** is produced by a

Fig. 22-10. A, the thoracic part of the pupa, cut away from the head and abdomen, remains alive for several months, but does not undergo metamorphosis. This part contains the prothoracic glands, which produce a "metamorphosis hormone," but the glands remain inactive unless stimulated by another hormone secreted by the "brain" (cerebral ganglia) of the insect. B, similar thoracic part into which living brain tissue has been implanted. This part has developed its adult characteristic. C, abdominal part of the pupa, isolated from the thorax and head. This part does not develop, though it does remain alive. D, abdominal part after implantation with both brain tissue and prothoracic glands. Note the development of adult structure (compare with Figure 22-9.) (Courtesy of Carroll M. Williams, Harvard University, and the *Scientific American.*)

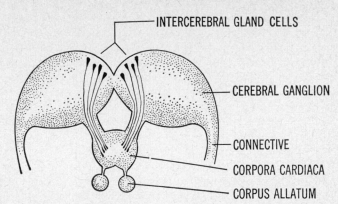

INTERCEREBRAL GLAND CELLS

CEREBRAL GANGLION

CONNECTIVE

CORPORA CARDIACA

CORPUS ALLATUM

Fig. 22-11. Diagram showing some of the endocrine glands of an insect. (After Bodenstein.)

specialized group of neurosecretory cells, situated in the brain, mainly near the cleft in the bilobed cerebral ganglion (Fig. 22-11). The nerve cell bodies then transmit the brain hormone, via their axons, to a pair of storage and distribution centers, the **corpora cardiaca** (Fig. 22-11). In some cases, the intercerebral gland cells of the pupa may temporarily become inactive until the pupa has experienced a period of dormancy **(diapause)** and has been subjected to chilling.

Molting, or Ecdysis. This process, by which an insect or other arthropod sheds the existing exoskeleton and develops a new one of larger size, is controlled by GDH, or ecdysone. In certain crustaceans at least, ecdysone is produced by the nervous system (cerebral ganglion), but is stored in and liberated from the **sinus gland,** a small mass of tissue embedded in the eyestalk. The evidence almost conclusively indicates, moreover, that ecdysone and the growth and differentiation hormone (GDH) are identical compounds.

CELLULAR ENDOCRINOLOGY

An ultimate goal, of course, is to under-stand how hormones act basically; that is, how they act on the cellular and subcellular level. In other words, one would like to know precisely how a particular hormone may change the metabolism or other cellular mechanism in the target organ and how these changes may be related to the over-all effects upon the body. This type of research, called cellular endocrinology, now constitutes a very active field in which important progress seems imminent.

In the case of insulin, for example, the recent evidence indicates that the hormone has an important effect upon cell permeability. Glucose cannot be metabolized properly in the absence of insulin because the sugar does not enter many of the tissue cells. But still we do not know precisely how insulin modifies the molecular structure of the cell membrane. And in the case of thyroxin, the recent evidence suggests that this hormone changes the structure of the mitochondria, enhancing their oxidative activity. But again we must ask: How and why? The outlook for further progress is excellent, however. Most of the hormones are now available in pure form and many new techniques of study are being developed.

TEST QUESTIONS

1. Slow and enduring coordinations tend to be under hormonal rather than under nervous control. Explain this statement exemplifying the discussion by comparing the flow of saliva with the flow of pancreatic juice.

2. Make a labeled diagram to show the placement of the various endocrine glands in man. Which of the glands are purely endocrine in function?

3. Carefully explain how deficiency, replace-

ment, and overdosage experiments have been used in obtaining evidence that the testis is an endocrine gland.

4. Explain two types of evidence that indicate that it is the interstitial tissue and not the seminiferous tubules of the testis that produces the testicular hormone.

5. The secondary sexual features, which differ entiate males from females, are related to differences in the sex hormones. Explain this statement in specific terms.

6. Differentiate between estrogen and progesterone on the basis of: (a) site of production; (b) chemical structure; (c) relative abundance during the menstrual cycle; (d) effects upon the uterine mucosa and mammary glands; (e) general functions.

7. Carefully explain the relationship between the corpus luteum and (a) implantation; (b) retention of the fetus in utero; (c) parturition (delivery of the fetus); (d) lactation.

8. Carefully discuss the thyroid hormone with special reference to: (a) its chemical composition; (b) dietary requirements for synthesis; (c) abnormalities of metabolism; (d) abnormalities of development.

9. Briefly discuss the parathyroids, adrenals (cortex and medulla), islands of Langerhans, and the pituitary (anterior and posterior lobes), specifying in each case: (a) the hormonal product or products (if known); (b) the general functions of each hormone; (c) effects of hypo- and hyperactivity of each gland.

10. Inspect the following list and for each condition specify: (a) the one or more hormones that may be involved; (b) the gland or glands in question; and (c) whether the glands are hypoactive or hyperactive: (1) cretinism; (2) gigantism; (3) persistent glycosuria, emaciation, and acidosis; (4) Graves' disease; (5) low blood calcium, with muscular tremors; (6) endemic goiter; (7) exophthalmic goiter; (8) myxedema; (9) fear and anger (as when a cat sees a dog); (10) drastic virilism; (11) diabetes mellitus; (12) diabetes insipidus; (13) very high basal metabolism; (14) delayed growth, retarded sexual maturity, atrophy of the adrenals and thyroid.

11. Explain why ACTH may be substituted for cortisone in the treatment of certain human diseases.

12. Define the terms *neurosecretion* and *neurohormone*. Provide examples from the endocrine systems of vertebrate and invertebrate animals.

13. What is a direct feed-back control mechanism? Explain how this and other control mechanisms operate to regulate secretional activity in the pituitary.

14. Discuss the endocrine system of insects, mentioning all of the following terms: (a) juvenile hormone; (b) corpora allata and cardiaca; (c) intracerebral gland; and (d) growth and differentiation hormone.

15. Explain the term *cellular endocrinology*.

FURTHER READINGS

1. *The Hormones in Human Reproduction,* by George W. Corner; Princeton, 1947.
2. *The Physical Basis of Personality,* by C. R. Stockard; New York, 1931.
3. *General Endocrinology,* by C. D. Turner; Philadelphia, 1960.
4. "Transplantation of the Testes," by A. A. Berthold; and "The Internal Secretion of the Pancreas," by Banting and Best; in *Great Experiments in Biology,* ed. by M. Gabriel and S. Fogel; Englewood Cliffs, N. J., 1955.
5. "The Juvenile Hormone," by Carroll M. Williams; in *Scientific American,* February 1958.
6. "The Parathyroid Hormone," by Howard Rasmussen; in *Scientific American,* April 1961.

23=*Responses of Higher Animals:*
The Receptors

THE PRECISE and rapid responses of complex animals would not be possible in the absence of a highly developed nervous system; the nerve cells of the body are constantly engaged in relaying excitations from the sense organs and other receptors to the muscles and other effectors of the body. First to be considered, therefore, are the sense organs and other receptors, which initiate most excitations.

THE SENSE ORGANS AND OTHER RECEPTORS

In man, the skin alone houses five distinct kinds of receptors—for touch, pressure, pain, warmth, and coldness; and in the head, there are the special sense organs of sight, hearing, taste, smell, and balance. Moreover, the muscles throughout the body are equipped with receptors of pressure, tension, and pain, and there are still other kinds of receptors, which will be mentioned later.

Cutaneous Receptors. Under the microscope a section of skin displays well-defined receptors for touch, pressure, coldness, and warmth (Fig. 23-1A,B), as well as many **free nerve endings,** which are susceptible to direct stimulation by various pain-inflicting agencies (Fig. 23-2). These cutaneous receptors can also be located by testing the sensitivity of the skin point by point, on the arm for example. A stiff bristle is used to demonstrate the tactile receptors, and a sharp needle will show the pain receptors; but a blunt metal stylus is required for the pressure and temperature receptors. The stylus is kept at body temperature in demonstrating the pressure corpuscles, but the stylus must be chilled or warmed in finding the points that are sensitive to cold and heat. Thus it is possible to plot a given area of skin, marking the exact localization of each kind of receptor; and such a plot shows a separate locus for each different receptor unit.

Reception of a stimulus involves the excitation of specialized cells in the sense organ,

419

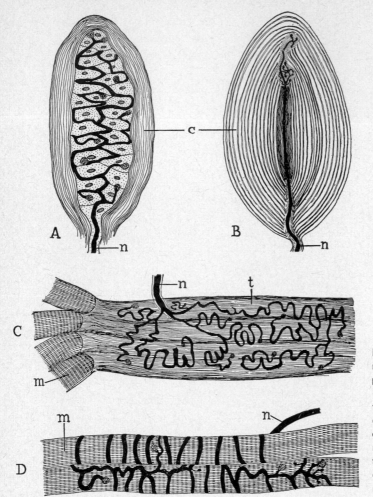

Fig. 23-1. Some types of mechano-receptors of vertebrates. A, tactile corpuscle (touch receptor) from the skin. B, Pacinian corpuscle (pressure receptor), found in deeper layers of the skin and in many internal organs. C, Golgi organ (proprioceptor) on a tendon. D, muscle spindle (proprioceptor) in skeletal muscle. n, afferent nerve fibers; c, connective tissue capsules; t, tendon; m, muscle fibers.

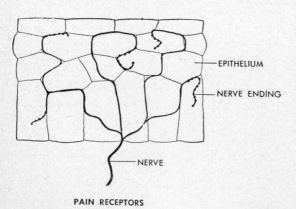

PAIN RECEPTORS

Fig. 23-2 Free nerve ending in epithelium. The terminal branches of the afferent nerve fiber end freely among the epithelial cells.

as is shown in the case of a tactile corpuscle (Fig. 23-1A). Such receptor cells are usually separate from the sensory nerve cells, which conduct the excitations to the central parts of the nervous system; but in some cases—for example, the pain receptors—the sensory nerve cells act as conductors as well as receptors (Fig. 23-2).

The receptors of touch and temperature are restricted mainly to the superficial parts of the body, especially in the skin, and on the lips and cornea; but pressure and pain receptors are also found in many deep-lying parts.

Receptors of Taste and Smell. Each animal discovers and recognizes its food by means of **chemoreceptors**, which are extremely sensitive to chemical stimulation. The taste buds of the oral cavity (Fig. 23-3) and the olfactory receptors of the nasal passages (Fig. 23-4) are representative of chemoreceptors generally, and these structures were discussed previously (Chap. 16).

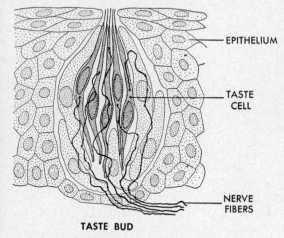

EPITHELIUM

TASTE CELL

NERVE FIBERS

TASTE BUD

Fig. 23-3. A taste bud from the tongue.

Receptors of Light, Especially the Eye. Light-receptive cells always contain one or more **photosensitive** substances, which undergo chemical reaction when energized by the absorption of the proper kind of light; and most photochemical substances are highly selective as to the wavelength of the light absorbed.

The simplest photoreceptors are the red-pigmented "eyespots" of many flagellates and unicellular algae (p. 167). Eyespots are sensitive to changes in the quality, intensity, and direction of light, but are not capable of recording *images* of the form and pattern of surrounding objects. A true eye, in contrast, is a complex organ, which possesses a multi-cellular **photosensory surface,** together with a focusing mechanism, which projects a well-defined image upon the surface.

Invertebrate animals have developed quite a variety of eyes, among which the simple and compound eyes of insects and other Arthropoda are most frequently encountered. Essentially the simple eye of an insect consists of a very small lens that focuses upon a group of light-sensitive nerve endings. The lens is anchored in a fixed position and cannot vary as to curvature. Consequently simple eyes possess no focusing capacity, and they do not form very clear images. The compound eye of the arthropod is more useful. The compound eye, being an aggregate of many simple eyes, constructs a mosaic of the light and dark regions of the surrounding locale, and is quite effective in detecting moving objects in the environment. A few invertebrates, such as the squid and octopus, possess eyes that can vary the focus for near and distant objects, and these eyes form fairly accurate images of the surroundings.

The eye of man and other mammals is in many ways like a modern camera, equipped with color film. The human eye (Fig. 23-5) possesses a high-speed **lens** with an accurately variable focusing capacity; an efficient diaphragm, called the **iris,** which controls the diameter of the **pupillary opening;** and a color-sensitive **retina** (Fig. 23-5). The eye is sturdily built, being protected at the sides and back by the tough opaque **sclerotic coat,** and in front by the strong transparent **cornea.** The black-pigmented **choroid coat,** which intervenes between the retina and the sclera, functions like the black paint on the inner walls of a camera. The choroid coat

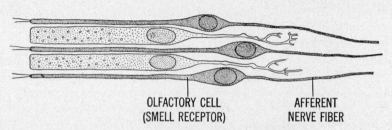

OLFACTORY CELL (SMELL RECEPTOR)

AFFERENT NERVE FIBER

Fig. 23-4. Olfactory cells from mucosa of the nose.

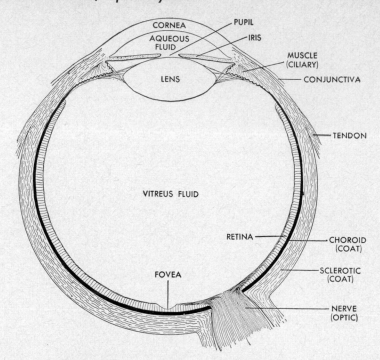

CORNEA
PUPIL
AQUEOUS FLUID
IRIS
MUSCLE (CILIARY)
LENS
CONJUNCTIVA
TENDON
VITREUS FLUID
RETINA
CHOROID (COAT)
FOVEA
SCLEROTIC (COAT)
NERVE (OPTIC)

Fig. 23-5. Section of the human eye.

makes the eyeball more opaque and prevents a scattering of light not absorbed by the retina. And lastly, a free rotation of the eyeball within its bony socket is effected by six small muscles, which permit the vision to be directed according to the situation (see Fig. 23-5).

The lens of the eye *accommodates* for near and distant vision by changes of curvature; and these curvature changes are controlled partly by the elasticity of the lens itself, and partly by the action of the **ciliary** muscle (Fig. 23-5). This circular band of muscle surrounds the margins of the lens, exerting a tension on the lens by means of the **suspensory ligament** (Fig. 23-5). Accommodation for near vision results when the ciliary muscle contracts, reducing the tension on the suspensory ligament and lens. When it is released of tension, the elastic lens assumes its unstrained form, which is quite thick and nearly spherical. For distant vision, on the other hand, the ringlike ciliary muscle relaxes, increasing its circumference. This restores the strain upon the suspensory liga-

ment and forces the lens to become flatter and broader.

The refractive power of the lens, which effects a precise focusing of the image on the retina, is augmented by the curvature of the cornea. The space in front of the lens contains a relatively nonviscous fluid, the **aqueous humor;** whereas the region behind the lens is filled with a viscous liquid, the **vitreous humor.**

The **retina,** or true photosensory surface of the eye, is composed mainly of a prodigious number of specialized receptor cells, called the **rods** and **cones** (Fig. 23-6). In each human retina there are more than 100 million rods and about 6 million cones. The cones are more numerous in the central area of the retina; they are concerned with ordinary "bright-light vision," in which colors and sharp outlines are clearly appreciated. Vision is most acute in a small depressed area, the **fovea centralis,** where rods are not present and the concentration of cones is at a maximum (Fig. 23-6).

The rods are most numerous in the periph-

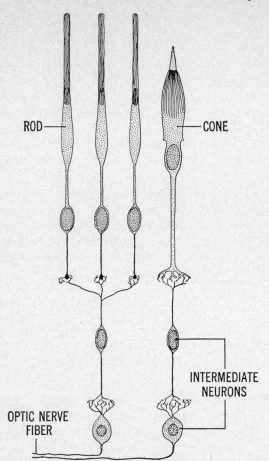

Fig. 23-6. Photoreceptors and associated nerve cells in the retina of the human eye.

eral areas of the retina, and they are employed mainly in "twilight vision." The rods are activated by relatively weak light, but they are not capable of distinguishing colors and sharp outlines—which accounts for the grayness and haziness of vision when the light is dim.

The Chemistry of Visual Excitation. Black-white, or *rod vision,* is somewhat different from color, or *cone vision.* Moreover, we have a better understanding of the chemistry of rod excitation, owing to the early (1925–1945) studies of Selig Hecht at Columbia University and a great many more recent investigations, pioneered most actively, perhaps, by George Wald at Harvard University.

The rods of a dark-adapted eye are almost unbelievably sensitive to light. Excitations, detected in the optic nerve, have been elicited by exceedingly brief flashes, enduring for only one microsecond (.000001 second). In fact, one or more of the rod cells may be excited by less than 10 quanta of light energy.

The light-absorbing agency of the rods has been identified as **rhodopsin;** prior to its chemical identification, it was called *visual purple.* Rhodopsin is a conjugated protein, formed by union between a pigment, **retinene,** and a protein, **opsin.** Essentially, light absorption by retinene and the consequent alteration in the molecular structure of retinene triggers excitation. Retinene is an aldehyde compound derived by action of a dehydrogenase upon vitamin A. This accounts, of course, for the well-known deficiency effect of vitamin A, namely night-blindness (p. 350).

The absorption of light alters the intramolecular structure of retinene. Retinene is changed from one stereoisomeric form (the *cis*-configuration) to another (the *trans*-configuration).[1] *Trans*-retinene, apparently, is the actual excitatory substance. Its presence in the rod cell leads to the generation of a volley of excitations in the axon of the rod (Fig. 23-6), and these excitations are transmitted to the serially arranged neurons of the system. The excitation does not persist, however. The *trans*-retinene-opsin complex, which has been called **lumirhodopsin,** is unstable. Soon *trans*-retinene breaks (by hydrolysis) off from the protein. Subsequently, a re-formation of active rhodopsin, available for further excitations, requires the expenditure of metabolic energy—to reverse the iso-

[1] *Cis-trans* changes in form depend upon the presence of a double bond between two carbon atoms in a molecule and upon a nonidentity between the two atoms or radicals that are in direct connection with each of these carbon atoms. For example, we may indicate the two forms of dichlorethylene as follows:

cis-dichlor-
ethylene

trans-dichlor-
ethylene

merism of the retinene and to recombine the *cis*-form with opsin.

The short persistence of excitation is important, however. Excitation from a very short flash enduring just 1 microsecond may persist as long as 0.1 second. This makes it possible for the eye to merge successive stimuli, forming a continuous visual image, as in the merging of the successive frames of a moving picture.

By dark adaptation, the sensitivity of the retina may be increased more than fifty thousand times. During a steady exposure to bright light, a significant part of the visual pigment of the rods in inactive, as a result of the relatively fast processes of breakdown and the relatively slow rate of resynthesis. In the dark, however, resynthesis of rhodopsin predominates, and within somewhat less than an hour maximum sensitivity is achieved.

Color vision, which is instrumented by the cones, is relatively more complex and less completely understood. Psychological analyses indicate that there are three kinds of cones. These are sensitive particularly to blue, green, and red light respectively, with intermediate colors appreciated by virtue of stimulation of two or more kinds simultaneously. The light-absorbing component likewise appears to be one or more retinene-protein complexes; but the opsin part of the molecules is not the same as in rhodopsin. Consequently the photosensitive pigment of the cones is called **iodopsin.** Whether there are different kinds of iodopsin, corresponding to the different kinds of cones, cannot be decided on the basis of present information. The different varieties of color blindness, apparently, result from an absence of one or another of the cones, and this, in turn, is determined by a deficiency or abnormality in one or more sex-linked genes (p. 498).

The Blind Spot. Impulses from the rods and cones are conveyed from the retina by two relays of sensory nerve cells (Fig. 23-6). The fibers of the second relay converge to form the **optic nerve,** which passes out from the eyeball at a point quite near the fovea cen-

tralis. Owing to a crowding of the nerve fibers at this point, rods and cones are entirely absent, and this small area of the retina is called the **blind spot,** because images falling upon it are not perceived (Fig. 23-5).

Receptors of Equilibrium. Typically the equilibrium organ of **invertebrate** animals is a hollow capsule, called the **statocyst** (Fig. 23-7). The statocyst is lined by hair-bearing receptor cells, and contains one or more grains of sand or other solid **statoliths.** The statoliths are free to fall in any direction, depending upon the position of the animal. Thus as an animal changes its position the statoliths fall upon and stimulate the different hair cells, initiating the movements by which the animal "rights itself."

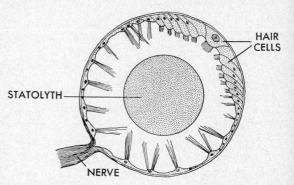

STATOCYST

Fig. 23-7.   Statocyst of a mollusk (Pterotraches). (After Claus.)

The lobster and other Crustacea have sand grains as statoliths, and new sand is taken into the statocyst from the environment each time the animal molts. Thus it is possible to introduce iron fillings instead of sand into the lobster's statocyst—in which case the animal will swim upside down, or in any other position, if a magnet is used to counteract the force of gravity.

The organ of equilibrium in lower vertebrates is a complex structure called the **labyrinth.** This labyrinth consists of three curved tubes, the **semicircular** canals, and two small chambers, the **saccule** and the **utricle** (Fig. 23-8). The whole system is filled

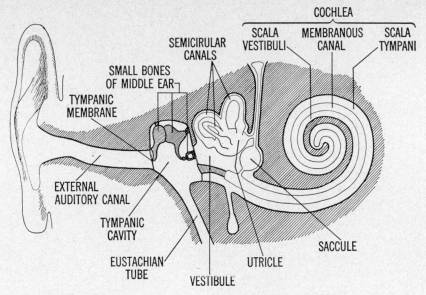

Fig. 23-8. Structure of the human ear. The shaded portions with heavy outlines represent bone; the lighter lines represent membranous structures.

with fluid and lined with hair cells. The saccule and utricle appear to function more or less like statocysts, but the semicircular canals are concerned with the perception of rotational movement, not of position. The different semicircular canals lie in different planes, each at right angles to the others, and when the body starts to move in a given direction, inertia displaces the fluid in some one of the canals, exciting some local group of the hair-bearing receptor cells. If the movement stops, the momentum of the fluid displaces the fluid in an opposite direction, which excites some other group of hair cells.

In fish and other lower Vertebrata, the labyrinth is mainly an organ of equilibrium; but in land vertebrates part of the labyrinth develops into the **cochlea,** the essential organ of hearing (Fig. 23-8). The cochlea contains a large number of hair-bearing sensory cells (Fig. 23-9), which are stimulated by sound vibrations, transmitted from the external air, through the **tympanic cavity,** to the fluid in the cochlea. Perception of the pitch and quality of sounds depends on the fact that the different hair cells of the cochlea are stimulated by vibrations of different fre-

quencies. Probably insects are the only other animals that possess specialized organs of hearing, but the ears of insects vary widely as to structure and position in the different species.

Proprioceptors. The perception of movement and position of the body *as a whole* is localized in the labyrinth, but each separate muscle and tendon is equipped with receptors, called **proprioceptors,** which play an essential role in coordinating the complex movements of the individual body parts. The proprioceptors of the muscles (Fig. 23-1D) and tendons (Fig. 23-1C) are sensitive to the changes of tension, and when a muscle is brought into play, its proprioceptors continue to discharge a series of excitations along the sensory fibers of its nerve supply. Thus each gradation of tension serves to condition the further activity of the muscle and bring it into synchrony with the activities of other muscles. Without the proprioceptors, skilled movements would not be possible; and because of the efficiency of the proprioceptors it is possible to perform skilled movements without the guidance of the eye—as, for example, the tying of a knot behind one's back.

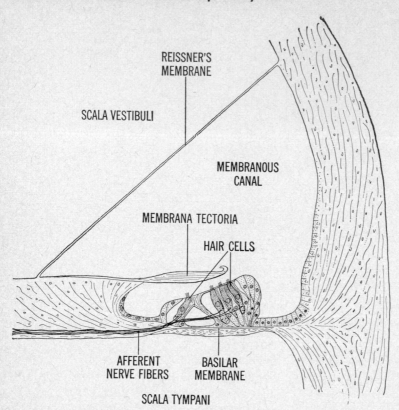

REISSNER'S
MEMBRANE

SCALA VESTIBULI

MEMBRANOUS
CANAL

MEMBRANA TECTORIA

HAIR CELLS

AFFERENT
NERVE FIBERS

BASILAR
MEMBRANE

SCALA TYMPANI

Fig. 23-9. Section through part of the cochlea. The **hair cells** are the essential receptors of sound vibrations.

Visceral Receptors. The **interoceptors,** which are localized in the internal organs, play an important role in governing the activities of the viscera. However, the interoceptors of the body are not so well defined as are the various exteroceptors, which have been discussed. The sense of **thirst** appears to originate in the throat, although the thirst receptors have not been identified definitely. A dearth of water in the digestive tract, and in the body tissues generally, seems to act as a stimulating agency that prompts the animal to seek and drink the necessary quantities of water.

Hunger sensations originate in the wall of the stomach. The empty stomach is swept by a series of rhythmic muscular contractions, and these *hunger contractions* exert a mechanical action upon the pressure receptors in the gastric wall. Likewise the urge to defecate and to urinate take origin from mechanoreceptors in the walls of the rectum and bladder respectively, as a result of ten-

sion that develops when these hollow organs become distended by their contents.

Nerve impulses from the interoceptors seldom cross the threshold of consciousness, because such impulses are not usually transmitted to the higher centers of the brain (p. 464). Nevertheless the visceral receptors are most important, especially the receptors in the walls of the blood vessels and heart, which initiate reflexes controlling the blood pressure and pulse rate. Moreover, the receptors in the walls of the lungs play a very important role in controlling the amplitude of the breathing movements (p. 367).

PERCEPTION OF SENSATIONS

The sense organs merely discharge excitations into the nervous system, and the receptor cells are not *directly* responsible for any sensation that may be experienced by the stimulated individual. What sensation, if any, may result depends not upon the activity of the receptors, but solely upon how the excitations are routed through the nervous system. Only such excitations as are transmitted to the cerebral cortex of the brain succeed in generating any conscious perceptions; this phase of responsiveness will be considered in Chapter 25.

Indirectly, however, the sense organs do determine the **quality** of sensations, because each sense organ is connected to a specific part of the nervous system by a specific set of sensory nerve fibers. The rods and cones, for example, generate sensations of light rather than of sound, because the rods and cones relay their excitations to the visual area of the brain via the optic nerves rather than to the auditory area via the auditory nerves. The nerve fibers and their connections, therefore, determine directly the quality of the sensation, and the stimulation of a certain group of nerve fibers gives rise to the certain kind of sensation; this is true even if these nerve fibers are stimulated artificially by electrical excitation, rather than naturally by impulses from one of the sense organs.

Likewise the **localization** of sensations is a function of the brain; but again the position of the stimulated receptors is an important determining factor. Some sensations, such as pain, are referred to a part of the body itself; but others, such as the warmth of a stove, are referred to the external environment. In either case, however, the location of the stimulated receptors is very important in determining where the sensation is localized by the mind. A cold floor stimulates the thermoreceptors of the soles of the feet, and consequently the coolness is judged to come from the floor; or if one burns oneself, the pain is referred to the injured organ, where the stimulated pain receptors are localized. In the case of pain originating in some of the internal organs, however, the mind is not very accurate in its judgments; quite frequently internal pain is referred to some specific external part of the body.

Judgments as to the **intensity** of a sensation are conditioned largely by the behavior of the stimulated sense organ. Ordinarily when a receptor is stimulated, it discharges not one, but a volley of excitations into the sensory nerves. The stronger the stimulus, the more prolonged is the volley from the receptor; but still more important, the **frequency** of excitations is greater if the stimulus is stronger. Thus a very dim light may stimulate the photoreceptors of the eye to discharge excitations at the slow rate of about 10 per second, as compared to more than 200 per second when the light is bright. Furthermore, stronger stimuli usually succeed in stimulating a greater *number* of receptor cells in the sense organ, and thus a greater number of sensory nerve fibers will carry excitation volleys toward the brain. All in all, therefore, the brain is influenced by several factors in mediating responses to stimuli of different intensities. With stronger stimuli, greater numbers of nerve cells become involved in spreading the excitation volleys, and the stronger the stimulus, the greater is the duration and frequency in the individual volleys.

BASIC MECHANISMS OF RECEPTION AND TRANSMISSION

A receptor becomes excited by a stimulus and it relays the excitation to one or more nerve cells. Basically these processes appear to involve: (1) a conversion, or **transduction**, of energy derived from the stimulus to electrical energy and (2) a utilization of the electrical energy for triggering excitations in associated neurons. These processes are extremely difficult to analyze. However, some progress in this direction has recently been made, under the leadership of H. K. Hartline, of Johns Hopkins University, Bernhard Katz, of University College, London, Donald Kennedy, of Stanford University, and a number of other workers. Exceedingly fine glass capillary ultramicroelectrodes, with tip diameters of less than half a micron, have been devised. These can be inserted without apparent injury into the cytoplasm of a sensory cell or associated neuron, small though these may be (Fig. 23-10). Such techniques have permitted investigators to detect and localize small changes in the membrane potentials of various sensory-neural couplets and to analyze the functional significance of these changes.

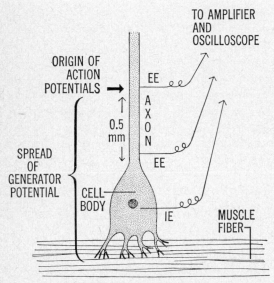

ORIGIN OF ACTION POTENTIALS →

TO AMPLIFIER AND OSCILLOSCOPE

EE

0.5 mm

SPREAD OF GENERATOR POTENTIAL

A X O N

EE

CELL BODY

IE

MUSCLE FIBER

Fig. 23-10. Unicellular "stretch receptor" of a crustacean muscle. One microelectrode (IE) is placed in the cytoplasm of the **body** of the receptor cell while the other electrode (EE) is moved from place to place along the axon. Each time the muscle fiber is subjected to a sudden stretch, a **generator potential** originates in the dendrites and cell body, followed by a volley of **action potentials** (nerve impulses) originating in the axon. (From Edwards and Ottoson; modified, diagrammatic.)

Whether a stimulus is chemical or mechanical, reception and transduction appear to involve a change in the resting potential (p. 191) of the receptor cell. This gives rise to what is called a **generator potential** (Fig. 23-10). The generator potential differs from an action potential. It is more sustained and it is seldom propagated for any great distance. Moreover, it suffers diminution, or *decrement,* during propagation. Essentially the generator potential appears to represent a partial depolarization (p. 191) of the membrane of the receptor cell, resulting from an increase in the permeability to ions. For mechanoreceptor cells, the increase in permeability results from a deformation of the membrane—by stretch, pressure, etc.—whereas for chemoreceptors, a chemical product, or **excitatory substance,** appears to be involved. Indeed, even in the case of mechanoreceptors it cannot be said with certainty that no excitatory substance is involved in the depolarization process.

The **generator potential** of a receptor cell, as the name implies, serves to trigger the firing of not one but a volley of action potentials, and these are conducted with great speed and without decrement away from the site of origin. If the receptor cell itself possesses an axon, the site of the triggering action of the generator potential appears to be near the point where the axon originates from the cell body (Fig. 23-10). Such sense cells, accordingly, display two plainly differentiated parts. One consists of the cell body and dendrites, if present, for receiving the stimulus and developing a generator potential. The other, an axon, serves to fire and conduct nerve impulses (p. 447). When no axon is present, the trigger point seems to be the *synapse* (p. 453), that is, the junction between the sense cell and the associated nerve cell (Fig. 23-3). In any event, it is important to realize that the frequency of firing in each volley is determined by the intensity of the generator potential, which keeps rising as the strength of the stimulus is increased (Fig. 23-11).

The essential excitatory agency in virtually all types of receptors appears to be either mechanical or chemical. Plainly the touch and pressure receptors are excited by mechanical deformations transmitted through the surrounding capsules (Fig. 23-1); and it is almost equally obvious that the hair cells of the hearing and equilibrium organs are excited mechanically, by disturbances in the labyrinthine fluids (Fig. 23-8). The proprioceptors are also excited by the strains of stretch and pressure, while the muscles are doing their work upon the tendons.

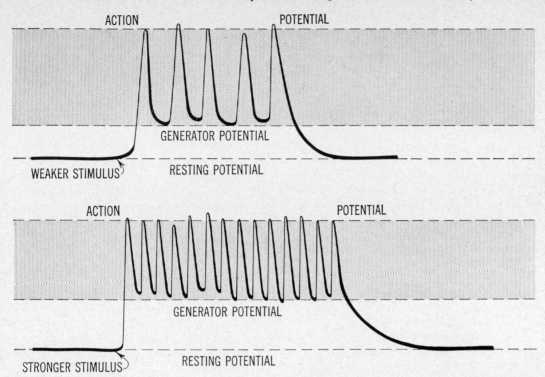

ACTION　　　　　　POTENTIAL

GENERATOR POTENTIAL

WEAKER STIMULUS　　　RESTING POTENTIAL

ACTION　　　　　　　POTENTIAL

GENERATOR POTENTIAL

STRONGER STIMULUS　　　RESTING POTENTIAL

Fig. 23-11. Diagram of an action potential recorded in a nerve near connection with a stretch receptor (muscle spindle, Fig. 23-1). The stronger the stimulus the greater is the **generator potential** and the greater the **frequency** of the spikes in the volley of action potential discharges. Presumably the generator potential originates in the receptor (spindle) and is transmitted to the associated nerve fibers, causing them to discharge impulses. (Based on the records of Bernhard Katz, University College, London.)

On the chemical side, the taste buds and olfactory cells respond very directly to the chemical action of impinging molecules; and probably the thermoreceptors are activated by chemical changes induced in the cells by heat and cold. The pain receptors respond to very strong stimuli of any kind, which indicates that excitation depends upon chemical substances released from damaged cells. And finally, photochemical reactions induced by light impinging on the retina constitute the true excitatory mechanism in the rods and cones.

The highly specialized sensory structures of complex animals all seem to have been evolved from the relatively simple mechanical and chemical receptors of lower organisms. The senses have great significance in survival, since the animal must rely upon its senses in the search for food and the avoidance of danger. No organism, so far as we know, has developed a sensitivity to magnetic fields, or to radio or cosmic waves, although certain bees seem to be sensitive to ultraviolet and infrared light, and bats are able to guide their flight in total darkness because they possess a sensitivity to high-frequency vibrations that are **supersonic** to other animals. And despite the fact that all cells are readily excitable by electric currents, few, if any organisms have developed specialized receptors for this type of stimulation. Animals have evolved without any direct appreciation of these other forces of the environment, probably because such forces, having little relation to survival, have not played a significant role in *natural selection* (Chap. 28).

TEST QUESTIONS

1. How many kinds of receptors are present in the skin? How is it possible to find where these receptors are localized in any given area?
2. How do pain receptors differ from most other kinds of sensory cells?
3. What is the justification for regarding the eye as a chemoreceptor and the ear as a mechanoreceptor? Explain.
4. Make a labeled diagram to show all essential structures in the human eye and state the function of each labeled part.
5. Differentiate between each pair of terms:
   a. the blind spot and the fovea centralis
   b. rods and cones
   c. the cornea and the lens
   d. the choroid and sclerotic coats
   e. the pupil and the iris
   f. a statocyst and a statolith
   g. the labyrinth and the cochlea
6. Differentiate between black-white and color vision on the basis of the basic receptors and on the basis of the photochemical reactions that are involved.
7. What is meant by the term *cis-trans* change of molecular configuration?
8. Explain why a dark-adapted retina is so exceedingly sensitive.
9. Explain the statement that accommodation for near vision demands work on the part of one of the eye muscles.
10. Explain the fact that the eyes of older individuals suffer a loss in their capacity to accommodate.
11. Explain the functioning of: (a) the saccule and utricle; (b) the semicircular canals; (c) the cochlea.
12. Specify two types of proprioceptors and explain the importance of the proprioceptors in relation to our muscular movements.
13. When a warm object is handled, what factors account for a person's capacity to judge: (a) the degree of warmth; (b) the size of the warm object; (c) the relative position of the object?
14. (a) What is a generator potential? (b) How does it differ from an action potential? (c) What techniques have made it possible to measure these potentials in small unicellular receptors?
15. Explain how the intensity of stimulation is related to the magnitude of the generator potential and to the frequency of nerve impulses in the volley of discharges.

FURTHER READINGS

1. *Smell, Taste and Allied Senses in the Vertebrates,* by G. H. Parker; Philadelphia, 1922.
2. *Vision,* by S. H. Bartley; New York, 1941.
3. *Hearing, Its Psychology and Physiology,* by S. S. Stevens and H. Davis; New York, 1938.
4. "How Cells Receive Stimuli," by W. H. Miller, F. Ratliff, and H. K. Hartline; in *Scientific American,* September 1961.
5. "The Initiation of Impulses in Receptors," by Donald Kennedy; in *American Zoologist,* February 1962.
6. *The Chemical Evolution of Vision,* by George Wald; Harvey Lecture Series; New York, 1945–1946.

24-*Responses of Higher Animals:*
The Effectors

THE MOST important effector organs in higher animals are the **muscles** and **glands.** But some complex animals, including both vertebrates and invertebrates, also possess (1) **luminous organs,** which give forth light; (2) **electric organs,** which generate high-voltage electrical discharges; and (3) **pigmentary effectors,** which execute rapid changes in the body color of the animal. Moreover, practically all multicellular animals possess unicellular effectors, such as the amoeboid cells of the blood and ciliated epithelial cells; these were discussed in Chapter 11.

THE SKELETAL MUSCLES

Skeletal muscles (p. 286) execute all external movements of the body and its parts. Typically each muscle has the form of a strong elongate strand that stretches from bone to bone of the skeleton (Fig. 24-1). Accordingly, when a muscle **contracts,** or shortens, it exerts a force upon some bone and tends to produce a movement at a joint where the particular bone is hinged to the rest of the skeleton.

Usually the two ends of a muscle are not exactly alike. At the proximal end, which is called the **origin,** there may be one or more tendons (Fig. 24-1), although usually the many individual fibers of the muscle fasten quite directly to the bone (see the triceps, Fig. 24-1). However, at the other end, which is called the **insertion,** there is almost always a **tendon** (Fig. 24-1). This tough *cablelike* strand of connective tissue intervenes between the muscle fibers and the bone and transmits the force of the contraction to the bone. Generally the origin maintains a relatively fixed position when the muscle contracts, and thus most of the force of contraction goes to produce a movement of the bone to which the insertion is attached (Fig. 24-1).

At least two muscles, acting antagonistically, control the movement at any particular joint. In the knee, for example, one set of muscles, called the **flexors,** acts to bend the knee; whereas the **extensors** are used to un-

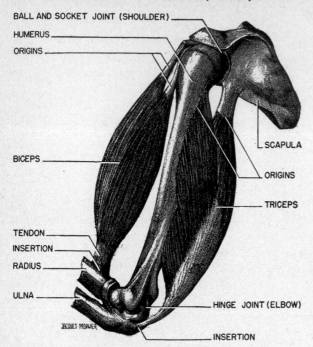

BALL AND SOCKET JOINT (SHOULDER)

HUMERUS

ORIGINS

SCAPULA

BICEPS

ORIGINS

TRICEPS

TENDON

INSERTION

RADIUS

ULNA

HINGE JOINT (ELBOW)

INSERTION

JACQUES PADAWER

Fig. 24-1. Two muscles of the human arm, having a more or less antagonistic action. Note that the biceps tends to bend (flex) the elbow, while the triceps straightens (extends) the joints. The biceps, however, has another main action, namely, to rotate the forearm.

bend, or straighten, the joint. If movement is to occur, the extensors must relax during the time that the flexors are contracting; and conversely, the flexors must relax in synchrony with the contracting extensors—as the joint undergoes bending and unbending.

Each *movement* of the body depends upon a reciprocal action of antagonistic muscles, but the maintenance of *posture* demands that the antagonistic muscles contract *synchronously*. While a person stands, for example, both the flexors and extensors of the knee are contracting simultaneously, locking the joint and converting the leg into a rigid pillar to support the weight of the body. Moreover an important function of a set of muscles is to *arrest* the movements of the antagonistic muscles. Thus, obviously, the contractions and relaxations of the interacting muscles must be coordinated by the nervous system, and each muscle remains inactive until it receives excitations from the nervous system.

In an average man, the weight of the muscles constitutes more than 50 percent of the body weight; and the strength of the larger muscles is very great. The extensor muscles

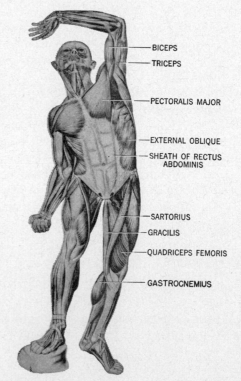

BICEPS

TRICEPS

PECTORALIS MAJOR

EXTERNAL OBLIQUE

SHEATH OF RECTUS ABDOMINIS

SARTORIUS

GRACILIS

QUADRICEPS FEMORIS

GASTROCNEMIUS

Fig. 24-2. Superficial muscles of man, anterior aspect. (Courtesy A. J. Nostrom Co.)

(quadriceps femoris, Fig. 24-2) of the knee, for example, act against an adverse lever ratio of more than 10:1. Yet an average man weighing 150 pounds can straighten his knees, lifting not only his own body but also that of another man. This means that the right and left extensors together can exert force enough to lift more than 3000 pounds, or at least 1500 pounds apiece.

Contraction: The Single Twitch. When a muscle is removed from the body, it retains its capacity to contract, and may survive for several days. Special precautions to maintain the temperature must be taken in the case of muscles from warm-blooded animals; but "cold-blooded muscles" keep very well at room temperatures. Thus frog muscles are studied most frequently; and usually it is the powerful gastrocnemius, or "calf muscle," that is selected for experimentation.

The apparatus shown in Figure 24-3 is designed to make a record of a single contraction, or **twitch,** which results when a muscle receives a single excitation. Mounted in a **moist chamber** to prevent drying, the muscle hangs by its origin from an immovable rod (Fig. 24-3). A cord, tied to the tendon of the muscle, penetrates a hole in the floor of the chamber, connecting the muscle to a lever. The marking point of this **muscle lever** makes contact with the **recording paper,** which covers the surface of a **revolving drum.** Thus each contraction lifts the lever and marks a record of the height and duration of the single twitch while the drum is turning.

Usually the muscle is stimulated by an electric shock, which is discharged directly into the muscle, as shown in the diagram; or the shock may be applied to the motor nerve, if it is still connected with the muscle. The instant of stimulation is recorded on the drum by an electrical **signal marker,** which is included in the stimulating circuit. Very frequently the *timing* of the twitch is also shown by a tuning fork, which makes a tracing of its vibrations (usually 100 per second)

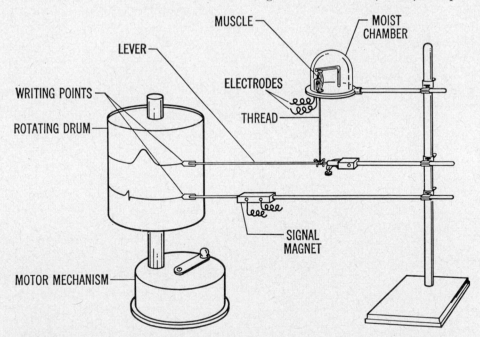

Fig. 24-3. Simple mechanical method of recording the contraction of a muscle. The moist chamber protects the muscle from drying; the signal magnet, which is in parallel circuit with the stimulating electrode, records the instant of stimulation; and the lever, lifted by the contracting muscle, records the extent and duration of the contraction on the paper cover of the moving drum.

upon the recording paper; and sometimes a simultaneous tracing of the action current of the muscle is made by means of a galvanometer.

The duration of a **single twitch** in a frog's muscle, at room temperature, is about 0.1 second (Fig. 24-4). This time can be subdivided by careful measurements into three periods: (1) the **latent period,** the very brief (0.003 second) interval following stimulation, before any sign of mechanical contraction can be detected; (2) the **contraction period,** the somewhat longer (0.047 second) time during which the muscle is engaged in shortening; and (3) the **relaxation period,** the longest (0.05 second) period, during which the muscle returns to its original length. Usually the **action potential,** which is the first indication that the stimulus has excited the muscle, reaches a peak and subsides during the latent period, before there is any mechanical sign of contraction (Fig. 24-4). Also before it contracts, at the very end of the latent period, the muscle displays a very slight, but definitely measurable relaxation (called the **latency relaxation**), as was first shown in 1948 by Alexander Sandow, at New York University.

Following a twitch, the muscle consumes oxygen and produces carbon dioxide and heat in excess of the normal resting quantities. This indicates that there is a **recovery period,** which restores the tissue to its original state. For a single twitch, the recovery period endures for about one minute. If a muscle is stimulated repeatedly and rapidly, so that the successive excitations occur before the muscle completes recovery from the preceding twitches, **fatigue** begins to appear. In this case, the twitches become feebler and feebler (Fig. 24-5), and the fully fatigued muscle will not respond to further excitation until it is allowed to rest in the presence of an adequate supply of oxygen.

Contraction: The Tetanus. The duration of a single muscle twitch varies in different animals, being about 0.1 second in the frog; 0.05 second in man; and 0.003 second in certain insects. However, most muscular movements in intact animals are not twitches, but more prolonged contractions, called **tetani.** A prolonged contraction, or **tetanus,** involves not one, but a volley of excitations. During any tetanus the excitations follow each other so rapidly that relaxation cannot occur between the successive contractions. Consequently the muscle remains in a contracted state until the volley ceases. Each separate excitation is, however, accompanied by its own electric discharge; and a continuous

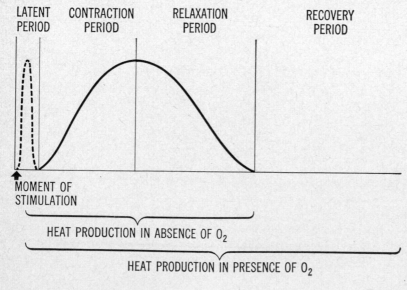

LATENT PERIOD CONTRACTION PERIOD RELAXATION PERIOD RECOVERY PERIOD

MOMENT OF STIMULATION

HEAT PRODUCTION IN ABSENCE OF O_2

HEAT PRODUCTION IN PRESENCE OF O_2

Fig. 24-4. Analysis of a muscle twitch. The dotted line represents the electrical response (change of electrical potential); the heavy line, the mechanical response (contraction and relaxation) of the muscle.

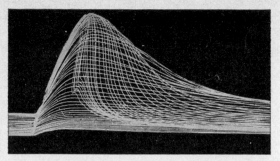

Fig. 24-5. Fatigue. Many successive twitches of an excised muscle, stimulated about 30 times per minute, are more or less superimposed. The earlier contractions reach higher levels, and the relaxations occur more quickly. Finally the capacity to contract is abolished completely. (From Gerard, *The Body Functions.* Permission of John Wiley and Sons, Inc.)

series of action potentials can be detected in the muscle, so long as the tetanus continues.

Gradation of Contractions. If a single fiber (Fig. 24-6) is isolated from the many that compose even the smallest whole muscle, the fiber contracts with maximal force each time it is excited successfully, regardless of whether the exciting stimulus is relatively strong or weak. This **all-or-none law** holds true for the single fiber, but it does not apply to the muscle as a whole. The intact muscle gives graded contractions according to the strength of the stimulus applied. Weaker stimuli do not arouse all the fibers of the muscle; and a maximal contraction, in the case of either a tetanus or a twitch, is obtained only when the stimulus is strong enough to bring all the fibers of the whole muscle into play.

Chemical Aspects of the Contractile Process. Even when completely deprived of oxygen, a muscle can perform many twitches and can sustain a fairly long tetanus. But without oxygen, fatigue sets in prematurely; or to state the matter more precisely, under aerobic conditions a muscle can do about four times more work than under anaerobic conditions.

Chemical analysis of a totally fatigued muscle reveals a number of changes in the tissue. The **glycogen** of the tissue, which in a rested muscle amounts to some 3 percent by weight, has declined considerably, and the quantity

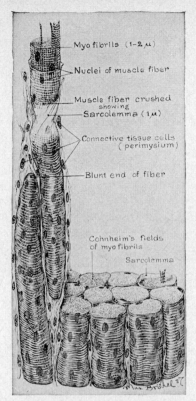

Fig. 24-6. Group of fibers of skeletal muscle. Formerly it was thought that the striations of the fibers were due to markings on the myofibrils (see p. 438). (Courtesy of Department of Art as Applied to Medicine, Johns Hopkins Medical School.)

of **inorganic** phosphate compounds has undergone considerable increase. Under anaerobic conditions, there is also an accumulation of lactic acid ($C_3H_6O_3$), in an amount equivalent to the missing glycogen.

One reaction known to occur while a muscle is working is the breakdown of glycogen into lactic acid. This process of **glycolysis** does not consume oxygen, as may be seen in the equation at the top of the next page.

Under aerobic conditions the muscle tissue oxidizes part (about $\frac{1}{5}$) of the lactic acid as it is formed, and thus the muscle obtains energy whereby the other part (about $\frac{4}{5}$) of the lactic acid is reconverted into glycogen. This reconversion accounts for the fact that lactic acid does not accumulate while a muscle has ample oxygen; and also it explains why glycogen is used up four times faster

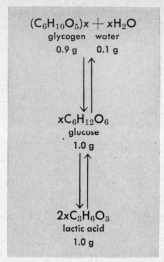

$$(C_6H_{10}O_5)x + xH_2O$$

glycogen   water
0.9 g   0.1 g

$$xC_6H_{12}O_6$$
glucose
1.0 g

$$2xC_3H_6O_3$$
lactic acid
1.0 g

than normally, when a muscle is deprived of oxygen.

Prior to 1930, glycolysis was thought to supply energy directly to the contraction process; but about this time several poisons were found that completely *inhibit* **glycolysis** *without blocking the contractions of the muscle.* In fact when a muscle is exposed to such glycolysis inhibitors, it behaves quite like one that is deprived of oxygen, except that poisoned muscles fatigue somewhat sooner than those that are asphyxiated. But the fact that a muscle can do considerable work, when no glycolysis is occurring, eliminates this reaction as the primary source of energy in contraction.

After 1930 it was discovered that the first chemical event to occur following excitation in muscle is the breakdown of a series of organic phosphate compounds. Indeed, the most direct source of energy in muscle contraction appears to be the hydrolysis of ATP (p. 143), a reaction that generates some 8 Cal per mole of phosphate liberated.

Also it is now known that glycolysis provides the energy through which the phosphate componds of the tissue are resynthesized, subsequent to their decomposition. Thus a recharging of the contractile mechanism, which follows each contraction, depends upon glycolysis; and the oxidative reactions, which extend throughout the long recovery period, are important not only because they conserve the glycogen stores of the muscle, by fostering the resynthesis of glycogen from lactic acid, but also because they prevent lactic acid from accumulating to a toxic level.

Two main proteins have been extracted from the myofibrils, namely **actin** and **myosin.** Also it is important to realize that myosin itself exerts a powerful catalytic action on the decomposition of adenosine triphosphate. Therefore, the recent discovery that artificial threads prepared of actin and myosin shorten energetically when treated with adenosine triphosphate has aroused great interest.

The fact that the restoration of the muscle to full efficiency depends upon glycolysis and other **anaerobic reactions** is of importance, especially for athletes. Frequently our muscles are called on for tremendous work, and despite the acceleration of respiration and circulation that accompanies exertion, the supply of oxygen to the muscles cannot keep up with the increased requirements. During such exertions, the muscles are being recharged largely by glycolysis, and lactic acid accumulates because it is not oxidized as fast as it is formed. But a well-nourished muscle has a good reserve of glycogen, and such a muscle can continue to function until the **oxygen debt** becomes excessive. After a hundred-yard dash, for example, the runner continues to breathe heavily for a number of minutes, and his muscles continue to utilize extra oxygen for almost half an hour. During this time the accumulation of lactic acid gradually subsides, as part is oxidized, and the remainder is rebuilt into glycogen. Thus the net result of muscular exertion is that a certain quantity of the glycogen store of the muscles has been consumed. The muscle may oxidize substrates other than lactic acid during the resynthesis of glycogen, in which case a greater proportion of the lactic acid is reconverted into glycogen.

Heat Production. The maximal efficiency of a muscle as a machine for delivering mechanical energy is about 40 percent, which compares very favorably with the 10 percent efficiency of the best steam engine. This means that under optimal conditions, 60 percent of the energy expended by a muscle appears as heat, and 40 percent as work. However, the heat put forth by the muscles during work is not wasted, since this heat contributes in large measure to the maintenance of the body temperature. The body does not possess any specialized effectors to function as heat producers, but the muscles are thrown into a special sort of action, namely **shivering,** whenever the body loses more heat than it gains from the general metabolism. None of the metabolic reactions throughout the body is 100 percent efficient in the fulfillment of its special end, and consequently heat is a by-product given off by all the cells; and since muscle constitutes the bulk of the tissues, the heat produced by the muscles plays a dominant role in maintaining the temperature of the body.

Fine Structure of the Contractile Mechanism. The banded pattern of single fibers in striated (skeletal and cardiac) muscles has been observed for many years, but a precise knowledge of the nature and significance of this pattern remained obscure until about 1957. Then two English workers, H. E. Huxley and A. F. Huxley,[1] simultaneously and independently, began to report their studies on the fine structure of muscle; their studies had utilized various modern techniques, such as electron microscopy and x-ray diffraction analysis, as well as interference and phase microscopy.

Previously it was thought that myofibrils were continuous strands of protein material that extended long distances along the length of the muscle fiber, and that a striated pattern resulted from alternating segments of denser material, regularly spaced and evenly aligned across the fiber (Fig. 24-6).

[1] These two Huxleys are not relatives.

Fig. 24-7. Fine structure of a skeletal muscle fiber (rabbit): electronmicrograph, magnified 24,000 diameters. Compare this photograph with the diagram of Figure 24-8. Be sure to identify the thick and thin filaments and the H-, A-, and Z-bands (see text description, p. 438). (Courtesy of H. E. Huxley and the University Postgraduate Medical School, Cambridge, England.)

Now, however, it is apparent that the myofibril is composed of subsidiary, exceedingly delicate threads, called **filaments** (Figs. 24-7 and 24-8). The filaments are of two kinds: **thick filaments,** of about 100 Ångstrom diameter, which appear to be composed of myosin, and **thin filaments,** about 50 Ångstroms in diameter, apparently composed of actin. Moreover, the filaments are not very long. The thick filaments terminate at the edges of the A-band (Fig. 24-8), so that their total length is about 1.5 microns. The thin filaments are slightly longer (about 2 microns). They extend from the margin of one H-band, through the Z-band, to the margin of the next successive H-band (Fig. 24-8). Thus the banded appearance of a striated myofibril results mainly from a regular pattern of overlapping in the filaments. This produces bands of greater and lesser protein density at regular intervals along the length of the fibril. Thin filaments are lacking in the H-band; both thick and thin filaments are present in the darker parts of the A-band; and thick filaments are lacking in the I-band (Fig. 24-8). The precise nature of the Z-band is still unknown, although it appears to be a membrane that supports each of the thin filaments at the center.

Decision as to the composition of the filaments is based mainly upon extraction experiments, although density measurements made by interference microscopy have yielded confirmatory results. Muscle fibers, subjected to extraction with solutions that dissolve myosin, yield electron microscope preparations that are devoid of thick filaments; whereas fibers treated with actin-dissolving

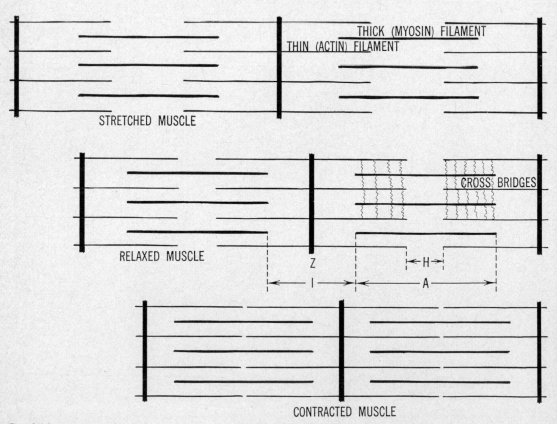

STRETCHED MUSCLE

THICK (MYOSIN) FILAMENT
THIN (ACTIN) FILAMENT

RELAXED MUSCLE

CROSS BRIDGES

Z   ←H→

←———— I ————→ ←———————— A ————————→

CONTRACTED MUSCLE

Fig. 24-8.   Fine structure of a skeletal muscle fiber, after H. E. Huxley. The diagram is based on analyses of electronmicrographs, such as the one shown in Figure 24-7. Note that the striated appearance of muscle results from the regimented overlapping arrangement of the thick and thin filaments (see text, p. 437).

media yield preparations in which there is only a small residue of thin fibers. There is some evidence that indicates that small amounts of a third muscle protein, called **tropmyosin,** may be represented in the structure of the thin fibers.

As mentioned previously, actin and myosin, extracted from muscle, unite chemically, forming actomyosin; and threads of actomyosin contract forcibly when treated with ATP. In the intact fibril, such an myosin-actin complex may be indicated by the numerous **cross bridges** that connect the thick and thin filaments (Fig. 24-8). The cross bridges originate from each of the thick filaments at very regular intervals (every 65 Ångstroms) along its length, and the points of origin of the bridges display a spiral arrangement, such that one helical turn is completed in a distance of about 400 Ångstroms. This arrangement permits a thick filament to establish a connection with each of the six surrounding thin filaments once in every complete spiral turn. The thickness of a thick filament is just great enough to accommodate four chains of myosin molecules, lined up in parallel; and it is reasonable to assume that the bridges may represent side branches from the regimented myosin molecules.

The precise mechanism of contraction is still far from clear, however. Formerly it was thought that shortening and lengthening, respectively, represented a coiling and uncoiling of the helical structure (p. 87) of the actomyosin complex, but this view seems scarcely tenable in view of recent studies. When a muscle is stretched, or when it is caused to contract in moderate degree, neither the thick nor the thin filaments show any change of length. Rather, the filaments slide past each other, as is shown in Figure 24-8. Only toward the end of a very strong contraction is there any detectable thickening and shortening of the filaments, and this appears to be confined to the ends, where the thin filaments are brought into contact with each other and where the thick filaments are finally brought into contact with the Z-partitions (Fig. 24-8).

The view proposed by a number of current workers is that contraction is mediated by the cross linkages between the myosin and actin filaments. Energy from the hydrolysis of ATP appears to be utilized in shifting the bonding sites along the filaments, causing them to be pulled along each other. And conversely a resynthesis of ATP is postulated to have the opposite effect, thus causing relaxation. However, many unanswered questions still remain. For example, how is contraction achieved in visceral muscle that is devoid of striated structure? And precisely how does ATP operate in causing the bonding sites to be shifted progressively along the length of the filaments?

VISCERAL AND CARDIAC MUSCLE

As to metabolism, cardiac muscle resembles skeletal muscle, and presumably visceral muscle is also similar, although very little information is available in this regard. But just as there are plain differences of structure among the three types of muscle, so there are differences in their physiological behavior. Skeletal muscle acts most rapidly, completing a single contraction and relaxation in 0.1 second or less—in comparison to 1 to 5 seconds for cardiac muscle, and 3 to 180 seconds for visceral muscle from various organisms.

A continuous mass of either visceral or cardiac muscle responds definitely in an all-or-none fashion. An excitation of one group of fibers keeps spreading until it involves all the fibers. In the heart there is a specialized system of modified fibers, which serves as a conducting system. In visceral muscle, however, the spread of a contraction may depend upon nervous conduction. Visceral muscle is permeated by a fine network of nerve fibers that cannot be removed by dissection.

An outstanding feature of cardiac muscle is the rhythmicity of its action. A frog's heart, for example, if skillfully handled, may keep on beating for more than a month after it has been excised from the body. This means that the contractions of the heart do not depend upon excitations from the central nervous system, although in the intact body, the strength and frequency of the heartbeat are altered considerably under the action of the cardiac nerves.

Each beat of the heart represents a single twitch, and it is not possible for the heart to undergo a tetanic contraction, because the refractory period (p. 449) of cardiac muscle extends into the contraction period. Consequently a second stimulus never elicits a contraction unless it comes after the heart has started to relax.

Sometimes visceral muscle also contracts and expands in rhythmic fashion, even in the absence of any apparent external stimulation. But the most important characteristic of visceral muscle is its capacity to remain in a contracted or semicontracted state even while "at rest." A sustained contraction, or tetanus, in skeletal muscle involves a series of excitations coming in usually at the rate of about 50 per second, and skeletal muscle continues to expend extra energy so long as the tetanus continues. But in visceral muscle, a state of sustained contraction, which is referred to as **tonus**, does not involve continuous excitation, nor does tonus demand any extra metabolism above that of the resting state. Thus any degree of tonus in the range between complete contraction and complete relaxation can be maintained with perfect efficiency, and extra metabolic activity is demanded only when the tonus is to be increased or decreased. Visceral muscle is not called upon for quick reversible movements, and consequently there is no need for visceral muscle to ready itself instantaneously for another full-scale contraction. Thus visceral muscle is able to maintain itself at any given status, and visceral muscle expends energy in shortening or lengthening its fibrils only when an appropriate stimulus is received.

GLANDS

These specialized **effectors of secretion** have been discussed previously (Chaps. 11 and 16), but a few general points will be considered in the present connection.

The exocrine glands secrete their products

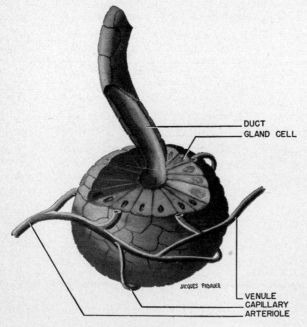

DUCT
GLAND CELL

JACQUES PADAUER

VENULE
CAPILLARY
ARTERIOLE

Fig. 24-9. Gland cells in relation to their blood supply. Each gland cell extracts substances from the blood (and lymph) and delivers them (with or without chemical alteration) into the duct system of the gland.

into ducts, and usually the active secretory cells are localized in bulbous chambers, called **acini,** at the blind ends of the finer ducts. Raw materials used by the gland cells in forming their special secretion are brought to the gland by the blood, which circulates through the capillaries, in close association with each acinus (Fig. 24-9).

Certain glands, such as the sweat and tear glands, synthesize no special substances, but merely extract the components of their juices from the blood. Such glands expend energy in selecting and concentrating their products, since tears and sweat, compared to blood, contain more salts and scarcely any organic substances, except for traces of urea. But most glands also perform the synthesis of specialized secretory products, for example, the enzymes of the digestive glands and the hormones of the endocrine glands.

Some glands, especially in the endocrine system, appear to secrete continuously, although this activity is subject to change by excitations from the nervous system, or by the action of hormones. But many glands discharge their products only in response to periodic stimulation, in which case each excitation is accompanied by a well-defined action potential.

Precisely how a gland cell discharges its secretion into its duct is not well understood. Secretory granules (p. 31), when present, may disintegrate just prior to their discharge (Fig. 24-10), or such granules may be swept bodily into the duct through the end of the cell bordering on the lumen. Probably the membrane at this end of the cell momentarily disintegrates, either partially or totally, allowing for the escape of synthesized products that do not ordinarily penetrate the membrane. Glandular activity requires an expenditure of energy, and the rate of respiration in some of the glands is higher than in any of the other tissues of the body.

ELECTRIC ORGANS

Galvanoeffectors are used as weapons of attack and defense by several kinds of fish, including the "electric eel" and the "stinging ray" (Fig. 24-11). Typically the electric organ is built up of disc-shaped cells that are stacked like coins in elongate columns. Each of the effector cells responds to excitation

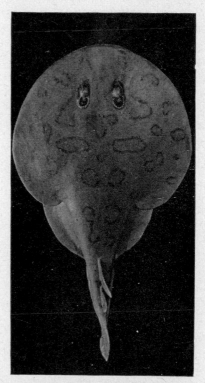

Fig. 24-11. Electric or stinging ray, *Torpedo occidentalis*. (Courtesy of the American Museum of Natural History, New York.)

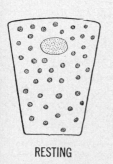 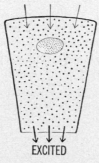

RESTING   EXCITED

Fig. 24-10. How secretion may occur. An increase of osmotic solute, together with increased permeability (or complete breakdown) of the membrane on the duct side of the cell, causes a flow of water from the lymph space through the cell, carrying its secretion out into the duct.

merely by discharging a volley of action potentials, but the cells are connected in series, like a string of serially wired batteries. Consequently the action potentials of the individual cells are summated, forming a total discharge of considerable magnitude. In some cases the total potential of the electric organ may exceed 400 volts, which is sufficient to stun or even kill a small fish if it receives the full charge. The amperage from an electric organ is not very great, because the effector cells have a rather limited electrical capacity, and each discharge endures for only about 0.005 second. However, enough current is obtained from the electric organ of a stinging ray to produce a series of brief flashes when a lamp bulb is brought into the circuit.

LUMINESCENT ORGANS

Light is emitted by a wide variety of organisms. These include a number of bacteria and fungi, as well as certain protozoans, sponges, coelenterates, mollusks, crustaceans, centipedes, millepedes, insects, and vertebrates. Among vertebrates, however, light production by the organism itself occurs only in certain fish, especially deep-sea species. Luminescence has not been observed in any of the amphibians, reptiles, birds, or mammals.

Certain bacteria and other fungi luminesce more or less continuously, when oxygen is available, and in this case the light appears to be an incidental by-product of oxidative metabolism. But most luminescent animals, like the firefly, give out flashes of light only when the specialized **luminescent organs** are stimulated. In some cases, the luminescent organs are glands, which give forth luminous secretions; but more specialized organs, such as are found among insects, crustaceans, mollusks, and fishes, produce their light intracellularly.

In the case of fireflies, at least, luminescent flashing provides a system of signals, based on timing, that guide the male flies to the females of the same species.

Chemistry of Bioluminescence. As was shown many years ago by Raphael Dubois in France and by E. Newton Harvey in the United States, it is possible to extract an organic substrate, called **luciferin,** and an enzyme, **luciferase,** from the luminescent organs. These extracts give a flash of light when they are mixed together in the presence of free oxygen (O_2). However, different organisms seem to have developed different varieties of luciferin and different luciferases. Bacterial luciferin, for example, appears to be a phosphorylated riboflavin-nucleic acid complex; whereas the luciferin from one of the Crustacea seems to be a yellow chromopeptid compound. Moreover, ATP seems to play an essential role in some cases, as in the flash emissions of the firefly. The color of the light, on the other hand, may vary according to what luciferase is being used.

The evidence indicates that the actual emission of light is from the molecules of an enzyme-substrate complex that becomes energized during oxidation. However, the energized state is short-lived. Free enzyme quickly is liberated and catalysis continues so long as free oxygen and other necessary substances are available.

Considerable progress has been made recently toward the purification and identification of the luciferin and luciferase components of the various luminescent systems. The bacterial system has been studied intensively by F. H. Johnson and co-workers at Princeton; the crustacean (cypridina) system also has been studied by Johnson in collaboration with an active group of investigators in Japan; and the insect (firefly) system has been investigated by W. D. McElroy and co-workers [1] at Johns Hopkins University. In the case of the firefly, it is now possible to specify the precise molecular structure of luciferin (Fig. 24-12); and it is well established that the firefly luciferase is a long-

[1] Grateful acknowledgment should also be given to the school children of Baltimore, who collected a vast number of fireflies and delivered them to the biological laboratory.

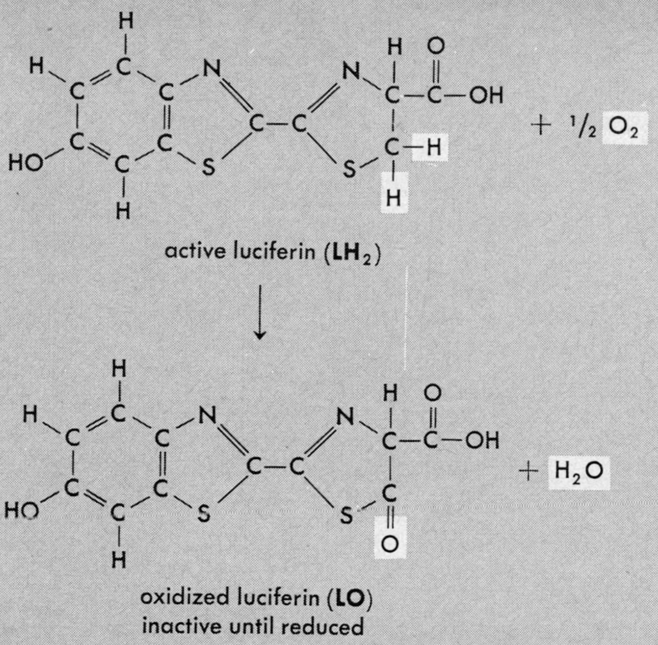

active luciferin (**LH₂**) $+ \frac{1}{2} O_2$

oxidized luciferin (**LO**)
inactive until reduced

Fig. 24-12. Molecular structure of the luciferins of the firefly.

chain protein, consisting of about 1000 precisely ordered peptide units. Moreover, it has been shown that for each molecule of active luciferin (LH_2) that is converted to the oxidized form (L:O), *one quantum of light* (and no heat) *is produced*. In other words, bioluminescence proceeds with remarkable efficiency and the frequently used term "cold light" is most appropriate.

PIGMENTARY EFFECTORS

Chromatophores, which enable an animal to change color or shade quickly and drastically, are possessed by a variety of creatures, including crustaceans, mollusks, fish, amphibians, and reptiles. As to structure, the chromatophores vary in different animals, but all are mechanical effectors in the sense that the response always involves the movement of pigment granules, which may or may not be contained within the protoplasm of the specialized effector cells.

Among invertebrates the chromatophores are usually multicellular organs in which the displacement of the pigment is controlled by muscles. But the chromatophores of vertebrates are single cells (Fig. 24-13), which are present in enormous numbers throughout the skin. The cytoplasm of these cells is densely packed with pigment granules, and the distribution of the pigment in the cells determines the shade and color of the skin

CHROMATOPHORES

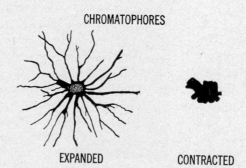

EXPANDED   CONTRACTED

Fig. 24-13. Unicellular chromatophores containing black pigment, from the scales of a fish (*Fundulus*). The light area at the center of the expanded cell marks the position of the nucleus. (After Spaeth.)

at any particular moment. Most of the pigment cells are **melanophores,** which contain black granules, although some are filled with granules of other colors.

A scale scraped from the skin of almost any fish provides an excellent preparation in which to study the behavior of the chromatophores under the microscope. Certain drugs, such as adrenalin, excite the melanophores to contract, in which case one can

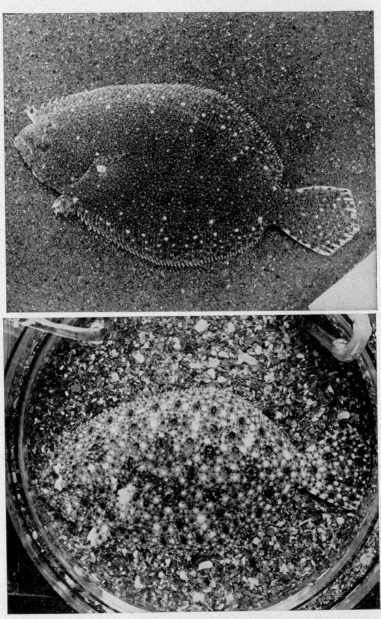

Fig. 24-14. Many fish can change their color and color pattern to match their background. *Above,* flounder against a background of finely mottled sand and mud. *Below,* same fish against a background of coarsely mottled shells. (Courtesy of the Fish and Wildlife Service, U.S. Department of the Interior.)

watch the pigment granules flow inward from the many fine branches of the pigment cell until they accumulate as a very small, deeply situated, mass around the nucleus (Fig. 24-13). Or by treating the scale with other drugs, such as acetylcholine (p. 455), one can watch the pigment granules dispersing into the many finer branches of the cell (Fig. 24-13).

The protoplasmic branches of the pigment cells were previously thought to be pseudopodia, capable of extension and retraction. But now it is known that the branches are relatively permanent, and that the pigment granules ebb and flow through the same channels with each successive "expansion" and "contraction." Thus the pigmentary response probably represents a type of protoplasmic streaming (p. 198) rather than a kind of amoeboid movement (p. 196).

In the intact animal, pigmentary responses are protective in nature, since they provide for changes in coloration in accordance with changes in the background of the environ-ment (Fig. 24-14). If a fish, for example, is placed in an illuminated aquarium with a white, or light-colored bottom, the skin of the fish blanches as a result of a regimented contraction of all the melanophores. But if the bottom of the aquarium is changed to black, the skin rapidly darkens, and all the melanophores are found to be expanded.

The normal stimulus that initiates the responses of the pigmentary effectors is light acting through the medium of the eyes and nervous system. Thus a blind fish usually remains permanently dark in contrast to the changing shades of its fellows in the aquarium. Among amphibians and crustaceans, however, excitations from the eyes are not transmitted to the pigmentary effectors; rather they act upon the endocrine system. In these animals, therefore, the immediate response is elicited by hormones. And even among fish and reptiles, the chromatophores are partially controlled by hormones, although excitations from the nervous system play a more dominant role (p. 454).

TEST QUESTIONS

1. Name five kinds of effector organs found in fish and other lower vertebrates. Which kinds are also found in man?
2. Distinguish the three kinds of muscle tissue on the basis of (a) structural differences and (b) functional differences.
3. What common structural and functional features are found in all muscle, regardless of type?
4. Specify three functions that could not be achieved unless the muscles were arranged in *antagonistic* groups.
5. Distinguish between a single twitch and a tetanus.
6. Draw a curve to simulate the single twitch of a frog's muscle, designating the name and duration of each part of the curve.
7. Explain the relationship between: (a) the duration of the recovery period and the susceptibility of a muscle to fatigue; (b) graded contractions and the all-or-none law.
8. When a working muscle is deprived of oxygen: (a) lactic acid accumulates more rapidly; (b) the glycogen reserves are used up faster; (c) inorganic phosphates accumulate; and (d) the muscle becomes fatigued more quickly and loses its capacity to contract. Explain these facts in the given order, emphasizing the relationships between them.
9. How is it possible for a muscle to do work even though it may have no available oxygen and no capacity to hydrolyze glycogen?
10. Explain how and why a steadily working muscle accumulates an *oxygen debt*. How is the extra oxygen used when a muscle is allowed to rest, and how is this usage related to a partial restoration of the glycogen reserves of the muscle?
11. Differentiate between myosin and actomysin. Explain the *dual role* of myosin in relation to the contractile process.
12. Discuss the efficiency of a muscle as compared to other machines.
13. What use to the body is subserved by the energy that escapes conversion into mechanical power during muscular work?

14. Explain the nature and function of shivering.
15. Make a diagram to show the *fine structure* of a single skeletal muscle fiber. Label the bands (A, H, I, and Z) and clearly differentiate between the thick (myosin) and the thin (actin) filaments.
16. Briefly explain a current theory as to how shortening (contraction) may occur.
17. Distinguish between a tetanic and a tonic contraction. Explain why the tonic contractions of visceral muscle are peculiarly well adapted to the functional responsibilities of this tissue.
18. All glands perform work in extracting the components of their secretions and in concentrating these substances, but some glands also achieve the synthesis of special products. Classify the glands of the body according to this criterion.
19. Briefly discuss electric organs in relation to: (a) the origin of the discharge; (b) the magnitude of the discharge; (c) the usefulness to the possessor.
20. Briefly discuss bioluminescence with reference to: (a) the occurrence in nature; (b) the use to the organism; (c) the metabolic origin of the light; (d) the efficiency compared to other kinds of light emissions.
21. Changes of color, shade, and pigment pattern in the skin of a fish (Fig. 24-14) are produced by unicellular effectors. Explain this statement carefully, using a diagram to show how the pigment cells behave when a fish darkens and pales according to the background.
22. To what extent are the pigment cells of the fish, amphibians, and reptiles controlled: (a) by the nervous system; (b) by the endocrine system?

FURTHER READINGS

1. *Muscular Movement in Man,* by A. V. Hill; New York, 1927.
2. *Color Changes of Animals in Relation to Nervous Activity,* by G. H. Parker; Philadelphia, 1936.
3. "The Contraction of Muscle," by H. E. Huxley; in *Scientific American,* November 1958.
4. "Biological Luminescence," by W. D. McElroy and H. H. Seliger; in *Scientific American,* December 1962.

25-Responses of Higher Animals: The Nervous System

THE RECEPTORS and effectors in higher animals are interconnected by the cells of the nervous system, which relay excitations from parts of the body where stimulation occurs to other parts where responses take place. Thus the nervous system *coordinates* activities throughout the body in such a way that each animal displays an integrated behavior as it confronts the problems of survival. Most animal responses are performed without benefit of previous training, because excitations that originate in a certain group of receptors tend to be transmitted by the nervous system to some specific and localized group of effectors. Such **unconditioned** responses (p. 468) are generally useful to the organism in that they are specifically adapted to the conditions of some particular habitat.

NERVE IMPULSES

The transmission of excitations is the specialty of nerve cells, and nerve cells transmit excitations at far greater speed than other tissues. Accordingly, *excitations traversing the nervous system are specifically referred to as* **nerve impulses.**

The speed of the nerve impulse varies in different animals, but it is always great compared to the transmission of excitations by unspecialized tissues. An activated egg cell, for example, propagates an excitation at the rate of only 1 cm per hour, and thus it is possible to watch the lifting of the fertilization membrane, which accompanies the spreading of the excitation over the surface of the egg. Likewise the sponge, which also lacks specialized nerve cells, transmits excitations at the comparatively slow rate of 1 cm per minute. But with the appearance of even primitive nerve cells, such as are found in jellyfish (p. 633), the rate of transmission climbs sharply to 10 cm per second; and in the well-developed nervous system of the earthworm, the speed is ten times greater. The maximum velocity is reached, however, in the nerves of warm-blooded vertebrates. In the nerves of man, for example, the largest fibers transmit at the rate of 120 meters per second, and even in the smaller fibers impulses are conducted almost as fast.

Aside from the speed of transmission, nerve impulses are fundamentally similar to excitations in other tissues (p. 190). Like excitations generally, the nerve impulse is a wavelike protoplasmic disturbance (p. 191) that is always distinguished by well-defined electrical, thermal, and chemical changes. Invariably the spikelike **action potential** keeps precisely in pace with the speeding impulse; and the passage of each impulse involves the liberation of a small amount of heat. At least 90 percent of this heat comes forth subsequent to actual transmission, while the nerve is consuming extra oxygen and consummating its *recovery*.

Compared to a working muscle, a transmitting nerve expends very little energy, although the total extra heat produced represents much more energy than is liberated by the actual process of transmission. The extra consumption of oxygen and production of carbon dioxide, which result from nervous activity, are so small that they could not be measured until quite recently. In fact, the heat produced by a stimulated nerve is equivalent merely to the energy liberated by the oxidation of 0.000001 gram of glycogen per gram of nerve per minute of continuous stimulation. Thus if the nerve contains only 1 percent of carbohydrate fuel, it could be stimulated continuously for a week without exhaustion. It is not surprising to find that *nerve fibers are,* in fact, *practically unfatigable,* provided an adequate oxygen supply is available.

EXCITABILITY IN NERVE FIBERS

With proper care, a nerve excised from the body of a cold-blooded animal, such as a frog, will remain alive and excitable for a period of more than 24 hours, and excised nerves have been widely employed in studying the phenomena of excitation. Usually such nerves are attached to a muscle, and the contraction of the muscle indicates the effectiveness of the stimulus, which is applied directly to the nerve. Each motor nerve is made up of many axon fibers (p. 453), which pass to the muscle in a common sheath, and these axons, though divorced from their centrons (p. 453), remain alive and excitable for an extensive period after the nerve has been removed from the body.

When any nerve is stimulated directly with an electric current, the excitation arises at the **negative electrode,** that is, at the point where the stimulating current abolishes the positive charge on the outer surface of the membrane (p. 190). Such a depolarization, or cancellation of the resting potential, results in the discharge of an impulse from the point of excitation. Then a rapid wave of depolarization, or action potential, travels along the length of the fiber, and each depolarized point, as it becomes excited, contributes its share of energy to the propagation of the impulse.

Immediately after transmitting an impulse, each part of a nerve fiber quickly recovers its capacity to be re-excited. The **absolute refractory period** (p. 449), during which the fiber cannot be re-excited by another stimulus, however strong, endures for only about 0.002 second (Fig. 25-1); but this is followed by a **relative refractory period** (0.012 second), during which an exceptionally strong stimulus can cause an excitation. Then, before the fiber returns to its original state, there is a brief **supernormal period.** During the supernormal period the fiber is susceptible to excitation by feebler stimuli.

Unlike an ordinary electric current, *the propagated action potential does not grow weaker* as the transmitting circuit becomes longer; this is because new energy is provided to the impulse as it passes each point along the nerve fiber. Moreover, nerve fibers, like muscle fibers, respond in an all-or-none fashion; each fiber discharges to the maximum of its capacity at the moment of excitation. This does not mean that all impulses are of the same magnitude. In fact, the mag-

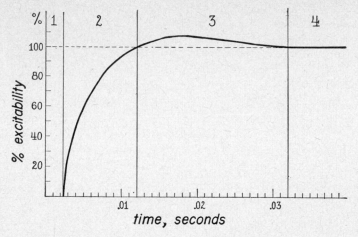

Fig. 25-1. Variation of excitability of a nerve after stimulation. 1, absolute refractory period; 2, relative refractory period; 3, supernormal period; 4, normal condition. (Adapted from Keith Lucas.)

nitude of an impulse provides a good index of the immediate condition of the transmitting fiber. Thus, for example, if one section of a nerve is slightly poisoned (Fig. 25-2), this section transmits weaker impulses so long as the toxic condition persists; but if impulses manage to traverse a damaged region of a nerve, the impulses regain full intensity as soon as they reach an undamaged section of the nerve.

THE NERVE NET OF HYDRA: A PRIMITIVE NERVOUS SYSTEM

One of the simplest types of nervous system is found in *Hydra* and other coelenterate animals. *Hydra* possesses a **nerve net** (Fig. 25-3) that extends throughout the body and

tentacles of the animal. The nerve net lies in close contact with the mesoglea (p. 630), but its branches make contact with the cells of both the ectoderm and endoderm. Some of these branches are equivalent to the sensory

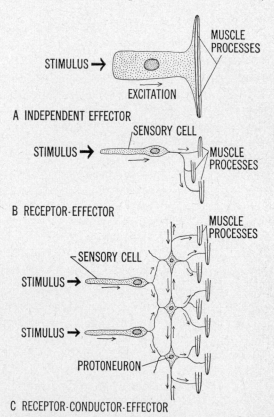

Fig. 25-3. Responsive mechanisms of *Hydra*. Note gradations of complexity from the independent effector to distinct receptor, conductor, and effector cells.

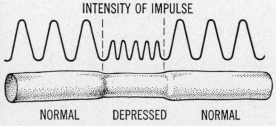

Fig. 25-2. The intensity of a nerve impulse traveling from left to right along a nerve fiber is indicated by the height of the action potential outlined above the fiber. The slightly shriveled region of the fiber indicates the depressed portion in which the impulse intensity is reduced. Note that the action potential, once past the depressed (perhaps drugged) section, regains its full intensity.

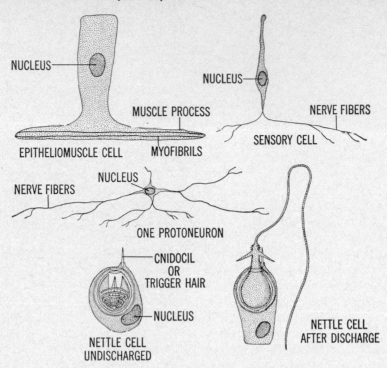

NUCLEUS

NUCLEUS

MUSCLE PROCESS

NERVE FIBERS

EPITHELIOMUSCLE CELL   MYOFIBRILS

SENSORY CELL

NERVE FIBERS

NUCLEUS

ONE PROTONEURON

CNIDOCIL
OR
TRIGGER HAIR

NUCLEUS

NETTLE CELL
UNDISCHARGED

NETTLE CELL
AFTER DISCHARGE

Fig. 25-4.   Specialized responsive cells of *Hydra*.

nerve fibers of higher animals, since they receive impulses from specialized receptor cells; but other branches of the net are motor fibers, since they transmit impulses to the epitheliomuscle cells of the ectoderm and endoderm.

The nerve net of *Hydra* is composed of primitive nerve cells, called **protoneurons** (Fig. 25-4), which differ from the **neurons** of higher animals. Protoneurons may not be discrete cells. In fact the whole nerve net may represent a syncytium, in which the protoneurons are in protoplasmic continuity with each other.[1] Moreover, protoneurons tend to send out fibers in many directions from the centron (p. 453), rather than along one main *linear* pathway of contraction, as is the case with the neurons of higher animals (p. 453).

In *Hydra,* impulses from the receptors in any part of the body tend to spread rather

indiscriminately in all directions throughout the nerve net. In fact, any strong stimulus tends to produce a very *generalized* response, such as a contraction of the hydra as a whole, since a large proportion of the epitheliomuscle cells are thrown into action more or less simultaneously.

There are, however, some factors that tend to *localize* responses, even in the hydra's primitive nervous system. Due to the elongate shape of the tentacles, the nerve net in these organs runs mainly in a lengthwise direction. This arrangement tends to orient the flow of impulses to and from the tentacles giving the tentacles some capacity for reacting on an individual basis. Moreover, protoneurons display a relatively *long refractory period*, so that recently excited parts of the nerve net are not immediately capable of propagating new excitations. Probably there are other factors, still unknown, that tend to localize the responses of *Hydra* more definitely.

[1] Recent electronmicrographic studies indicate that at least some synapses are present in the nerve net.

THE NERVOUS SYSTEM OF THE EARTHWORM

Such a diffuse and *uncentralized* nervous system is not characteristic of invertebrate animals generally. Many invertebrate animals have highly centralized nervous systems, especially among the annelids and arthropods.

In higher animals, the nerve cells are not scattered throughout the body, but are aggregated mainly in a *central nervous system.* The central nervous system of the earthworm has the form of an elongate **nerve cord** that extends lengthwise through the body. In the earthworm and most other invertebrates, the nerve cord lies **ventral** to the digestive tract, except at the anterior end, where it loops around the pharynx (Fig. 25-5). Anteriorly the nerve cord terminates in two distinct swellings, the **cerebral ganglia**, which lie dorsal to the digestive tract (Fig. 25-5); other swellings, or **ganglia,** occur in the ventral part of the cord, typically one pair in each **segment** of the body.

The ganglia are very important because these swellings mark the location of the cell bodies, or centrons, of the many nerve cells that compose the whole nervous system. Thus the interconnecting strands between the ganglia (Fig. 25-5) consist of **nerve fibers** (mainly axons), derived from the centrons in the ganglia; and likewise the *nerves,* which are associated with each ganglion (Fig. 25-5), consist of bundles of nerve fibers passing to and from the ganglia.

Central vs. Peripheral Parts of the Nervous System. In such a highly organized system, it is possible to recognize two main functional parts: (1) the **peripheral nervous system,** which consists of the many nerves extending out from the nerve cord; and (2) the **central nervous system,** which is the ganglionated nerve cord itself. Each peripheral nerve sends fibers to both the receptors and effectors in a certain segment of the body; and the central nervous system serves as an interconnection among *all* the peripheral nerves. Thus the nerves present in each segment of the earthworm (Fig. 25-5) are brought into communication with each other, and with all other nerves in the body, by way of the nerve cells of the central nervous system (Fig. 25-6).

The nerves of the earthworm are all mixed nerves, in that each nerve is made up partly of **sensory** (afferent) **fibers,** which convey impulses from the receptors *toward* the central nervous system; and partly of **motor** (efferent) **fibers,** which always transmit impulses *from* the CNS to the effectors. Thus each nerve consists of fibers supplying both the receptors

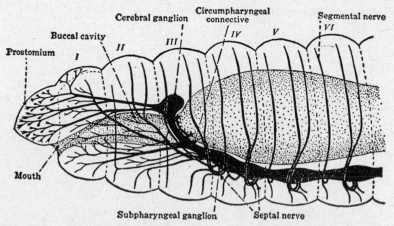

Fig. 25-5. Side view of anterior end of an earthworm, showing the cerebral ganglion and larger nerves. (After Hess. From Hegner, *College Zoology.* Permission of The Macmillan Co.)

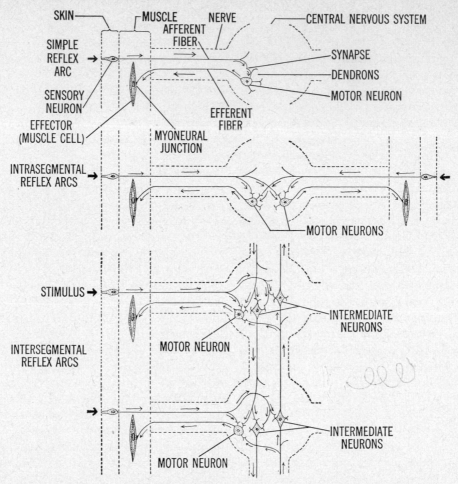

Fig. 25-6. Sensory-neuromotor mechanisms of the earthworm. Be sure to differentiate between intrasegmental and intersegmental reflexes.

and the effectors in a given region of the earthworm's body (Fig. 25-6).

The Reflex Arc. As is indicated in Figure 25-6, not one, but a series of neurons takes part in relaying impulses to the effectors, whenever the receptors of an earthworm are stimulated. But regardless of the number of neurons, the route taken by impulses in passing from the receptors to the effectors of an animal is designated as a **reflex arc.** In all cases impulses pass to the central nervous system via afferent fibers, and pass outward from the CNS via efferent fibers.

The many degrees of complexity displayed by reflex arcs are shown in Figure 25-6. The simplest arc (Fig. 25-6) is a **unilateral intra-** segmental reflex, which involves just one side of one segment of the animal's body; another simple arc is a **bilateral intrasegmental** reflex, which involves both sides of any one segment (Fig. 25-6). Similarly it is possible to recognize **intrasegmental reflex arcs** (Fig. 25-6), which may be either short or long, and either unilateral or bilateral in nature.

In the intact animal, each stimulus usually excites many receptors and throws a number of reflex arcs into simultaneous action. Moreover, each sensory neuron makes contact with several **association neurons,** as well as with a number of motor neurons. *Association neurons are localized entirely within the central* *nervous system,* and do not send fibers into the nerves. Association neurons make contact with other association neurons, as well as with sensory and motor neurons. In fact the interconnections of the association neurons are so extensive throughout the central nervous system that impulses coming in from any sensory nerve can find their way to *any* motor nerve. However, impulses in all higher animals tend to follow well-defined and localized pathways, which are determined by a variety of factors (see later).

THE NEURONS OF VERTEBRATE ANIMALS

The neurons of all higher animals are uninucleate cells. Typically each neuron (Fig. 25-7) displays one or more **dendron fibers,** which conduct impulses *toward* the nucleated cell body, or **centron;** and each neuron has one (occasionally two or more) well-defined **axon fiber,** which transmits impulses *away* from the cell body. Both dendrons and axons may display side branches, or collaterals, and

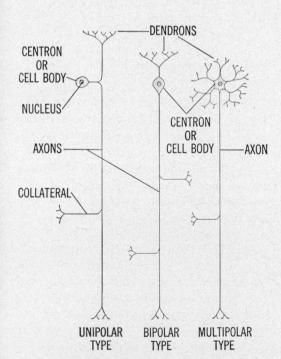

Fig. **25-7.** Types of neurons, or nerve cells, found in man.

each fiber terminates in a number of twiglike **nerve endings.**

The neurons of vertebrates are essentially comparable to those of invertebrate animals, but the vertebrate nervous system represents a much more intricate complex of reflex arcs, as is shown diagrammatically in Figure 25-8.

The Synapses and Other Relay Points in the Reflex Arc. One main function of each neuron is to relay impulses either to one or more other neurons, or directly to an effector structure. Thus even a relatively simple reflex arc is interrupted by one or more **synapses,** which are the *points of contact between successive neurons.*

Other types of synaptic junctures are encountered: at points where receptor cells make contact with the sensory neurons (Fig. 25-8), and at points where motor neurons join the muscle fibers or other effector cells. However, the physiological properties of the **sensory-neural** and **myoneural synapses** may be somewhat different from those of **interneural synapses.**

Electronmicrographic studies demonstrate beyond doubt that the synapses are points of discontinuity between the successively arranged cells of the sensory-neural-muscular system. The gap between the membrane at the tip of an axon branch and the membrane of a dendron branch—and this is a typical synapse—measures some 125 ± 25 Ångstrom units across. Generally there are a number of microvesicles, called **neurosecretory** vesicles, situated at the axon terminal, near the synaptic membrane.

The transmission of impulses across a synapse involves **relay mechanisms** that are far from simple. The synapse may act as a resistance point at which impulses are damped off completely. Synaptic resistance varies, however, in the different reflex arcs, and consequently the synapses play an important role in routing impulses through the nervous system and in *localizing* responses in the organism. But even more important, perhaps, is that the pattern of impulses in the postsynaptic neuron is usually not a carbon copy

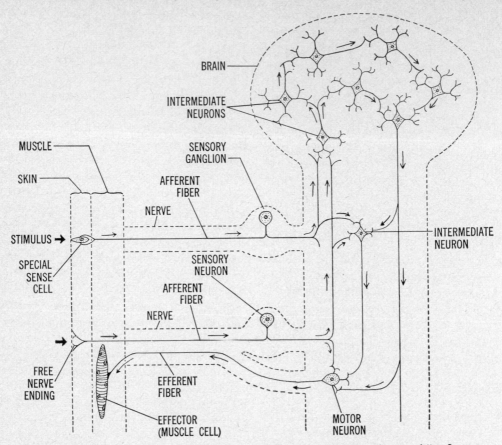

Fig. 25-8. Sensory-neuromotor connections in the vertebrate. Note that "long path" reflexes are conducted through the brain; whereas intra- and intersegmented reflexes are restricted to the spinal cord.

of the pattern in the presynaptic nerve cell. The rate of firing (frequency of impulses) may be increased or decreased as a result of the relay. And if the postsynaptic neuron possesses more than one axon, the rate of firing may be different in the different axons. Also, neighboring synapses may mutually exert an influence upon each other. In short, the synapses are very important in determining the *integrative functions* of the nervous system, as will be discussed more fully later (p. 455).

Basic Nature of Synaptic Transmission. The question of whether synaptic transmission is chemical or electrical remained a matter of controversy for many years. Now, however, most neurophysiologists agree that both chemical and electrical agencies are gener-

ally involved. However, a few cases of purely electrical synaptic excitations, not involving any chemical agency, have been demonstrated—particularly in arthropods.

The first demonstration of a **neurosecretion**, or **neurohumor**, was made by Otto Loewi, in 1921, while studying the isolated heart of the frog. Such a preparation will keep beating for many hours. And if two hearts are arranged in the fashion indicated in Figure 25-9, stimulation of the decelerator (**vagus**) nerve to the upper one not only causes this heart to slow down but also leads, a few seconds later, to a slowing of the beat of the lower heart. Obviously these hearts are not connected by any nerves. Consequently the effect must be transmitted by some chemical agent, liberated into the saline fluid that

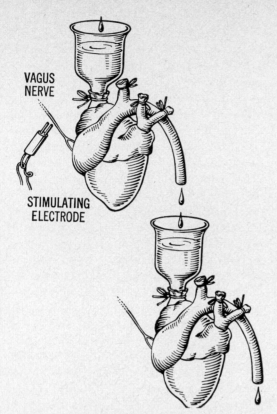

VAGUS
NERVE

STIMULATING
ELECTRODE

Fig. 25-9. Diagram of Otto Loewi's experiment, demonstrating the *neurohumor,* **acetylcholine.** Stimulation of the vagus nerve of the upper heart soon retarded the beating of the lower heart as well.

flows from one heart to the other. Similarly, excitation of the accelerator (**sympathetic**) nerve to the upper specimen accelerated the beat in both hearts. This indicated the liberation of another neurosecretion, or **excitatory substance.**

Subsequent work resulted in the isolation and identification of the cardiac **decelerating** factor. It is a fairly simple nitrogenous compound, namely, **acetylcholine.** Acetylcholine is secreted by the terminal axon branches in many parts of the nervous system. It serves as the excitatory agency (1) at the myoneural synapses of all motor neurons, (2) at all synapses in the parasympathetic (p. 465) system, and (3) at the synapses of the preganglionic neurons of the whole sympathetic (p. 466) nervous system. Acetylcholine is probably produced also at many synapses within the central nervous system, that is, at the synapses joining the successive association neurons of various reflex arcs. Collectively, therefore, such neurons, which are excited by acetylcholine, are said to be **cholinergic.**

Acetylcholine is liberated, probably, from the microvesicles of the axon tips, into the synaptic gaps. Here it contacts the dendritic membranes, causing excitation. Such excitation is short-lived, however. A special enzyme, **cholinesterase,** soon initiates a hydrolytic breakdown of the excitatory substance into acetate and choline which are inactive.

The heart **accelerator** factor has also been identified. It is **noradrenaline** (p. 406), formerly referred to as sympathin. Noradrenaline has a more restricted action as a **synaptic transmitter.** It is produced by the postganglionic neurons of the sympathetic system and, perhaps, by some neurons in the brain stem (p. 459). Neurons that are excited by noradrenaline are referred to as **adrenergic.**

In addition to acetylcholine and noradrenaline, at least three other synaptically active substances are indicated by current research. These are **serotonin** (5-hydroxytryptamine), **factor S,** and **factor I.** Serotonin may act as a synaptic transmitter in some neurons within the central nervous system; factor S (*sensory factor*) appears to be involved in the formation of the generator potential (p. 456) in receptors generally; and factor I (*inhibition factor*) appears to mediate the inhibitory effects of certain nerve cells in the central nervous system.

FUNCTIONS OF NERVE CELL BODIES AND DENDRITES

Previously it was thought that the sole function of the cell body, or **centron,** was to nourish its connected fibers (dendrites and axons). The nucleus, of course, lies in the cell body, and if an axon or dendrite is divorced from its centron it begins to degenerate after several days. In fact, following the pathway of such degeneration has enabled neuroanatomists to trace out many of the principal sensory and motor pathways (p. 463) in the nervous system. Likewise, a study of axon regeneration, which follows the channel of degeneration in the central nervous system, has yielded a great deal of confirmatory evidence.

Recent studies indicate that the cell body has other important functions. Neurosecretory products, apparently, are synthesized mainly in the centron. They are then carried by a sort of "peristalsis" along the fibers to the tips (p. 414), where storage and utilization occur. But even more important, perhaps, is the fact that the cell body, together with its associated dendrites, is not just a passive transmitter of such impulses that are brought to it. These parts may profoundly modify the pattern of such impulses, before passing them on. This newly discovered fact has had great impact upon current thinking on the question of how the nervous system achieves its complex integrative functions.

Some nerve cells discharge impulses spontaneously in rhythmic fashion. This phenomenon was demonstrated most clearly by T. H. Bullock of the University of California, working on the **pacemaker neurons** of the heart of the lobster. An exceedingly fine microelectrode (p. 428) inserted into the centron of such a cell reveals an alternating series of depolarizations and repolarizations in the membrane potential of the dendritic region of the cell. As depolarization reaches a critical level, one or more spikelike action potentials are fired, causing cardiac contraction. Immediately after the spike, however, repolarization commences, and the next action potential is not discharged until another depolarization occurs in the changing cycle of the **"pacemaker potential."**

Impulses coming to a pacemaker neuron across synaptic contacts from other neurons do not directly lead to the firing of impulses to the heart. They merely change the rate of firing. Some fibers cause acceleration and others deceleration; and presumably these effects are mediated by two different synaptic transmitter substances. A neuron does not necessarily fire off an exact carbon copy of the pattern of impulses received by its dendrites.

The **generator potential,** previously discussed (p. 428), provides another example of specialization and versatility among neuronal cells and synaptic junctions. Some small neurons in the central nervous system, apparently, do not handle true nerve impulses—conducted in all-or-none fashion and without decrement—as do the axons of most nerve cells. They conduct slow changes of potential that suffer decrement during propagation. Impulses arriving at a synapse may either raise or lower the dendritic membrane potential of the postsynaptic cell. Also they may either excite or inhibit, depending upon several factors, such as the intrinsic nature of the presynaptic and the postsynaptic cells, and local conditions, both past and present. Presumably these activities are mediated by synaptic transmitter substances. However, much remains to be learned, although the known mechanisms are sufficiently complex and versatile to account for the great complexity and versatility of the nervous system.

"One-Way" Conductivity: The Law of "Forward Direction." In the intact animal, sensory impulses always travel inward, toward the central nervous system, and motor impulses always pass outward from the CNS. However, this law of "forward direction" is determined, not by the conductivity of the neurons, but by the fact that *synapses can conduct in one direction only*. An excised nerve will conduct impulses equally well in either direction, but *in the body* an impulse traveling "backward" through a neuron is always stopped when it reaches a synapse. In other words, impulses may be transmitted from axons to dendrons in successive neurons, but not from dendrons to axons.

The "two-way" conductivity of nerve fibers, in contrast to the "one-way" conductivity of the synapses, may be demonstrated by experiments in which the nerves of an animal such as a frog are exposed and stimulated directly. The simplest method is to expose a motor nerve that consists mainly of efferent axons, passing toward some muscle. When such a nerve is excited—as by pinching—a series of action potentials can be detected by an **oscilloscope.** These impulses pass not only outward toward the muscle (causing it to contract); but they also pass inward toward the spinal cord. However, the backflow of impulses dies out as soon as it reaches the spinal cord. At the spinal cord the impulses encounter the synaptic junctures between the motor neurons and the other neurons of the central nervous system (Fig. 25-8), and these synapses are not able to conduct in a central direction.

Apparently the dendrons represent the "receptive" portion of a neuron. The dendrons of a postsynaptic neuron may be excited by impulses coming from presynaptic axons, but axons cannot be excited by impulses coming from the dendrons.

Synaptic Resistance: Localization of Responses. Even when impulses approach a synapse in the proper direction, they may or may not be transmitted, depending on a variety of factors. The resistance to the passage of impulses is extremely variable from synapse to synapse, and in any one synapse from time to time. Impulses entering the central nervous system from a stimulated sense organ tend to follow certain paths that carry the impulses to some limited and localized group of muscles or other effectors. In other words, certain reflex arcs transmit impulses more readily than others, and consequently the application of a particular stimulus frequently results in the performance of one or more definitely localized **reflex acts.** However, the forces and factors that determine synaptic transmission are very complex and not fully understood at present.

Synaptic Summation. A single stimulus, *applied to an* **afferent nerve,** may fail to evoke any response, even though the stimulus is not too weak to excite the nerve itself. But the same or even a weaker stimulus may evoke the response, if repeated a number of times in rapid succession. This phenomenon of **synaptic summation** indicates that a series of impulses leads to the accumulation of some force or substance, which finally may overcome a synaptic block. The success of a summation depends upon the exact timing of the succession of impulses arriving at the synapses, and this fact is important in determining the reflexes of the intact animal. Ordinarily when a sense organ is stimulated, it discharges not one, but a volley of impulses into the afferent nerve; and in the volley, the frequency of the impulses increases steadily as the strength of the stimulus is raised. Thus a single weak stimulus, *applied to a sense organ,* may fail to evoke a reflex, whereas a stronger stimulus, even when applied just once, may be entirely successful.

Synaptic Fatigue. A *prolonged and continuous* repetition of the same stimulus sooner or later results in a failure of the response. This block is not necessarily due to a fatigue of the synapses of the particular reflex arc, since the receptor cells themselves may not continue to discharge impulses if the stimulation is continued unduly. But even when the sensory nerve is excited directly by a continuous series of stimuli, a block is finally effected by **synaptic fatigue.** Synapses are much more quickly fatigued than myoneural junctures, which, in turn, are fatigued much sooner than a muscle; nerve fibers proper are practically unfatigable. Fatigue of the synapses, like that of other tissues, is a reversible process, and the synaptic block disappears during periods of rest, if an adequate supply of oxygen is available.

Facilitation: Habit, Memory, Learning. Assuming the fatigue is avoided, the mere transmission of a series of impulses across the synapses of a given reflex arc results in an enduring increase in the conductivity of this arc to the passage of subsequent impulses. Thus it is always easier for an animal to *repeat* a given response than to perform the action for the first time. This effect, which is called **facilitation**, is especially characteristic of the brain synapses of higher animals—particularly in higher vertebrates, such as birds and mammals. This effect is very important, because facilitation may underlie the phenomena of *habit, memory,* and *learning.* In fact, all **conditioned reflexes,** which enable an animal to *modify behavior in relation to past experience,* appear to be dependent upon the facilitation effect.

If fatigue is avoided, facilitation becomes more and more pronounced as the synapses of a given arc continue to be used, until a certain maximum is reached. The degree of repetition required to reach this maximum varies widely from species to species, and from individual to individual in the same species. Moreover, facilitation tends to endure for considerable time—sometimes throughout the life of the individual. The fading of facilitation—and this is the underlying basis of *forgetting* and *loss of habit*—usually proceeds at a gradual pace, during periods when there is a prolonged disuse of the synapses concerned with a particular response. However, there are many facets to the problem of facilitation that still remain obscure.

THE NERVOUS SYSTEM OF MAN AND OTHER VERTEBRATES

The vertebrate nervous system is far more complex than that of invertebrate animals, although no *fundamental* differences have been found between the systems.

The Central Nervous System. In vertebrate animals, the central nervous system consists of the **brain** and **spinal cord,** which form a thick-walled **tubular** mass of nerve tissue extending lengthwise in the mid-line of the **dorsal** body wall. At its anterior extremity the nerve tube is enlarged and modified, forming the **brain;** but most of the tube forms the **spinal cord,** which has a relatively simple cylindrical form (Fig. 25-10). The brain lies within a strong (usually bony) encasement, called the **cranium;** and the spinal cord is surrounded by the segments of the **vertebral column.**

The form of the spinal cord does not vary

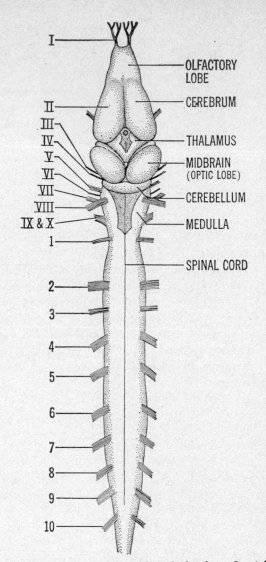

Fig. 25-10. Brain and spinal cord of a frog. Cranial nerves are indicated by Roman numerals, I-X; spinal nerves, by Arabic numbers, 1-10.

very much in different vertebrates, except in size and length (Fig. 25-11). The brain, however, becomes proportionately larger and displays an increasing complexity of form and function in higher vertebrates, especially in man and other mammals (Fig. 25-12).

Structure of the Spinal Cord and Brain. A section of the spinal cord (Fig. 25-13) reveals two regions: (1) an outer mass of **white matter,** composed mainly of axons running lengthwise in the cord; and (2) an inner

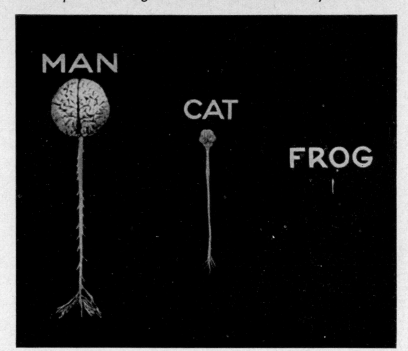

Fig. 25-11. Brains and spinal cords of man, the cat, and the frog, showing the relative sizes and proportionately greater development of the brain in man and the cat. (From *The Nervous System*. Encyclopedia Britannica Films, Inc.)

mass of **gray matter,** consisting mainly of nerve cell bodies, together with the dendrons and axons that connect with the centrons. The grayness of the central area is due to an absence of **myelin.** This whitish lipoid material invests the axons only after they emerge from the gray matter and start running upward or downward through the cord. Some of the centrons, especially in the two **ventral horns** of gray matter (Fig. 25-13), are the cell bodies of **motor neurons,** which dispatch their axons directly out into the motor nerves; but the other centrons belong to **association neurons,** which lie entirely in the central nervous system.

The **brain stem,** or lower part of the brain, has much the same structure as the spinal cord, but the walls of the upper part of the brain are greatly expanded, forming the so-called **higher centers.** The most prominent higher centers—in man and other mammals —are the **cerebrum** and the **cerebellum** (Fig.

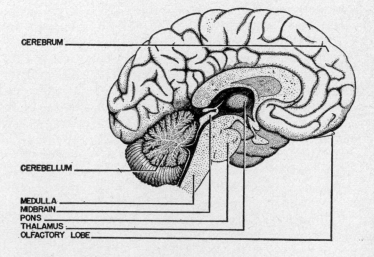

CEREBRUM

CEREBELLUM

MEDULLA
MIDBRAIN
PONS
THALAMUS
OLFACTORY LOBE

Fig. 25-12. Median longitudinal section of human brain.

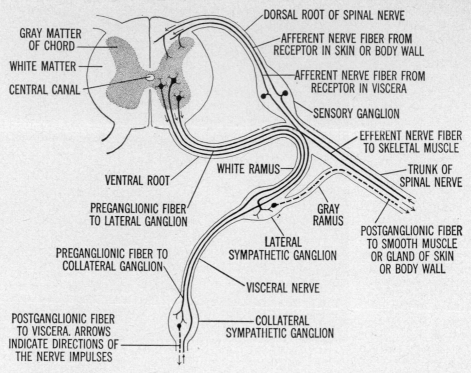

GRAY MATTER OF CHORD

WHITE MATTER

CENTRAL CANAL

DORSAL ROOT OF SPINAL NERVE

AFFERENT NERVE FIBER FROM RECEPTOR IN SKIN OR BODY WALL

AFFERENT NERVE FIBER FROM RECEPTOR IN VISCERA

SENSORY GANGLION

EFFERENT NERVE FIBER TO SKELETAL MUSCLE

TRUNK OF SPINAL NERVE

WHITE RAMUS

VENTRAL ROOT

PREGANGLIONIC FIBER TO LATERAL GANGLION

GRAY RAMUS

POSTGANGLIONIC FIBER TO SMOOTH MUSCLE OR GLAND OF SKIN OR BODY WALL

PREGANGLIONIC FIBER TO COLLATERAL GANGLION

LATERAL SYMPATHETIC GANGLION

VISCERAL NERVE

POSTGANGLIONIC FIBER TO VISCERA. ARROWS INDICATE DIRECTIONS OF THE NERVE IMPULSES

COLLATERAL SYMPATHETIC GANGLION

Fig. 25-13. Diagrammatic cross section of the spinal cord (man), showing connections with the sympathetic ganglia on one side of the body.

25-12). The higher centers—particularly the **cerebral hemispheres**—increase in size and complexity from the lower to the higher vertebrates, until in man they overgrow practically all other parts of the brain. In both the cerebrum and cerebellum there is an external layer of gray matter, called the **cortex,** which is formed by an outgrowth from the deeper gray matter and which completely covers the *outer surface* of these organs. This cortex, in both the cerebrum and the cerebellum, consists entirely of **association neurons,** which relay impulses to and from the underlying white matter. The cortex neurons are extremely numerous; several billion are present in the cerebral hemispheres of man. Accordingly it is not possible to trace the exact path of the impulses in the higher centers; nor is it possible to predict the precise outcome of a response if the reflex arc involves a higher center of the brain.

The cortical regions of the higher centers are very important, because (1) *consciousness* occurs only in relation to nerve impulses that pass through the cerebral cortex; and (2) the capacity of vertebrate animals to form **conditioned reflexes** is localized mainly in the cortical areas of the cerebrum and cerebellum.

The Craniospinal Nerves: Somatic Reflexes. All movements of the limbs and other external body parts are performed by **skeletal muscles,** and the skeletal muscles are all activated by motor neurons from the spinal cord and brain. Thus the **spinal nerves** and the **cranial nerves** are directly concerned with all **somatic reflexes,** which determine the activities of the **skeletal muscles.**

The Spinal Nerves. The **segmented character** of the vertebrate nervous system is clearly shown by the arrangement of the spinal nerves (Fig. 25-10). The spinal nerves originate from the spinal cord in bilaterally symmetrical pairs, and each spinal nerve innervates all the receptors and effectors on one side of *one segment of the body.* Each spinal nerve is a mixed nerve, since it carries sensory fibers from the receptors to the cord, and motor fibers from the cord to the muscles, in a particular body segment.

The junction between each spinal nerve and the cord is effected by *two* roots: a **dorsal root** and a **ventral root** (Fig. 25-13), and these two roots are different as to function. All **sensory fibers** in the nerve *enter* the spinal cord *via the dorsal root;* whereas all **motor fibers** *emerge from the cord via the ventral root* (Fig. 25-13). The dorsal root is also distinguished by an appreciable swelling, the **dorsal root ganglion,** which contains the **centrons** of all the **sensory neurons** of the corresponding side of a particular body segment. Each of the neurons shown in Figure 25-13 represents a type, of which *many* are present in the actual nerve—so that a spinal nerve innervates all the receptors and effectors on the corresponding side in a particular body segment. Not shown in the diagram are the association neurons in the gray matter of the cord, which serve to transmit impulses from the sensory neurons to motor neurons, not only in the same segment of the body, but also in segments that lie above and below a particular spinal nerve.

It is not difficult to demonstrate the functional differentiation between the dorsal and ventral nerve roots. If a **dorsal** root is cut, the animal suffers an **anesthesia,** which is limited strictly to one side of one segment of the body. No sensations can originate from the receptors of this segment, nor can any reflexes be initiated if stimuli are applied in this area of the body. However, the muscles of the segment are not paralyzed, since these muscles can take part in other reflexes, provided these reflexes originate in other segments of the body.

If the **ventral** root of a spinal nerve is cut, there is a localized unilateral **paralysis** involving only the muscles supplied by the particular nerve. After the operation these muscles cannot participate in any reflex. The segment suffers no anesthesia, however, and reflexes involving other muscles of the body

can originate from the receptors of the segment. Essentially, the cutting of one or more **ventral** roots simulates the main symptoms of infantile paralysis, and, in fact, the virus of infantile paralysis does produce a degeneration of the motor neurons that pass out from the spinal cord via the ventral roots.

When a nerve is cut, the fibers that have been divorced from their cell bodies gradually degenerate. Later, however, a new set of axons and dendrons may grow out along the remnants of the old fibers; and this trail of degeneration and regeneration makes it possible to trace out the origin and distribution of a given set of nerve fibers, even within the mazes of the central nervous system.

The Cranial Nerves. In primitive vertebrates, the cranial nerves develop on a segmental basis, but the brain of modern vertebrates has become so highly modified that the segmentation is obscured. The cranial nerves originate from the brain—or more precisely, from the sides of the brain stem (Fig. 25-10). Most vertebrates possess *twelve* pair of cranial nerves; Table 25-1 shows the cranial nerves of man. Reptiles, birds, and mammals possess the same nerves as man; but only the first ten pair are fully developed among the fish and amphibians. Some of the cranial nerves (I, II, and VIII) are purely sensory; others are mainly motor (III, IV, VI, XI, and XII); and the others (V, VII, IX, and X) are mixed nerves, containing sensory and motor fibers in fairly equal proportions. The sensory neurons of the cranial nerves, like those of the spinal nerves, have their cell bodies localized in **ganglia** situated near the nerve roots.

The cranial nerves function like the spinal nerves, except that in many cases the cranial nerves are more closely associated with the higher centers of the brain. This is especially true of the main sensory nerves—from the eyes, ears, tongue, and nose—in which the fibers are routed almost directly to the cerebral cortex.

Main Conduction Paths: Somatic Reflexes. The simplest possible reflex in a vertebrate

Table 25-1—The Cranial Nerves of Man

Number	Name	Origin of the Sensory Fibers	Termination of the Motor Fibers
I	Olfactory	Olfactory mucous membrane of nose (smell)	None
II	Optic	Retina of the eye (vision)	None
III	Oculomotor	Proprioceptors in eye muscles (muscle sense)	Muscles that move the eye (with IV and VI). Muscles of accommodation (lens). Iris (constriction of pupil)
IV	Trochlear	Eye muscles (muscle sense)	Muscles that move the eye (with III and VI)
V	Trigeminal	Teeth. Skin of face	Some of the muscles used in chewing
VI	Abducens	Eye muscles (muscle sense)	Muscles that move the eye (with III and IV)
VII	Facial	Taste buds of anterior two-thirds of tongue	Muscles of the face. Salivary glands (submaxillary and sublingual)
VIII {	Auditory	Cochlea (hearing)	None
	Vestibular	Semicircular canals, sacculus, utriculus (senses of movement, balance, rotation)	None
IX	Glossopharyngeal	Mucous membrane of pharynx (swallowing reflex). Taste buds of posterior one-third of tongue	Muscles of pharynx (swallowing). Salivary glands (parotid)
X	Vagus	Lungs (reflex control of respiratory rhythm). Mucous membrane of larynx. Arch of aorta (control of blood pressure). Stomach (hunger)	Heart (inhibition). Stomach, small intestine (augmentation of peristalsis). Muscles of larynx (speech). Muscles of esophagus (swallowing). Gastric glands (secretory)
XI	Spinal accessory	Muscles of shoulder (muscle sense)	Muscles of shoulder girdle (shoulder movements)
XII	Hypoglossal	Tongue muscles (muscle sense)	Muscles in tongue (tongue movements)

animal involves at least one **sensory neuron** and one **motor neuron,** to which impulses are passed directly in the gray matter of the same segment of the spinal cord (Fig. 25-14). However, such two-neuron arcs play no essential role in behavior, except *possibly* in the case of very simple reflexes like the "knee jerk" and other proprioceptive reflexes from the tendons and muscles. Most responses in the intact animal involve a number of **association neurons;** and in the case of **suprasegmental reflexes,** which involve the relaying of impulses through a higher center of the brain, the number of association neu-

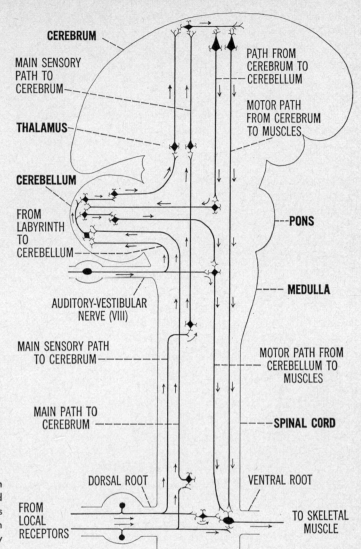

CEREBRUM

MAIN SENSORY
PATH TO
CEREBRUM

THALAMUS

CEREBELLUM

FROM
LABYRINTH
TO
CEREBELLUM

AUDITORY-VESTIBULAR
NERVE (VIII)

MAIN SENSORY PATH
TO CEREBRUM

MAIN PATH TO
CEREBRUM

DORSAL ROOT

FROM
LOCAL
RECEPTORS

PATH FROM
CEREBRUM TO
CEREBELLUM

MOTOR PATH
FROM CEREBRUM
TO MUSCLES

PONS

MEDULLA

MOTOR PATH FROM
CEREBELLUM TO
MUSCLES

SPINAL CORD

VENTRAL ROOT

TO SKELETAL
MUSCLE

Fig. 25-14. Some main conduction pathways in the brain and spinal cord of man. Although the sensory pathways are shown on the left and motor path on the right in this diagram, actually both types of pathways are bilateral.

rons may be exceeding large indeed (see Fig. 25-14).

The spinal cord serves as the conduction pathway for impulses traveling upward to the higher centers and downward from the higher centers to effectors situated below the level of the head. In the spinal cord, moreover, impulses of different origins and destinations tend to follow certain rather specific **main fiber tracts.**

Main Sensory Tracts. The association neurons that carry impulses from the *pain* and *temperature* receptors. *cross over imme-*

diately to the opposite side of the cord and then pass upward toward the brain. But impulses from the *touch* and *pressure* receptors, and impulses from the **proprioceptors** of the muscles and tendons, *do not cross over*, but pass upward in the cord on the same side, that is, on the side where the stimulated receptors are located.

The localization of the main **sensory tracts** is clearly demonstrated in cases of unilateral injuries of the spinal cord. If only the right side of the spinal cord is crushed or damaged, the subject suffers a loss of "muscle sense" and of touch and pressure sensations when stimuli are applied on the right side of the body, *below the level of the lesion;* but the loss of temperature and pain sensations is localized on the left side of the body, likewise below the damaged level.

Localization of Impulses in the Higher Centers, Especially the Cerebral Cortex. Proprioceptive impulses passing upward in the spinal cord are routed mainly to the cerebellum, where the complex movements of the body are coordinated, but other types of impulses go mainly to the cerebrum. In either case, however, the *crossing over of* **all** *impulses* is completed by the time they reach the higher centers. Thus pain and temperature impulses are shunted across at a relatively low level in the spinal cord, but other impulses pass across at a higher level, in the **brain stem.** Each half of the cerebrum and cerebellum, therefore, is concerned with the transmission of impulses that are derived from the receptors on an opposite side of the body.

As is shown in Figure 25-15, the cerebral hemispheres sort out the different kinds of impulses and transmit the several kinds through different areas of the cortex. Thus sensations and reflexes initiated in the receptors of the trunk and limbs are abolished by damaging specific areas in the upper midregion of the cortex; whereas sensations and reflexes originating from the special sense organs are definitely localized in other *specific areas of the cortex.*

The Main Motor (Pyramidal) Tract. The main **motor area** of the cerebral cortex, which sends impulses to the muscles of the arms, trunk, and legs, lies just anterior to the **sensory area** of the corresponding parts of the body (Fig. 25-15). Direct stimulation of this motor region produces convulsive movements in the different body parts, according to the focal point of the applied stimulus. Such movements tend to simulate the convulsions that are commonly recognized in epilepsy; it is generally agreed that some forms of epilepsy represent an abnormal hyperexcitability of the neurons of the motor area of the cerebral cortex.

The neurons of the motor area possess very elongate axons that pass downward through the brain stem to all levels of the spinal cord. These axons form a compact bundle of fibers, called the **pyramidal tract,** that begin to cross over in the lower part of the brain stem, at the level of the **pons** (Fig. 25-12). Thus the pyramidal fibers from one side of the cortex finally reach the motor neurons of the various spinal nerves *on the*

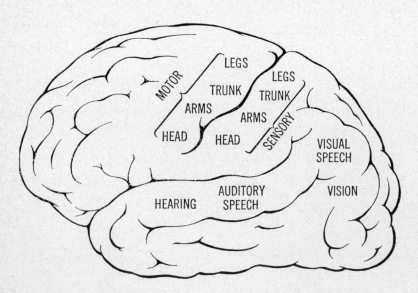

Fig. 25-15. Lateral surface of the left cerebral cortex of man, showing the sensory and motor areas that directly connect with the lower parts of the nervous system.

opposite side of the body. Injury to the spinal cord, therefore, results in serious motor impairments, in addition to the sensory losses mentioned previously. If only one side of the cord is crushed, all the muscles of that side, in segments below the level of the damage, are divorced from the higher centers and cannot be utilized for voluntary movements. The paralysis is not complete, however, since below the level of the injury, the intrasegmental and intersegmental reflex arcs are still intact, permitting the fulfillment of local reflexes after the animal has recovered from a "temporary shock," which lasts for some hours after the injury.

The Autonomic Nerves: Visceral Reflexes. The responses of the internal organs, in the digestive, respiratory, urogenital, and circulatory systems, are performed mainly through the agency of visceral muscle and glands, or, in the case of the heart, by cardiac muscle. These **visceral effectors** differ from skeletal muscles, in that each receives a *double* set of *motor fibers* from the central nervous system. One set of fibers comes to the organ by way of the **sympathetic nerves,** and the other fibers by way of the **parasympathetic nerves.** Moreover, the sympathetic and parasympathetic fibers always antagonize each other as to their action upon the visceral organ. Thus if one set of fibers augments activity, the other invariably depresses activity in the organ, as may be seen in Table 25-2.

By means of such a mutually antagonistic action, the sympathetic and parasympathetic nerves exert a joint control in all visceral reflexes; and thus it is convenient to designate the sympathetic and parasympathetic nerves collectively as the **autonomic nervous system** (Fig. 25-16). Actually the autonomic system is just a physiological subdivision of the peripheral nervous system, and the autonomic nerves, like other peripheral nerves, depend upon the brain and spinal cord for *central connections* in the completion of all reflex arcs. Visceral reflexes, however, generally have their association centers in the brain stem (medulla), and visceral reflexes seldom reach the level of consciousness, or voluntary control. Thus the rhythm of the

Table 25-2—Action of the Autonomic Nerves

Effector Organs	*Sympathetic* (**Adrenergic**) *Nerves (Action of)*	*Parasympathetic* (**Cholinergic**) *Nerves (Action of)*
Digestive tract (stomach, small intestine, colon, rectum)	Depresses activity; slows peristalsis; decreases tone	Augments activity; accelerates peristalsis; increases tone
Heart	Augments activity; strengthens and accelerates the beat	Depresses; weakens and slows the beat
Blood vessels, especially the arteries and arterioles of skin and viscera	Augments tone; vasoconstriction; elevates blood pressure	Depresses tone; vasodilation; lowers blood pressure
Muscle fibers in walls of the bronchi and other respiratory passages	Depresses; dilates passages; easier breathing	Augments tone; constricts passages; harder breathing
Iris muscle fibers in eye	Depress tone; dilates pupil	Augments tone; constricts pupil
Urinary bladder	Depresses tone; dilates bladder	Augments tone; constricts bladder
Hair erector muscle	Augments tone; erects the hair	Depresses tone; hairs lie flat
Sweat glands	Augments secretion; profuse perspiration	Depresses secretion; scanty perspiration

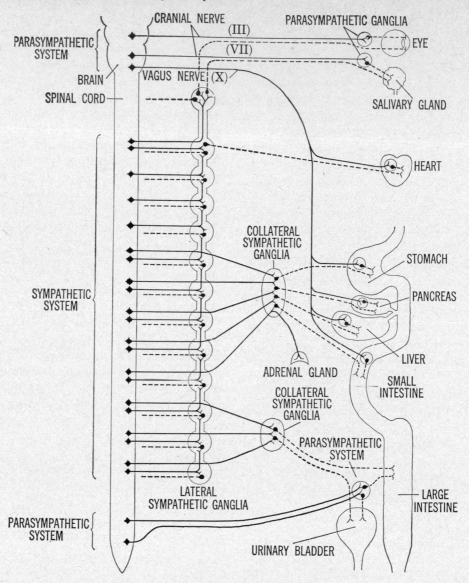

PARASYMPATHETIC SYSTEM

BRAIN

SPINAL CORD

SYMPATHETIC SYSTEM

PARASYMPATHETIC SYSTEM

CRANIAL NERVE

(III)

(VII)

VAGUS NERVE (X)

PARASYMPATHETIC GANGLIA

EYE

SALIVARY GLAND

HEART

COLLATERAL SYMPATHETIC GANGLIA

STOMACH

PANCREAS

LIVER

ADRENAL GLAND

SMALL INTESTINE

COLLATERAL SYMPATHETIC GANGLIA

PARASYMPATHETIC SYSTEM

LATERAL SYMPATHETIC GANGLIA

LARGE INTESTINE

URINARY BLADDER

Fig. 25-16. Distribution and connections of the autonomic nervous system. The heavy lines represent preganglionic fibers; the dotted lines, postganglionic fibers.

heartbeat, or the peristaltic movements of the gastrointestinal tract, although regulated by reflexes, cannot be controlled on a volitional basis.

One peculiar feature of the autonomic nerves lies in the fact that *motor* impulses, leaving the spinal cord or brain, reach the effector organ, not by way of a single neuron, as in the case of the skeletal muscles, but always by a relay of *two* neurons. In every case the autonomic nerve is interrupted by a motor ganglion in which the **preganglionic neurons** establish synaptic connections with a second relay of **postganglionic neurons** (Fig. 25-16). Each preganglionic neuron transmits its impulses to several or many postganglionic nerve cells, and this arrangement tends to spread visceral responses rather diffusely, making them less precisely localized than somatic reactions. In the autonomic system, all preganglionic fibers are covered by myelin sheaths, but all postganglionic fibers are nonmyelinated.

Most of the ganglia of the **sympathetic** system are **lateral ganglia,** which lie in close proximity to the roots of the spinal nerves, in the so-called **sympathetic chain.** This ganglionated strand of nerve tissue extends along the vertebral column on either side of the body, from the neck, through the thorax, to the abdomen (Fig. 25-16). A few of the sympathetic ganglia, such as the **coeliac** and other **collateral ganglia,** lie in the abdominal mesentery, some distance from the cord. In either case, however, each sympathetic ganglion exchanges numerous fibers with the nearest spinal nerve. As may be seen in Figure 25-13, some of these fibers are sensory fibers derived from receptors in the visceral organs; others are preganglionic fibers passing to the lateral or collateral ganglia; while the rest are postganglionic fibers, which return from the lateral ganglion to the spinal nerve. Thus each spinal nerve distributes quite a number of sympathetic fibers to the visceral effectors (arterial walls, sweat glands, and hair-erection muscles) in each segment of the body wall. From the collateral ganglia, however, all the postganglionic fibers proceed to the various visceral organs by way of a number of relatively fine nonmyelinated nerves (Fig. 25-16).

The preganglionic fibers of the **parasympathetic system** are *mainly* distributed by the vagus nerves. This tenth and largest pair of the cranial nerves arises from the brain stem and passes posteriorly through the neck, thorax, and abdomen, sending branches to the heart, respiratory organs, and to the gastrointestinal tract as far as the small intestine. The vagus, however, is not the only channel for transmitting parasympathetic fibers to the visceral effectors. The lens, pupil, and salivary glands receive their parasympathetic innervation via other cranial nerves (III and VII); while the urogenital organs and the large intestine are supplied by parasympathetic nerves originating from the spinal cord in the **pelvic region,** close to the posterior termination of the cord (Fig. 25-16).

The preganglionic fibers of the vagus and other parasympathetic nerves establish synaptic contact with postganglionic fibers in the **parasympathetic ganglia,** which lie very close to the organs that receive the innervation (Fig. 25-16). Thus all postganglionic neurons in the parasympathetic group possess relatively short axons, which terminate in contact with effector cells in some particular visceral organ.

As stated previously (p. 455) the synaptic transmitter, or excitatory substance, of the postganglionic neurons of the parasympathetic system is acetylcholine; whereas the equivalent agency in the sympathetic system is noradrenaline.

BEHAVIOR

To analyze the full pattern of responses in the individual animal—in short, to study the behavior of the organism as a whole—would be to usurp the subject matter of **psychology.** Consequently the present account of behavior will be limited very strictly to considerations of general biological importance.

The modern tendency is to explain all **discontinuous responses** (p. 189) in terms of the intricate interconnections of the nervous system. The nervous system consists essentially of a very extensive network of reflex arcs, some simple and others very complex, but all interrelated both anatomically and functionally, via a multitude of association neurons in the brain, spinal cord, and affiliated ganglia.

Vertebrate animals are able to perform quite a number of fairly complex, though highly standardized, responses, even without any preliminary training or conditioning. The human infant, for example, immediately begins responding to the manifold stimuli of the environment by performing a number of complex actions, and the child executes these responses just as well initially as subsequently. The infant starts breathing; it sucks upon the breast; it salivates when anything is placed in the mouth; and so forth. In fact, even before birth, while the fetus is *in utero*, many visceral responses, such as the heartbeat and the peristaltic movements of the gastrointestinal tract—and some somatic responses, such as movements of the arms and legs—begin to take place at appropriate stages in development.

Unconditioned Reflexes. Regardless of complexity, any standardized response to a standardized stimulation, which can be executed by an organism without benefit of previous experience, is called an **unconditioned reflex.** In higher animals such responses indicate the existence of a number of *highly conductive* **reflex arcs,** in which the synapses offer virtually no resistance to impulses, *even in the absence of the facilitating effects of previous transmission.*

Depending on complexity, **unconditioned reflexes** are classified as (1) **simple unconditioned reflexes,** which involve only a few quite localized receptors and effectors; and (2) **compound unconditioned reflexes**—formerly known as **instincts**—which involve many receptors and effectors, acting in sequence. Essentially, it is thought, compound reflexes represent a train of interlocking simple reflexes, each touched off by its predecessor. However, the line of distinction between simple and compound reflexes is quite arbitrary. In man, for example, coughing, salivating, and swallowing are usually classified as simple reflexes, whereas sucking, chewing, and spitting out disagreeable material are regarded as compound reflexes.

A conspicuous feature of unconditioned reflexes is their survival value to the organism. In most cases, they serve in one way or another to secure the welfare of the individual and to foster the perpetuation of the species. This characteristic, however, does not imply any consciousness on the part of the animal as to the consequences of its acts. It merely means that different organisms have developed a structural and functional capacity to execute certain self-preserving responses, and these organisms continue to survive and perpetuate themselves, each according to its kind.

The lack of any "conscious purpose" in unconditioned reflexes is clearly shown by the fact that their "usefulness" applies only under the natural conditions of the animal's age-old habitat. When some feature of the natural environment is changed, the animal still responds in the same old way to the same old stimulus, even though the response may now be useless, or even injurious. Moths, for example, always fly toward the light. Under primeval conditions this was undoubtedly a useful response, since the moth is a nocturnal flyer and depends upon white or light-colored flowers as a source of nectar. But with the introduction of fires and lamps into the moth's environment, this response became virtually suicidal—but nevertheless it persists. The moth flies into the flame for the same reason that it flies to a white flower —not because it knows the flower to be nutritious, nor because it thinks the flame to be a flower—but because its eyes, nervous system, and wing muscles are so connected that an unequal illumination of the two eyes sets up reactions that automatically turn it toward the light. Likewise, a majority of the complex and seemingly purposeful actions of lower vertebrates—such as fish, amphibians and reptiles—are machinelike and unvarying in nature. And even in the birds and mammals, many of the reactions most essential to survival are purely unconditioned, that is, quite independent of experience and learning.

Modifiability of Behavior: Conditioned Reflexes. In higher animals especially, the same stimulus does not invariably elicit the same response, and there are a number of factors that may, to a greater or lesser extent, modify the outcome of a given stimulation. *Combinations* of two or more stimuli, applied simultaneously or in close succession, often change the response that would be evoked by either one alone. This change may consist in (1) **reinforcement,** a stronger response than usual; (2) **inhibition,** a weaker response, or none at all; or (3) **modification,** a different response than either stimulus alone would evoke. All these phenomena depend upon the particular connections, within the nervous system, of the reflex arcs involved, and also upon the time and intensity relations of the nerve impulses traversing the various arcs. Thus the behavior of an individual is determined not by a single stimulus, but by the entire *situation,* that is, the total pattern of stimuli impinging on the animal at any given moment.

All learned responses of an animal, the fulfillment of which depends upon previous training or experience, fall into the category of **conditioned reflexes.** Such conditioned reflexes are frequently extremely complex and indirect; and the many factors that determine this type of behavior are difficult to investigate experimentally. However, the classical experiments of Pavlov, which were mentioned previously (p. 307), have served to initiate many experiments on the learning process.

Conditioned responses are superimposed upon the unconditioned reflexes of an animal, such as a dog, by a process of substituting one kind of stimulation for another. In an unconditioned dog, for example, only the actual presence of food or other material in the mouth will elicit the salivation reflex; but if another kind of stimulus is applied each time the animal is fed, soon the foreign stimulus alone will evoke a flow of saliva. In other words, the dog has "learned" to salivate at the sound of a dinner bell, or at the smell of a tasty morsel—or whenever any other stimulus, however bizarre, is applied repeatedly, in close association with the original stimulus.

The capacity to form conditioned reflexes is more highly developed in vertebrates as compared to invertebrate animals, and in birds and mammals as compared to lower vertebrates. Among vertebrates, the conditioning potentiality is definitely related to the development of the cerebral cortex; and if this part of the brain is destroyed, the animal loses almost all previously acquired learning as well as virtually all capacity for forming new conditioned responses. Apparently impulses from all the receptors of the body converge upon the association neurons of the cerebral cortex and tend to be shunted into motor pathways that at the moment are superexcitable because they are simultaneously engaged in carrying out some well-established reflex. Consequently other stimuli acting simultaneously with an original stimulus tend to establish an associative connection with the original stimulus. Furthermore, any repetition of this association tends to *facilitate* the new synaptic connections and to establish the "habit" of the new response.

Birds and mammals stand strikingly above all other animals in their ability to learn. Among mammals, an especially high degree of educability is found in some of the larger carnivores and herbivores, such as dogs, horses, and elephants. These animals are not intelligent because they are domesticated— they are domesticated because of their intelligence, that is, their ability to be trained. The highest development of intelligence, however, is found in the primates—monkeys, apes, and man. There can be no doubt that monkeys—even after making all due allowance for their enormous advantage in the possession of hands—display distinctly more intelligence than four-footed mammals. Monkeys quickly learn to employ tools as a means to an end—for example, a stick to secure food that is out of reach. Monkeys also display more initiative and curiosity than other animals, and in these features their behavior approaches that of man. Moreover, the anthropoid apes—which resemble man most closely in the structure of their bodies and especially of their brains—are more nearly "human" in their behavior than the tailed monkeys.

Behavior of Man: Language. An older point of view regarded human behavior as sharply distinct from that of other animals. Man was said to act by "reason," in contrast to the instinctive behavior of other animals; but no such sharp distinction can be drawn. Man displays many simple reflex and instinctive responses, while many of the higher animals show more or less intelligent behavior. On the other hand, many writers, in attempts to minimize the differences between human and other animal behavior, have perpetuated highly exaggerated accounts and utterly uncritical interpretations of the "intelligent" behavior of animals. The truth probably lies in the other direction: that is, far more of human behavior than is commonly supposed is purely instinctive and automatic. Nevertheless, there is an enormous gap between the achievements of man—at least of civilized man—and those of other animals. The essential clue to this difference seems to lie in one peculiar feature of human behavior: language. Every known race of man has some kind of language; and there is no good evidence that any other animal has developed any truly equivalent system of communication.

A word is both a response and a stimulus. On the one hand, a word is a conditioned reflex that may be elicited by a variety of substituted stimuli; and on the other hand, it is a stimulus that has been substituted for many other stimuli. In short, a word is a relatively simple motor act that "sums up" a vast amount of experience. A word is a vehicle of experience; and this distinguishes words from purely instinctive or emotional sounds, which are uttered by many animals. Language consists not merely of words, but of combinations of words. The separate words are, in general, purely imitative, but the word combinations are largely original. Every conditioned reflex involves an element of originality, in a sense; that is, it represents a new combination of stimuli and responses, so far as the individual animal is concerned. Thus language may be described as a mode of behavior that enormously extends the range of original responses in all mankind.

TEST QUESTIONS

1. Explain how the nerve impulse (a) differs from, and (b) is similar to, the state of excitation in cells generally.
2. Discuss the fatigue susceptibilities of nerve and muscle and relate this problem to the relative rates of oxidative metabolism.
3. Differentiate between the members of each pair of terms:
    a. the absolute and relative refractory periods
    b. the relative refractory period and the supernormal period
    c. centralized and decentralized nervous systems
    d. the peripheral and central parts of the nervous system
    e. afferent and efferent nerve fibers
    f. neurons and protoneurons
    g. a nerve fiber and a neuron
    h. axons and dendrons
4. Nerve impulses do not grow weaker as they are transmitted along an axon. Explain this statement carefully.

5. Differentiate between the members of each pair of terms:
    a. a reflex arc and a reflex act
    b. unilateral and bilateral reflexes
    c. intrasegmental and intersegmental reflexes
    d. association neurons and other neurons
6. What are the synapses and why have synapses been studied so intensively?
7. Explain the interrelationships between the synapses and the law of "forward direction."
8. Discuss briefly each of the following topics in relation to the behavior of an intact animal: (a) synaptic block; (b) synaptic resistance; (c) synaptic summation; (d) synaptic fatigue; (e) facilitation.
9. Explain how electron microscopy has contributed to our knowledge about synapses.
10. Explain the meaning and significance of the following terms: (a) neurosecretions, or neurohumors; (b) synaptic transmitters; (c) acetylcholine; (d) cholinesterase; (e) cholin-

ergic; (f) noradrenaline; (g) adrenergic; (h) microvesicles, or microsecretory vesicles; (i) serotonin; (j) factor S; (k) factor I.

11. Discuss the various functions of the cell body and dendritic regions of neurons.

12. Explain the terms: (a) pacemaker potential; (b) decremental conduction; (c) generator potential.

13. How does the central nervous system of a vertebrate such as man differ from that of an invertebrate such as the earthworm in regard to: (a) general structure and position in the body; (b) relative development of the "higher centers"; (c) general function?

14. Differentiate between gray matter and white matter: (a) in general; (b) in the spinal cord; (c) in the cerebrum and cerebellum.

15. Differentiate between: (a) somatic and visceral reflexes; (b) the cranial and the spinal nerves; (c) the dorsal and ventral roots of a spinal nerve.

16. Carefully describe the results of each of the following operations:
    a. cutting the dorsal root of one spinal nerve
    b. cutting the ventral root of a spinal nerve
    c. a right hemisection of the spinal cord
    d. cutting the olfactory nerves (cranial nerve, I)
    e. cutting the facial nerves (VII)
    f. cutting the vagus nerves (X)

17. Differentiate between:
    a. the functions of the cerebrum and the cerebellum
    b. the sensory and motor areas of the cerebral cortex
    c. sensory and motor tracts
    d. the pain-temperature tracts and the touch-pressure tracts

18. How do visceral reflexes differ from somatic reflexes in regard to: (a) the innervation of the effector organs; (b) myelination of the motor nerve fibers?

19. Explain the antagonistic action of the sympathetic and parasympathetic nerves, using the heart and the digestive tract to exemplify the discussion.

20. Differentiate between:
    a. lateral and collateral ganglia
    b. sympathetic and parasympathetic ganglia
    c. preganglionic and postganglionic neurons

21. Describe an experiment that demonstrates the existence of: (a) a parasympathetic excitatory substance (acetylcholine); (b) a sympathetic neurohumor (noradrenaline).

22. Distinguish clearly between (a) simple and compound reflexes and (b) conditioned and unconditioned reflexes, citing at least one example in each case.

23. Briefly discuss the relations between:
    a. unconditioned responses and the survival of a species
    b. facilitation and the establishment of conditioned reflexes
    c. the development of the cerebral cortex and an animal's capacity to form conditioned reflexes

FURTHER READINGS

1. *Forced Movements, Tropisms, and Animal Conduct,* by Jacques Loeb; Philadelphia, 1918.

2. *The Integrative Action of the Nervous System,* by C. S. Sherrington, New York, 1947.

3. *Lectures on Conditioned Reflexes,* by I. P. Pavlov; New York, 1928.

4. Articles by Donald Kennedy, Ernst Florey and Theodore H. Bullock in *American Zoologist,* vol. 2, no. 1, 1962.

PART IV-*Heredity and Evolution*

26-*Heredity*

THE DISTINCTIVE **individuality** of each living thing depends not only upon parental heritage but also upon environmental experience. However, the potency of the environment in shaping the form and function of each individual will be disregarded for the present, and all attention will be focused upon the factors of heredity.

IDENTIFYING THE MACHINERY OF HEREDITARY TRANSMISSION

Heredity depends upon the protoplasmic continuity between parent and offspring. But all that a parent generally contributes to the offspring is a small sample of its own protoplasm, usually in the form of a single gamete cell.

Excluding asexual modes of reproduction, which will be considered separately, only the gametes establish continuity between parents and offspring, and consequently the mechanism of hereditary transmission must operate across this exceedingly slender protoplasmic bridge.

The processes of sexual reproduction indicate very clearly that the hereditary potency of the cytoplasm is not nearly as great as that of the nucleus. In a vast majority of organisms, the male gamete contains virtually no cytoplasm as compared with the large amount present in the egg—and yet the male and female gametes contribute equally to the hereditary qualities of the offspring. This indicates that the machinery of inheritance lies mainly in the nuclei—or more particularly in the chromosomes—of the gamete cells. The chromosomes, in fact, are the only entities that are always passed on in *equal* quantities from parents to offspring in sexual organisms generally.

Modern genetics began to develop very rapidly in 1910 under the leadership of Thomas Hunt Morgan, and since that time geneticists in all parts of the world have cooperated in establishing the **chromosome theory of heredity.** In fact there now exists a vast amount of experimental evidence that proves conclusively that (1) chromosomes are the essential agencies in the transmission of hereditary traits; (2) each chromosome is made up, essentially, of a linear series of definitely localized units, called **genes;** (3) each gene is a decisive factor in determining one or more hereditary qualities in every individual organism.

CONTINUITY OF THE GERM CELLS

In multicellular species, some but not all of the cells retain the potentiality of transmitting their chromosomes to the cells of the next generation. These **germ cells** stand in contrast to the **somatic cells**, which cannot perpetuate their chromosomes beyond the lifetime of the individual organism. The somatic cells of an organism are destined to die with the individual, but the germ cells are potentially immortal (Fig. 26-1). Only the germ cells establish continuity from individual to individual in each successive generation, and *only changes in the germ cells are effective in changing the hereditary destiny of the species.* Accordingly, it is necessary to follow the germ cells and to determine how these cells transmit their chromosomes to the gametes and to the offspring.

Among sexual organisms, any cell that stands in line of descent of the eggs or sperm is a germ cell. The germ cells include not only the sperm and eggs but also the zygote and some of the cells of the developing embryo, even before the gonads become differentiated (Fig. 26-2). These early **primordial germ cells** eventually come to lie in the gonads— but now they are called by a different name. In the gonads, while they are multiplying by repeated **mitotic** divisions, the germ cells of an animal are called **gonia**; more specifically, in the testis of the male animal the germ cells are called **spermatogonia**, in contrast to the **oögonia**, which lie in the ovaries of the female.

Gametogenesis: Maturation of the Gametes. In the gonads of the *adult,* the eggs and sperm begin to undergo **maturation**; and during maturation the chromosomes of the ripening eggs and sperm go through similar stages of development. However, there are

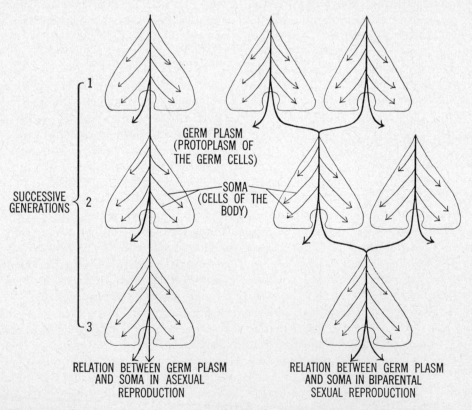

SUCCESSIVE GENERATIONS

1

2

3

GERM PLASM (PROTOPLASM OF THE GERM CELLS)

SOMA (CELLS OF THE BODY)

RELATION BETWEEN GERM PLASM AND SOMA IN ASEXUAL REPRODUCTION

RELATION BETWEEN GERM PLASM AND SOMA IN BIPARENTAL SEXUAL REPRODUCTION

Fig. 26-1. The germ cells maintain continuity from generation to generation, whether the reproduction is sexual or asexual.

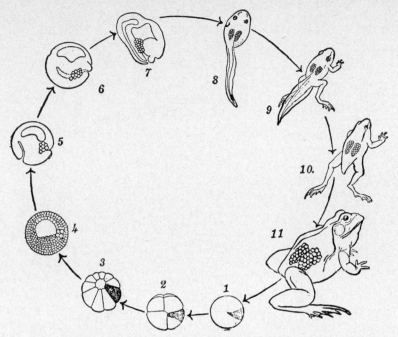

Fig. 26-2. Continuity of the germ cells in the life cycle of the frog. 1, the fertile egg—the shaded area becomes cytoplasm of the germ cell; 2, 8-celled stage; 3, 32-celled stage; 4, blastula showing 4 germ cells; 5-7, successive stages in the development of the gastrula, showing germ cells; 8-10, metamorphosing frogs; 11, mature frog with eggs in ovary ready to be discharged. (After Conklin. From Guyer, *Animal Biology*. Permission of Harper and Row.)

certain differences, and this makes it necessary to give a separate description of the maturation of the two kinds of gametes.

A very brief description of the maturation of the sperm was given previously (Chap. 3), but now it is necessary to follow the process more closely. In the testes, when a spermatogonium stops multiplying by mitosis and begins to grow, it is a sign that the **meiotic divisions** are about to occur (Fig. 26-3). Now each germ cell is called a **primary spermatocyte** and each primary spermatocyte is destined to form *four* sperm (Fig. 26-3). In fact, the growth of the primary spermatocyte proceeds simultaneously with the long prophase of the first meiotic division; and during this growth stage the pairs of chromosomes engage themselves in **synapsis** (Fig. 26-4). After growth and synapsis, the first and second meiotic divisions usually proceed quite rapidly. First the two **secondary spermatocytes**

are formed, and then each secondary spermatocyte divides. This second of the meiotic divisions forms the four **spermatids,** which soon grow tails and become actively motile sperm (Fig. 26-3).

The diploid nature of the germ cells prior to the meiotic divisions follows from the fact that they are derived entirely by mitosis from the original zygote that produced all the cells of the individual. But when the meiotic divisions have been completed all the sperm are haploid (Fig. 26-4). The single haploid set of chromosomes that is carried by the sperm represents the essential contribution of the male parent toward the hereditary constitution of the offspring.

Oögenesis differs from **spermatogenesis** mainly as to the behavior of the cytoplasm during the meiotic divisions. In the case of the ripening egg (Fig. 26-3), the growth period, during which synapsis occurs, is more

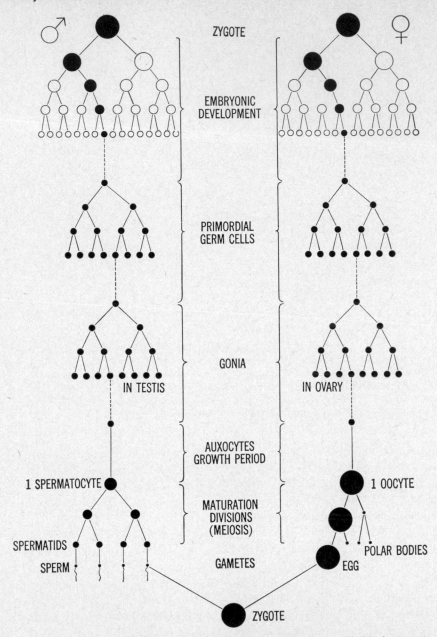

Fig. 26-3. History of the germ cells in multicellular animals; germ cells black, somatic cells white. The number of cell divisions is actually much greater than shown here (except in the maturation period). (Adapted from Wilson.)

pronounced; and due to an accumulation of yolk, the primary oöcyte becomes very much larger than the primary spermatocyte. But more important still is the fact that the two meiotic divisions that follow are highly unequal as to the apportionment of cyto-plasm among the four resulting daughter cells (Fig. 26-3). One cell, which is the *ripe egg*, receives virtually all the accumulation of yolk and cytoplasm, whereas the **polar bodies** receive only an insignificant fraction (Fig. 26-5). Thus the ripe egg, if fertilized, is

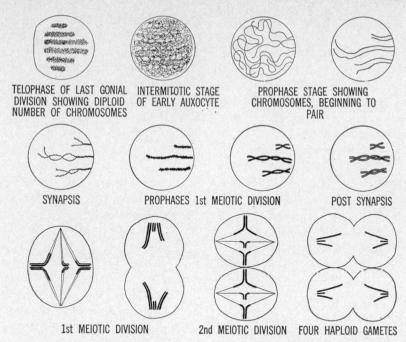

TELOPHASE OF LAST GONIAL DIVISION SHOWING DIPLOID NUMBER OF CHROMOSOMES

INTERMITOTIC STAGE OF EARLY AUXOCYTE

PROPHASE STAGE SHOWING CHROMOSOMES, BEGINNING TO PAIR

SYNAPSIS

PROPHASES 1st MEIOTIC DIVISION

POST SYNAPSIS

1st MEIOTIC DIVISION

2nd MEIOTIC DIVISION   FOUR HAPLOID GAMETES

Fig. 26-4.   Diagram of meiosis in a cell possessing three pairs of chromosomes.

equipped to develop into an embryo, but the polar bodies are not.

The behavior of the chromosomes during the maturation of the eggs is precisely the same as it is during the maturation of the sperm (Fig. 26-4). Consequently the net result of oögenesis is the production of four haploid cells, but only one of these can function as the female gamete. When fertilization occurs, this ripened egg transmits its haploid set of chromosomes to the nucleus of the zygote, and this is the essential donation of the female parent to the genetic constitution of the offspring.

Free Assortment of Chromosomes during Meiosis. As was emphasized previously (p. 51), the fact that only *one* division of the chromosomes occurs during the *two* meiotic divisions results inevitably in a reduction of the chromosome number of the gametes as compared to the other cells of the animal. At one point or another during meiosis the

Fig. 26-5.   Second polar body forming at the surface of the maturing egg of the whitefish. This photograph shows the telophase of the second meiotic division. Note that the polar body (above) receives a full (haploid) set of chromosomes, but only a very small fraction of the cytoplasm. Most of the cytoplasm is retained by the ripe egg cell. (Copyright, General Biological Supply House, Inc.)

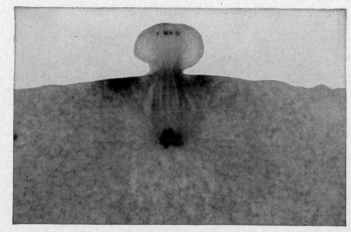

members of each homologous pair of chromosomes become separated from each other, and each mature gamete comes to possess just a single member of each chromosome pair. It is, however, entirely a matter of chance as to which member of any chromosome pair goes to a particular gamete, and the various possibilities occur with equal frequency.

Take for example the sperm formed from spermatogonia possessing two pairs of chromosomes, namely:

$$A\,a$$
$$B\,b$$

During spermatogenesis, this type of germ cell can produce only four *kinds* of sperm, namely:

$$A \quad a \quad A \quad a$$
$$B \quad b \quad b \quad B$$

These sperm will be produced in equal numbers, since each chromosome has the same chance of finding its way into any of the gametes. Similarly, oögonia with two pairs of chromosomes can produce only four kinds of eggs, with corresponding combinations of chromosomes.

But if the spermatogonia (or oögonia) possess *three* pairs of chromosomes, namely:

$$A\,a$$
$$B\,b$$
$$C\,c$$

the following eight kinds of gametes will be produced in equal numbers:

$$A \quad a \quad A \quad a \quad A \quad a \quad A \quad a$$
$$B \quad b \quad B \quad b \quad b \quad B \quad b \quad B$$
$$C \quad c \quad c \quad C \quad C \quad c \quad c \quad C$$

When an individual animal produces eggs or sperm, therefore, the several chromosomes that were received from its maternal and paternal parents are free to assort themselves at random in the next generation of gametes; however, *one member of every pair of chromosomes is always (normally) represented in every gamete produced.*

In *plants,* the origin of the haploid gametes is less direct than in animals, but essentially the same system of transmitting chromosomes from parent to offspring is at work. Among plants, fertilization does not take place immediately after meiosis. Instead, a whole haploid generation, the gametophyte generation, intervenes—and the diploid condition is not restored until the gametes unite, forming a zygote and initiating the sporophyte generation. This peculiarity, however, does not fundamentally alter the processes of heredity, which are essentially similar in all sexual organisms.

BREEDING EXPERIMENTS

The first accurately controlled and thoroughly documented breeding experiments were published in 1866 by Gregor Mendel. This Austrian monk worked with garden peas; and by strictly controlling the pollination of his plants, Mendel discovered a well-defined pattern that governed the transmission of a number of hereditary features, such as color, height, hardiness, etc., throughout many successive generations. The importance of Mendel's experiments was not recognized, however, until about 1900. By this time much more had been learned about chromosomes; and now biologists were ready to recognize the crucial role of the chromosomes in the fulfillment of the Mendelian laws.

Genetic experiments presuppose a very accurate knowledge of the stocks that are to be crossed. The aim is to study the transmission of *single hereditary differences,* either separately or in combination, by crossing two stocks and determining the numerical distribution of the hereditary peculiarities among the offspring. But unless the number of differences is relatively small, an analysis of the results becomes very complex. Consequently it was most fortunate that Mendel began his work with a self-pollinating species of plant, in which the original stocks possessed a high degree of genetic homogeneity.

Modern genetics owes a great debt to a

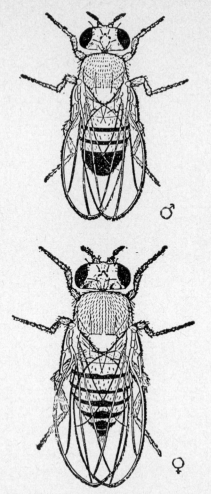

Fig. 26-6. Male and female fruit fly, *Drosophila melanogaster.* (After Morgan. From Guyer, *Animal Biology.* Permission of Harper and Row.)

diminutive animal, *Drosophila melanogaster,* commonly called the fruit fly (Fig. 26-6). Morgan and his students found that *Drosophila* is ideally suited for experimental breeding. At the age of 12 days these little flies begin to breed; and by the end of three weeks a single female can produce 300 offspring. Accordingly, within 3 years it is possible to study more than 60 generations of *Drosophila*—or about as many generations as have accrued to mankind during all the Christian era. Furthermore, many specimens of *Drosophila* can be housed in a single milk bottle; and the food of *Drosophila,* which is mainly yeasts, growing on fermenting ba-

nanas, is a negligible laboratory expense. Because of these advantages, experiments on *Drosophila* have pioneered practically all advances in modern genetics. However, the laws of heredity, as worked out in *Drosophila* and other lower forms, have proved to be generally applicable to man and all other higher organisms.

Mendelian Inheritance: Segregation. The **law of segregation** deals with the transmission of a *single hereditary difference* from parent to offspring in successive generations. Mendel worked out the law of segregation by studying the inheritance of flower color; but our first example will be chosen from a special breed of chicken, the *Andalusian fowl* (Fig. 26-7).

Two stocks of Andalusians have been cultivated for many years: one white and the other black. If these stocks are **inbred,** white to white, or black to black, no change of feather color ever appears: white crossings never (barring mutation) yield anything but white offspring, and black crossings yield only blacks.

If a white hen (or rooster) is crossed to a black mate, *all the offspring* display an intermediate pigmentation—a sort of gray-blue. But if any two of these offspring are inbred, 25 percent of the offspring are pure white, like the one grandparent; 50 percent are blue, like the immediate parents; and 25 percent are pure black, like the other grandparent. Or, to state these results more technically, when the P_1 (first parental) generation of Andalusians are pure white and black respectively, all individuals of the F_1 (first filial) generation will be blue; but the F_2 (second filial) generation, obtained by inbreeding the F_1, consists of white, blue, and black fowl in a ratio of 1:2:1 (Fig. 26-7). Furthermore, by inbreeding the different kinds of F_2 individuals the same results are obtained: whites always give only whites; blacks give only blacks; a white and black yield all blues; and a blue crossed with a blue gives a 1:2:1 ratio of whites, blues, and blacks.

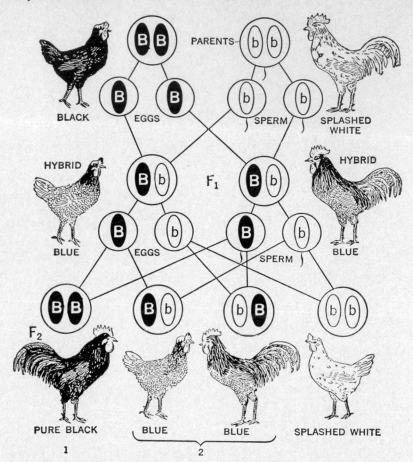

Fig. 26-7. Cross between a splashed white and a black Andalusian fowl. The hybrid is popularly called a "blue" Andalusian fowl. (Jane Wyatt. From MacDougall and Hegner, *Biology*. McGraw-Hill Book Co.)

Provided the **F₁ hybrids** are clearly distinguishable from both of the pure line parents, similar results are always obtained in any **one-factor cross,** in which the mated individuals possess just a single hereditary difference.

The results of this and all other similar breeding experiments can be explained by a very simple hypothesis, which has been substantiated by many lines of evidence. The feather color differences are due to a single **pair of genes** that are localized in a particular pair of homologous chromosomes. Black fowls, when inbred, never give rise to any white offspring, and consequently it is certain that the black stock has *both* of the feather color genes of the same kind (*B*),

which fosters the production of black pigment (Fig. 26-7). Similarly, inbred white fowls always produce only white progeny, so that both of the feather color genes of this stock must be of the same kind (*b*) which is not a pigment producer (Fig. 26-7). Or to phrase these ideas more technically, the black Andalusian is said to be homozygous (*BB*) with reference to the "black gene"; whereas the white fowl is homozygous (*bb*) as to the "white gene." Furthermore, this genic condition obtains in all the diploid cells of the organism, since all the cells have been derived by mitosis from the same fertilized egg.

Granting these assumptions, the results of the breeding experiments follow automatically from the known events of gametogenesis and fertilization—as may be seen in Figure 26-7. As to feather color genes, each of the P_1 fowls can produce only one kind of egg, or sperm, depending on the sex. Consequently all F_1 individuals must be alike; all are **heterozygous** (Bb) as to the feather color genes. But when the F_1 hybrids form gametes, each fowl produces **two kinds of gametes** in equal numbers. Half the eggs and half the sperm must carry the B gene, and half must carry the b gene. Consequently, depending entirely on the chance union of the gametes, the F_2 offspring must be homozygous black (BB), heterozygous (Bb) blue, and homozygous white (bb) in a ratio of 1.2.1 as is indicated in the following **Punnett Square:**

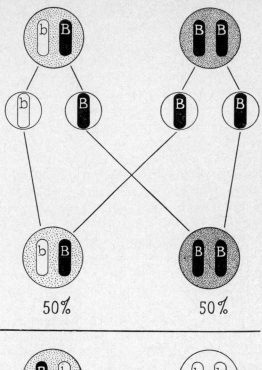

50%   50%

F_1 eggs	B	b	
F_1 sperms B	BB black	Bb blue	} F_2 zygotes
b	Bb blue	bb white	

All other matings among Andalusians can be explained by the same mechanism. A blue hen mated to a black cock produces blues and blacks on a 1:1 basis; and similarly a cross between a blue and a white fowl gives blues and whites in a 1:1 ratio (Fig. 26-8). In fact the chromosome hypothesis has been validated by experiments on a countless number of unit hereditary differences, taken singly and in combination, in practically every kind of plant and animal.

The results so far indicate that a parent transmits hereditary qualities to the offspring through the agency of **discrete material units,** called **genes,** which are borne in the chromosomes of the germ cells. All the diploid cells of the organism are equipped with at least two genes that influence the development of any one characteristic. In exerting its effect, each gene maintains a discrete individuality. Its effect upon the organism may be blended with the effects of other genes, but the gene itself *is not changed* by this association. During meiosis in the succeeding generation, the members of each

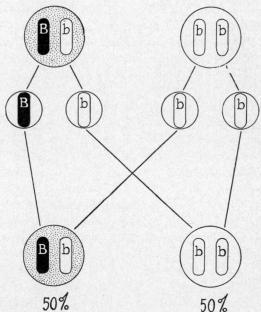

50%   50%

Fig. 26-8. *Above, cross of blue and black Andalusians; Below, cross of blue and white.*

pair of genes become *segregated* into separate gametes, so that each gamete can transmit only one of any given pair of genes.

All of the foregoing ideas are implicit in the work of Mendel, except that Mendel referred to "factors" rather than genes, and Mendel did not realize that the factors are localized in the chromosomes. The central and pre-eminently important concept of Mendelian inheritance is the realization that the genes are **stable self-perpetuating units** that are transmitted, without change, throughout many generations. This means that the characteristics of a stock are not lost by dilution, but tend to appear without alteration generation after generation. Heredity is, indeed, more a matter of "shuffling" (not mixing) the genes during the processes of meiosis and fertilization. Or, in other words, heredity is **particulate**—a process of transmitting discrete particles, which are the genes. This is in sharp contrast to many older concepts of heredity. These older views considered heredity to depend upon a sort of blending process in which inevitably the characteristics of a stock would be further and further attenuated with each succeeding generation of outbreeding.

Allelic Genes. Each gene occupies a **specific locus** in a **specific chromosome** of the species, and all genes occupying this locus in a given pair of chromosomes are said to be **allelic** to each other. Among Andalusians, for example, the "black" gene (*B*) is the allele of the "white" gene (*b*), since these genes occupy corresponding loci in the same chromosome pair. In other words, just as the chromosomes in the diploid cells of the organism occur in **homologous pairs,** so the genes are present as **allelic pairs;** and if one of the alleles of a certain pair has been derived from one of the parents, the other inevitably was derived from the opposite parent.

Dominant Genes. The case of the Andalusian fowl was taken as a first example in Mendelian inheritance because neither of the allelic genes determining feather color obscures the effects of the other. In many cases, however, one member of an allelic pair may totally hide the effects of the other. Such **complete dominance** is shown in the following experiment, which deals with the inherit-

ance of **seed color** in garden peas, a material used by Mendel in his original studies.

Two stocks of the garden pea have been cultivated: one with yellow seeds, the other with green. Both stocks breed true when self-pollinated; that is, no greens are obtained from the yellows, and vice versa. When such stocks are cross pollinated, in either direction, all the F_1 seeds display a yellow color. Proceeding to the F_2 generation, obtained by self-pollinating the plants grown from the yellow seeds, 75 percent of the F_2 seeds are yellow and 25 percent are green.

Figure 26-9 shows that this case is similar to the experiment with the Andalusians, except that one of the gene pair determining seed color, *being dominant,* suppresses the effects of the other (*recessive*) gene. The P_1 green-colored seeds must have been homozygous (having the two genes of the allelic pair identical) as to the "green gene" (*g*) and the yellow-seeded stock must likewise have been homozygous for the "yellow gene" (*G*); otherwise neither of these stocks would breed completely true with successive self-pollinations. Consequently only one kind of gamete is produced by each of the P_1 parents, and all of the F_1 hybrids are inevitably alike (Fig. 26-9). Due to the dominance of G gene, however, all the F_1 seeds display a yellow color. But during meiosis, when segregation occurs, the F_1 plants form two kinds of spores, and subsequently, the same two kinds of gametes (Fig. 26-9). Consequently when the F_1 eggs and sperm combine at random, the F_2 seeds must come out "yellow" and "green" in a ratio of 3:1, as is shown by the following Punnett Square:

F_1 eggs	G	g	
F_1 sperm			
G	GG yellow	Gg yellow	$\Big\}$ F_2 zygotes
g	Gg yellow	gg green	

Genotype vs. Phenotype. Although all *look* alike, not all the yellow-colored F_2 seeds *are* identical in their genetic constitution

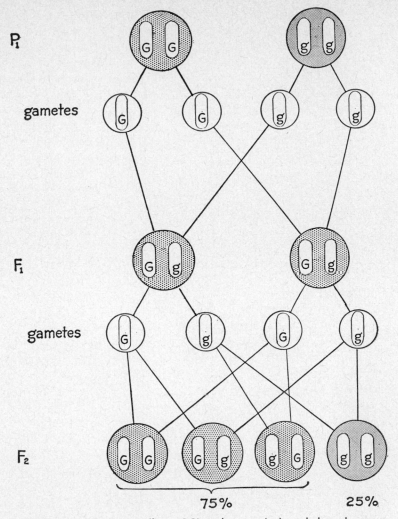

P₁

gametes

F₁

gametes

F₂

75%   25%

Fig. 26-9. Cross between yellow- (GG) and green- (gg) seeded garden peas. Due to the dominance of the "yellow gene" (G), heterozygous (Gg) seeds display the same appearance as homozygous (GG) ones.

(Fig. 26-9). All the F₂ yellow seeds belong to the same **phenotype** (a type of organism judged on the basis of its appearance), but two different **genotypes** (types based on the genic constitution) are represented. Some of the yellow F₂ seeds (Fig. 26-9) are homozygous (*GG*) but others are (*Gg*), or **heterozygous**; that is, the two genes of an allelic pair are not the same.

A dominant-recessive relation between allelic genes is the general rule rather than the exception among animals and plants, although frequently the dominance is not al-together complete. When the dominance is complete, as in the present case, the presence of a single recessive gene cannot be determined by the appearance of its possessor, but only by the breeding potentialities. If the recessive gene is present, the corresponding trait will turn up in a subsequent generation, as soon as the homozygous condition happens to be established at the conception of some future individual. In other words, although organisms of the same phenotype may look alike, they do not *breed* alike, unless they also belong to the same genotype.

In comparing the experiments so far, garden peas give exactly the same results as Andalusians, if one determines the F_2 ratios in terms of genotypes rather than in terms of the phenotypes. The ratio is 1:2:1, with reference to genotypes (BB), (Bb), and (bb) in the Andalusian; and also 1:2:1 for genotypes (GG), (Gg), and (gg) in the garden pea (Figs. 26-7 and 26-9). The different phenotype ratios—1:2:1 for Andalusians, and 3:1 for the peas—merely indicate that among Andalusians, each different phenotype represents a distinct genotype; whereas among garden peas, the yellow phenotype, due to dominance, consists of two genotypes.

Backcrossing to Determine Genotype. The simplest method of determining the genotypes present in a given phenotype is to **backcross** the unknown F_2 individuals. This procedure involves mating the unknown to its *homozygous* **recessive** grandparent (Fig. 26-10). The advantage of the backcross is that it gives

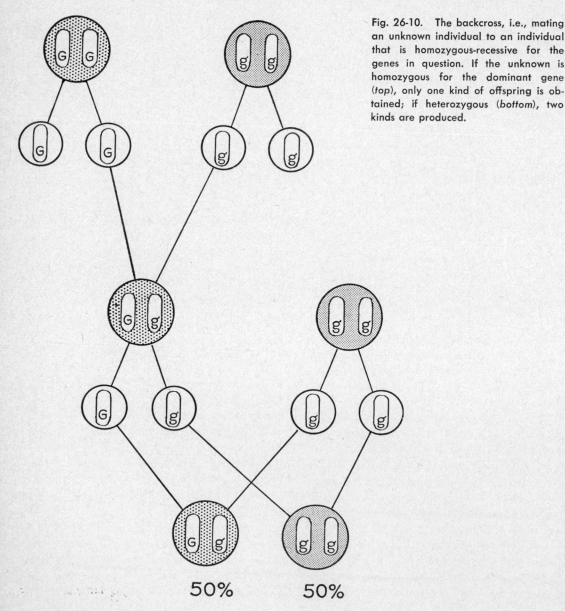

Fig. 26-10. The backcross, i.e., mating an unknown individual to an individual that is homozygous-recessive for the genes in question. If the unknown is homozygous for the dominant gene (*top*), only one kind of offspring is obtained; if heterozygous (*bottom*), two kinds are produced.

50%   50%

very simple results, which are easy to analyze —as may be seen in the following experiment.

Any yellow-seeded F_2 pea (Fig. 26-9), which may be either homozygous (GG) or heterozygous (Gg), is backcrossed to a green-seeded (gg) plant and the offspring are examined. If the unknown is of the (GG) genotype, all the offspring will have yellow seeds, as is shown in Figure 26-9 (the F_1 generation). But if the unknown is genotype (Gg), only half the offspring will be yellow and the other half will be green, as is shown in Figure 26-10. Thus the backcross gives a simple 1:1 ratio, if one deals with a heterozygous individual, as compared to the single product obtained from a homozygous specimen.

Dominance does not in any way alter the mechanics of transmission of a gene, but merely changes the potency of the gene as a determinant of developmental processes in the organism. But how the genes, which are transmitted via the zygote to all the cells of the body, manage to produce their profound effects upon developmental processes is a problem that will be discussed later (p. 529).

Independent Assortment: Two or More Gene Pairs in Separate Chromosome Pairs. During gametogenesis several or many pairs of chromosomes are "dealt out" simultaneously to the maturing gametes; and consequently it is impossible to predict the exact hereditary constitution of any given egg or sperm. But two or three gene pairs, even if *localized in different pairs of chromosomes,* can be followed. This permits the hereditary results to be predicted very accurately, as in the following experiment on the inheritance of *hair characteristics in guinea pigs.*

The experiment starts with two well-known laboratory stocks of the guinea pig. One stock with *black, smooth hair* (Fig. 26-11) has been inbred for many generations without any change in the color and texture of the coat; and the same is true of the other stock, which has *white hair* and a *rough coat.* When crossed, these stocks produce nothing but *black-rough* individuals in the F_1 genera-

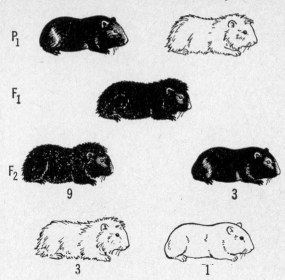

Fig. 26-11. Cross between a black-smooth and a white-rough guinea pig. The F_1 individuals are all black-rough; but when inbred, these produce four kinds of offspring in the proportions: 9 black-rough, 3 black-smooth, 3 white-rough, and 1 white-smooth.

tion. But when inbred, the F_1 pigs give F_2 offspring that are black-rough, black-smooth, white-rough, and white-smooth, respectively, in a ratio of 9:3:3:1.

On the basis of the known history, the genotype of the P_1, black-smooth stock must be $(WW\ ss)$—that is, homozygous for both the "black gene" (W) and for the "smooth gene" (s); and the genotype of the white-rough pigs must be $(ww\ SS)$—that is, homozygous for both the white (w) and rough (S) genes (Fig. 26-12). Consequently each P_1

F_1 eggs	W S	W s	w S	w s	
F_1 sperm W S	WW SS ① black-rough	WW Ss ② black-rough	Ww SS ③ black-rough	Ww Ss ④ black-rough	
W s	WW Ss ② black-rough	WW ss ⑤ black-smooth	Ww Ss ④ black-rough	Ww ss ⑥ black-smooth	F_2 zygotes
w S	Ww SS ③ black-rough	Ww Ss ④ black-rough	ww SS ⑦ white-rough	ww Ss ⑧ white-rough	
w s	Ww Ss ④ black-rough	Ww ss ⑥ black-smooth	ww Ss ⑧ white-rough	ww ss ⑨ white-smooth	

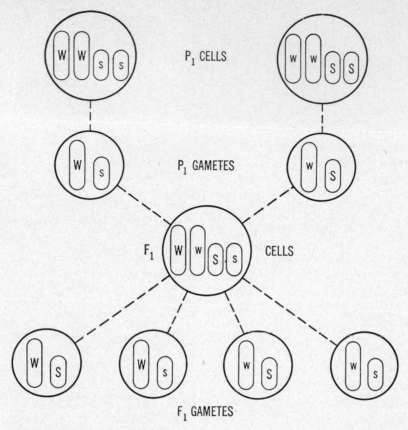

Fig. 26-12. The P_1 and F_1 gametes of a "two-factor cross" involving hair color and hair length in guinea pigs.

stock produces only one kind of gamete, and all the F_1 pigs must be alike (Fig. 26-12). But the F_1 hybrids produce four kinds of eggs, and a similar four kinds of sperm (Fig. 26-12). Consequently when these gametes unite to form the F_2 generation, the combinations shown at bottom of page 487 are obtained.

These combinations account for the phenotype ratio in the F_2 generation, namely:

black-rough		black-smooth
9	:	3
white-rough		white-smooth
3	:	3

and also for the ratio of the *nine* genotypes (which are numbered in the Punnett Square):

① ② ③ ④ ⑤ ⑥ ⑦ ⑧ ⑨
1 : 2 : 2 : 4 : 1 : 2 : 1 : 2 : 1

The random combinations of the F_1 eggs and sperm, as indicated by the Punnett Square, shows that four different genotypes, ①, ②, ③, and ④, are represented in the black-rough phenotype; and this is borne out by backcrossing experiments. Thus, if the unknown is genotype ④, the offspring of the backcross will show a 1:1:1:1 ratio of black-rough, black-smooth, white-rough, and white-smooth, as may be seen in Figure 26-13. Similarly genotypes ①, ②, and ③ may be determined, if the backcross yields, respectively, (1) nothing but black-rough offspring; (2) half and half black-rough and black-smooth; or (3) half and half black-rough and white-rough (as should be worked out by the student).

The complete independence of each of the two gene pairs, during the inheritance

Gametes produced by genotype ④ *Ww Ss*	*W S*	*W s*	*w S*	*w s*
All gametes of a "double recessive" pig are the same.	*w s*			
Offspring of the backcross	genotypes	*Ww Ss* black-rough	*Ww ss* black-smooth	*ww Ss* white-rough	*ww ss* white-smooth
	phenotypes	1 :	1 :	1 :	1

Fig. 26-13. Backcross involving two independently assorting pairs of genes. The backcross is the simplest method by which an unknown genotype may be determined.

of hair color and hair texture in guinea pigs, can also be emphasized from another viewpoint. By dissociating the color and texture characteristics the F_2 offspring may be classified as follows:

$$
\begin{array}{lccccc}
 & \text{rough} & & \text{smooth} & & \\
\text{black} & 9 & + & 3 & = & \dfrac{12}{4} = 3 : 1 \\
\text{white} & 3 & + & 1 & = & \dfrac{}{} \\
\hline
 & 12 & : & 4 & = & 3 : 1
\end{array}
$$

This shows that the 9:3:3:1 ratio of the F_2 generation is obtained merely by superimposing two 3:1 ratios. As to color the ratio is 12 blacks to 4 whites; and as to texture the ratio is 12 roughs to 4 smooths. In other words, the guinea pig experiment is just like the case of the garden pea, except that two pairs of genes, instead of one pair, are being transmitted to the offspring, each independently of the other.

In the organism many allelic pairs of genes are simultaneously undergoing *independent assortment* as they are transmitted from generation to generation, although only gene pairs that are localized in separate pairs of chromosomes are able to assort independently. In the case of an organism that is heterozygous for *three* pairs of genes—for example, *Aa, Bb,* and *Cc*—eight kinds of gametes:

$$
\begin{array}{cccccccc}
A & a & A & a & A & a & A & a \\
B & b & B & b & b & B & b & B \\
C & c & c & C & C & c & c & C
\end{array}
$$

will be formed, provided the allelic genes have loci in *different* chromosomes. Or, to generalize completely, a heterozygous individual will form 2^n classes of gametes in equal numbers, when n is the number of heterozygous allelic genes with loci in different chromosomes.

Variations of Genic Potency. The discussion so far has indicated that each gene exerts an "all-or-none" sort of action—but this is not always true. In fact, quite a few cases are known in which a homozygous pair of recessive genes, or a dominant gene whether homozygous or heterozygous, may fail to find any expression in a certain percentage of the offspring. Such an incomplete **penetrance** of certain genes increases the difficulty of genetic analysis. However, the degree of penetrance may often be increased to approximately 100 percent by suitably adjusting environmental conditions during the embryonic period. In such cases the expected Mendelian ratios are obtained among the offspring.

Variations in **expressivity**, which is somewhat analogous to **penetrance**, have also been observed in some cases. That is to say, certain genes, whether in heterozygous dominant-recessive or homozygous recessive combination, may show large quantitative variations in the degree to which the phenotypic characteristic may appear among the offspring. One recessive gene in *Drosophila*, for example, always (when homozygous) yields a shortening and scalloping of the wing. But the degree of this effect varies widely according to the environmental conditions (especially temperature) that are experienced by the individual fly during its developmental stages. Variations in both penetrance and expressivity, therefore, make the genetic analysis of certain characteristics more difficult. On the other hand, a study of these characteristics is beginning to yield valuable data in regard to the basic manner in which genes operate during embryonic development.

Complementary and Supplementary Genes. In recent years there have been frequent reports indicating that interaction may occur between two or more different gene pairs, and it now is possible to designate two main types of interacting genes. In the case of **complementary genes,** two nonallelic dominants are involved, but neither of these dominants can express itself in the absence of the other. With **supplementary genes,** on the other hand, two dominants are again involved, but in this case the first dominant produces its effect when the other is absent, but the second dominant remains inactive unless the first is present. Obviously genetic experiments dealing with complementary or supplementary gene pairs are apt to yield unusual ratios. Therefore a clarification of these types of genic interaction has helped to solve several rather baffling cases, which previously were regarded as non-Mendelian types of heredity.

Mendel's Laws. The experiments that have been presented up to this point exemplify the first two laws of genetics. These are called Mendel's laws, although Mendel had little knowledge about chromosomes and phrased the laws in different terms.

1. *Law of segregation: the genes of every allelic pair are always segregated into separate gametes, each gene remaining completely uncontaminated by the other.*

2. *Law of independent assortment: provided the gene pairs have loci in dif-*

ferent pairs of chromosomes, they are assorted among the gametes each independently of the others.

Linkage (Dependent Assortment). The number of groups of allelic genes that assort independently cannot be greater than the number of *pairs* of homologous chromosomes of the species (Table 26-1), although the total number of genes in any organism is always much greater than the number of chromosomes. Each chromosome provides loci for many genes, and the genes of each chromosome tend to be *linked* together during their hereditary transmission.

Table 26-1—Chromosome Numbers of Some Familiar Organisms

Common Name	Species	Diploid Number of Chromosomes
Hydra	*Hydra fusca*	12
Pinworm ..	*Parascaris equorum*	2
Fruit fly ..	*Drosophila melanogaster*	8
Dogfish ...	*Scyllium canicula*	24
Bullfrog ..	*Rana catesbiana*	26
Dog	*Canis familiaris*	22
Man	*Homo sapiens*	46
Spirogyra .	*Spyrogyra neglecta*	24
A liverwort	*Riccia lutescens*	8
A moss....	*Bryum capillare*	20
A fern.....	*Pteris aquilina*	64
Corn	*Zea mays*	20

Drosophila melanogaster provides excellent material for the study of linkage, because this species has only four pairs of chromosomes (Fig. 26-14). Thus the several hundred genes that have been identified in the fruit fly all fall into four linkage groups, which correspond to the four chromosomes.

Linkage can be demonstrated by following the transmission of two or more gene pairs having loci in the *same* pair of chromosomes. In *Drosophila* this specification is met by

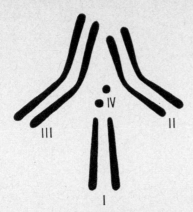

Fig. 26-14. Diploid chromosomes of Drosophila melanogaster (female). I, II, III, and IV indicate the chromosomes that are mapped in Figure 26-19.

two pairs of genes that determine the *body color* and *wing length* of the flies.

In crossing one stock of fly, which self-breeds true for black body and vestigial (reduced) wing, with another true-breeding stock having gray body and large wings, the F_1 individuals are found to have gray bodies and long wings (Fig. 26-15). Accordingly, the gray (*B*) gene dominates black (*b*) and the normal long wing gene (*V*) is dominant to the vestigial (*v*); also both of the P_1 flies are homozygous as to both allelic pairs (Fig. 26-15). Thus when an F_1 hybrid *male* is **backcrossed** to the double recessive *female,* instead of getting four kinds of offspring such as would be obtained if the genes assorted independently, only two kinds of flies are obtained (Fig. 26-15). Fifty percent of the backcross offspring have black bodies and short wings, and the other 50 percent have gray bodies and long wings. In other words, the black body and short wing, and the gray body and long wing, are *linked* as to their inheritance, since both of these gene pairs have loci in the same pair of chromosomes.

Incomplete Linkage: Crossing Over. The foregoing case is called complete linkage because the two gene pairs in the one pair of chromosomes are always inherited together. But complete linkage is a rare phenomenon: it occurs only in the *male Drosophila* and very few other known organisms. A back-

cross between a *female* F_1 hybrid and a double recessive male gives very different results, in that the offspring are of four types: gray-vestigial, gray-long, black-long, and black-vestigial; but these offspring are *not* produced in *equal* numbers (Fig. 26-16). In fact the results of such a cross cannot be stated as a simple ratio, but only on the following *percentage* basis:

gray-long ....41% ⎫
black-vestigial ....41% ⎬ 82%
gray-vestigial .... 9% ⎫
black-long .... 9% ⎬ 18%

In all cases of incomplete linkage, the *original* combinations of characters—those possessed by the P_1 parents—are found in a majority of the offspring: but *new* combinations occur in a minority of the progeny. Moreover, the two majority classes are always equal to each other—as is also true of the minority classes.

To explain these results, attention must be focused upon the F_1 *female* hybrid. This hybrid received chromosomes $\begin{vmatrix} b \\ v \end{vmatrix}$ and $\begin{vmatrix} B \\ V \end{vmatrix}$ from her homozygous parents and transmitted these chromosomes without change to a large majority of the eggs (Fig. 26-16). But some of the eggs of the hybrid fly, due to a shift in the gene loci, received $\begin{vmatrix} b \\ V \end{vmatrix}$ and $\begin{vmatrix} B \\ v \end{vmatrix}$ chromosomes, and these eggs gave rise to the minority classes.

An equal exchange of genes between the chromosomes of a homologous pair is called **crossing over,** and crossing over has important genetic consequences. In fact a careful study of the cross-over phenomenon has yielded a determination of the exact sequence of location of virtually all known genes in the different chromosomes of *Drosophila*.

Crossing over takes place during **synapsis** (p. 479), while the homologous chromosomes are entwined about each other so intimately that in many cases they appear to fuse completely.

After synapsis it usually is not possible to

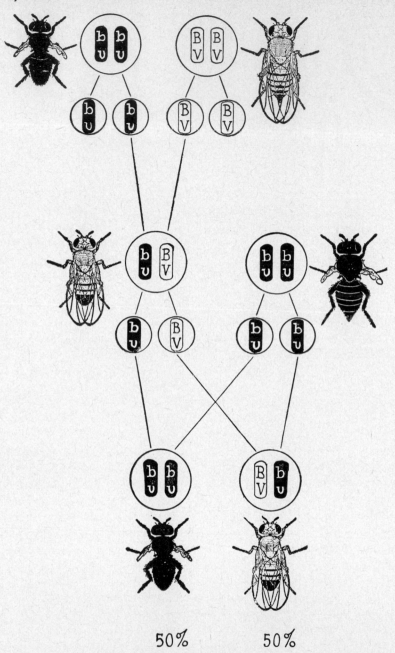

Fig. 26-15. Complete linkage: F₁ male, from cross of black-vestigial and gray-long, back-crossed to black-vestigial female. (Adapted from Morgan.)

see that crossing over has occurred, because usually the members of each synapsing pair are identical in their appearance. But the genetic evidence is altogether convincing and cytological corroboration has been obtained in certain cases. It is known from the law of segregation that the individual genes do not fuse, and that each gene retains its identity without contamination by other genes. But equal blocks of genes may be exchanged between the synapsing mates, as is indicated in Figure 26-17. The two chromo-

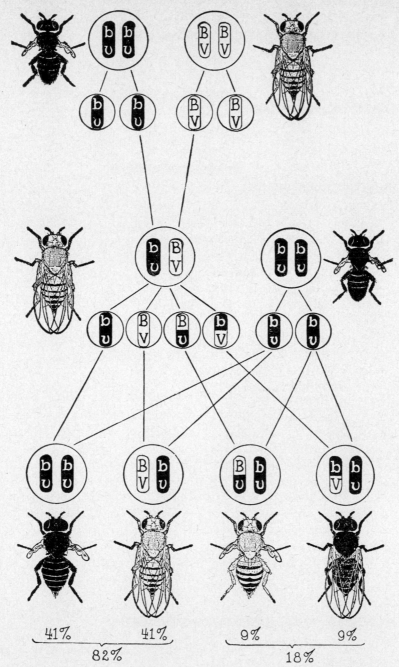

Fig. 26-16. Incomplete linkage: F_1 female, from cross of black-vestigial and gray-long, back-crossed to black-vestigial made. (Adapted from Morgan.)

41%   41%   9%   9%
82%   18%

somes break at corresponding points, and an exchange of connections occurs at the ruptured points. If the break takes place *between* any two genes, the linkage between these genes is changed. In the present case, for example, this change in the linkage relations is from $\begin{vmatrix} B \\ V \end{vmatrix} \begin{vmatrix} b \\ v \end{vmatrix}$ to $\begin{vmatrix} B \\ v \end{vmatrix} \begin{vmatrix} b \\ V \end{vmatrix}$, in a certain percentage of the gametes.

Localization of the Genes in the Chro-

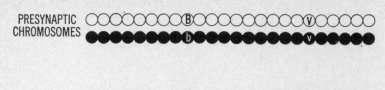

PRESYNAPTIC CHROMOSOMES

SYNAPSIS

POSTSYNAPTIC CHROMOSOMES

Fig. 26-17. Crossing over. If a cross over occurs at a point that lies between the location of the genes B and b and that of the genes V and v, these genes, as the diagram shows, will occur in new combinations in the postsynaptic chromosomes.

mosomes. The frequency of **crossing over**—which technically is called the **cross-over value**—provides a valuable index as to the relative distance between any two pairs of genes having loci on the same pair of chromosomes. Cross-over breaks can occur with equal facility along the length of the synapsing chromosomes. Consequently, the farther apart are the loci of any two genes, the greater is the likelihood that a cross over will occur between them. And conversely, the nearer together are the loci, the less is the chance of a cross over. Moreover, the cross-over values, expressed on a percentage basis, are *additive* when one studies a given series of genes; and this proves that the loci are arranged in a specific linear order in each chromosome. These important facts are shown, for example, by the cross-over values between the genes in chromosomes I of *Drosophila,* which may be summarized as follows:

yellow
$\left. \begin{array}{l} \\ \end{array} \right\} 1.0$
prune
$\left. \begin{array}{l} \\ \end{array} \right\} 0.5 \left. \begin{array}{l} \\ \end{array} \right\} 1.5$
white
$\left. \begin{array}{l} \\ \end{array} \right\} 1.5 \left. \begin{array}{l} \\ \end{array} \right\} 3.0$
facet
$\left. \begin{array}{l} \\ \end{array} \right\} 2.5 \left. \begin{array}{l} \\ \end{array} \right\} 4.0 \left. \begin{array}{l} \\ \end{array} \right\} 5.5$
echinus
$\left. \begin{array}{l} \\ \end{array} \right\} 2.0 \left. \begin{array}{l} \\ \end{array} \right\} 4.5 \left. \begin{array}{l} \\ \end{array} \right\} 7.5$
ruby

Crossing over between two consecutive gene pairs is relatively rare, so that linkage between such genes is almost complete. But between more distantly localized gene pairs cross overs are frequent, although, if the distance is too great, the cross-over values are difficult to analyze—because double (Fig. 26-18), or even triple cross overs may occur.

The mathematical relation displayed by the cross-over values of the yellow to ruby

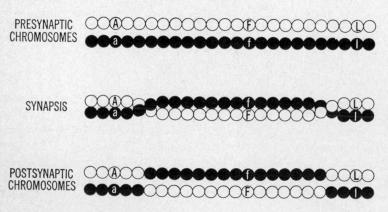

PRESYNAPTIC CHROMOSOMES

SYNAPSIS

POSTSYNAPTIC CHROMOSOMES

Fig. 26-18. Double crossing over. If cross over occurs at the points shown in this diagram, the genes A and L, and also a and l, will occur in their original combinations in the postsynaptic chromosomes; but the cross over will be evidenced by the interchange of the genes F and f at an intermediate locus.

gene series likewise holds true for *all* genes in each of the other three pairs of chromosomes in *Drosophila*. In fact there is *one, and only one*, **linear order** that shows this relation. Accordingly, the only possible interpretation of these facts is that the genes are arranged in the chromosomes in a precisely determined linear order, like a string of beads.

As a result of such experiments, accurate **chromosome maps** (Fig. 26-19) have been prepared for *Drosophila* and, to a lesser extent, for a number of other organisms. Although *Drosophila* has been studied much more intensively than other organisms, not all the genes of *Drosophila* are known. In *Drosophila* there are probably about three thousand genes, of which about half of those known are shown on the maps. Map I is for the long straight pair of the fruit fly's chromosomes; II and III are for the smaller and larger of the V chromosomes, respectively; while IV is for the very small pair (Fig. 26-14). All the genes in each pair of chromosomes assort independently of genes in the other three pairs; and the genes localized in each pair of chromosomes display a linked inheritance—which is complete in male animals and incomplete in females. A cytological study of the germ cells during the prophase of the first meiotic division indicates that synapsis, *as it occurs in the male Drosophila*, is more transient and less intimate than is the general rule. But precisely why crossing over is entirely aborted in the male fruit fly, whereas it occurs successfully in both sexes of almost every other species of animal, cannot be said with certainty.

Morgan's Laws. The phenomena of linkage apply to virtually all organisms, although they were worked out by Morgan and his students mainly in *Drosophila*. Thus it is customary to designate the last four of the six well-recognized laws of inheritance as **Morgan's laws:**

1. *All the genes of a species are arranged into linkage groups that correspond exactly to the chromosomes of the species; and the genes in any one pair of chromosomes are assorted during hereditary transmission independently of the genes in the other pairs.*

2. *All genes in the same chromosome are linked in heredity, maintaining their original combinations throughout successive generations, either always (complete linkage), or more often than not (incomplete linkage).*

3. *The genes in each chromosome are arranged in a specific linear order. Thus the cross-over frequencies between them have the same mathematical relations as distances between points in a straight line.*

4. *Crossing over at any one point interferes with cross overs at neighboring points; for short intervals this interference is complete, so that for genes relatively close together in a series, the observed percentage of recombinations is an accurate measure of the cross-over frequency.*

INHERITANCE OF SEX

As a general rule among sexual organisms, males and females are produced in equal or almost equal numbers in every generation, and each of the sexes can mate successfully only with the other.

The inheritance of sex in a majority of organisms shows that a single pair of chromosomes is the differential that determines whether an individual is to be male or female. Actually the situation is somewhat more complex than this, as will become apparent presently. Nevertheless it is certain that the sex differences between individuals of the same species are almost always transmitted via genes, although in the case of some animals, the developmental effects of the "sex genes" are mediated largely through the endocrine glands.

In many species the chromosomes of the female are visibly dissimilar from those of the male. In the *female Drosophila*, for ex-

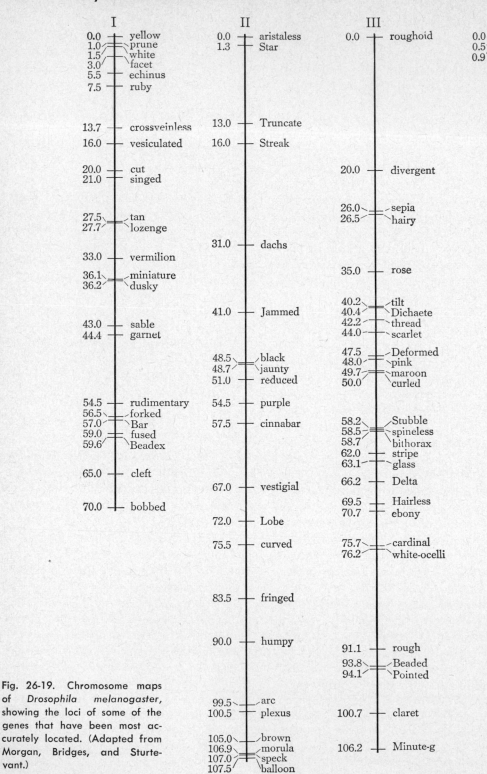

Fig. 26-19. Chromosome maps of *Drosophila melanogaster*, showing the loci of some of the genes that have been most accurately located. (Adapted from Morgan, Bridges, and Sturtevant.)

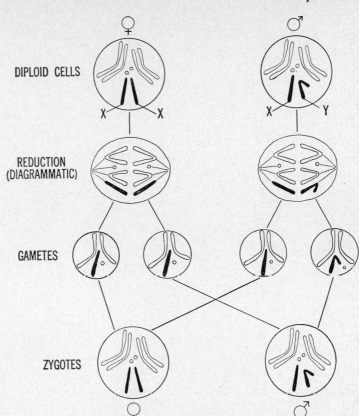

DIPLOID CELLS

REDUCTION (DIAGRAMMATIC)

GAMETES

ZYGOTES

Fig. 26-20. Diagram showing the distribution of the sex chromosomes of *Drosophila melanogaster*. Sex chromosomes, black; autosomes, white.

ample, chromosome pair number 1 consists of two straight rods, each the apparent duplicate of the other; but in the *male Drosophila,* one member of pair I is bent, and is plainly longer than the other (Fig. 26-20). In *Drosophila* the **sex-differentiating genes** are carried in the chromosomes of pair I. Accordingly these chromosomes are called the **sex chromosomes,** in contrast to the other **autosomes,** which ordinarily are neutral in their effect upon sexual development. Moreover, the sex chromosomes of *Drosophila* are of two types: the straight type is called the **X chromosome,** and the bent type, the **Y chromosome.**

The sex chromosomes, like the autosomes, are transmitted to the offspring in the usual fashion, as may be seen in Figure 26-20. But due to the dissimilarity between the X and the Y, equal numbers of males and females are conceived in each new generation of the species. As to their bearing on the sex of the

offspring, all the eggs of a female are of one kind, in that all carry an X chromosome. But a male produces *two* kinds of sperm— half X-bearing and half Y-bearing. When one of the X-bearing sperm succeeds in fertilizing an egg, the offspring will be female; and the Y-bearing sperm can only give rise to male progeny.

These microscopically visible facts suggest that each X chromosome carries a recessive gene for femaleness, and that each Y chromosome carries a dominant gene for maleness; but this is not true. Actually the Y chromosome has no direct effect in determining sex. By certain rare abnormalities in the maturation divisions, individuals of *Drosophila* are produced that have one X and no Y chromosome; and these individuals are always males. In fact some animals transmit the sex differences in just this fashion; that is, in males, the X chromosome has no homologous mate. In such cases half of the

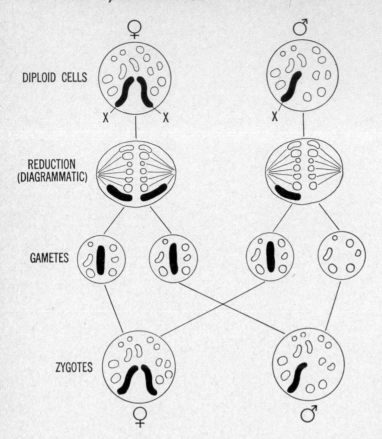

Fig. 26-21. Distribution of the sex chromosomes in *Protenor*, a bug that has no Y chromosome. Sex chromosomes, black; autosomes, white.

sperm cells contain an X chromosome, but the other half contain no sex chromosome (Fig. 26-21). Occasional individuals of *Drosophila* (resulting from abnormal maturation divisions) contain two X's and a Y, or even two X's and two Y's, and such individuals are always females.

Summarizing the evidence, *Drosophila* possesses a group of genes that determine the female characteristics of the species, and these "female genes" are localized mainly in the X chromosomes. The male characteristics, in contrast, are determined by another group of genes, but the "male genes" have their loci mainly in the **autosomes**. All individuals are homozygous for the male sex genes so that no difference is found between males and females with reference to the genes for maleness. Thus the primary sex difference is that females, which receive two X chromosomes, possess a double set of "fe-

male genes," and in such individuals the female characteristics dominate over the male. But male individuals receive only a single set of female determinants, and in these individuals the male characteristics dominate over the female.

In man and a majority of other organisms, the sex-determining mechanism resembles that of *Drosophila*.[1] But in some species the female rather than the male displays a dissimilarity of the sex chromosomes, although otherwise the mechanism of sex inheritance is similar to that of *Drosophila*.

Sex-Linked Genes and Characters. The Y chromosome of *Drosophila* and many other species is most unusual. The Y chromosome not only is devoid of sex genes, but it carries scarcely any other genes. In fact, the Y chromosome can almost be considered as a

[1] In man, however, the combination XXY yields an abnormal male, as is explained later (p. 507).

"dummy" chromosome. The Y chromosome has very little influence upon the characteristics of the organism, except that, by replacing one of the X chromosomes, it plays a deciding role in the determination of the sex of the organism.

The X chromosome, in contrast, carries many genes (Fig. 26-19). These genes are transmitted along with the sex-determining genes, and consequently a number of hereditary traits tend to be associated with the sex of the individual. Characteristics for which the genes have loci in the X chromosomes are said to be **sex-linked;** and sex linkage influences the inheritance of many characteristics—as shown in the following experiments.

In *Drosophila,* white (*w*) eye color is a sex-linked recessive character, and the allelic gene for red (*W*) eye is dominant. Thus if a white-eyed female (Fig. 26-22) is crossed with a red-eyed male, all the F_1 daughters are found to have red eyes, but all the sons have white eyes. Moreover, if these F_1 individuals are **inbred**, the F_2 generation gives 25 percent white-eyed daughters, 25 percent red-eyed daughters, 25 percent white-eyed sons, and 25 percent red-eyed sons (Fig. 26-22). Or if the experiment is started oppositely (Fig. 26-23)—by crossing a homozygous red-eyed female with a white-eyed male—all the F_1 offspring have red eyes; and in the F_2 generation, all the daughters have red eyes, but the sons show an equal distribution of the red and the white eye color (Fig. 26-23).

The foregoing experiments show that the inheritance of the eye color in *Drosophila* is linked with the inheritance of sex. It is plain also that the Y chromosome, other than displacing the X chromosome, plays no essential role in the determination of the characteristics of the individual.

In man, several types of abnormality, such as **red-green color blindness** and **hemophilia** (p. 323), are sex-linked, recessive characteristics, which are inherited exactly like white eye color in *Drosophila*. As to color blindness, for example, all the sons of a color-blind mother by a normal father will show the defect, although all the daughters will have normal vision. These daughters can transmit color blindness, however, since none is homozygous for the normal gene. Thus if we designate the recessive color-blind gene as (*b*), and the dominant allelic normal gene as (*B*), the mother would be ($X_b X_b$), the father ($X_B Y$), the sons ($X_b Y$), and the daughters ($X_B X_b$) as to their respective genotypes. In other words, the inheritance of this type of color blindness follows the same pattern as the inheritance of white eye color in *Drosophila* (Figs. 26-22 and 26-23).

Nongenetic Sexual Differentiation. A few species display no **genetic** difference between the sexes; and in such cases a zygote can give rise to either a male or a female, depending on environmental factors such as food. This type of sex determination is quite rare, however, being encountered in only a few worms and other relatively simple invertebrate animals.

Identical vs. Fraternal Twinning. In a majority of organisms only one individual arises from each fertilized egg; but in a few species (for example, the nine-banded armadillo), the embryo regularly divides at an early stage of development, producing two or more genetically identical individuals from the same zygote. This phenomenon of **polyembryony** is not common among higher animals. However, polyembryony sometimes occurs in man and other mammals, resulting in the production of **identical twins and triplets** (Figs. 26-24 and 26-25). Identical twins, in contrast to **fraternal** twins, are always of the same sex. Moreover, identical twins bear a remarkable resemblance to each other, not only as to visible appearance, but also as to characteristics of mind and personality (p. 509).

ASEXUAL REPRODUCTION IN RELATION TO HEREDITY

Asexual processes of reproduction—excluding meiotic sporulation and parthenogenesis

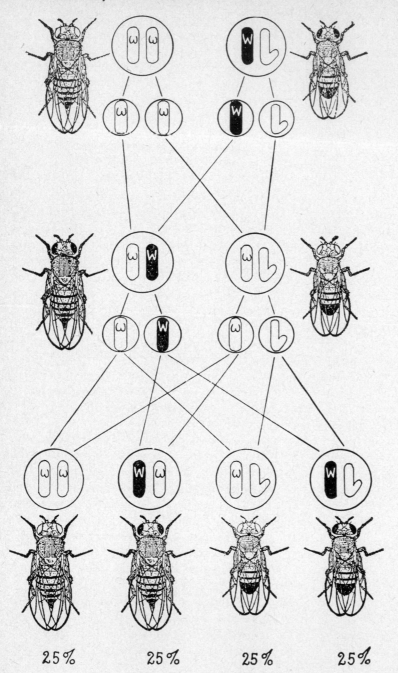

25% 25% 25% 25%

Fig. 26-22. Cross of white-eyed female and red-eyed male; F₁ inbred. (Adapted from Morgan.)

—tend to produce offspring that are genetically identical. All the cells of the offspring are derived entirely by **mitosis** from the cells of the parents; and the mitotic type of cell division operates to perpetuate the existing combination of genes affording no opportunity for any recombination of genetic traits.

This stability of asexual inheritance is of great advantage in the propagation of commercially valuable plants—such as fruit trees and potatoes. Any cutting or grafting derived from a valuable stock can be relied upon to

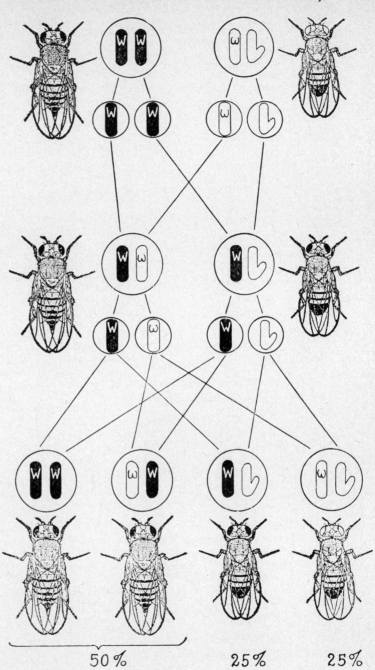

Fig. 26-23. Cross of red-eyed female and white-eyed male; F_1 inbred. (Adapted from Morgan.)

50%   25%   25%

perpetuate its favorable combination of qualities. Opportunity is not afforded for the loss of advantageous genes, or the gain of disadvantageous ones, because recombination and random assortment can occur only when meiosis is permitted to intervene between the generations. Propagation by seed, even when artificial self-pollination is practiced, usually gives rise to considerable variability among the offspring, because most stocks, unless inbred for many generations, are heterozygous for many genes.

IDENTICAL TWINS
Are products of

A single   and   A single
sperm   egg

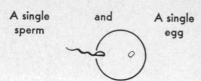

In an early stage
the embryo divides

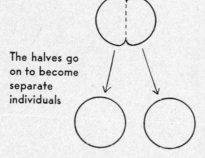

The halves go
on to become
separate
individuals

Usually — but not always — identical
twins share the same placenta and
fetal sac

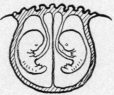

But regardless of how they develop,
they carry the same genes and are
therefore

Always of the same sex — two boys
or two girls

FRATERNAL TWINS
Are products of TWO different eggs fertilized by TWO different sperms

They have different genes and may
develop in different ways, usually—
but not always — having separate
placentas and separate fetal sacs

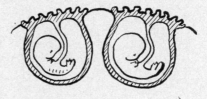

Also, as they are totally different individuals, they may be

Both
of the
same sex

—Or a
mixed
pair

Two boys

—or two girls

One   One
boy   girl

Fig. 26-24.   (From Scheinfeld, *You and Heredity*. Permission of J. B. Lippincott Co.)

HOW TRIPLETS MAY BE PRODUCED

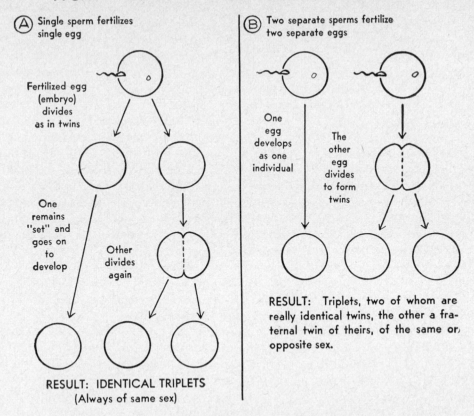

(A) Single sperm fertilizes single egg

Fertilized egg (embryo) divides as in twins

One remains "set" and goes on to develop

Other divides again

RESULT: IDENTICAL TRIPLETS
(Always of same sex)

(B) Two separate sperms fertilize two separate eggs

One egg develops as one individual

The other egg divides to form twins

RESULT: Triplets, two of whom are really identical twins, the other a fraternal twin of theirs, of the same or, opposite sex.

(C) A third type, of "unmatched" triplets, can result from the union of three separate sperms and three separate eggs.

Fig. 26-25. (From Scheinfeld, *You and Heredity*. Permission of J. B. Lippincott Co.)

MULTIPLICITY OF GENIC EFFECTS

Each part and characteristic of an organism is *usually* affected not by a single pair of genes, but by several or many pairs. There are, for example, at least 50 different genes that are known to have an influence upon the eye color of *Drosophila;* and under natural breeding conditions, all these different genes cooperate in determining the eye color of the individual offspring.

A cross between the red-eyed and white-eyed flies can be called a "one-factor cross" only when the original P_1 stocks are **homozygous** and **similar** as to all other gene pairs having any influence on the eye color. Deliberately, the stocks selected for most genetic experiments differ from each other by only one or two hereditary factors; and a long preliminary process of inbreeding is necessary to secure such stocks. In a sense, therefore, the breeding experiments of the laboratory geneticist, which yield such simple ratios among the offspring, are somewhat artificial and arbitrary. Wild flies, obtained directly from their natural habitat, tend to be heterozygous for many genes. Consequently many different recombinations appear among the offspring. Under these conditions, it is not possible to predict the results of a given mating very accurately. Without the inbreeding technique, therefore, geneticists might not have been able to ascertain the mechanism of heredity, except among a minority of plants that practice inbreeding (self-pollination) on a natural basis.

It is also important to realize that most genes affect several or many characteristics in the organism. The white-eye gene (*w*), which was used to exemplify sex linkage, received its name because its eye color effect is more dramatic and easier to follow than its other effects. Careful study, however, reveals that the white (*w*) gene has many other effects. Flies that are homozygous for this gene lack pigment in many of the internal organs; they develop more slowly and display less vigor than red-eyed flies; and homozygous white-eyed flies produce fewer offspring than their wild-type relatives. And what is true of this gene is probably true of all the genes in every organism: each gene has various effects upon many different parts and functions. Thus, to speak of the "gene for white eyes," or the "gene for vestigial wing," is merely to identify a certain gene by its most conspicuous and obvious effect.

HEREDITY IN MAN

Great difficulties have beset the scientific study of human inheritance. The impossibility of controlled experimental breeding, particularly as to the technique of inbreeding; the long period between generations; the relatively small number of offspring; and finally the large number of man's chromosomes—all have combined to hamper the progress of a detailed analysis of human heredity. In fact, human geneticists have had to depend largely upon family pedigrees; and sometimes such data are not completely reliable.

Despite these difficulties, a great deal has been learned about human inheritance. Reliable statistical methods for the analysis of human populations have been developed, and it is now evident that man and other organisms possess essentially similar genetic processes. Other mammals—especially mice, rats, guinea pigs, and rabbits—are much more favorable than man for genetic studies;

and a vast amount of data prove conclusively that mammalian heredity proceeds along the same lines as were first mapped out in *Drosophila*.

Population Genetics. The currently active field of population genetics was opened up in 1908 as a result of the mathematical and statistical studies of Hardy and Weinberg. The Hardy-Weinberg method of analysis, based on an extension of the binomial equation, makes it possible to determine the genetics of a given trait on the basis of its statistical occurrence in a population, provided that the population and sampling are large enough to yield valid probabilities.

A few of the results of human population analysis are indicated in Table 26-2. Take, for example, the case of the recessive gene of **albinism.** The homozygous condition, which produces an overt **albino,** occurs in only 1 in 20,000 individuals; the heterozygous combination, however, which yields a **carrier,** is found in 1 of every 70 people. In addition to the several examples cited in Table 26-2, the inheritance of a **tasting capacity** (ability in man to taste a special chemical, namely phenylthiocarbamide) deserves fuller consideration. This classic case was analyzed very completely by L. H. Snyder of the University of Hawaii.

Snyder tested the tasting capacity of some 3500 subjects and found that 29.8 percent were insensitive to the bitter taste of phenylthiocarbamide (PTC). Then, working on the assumption that the "taste gene" is dominant to the "nontaste gene" and that PTC-tasting is determined by a single pair of genes, an analysis was made of the occurrence of sensitivity among children derived from a number of taster × taster and taster × nontaster marriages. The actual values derived from these unions were 12.3 percent and 33.6 percent of nontasters, respectively. These values corresponded very closely with the mathematically predicted values of 12.4 percent and 35.4 percent, which proves that the original assumptions were valid.

The importance of the Snyder analysis,

Table 26-2—Partial List of Heritable Traits in Man, with Probable Genic Relations

	Dominants	*Recessives*
Eye characteristics	Brown Hazel or green Astigmatism Farsighted Nearsighted Long lashes Long orbed	Blue or gray Blue or gray Normal Normal Normal Short lashes Small orbed
Facial features	Broad lips "Roman" nose Flaring nostril Narrow bridge (nose)	Thin lips Straight bridged Nonflaring Broad bridge
Hair characteristics	Dark Nonred Curly Abundant (on body) Balding tendency (males) White forelock	Blond Red Straight Sparse Normal Normal
Other characteristics	Short stature (multiple genes) Muscular distrophy A, B, and AB (blood groups) Normal Normal Normal Free lobes (ear) Normal	Tall stature Normal Group O Diabetes mellitus Congenital deafness Hemophilia (sex-linked) Attached Albinism (absence of pigment in hair, skin, eyes, etc.)

however, is not so much that it proved that nontasting is determined by a single pair of recessive genes, since this could be ascertained directly by noting the absence of tasters among the offspring of nontaster × nontaster unions. The true importance lies in the validation of the analytical methods used in population genetics—methods that are now being used extensively by many workers.

Heritable Defects of Metabolism. In 1908, Archibald Garrod, an English physician of outstanding scientific insight, reported upon a number of "inborn errors of metabolism," which appeared to be caused by heritable defects in one or another of the metabolic enzymes of various patients. Subsequently Garrod's viewpoint has been amply substantiated. Now, in fact, about a dozen such metabolic defects are recognized. Among these, perhaps the most important are: **alkaptonuria, phenylketonuria, agammaglobulinemia, galactosemia, sickle cell anemia,** and **albinism.** In each case the lack of a single enzyme appears to be responsible for the condition, and the inheritance is mediated by a single pair of mutant, or defective, genes, usually of recessive character. Moreover, a study of the inheritance of these metabolic defects has provided considerable support to the "one gene, one enzyme" hypothesis (p. 530) as to the mechanism of genic action (Chap. 27).

The missing or defective enzymes responsible for **phenylketonuria, alkaptonuria,** and **albinism** are indicated in Figure 26-26. Phenylketonuria, in which a high concentration of phenylpyruvic acid (Fig. 26-26) accumulates in the blood and urine, is an exceedingly serious condition. Always it is accompanied by a grave degree of mental deficiency. The condition can be partially controlled, however, by careful regulation of the phenylalanine intake of the patient. This is difficult, however, because phenylalanine is one of the essential amino acids (p. 137) that cannot be eliminated from the diet completely and because phenylalanine is a constituent of almost every protein food. Alkaptonuria and albinism, on the other hand, are not so seri-ous. The urine of an alkaptonuric individual turns black upon exposure to air, because **homogentisic acid,** the substance that accumulates in the blood and urine, spontaneously undergoes oxidation into a blackish end product (Fig. 26-26). An albino is over-sensitive to sunburn and glare. Melanin (p. 530), the principal light-absorbing pigment of the skin, hair, and eyes, cannot be manufactured in the absence of the proper enzyme. (Fig. 26-26).

The rare infant who suffers from **galactosemia** cannot metabolize galactose, which is absorbed, of course, from milk (p. 80). Accordingly, this sugar accumulates to toxic levels in the body fluids, although considerable amounts are excreted via the urine. Specifically, the missing enzyme is **galactosephosphate transferase.** This enzyme is necessary for the conversion of the milk sugar-phosphate to glucose-phosphate, as was

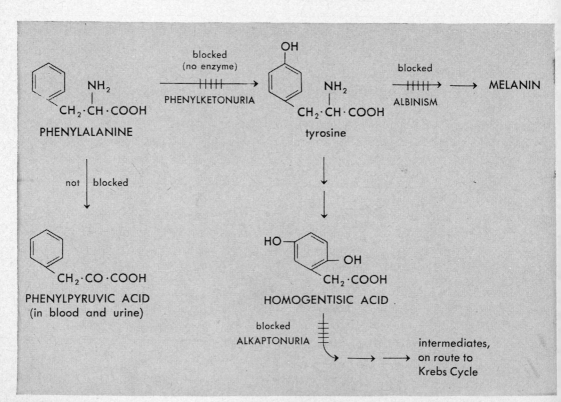

Fig. 26-26. Enzymes missing in certain heritable metabolic diseases, namely albinism, alkaptonuria, and phenylketonuria.

shown by Herman Kalckar and co-workers at the National Institutes of Health. The condition may be alleviated by withholding milk from the diet. This is difficult, however, because milk is used in the preparation of many foods.

The enzyme deficiencies of **sickle cell anemia** and **agammaglobulinemia** are both concerned with faulty protein synthesis. In the sickle cell patient, the determining gene appears to carry a defective code (p. 526) for the synthesis of hemoglobin. The amino acid sequence in this peptide chain is almost perfect, except that valine is substituted for glutamic acid at one point. As a result of the defect, the erythrocytes are not biconcave discs. Instead, they are sickle-shaped (concavo-convex), they have a faulty oxygen-binding capacity, and they are *abnormally fragile*. The anemia that results may be very mild, in the case of heterozygous individuals, or quite severe, when the homozygous condition obtains. This indicates, of course, that the "sickle cell gene" is not completely recessive to its normal allele.

The code carried by the "agammoglobulin gene" appears to be hopelessly scrambled, since the gamma globulin fraction of the plasma proteins is absent. This, of course, is the "antibody fraction" and consequently agammaglobulinemic patients are exceedingly susceptible to infection (p. 320).

Chromosomes of Man; Normal and Abnormal Complements. The diploid complement of chromosomes in man was difficult to determine precisely. Man's chromosomes are numerous and they are crowded together in the metaphase plate (p. 46). Moreover, there are only small differences in the size and morphology of the various pairs, as is shown in Figure 26-27.

An early approach toward an accurate picture of man's chromosomes was made by T. S. Painter at the University of Texas in 1921. Painter counted 24 pairs, and this count was generally accepted until 1956. Meanwhile, the counting problem was greatly simplified by the development of three techniques: (1)

the tissue culture technique, which enabled the investigator to study the division stages of human cells, particularly leucocytes, after removal from the body; (2) the use of *colchicine* to block mitosis at metaphase, when the chromosomes are very clearly differentiated; and (3) the use of hypotonic media to separate the chromosomes from one another more sharply.

In 1956, J. H. Tjio and A. Levan in Sweden and C. E. Ford and J. L. Hamerton in England were able to achieve the first perfect counts—counts that have been verified subsequently by many workers throughout the world. Therefore it can now be said without equivocation that man's normal complement of chromosomes is **23 pairs**: 22 pairs of **autosomes** and 1 pair of **sex chromosomes**, as is shown in Figure 26-27.

The newly developed accuracy of counting has led to some important medical discoveries. It now is known definitely that at least three serious pathological conditions—**mongolism**, the **Klinefelter syndrome**, and the **Turner syndrome**—are related to abnormalities in the chromosome constitution. In some cases, an extra chromosome may be present; but in other cases, a chromosome may be missing.

Mongolism, an unfortunate term as well as an unfortunate condition, results from the presence of an extra member of pair 21 (Fig. 26-27). Or, more technically stated, the mongoloid condition is related to **trisomy** in chromosome 21. During oögenesis, apparently, nondisjunction (p. 515) occurs in this pair of chromosomes, resulting in the formation of an egg that is diploid for this pair. Such nondisjunction is relatively rare, however. Only 1 in 650 cases appears among children generally. However, the incidence among children produced by older mothers (but not by older fathers) reaches 3 percent when the mother's age is 45 or over. The term "mongoloid" is apt only in the sense that such children display an extra fold of skin in the upper eyelid, giving an oriental appearance to the eyes. The more serious aspects of the

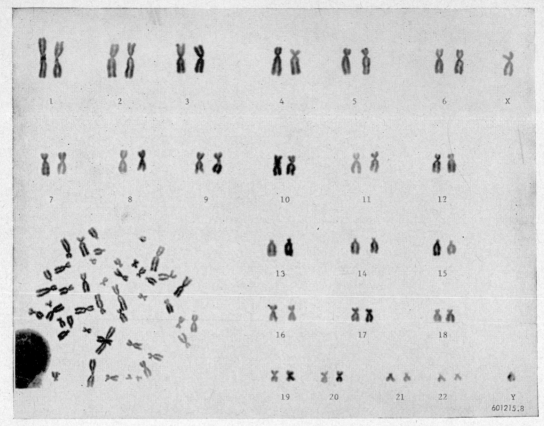

Fig. 26-27. Diploid set of chromosomes in man, derived from a cell at metaphase. By this time each chromosome has undergone replication, but a complete separation of the sister replicas has not occurred. Selection of the paired members requires a precise study of the morphology, including the centromere (constricted point) positions, of the randomly arranged chromosomes of an original preparation (lower left of photo), utilizing a magnification considerably higher than is shown here. Then the paired members are arranged and numbered, forming what is called a **karyotype**, which may be normal or abnormal. (Courtesy of Alexander G. Bearn, The Rockefeller Institute, New York.)

condition include a malformation of the tongue and a very severe retardation of growth, both physical and mental.

The Klinefelter and Turner syndromes both are related to abnormalities in the *sex chromosomes*. The Klinefelter patient is always a male with an XXY constitution. Typically the stature is tall, and usually some degree of mental deficiency is present. Sperm production is reduced to the point of virtual sterility and the breasts show a tendency toward overdevelopment. The Turner patient, on the other hand, lacks a Y chromosome; that is, the genetic constitution is XO. The condition is associated with malforma-

tions of the aorta, deafness, shortness of stature, and some degree of mental retardation.

Other Aspects of Human Inheritance. Most *normal* differences among human individuals—such as size, weight, color of skin, hair, and eyes—are, as in other animals, influenced by many genes; and there are no very closely inbred stocks in man. All human individuals are heterozygous for many genes, and consequently it is difficult to forecast the precise distribution of most characteristics among human offspring. Moreover, many characteristics—such as height and weight— are very susceptible to nutritional influences, and this makes the genetic analysis more difficult.

In the case of eye color, which is relatively insensitive to environmental influence, the analysis has been quite successful. *Pure blue* eyes are inherited as a simple recessive, but the various darker shades of eye color are determined by several other genes—the darker alleles being usually dominant to the lighter. Hair color and skin color are likewise determined by more than one gene pair. In the case of skin color, all the F_1 offspring of a *pure* white-black cross display a fairly uniform intermediate (mulatto) shade—which shows that each of the original stock is homozygous for the skin color determination. But the F_2 children derived from first-generation mulatto parents are of many shades, ranging from pure black to pure white.

One analysis indicates that skin pigmentation in man is determined by two pairs of genes, which, in the F_1 mulatto, are *Aa* and *Bb*—the capitals indicating partially dominant genes, which tend to make the pigmentation darker in an **additive** fashion. Consequently the F_2 offspring of F_1 mulatto parents are distributed as follows:

1 with 4 dominants—*AABB* (phenotypically Negro)
4 with 3 dominants—2 *AaBB* and 2 *AABb* (phenotypically dark)
6 with 2 dominants—4 *AaBb*, 1 *AAbb*, and 1 *aaBB* (phenotypically mulatto)
4 with 1 dominant—2 *Aabb*, 2 *aaBb* (phenotypically light)
1 with no dominants—*aabb* (phenotypically white).

Such a situation allows for a graded type of variation among the F_2 generation. In fact, such cases where the same character is influenced in the same way by two or more independent pairs of genes acting additively are generally designated as **multiple-factor** characters, and the results have been referred to as **blended inheritance.** Moreover, the greater the number of independent heterozygous gene pairs involved in the determination of a single character, the less perceptible will be the gradations among the offspring. It is interesting to note, therefore, that many characteristics in man—such as height, weight, and intelligence—and many characteristics in commercially valuable species—such as milk production in cows and egg production in chickens—are undoubtedly inherited on a multiple-factor basis.

An analysis of the inheritance of the factors determining the blood-group agglutinogens (p. 325) in man and other mammals indicates that these are transmitted as a set of **three allelic genes,** namely, A, A_B, and a. Genes A and A_B, which respectively determine agglutinogens A and B, are both dominant to the recessive gene a, which gives rise to no agglutinogens when it is homozygous. However, neither A nor A_B is dominant to the other, so that the heterozygous combination AA_B determines an individual belonging to group AB. The inheritance of the Rh agglutinogens, on the other hand, is determined by a more complex set of allelic genes.

In addition to the cases cited previously (p. 507), there are several other genes known to be concerned with the hereditary transmission of abnormalities in man. Polydactyly (extra fingers and toes), brachydactyly (shortened fingers and toes), certain cases of dwarfism, and a number of other relatively rare and deleterious characters—all are transmitted by single pairs of genes. Moreover, the gene pairs concerned with the transmission of abnormalities tend to be **recessive** in nature. To "remain in circulation," in fact, such deleterious factors are quite apt to be recessive, because dominant abnormalities tend to be "bred out" of the species by a natural tendency of most individuals to choose a "normal" mate.

The inheritance of mental and other less tangible characteristics in the human species constitutes an even more perplexing problem. In the case of mental qualities, particularly, exact measurements are difficult to make; and it is hard to disentangle genetic factors from the manifold influences of the child's environment. The best evidence regarding the inheritance of mental traits comes from the study of **identical twins,** in whom there is an exact duplication of all genetic factors. Such twins, even if they have grown up in separate and different environments, always show a very high correlation of intelligence, as measured by several of the available kinds of "intelligence tests." These measurements are admittedly arbitrary, but they do provide strong evidence that an individual's capacity to learn is largely determined by genetic factors. Other traits, such as are commonly designated as "personality" and "character," are less highly correlated in given pairs of twins. This may merely mean that the measurements of personality and character are not very reliable; or more probably, it indicates that personality characteristics are very susceptible to the modifying influence of environmental experience.

It has often been noted that "feeble-mindedness" and a few forms of insanity show a marked tendency to "run in families"; and the same is true for supernormal talents of one sort or another. But closely related individuals tend to be exposed to the same environment, especially during the formative period of childhood, and the potency of the environment cannot be ruled out under these circumstances. On the basis of our present knowledge, it is possible to say, however, that the mental as well as the physical traits of the individual are determined in highly significant degree by genetic factors; but the details—as to what and how many genes are involved, and as to how the action of these genes may be influenced by disease, malnutrition, education, economic welfare, and other environmental factors—have not yet been brought into focus very clearly.

The laws of heredity have already yielded a rich practical harvest in the improvement of domestic animals and plants by **selective breeding.** Naturally high hopes have also been engendered as to the improvement of the human species. But these hopes are hampered by enormous difficulties. Our knowledge of human heredity is still relatively meager in detail, and there is no agreement as to what goals should be "bred for" in any large-scale eugenics program. As to an ideal feminine type, for example, college men might insist upon the slim exotic beauty of some current "pin-up" girl; whereas a chauvinistic dictator might want to foster the sturdy and fecund qualities of a peasant mother. Moreover, mankind is averse to tampering with individual rights and preferences; and it does not seem likely that human matings will ever be governed, to any great extent, by the dictates of genetic principle. Accordingly, the greatest hope for human advancement, at least in the near future, still lies in the amelioration of the social, educational, and economic conditions of human life.

MUTATIONS

All the facts of heredity emphasize the **stability** of the genes, since the genes of a species are generally transmitted without change through many successive cell divisions, and through many generations of the organism as a whole. All the genes of the zygote multiply successively as the many cells of the developing embryo are formed, so that every cell of the adult receives a duplicate of every gene originally present in the zygote. Moreover, every gene in the diploid germ cells of the organism has an equal chance of passing on into the next generation by way of the gamete cells of the current generation.

But the stability of genes is by no means *absolute.* On rare occasion a certain gene may change, suddenly and dramatically, into a new and different gene. This important phenomenon is called **mutation.**[2] As a result of

[2]Strictly speaking, such a change of one gene into another is referred to as a **point mutation.** Some heritable changes may result from chromosomal phenomena, such as translocation, duplication, or deletion (p. 523), and these are called **chromosomal mutations.** Presumably a point mutation involves a change in the nucleotide sequence (p. 88) of the genic material, which is the code of information transmitted by the gene (p. 527).

mutation, a new hereditary factor will suddenly appear, and this new gene will influence the destiny of the species in a small or large degree, depending on the nature of the change. Quite a number of drastic mutations are known to have played an important role in animal husbandry. Mutant stocks of domestic animals—such as hornless cattle, short-legged Ancon sheep, and white turkeys —have distinctive features that may be more desirable than those of the original stock (Fig. 26-28).

A

B

Fig. 26-28. The silver fox (A), which has a highly valued pelt, arose by mutation from the wild-type red fox (B). (A, courtesy of the U.S. Department of Agriculture and the American Museum of Natural History, New York. B, courtesy of the American Museum of Natural History, New York.)

A mutation gives rise to a new gene that *usurps the locus of the old.* Consequently the mutant gene becomes allelic to the normal gene from which it has arisen. In diploid cells, only one gene of any allelic pair has been known to mutate at a given time, and the mutant gene may bear either a recessive or a dominant relation to its nonmutated mate. In any event, the mutant gene immediately occupies the old position in a particular chromosome; and thereafter the mutant gene enjoys the same linkage relations as its normal progenitor. In *Drosophila* many mutations have arisen in pedigreed stocks kept under meticulous observation, so that in each case it is possible to specify which gene is the mutant and which is the normal allele. For example, the gene (w) that determines white eye mutated from (W), the red-eye gene; and the gene (b) for black body came from (B), the gray-body allele. Nevertheless, little distinction exists between a mutant gene and the normal original, except when the former is known to have arisen from the latter. In wild stocks, wherein no pedigrees are known, it is not possible to tell which member of an allelic series is the "original" and which are the mutant genes. In fact a study of evolution from the viewpoint of heredity leads to the conclusion that *virtually all* genetic differences—between individuals of the same species, and between the different species—have resulted from an age-old series of mutations extending back to the beginnings of life.

The sudden and unexpected appearance of a new heritable characteristic in a known stock does not always indicate a mutation— in the strictest sense. Such changes sometimes result from chromosomal **duplications** or **deficiencies,** such as arise from abnormalities in the divisions of the germ cells; they may come from the deterioration of one or more genes in the germ cell line; or, they may indicate a shift in the position of genes in a chromosome—since there is a distinct **position effect,** which may modify the behavior of the genes. These phenomena are sometimes called "mutations"; but a stricter usage, confining the term "mutation" to the transformation of one gene into another, will be adhered to in the present account.

Mutations are recognized by their phenotypic effects, but recessive mutants do not produce these effects until the next generation, that is, until homozygous offspring have been produced. Mutations may also occur in the somatic cells of the organism, but in this case the effects are usually limited to some particular part or parts of the body; and such changes are not perpetuated in subsequent generations. Thus, a somatic mutation usually produces a **mosaic organism,** such as a drosophila having a red eye on one side and a white eye on the other.

The phenotypic change induced by a mutant gene may be so slight that it can be detected only by extremely careful study, or, the change may be drastic enough to kill the organism. On the basis of the degree of phenotypic change (induced by the mutant when it is homozygous), mutations are usually classified as (1) **slight mutations,** which can be recognized only by statistical analysis and other special methods; (2) **visible mutations,** which can be recognized at a glance; and (3) **lethal mutations,** which are so drastic that the homozygous organism dies before reaching sexual maturity.

Mutation Frequencies. Rare though they are, mutations are not so rare as was first supposed, *if all types are considered.* In *Drosophila melanogaster,* some 500 different **visible** mutations were distinguished in surveys covering 25,000,000 individuals of known genetic stock; that is, about 1 fly in 50,000 plainly showed a mutant quality. And when special methods were employed for the detection of **lethals,** this type of mutation was found to occur about six times more frequently than visible mutations.

The methods for estimating the frequency of slight mutations are not exact, but many experts believe that slight mutations may take place even more often than either of the other types. In fact there are now reliable estimates for *Drosophila* that indicate that between 1 and 10 percent of the gametes in each generation display at least one mutation of one type or another. In man, the estimates indicate that each of us, on the average may receive one mutated gene, via the egg or sperm, at the time of conception.

A particular mutation, on the other hand,

will not occur, except rarely, although different genes vary considerably as to their mutability. Among certain colon bacteria, for example, the mutation that makes the bacilli resistant to streptomycin shows up in only about one cell per billion in each generation; whereas the mutation responsible for hemophilia in man appears at least once in every 100,000 gametes.

The same gene may mutate successively in several different directions, giving rise to a **series of allelic genes.** In the fruit fly, for example, the gene W, the normal allele of white (w) gene, has given rise to 11 mutant alleles, each having a different effect upon eye color and upon other phenotypic characteristics. Several of these mutations have been duplicated in different stocks on different occasions; and in some cases the same mutant has arisen from two different alleles. Thus in the white (w) series, the gene w^e (eosin) has arisen not only from W (red) but also from w (white); and eosin has mutated back to white and also to red.

As a general rule the mutant gene has its chief effects upon the same part or character as the normal counterpart, though the effects may vary widely as to quality and intensity. Except for this fact, however, mutations appear to be quite random in their phenotypic effects; and this is probably why so many mutations are lethal in result. In the delicate balance of developmental and functional processes in a complex organism, any considerable change is more likely to "gum up the machinery" than merely to modify its operational behavior.

Some insight is currently being gained into the mechanisms of mutation (p. 525). The frequency of mutation is known to increase at higher temperatures. Moreover, the mutation rate is much higher when the organism is exposed to short-wave radiations such as x-rays, radioactivity, and cosmic rays, and when cells are treated with certain chemicals, notably some of the "nitrogen mustard" compounds. There is approximately a threefold increase in the frequency of mutation for each 10-degree elevation of the temperature, within the range that the organism can tolerate. This high degree of temperature sensitivity is strong evidence that a chemical rather than a purely physical reaction is involved, and this is in good agreement with current theory (p. 525).

GENETIC vs. ENVIRONMENTAL VARIATIONS

Even among offspring of the same parentage the interplay of genetic and environmental factors results in great variation among organisms—and this accounts for the familiar fact that no two organisms are ever *exactly* identical. But sharp distinction must be made between **environmental variations**, which are not perpetuated by the mechanisms of heredity, and **genetic variations**, which are so perpetuated. Environmental variations are referred to more technically as **modifications;** but the importance of modifications will be discussed later (Chap. 28).

The following classification serves to summarize and systematize the several kinds of **genetic variations** that have been mentioned during the discussion on heredity:

1. **Recombinations.** Differences among offspring due to segregation, independent assortment, crossing over, random fertilization, and other *normal* operations of the chromosomal mechanism.

2. **Aberrations.** Variations due to occasional *irregularities* in the behavior of the chromosomes.

3. **Mutations.** Transformations by which one gene changes into another.

Recombination. The numbers of different phenotypes and genotypes produced in several simple crosses were analyzed previously. These results may be extended and generalized as follows. Assuming the absence of *complete* linkage (and this is generally true), any organism that is heterozygous for n pairs of genes will produce 2^n genetically different kinds of gametes. Or if one parent is heterozygous for m pairs, and the other for n different gene pairs, there will be $2^{(n+m)}$ different genotypes among the offspring. Or if both parents are heterozygous for the same n pairs of genes, the number of genotypically different offspring will be 3^n. If dominance is entirely lacking, the numbers of phenotypes and genotypes will be equal; otherwise the number of phenotypes will be less, although the recessive genes will all appear in subsequent generations and frequently a recessive gene may have significant "side effects" in each generation.

In general, therefore, the number of genetically different offspring increases more and more rapidly as the parents become heterozygous for more and more gene pairs; or in mathematical language, genetic variation increases exponentially with heterozygosity.

Only a small minority of species are self-fertilizing; and a majority of organisms, as a result of random mating, are heterozygous for many genes. Under these conditions, consequently, the production of two genetically identical offspring becomes virtually impossible, except where more than one individual arises from the same zygote (identical twins, triplets, etc.). In man particularly, owing to random mating and the conservative rate of breeding, genetic identity between any two children lies quite beyond the range of practical possibility.

Aberration. The processes of mitosis and meiosis are extremely precise and regular, but now and again a slip-up may occur while the countless cells of the species proceed with their divisions. Sometimes a chromosome, or a whole set of chromosomes, may be gained, lost, or misplaced; or just a fragment of a chromosome may experience a similar fate. Moreover, if such an **aberration** occurs in the cells of the germ cell line, a new and different complex of chromosomes will automatically be transmitted to the offspring; and the changed genetic constitution of the species will be perpetuated.

The commonest and most important type of aberration involves the gain of one or more *whole sets* of chromosomes. This may result if a nucleus fails to divide after the chromosomes have divided, or if two daughter nuclei fuse before the cell divides. Such an aberration occurring in a germ cell may lead to the production of **diploid** ($2n$) gametes. Such gametes give rise to **triploid** ($3n$) offspring if fertilized by normal (n) gametes; or to **tetraploid** ($4n$) offspring if fertilized by other diploid gametes.

Both triploid and tetraploid individuals have been found in many species (Fig. 26-29). Tetraploids particularly are apt to be larger than their diploid prototypes; and a number of other phenotypic differences may accompany the aberration.

As to the production of gametes, triploid and tetraploid individuals differ quite markedly. Usually all the gametes of a tetraploid are diploid, and all are capable of taking part in fertilization. But the gametes of a triploid individual vary as to their chromosome count, all the way from n to $2n$, with a *majority* falling in the intermediate range. And since only the n and $2n$ gametes can participate successfully in fertilization, **triploid individuals** *are highly sterile*.

In nature many tetraploid stocks are found among plants, but very few animal tetraploids occur. Among cross-fertilizing species there is little chance that both parents should simultaneously produce aberrational ($2n$) gametes; and unless this occurs the aberration is almost certain to be eliminated in the next generation, due to the sterility of the triploid offspring. But among self-pollinating plants, a single aberration may reach both the male and female gametes, and thus tetraploidy has a fair chance of becoming estab-

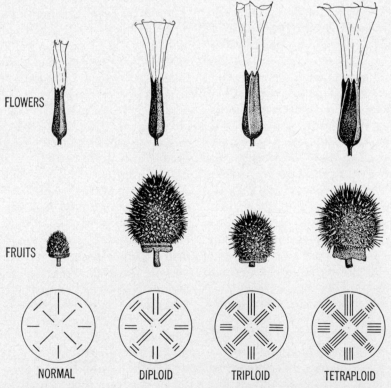

Fig. 26-29. Flowers, seed capsules, and chromosome groups of haploid, diploid, triploid, and tetraploid Jimson weeds (*Datura stramonium*). The small size of the seed capsules of the haploid and triploid plants is due to the low fertility of these forms, producing relatively few seeds. (Adapted from Blakeslee.)

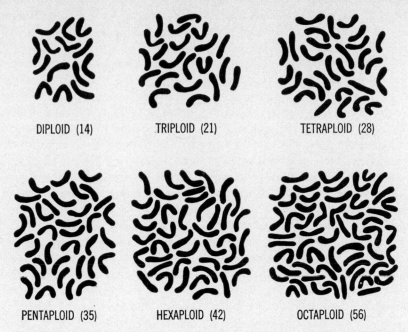

DIPLOID (14)   TRIPLOID (21)   TETRAPLOID (28)

PENTAPLOID (35)   HEXAPLOID (42)   OCTAPLOID (56)

Fig. 26-30. Chromosome groups of different species of roses. Some of these forms (those with odd chromosome numbers, at least) are probably hybrids. (After Tackholm.)

lished in such species. In fact quite a number of species in closely related plant groups have chromosome numbers that are multiples of a common factor (Fig. 26-30). In any tetraploid stock, subsequent aberrations occurring over a period of many years may result in the production of other stocks that are hexaploid (6*n*), octaploid (8*n*), and so forth.

Other types of aberration, which also can be important in the origin of species, display quite a variety of forms (Fig. 26-31). **Deficiencies,** because of the loss of one chromosome, or any fragment of a chromosome; **duplications,** as a result of the presence of an *extra* chromosome or any of its pieces;

translocations, owing to the attachment of a piece to some other chromosome; and **inversions,** resulting from the rejoining, by the wrong ends, of two pieces of a single chromosome—all have important genetic consequences that have been studied very intensively in *Drosophila*. Irradiation of animals and plants with x-rays greatly increases the occurrence of such aberrations, since the x-ray treatment tends to produce a fragmentation of the chromosomes. Careful studies of the chromosomes of several closely related species have shown that the difference between two *species* may, in some cases, arise suddenly by chromosomal aberration. In one case, for example, a single inversion occur-

Fig. 26-31. Types of aberrations. In each case the normal chromosome is shown on the left, the abnormal one on the right.

DEFICIENCY

DUPLICATION

TRANSLOCATION

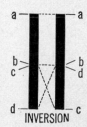

INVERSION

ring in just one chromosome produced a new stock that was sufficiently different from the old to be considered as a separate species.

Selective Breeding: Artificial Selection. Except for species with a long history of self-fertilization, animal and plant populations tend to be extremely mixed; that is, composed of individuals that are heterozygous for many different pairs of genes. In consequence of this heterozygosity, most species display a high degree of genetic variability, and such species are very plastic from the viewpoint of experimental breeding.

Artificial selection has produced many "breeds" of animals and plants, according to man's need or fancy. Attempts to improve the quality of domesticated animals and plants were started long before the laws of heredity were understood, and many valuable breeds were created by hit-or-miss methods. However, modern genetics has greatly accelerated the processes of selective breeding, because modern breeders select their crosses logically and efficiently, according to the laws of segregation, assortment, linkage, etc. Accordingly, it is now possible to "pick apart" the hereditary qualities of a given species and to assemble its desirable qualities into a new stock that can be depended upon to breed true in subsequent generations.

Animal breeding is more difficult because none of man's domestic animals can be self-fertilized. However, pure lines of true-breeding animal stocks can eventually be obtained by persistent and continued **inbreeding.** Strictly speaking, inbreeding involves brother-sister matings in every generation; but in practice first cousin crosses are more frequently employed. The final goal of the inbreeder is to establish complete homozygosity with reference to all gene pairs that have any effect upon the qualities of the organism that are being "bred for." In the case of self-fertilizing species this goal may be reached in six generations of inbreeding; but brother-sister inbreeding requires about three times as many generations, and cousin crosses even more.

To take a crude example, suppose that the problem is beef production, and the cattleman owns a large herd with a long history of **random** mating. In this case, the muscle weight of the herd would show tremendous variation between the heaviest and lightest animals. If the two heaviest specimens of the herd are selected as parents, the offspring will still vary widely in weight, but the **average weight** of the selected group will be greater than that of the herd as a whole. Similarly if the two champions of the selected group are crossed, the average weight of the F_2 selectees will be still greater. Finally, however, after about 20 generations of such selective inbreeding, a maximum weight will be reached. Continued inbreeding will maintain the heavily meated stock, but further improvement will not occur. The stock has become homozygous for all genes concerned with muscle weight and, therefore, no further improvement can be expected, except on the rare chance of a favorable mutation or aberration. The breeder must now resort to **outcrossing** with the champion of some other famous pedigreed herd, in hopes that a still more favorable combination of "meat genes" may be obtained. If so, the process of selection may proceed again until a peak of homozygosity is gained in the new and better stock.

In practice, the problem is not so simple as is indicated by the foregoing description. The breeder must simultaneously select for other qualities in addition to "meat weight." Of what avail is a meat champion if the new stock is susceptible to disease, cold, or other unfavorable environmental factors; or if the stock displays a reduced capacity to multiply? In fact, the very process of inbreeding may lead to a decrease in the general vigor of the inbred line as compared to the mixed population, unless the breeder pays close attention to the factors of health and resistance in making his parental selections. The tendency of an inbred stock to lose vigor is not due to inbreeding as such, but to an accidental accumulation of deleterious recessive genes as the degree of homozygosity increases. Unfavorable recessives are apt to be widely spread in any mixed population, since heterozygous individuals, which suffer none of the injurious effects, continue to act as carriers. But inbreeding tends to increase homozygosity and there is always a good chance that unfavorable recessives may become homozygous in the selected stock. On the other hand, it is quite possible, by selecting only the most vigorous and fertile individuals of each generation, to produce a highly inbred line that is superior to the original mixed population as to general health, vigor, and fecundity.

The results of artificial selection can be most startling. Among dogs, for example, one can scarcely believe that the "pocket Mexican hairless" belongs to the same species as the gigantic Great Dane. But always a limit is reached as to how far a certain quality may be carried in a given direction; and barring mutations and aberrations, this limit cannot be exceeded by selection. Artificial methods of increasing the frequency of mutations are too recent to have yielded many practical results, but perhaps these methods can eventually be adapted to utilitarian purposes.

TEST QUESTIONS

1. Explain how and why the known processes of cell division and sexual reproduction convinced biologists, even before they knew anything about genes, that the mechanisms of hereditary transmission must reside in the nuclei of the gametes (and other germ cells).

2. Explain the meaning of the phrase "continuity of the germ cells," exemplifying the discussion by describing the "germ cell cycle" of the frog.

3. How does the prophase of the first maturation (meiotic) division, as it occurs in spermatogenesis (and oögenesis), differ from the prophase of an ordinary (mitotic) division? (At least three differences should be mentioned.)

4. Answer the foregoing question with reference to (a) the metaphase of the first maturation division and (b) the prophase of the second maturation division.

5. Discuss the similarities and differences between spermatogenesis and oögenesis, emphasizing the functional importance of these points of comparison.

6. What is synapsis? When does it occur? What are its genetic consequences?

7. Define and localize: (a) spermatogonia (and oögonia); (b) tetrads; (c) secondary spermatocytes (and oöcytes); (d) spermatids; (e) polar bodies, and (f) ripe ovum.

8. Explain the meaning of the phrase "free assortment of the chromosomes during meiosis," using the sperm produced by a spermatocyte with two pairs of chromosomes (*Aa* and *Bb*) to exemplify the discussion.

9. Make a series of labeled diagrams to show all the stages of maturation in a spermatocyte having two pairs of chromosomes (*Aa* and *Bb*).

10. Specify all the possible types of gametes that can be formed by each of the following types of spermatocyte:
    a. *AA bb cc*
    b. *AA Bb Cc*
    c. *Aa Bb Cc*

11. All the offspring produced by crossing red four-o'clocks with white ones have pink flowers. What proportions of what flower colors will be yielded among the direct offspring of each of the following crosses:
    a. pink × pink
    b. pink × red
    c. pink × white
    d. red × white

12. Among the various offspring from the foregoing crosses, indicate those that are (a) homozygous and (b) heterozygous.

13. In summer squashes, white fruit (*Y*) is dominant over yellow fruit (*y*). If a squash plant homozygous for white is crossed with one homozygous for yellow, what will the genotype and phenotype ratios be:
    a. if two of the F_1 individuals are inbred
    b. if one of the F_1 is mated with its white parent
    c. if one of the F_1 is mated with its yellow parent

14. In the fruit fly, long wing (*V*) is dominant over vestigial wing (*v*). What results would be obtained when a heterozygous long-

winged fly is crossed with a short-winged individual?

15. What is a backcross experiment? Why is the backcross so useful in genetics?

16. Rough-coated guinea pigs crossed to smooth-coated pigs produce only rough-coated F_1 offspring. What results would be obtained:
   a. by inbreeding the F_1 individual
   b. by backcrossing one of the F_1 pigs

17. Twenty-five percent of the offspring of a certain pair of white sheep are black. What was the genotype of the parents?

18. Explain the statement that hereditary transmission is particulate in character.

19. After many generations, what result would be anticipated if one black sheep (see Question 17) were introduced into a herd of pure-bred (homozygous) whites:
   a. assuming the heredity to be particulate (as it is)
   b. assuming a "blending type" of heredity (as it is not)

20. In summer squash, white fruit (Y) is dominant to yellow (y), and flat fruit (R) is dominant to round (r). The selected parents are a plant with white, flat fruit (YY, RR), and a plant with yellow, round fruit. Specify the phenotypes and genotypes and their respective ratios:
   a. in the F_1 generation
   b. in the F_2 generation (inbreed the F_1 plants)
   c. among the offspring obtained by back-crossing one of the F_1 plants

21. An albino (pure white) guinea pig with a rough coat is mated with a black one with a smooth coat. The F_1 offspring are all black and rough. What would be the genotype and phenotype ratios in the F_2 generation?

22. A heterozygous black, smooth-haired guinea pig (Question 21) is crossed to a white, heterozygous, rough-haired mate. What phenotype and genotype ratios would be expected among the direct offspring of this cross?

23. Carefully differentiate between the members of each pair of terms:
   a. the phenotype and the genotype of an individual
   b. a homozygous and a heterozygous individual
   c. sex chromosomes and autosomes

d. sex linkage and ordinary linkage
e. complete and incomplete linkage

24. In tomatoes, red fruit (Y) is dominant to yellow (y) and tallness (D) is dominant to dwarfism (d); the two pairs of genes have their loci in the same pair of chromosomes; and the linkage is complete. What phenotype and genotype ratios would be expected among the direct offspring if both of the parents are red (heterozygous) and tall (heterozygous).

25. Assume that the linkage relation in the parents given in Question 24 is $\begin{array}{c|c} Y & y \\ D & d \end{array}$ and that the cross-over value between the gene pairs is 10 percent. Specify the gametes of such a parent and indicate the relative abundance of each gamete type.

26. In rabbits, black coat (B) is dominant to brown (b) and long hair (S) is dominant to short (s). Derive the phenotypes and genotypes to be expected when a heterozygous long-haired pig is crossed to a brown short-haired mate:
   a. assuming that the two gene pairs have their loci in separate pairs of chromosomes
   b. assuming that the loci are in the same pair of chromosomes and that the linkage is complete

27. Make a diagram to show how sex is inherited in *Drosophila* (and in man and many other organisms).

28. What is the basis for referring to the Y chromosome of *Drosophila* as a "dummy"?

29. In the fruit fly, red eye (W) is *sex-linked* and dominant to white eye (w). Specify the distribution of eye color (a) among the males, and (b) among the females, derived from each of the following crosses:
   a. white-eyed female $\times$ red-eyed male
   b. heterozygous red-eyed female $\times$ white-eyed male
   c. heterozygous red-eyed female $\times$ red-eyed male

30. In man, normal vision (B) is dominant to red-green color blindness (b), and this trait is *sex-linked*. Specify the distribution of normal and defective eyes among the sons and daughters produced by each of the following matings:
   a. color-blind mother and normal father

b. heterozygous normal mother and color-
blind father

c. heterozygous normal mother and normal father

31. Enumerate the problems that have made it
difficult to analyze the details of human
heredity.

32. If each phenotypic characteristic of the organism is determined by several or many
pairs of genes, how is it possible that simple
ratios (for example, 3:1 and 1:2:1) are obtained in the F_2 generation when the inheritance of a particular characteristic is studied?

33. Define the term *population genetics*. Illustrate this explanation with reference to Snyder's study of the inheritance of "tasting
capacity."

34. Who coined the phrase "inborn errors of
metabolism"? Give three examples of this
phenomenon. Explain how and why a study
of these metabolic defects lends support to
the "one gene, one enzyme" hypothesis (p.
529).

35. What difficulties were encountered in determining the exact chromosome complement
of man? Explain how these difficulties were
surmounted. Explain how certain chromosomal aberrations are related to certain grave
pathological situations.

36. Discuss the phenomena of mutation, according to the following topics:
a. definition of the process
b. types of mutation
c. frequency of the types
d. factors that may modify the frequency
e. proof that a mutation cannot represent
the mere loss or destruction of a gene
f. relation of mutations to evolution

37. Carefully differentiate between the members
of each pair of terms:
a. genetic and environmental variation
b. an aberration and a true mutation
c. a deficiency and a duplication
d. translocation and inversion
e. triploidy and tetraploidy
f. artificial and natural selection

38. Discuss the problems of selective breeding,
emphasizing particularly:
a. the general technique
b. relation between inbreeding and homozygosity
c. the dangers of inbreeding and how
these may be overcome
d. the practical value of the method
e. the limitations of selective breeding

FURTHER READINGS

1. *You and Heredity,* by Amram Scheinfeld;
New York, 1950.

2. *Multiple Human Births: Twins, Triplets,
Quadruplets, and Quintuplets,* by H. H. New-
man; New York, 1940.

3. *Science in Progress,* chapter by G. W. Beadle;
New Haven, 1949.

4. *Principles of Human Genetics,* by C. Stern;
San Francisco, 1960.

5. *Genetics in the 20th Century,* L. C. Dunn,
editor; New York, 1951.

6. "The Chemistry of Hereditary Disease," by
A. G. Bearn; in *Scientific American,* December 1956.

7. "Chromosomes and Disease," by A. G. Bearn
and J. L. German III; in *Scientific American,*
November 1961.

27-Genes: Nature and Mode of Action

THREE GENERAL conclusions as to what genes are and how they act are now widely accepted: (1) each gene is part of a specific DNA compound; (2) genic effects upon development are mediated mainly by enzymes; and (3) each gene is responsible for guiding the synthesis of some particular one of the protein catalysts of the organism. These important conclusions have been reached within the past five years, although the origins go back almost a full century. In 1869 Friedrich Miescher first extracted a type of material, which he called *nuclein,* from fish sperm and from the nuclei of thymus gland tissue. Since then the trail of evidence that finally has led to the identifying of DNA as the code bearer in heredity has been long and complex. Only a few of the principal clues can be given in any short account, however.

IDENTIFICATION OF DEOXYRIBONUCLEIC ACID (DNA) AS THE GENIC MATERIAL

It was first realized in 1914, as a result of a staining technique devised by Robert Feul-gen, that **deoxyribonucleic acid** is the one kind of substance found almost exclusively in nuclei and that a large proportion of the chromosomal material consists of **DNA.** But it was almost 1950 before quantitative measurements—by A. E. Mirsky and Hans Ris of the Rockefeller Institute and by A. Bowin and C. Vendrely of the University of Strasbourg—showed that the DNA content of the nuclei in each organism is of a definite quantity in each species. Moreover, the haploid nuclei of a species contain exactly half as much DNA as the diploid nuclei; and if tetraploid nuclei occur, as they do occasionally in some tissues (for example, liver), these polyploid nuclei contain quadruple the haploid amount of DNA.

The foregoing observations indicated that there must be a very close relationship between DNA and the genic material. Then, later, a more direct demonstration that DNA determines hereditary transmission came from the **bacterial transformation** experiments of F. Griffith in England and of O. T. Avery, C. M. MacLeod, M. McCarty, and R. Hotchkiss working in the United States.

Bacterial Transformation. Previous to the discovery of bacterial transformation, it was generally believed that the only manner in which genes could be passed on from generation to generation was by way of chromosomes, transmitted by the complex mechanisms of mitosis, meiosis, and fertilization. The transformation experiments, on the other hand, led inevitably to the conclusion that certain bacterial genes can be passed from cell to cell through the culture medium in which the bacteria are growing, and that the transmitting agency must be DNA.

Some 30 different bacterial transformations have now been studied. Here, however, only one will be described. This deals with the inheritance of a protective capsule in *Diplococcus pneumoniae,* the pathogenic agent that causes bacterial pneumonia in man.

Two strains of this bacterium can be distinguished—one *naked,* the other *covered* by an easily visible capsule. Each of these strains, cultured separately, breeds true; that is, the naked and the covered types each give use only to their own kind. However, if naked cells are exposed to a medium prepared from *killed, broken-up, covered* cells, quite a number of the previously naked cells now develop capsules. Following this transformation, moreover, the newly encapsulated strains retain this characteristic from generation to generation indefinitely. In other words, a heritable change has been stamped upon an organism by material transmitted through the environment.

Further experiments clearly showed that the *bacterial transforming material* is always one or more of the high molecular weight DNA compounds, devoid of any protein. In some experiments, two transformations—for example, encapsulation and drug resistance—have been induced to occur simultaneously; and such changes may display linkage phenomena when their further hereditary transmission is followed. Moreover, the bacteria show waves of susceptibility to transformation, which may be correlated with the division cycles of the cells.

MACROMOLECULAR STRUCTURE OF DNA

A tremendous impetus to the study of **biochemical genetics** resulted in 1953 from the collaboration of F. H. C. Crick, an English worker, and J. D. Watson, an American. The Watson-Crick model of the molecular structure of DNA, which is shown in Figure 27-1, represented a synthesis of data from many sources; subsequently the essential features of this structure have been validated by many kinds of evidence. Consequently it was not surprising that a Nobel Prize was awarded to Crick and Watson, in 1962.

Previous analytical work by E. Chargaff at Columbia University, and by Mirsky and co-workers at the Rockefeller Institute, provided helpful preliminary information. Unit for unit **adenine** and **thymine** are always equal to each other in any DNA molecule, and the same is true for the other two organic bases, **guanine** and **cytosine** (Fig. 27-1). Moreover, the molecular dimensions of DNA structure (Fig. 27-1) were ascertained by the x-ray diffraction studies of M. H. F. Wilkins and others at King's College, London. The Watson-Crick structural model recognized these (and other) features. The analysis showed that only a **double helix,** such as is shown in Figure 27-1, would fit all the specifications.

The rungs of the coiled ladderlike structure of DNA are constituted by base pairs—cytosine-guanine and adenine-thymine—attached to one another by **hydrogen bonds** (p. 87). The sides of the ladder are formed by two (deoxyribose) sugar-phosphate chains, running in opposite directions, on either side. The space is restricted, however. Only a *purine-pyrimidine* pair (C—G or G—C or A—T or T—A) can achieve hydrogen bonding across the rungs of the ladder (Figs. 27-1 and 27-2).

The length of the double helix of a DNA

macromolecule may be exceedingly long. Frequently more than a thousand base pairs are

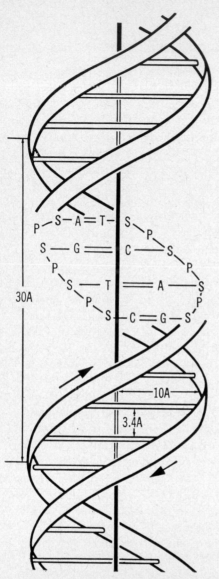

Fig. 27-1. Diagram of the Watson-Crick model of a section of a DNA molecule. Note that the double **helix** is formed by two sugar-phosphate chains (—S—P—S—P—), which run parallel to each other in opposite directions. The "cross bars" or "rungs," which hold the coiling sides of the "ladder" together, are constituted by **base pairs**, adenine≡thymine (A≡T) and guanine≡cytosine (G≡C), bound to each other by **hydrogen bonds** (≡). The base pairs may occur in any sequence, but the specific sequence in any one DNA molecule serves to determine the triplet code of protein synthesis. (After Watson and Crick.)

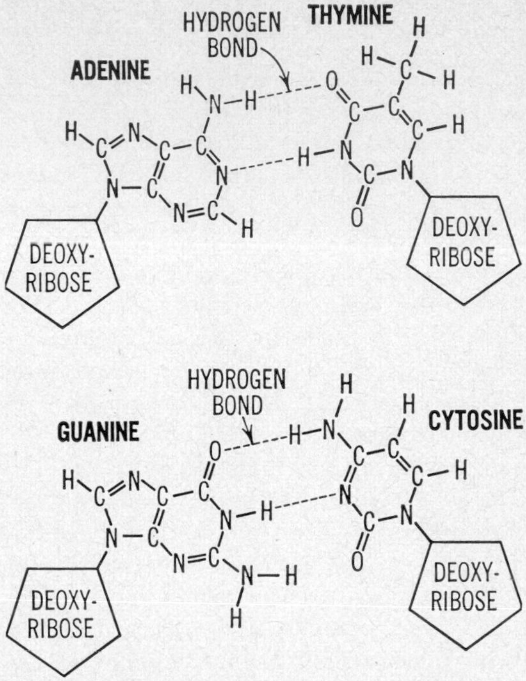

Fig. 27-2. **Base pairs** that form the "cross bars" of a DNA molecule. The size and shape of these **purine** and **pyrimidine** units determine their capacity to be bound together by **hydrogen bonds**, which stabilize the macromolecular structure. (After Crick.)

represented. Moreover, a different molecule occurs each time the sequence of the base pairs is shifted. Therefore it is safe to say that an almost infinite variety of DNA molecules exist—corresponding to the almost infinite variety of genes that have arisen during the evolution of our many species.

Self-templated Replication of DNA. A self-guided type of replication must be a prime requirement for any genic material. Accordingly, a mechanism for the replication of DNA has been proposed by Crick and others. This is diagramed in Figure 27-3.

The double helix presumably uncoils and separates into single strands, on which the bases of the successively arranged nucleotides occupy exposed positions. Then, if an adequate supply of the proper kinds of **free nucleotides** is present in the cell, these nucleotides become bonded in proper order—by virtue of the **base-pair rule** (p. 134)—

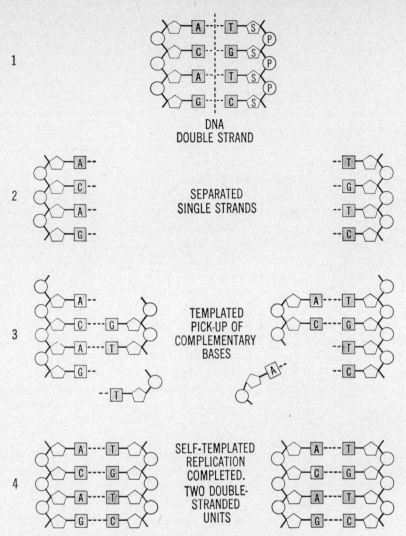

1

DNA
DOUBLE STRAND

2

SEPARATED
SINGLE STRANDS

3

TEMPLATED
PICK-UP OF
COMPLEMENTARY
BASES

4

SELF-TEMPLATED
REPLICATION
COMPLETED.
TWO DOUBLE-
STRANDED
UNITS

Fig. 27-3.   Crick hypothesis on the mechanism of DNA replication. Note that the **base-pair rule** operates in the assembling of the nucliotides. As a result of such self-templated replication, each of the new DNA units is an exact copy of the original. Symbols in the sugar-phosphate chain are S and P, respectively; in the base pairs, A, T, G, and C are adenine, thymine, guanine, and cytosine, respectively.

along each of the separate single strands. Finally a new sugar-phosphate chain is formed, and a re-coiling of the double helix occurs. In short, each single strand serves as a template for the building of a complementary strand; and finally, each of the new double helices constitutes an exact replica of the original one. A complex sort of **auto-catalysis** has occurred.

Recent evidence strongly supports this con-

cept of the mechanism of DNA replication. Particularly important in this regard are the experiments of Arthur Kornberg at Washington University. Kornberg worked on the synthesis of DNA in cell-free bacterial preparations (see below). Also important are the studies on viral DNA replication conducted by T. F. Anderson and S. S. Cohen at the University of Pennsylvania, A. D. Hershey and M. W. Chase at the Carnegie Laboratory in Cold Spring Harbor, N.Y., and Seymour Benzer at Purdue University.

Kornberg demonstrated self-templated synthesis of DNA in a medium prepared from disrupted bacterial cells. This preparation contained a good supply of the four varieties of free nucleotides and an enzyme designated as DNA **polymerase,** which catalyzes the formation of linkages in the sugar-phosphate chain. No synthesis of DNA occurred, however, unless some preformed DNA was added to the system. But when just a small amount of preformed DNA was added as a primer, new DNA was synthesized vigorously. And, most important of all, the "new" DNA appeared to be identical to the "old." A statistical analysis showed that the base-pair constitution of the newly synthesized DNA was exactly the same as that in the priming sample—regardless of the source and nature of this sample. In some cases, DNA from the same bacterial species was used; but in other cases the primer DNA was of viral origin or even more remarkable, DNA extracted from animal cells.

Replication of Viral DNA. Viruses, of course, display many resemblances to genes. Some biologists, indeed, regard viruses as "parasitic genes." In any event, the mechanisms of replication in genes and viruses are very similar, if not identical. Consequently the recent experiments on virus replication are highly significant.

Most of the experiments were done with the bacteriophage virus (strain T_2), which is shown in Figure 1-4; and the bacterial host was one of the human colon bacilli, *Escherichia coli,* also shown in Figure 1-4. The DNA fraction of the virus was labeled by incorporating radioactive phosphorus (P^{32}) into the phosphate parts of the molecule, and the protein fraction was identified by the incorporation of radioactive sulfur (S^{35}). In some experiments the viral DNA and protein were radioactively labeled in advance; but in others, the precursory compounds (phosphate and amino acids) containing radioactive atoms were added to the culture medium in which the bacteria (and viruses) were growing.

A bacterium infected by one particle of virus is destined to survive for only 24 minutes (at 20°C). Then the bacterial cell suddenly disintegrates. This liberates about 200 new virus particles into the culture medium, each ready to carry the infection to another bacterium. It is important, therefore, to determine precisely how this remarkable process of replication is achieved.

A study of the virus particle shows that all its content of DNA lies in the so-called "head" (Fig. 1-4B), a swollen rounded part; whereas the "tail" is formed solely of protein, which also forms a thin skin covering the DNA core of the head. When infection occurs, the tail makes contact with the surface of the bacterium, but only the DNA part of the virus actually enters into the bacterial cell. The protein part remains attached to the cell surface and eventually weakens this surface, by virtue of an enzymic activity. The whole responsibility for achieving a reduplication of the virus is assumed by the DNA fraction, which penetrates into the interior of the bacterial cell. The protein is important, however, in spreading the infection and in causing a lysis of the cells, but it is not essential to the actual process of replication.

The fate of the DNA, which goes into the bacterium, can also be followed, at least to some extent. Within 12 minutes, the viral DNA increases to about 200 times its original amount. About one third of this increase is at the expense of preformed nucleotides present in the bacterium, but mainly it represents new synthesis that utilizes inorganic phosphate from the culture medium. And while the viral DNA increases quickly, viral protein slowly begins to appear inside the bacterium, where at first it was completely absent. Indeed, no complete new virus particles (viral DNA plus viral protein) can be found in the bacterium until the very last part of the infection cycle. By this time, however, the viral protein has also increased about two hundredfold. Finally, therefore, about 200 complete new virus particles can be liberated, when the infected bacterium goes to pieces.

These studies on viral replication are important. Not only do they demonstrate that a self-templated synthesis of viral DNA occurs, but they also show that a close relationship exists between DNA and protein synthesis. Genic materials, apparently, are capable of templating the synthesis of other substances, as well as of themselves. In a sense, therefore, genes are both **autocatalytic** and **heterocatalytic**.

DNA-RNA-PROTEIN INTERRELATIONSHIPS

That **ribonucleic acid (RNA)** is essential for the synthesis of proteins, including enzymes, was suggested some twenty years ago by the work of T. O. Casperson of Stockholm and of Jean Brachet of Brussels. But only within the past five years, as the result of many studies, has it become apparent that the processes by which DNA, RNA, and proteins are synthesized are related to one another in a complex and fascinating manner.

In the ordinary cycle of cell division, an active new synthesis of DNA does not occur during mitosis or meiosis—while the chromosomes are compactly formed—but in between times—when the chromosomes are greatly extended (Fig. 2-11B) and when (presumably) the helical structure of the DNA is to a large extent uncoiled.

It has recently been proved that DNA can *template the synthesis of RNA* as well as of itself. Each single strand of uncoiled DNA assembles a complementary strand of RNA. This assembling process follows the **base-pair rule**—except that thymine (which is absent from RNA) is replaced by **uracil** in the pairing. Affiliation between the strands of DNA and RNA is short-lived, however. After separation, the RNA remains in single-stranded state. But eventually, after self-templated synthesis has occurred, DNA resumes its double-stranded helical form. The sugar of the sugar-phosphate chain, in the case of RNA is ribose, of course, rather than deoxyribose.

Such a heterocatalytic templating of RNA synthesis has been demonstrated most directly in cell-free bacterial preparations by Samuel Weiss at the University of Chicago and by Jerard Hurwitz at New York University; and in phage virus replication by Elliot Volkin, at the Oak Ridge National Laboratory. Moreover there has been considerable confirmatory evidence derived from the cells of higher organisms.

By templating the synthesis of RNA, DNA assumes indirect control over the synthesis of the enzymes and the other protein components of the organism, as was partly explained in Chapter 4.

Kinds of RNA. There are at least three kinds of RNA and each has a different mission to fulfill in the cytoplasm. **Ribosomal RNA**, a very stable form of high molecular weight, takes up a fixed position in the ribosomal membranes (p. 25). Here, presumably, it determines the alignment of the second kind, called **template RNA**. Template RNA (also called **messenger RNA**) is likewise of large molecular size, but it is relatively unstable. Template RNA keeps breaking down as its mission in protein synthesis is consummated. Consequently new template (messenger) units must, from time to time, originate from the nucleus. *Template (messenger) RNA, moreover, is the bearer of the genetic code.* The base sequence in this fraction determines the amino acid sequence in the protein being synthesized. In other words, the template for protein synthesis is carried by the messenger, or template, form of RNA.

The third form of RNA is of low molecular weight and it is freely dissolved in the cytoplasm. This form is called **transfer RNA** (also sRNA, or soluble RNA) because it serves to pick up amino acids from the cytoplasmic pool and to bring these units of protein structure into proper alignment upon the synthesizing template. And here again the base-pair rule operates to determine the affiliations between the transfer and the template forms of RNA. Thus the base-pair rule plays a crucial role in determining the precise order of amino acids in the peptide chain of the synthesized protein (Fig. 4-20). In the last analysis, therefore, the base-pair sequence of the genic DNA eventually determines the amino acid sequence in the protein components of each organism.

The situation is even more complex, however. Not only is a specific enzyme required for each amino acid as it affiliates with transfer RNA, but energy, provided by ATP, must be available. Moreover, the formation of peptide bonds, which link the amino acids together after they have been aligned properly upon the template, requires a further fund of energy. This is provided by another high-energy phosphate compound, namely **guanine triphosphate** (GTP). The fact remains, however, that the base order of the genic material finally determines the amino acid sequence in the proteins of the organism. Thus the specific enzymes of a species are a product of its genes.

THE GENETIC CODE

Deciphering the code of *biochemical instruction,* which is built into the DNA inheritance of an organism, represents a truly formidable problem. Considerable progress has recently been made, however, mainly as a result of experiments by Crick, Ochoa, Nirenberg, Benzer, Hurwitz, and others. Two principal methods have been valuable: (1) studies on protein synthesis in cell-free bacterial preparations (p. 524) to which are added artificially synthesized samples of (template) RNA—*in which the sequence of bases is known;* and (2) studies on the transmission of hereditary defects in the DNA component of bacteriophage viruses in doubly infected bacteria (see below).

Since there are only four bases—cytosine (C), guanine (G), thymine (T), and adenine (A)—present in a DNA molecule, and since there are some 20 amino acids to be coded, it is not possible for each amino acid to be coded by a single base. In fact, two bases per amino acid are not enough, because this system would yield only 16 (4×4) combinations. The simplest possible code, therefore, must consist of three bases, which provides for a system in which 64 ($4 \times 4 \times 4$) "words" are available.

Such a **triplet code** is shown in Table 27-1. Almost beyond doubt this is the code utilized by organisms generally. In this system, some amino acids are coded by more than one triplet, as has been verified in a number of experiments. In other words, using the special language of the code maker, the genetic code is a degenerate one.

Simplest Concept of a Gene. In order to code the synthesis of an average protein, which is a peptide chain consisting of some 500 to 1000 amino acid units, the DNA molecule must carry 500 to 1000 triplets, arranged precisely in a specified sequence. The simplest concept of a gene, accordingly, would be a segment of a DNA molecule in which, on the average, some 1500 to 3000 base pairs are represented. This is not an unduly large number, however. Most DNA molecules are exceedingly long. The DNA of the T_4 bacteriophage, for example, encompasses more than 200,000 base pairs, which would represent about 200 genes.

DNA in a chromosome is always combined with protein material. This, presumably, stabilizes the morphology of the chromosome. In any event, when chromosomes are subjected to digestion with deoxyribonuclease, the Feulgen-positive fraction disappears, leaving a sort of "ghost." But if chromosomes are treated with proteolytic enzymes, they tend to break into fragments of Feulgen-positive material.

BASIC NATURE OF MUTATION

As a by-product of the decoding studies of Crick and of Benzer, some insight has been gained as to the nature of mutational change. A heavy treatment of bacteria with two kinds of phage DNA (p. 524) often results in a

Table 27-1—The Genetic Code after Transfer from DNA to RNA

Coded Amino Acids	RNA Code Triplets			
Alanine	CCG	UCG *		
Arginine	CGC	AGA	UCG *	
Asparagine	ACA	AUA		
Aspartic acid	GUA			
Cysteine	UUG *			
Glutamic acid	GAA	AGU *		
Glutamine	ACA	AGA	AGU *	
Glycine	UGG	AGG		
Histidine	ACC			
Isoleucine	UAU	UAA		
Leucine	UUG	UUC	UUA	UUU *
Lysine	AAA	AAG *	AAU *	
Methionine	UGA *			
Phenylalanine	UUU			
Proline	CCC	CCU *	CCA *	CCG *
Serine	UCU	UCC	UCG	
Threonine	CAC	CAA		
Tryptophan	GGU			
Tyrosine	AUU			
Valine	UGU			

After M. W. Nirenberg.
* Not absolutely certain; data scanty.

double infection. Thus each bacterial cell may receive two kinds of viruses. When replication has been completed (p. 524), the liberated viruses may be (1) all of one kind; (2) some of one kind and some of the other; or (3) a **recombination** of the original two kinds —indicating that some kind of exchange has occurred between the strands of DNA material. The viruses are very favorable for such genetic studies, because millions of individual viruses are produced in each experiment and

the production of each new generation requires less than half an hour (p. 524).

Mutations, whether "spontaneous" or induced experimentally (p. 530), result apparently from one or more structural changes in the genic DNA. Such changes may involve (1) substitution in one or more of the base pairs; (2) subtraction of one or more base pairs; (3) addition of one or more base pairs; or (4) combinations of the foregoing. Such changes are heritable—provided they are not lethal (p. 512)—because each segment of a DNA molecule is able to self-template its own replication. A mutation, accordingly, may involve a structural change at one or more points along the length of a gene, and it is perfectly possible that more than one mutational change may occur within the limits of a single gene.

Crick's addition-subtraction analysis of the B gene of the T_4 virus indicates that the code within a single gene is written serially in triplets. Also it indicates that the code starts at one end of a genic segment. Thus, if a single addition or subtraction occurs near the start of a genic series, the whole code is disrupted; that is, the whole gene becomes inoperative. Consider, for example, one end of a gene that carries (via RNA) the following code:

alanine -- cysteine -- glycine -- alanine --
   CCG... UUG... UGG... CCG... U...etc.

If, however, a subtraction occurs at the first C, code would now read:

CGU ... UGU ... GGC ... CGU ... etc.

Thus the code would be completely changed and the gene could not fulfill its proper function. If, however, a subtraction near the beginning of a genic series is balanced by a nearby addition, most of the gene triplets would remain unchanged. Then the gene might continue to function, although there might be some slight change in its effects. Perhaps an altered triplet, if it still remains a triplet, might summon a single different amino acid into a protein chain. This, indeed, appears to be the case in certain heritable changes, such as sickle cell anemia (p. 505).

An interesting phenomenon is observed in the replication of T_4 phage virus, when two differently mutated viral strands are undergoing replication in a single bacterial cell. An exchange of DNA material between the strands may take place; and the points at which such exchanges occur *do not necessarily lie between two genic segments*. Sometimes, indeed, a break may be localized *within a genic segment*.

Simplest to analyze are cases where **deletions** have been induced within the same

PARTS OF A GENIC SEGMENT OF DNA

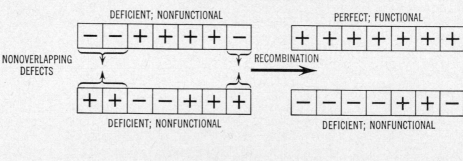

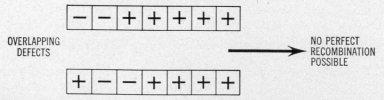

Fig. 27-4. Recombination within a genic segment. Each minus sign (—) indicates a deficiency—presumably a missing base pair. Plus sign (+) indicates normal base pairs. (Modified from Benzer.)

genic segment in both of the replicating DNA strands (Fig. 27-4). In this case, neither gene can function by itself. But if the two strands are replicating simultaneously in the same bacterial cell, an exchange of parts within the limits of the single gene may give rise to one perfect unit (Fig 27-4). This can only occur, however, *if there is no overlapping of the deficient sections,* as is shown diagrammatically in Figure 27-4.

An analogous phenomenon has been reported by Green and Green, studying the inheritance of three mutational changes in *Drosophila.* These mutations appear to be localized very near each other in the chromosome, probably at different points along the length of the same gene. All three mutations have a similar effect upon the shape of the eye. Each produces what is termed a "lozenge eye" when it is homozygous. Consequently, these mutations have been designated as lz^1, lz^2, and lz^3.

The curious thing about the inheritance of the *lz* mutations is that they reach expression, even when heterozygous, if *they are localized oppositely (trans-position)* in the pair of chromosomes—as is shown in Figure 27-5. When the loci are in the same chromosome *(cis-position)* the mutant genes are inactive. One perfect *(nonmutated)* genic unit seems necessary for the production of a normally formed eye, just as a complete unit is necessary for function in T_4 bacteriophage. Some recent workers prefer to call such an integrated series of mutational sites a *cistron,* rather than a gene, but this appears to be mainly a matter of semantics.

ROLE OF THE GENES IN DEVELOPMENT: THE ONE GENE, ONE ENZYME CONCEPT

Even before it was known that DNA can determine the synthesis of enzymes and other proteins, considerable evidence indicated that genic defects were correlated with enzyme deficiencies. Several examples of such a relationship have already been cited; for example, the case of *phenylketonuria,* in which

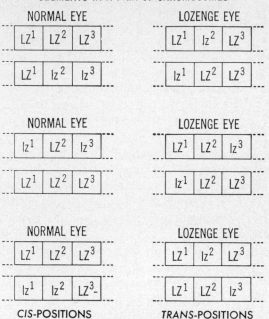

SEGMENTS IN A PAIR OF CHROMOSOMES

Fig. 27-5. The effects of a series of mutational changes may depend upon their relative positions in a pair of chromosomes. The development of a normal eye depends upon the existence of one normal gene (or gene series) in at least one of the chromosomes. LZ^1, LZ^2, and LZ^3 are nonmutated sites, which in series yield an eye of normal shape; lz^1, lz^2, and lz^3 are mutant sites, which yield an abnormal (lozenge-shaped) eye if they interrupt a series of nonmutated sites.

a defective gene determines the absence of one enzyme, and of *alkaptonuria,* in which another deleterious mutation is associated with another missing enzyme (Chap. 26). But final demonstration that such a relationship frequently (if not always) obtains awaited the ingenious experimental work of Beadle and Tatum.

Beadle and Tatum studied the inheritance of mutational changes induced by x-ray irradiation in the red baker's mold, *Neurospora crassa.* This mold provides an exceedingly favorable material. It has a short (10-day) life cycle and the mycelium that grows from each spore is haploid. Thus any recessive mutation is not obscured by a dominant allele; that is, the effect can be observed in the first generation. Moreover, the hereditary transmission of the mutation, as a single recessive gene, can be followed readily in the next generation, when a mutant strain is allowed to conjugate with a nonmutant. The diploid sporocytes in the sporangium of such a sexually produced mycelium (Fig. 12-10) will possess the mutant gene balanced against a nonmutant allele. But these genes soon become segregated from one another during meiosis, which follows immediately. Therefore, by collecting the individual spores from each sporangium and by culturing the spores separately, it is possible to determine that half the spores possess the mutant (usually defective) gene and half carry the normal nonmutant allele.

Normally *Neurospora* grows excellently on a medium that contains only inorganic salts, sugar, and **one vitamin,** namely **biotin** (p. 353). After irradiation, however, various mutant strains are found that cannot grow unless the mold is provided with one or more additional vitamins, such as niacin, thiamine, etc. The data show that each genic deficiency is inherited as a simple recessive and is related to the loss of a particular enzyme. The synthesis of **niacin,** for example, passes through a series of intermediates: *anthranilic*

$$acid \xrightarrow{E_1} \xrightarrow{E_2} indole; indole + serine \xrightarrow{E_3} trypto\text{-}$$

$$phan \xrightarrow{E_4} \xrightarrow{E_5} 3\text{-}hydroxyanthranilic\ acid \xrightarrow{E_6} \xrightarrow{E_7}$$

niacin. Each of these seven steps is catalyzed by a different enzyme (E_1, E_2, . . . E_7). But the important point is that each time a single gene is damaged by the radiation, one and only one enzyme is lost in the series. Probably most of the individual genes of an organism carry the code for the production of a particular enzyme. However, some genes may determine the synthesis of other proteins.

One more example of a one gene, one enzyme relation will suffice, although many others could be cited among higher as well as lower organisms. Certain flounders are known to lack black pigment in their melanophores, and this lack, which prevents the fish from changing its shade in accord-

ance with the background of the environment, is determined by a recessive allele of the normal "pigment gene." Accordingly, when heterozygous pigmented flounders are inbred, they produce pigmented and unpigmented offspring in a ratio of 3:1. But the significance of this study is revealed by further data. When the melanophores of the nonpigmented individuals are tested, these cells are found to lack one specific oxidizing enzyme (**dopa oxidase**), which is present in all normal melanophores. Thus the black pigment, *melanin,* which is an oxidation product derived from *dopa,* a colorless precursory compound, cannot be formed in the melanophores of the nonpigmented fish. From this experiment it may be concluded that the normal "pigment gene" achieves its phenotypic effect in the melanophores of the flounder by determining the production of a specific metabolic enzyme; a similar situation has been found in reference to the formation of black hair pigment in guinea pigs and other mammals.

Determining, as they do, the enzymes of an organism, the genes are a tremendously potent force. They govern not only the metabolism of the cells of the adult, but also the metabolism of the cells throughout all stages of embryonic development. This, indeed, is generally believed to be the principal mechanism by which the complex and beautifully integrated processes of development are guided. However, the presence of a particular gene in a particular cell does not mean that the enzyme templated (indirectly) by that gene must necessarily also be present in the cell. Genes may remain dormant until activated by the conditions of their intracellular environment. A central problem in experimental embryology is, therefore, to find out how the intracellular environment provides for the intricate system of checks, balances, and controls for genic activity throughout development.

Enzyme Induction Phenomena. A study of enzyme induction, particularly among bacteria, has provided some clue as to one mechanism of genic control. A particular bacterial cell, for example, may be capable of metabolizing a wide variety of organic substrates including, let us say, sucrose and lactose. If such bacteria are cultured for some time in a medium containing sucrose but not lactose, the presence of sucrase but not lactase [1] can be demonstrated in the cells. When lactose is added to the medium, therefore, this sugar cannot be utilized at first. Gradually, however, in the course of about half an hour, lactase begins to be produced by the cells and lactose begins to be metabolized more and more vigorously. Apparently the presence of a particular substrate in the cell has induced the production of the proper enzyme. Presumably the particular gene capable of guiding the synthesis of the enzyme had been present in the cells throughout but this gene had remained dormant until stimulated by the particular substrate.

Induction of specific enzymes by specific substrates, although studied most intensively among bacteria, appears to be a general phenomenon of widespread occurrence in many, if not all, cells. Probably, therefore, such induction plays an important role in mediating genic influences upon developmental processes.

EXPERIMENTAL EMBRYOLOGY

A principal goal in the field of experimental embryology is to reach a fuller understanding of what is sometimes called the **mechanics of development.** In essence, the experimental embryologist is trying to find out how, when, and where the genes produce their developmental effects.

One perennial question continues to be: How does differentiation occur? Usually all the cells of a young embryo appear to be alike. Yet marked differences soon appear as the specialized tissues—nerve, muscle, cartilage, bone, and so forth—come into being, and as the tissues become fitted together in the final structure of the adult organs.

[1] Also called β-galactosidase.

Since all the cells of the embryo arise by repeated mitosis from the original fertilized egg cell, it seems probable that all must receive identical sets of genes. The possibility exists, however, that somehow genic differences may arise among the embryonic cells. Consequently, the experiments of Robert Briggs and Thomas King of the Institute for Cancer Research at the Lankenau Hospital in Philadelphia are of particular interest. These workers have succeeded in removing the zygote nucleus from frogs' eggs, and in *substituting other nuclei,* taken from the individual cells of frog embryos at different stages of development. Generally speaking, this work indicates that up until the early gastrula stage, at least, a nucleus from any one of the many cells present in the young embryo can be substituted for the zygote nucleus without impairing the capacity of the egg to fulfill its developmental destiny. Nuclei from later stages, however, are not successful substitutes. But whether this failure results from the reduced size of such nuclei, or from some change in genic constitution, remains an open question. At present there does not seem to be any convincing evidence to show that the various embryonic cells do acquire distinctive differences in their genic constitutions. It seems necessary, therefore, to look elsewhere in trying to solve the problems of cellular differentiation.

In general, it would seem, the genes received by a particular embryonic cell determine the developmental *potentiality* of that cell, but the environment of the genes and of the cell as a whole determines the *actuality* of development. Sooner or later the genes in the different cells come under the influence of many *small differentials of local environment.* Differences in relation to the *position of the cells in the embryo* and differences in the cytoplasmic composition begin to appear, and these small differences seem to play a crucial role in cellular differentiation.

The cytoplasm represents a part of the environment of any set of genes; and a given set of genes may produce totally different effects, owing to small differences in the composition of the surrounding cytoplasm. Even at the time of fertilization there are always significant differences in cytoplasmic composition at the poles of the zygote. Moreover, the cytoplasm of the animal pole goes mainly to an upper group of cells, during normal cleavage (Fig. 15-2); and the cytoplasm of the vegetal pole goes to the lower cells. Inevitably, therefore, differences occur between the cells at a very early stage of development. And as development continues, many other differentials develop in the genic environments of the various regions of the embryo. The chemical environment is not uniform, since some cells come to lie in a more advantageous position with reference to the supply of oxygen and other nutrients, and some cells have an easier problem in disposing of their metabolic wastes. Substrates present in one cell may become different from those in another, and consequently different enzymes may be induced to form. Also, the distribution of physical factors—such as pressure (from other cells), light, heat, and electric fields—do not impinge uniformly upon the different cells. All these chemical and physical forces appear to cooperate in determining the differential action of the genes in the different cells of the embryo. One main problem in experimental embryology is, therefore, to determine which of these environmental factors play crucial roles in the differentiation of particular structures, and when this control is exerted in the case of each different kind of cell.

Pressure from neighboring parts of the embryo may greatly influence developmental processes, as is demonstrated by a classic experiment on the frog's egg. If the two blastomeres are separated in the two-cell stage of development, each of the separated cells develops into a small but perfectly *whole* embryo. But if one of the two cells is merely killed and left in contact with its companion, the remaining cell develops into only *half* an embryo. This shows that pressure, or at least some other factor associated with the con-

tiguous cell, dead though it be, has had a very profound influence upon the developmental destiny of all the other cells of the embryo.

Some Problems of Morphogenesis. A number of investigators are currently attempting to analyze the various factors and forces that operate to determine the form and arrangement of the aggregated cells of the embryo during development. Here, however, it is possible to give only a very brief account of results obtained by T. Gustafson of Stockholm and L. Wolpert of London (working in collaboration) and by J. T. Bonner (Princeton University), B. Shaffer (Cambridge University), and A. A. Moscona (University of Chicago).

Wolpert and Gustafson in their time-lapse cinematographic studies of morphogenesis in sea urchin embryos have emphasized the importance of four simple factors: (1) changes in the areas of cohesion between contiguous cells; (2) changes in the areas of adhesion between the cells and some supporting membrane; (3) pseudopodial activity; and (4) adhesion between the pseudopodia and stationary cells that are contacted by them.

An indication of how the first two factors (cohesion and adhesion areas) may operate is given in Figure 27-6. Furthermore, it is not difficult to visualize how the other two factors may come into play. Shortly after a blastula is formed, a number of cells lose contact with the supporting membrane at the surface of the embryo. These cells then become crowded into the blastocoel, where they display vigorous pseudopodial activity. The pseudopodial out-thrustings appear to be random. However, there are certain areas, bordering the blastocoel, where the amoeboid cells, or rather their pseudopodia, tend to stick. By a contraction of the pseudopodia, therefore, the migratory amoeboid cells may come into close association with certain cells on the surface of the blastula. In other words, localized changes in the cohesive and adhesive properties of cells, together with cellular motility, are important factors in deter-

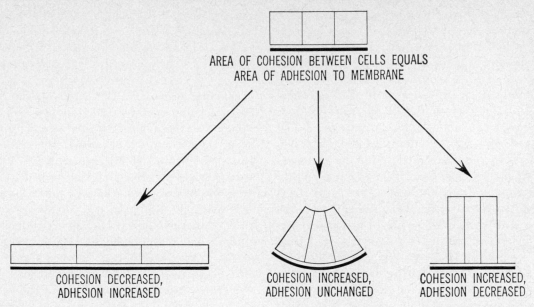

AREA OF COHESION BETWEEN CELLS EQUALS
AREA OF ADHESION TO MEMBRANE

COHESION DECREASED,
ADHESION INCREASED

COHESION INCREASED,
ADHESION UNCHANGED

COHESION INCREASED,
ADHESION DECREASED

Fig. 27-6. How changes in cohesion between cells and adhesion to a supporting membrane may affect the form of aggregated cells, in an embryo or in a tissue. It is assumed that no change has occurred in the volume of the cells. (After Gustafson and Wolpert.)

mining morphogenesis. But precisely how these forces and factors are controlled by the genes remains an open question.

Special affinities of association between cells, which seem to depend upon mutal cohesiveness, have also been demonstrated by the work of Moscona and associates. The technique of these experiments is to grow mixed cultures of different cells in a common fluid medium that is being stirred constantly. The cells of a sponge, for example, tend to recongregate, forming a complete organism, after they have been subjected to experimental treatments that cause them to be dispersed individually. The observations indicate, however, that the reassociation is not random. If the dispersed cells of a yellow and red sponge are stirred in a common medium, the yellows always aggregate with yellows and the reds with reds. Or if liver, retina, and kidney cells from a chick embryo are circulating together in a common culture medium, each kind tends to form aggregates with its own kind. Moreover, in certain tissues at least, definite points of attachment may be formed between contiguous cells, as

has been shown by the electronmicrograph studies of Keith Porter of Harvard University.

In some cases, specific substances may mediate an aggregation, causing mutual attraction between cells. One such substance, *acrasin,* has recently been isolated by Shaffer. This substance controls the aggregation of cells in the slime mold, *Dictiostelium* (Fig. 2-23), which has been studied so intensively by Bonner and others. Genic control of such associative phenomena does not seem difficult to understand, because genes are able to govern the production of specific enzymes, which, in turn, determine the synthesis of specific end products.

Determination. Sooner or later, each cell in the embryo finally "takes its destiny into its own hands" and becomes **determined** as to its eventual differentiation. But the time at which determination occurs differs widely in different embryos, and in the different cells of the same embryo. In a few embryos, the cells are determined very early, even at the two-cell stage—in which case each of the separated blastomeres can give rise to only half an embryo. But in most cases a determination of the cells comes much later in the embryonic period.

In the frog embryo **during gastrulation** (p. 277), small groups of cells may be *transplanted* from almost any part of the embryo and induced to grow in various new positions in the same embryo. Such transplanted cells usually change their destiny and develop into structures that are normal for the region *to* which they have been moved. But if similar transplantations are made at a later stage, the results are altogether different. Now the transplanted cells give rise to structures characteristic of the region *from* which they have been moved. The cells of a **limb bud,** for example, moved from the shoulder region to the side of the abdomen, now cling to their original destiny, giving rise to a forelimb that is quite normal except for the peculiarity of its position. At some time between

gastrulation and the appearance of the limb bud, these cells have lost their **totipotency;** that is, they have become **unipotent,** or **determined,** as to their eventual fate, or destination.

Embryonic Organizers. One group of cells in the frog embryo becomes determined much earlier than the others. During gastrulation the cells constituting the **dorsal lip** of the **blastopore** (Fig. 27-7), if transplanted to another part of another embryo, go on developing in the same manner as they would have done had they not been moved. Moreover, the transplanted **dorsal lip** not only determines its own development, but it also *organizes* the development of the neighboring cells. Soon an *extra* **neural tube** begins to form in the host embryo, in front of the site of the transplanted dorsal lip (Fig. 27-8); and an extra vertebral column, together with associated structures, is *induced* to form in

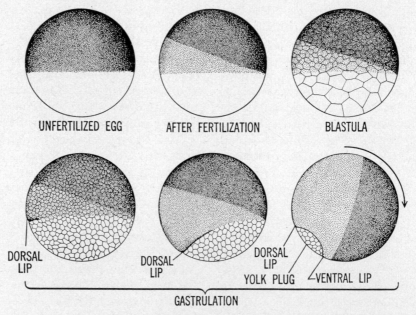

UNFERTILIZED EGG   AFTER FERTILIZATION   BLASTULA

DORSAL LIP   DORSAL LIP   DORSAL LIP   YOLK PLUG   VENTRAL LIP

GASTRULATION

Fig. 27-7. Early development of a frog embryo. The primary axis of the unfertilized egg is vertical; i.e., the animal pole is on top. After fertilization, the gray crescent (left) appears. The secondary axis is now horizontal and the median plane corresponds with the surface of the page. During gastrulation the whole embryo rotates as indicated by the arrow, so that the primary axis originally vertical, becomes the longitudinal axis, with the animal pole at the anterior end; the secondary axis, originally horizontal, becomes the dorsoventral axis, with the original gray crescent region on the dorsal side.

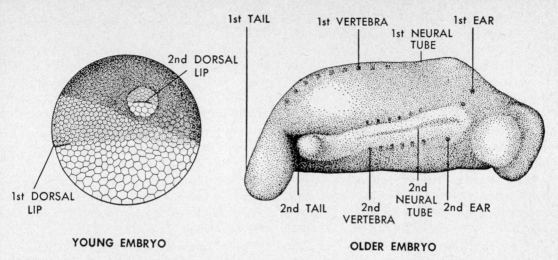

Fig. 27-8. *Left,* an embryo at the beginning of gastrulation. An organizer from another embryo of the same stage has been transplanted, in the position shown. *Right,* the same embryo at a later stage.

an entirely foreign region of the embryo. Thus the **dorsal lip** of the blastopore serves as the **primary organizer** in the vertebrate embryo. In fact the organizing capacity of the lip region can be traced back before gastrulation. If the corresponding part of a fertilized egg is removed, such an egg never develops into anything but a ball of cells; whereas if other small parts of the egg are taken away, the egg still gives rise to a normal or approximately normal embryo.

After gastrulation, other parts of the embryo, especially those lying near the primary organizer, gradually become determined. Soon a bit of ectoderm, transplanted from the dorsal surface quite some distance anterior to the blastopore, will develop into nerve cord regardless of its new location. Moreover, this ectoderm acts as a **secondary organizer** in that it determines not only its own development, but also that of nearby parts. And in like manner, other parts of the embryo, once they have been determined and launched upon some special line of independent development, may act as organizers of such parts as may still remain in a nondetermined state.

Precisely how an organizer "organizes" is quite unknown. Perhaps it produces special substrates that, transmitted to neighboring cells, change the enzyme induction pattern of these cells. The dorsal lip tissue will induce the formation of a neural tube even if the lip tissue is *killed* before it is introduced into the host embryo. In fact, supernumerary neural tubes have been induced by a variety of chemical and physical agencies, some quite foreign to the normal embryonic environment. At present, all that can be said is that the organizer introduces some kind of differential into the environment of the genes of neighboring cells, and this differential induces a change in the subsequent behavior of these genes. Certainly the different parts of an embryo have ample opportunity for affecting one another: mechanically, as a result of mutual pressure; chemically, as a result of differences in the rates and qualities of metabolism; electrically, by way of bioelectric phenomena; and so forth. Moreover, other factors that are still obscure may play upon the genes in the different parts of the embryo, determining the course of their performance within the sphere of their potentiality.

Probably every gene is present in all the diploid cells of the organism, and therefore every gene may have some effect upon the metabolism of every cell. More or less constantly the genes must continue to use up substances needed in their self-templated synthesis, and very probably the genes produce other substances as by-products of self-synthesis. Every such removal and addition must have a definite influence upon the complexly interrelated reactions of metabolism, and consequently every gene must have some metabolic importance in every cell of the body at every stage of development. No doubt the importance of a given gene is much greater in some parts of the body as compared to others. If a gene is to change the pigmentation of the eye, for example, this effect can appear only in such cells as may contain the precursory substances from which the eye pigment is to be formed. It seems probable that these precursory substrates serve not only as raw materials for pigment synthesis, but also as activators of the genes that produce the proper enzymes. Thus, each gene may produce several or many effects in the different cells of the organism, depending upon chemical and physical conditions in the different cells; and the destiny of a cell depends not only on its genes, but also on the factors of its environment, and, in addition, on the intrinsic composition and structure of its own cytoplasm.

GENIC DETERMINATION OF HORMONES

Recent studies have made steady progress in determining precisely how specific genes may exert their developmental influence upon the phenotypic characteristics of various organisms, but only one such study will be mentioned. It has been shown, for example, that dwarfism in mice, which is inherited as a single recessive factor, is mediated through the pituitary gland. The pituitary of a mouse that is homozygous for the "dwarf gene" displays a deficiency in the enzyme system of the particular cells that are responsible for the production of the growth hormone (p. 410). Thus if such a genetically dwarfed individual receives growth hormone injections, it achieves full stature and cannot be distinguished from a genetically large mouse.

In conclusion it may be said that our newly acquired knowledge about the structure and mode of replication of DNA and about how the genic materials influence synthetic metabolism in every cell has given great impetus to the study of biochemical genetics and biochemical embryology, and one can now expect a rapid "breakthrough" on these scientific fronts.

TEST QUESTIONS

1. Summarize the main evidence that indicates that DNA represents the essential genic material.
2. Differentiate between double- and single-stranded DNA. How is this difference related to self-templated replication and to the synthesis of RNA?
3. Distinguish between transfer RNA and messenger RNA. What other terms are used in this connection?
4. What is the base-pair rule? How is this rule related to the *triplet code?*
5. Explain why a doublet code would not be adequate in determining protein synthesis.
6. Mention the names of five men who have made important contributions in biochemical genetics and explain the work of each.
7. What is meant by the term "bacterial transformation"? How do the transformation experiments identify DNA with the genic materials?
8. Cite experimental evidence that indicates that DNA is important in determining protein-enzyme synthesis.
9. How does the bacteriophage virus achieve self-duplication? What seems to be the role of DNA in this process?
10. How and why do the experiments on the red baker's mold (*Neurospora*) indicate that there is a close relationship between genes, enzymes, and vitamins?
11. Although all the cells of an embryo are equal as to their genes, all the cells do not remain alike as development proceeds. In general terms, how can this differentiation of the embryonic cells be accounted for?

12. Briefly discuss and *exemplify* each of the following topics:
   a. an experimental technique that demonstrates whether a given part of the embryo is determined or not determined
   b. an experiment that shows that the presence of one cell (dead or alive) can influence the development of all the other cells in the embryo
   c. the role of the dorsal lip of the blastopore as an embryonic organizer
   d. the time at which determination occurs in the different parts of a frog embryo
   e. the nature of the organizing influence of the dorsal lip
13. Discuss briefly the possible ways in which the genes may affect the metabolism and hence the development of a given cell.

FURTHER READINGS

1. *Experimental Embryology,* by T. H. Morgan; New York, 1927.
2. *An Introduction to Experimental Embryology,* by G. R. DeBeer; New York, 1934.
3. *Principles of Development,* by Paul Weiss; New York, 1939.
4. Section on "Bacterial Transformation," by O. T. Avery, C. M. MacLeod, and M. McCarty, in *Great Experiments in Biology,* ed. by M. Gabriel and S. Fogel; Englewood Cliffs, N. J., 1955.
5. Articles in *Scientific American* by G. W. Beadle (September 1948); R. D. Hotchkiss and E. Weiss (November 1956); F. H. C. Crick (October 1954 and October 1962); and M. W. Nirenberg (March 1963).

28-*Natural Selection;*

Origin of Species

IT IS certain that the plants and animals of today have descended from species that occupied the earth in previous times. Moreover, there are only two alternatives as to the nature of this descent. Either there has been a **fixity** *of the species,* such that the existing species have *descended without change* from the pre-existing species; or **evolution** *has occurred,* in the sense that the species have undergone change during the course of their descent from pre-existing forms.

The idea of evolution extends back into ancient times, but Darwin, in 1859, first succeeded in marshaling a convincing array of basic evidence. However, it was not until the present century that modern genetics provided many missing clues as to how the known processes of heredity and reproduction inevitably lead to evolution.

Under natural conditions every species of plant and animal is constantly subjected to a process of **selection.** The parents selected to perpetuate each species in every generation are not chosen artificially according to the specifications of mankind, but naturally, according to their *ability to live and reproduce* under the conditions of their particular environment. This process of **natural selection,** as will be apparent shortly, results inevitably from the normal tendency of every organism to multiply at a rate that exceeds the capacity of the environment to support all the offspring of any given species.

MULTIPLICATION OF ORGANISMS; A GEOMETRICAL PROGRESSION

Every kind of organism tends to multiply at a characteristic *rate.* Perhaps the highest rate occurs among certain bacteria, which, under favorable conditions, will divide once every half hour. At this rate the population would be quadrupled every hour, and in 24 hours the descendants of a single bacterium would number 2^{48} (more than 280 million million), *if they all survived.* A million seeds, or spores, per year are not uncommon for an individual plant, and many invertebrates, and even lower vertebrates like fish, produce more than a million fertilized eggs annually. Higher vertebrates, especially birds and mammals, do not produce so many eggs, but these animals provide more care for the developing young, so that a larger proportion of the offspring can survive. Probably the slowest multiplication rate is that of the elephant. This animal begins to breed at the age of 20 and continues until 60, producing an average of six calves during the reproductive period. Even at this exceedingly slow rate, *if every elephant survived,* the descendants of a single pair would number more than 18,000,000 in 750 years; and in three or four additional centuries, the earth could provide "standing room only, for elephants only."

These facts are summarized by realizing that every kind of organism, whether its multiplication rate is slow or fast, tends to increase in geometrical progression: $n, n^2, n^3,$ . . . etc. where n is the average number of offspring per individual parent per generation, and the exponential numbers designate the sequence of the generations. Graphically this relation is shown by curve A in Figure

28-1, which is often called the curve of compound interest, or the **growth curve.** In this natural type of multiplication, the rate of increase grows greater and greater as the population increases. Accordingly, if all the offspring survived and reproduced, every species, even those with the slowest natural rates of reproduction, eventually would increase until it covered the earth, and this eventuality would be fulfilled within a relatively short time in relation to terrestrial history.

Limits of Population Increases. Obviously, plant and animal populations do not actually increase in this manner, for they are limited by the food supply and by a number of other *environmental conditions.* This limitation is illustrated by the lower curve in Figure 28-1, which shows the actual multiplication of yeast cells in a definitely limited amount of nutrient. Initially the actual growth curve follows the theoretical growth curve very closely, but soon the rate of increase falls off, and finally the number of cells reaches a constant value beyond which there is no further increase. Under comparable conditions, a population of any species behaves

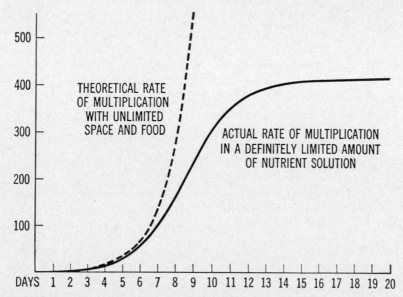

Fig. 28-1. Multiplication of yeast cells: abscissas, time in days; ordinates, number of cells (in millions).

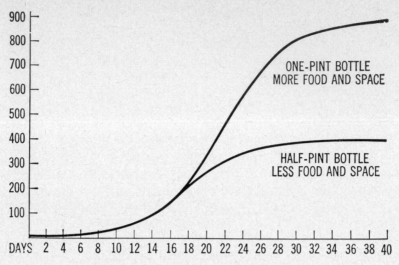

Fig. 28-2.   Multiplication rates in *Drosophila*.

similarly, as is shown for *Drosophila* in Figure 28-2 and for man in Figure 28-3. In each case the population reaches a constant maximum, under a given set of conditions; and this maximum is attained in a relatively short time, that is, within a relatively small number of generations. The level of this maxi-

mum is determined largely by environmental conditions, as may be seen in Figure 28-2. After the maximum is reached, a population may fluctuate from year to year or—within shorter periods, in rapidly reproducing organisms—in accordance with the food supply and other environmental conditions. But by

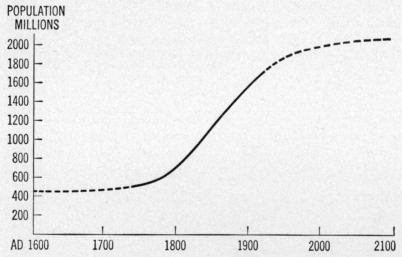

Fig. 28-3.   Human population of the earth: abscissas, years; ordinates, population in millions. The solid portion of the curve is based on actual data; the dotted portions are purely theoretical, calculated from the equation of the curve. The increase in population during this period, from its previous stationary level, is the result of the great change in environmental conditions caused by the Industrial Revolution. The upper, dotted portion of the curve predicts the future population on the assumption that there will be no further great environmental changes—a very doubtful assumption. (Adapted from Pearl.)

and large, over any long period, the average level of the population remains fairly constant, provided environmental conditions do not undergo a permanent change.

Limitations of the Environment. In general, the principal factor that limits a given population is the **food supply**—using this term in the very broadest sense. Among animals and colorless plants, the fund of organic foods available in the particular habitat is especially important, although water, oxygen, or other inorganic nutrients may be limiting factors in some environments. But among plants, the primary nutritive factor is apt to be the quantity of accessible **light,** although the available quantity of inorganic foods, such as water or salts, is sometimes very important.

A number of other environmental factors act directly in determining the population levels of different animals and plants, in addition to having indirect effects upon the food supply. Climatic conditions (heat, cold, wind, ice, snow, fog, etc.) impose definite limits on the extent of territory that can be occupied by a given species; **predaceous** and **parasitic** enemies (Chap. 30) may prey upon the populations, and a variety of minor factors may assume importance in particular cases. But for any particular species, under unchanging environmental conditions, a balance is reached between its natural tendency to increase and the limiting factors of its particular environment.

NATURAL SELECTION

The fact that each species in every generation produces so many offspring that only a fraction can possibly achieve the age of sexual maturity gives rise to two important questions: What selecting agency scrutinizes the many offspring and chooses the few that are to survive and perpetuate the species; and what characteristics qualify the individuals that are selected?

Generally speaking, organisms that are *fittest to survive and reproduce* under the conditions of their particular environment are automatically selected to perpetuate each species. The selecting agency is the natural environment of each species, and the main qualification for selection is a *fitness to survive and reproduce in competition with other organisms* that seek to utilize the same environment. Inevitably each organism encounters a ceaseless *struggle for existence*— using this term in the broadest sense—since potentially *unlimited* numbers of each kind of organism are competing for sustenance in a definitely *limited* environment.

The struggle for existence does not imply direct and active combat, except in the case of some predaceous animals. Survival depends more on the organisms' capacity to withstand adverse physical conditions (temperature, light, etc.) and unfavorable conditions (drought, soil fertility, etc.) in the chemical environment. But above all, the struggle is a competition for the *necessities* of life, of which the supply is strictly limited. This aspect of the struggle for existence, indirect and obscure though it frequently may be, reaches a climax of intensity among organisms of the same or closely related species, because such organisms are competing for the *same,* or very similar necessities.

Take, for example, a group of annual plants sprouting on a limited plot of ground. At first the ground may be thickly covered with a large number of small seedlings; but as the season progresses, the *number* of survivors falls off, while their *size* increases. Finally there are just a few individuals left and these completely occupy the area in which hundreds of seeds originally germinated. Among such plants the struggle is primarily for a "place in the sun," and the struggle is especially keen because light is absolutely essential to every competitor. The seedlings that spread their leaves a little faster and farther overshadow the others, cutting off their light and assuring their starvation. But the survivors go on and produce the next year's crop of seeds, whereupon the process is repeated. Thus a selection has been made in the direction of the faster growing seedlings, and the selecting agency has been the environment. Similarly among animals, the primary selecting factor is very frequently a competition for the limited supply of organic food; and since individuals of the same species have the same food requirements, the struggle is keenest within such a population.

Of course there are wholesale and indiscriminate forces of destruction (storms, floods, glaciers, etc.), which may reduce a population without any regard for the capacity of the individual to *survive* and *reproduce.* Also an individual's survival may hinge upon sheer accident. Some seeds fall on good ground and some on stony ground—through no virtue of the former or fault of the latter. But over and above such nonselective eliminations, *speaking in terms of the average,* the individuals of a species that are most healthy, vigorous, capable of securing food and escaping or protecting themselves from enemies, resistant to disease and unfavorable weather, and so forth, and so forth—in short, those that are *fittest to survive and reproduce* under the given conditions—are most likely to be the perpetuators of the species. Thus variations—or more particularly variations of the heritable type—play a very definite role in survival by providing the material upon which the environment exerts its selective action.

Natural selection differs from **artificial selection** not only as regards the criteria by which the surviving individuals are chosen, but also as to the *time element.* Progress ceases in an artificially selected line when all genes favorable to the chosen characteristics have been collected in a group of purebred individuals. This is because man does not have *time* to wait for "lucky" mutations in a desired direction. But natural selection has no such limitation. Natural selection has "all the time there is." Generation after generation, century after century, millennium after millennium, the struggle for existence goes on, selecting the fittest and eliminating the less fit. A great majority of mutations, probably, are soon eliminated because they are unfavorable, and many mutations may be indifferent as to their survival value. But some favorable mutations—especially of the slight type—are bound to appear periodically. Even favorable mutations may accidentally be eliminated; but *on the average,* if a mutation gives any advantage to its possessors, the mutant individuals will have a greater chance than the nonmutant individuals of surviving and transmitting the new trait to their descendants, and in the next generation, the mutants, in turn, will be similarly favored in the struggle for existence. In the long run, therefore, every mutation that is favorable to survival or reproduction stands a good chance of being permanently incorporated in the genetic constitution of the species.

Artificial and natural selection differ, broadly, in that artificial selection operates chiefly by the more rapid but limited method of selecting favorable **recombinations** of existing genes; while natural selection operates by the slower but potentially unlimited method of selecting favorable **new mutations.** To some extent both methods operate in both cases, since both the artificial and the natural processes actually select the surviving parents on the basis of their phenotypic characteristics, regardless of how these arose. The great difference lies in the time factor; artificial selection has operated for only a few centuries, at most, but natural selection has gone on for millions of years. Natural selection proceeds in a bungling, haphazard, hit-or-miss fashion, and therefore it is very slow. But given an infinity of time, even such a slow and halting process can produce tremendous results—as is witnessed by the great diversity of living forms inhabiting our earth today.

Even on a short-term basis mutational changes may be of great selective value to a species, as is shown by the recent work of Milislav Demerec at the Carnegie Institution in Cold Spring Harbor, N.Y. Demerec found that among colon bacilli (*Escherichia coli*) a mutation that makes the bacterium *resistant* to the sterilizing effects of *streptomycin* occurs, on the average, in 1 out of every 1,000,000 individuals. In an ordinary environment such resistant mutants have no survival advantage and consequently they remain in circulation only as an insignificant minority (Fig. 28-4). When, however, streptomycin is introduced into the environment, the resistant mutant becomes dominant—to the virtual exclusion of the original nonresistant form (Fig. 28-4). In fact, the appearance of mutant forms of various bacteria that are resistant to one or another of the antibiotic compounds has become a real problem in modern medical practice.

ADAPTATION

Under natural selection each species must attain a fitness to survive and reproduce, or otherwise it faces extinction. Consequently it is not surprising to find many qualities of "fitness," or **adaptations,** in all kinds of living things.

The most obvious adaptations have to do with the *external features* of the organism, taken in relation to its particular environment. Among animals, for example, the coloration tends to be inconspicuous in relation to the background of a particular habitat; or the mouth parts are shaped for handling a certain kind of food; or the appendages are fitted for locomotion on land, in the sea, or in the air—and so forth. Among plants, the roots, stems, leaves, and other organs are variously modified according to conditions in different localities. Many of these obvious **external adaptations** are important in relation to survival, but **internal adaptations,** which are not so obvious, are probably even more important.

Each organism consists of an intricate system of interacting components, ranging from ultramicroscopic units such as enzymes and substrates, up to the macroscopic organs of the body. Internal adaptation embraces the sum total of these parts and their interactions, and internal adaptation assumes a paramount, though frequently hidden, importance in survival. If a mutation unbalances any of the delicate internal functions, the organism cannot survive at all, regardless of the particular environment. Therefore, the only mutations that can possibly lead to a greater degree of external adaptation are those that also have a neutral or advantageous effect upon internal adaptation. Likewise, some mutations may be perpetuated if they have a favorable effect upon the internal adaptation of the species, even

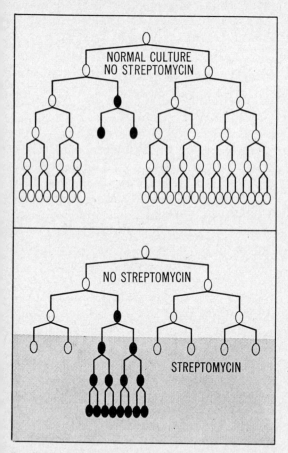

Fig. 28-4. Selection of a mutant form by a change of environment. Mutant forms, resistant to streptomycin, are very rare (1/1,000,000) in an ordinary culture (upper diagram) of colon bacilli. In a new environment with streptomycin added (shaded area of lower diagram), the mutant form soon predominates. (After Th. Dobzhansky.)

though the more obvious external phenotypic effects of such mutations are partially disadvantageous to survival. Such internal effects seldom involve any visible changes of structure, but presumably they involve changes, however slight, in the chemical composition or ultramicroscopic structure of the tissues. They are usually referred to rather vaguely as changes in the "viability" or "fertility" of the stock. But despite the fact that they are invisible and very difficult to study, these internal variations are most important. Natural selection must—and demonstrably does—deal with many such intangible characteristics.

External adaptations include all the visible characteristics of the individual that fit it to survive and reproduce in its own *particular* environment. The shaping of all external structures with reference to food getting, respiration, self-defense, protection, reproduction, and so forth, all fall into the category of external adaptations. But even more important, perhaps, is the external **behavior** of the organism: its responses to particular environmental situations. Natural selection has preserved individuals and races whose responses are useful—to themselves, of course—and has eliminated those whose behavior was less favorable to survival. Accordingly, it is found that most unconditioned responses—tropisms, instincts, etc.—are strikingly adapted to the conditions of the natural habitat of the particular organism.

The environment of any organism is an extremely complex set of conditions. It includes not only the many physical and chemical conditions of inanimate nature, but also the multitude of *living* things with which each organism comes into various kinds of relations—predatory, parasitic, symbiotic, competitive, cooperative, and so forth. In fact, the study of organisms in relation to the factors of their environment, which is called **ecology**, represents an important branch of biology (see Chap. 30). So complex are these ecological interrelations and so delicate is the balance between the processes of multiplication and destruction in any given species, that the very slightest factor may tip the scales, determining whether the individual, the race, or the species shall perish or survive. Without most careful study, therefore, it is very risky to judge that a particular characteristic has no survival value for the organism. On the other hand, it is not necessary to assume that every visible characteristic—such as the humps of the camel, the bumps of the wart hog, or any other peculiarity of form, color, or habit—must necessarily have some adaptive significance. In many cases such features are merely incidental effects of genes that have less obvious but more important effects upon the internal functions of the organism.

STABILITY OF THE SPECIES

Since most mutations are not favorable, natural selection acts to preserve a high degree of *uniformity* in each species by eliminating a majority of these heritable changes as fast as they appear. Wild species display less variability than domesticated animals and plants. In the case of domesticated species, man has interrupted the natural struggle for existence and has artificially preserved a number of less viable variants, which, under natural conditions, could not have survived in competition with their wild-type relatives. But even wild species are genetically heterogeneous for many genes with relatively slight phenotypic effects, because natural selection tolerates a number of *slight mutations,* even though it almost always eliminates the larger ones.

Provided the environment does not change, any species that has occupied a particular habitat for a great many generations becomes about as well adapted to conditions as its inherent genetic nature will permit. In other words, after a long time, the possibility of new favorable mutations becomes rather small. Under these conditions, therefore, most species are fairly stable with reference to the *average* of their characteristics, although seasonal variations, due to temporary selections of more favorable combinations of existing genes, still allow for a certain degree of fluctuation.

However, the stability of species cannot withstand any long-enduring *change* in the environment. Considered over a period of a few years, or even a few centuries, most *natural* environments—that is to say, environments that are not greatly modified by man's activities—remain fairly constant as to the average of the cyclic changes of the day and season. But considered over longer periods, practically every environment repeatedly has undergone great changes.

Geological Changes in the Environment. The most obvious long-range environmental changes are geological in nature. Even within the period of human history—which is just a moment in relation to the whole history of the earth—certain regions of Asia that once supported a flourishing civilization have become deserts virtually devoid of life. Going back some few thousand years further—still within the existence of the human species—vast regions of the earth, in North America, Europe, and Asia, have several times been subjected to arctic conditions due to glaciation, while alternately these regions have experienced tropical or subtropical climates. And if we look still further back into geological time—millions of years—we see continents rising and sinking, changing their contours and connections, and mountain ranges elevated and worn down. In fact, practically every region on the surface of the earth, during the period in which life has existed, has experienced virtually every kind of environment: salt water, fresh water, highland, lowland, desert, swamps, under every type of climate, ranging from arctic to tropical temperature (Fig. 28-5).

These great physical fluctuations, while most impressive, are not the only important kind of change. The environment of a species also consists of its relations to *other organisms;* and whenever a species invades new territory, increases or decreases in numbers, or changes its mode of life in any respect, quite a number of other organisms are likely to be affected directly or indirectly. Consequently each significant modification of the inanimate environment is always attended by many changes in the animate environment of all species in the affected region.

Origin and Extinction of Species. Every long-range change in the climate and other environmental conditions has, owing to these many factors, many effects upon the species of the region: some species decline or even become extinct; other species increase their numbers and extend their range. Slight variations that were barely tolerated by the previous environment may assume real survival value under the changed conditions, and thus these particular variants will displace the species types that dominated under the old conditions.

When an environmental change is favorable to a given species, its population will increase, and during this period of less rigorous competition a larger proportion and a wider variety of offspring will be tolerated for a number of generations. By chance some of the new variants may be adapted to slightly different environments, which enables the species to extend its geographical or its ecological range. When, however, environmental conditions become harder for the species, many of its less fit or weaker varieties may be wiped out, leaving just a few sharply distinct varieties—or incipient new species. In good times, generally speaking, a species tends to increase in number and variety, and greatly extends its range of territory. Then when hard times come, the species may become extinct over large areas of its former territory, leaving a few exceptionally fit and perhaps very sharply different varieties, each quite *isolated* from the others, in different parts of the former range. This factor of **isolation**, whether due to *geographical separation* or to other conditions, is very important in the origin of species. Whenever two varieties are isolated and prevented from intercrossing for many generations, the muta-

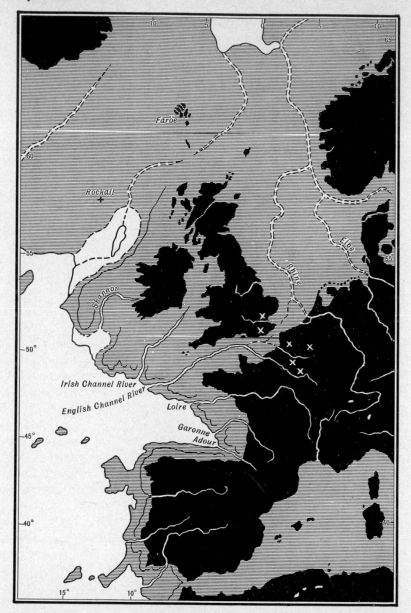

Fig. 28-5. Land areas of Western Europe in the third interglacial stage. Present areas, in black; former areas, lighter. (From Osborn, *Men of the Old Stone Age*. Permission of Charles Scribner's Sons.)

tions of one group cannot spread over into the other. Continually and gradually the stocks become very different, and finally a genetic incompatibility will result. Thus, when interbreeding becomes impossible, the isolation is complete, and the further evolution of the stocks must be as separate species.

Natural selection, acting upon a group of closely related organisms, over a long period of time, inevitably produces results such as are shown in Figure 28-6. The letters at the left represent a group of seven closely related species or—starting one step earlier—seven isolated varieties of a single species; and the

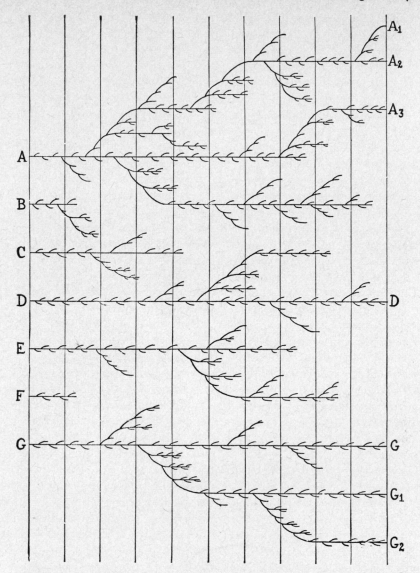

Fig. 28-6.   Origin and extinction of varieties and species by natural selection. The horizontal dimension represents time (i.e., the succession of generations); the vertical dimension, variation. The very short branches represent the numerous mutations that are quickly eliminated by natural selection; the longer branches, those that persist for longer periods. Letters at left indicate original species; those at right, surviving species. (Adapted from Darwin.)

intervals between the successive vertical lines in the figure may be taken to indicate approximately a thousand generations. Each species continues to produce new mutant varieties, and although most of these varieties are quickly eliminated by natural selection, some persist for longer periods. Thus, in the course of 10,000 generations, the several original species may meet with totally different fates, as may be seen in the figure. One species has given rise to several new forms, while the original species has disappeared; in another case, the original species has persisted without changing, while all its offshoots have perished; in a third species, both the parent form and some of its offshoots have survived; and lastly, the other species of the original group have become entirely extinct, leaving no descendants, after surviving for a shorter or a longer period. At the end of 10,000 generations, the number of distinct forms—species or varieties—may be no greater than originally, although a much greater number of forms has meanwhile appeared and disappeared. The surviving species, also, are related more or less closely to each other, because of their method of origin.

Thus the original group of species has given rise to a number of more sharply separated—or more distantly related—species, which tend to assemble themselves, according to relationship, into several larger groups. Perhaps these larger groups are already sufficiently distinct to be considered as separate **genera,** or perhaps the separative action of a greater number of generations will be required before this point is reached. In any event, natural selection, operating through ages of time, continues the fateful processes of diversification and extinction. It creates new species, not abruptly and *de novo,* but gradually, from pre-existing species. And as a result of the relentless processes of natural selection, working in conjunction with an ever-changing environment, man finds himself upon this earth today—together with a tremendous variety of other living species, all variously adapted to current environmental conditions, and all variously interrelated as to their origins. Also man finds within the earth itself the telltale remnants of a vastly greater number of plant and animal species, which have become extinct in past ages (Chap. 29).

NATURAL SELECTION AND MODERN GENETICS

The origin of species by natural selection was first explained by Darwin in 1859; but at that time very little was known about the laws and mechanisms of hereditary and varia-

tions. Darwin based his conclusions on the unquestionable facts: that all organisms do vary; that *some* variations are heritable; and that large variations are generally less viable than slighter ones. Since Darwin's time— chiefly in the last 40 years—the mechanisms of heredity have been thoroughly clarified and much has been learned about the origin and nature of variations. Prior to these developments, the chief objections to the theory of natural selection were that the theory did not account for the appearance of many apparently useless features in different organisms; and that variations, especially slight ones, would be lost by "dilution" when the variant individuals continued to interbreed with the more numerous members of the species not possessing the particular variations in question.

Both of these objections are eliminated completely by an understanding of genetic principles. The visible differences between closely related species are not necessarily of critical importance in survival, since frequently these visible characteristics are incidental effects of the *same genes* that produce invisible effects having great survival value. Furthermore, the idea of "dilution" has proved to be altogether fallacious: when mutant individuals continue to cross with the original type, the processes of **particulate inheritance** guarantee a distribution of the mutant gene throughout the whole population without any alteration of the new gene throughout successive generations.

Imperfections in an organism, or the possession of features that *seem* to reduce its fitness in relation to its particular environment, are not difficult to understand if the limitations of natural selection are carefully considered. Natural selection cannot *produce* favorable variations, it can only preserve them as, *by chance,* they do arise. The possibilities of favorable variations are strictly limited by the existing genetic constitution of the particular organism: the possible ways in which its various genes can undergo change without disrupting the delicate balance of existing functions within the organism. Thus natural selection is restricted mainly to small changes and must, therefore, work very slowly. Moreover, since heredity is particulate in nature, each new gene must be selected or discarded *as a whole.* This means that disadvantageous phenotypic effects may be carried along with advantageous ones, if the former are less important in survival. The survival of a particular individual or race is determined, not by the perfection of any one characteristic, but by the aggregate fitness of all its characteristics. The survivors in the struggle for existence need not be perfectly adapted, but merely sufficiently adapted to "get by" until they produce an adequate number of offspring. Each organism is "made over" and "patched up" to meet its new environment each time there is a swing in the mighty pendulum of geologic time. Consequently, each plant and animal may possess a number of useless or even definitely harmful characteristics, resulting from the sorting out of innumerable *chance* variations. Survival does not require perfect adaptation. It merely demands that the individual be as well adapted as its competitors—all of which have also been produced by the same method.

LAMARCKISM: AN EARLY THEORY OF EVOLUTION

Prior to Darwin, evolution had many proponents, and several theories were advanced as to how evolution had wrought its slow but tremendous changes in the species. These theories rested mainly on the supposition that *all* variations in the characteristics of the organism are transmitted to the offspring— a weakness that is well exemplified by the theory of Lamarck. This work on evolution was published in 1809; and Lamarck's contribution was important, despite the fact that the central theme—as to the mechanism of evolutionary change—is not tenable in the light of modern genetics.

According to the Lamarckian view, each organism is molded by its contacts with the environment, and these *acquired characteristics* are subsequently transmitted to the offspring. In other words, Lamarck held that the environment *produces* heritable variations that fit each organism to cope with the particular conditions of its habitat; and that the perpetuation of these acquired characters produced changes in the species in accordance with the geological changes of the environment.

Lamarck's ideas had great appeal in the early part of the nineteenth century, and the theory was not abandoned until it was proved beyond reasonable doubt that *acquired characteristics are not inherited.* The environment, to be sure, is very effective in determining the qualities of every individual, but these *modifications* are localized in the *somatic tissues of the body,* and the *germ cells* remain unchanged.

To exemplify the noninheritance of acquired characters, we will consider a **homozygous stock** of garden peas. When grown in well-watered soil these plants develop a moderately extensive root system. But if the same plants are grown in unusually dry soil, the roots become distinctly deeper and broader up to a limit that is determined by the genetic potentiality of the stock. In fact, so long as the same relatively dry environment is maintained, the well-developed root system will continue to appear, generation after generation; but no *progressive* improvement is likely to occur within any reasonable span of time. Moreover, when the seedlings of this stock are finally restored to normal conditions, no permanent change in the root system can be observed. The dry environment has brought out the utmost of root development in the given stock, but the environment has not been effective in molding the genetic constitution of the stock in the direction of greater fitness to cope with the dry condition. Aside from the remote possibility that a favorable mutation might occur during the period of the study, the plant experimentalist has no hope of improving any **homozygous** stock as a result of directive influences from the environment. The environment, to put it more technically, is able to effect a limited improvement in the developmental performance of the group of genes determining the root system of the stock, but the environment has not been able to produce any measurable change in the intrinsic nature of these genes.

Similarly a great many experiments have been performed on other organisms, using a variety of adverse environmental conditions, such as chronic alcoholism. One inbred stock of white rats was daily subjected to extreme alcoholism from the time of weaning until death, for more than ten generations. During this period of extreme debauchery, there were among the litters a very high proportion of feeble, stunted individuals, but the offspring of all such rats were restored to a full measure of growth and vigor as soon as they were taken off the alcoholic treatment. The alcohol did not alter the genic complex of the treated animals, and consequently none of the adverse *acquired characteristics* found a permanent place in the heritable constitution of the race.

Lamarck's theory laid great stress on the question of *use and disuse* of the various organs of the species. The horse, for example, was considered to have arisen from a slower running form that inhabited the open plains, where a constant exercise of speed was essential in the avoidance of carnivorous enemies. Accordingly, improvements in the skeletal and muscular structures of the legs were thought to have occurred gradually as a result of the excessive use of these organs demanded by the environmental conditions. And conversely, blind species, which are found inhabiting deep, dark caves, were thought to have arisen as a result of a gradual degeneration of the eyes, due to many generations of disuse.

Two main fallacies of the use and disuse theory are: (1) all experiments designed to prove an inheritance of environmentally induced changes in somatic structures have been unsuccessful; and (2) although certain factors in the environment, such as heat and short-wave radiations, may accelerate the appearance of mutations, these heritable variations are random and are not directed by the environment toward a greater fitness of the variant with reference to its habitat. One such experiment involved the rearing of fruit flies in total darkness for more than 60 generations—an equivalent of many centuries in human history. When this experiment was finished and the flies at long last were restored to light, no changes could be found, either in the structure of eyes or in the responses of the flies to light. Similarly, the old custom of binding the feet of high-caste Chinese women—which made it virtually impossible for these individuals to walk —has had no heritable effect upon the foot dimensions of the race, even after many centuries. Likewise, many sorts of mutilation, including the surgical removal of certain organs, have been adhered to religiously by various peoples since the dawn of human societies—without leaving the slightest mark upon the genetic constitution of any race. These environmentally induced modifications do not penetrate to the level of the germ cells of the species; and no change can play a significant role in evolution unless it involves the genes of the germ cells. Thus it can be said that the environment has no directive influence upon germ cell mutations, except that the environment eliminates such mutations as may decrease and selects such mutations as may increase the general fitness of the species.

The impact of modern genetics upon the theory of natural selection has thus been to clarify and strengthen it, without essentially modifying this theory as developed by Darwin. The known laws of variations and heredity operate by providing material that is sifted and screened by natural selection. These somewhat haphazard processes logically account for the origin of the species of animals and plants that exist today; and science can see no other alternative.

TEST QUESTIONS

1. Calculate the number of offspring that would be derived from a single pair of cats in ten generations, assuming that the average number of kittens produced in each generation were four and that all the offspring were to survive and reproduce. Plot the theoretical growth curve of this population of cats.

2. A certain troutless pool, in which the food supply can sustain no more than 100,000 trout, is seeded with 5 pairs of fingerlings. Assuming that each pair produced 100 offspring annually, what percentage of the offspring can survive: (a) in the first year; (b) in the second year; (c) in the third year; (d) in each succeeding year.

3. Predict ten factors in the *inanimate* environment that might exert a selective action upon the population of trout in the foregoing pool, and explain the type of variation that would be probably favored by each of the given factors.

4. Consider Question 3 in terms of several possible factors in the *animate* environment of the pool.

5. To what extent does Question 3 illustrate: (a) the "struggle for existence"; (b) the "survival of the fittest"; (c) natural selection generally?

6. Point out the essential similarities and differences between natural and artificial selection.

7. Differentiate between external and internal adaptations.

8. Explain how the external adaptations of fish generally equip these animals for life in the aquatic environment.

9. Explain how the external adaptations of a particular species of fish may equip it for life in a particular kind of aquatic environment (for example, in a particular pool).

10. In terms of some particular animal explain how some essential internal adaptation may be responsible for perpetuating some neutral or disadvantageous characteristics in the species.

11. To what extent has the environment of the different areas of the earth (for example, New York State) undergone drastic change during the ages of prehistoric time?

12. In general, how is a species affected in number, diversity of variation, and area of habitation: (a) during periods when the environment is especially favorable; and (b) during periods when the environment is especially unfavorable? Explain.

13. Explain why isolation is a very important factor in determining the origin of new species. Explain several ways in which two or more varieties of a species may become isolated from each other.

14. How may isolation from competitors affect the perpetuation of a given species (for example, the various monotremes and marsupials [p. 673] of Australia)?

15. Differentiate between genetic variations and environmental variations (modifications). Cite five examples to illustrate how a given animal (for example, man) and a given plant (for example, a fruit tree) are susceptible to the modifying influence of environmental factors.

16. Summarize the evidence that strongly supports the view that environmental modifications are noninheritable (choose at least two specific examples).

17. Carefully explain the Lamarckian concepts of the mechanism of evolutionary change. What has been the basis for discarding these concepts?

18. Carefully summarize the modern concepts as to the mechanism of evolutionary change.

FURTHER READINGS

1. *The Origin of Species,* by Charles Darwin; London, 1859.
2. *The Scientific Basis of Evolution,* by T. H. Morgan; New York, 1935.
3. *What Evolution Is,* by G. H. Parker; Cambridge (Mass.), 1925.
4. *The Causes of Evolution,* by J. B. S. Haldane; New York, 1932.
5. *Biochemical Evolution,* by M. Florkin; New York, 1949.
6. *Genetics and the Origin of Species,* by T. Dobzhansky; New York, 1951.
7. *The Material Basis of Evolution,* by R. Goldschmidt; New Haven, 1940.

29 - The Consequences
of Evolution

EVERY MUTATION or other heritable change, if it becomes established in a species, either by natural or artificial selection, represents a definite evolutionary step, and in this sense evolution is directly demonstrable by experiment. But the conclusion that all existing species have originated by similar processes occurring in past ages cannot—in the nature of the case—be subjected to *direct* proof. In accordance with the scientific principle of the *uniformity of nature,* however, evolution represents a logically predictable consequence of known forces and processes. Geology and physics provide good evidence (p. 559) that organisms have lived on earth for more than *three billion years,* while the environment, aside from large-scale fluctuations in local conditions, has not undergone great change. It may be assumed, therefore, that variation and selection have operated during these past ages at much the same rate as they do today, and this rate, operating through this expanse of time, seems ample to account for the evolution of the great

diversity of existing species. Moreover, evolution has left indelible imprints upon many structural and functional characteristics in every organism, and the crust of the earth contains the fossilized remnants of many kinds of pre-existing organisms. Thus an accumulation of evidence from many sources impels the scientific mind to accept the evolutionary viewpoint. Organic evolution does not necessarily demand that all existing organisms have arisen from a *single* primitive ancestral form, but the bulk of evidence indicates that early primordial life was very simple and did not consist of any great diversity of forms.

Evolution has left its mark upon every phase of biology, as has been noted in many places throughout the earlier chapters. In summary, therefore, the consequences of evolution will be considered very briefly, under the topics of: **classification, comparative anatomy, embryology, biochemistry,** and **paleontology** (a systematic comparative study of fossils).

EVOLUTIONARY BASIS OF CLASSIFICATION

According to their similarities and differences, organisms have been classified into groups and subgroups—that is, into the various phyla, classes, orders, and so forth—of the plant and animal kingdoms (Appendix I). This classification is not an arbitrary system, as is witnessed by the fact that all organisms in a given group, however large this group may be, resemble each other not merely as to one characteristic, but as to many. Originally the classification was laid out on the basis of the gross structures mutually possessed by members of each group, but subsequent study has usually revealed many other resemblances—as to developmental, biochemical, and physiological features—which were entirely unknown to the biologists who first devised the classification. Such facts very clearly indicate that there are real, natural relationships underlying the classification system. In fact, the main intent of classification is to group organisms according to their genetic relationships with other organisms. On the average, those organisms most closely related by descent will mutually possess the greatest number of similar or identical genes, and organisms possessing the greatest common fund of similar genes will resemble each other most closely as to their phenotypic characteristics. Of course there are exceptions to these general rules: identical genes may arise independently even in species of fairly distant relationship, and, on occasion, the phenotypic effects of one set of genes may simulate quite closely the effects of a different set of genes. Therefore, resemblance in one or a few characteristics is not a safe criterion of genetic relationship. But it is not probable that such coincidences should occur frequently, and the more characteristics a group of organisms possess in common, the greater is the certainty that these resemblances are due to common genes derived from a common ancestry. And whenever it is possible to test this question by breeding experiments, organisms that appear to be most closely related on the basis of their phenotypic features are in fact generally found to possess the greatest number of common genes. Actually the modern system of classification considerably antedates the methods of modern genetics, but the criteria that were used in establishing the classification of organisms have proved, on the whole, to be quite valid.

It is possible to subdivide existing species into well-defined groups, only because a large proportion of intermediate organisms have become *extinct*. If every species and subspecies that ever lived were still alive today, there would be no definable groups, but a continuous series of intermediate forms connecting every type of organism with every other type by insensibly small degrees of difference. Classification depends in a large measure upon the accidents of extinction, and thus we do not find a neat symmetrical scheme, but rather a confusing system of large, small, well-defined, ill-defined, remotely different, and closely similar species, genera, families, orders, classes, and phyla, making up both the plant and animal kingdoms. Existing species are frequently and aptly compared to the surviving twigs of a buried tree, of which the main limbs and branches have decayed and disappeared. Classification must seek to assign each twig to the proper branch and subbranch from which it initially originated. In many cases this task is simplified by the uncovering of a few more or less imperfect remnants (fossils) of the former connections; but under the circumstances it is not surprising that there are many uncertainties and differences of opinion. In some cases there are so many intermediate forms between two different groups that the line of separation must necessarily be altogether arbitrary—as is the case of the line that separates the animal and plant kingdoms. In other cases the opposite difficulty arises: so much extinction has occurred that certain small groups of species are left, isolated with no obvious relations to any other larger group—as in the case of several invertebrate phyla (Nemertinea, Rotifera, etc., p. 680). All in all, therefore, classification, or **taxonomy,** is a very difficult science, fraught with uncertainty and controversy. But experience has shown that this natural system is very useful. In giving the phylum, or class, or other lesser category of any animal or plant, the name of the group immediately specifies that this organism possesses a long list of structural, functional, and developmental characteristics, in common with all other members of the same group.

COMPARATIVE ANATOMY IN RELATION TO EVOLUTION

Each large group of organisms, such as the phyla and classes of the animal and plant kingdoms, displays a fundamental architectural plan of body structure that underlies the diverse specializations of the different body parts. Invariably all the members of such a group possess a number of **homologous** organs that display unmistakable similarities of structure and development, although the particular organ in the different species may be adapted to totally different functions. Generally speaking, the *differences* between homologous organs show an adaptive relationship to differences in the environments of the several species—as would be expected as a result of natural selection. But the *similarities* between homologous organs seem to have no logical explanation, except in terms of genetic relationship.

To exemplify **homology,** let us take the skeletal system of vertebrate animals, or more particularly the bony structure of the forelimbs throughout the vertebrate group. Regardless of whether the forelimb is adapted for walking, swimming, flying, or other special function, the same grouping of homologous bones can easily be recognized in any vertebrate—as is shown in Figure 29-1. This does not mean that such a skeletal structure is ideally suited for all these purposes. The walking, swimming, and flying appendages

of insects are just as well adapted to each of these same functions, although insect appendages display a totally different plan of structure. The *differences* between the forelimbs of various vertebrates are obviously correlated with their different environments and functions, while their underlying *similarities*—as to the form and arrangement of the homologous bones and muscles—must be ascribed to the fact that all vertebrates are genetically related to each other more closely than to other animals.

Similarly the whole skeletal system, as well as all the muscles, nerves, sensory organs, digestive organs, reproductive structures, etc., of vertebrate animals display innumerable homologies of structure and development. The same general architectural plan can be seen in the body structure of every vertebrate, and no other group of animals conforms to this particular plan. Variation and selection have modified the plan to fit a wide variety of special environmental conditions in a wide variety of species; but the plan itself remains to testify as to the common inheritance that all vertebrates have received from a common ancestral stock.

Vestigial Organs. Some organs in every species appear to be quite useless and degenerate as compared to homologous structures in related species, and such **vestigial organs** are by no means rare. The complete list of vestigial structures in the human body, for example, probably numbers more than a hundred; and the list includes a number of familiar structures, such as the vermiform appendix, the coccyx (tail vertebrae), the nictitating membrane of the eye, and the small muscles that can be trained to "move the ears." Moreover, comparable numbers of vestigial organs are found in other groups of animals and plants—in proportion to the complexity of their structure, and to the care and thoroughness with which they have been studied.

A vestigial organ is presumed to represent the surviving remnant of an organ or structure that was well developed and functional

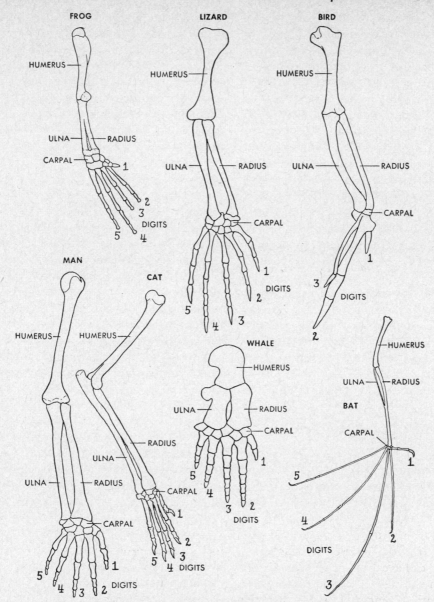

Fig. 29-1.   Homologous bones of the forelimbs of various vertebrates.

in some ancestral species. Or to state the matter more specifically, the vestigial organ is the product of a surviving group of genes derived from genes that previously governed the development of some useful organ in an ancestral species. As a general rule, organs that become useless to a species as a result of changes in its habits and environment tend, in the course of evolution, to degenerate in size and refinement of structure. The eyes, for example, of many cave-dwelling species of crustaceans, fishes, and amphibians, are blind and degenerate, although these nonfunctional eyes still show a similarity of structure and development to the functional eyes of closely related daylight-dwelling species. Given adequate time, such an evolutionary degeneration of useless organs would seem to be inevitable on the basis of mutation and natural selection. Mutations are random and prone to decrease, rather than increase, the size and perfection of the affected parts. So long as the organ in question has value in the survival of the species, such detrimental mutations are quickly eliminated by natural selection. But if a structure has become nonessential to survival, detrimental mutations will tend to accumulate and spread throughout the population. In fact, the displacement of a useless organ will be accelerated by natural selection, because the whole organ would require a greater share of the organism's food supply compared to its partly degenerate counterpart. Natural selection tends to reduce and eliminate useless structures, although a long-enduring persistence may occur as a result of the random nature of the degenerative changes, or as a result of hidden effects of the persistent genes, which may be favorable in relation to the internal adaptation of the species (p. 543).

EMBRYOLOGY AND EVOLUTION

In any group of related species the embryonic stages tend to resemble each other much more closely than the adults (Fig. 29-2) for reasons that are not very difficult to find.

In the earlier embryonic stages, all organisms are relatively simple as to their gross structure, so that little opportunity is afforded for drastic differences to appear. Moreover, many genes produce their phenotypic effects relatively late in embryonic development, so that differences induced by these genes are added to the differential effects of earlier acting genes. Thus in some cases the embryonic stages of a species reveal genetic relationships that would scarcely be suspected on the basis of adult structure. This is particularly true of parasitic or otherwise degenerate forms in which the adults lose many of the characteristics of the group to which they belong. Frequently the mutations responsible for these losses have their main effects relatively late in development, so that the early development of the species displays an unmasked resemblance to the embryos of the other members of the group.

In some cases, however, the **larvae** of related animals do *not* resemble each other more closely than the adults, but such larval differences usually show a distinct adaptive relation to the habitat in which the larvae live. Highly distinctive larvae are particularly characteristic of insects and other forms that spend a considerable proportion of their life span in the larval stage. In such cases, apparently, natural selection has acted to

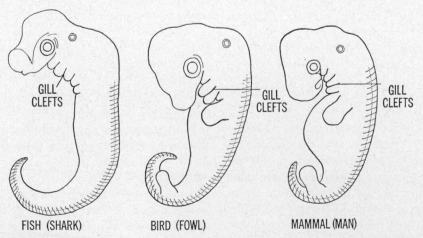

Fig. 29-2. During early development the embryos of various vertebrates are strikingly similar.

preserve a number of early acting mutations that have survival significance during the larval stages. Later in development many of these special larval adaptations are lost, for during metamorphosis, the structures of the adult are derived from less specialized parts of the larva. In short, differences between related species may appear at any stage of development—embryonic, larval, or adult—although it is undeniably true that genetic relationships are apt to be plainer in the earlier stages of development.

Higher animals, due to the greater complexity of their mature structure, tend to differ more drastically from their respective embryos than do their lower, or simpler, relatives. For this reason, the embryonic stages of higher animals are apt to exhibit striking resemblances to the adult stages of lower species. For instance, the embryos of all vertebrates develop gill slits in the pharynx (Fig. 29-2); and in lower vertebrates (fish) these gill slits remain as functional respiratory channels in the adult species. But in the embryos of higher air-breathing vertebrates (Fig. 29-3), the gill slits are closed, except for the first pair, which becomes modified to form the Eustachian tubes (p. 283). Apparently the genes responsible for the development of gill slits in the ancestral vertebrate stock have persisted, while other genes, which decree the closing of these channels, exert their developmental effects later in the embryonic period. In a sense, therefore, gill slits are to be regarded as embryonic vestigial structures.

Biologists of the eighteenth and nineteenth centuries were deeply impressed by the resemblance of early embryonic stages of higher animals to the adult stages of lower members of the same class or phylum. In fact these observations formed the basis of the **theory of recapitulation,** which was accepted very widely. Briefly, the recapitulation theory held that every species, in passing through its embryonic stages, repeats the evolutionary stages by which the species has reached its present status. Without question the recapi-

tulation theory served a useful purpose in emphasizing the general similarity between embryonic development and evolutionary development. All multicellular animals do, in fact, revert to the unicellular condition at conception; and the blastula, gastrula, and other generalized stages of embryonic development do tend to resemble the early steps of evolutionary development. But the theory cannot sustain a very detailed analysis, as might be expected in the light of our modern knowledge of genetics and development. So long as a given set of genes survives in any kind of organism, these ancient genes will continue to preserve the ancient characteristics of the stock, although newer genes may modify and obscure these old effects at any stage of development. Moreover, some genes in every stock seem to be so crucial in embryonic development that few, if any, mutations in these genes are tolerable to the organism. Consequently such genes are preserved in the course of natural selection and are responsible for the recapitulation of certain age-old characteristics in every species.

BIOCHEMICAL RELATIONSHIPS AMONG ORGANISMS

Genetic relationships between different organisms are clearly indicated not only by their structural and developmental characteristics, but also by their chemical composition—particularly with reference to their protein components. The proteins extracted from corresponding tissues of closely related animals tend to be very similar, or sometimes identical; whereas more distantly related species show much greater differences in this respect. Take, for example, the blood proteins of vertebrate animals, which have been studied very extensively in recent years. The antigenic reactions (p. 335) of bloods from the various races of man prove to be practically identical, and almost identical with the antigenic reactions of bloods from the anthropoid apes. The bloods of Old World monkeys come next in their relationship to

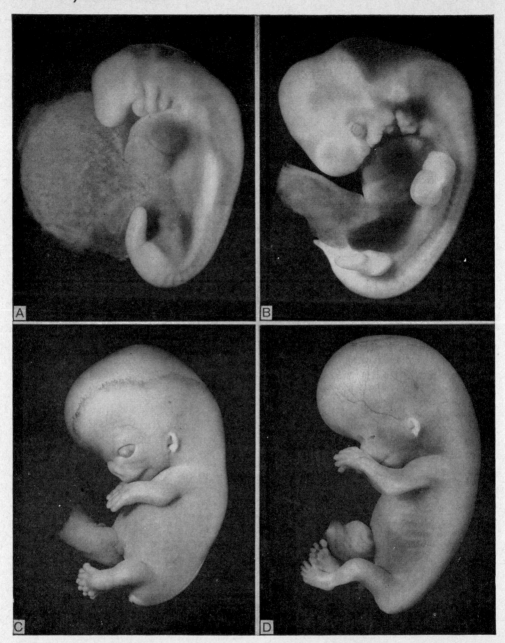

Fig. 29-3. Human embryos: A, 26 days after ovulation (note particularly the gill slits, yolk sac, and tail). B, 34 days (note the limb buds, eye, and brain). C, 43 days (note the well-developed face and limbs and the umbilical cord). D, 56 days. In A, the magnification is some five times greater than in D. (Courtesy of Dr. G. W. Corner, Carnegie Institution of Washington.)

human blood; while the bloods of New World monkeys and lemurs (Fig. 29-4) show a less and less intimate relationship. In this way many degrees of relationship between the bloods of all mammals can be demon-strated (Fig. 29-5); similarly all birds are found to have a fairly close relationship to each other, and more distant ties to members of the reptile group (Fig. 29-6). All in all, more than a thousand animals, in several dif-

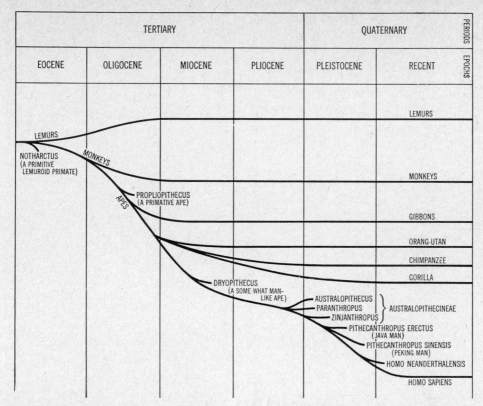

	TERTIARY			QUATERNARY		PERIODS
EOCENE	OLIGOCENE	MIOCENE	PLIOCENE	PLEISTOCENE	RECENT	EPOCHS

LEMURS

NOTHARCTUS
(A PRIMITIVE LEMUROID PRIMATE)

MONKEYS

APES

PROPLIOPITHECUS
(A PRIMATIVE APE)

DRYOPITHECUS
(A SOME WHAT MAN-LIKE APE)

LEMURS

MONKEYS

GIBBONS

ORANG-UTAN

CHIMPANZEE

GORILLA

AUSTRALOPITHECUS
PARANTHROPUS } AUSTRALOPITHECINEAE
ZINJANTHROPUS

PITHECANTHROPUS ERECTUS
(JAVA MAN)
PITHECANTHROPUS SINENSIS
(PEKING MAN)
HOMO NEANDERTHALENSIS

HOMO SAPIENS

Fig. 29-4. Probable interrelations of the primates, and the fossil forms most closely in the line of human ancestry.

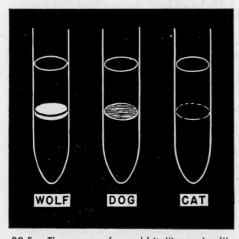

Fig. 29-5. The serum of a rabbit "immunized" with wolf blood will cause a heavy precipitate of the proteins of wolf plasma when this plasma is added to the rabbit serum in a test tube. The chemically similar proteins of dog blood give a faint precipitate, but the quite different ones of cat blood react scarcely at all. (From Gerard, *Unresting Cells*. Permission of Harper and Row.)

ferent phyla, have been classified in accordance with their blood and tissue reactions, and generally speaking, these tests indicate the same relationships as were derived from structural and developmental studies. Thus these biochemical relations—which were discovered long after the theory of evolution had gained general acceptance—strikingly confirm the conclusions that were based originally upon totally different grounds. Apparently the biochemical similarities between related species come from the same sources as their structural and developmental similarities—the possession of a common fund of genes derived from a common ancestry.

PALEONTOLOGY: THE FOSSIL RECORD

A **fossil** is any sort of remnant, or trace, left by an ancient pre-existing form of life

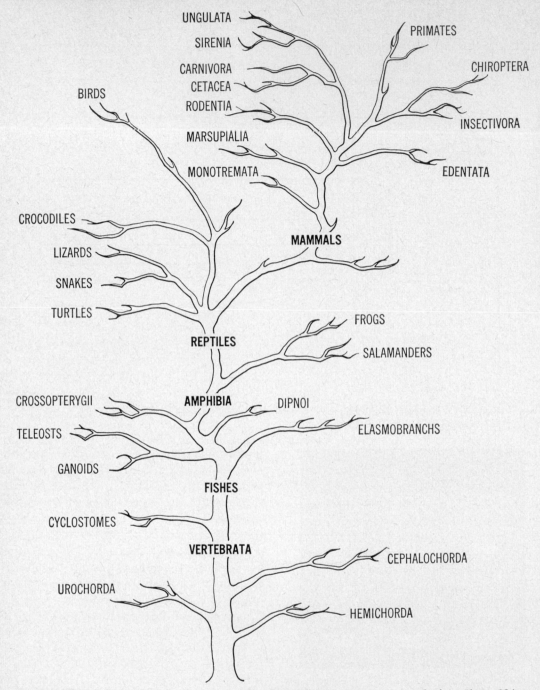

Fig. 29-6. Probable interrelations of the chordates. (These groups are described in Chap. 32.)

Fig. 29-7. Part of the leg of a dinosaur, *Diplodocus*, as uncovered in the Bone Cabin Quarry, Wyoming. (Courtesy of the American Museum of Natural History, New York.)

and circumstance necessary for the formation, preservation, and discovery of fossils. Usually only the hard parts of any creature—such as shell, bone, or wood—are likely to survive as fossils, and since a majority of very early organisms never possessed any skeletal parts, vast multitudes of ancient forms have left only the barest traces of their existence. Also the fossils found in sedimentary rock, by the nature of their origin, are derived mainly from aquatic organisms or, more especially, from species that have dwelt in the ocean. Only rarely does it happen that the remains of a land-dwelling form find its way to the oceanic floor, and consequently terrestrial species, on the whole, are rather poorly represented in the fossil record. Moreover, sedimentary rocks are deposited only under certain conditions—relatively near the shore, where large amounts of sediment are accumulating, in areas that are *sinking*—so that the accumulation may reach considerable depth. And once formed, fossils are susceptible to destruction. Very deeply buried sedimentary rocks begin to suffer distortion or **metamorphosis,** as a result of great pressure or heat, and these factors may destroy or obliterate a large part of the fossil content. If, on the other hand, such rock is *raised* and exposed to the *eroding* action of running water, wind, rain, sleet, frost, etc., again there may be a wholesale destruction of the fossil record. And finally, fossils that escape the vicissitudes of the ages can be discovered during this present age only if they happen to lie at or near the surface of the earth, in some accessible region (Fig. 29-9). Considering all these factors, therefore, it is not surprising that the record of pre-existing species

(Figs. 29-7 and 29-12); and the study of fossils constitutes the science of **paleontology.** A few fossils are found in sand drifts, asphalt, amber (petrified resin), and in the ice of arctic regions, but a vast majority of fossils are found in **sedimentary rocks.** These stratified rocks are formed *under water,* by the slow deposition of sand, clay, mud, or lime, which subsequently harden into rock, under the action of high pressure and a series of slow chemical transformations.

The fossil record, as it is known today, provides only a very fragmentary history of the life of past ages, but this fact is not surprising in view of the peculiar chain of chance

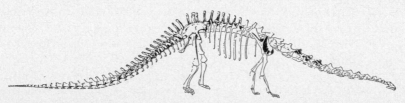

Fig. 29-8. Total skeleton of a dinosaur, *Diplodocus*. (Courtesy of the American Museum of Natural History, New York.)

Fig. 29-9. Layer after layer of stratified rock, exposed in the Grand Canyon of the Colorado River. (Union Pacific Railroad Photograph.)

is far from complete. In fact, it is surprising that so much has been preserved and discovered. Since the time of Darwin—who emphasized the meagerness of fossil data—paleontologists have advanced great lengths toward the completion of the record (Fig. 29-10), especially with reference to species that became extinct during the more recent periods of geological time.

Geological Strata and Their Relative Ages. The layers, or **strata,** of sedimentary rock, because of the nature of their origin, occur in the sequence of their deposition, such that all newer (later) strata are superimposed upon the older (earlier) layers. Consequently the deeper the stratum, the older its content of fossils. However, the problem of determining the *relative ages* of the various geological

strata is not always so very simple, because not all strata are to be found in any one locality. Some land areas were exposed at times when others were submerged, so that great gaps may be present in the strata of any given region. Also some areas experienced resubmergence after many centuries of exposure—during which erosion carried away many of the upper strata. Therefore, in some cases, relatively recent strata are found superimposed directly upon very ancient layers. But despite the gaps, the older strata in any one locality are always found to be deeper than the newer layers, except in rare cases where there has been a demonstrable folding of the crust of the earth and an inversion of the strata. And once the relative age of a certain stratum has been determined on

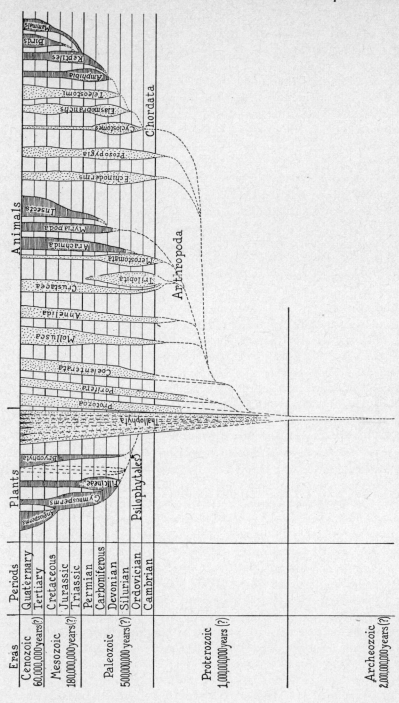

Fig. 29-10. History of the main groups of organisms of which fossil remains are known. Shaded spaces indicate known fossils; dotted areas indicate chiefly aquatic, crosslines chiefly terrestrial, groups. The varying widths of these spaces indicate increases and decreases in number of species within each group. Dotted lines indicate presumed existence and probable derivation of these groups.

other grounds, the fossils of this stratum provide an invaluable clue for the identification of the corresponding stratum in other regions of the earth.

Eras and Periods of Geological Time. The earlier geologists were able to identify five well-defined *series* of strata, but found considerable gaps between the series, and smaller gaps within each series. On the basis of these gaps, the strata were divided and subdivided into the eras and periods of geological time, as is shown in Table 29-1. Subsequently the study of the strata has progressed considerably, extending to ever wider regions of the earth. Thus many of the gaps have been filled in, and the lines of demarcation between the eras and periods are becoming less sharply and arbitrarily defined.

The *relative* duration of the eras and periods of geological time is quite plainly indicated by the thickness of their strata, although considerable variation must have occurred in the rate at which sedimentary rock was deposited in different areas and at different times. In fact, until recently there was little hope of obtaining reliable estimations as to the *absolute* duration of the geological periods. Now, however, physicists have found that the proportion of radioactive elements contained in certain rock provides an excellent index of the absolute age. Uranium, for example, gradually transforms into lead by a series of radioactive disintegrations, and the rate of this disintegration is independent of temperature and the other variables of the environment. Specifically, it requires 4.5 billion years for half of a given sample of uranium to degrade into lead. Therefore, in rocks that are devoid of lead except for that which has been derived from uranium, the lead:uranium ratio gives an accurate measure of the absolute age. These age measurements are in excellent agreement with the most recent and reliable data based on sedimentation rates. Consequently the durations of the eras, as specified in Table 29-1, can be accepted with a fair degree of confidence.

Brief Survey of the Fossil Record. The main outlines of the history of pre-existing life are shown in Figures 29-10 and 29-11 and Table 29-1; and the ensuing account will attempt little more than to exemplify a few of the major evolutionary trends.

No recognizable fossils are found in the Archeozoic strata, but all these rocks are badly metamorphosed and eroded. However, the presence of graphite and other materials of presumably organic origin indicates that the very earliest forms of life had their first beginning quite early in the Archeozoic period.

In Proterozoic rocks, fossils are still relatively scarce and poorly preserved, but quite a few are plainly recognizable. The very earliest fossils are identified as primitive Schizomycophyta; and most biologists agree that the earliest cellular organisms were colorless plants somewhat similar to the modern bacteria (p. 601). In the upper Proterozoic strata there are unmistakable fossil remains of algae (akin to the modern Thallophyta), numerous Protozoa, a few sponges (Porifera), and—near the very top—a few other invertebrate groups (Fig. 29-10).

A considerable gap exists between the strata of the early Paleozoic and the late Proterozoic eras; that is, no sedimentary rocks formed during this interval have been found on the land surfaces as they exist today. In fact the geological evidence indicates that most of the land areas of today were also land areas toward the end of the Proterozoic period. The earliest Paleozoic (Cambrian) strata contain a rich fossiliferous record, with an abundance of algae and some representatives of all the principal invertebrate phyla. However, the Cambrian strata show few, if any, true vertebrates, no plants higher than the Thallophyta, and, in fact, *no terrestrial organisms of any kind.* All life at this time was still aquatic. Moreover, Cambrian animals while belonging to the same phyla as our modern species, were generally quite different. On the whole they were more primitive than the present species, and in many

Table 29-1—Origin of Organisms in Relation to the Earth's History

Eras	Periods	Main Characteristics of the Environment	Existing Forms of Life
Cenozoic ±60 million years	Quaternary	Land areas like today's; periodic glaciation	Continuance of all pre-existing phyla; origin and rapid spread of man; rise of the grasses; replacement of archaic mammals by the modern placentate forms
	Tertiary	Elevation of mountains, including Alps and Himalayas; climate growing colder	
Mesozoic ±180 million years	Cretaceous	Extensive swamplands, followed by elevation of the Rocky and Andes mountain ranges	Continuance of all pre-existing phyla; origin of the birds and mammals; rise and fall of gigantic reptiles (dinosaurs), flying reptiles (pterodactyls) and toothed birds; spread of the cycads and conifers; extinction of forests of large ferns, horsetails, and club mosses
	Jurassic	Small continents; much lowland near the sea	
	Triassic	Great desert areas	
Paleozoic ±500 million years	Permian	Mountain building	No birds or mammals, and only a few primitive angiosperms; primitive bryophytes, primitive tracheophytes and gymnosperms, starting in the Devonian strata; origin of the mollusks, annelids, arthropods, echinoderms, and chordates as early as the Cambrian period; land vertebrates start in the Carboniferous; great dominance of trilobites (primitive arthropods) in early periods, but extinction in the later
	Carboniferous	Large continents, rising mountains; warm humid climate	
	Devonian	Smaller inland seas; land emergence	
	Silurian	Great inland seas; warm climate	
	Ordovician	Land submergence; warm even in the Arctic	
	Cambrian	Extensive lowlands	
Proterozoic ±1,000 million years		Little known; some evidence of extensive repeated glaciation	Mainly unicellular plants (Cyanophyta and Schizomycophyta) and animals (Protozoa); and, toward the end, a few simple thallophytes and sponges (Porifera). No higher invertebrates, nor any vertebrates
Archeozoic ±2,000 million years		Conditions altogether problematical	No recognizable fossils; indirect evidence indicates some primitive organisms toward the end of the Archeozoic era

PLANT KINGDOM   ANIMAL KINGDOM

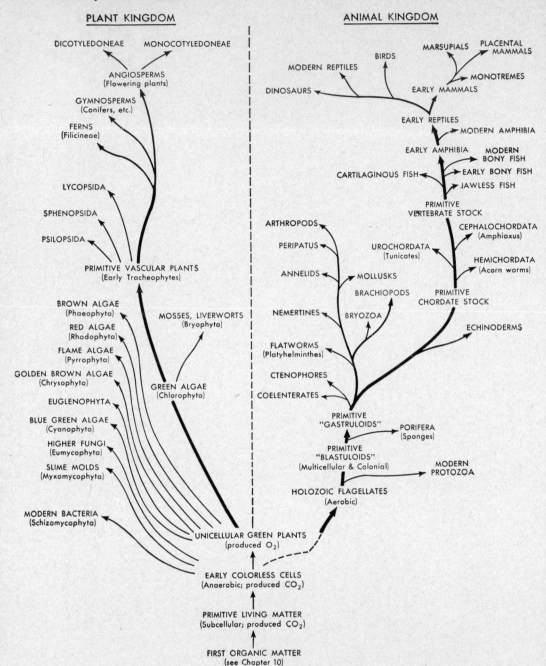

Fig. 29-11. Probable relations of the main phyla of plants and animals.

cases like the Trilobita (Fig. 32-31), they belong to groups that are now extinct.

Quite early in the Paleozoic era (Ordovician strata), *fossil Vertebrata* begin to be well represented, as primitive fishlike forms.

Shortly thereafter (Silurian strata) the *first land plants* appear, followed (in the Silurian and Devonian periods), by primitive **amphibians** and **reptiles**, which also began to invade the land. The later strata of the Paleozoic

Fig. 29-12.   Fossil of a Paleozoic insect (*Dunbaria fasciipenis*). (Courtesy of the Yale Peabody Museum.)

era continue to show a rich though varying representation of most of the earlier groups, but in addition they reveal the flourishing of many *land-dwelling* species: Bryophyta and Gymnospermae, among the plants; reptiles and Amphibia, among the Vertebrata; and insects (Fig. 29-12) and other Arthropoda among the invertebrates. Extensive swampland forests (Fig. 29-13), composed of gigantic ferns and other primitive Tracheophyta together with a few primitive Gymnospermae, flourished in the latter parts of the Paleozoic period; and fish became the dominant animals of the sea. However, none of the flowering plants (Angiospermae), nor any of the birds and mammals appear to have arisen much before the termination of the Paleozoic era.

Fig. 29-13.   Restoration of a carboniferous swamp forest. Note the giant ferns, horsetails, and club mosses; the primitive conifers (primitive gymnosperms); and the large primitive insect (center, right, look closely). (Courtesy of the Chicago Natural History Museum.)

Fig. 29-14. Whole skeleton of another dinosaur, *Tyrannosaurus rex*, from the Cretaceous strata of Hell Creek Basin, Montana. (Courtesy of the American Museum of Natural History, New York.)

The early Mesozoic strata show a great diversification of the reptile group, not only as to forms resembling the modern lizards, turtles, snakes, and so forth, but also as to archaic forms like the gigantic **dinosaurs** (Figs. 29-14 and 29-15), and the flying reptiles (**pterosaurs**). Also in the early Mesozoic rocks one finds the first **primitive mammals.** But the first *birds,* such as the toothed and clawed *Archaeopteryx* (Fig. 29-16), are not found

Fig. 29-15. *Tyrannosaurus* and *Triceratops*, a restoration by Charles R. Knight. (Courtesy of the American Museum of Natural History, New York.)

until the middle Mesozoic strata, and only in the upper Mesozoic strata does one begin to find flowering plants and *modern* insects. The close of the Mesozoic era also marks the extinction of most of the numerous ancient reptilian hordes that had dominated the land and air for a hundred million years. Hardly a single fossil trace of the many kinds of dinosaurs, pterosaurs, and other primitive types of reptiles are to be found in any of the Cenozoic strata.

The Cenozoic era, in which we live, is characterized by a very abundant fossil record; but to consider the details of this record would carry us far into the field of paleontology. Very briefly it can be said, however, that the Cenozoic era is the **age of mammals and angiosperms.**

By the beginning of the Tertiary period quite a variety of **archaic mammals** had usurped the place of the dinosaurs. These mammals displayed a very primitive structure. Their teeth, unlike the differentiated cutting (incisor), tearing (canine), and grinding (molar) teeth of modern mammals, were all essentially the same—like typical reptilian teeth. Moreover, the archaic mammals

Fig. 29-16. A primitive Jurassic bird, *Archaeopteryx*. Note the teeth, the elongate tail, and the clawed wings. (Courtesy of the American Museum of Natural History, New York.)

walked, not on their toes, but on the soles of their feet; they had five (the full primitive number) of digits on both fore and hind feet; and their cranial cavities were small compared to those of most modern mammals. In fact, very few of the **archaic mammals** survived until the end of the Tertiary period. Gradually they were displaced by the ancestors of the modern types, which had begun to appear simultaneously in early Tertiary times.

By the middle of the Tertiary period most of the *modern orders of mammals* (p. 673) had become numerous and well established. Here we find the richly documented evolutionary stages of the Ungulata (horses, camels, elephants, cattle, swine, etc.); the Carnivora (tigers, lions, cats, dogs, etc.); Rodentia (squirrels, rabbits, rats, mice, etc.); Primates (monkeys, apes, lemurs, etc.); and so forth. In fact, the peak of the ascendancy of the mammals (excluding man) was reached before the close of the Tertiary period. In the latter part of this period, there were great herds of mastodons (Fig. 29-17); but these elephantine creatures became extinct before the onset of the recent epoch.

The Tertiary period also records the rise of the angiosperms to ascendancy in the plant kingdom. Particularly important was the spread of the grasses, which provided food for the herbivorous mammals; and the extension of the deciduous forests, which afforded protection for a wide variety of mammalian types.

The first manlike fossils began to appear quite late in the Tertiary (Fig. 29-4); but undeniable evidence of the genus *Homo* is not found until early in the Quaternary period. The fossil record of the descent of man is not so complete as that of many other mammals (for example, the horse, camel, elephant, etc.), due probably to the fact that the forest habitat and mode of life among the early primates were not conducive to fossilization. However, the evidence is clear enough to show that man owes his origin to apelike creatures (Fig. 29-18), which in turn were de-

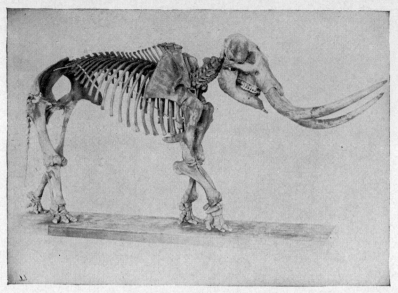

Fig. 29-17. Mastodons were very numerous toward the end of the tertiary period. (Courtesy of the American Museum of Natural History, New York.)

rived from lower primates. In fact, when one traces the fossil record, it is impossible to draw a sharp line between the apes and the several species of "man" that existed in the Pleistocene epoch. Also it is clear that all races of man that are alive today belong to a single species, *Homo sapiens;* and that the oldest fossil remains of this species are found in Pleistocene strata, formed about 250,000 years ago.

TEST QUESTIONS

1. Explain how a study of the classification of a given group of organisms (for example, vertebrates) leads to the conclusion that all the types belonging to the group (for example, fish, amphibians, reptiles, birds, and mammals) are variously interrelated by descent.

2. List twenty features possessed by all vertebrate animals but not by any other group of animals.

3. Explain how and why a biologist can predict many things about an animal or plant he has never seen, provided he is merely told the phylum and the class of the unknown organism.

4. Specify:
   a. five human bones that have homologous parts in the frog's skeleton
   b. four parts of man's digestive tract for which there are homologous organs in the frog

   c. four parts of man's excretory system for which there are homologous organs in the rat
   d. five parts of man's nervous system for which there are homologous parts in all other vertebrates

5. What is the justification for considering that the arm of a man is homologous to: (a) the wing of a bird; (b) the forelimb of a frog?

6. Explain the basis for the statement that a reptile, essentially, is "a patched up and made over amphibian."

7. What is a vestigial structure? Mention three of man's vestigial structures. How are vestigial structures to be accounted for?

8. How does a human embryo resemble the embryos of fish (and other vertebrates) in regard to:
   a. origin, position, and structure of the nervous system

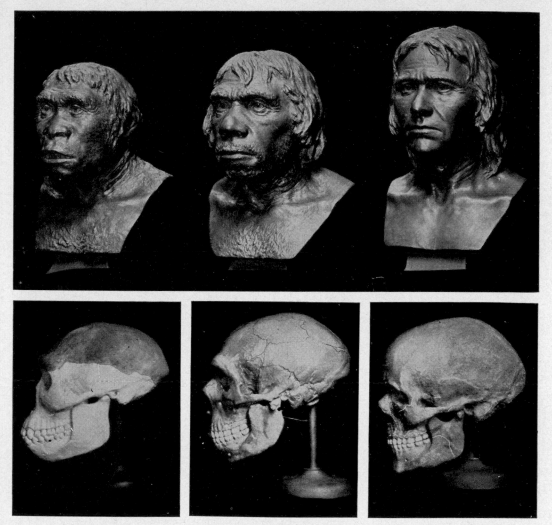

Fig. 29-18.   Skull and facial restorations of various prehistoric men, by J. H. McGregor. From left to right: 1, the Java man, *Pithecanthropus*; 2, the Neanderthal man; and 3, the Cro-Magnon man. In 1, the lighter parts are restorations, deduced from the anatomy of the other parts. (Courtesy of the American Museum of Natural History, New York.)

    b. stages in the development of the skeletal system
    c. origin and development of the circulatory organs?

9. To what extent does a human embryo in the "gill slit stage" tend to resemble a fully developed fish?

10. Explain and discuss the theory of recapitulation, pointing out its strengths and weaknesses.

11. Explain the genetic basis of the recapitulation tendency.

12. Explain how a study of the comparative biochemistry of the tissues (for example, blood) of various groups of animals and plants can be used to reveal genetic relationships among the groups.

13. Carefully define: (a) paleontology; (b) a fossil; (c) sedimentary rock; (d) erosion; (e) metamorphosis (of rock); (f) a geological stratum.

14. Explain how it is possible to estimate: (a) the relative age of a given geological stratum; (b) the absolute age of certain strata.

15. Distinguish between the eras and periods of geological time.

16. Briefly discuss each of the following topics:
    a. origin of the Schizomycophyta and Protozoa
    b. origin of the Thallophyta and Porifera
    c. origin of the higher invertebrate phyla, and of the earliest vertebrates
    d. first appearance of land plants (mosses, ferns, and seed plants); origin of land vertebrates
    e. origin and extinction of the forests of giant ferns
    f. the rise and fall of the dinosaurs and other primitive reptilian forms; origin of the birds and mammals; the heyday of the cycad and conifer forests
    g. the replacement of the archaic mammals by the modern mammalian forms
    h. the rise of man

17. List at least ten different fields of study that contribute significant evidence as to the probable mechanism and the actual course of evolution.

FURTHER READINGS

1. *Man and the Vertebrates,* by A. S. Romer; Chicago, 1941.
2. *Men of the Old Stone Age,* by H. F. Osborn; New York, 1918.
3. *Organic Evolution,* by R. S. Lull; New York, 1929.
4. *Embryos and Ancestors,* by G. R. DeBeer; Oxford, 1940.
5. *Tempo and Mode in Evolution,* by G. G. Simpson; New York, 1944.
6. *Up from the Ape,* by E. A. Hooton; New York, 1945.

30-*Ecology and Evolution*

THE ORGANISM AND THE ENVIRONMENT

Throughout the ages living things have been forced to change as they survived the everchanging conditions of natural selection. Each kind of organism, in fact, has been molded and remolded according to its capacity to live and reproduce at such times and in such places as it happened to exist during its evolutionary history. Today, therefore, existing species tend to be well adapted to their present environment. Each displays a variety of **adaptations** of form, function, and behavior. These adaptations fit each species to survive and multiply not only under the conditions of the environment as a whole but also—and this is even more important—under the special conditions of its own particular **natural habitat.**

A systematic study of the manifold interactions between organisms and the environment constitutes the science of **ecology.** Organisms, of course, have been tailored by natural selection to fit some particular environment; but it is equally true that the environment is subject to profound change by virtue of the organisms that live within it. Obviously ecology impinges upon every as-

pect of biology, and the following summary must therefore be brief and fragmentary.

BIOTIC AND ABIOTIC ASPECTS OF THE ENVIRONMENT

Living things are exposed to two kinds of environmental influences: (1) contacts with other organisms (the **biotic environment**); and (2) contacts with the nonliving elements of nature (the **abiotic environment**). The biotic and abiotic parts of the environment always work together in shaping the evolutionary destiny of the species, but it is easier to discuss them separately.

The Biotic Environment. Directly or indirectly the animals of a given region are dependent upon the green plants of the area, since green plants provide the major source of all organic food. But above and beyond this basic fact, there are many other biotic relationships that enmesh the species in a common web of destiny. Indeed, the equilibrium that exists is so delicately balanced that any significant change in the population of one species inevitably has an influence on all neighboring species.

Interdependence of Species. Sometimes it is

possible to catch a glimpse of the chain of circumstances that interlinks the species of a region, even though biotic interrelationships are extremely complex and difficult to study. In 1931, for example, a fungus disease, caused by a parasitic slime mold (*Labyrinthula*), suddenly destroyed almost all of the eelgrass (*Zostera marina*) that for centuries had flourished in the shallow bays and inlets along the Atlantic coast. Such a wholesale extermination of the eelgrass produced enormous changes in the fauna and flora of the coastal region. Most people noticed these changes, because scallops and mussels became extremely scarce and because certain migratory ducks (which feed upon the eelgrass) were no longer available. But more important still was the extermination of many species of marine worms and other tidal organisms, which died off in prodigious numbers. Without eelgrass, the mud flats were no longer anchored against erosion by the shifting tides, and large areas of this richly populated habitat were destroyed all along the coast.

Another example of the interdependence of species in a given locality may be cited from the work of Darwin. For years Darwin studied the periodic fluctuations in the abundance of red clover in an English countryside. Generally speaking, it was found that red clover became exceptionally abundant whenever the population of cats increased. These changes were correlated with changes in the population of field mice and bumblebees in the locality. The red clover produced more seeds whenever there were larger numbers of bumblebees to pollinate the flowers; and since field mice gain a living by preying upon the nests of the bumblebees, the bees became abundant when the current generation of cats was adequate to hold down the number of field mice. Consequently, both bumblebees and red clover began to prosper whenever there were many cats to check the depredations of the mice.

Animal Populations and the Food Supply. Although the green plants of a region provide an ultimate nutritive base for the animal species, many large animals feed directly upon smaller animals, and smaller animals, in turn, gain a living by devouring a variety of still smaller creatures. Moreover, large carnivorous animals cannot survive unless they find an abundance of smaller creatures to feed on—as is witnessed by the fact that an adult lion may kill as many as fifty zebras every year (Fig. 30-1). As a result of these factors, the carnivorous species of a region tend to display a pyramidal distribution. Generally one finds, at the base of the pyramid, large numbers of small plants and animals, which provide food for the larger animals. And at the apex of the pyramid there are only a few very large animals which feed upon the lesser species.

Fig. 30-1. African lions at the kill (a zebra). (Courtesy of the American Museum of Natural History, New York.)

This pyramidal distribution of animals, according to size and the magnitude of the food requirements, may be observed in a variety of localized environments. In many ponds, for example, there are billions of bacteria, but only millions of paramecia and other large Protozoa can be supported by the bacterial population. Then there will be a lesser number—perhaps hundreds of thousands—of semimicroscopic animals, such as *Daphnia* and *Cyclops,* and only thousands of easily visible creatures, such as carnivorous beetle larvae and small fish. Finally, at the apex of the pyramid, the number of truly large predaceous fish may be so restricted that an angler may need patience to make a single catch.

A study of the fauna in a summer forest reveals a similar arrangement. Vast numbers of aphids and other small herbivorous animals provide a broad food base for the carnivorous species of the region; and a fairly large population of spiders, beetles, and other medium-sized carnivorous animals are able to prosper on this base. But the number of insectivorous birds, such as warblers, will not be very great; and only two or three hawks (Fig. 30-2) or other predatory birds will be able to gain a living in a particular forest—even though the range of flight of such hunting birds is extensive.

Fig. 30-2.   Red-shouldered hawk (*Buteo lineatus*) with a field mouse in its talons. (Courtesy of the American Museum of Natural History, New York.)

In short, the smallest animals at the base of a food chain, owing to the modesty of their food needs and the efficiency of their reproductive processes, tend to populate a given habitat in great abundance, whereas the largest animals, at the apex of the food chain, are much more restricted in numerical abundance—with the medium-sized species falling in between the two extremes. Moreover, the height of the pyramid is limited, since the population of a dominant species tends to be so sparse that no other animal can gain a living by preying upon it.

The Adaptation of Species to Species. During evolution, many species had a profound influence upon the development of other species. In this regard, the insects provide many good examples. Insects have been abundant since early in the Cenozoic era, at which time the flowering plants began their evolution. Consequently, natural selection had ample time to create a rich variety of modern flowers. Thus, many present-day flowers possess both color and fragrance with which they attract insects seeking food and, incidentally, pollinating flowers. Likewise, the prevalence of insects during such an extensive evolutionary period accounts for many other adaptations in modern plants and animals. In this category we find the insect-trapping leaves of certain plants (Fig. 14-2); the wings, eyes, and mouth parts of insect-catching birds; and the mouth parts and sensory organs of many fish, reptiles, and mammals that prey upon insects or insect larvae. And although insects, owing to their unusual prevalence, were particularly potent in shaping the adaptations of other species, it seems probable that every kind of animal and plant, whether it persisted or became extinct, has had some influence on the evolutionary destiny of neighboring species.

Predatism: Mechanisms of Offense and Defense. Impacts between species have been of many kinds, but only such adaptations as have arisen in relation to **predatism** and **parasitism** will be considered in the present account.

Even a cursory survey of familiar species reveals a wide variety of adaptations that enable animals to catch, kill, and feed upon their living prey. Many one-celled animals such as *Amoeba* have pseudopodia that entrap the prey; *Didinium* (Fig. 32-4) uses a pointed drill to pierce and kill other microscopic animals; and *Suctoria* (Fig. 30-3) catch and hold their prey with tentacles tipped by suction discs. Multicellular animals also display a bizarre variety of offensive devices. These include stinging organs (jellyfish, bees, wasps, spiders, scorpions, etc.); webs for ensnarement (spiders, etc.); claws for catching, holding, or tearing victims (eagles, lions, tigers, etc.); and teeth for tearing flesh and crunching bone (carnivorous mammals).

Defensive devices are also widespread in nature. Ciliates often possess **trichocysts**, which may be used in warding off attack; and many animals possess *shells, scales,* and other types of *armor* (Fig. 30-4). There are numerous other protective devices of greater or lesser importance. These include many familiar examples—such as spines (cactus, roses, and porcupines); poisonous secretions (numerous plants and animals); *unpleasant tastes* and *odors* (many plants, caterpillars, and toads); and last but not least, *protective mimicry* (Fig. 30-5) and *protective coloration* (many insects and other animals). Also there are many less familiar defensive adaptations, such as the *ink sac* of the octopus. This contractile reservoir is able to eject such a dense cloud of inky fluid that an enemy has difficulty finding its intended victim in the darkened sea.

Parasitism. Practically every plant and animal serves as host to one or more parasitic species. Moreover, the association between host and parasite often extends far back into the evolutionary history of the species; and a high degree of specificity may develop

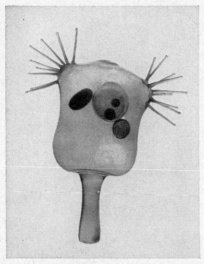

Fig. 30-3. This one-celled animal, a suctorian, uses its two batteries of tentacles to catch, hold, and penetrate into other Protozoa. Then it "sucks out" the protoplasm from the victim. Photograph of a glass model of *Tokophrya cyclopum*. Note the nucleus (dark, oval, left), an internal reproductive bud (center), and a rounded mass of semidigested food (right). (Courtesy of the American Museum of Natural History, New York.)

Fig. 30-4. Female box turtle (*Cistudo carolina*) with egg. (Courtesy of the American Museum of Natural History, New York.)

Fig. 30-5. The leaf butterfly, an outstanding example of protective mimicry. (Courtesy of the American Museum of Natural History, New York.)

between the parasite and its host. Seldom can a particular parasite infest a wide variety of different hosts, and frequently the parasitic relation is altogether *species specific*.

Undoubtedly the adaptation of a parasite to life on or in a host represents a gradual evolution. By slow degrees the parasite develops an increasing fitness to live on or in the body of a particular host; and simultaneously the host develops countermeasures to limit the growth of the parasite and to neutralize its damaging effects. If the total population of the host should succumb to the ravages of a parasite, the parasite itself would face extinction. Obviously, therefore, the survival of a parasitic species depends in certain measure upon the survival of the host species.

EFFECTS OF PARASITISM ON THE PARASITE. Some parasites, especially ectoparasites (p. 178) like the mosquito, do not remain in continuous contact with the host species, and such organisms do not display very drastic adaptations to the parasitic habit. The mosquito, for example, is an insect that has mouth parts that are plainly designed for piercing the skin and sucking blood from the host; and the saliva of the mosquito contains an anticoagulant, which prevents the blood from clotting as it is being imbibed. But otherwise the mosquito displays little

divergence from other closely related insects. Other ectoparasites, however, maintain a closer contact with their hosts, and these display more drastic adaptations. The flattened body and spiny legs of the flea, for example, enable this parasite to force its way through the matted hair of the dog; and the clasping talons of the louse (Fig. 30-6) make it difficult for this pest to be dislodged from the surface of the skin. In extreme cases, indeed, the fixation of a parasite to the host may be so complete that the parasite loses virtually all capacity for independent life. For example, *Sacculina,* a parasitic crustacean, displays so drastic a degeneration of its eyes and other sensory structures, and such an atrophy of its locomotor organs, that it bears very little resemblance to closely related species. However, *Sacculina* displays free-living larval stages by which it can be identified as a true crustacean.

Obligatory parasites may encounter serious difficulty at times when it is necessary to abandon one host and find access to another. In fact there are various adaptations that facilitate the transfer of parasitic species from host to host. However, only two such adaptations will be considered, namely: (1) a tendency of parasitic species to produce vast numbers of offspring, and (2) the ability of many parasites to invade one or more intermediary

Fig. 30-6. Enlarged model of the body louse, *Pediculus vestimenti*. Note the adaptations that enable this ectoparasite to cling to its host. (Courtesy of the American Museum of Natural History, New York.)

hosts as a means of regaining access to a primary host.

Many parasitic species display enormous powers of reproduction—which assures a reasonable chance that some of the offspring may gain access to a proper host. In an adult tapeworm, for example, each of the many body sections usually bears two ovaries and many testes, and the number of self-fertilized eggs produced by a single tapeworm amounts to many millions. Also many parasites multiply asexually during one or more stages of the life cycle. Thus, large numbers of offspring may be produced by fission, budding, or sporulation during one or more asexual stages (Fig. 30-7).

In regaining access to a primary host, a parasite may develop the capacity to infest intermediary hosts; and such an intermediary host may become a **vector,** which facilitates the transfer of the parasite back to the primary host (Fig. 30-7). This tendency, indeed, accounts for the complexity that is characteristic of the life cycles of many parasites. The parasite must adapt itself to a series of intermediary hosts, and perhaps also to one or more free-living periods between successive hosts before it comes back to its primary host.

EFFECTS OF PARASITISM ON THE HOST: PARASITIC DISEASES. Although a parasite may not harm its host very seriously, or at all, parasites generally are responsible for **infectious diseases.** This is true among plants, as well as animals, including man (see Table 30-1). When a virus, fungus, protozoan, or other parasitic species invades the tissues, fluids, or hollow organs of a host, the parasitized individual often suffers damage, and often the host displays symptoms of a definite disease.

A parasite may harm the host in various ways: (1) by digesting and destroying the living tissues (*Amoeba hystolytica,* in amoebic dysentery); (2) by producing toxic products (fever-producing organisms); (3) by causing internal bleeding (hookworm); (4) by appropriating organic food from the digestive tract of the host (tapeworms); or (5) by combinations of these and other effects.

DISEASE RESISTANCE: NATURAL DEFENSES. Natural defenses against infective organisms have been evolved in every species. In man, for example, the skin, because of its toughness and dryness, offers an effective barrier against the penetration of potential parasites, which often may gain access to the more vulnerable deeper tissues only when the skin is broken. Moreover, a parasite, once past the

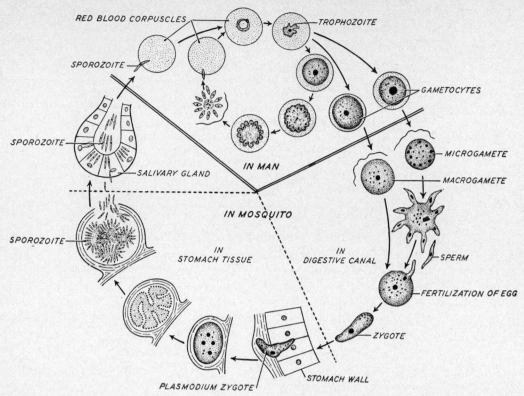

RED BLOOD CORPUSCLES

TROPHOZOITE

SPOROZOITE

GAMETOCYTES

SPOROZOITE

MICROGAMETE

SALIVARY GLAND

MACROGAMETE

IN MAN

IN MOSQUITO

SPERM

SPOROZOITE

IN
STOMACH TISSUE

IN
DIGESTIVE CANAL

FERTILIZATION OF EGG

ZYGOTE

PLASMODIUM ZYGOTE

STOMACH WALL

Fig. 30-7. Life cycle of one of the malaria parasites, a protozoan (Class, Sporozoa; Genus, *Plasmodium*). Note the three separate reproductive stages and the several adaptations to different conditions in two hosts. In man, the malarial fever flares up whenever swarms of the parasites emerge from one set of corpuscles (which are destroyed) and pass, via the plasma, into another set of corpuscles. (From Buchanan, *Elements of Biology*. Harper and Row.)

skin, may be phagocytized by leucocytes, either locally at the site of the infection (p. 334), or in the lymph nodes, which filter the lymph as it drains from the infected area (p. 335). Or the parasite may be immobilized by encasement within a tough-walled cyst, which is constructed by the local connective tissues in response to the irritating presence of the foreign organism. But by far the most important defensive adaptation of organisms generally is a capacity to produce specific **antibodies.** Each antibody is a specific chemical compound that is formed by the tissues of the host and serves to limit the growth or to neutralize the toxins of some particular infective agent.

Disease Resistance: Artificial Defenses. **Vaccines** and **antisera** are widely used in modern medicine to augment the natural antibody defenses of man and other animals. The vaccine with which an individual is inoculated (or vaccinated) always contains a specific antigen (p. 320) that stimulates the subject to produce the proper antibody. The vaccine may be an extract of an infectious organism; or the infectious organism itself may be used for the inoculation. But in the latter case, the infectious organism must first be killed or weakened (attenuated), or it must be selected from a nonvirulent strain. An antiserum, on the other hand, is an antibody-rich serum obtained from an animal (for example, horse or cow) that previously was vaccinated against a particular infection.

Man has developed many other weapons to combat the ravages of parasitic organisms (see Table 30-1). In addition to natural

Table 30-1—Some Infectious Diseases of Man

Types of Parasitic Diseases	Locus of Infection	Preventive or Curative Treatment
Bacillus Infections		
Tetanus (lockjaw)	Brain and spinal cord	Antiserum, penicillin
Cholera	Gastrointestinal tract	Vaccine
Diphtheria	Upper respiratory tract; generalized in later stages	Antiserum (antitoxin)
Tuberculosis	Lungs, bones, etc.	Antibiotics
Typhoid fever	Intestinal tract	Vaccine
Whooping cough	Trachea and bronchi	Vaccine, human antiserum
Coccus Infections		
Pneumonia (typical)	Lungs; generalized in later stages	Antibiotics and antiserum
Gonorrhea	Urogenital organs, eyes, joints	Penicillin and streptomycin
Spirochete * *Infections*		
Trench mouth	Mouth and throat	Various antibiotics
Syphilis	Genital organs, blood, and, in late stages, other organs of the body	Penicillin and other antibiotics
Virus Infections		
Smallpox	Generalized	Vaccine
Mumps	Salivary glands, mammary glands, and (sometimes) the testes	Vaccine
Measles	Generalized	Vaccine
Rabies	Brain	Vaccine
Poliomyelitis	Brain, spinal cord	Vaccine
Pneumonia (atypical) ...	Lungs	Vaccine (?)
Influenza	Lungs, etc.	Vaccine
Protozoan Infections		
Malarias	Blood stream	Several recently synthesized antimalarial compounds
Amoebic dysentery	Intestinal tract	Combinations of antibiotics
Rickettsia † *Infections*		
Rocky Mountain spotted fever	Heart, blood vessels, etc.	Vaccine, antiserum
Epidemic typhus	Heart, blood vessels, etc.	Vaccine, antiserum

* The spirochetes are unicellular organisms that appear to be intermediate between bacteria (spirilla) and protozoans (flagellates).

† Rickettsia are infective agents that are smaller than typical bacteria but larger than typical viruses.

drugs, which are mainly plant products, there are the artificially synthesized **chemo-therapeutic agents,** such as salvarsan (which was used for many years against *Treponema pallidum,* the syphilis parasite), the sulfonamides (which are effective against many bacterial infections), and several synthetic antimalarial compounds.[1] Also to be mentioned are the **antibiotic compounds,** like penicillin, streptomycin, and aureomycin, which are extracted from certain molds, bacteria, and other fungi. These advances are very encouraging, but the problem of finding a particular compound that is effective against a specific parasite is not an easy one. Most compounds that are toxic to a parasite are also toxic to the cells and tissues of the host. If the compound is administered in amounts that are adequate to eliminate the parasite, the host itself is unable to tolerate the dose. In each case, therefore, the essential problem is to find a compound that is at the same time *specifically* toxic to the cells of the particular parasite and relatively nontoxic to the cells of the host (man).

DISEASE VECTORS. Various blood-sucking creatures frequently serve as transmitters of disease, as has been acknowledged since 1893, when Theobald Smith first proved that the blood-dwelling parasite of Texas cattle fever is transmitted from animal to animal by the bite of a common tick. Subsequently, as a result of many investigations, the importance of vector organisms, especially insects, in relation to human disease became increasingly apparent. Today, in fact, it is common knowledge that various mosquitoes are mainly responsible for the spread of malaria, yellow fever, dengue, and filaria infections; that the tsetse fly transmits African sleeping sickness; that lice carry typhus; that fleas spread the "black plague"; and finally that ticks are the main purveyors of Rocky Mountain spotted fever. Moreover, a study of vectors has greatly aided man's fight against disease. Mosquito

control made it possible to complete the Panama Canal, after a first attempt had been abandoned owing to the ravages of yellow fever; and more recently, a drive against lice enabled the American Army to overcome a grave epidemic of typhus in the Naples area, during the Italian campaign of World War II. Likewise, the development of modern insecticides, such as DDT, has provided a new and powerful weapon against the insect-borne diseases.

The Abiotic Environment. Throughout the universe living matter has been found only on the earth, a relatively small planet in the solar system. In fact, no other region has been discovered where the environment is chemically and physically suitable for the existence of living things, although probably other life-supporting planets do exist through the universe (p. 187). Protoplasm is an extremely sensitive and unstable form of matter. It can exist and perpetuate itself only under a very limited set of physical and chemical conditions such as have prevailed on the earth for many ages.

The general fitness of the terrestrial environment in relation to living organisms is determined by a wide variety of conditions. However, only four physical factors, namely **temperature, light, gravity,** and **pressure,** and only one chemical factor—the **water supply**—will be considered in this brief account.

Temperature. A tremendous variation of temperature occurs within the universe— from the frigid stillness of interstellar space, where the temperature approaches absolute zero—to the shattering heat of the sun, where the temperature exceeds 10,000,000 degrees centigrade. The range of temperature that is tolerable to living things is very limited, however. Few organisms can survive except at temperatures between 0° and 50° C; and if such temperatures had not prevailed for many years over large areas of the earth, life as it is today could not have evolved.

The sensitivity of living things to cold and heat derives mainly from the fact that water and proteins are main components of living

---

[1] Antimalarial research during World War II led to the discovery of several compounds that have proved to be more effective than atabrine.

matter. If protoplasm freezes,[2] the formation of ice crystals tends to isolate the water as a separate phase—and without water, the protoplasmic structure disintegrates beyond repair. Conversely, if protoplasm continues to absorb heat, even though the heat capacity is high, a point is finally reached where the enzymes and other protein components of the cell become denatured, and the protoplasmic structure is destroyed.

Although living organisms can remain active only when the body temperature keeps within certain limits, many species possess adaptations that permit them to inhabit regions of unusual heat or cold. This is especially true of **homeothermic** animals— namely the birds and mammals—which possess mechanisms for controlling the body temperature at a relatively steady level even when there are great changes in the environmental temperature. But even the birds and mammals vary widely as to their capacity to endure the extremes of cold and heat. Cold-adapted species (Figs. 30-8 and 30-9) tend to possess specialized integumentary coverings (feathers or fur) and thickened layers of subcutaneous fatty tissue—which are effective in insulating the body against the loss of heat; and polar species are apt to maintain a very high basal metabolism—which produces heat as a by-product (p. 436). Conversely, tropical species tend to limit their basal metabolism to a minimum, and such organisms usually display a well-developed capacity for dissipating heat from the body surfaces.

Poikilothermic organisms, in which the body temperature changes constantly with the surrounding temperature, likewise are variously adapted in relation to the tempera-

[2] By the "quick-freezing" technique, which involves a very rapid reduction to subfreezing temperatures, protoplasm may solidify without the separation of ice crystals, and without a disruption of structure. However, the conditions for "quick freezing" seldom prevail in nature, and probably this phenomenon has little evolutionary significance. Also many cells can tolerate subfreezing temperatures temporarily, if the formation of ice crystals is delayed (as in supercooled solutions) by an absence of crystallizing foci, or if much of the intracellular water is in "bound" form.

Fig. 30-8. Polar bear on an iceberg off Greenland. (Courtesy of the American Museum of Natural History, New York.)

ture range of their native habitat. In most cases the metabolic enzymes are keyed to operate efficiently only within some rather restricted range of temperature, which may be high or low according to the evolutionary experience of the species. In fact, there are

Fig. 30-9. Female fur seals. (Courtesy of the American Museum of Natural History, New York.)

very few species, at least among poikilo-thermic organisms, that have extended their range of habitat widely enough to include all kinds (tropical, temperate, and frigid) of climatic conditions.

Lastly, some organisms display a capacity to become dormant during periods of very low or high temperature, and frequently the dormant protoplasm is especially adapted for enduring adverse conditions. This is especially true of seeds, spores, and cysts, which sometimes remain alive after they have been exposed to subfreezing or near-boiling temperatures. Usually such a great temperature resistance indicates that the protoplasm has undergone reorganization. The cells eliminate part of their normal water content, and in a partially dehydrated condition the proteins are less susceptible to denaturation by low and high extremes of temperature.

Light. Almost all the radiant energy received by the earth comes from the sun, and if the sun grew dim, all parts of the world would become too cold for the survival of any living thing. Light striking the earth is transformed mainly into heat, and this maintains the environmental temperature. But a small fraction of sunlight provides energy for the growth of green plants. And since organic compounds synthesized by plants are essential for the sustenance of virtually all other organisms, the importance of light in the general economy of life cannot be overemphasized.

A competition for light among green plants is a primary factor in their struggle for existence. Treelike species survive by overshadowing their smaller competitors, although sometimes a smaller species, by dint of numbers, will pre-empt a certain region, making it difficult for the seedlings of a larger species to gain a foothold. Small annual plants may also succeed in growing on the floor of very dense deciduous forests, but such plants tend to sprout very early in the springtime and to produce their seeds before the overlying foliage has had a chance to blanket them from the sun. Thus, one trend

of natural selection among woodland flowers has been toward a very quick and abundant production of seeds.

Among animals, light has been a primary factor in the development of eyes and other photoreceptive organs, which play a paramount role in the acquisition of food, the finding of shelter, the avoidance of danger, and the fulfillment of the reproductive functions of the species. Creatures that live entirely in a dark environment—as in deep caves, underground burrows, or in the abysmal depths of the ocean—are usually sightless. This may be due either to a degeneration (Fig. 30-10) of photoreceptive organs that once were possessed by the ancestral species, or to a failure of the ancestral species to develop such organs initially—depending on the earlier evolutionary background.

The breeding activities of many birds and mammals are initiated in the springtime

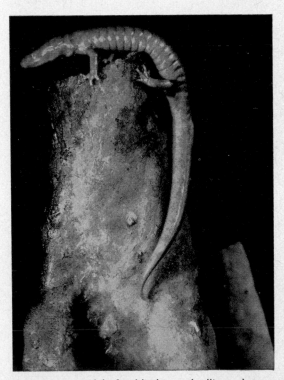

Fig. 30-10. Model of a blind cave-dwelling salamander, taken from the Ozark Mountains (see text). (Courtesy of the American Museum of Natural History, New York.)

when the days grow steadily longer. Carefully controlled experiments have proved that the stimulus for this ripening of the eggs and sperm often originates from the increased time of exposure to light rather than from an increase in the total amount of light received. This fact, indeed, has been used by modern hatcheries, which force the brood hens to lay prematurely, using artificial lights to duplicate the approach of spring. Also many plants display a similar **photoperiodicity,** putting forth buds, flowers, and fruits on a schedule that is determined mainly by the waxing or waning of the daylight in the different seasons of the year (p. 265). However, other plants are more sensitive to the thermoperiodic fluctuations of their environment.

Gravity. The gravitational force of the earth has remained quite constant for eras, but the magnitude of this force has influenced the evolution of all organisms. In fact, if the earth had been a significantly larger or smaller planet (such that the force of gravity were correspondingly greater or lesser) the end results of evolution would necessarily have been quite modified.

Aquatic plants and animals are buoyed up by the surrounding water and thus are protected from the full impact of gravity. Consequently the supporting structures of aquatic organisms, compared to terrestrial forms, are not subjected to so great a strain. Some seaweeds, for example, are able to grow four or five hundred feet up from the ocean floor, despite the fact that these algae lack any specialized strengthening tissues such as are present in the higher plants. Among terrestrial plants mainly those that have evolved a capacity to deposit strong annual rings of xylem tissues are able to achieve a very tall treelike form.

Many aquatic animals possess skeletal materials that are relatively light and weak, such as the cartilage of the elasmobranchs (p. 669) and the delicate porous bones of many fish. But land animals require a heavier skeleton to sustain their fleshy bulk, and this imposes a definite restriction upon their growth. In fact, the unwieldy skeletal weight of some dinosaurs is known to have been a handicap that partly accounted for their extinction.

Pressure. Land organisms do not often experience great changes in the pressure of their surroundings. At sea level the pressure is only about 15 pounds per square inch (one atmosphere), and even at the highest altitudes where living things are found, the pressure seldom drops to less than half an atmosphere. But many marine species live at oceanic depths of more than three miles, where the pressure exceeds 8000 pounds per square inch. Here pressure introduces a number of interesting ecological problems.

Most deep-sea forms, if they are suddenly brought to the surface, cannot survive the change. Fish with swim bladders are particularly vulnerable in this respect, although most truly deep-sea forms do not have swim bladders. Nevertheless some fish, living at moderate depths, are literally torn apart, so great is the expansion of the gas in the bladder when the surrounding pressure is reduced. But even if the swim bladder is lacking, the fish or other deep-sea form is apt to die as a result of decompression; and conversely, surface forms do not usually survive when exposed to deep-sea pressures.

An animal may be protected partly from the effects of decompression if it is cooled as the pressure is reduced. Thus deep-sea forms may remain alive and active at sea-level pressure if the water in the aquarium is cooled nearly to the freezing point. Low pressure, apparently, is counteracted by low temperature, and such an antagonistic action between pressure and temperature has been demonstrated in many experiments. Generally speaking, the metabolic reactions of an organism are equally sensitive to both pressure and temperature, and increasing temperature shifts the metabolic equilibria oppositely to increasing pressure. Moreover, the metabolic reactions of deep-sea and surface forms are keyed to different combinations of temperature and pressure. Consequently such animals cannot usually exchange environments without suffering drastic derangements in their metabolism.

Man represents an exception to the rule that land organisms do not encounter significant changes in the environmental pressure. Deep-sea divers and workers in pressure caissons may experience sudden compressions and decompressions amounting to several atmospheres, and a modern aviator may gain or lose altitude so fast that the pressure change becomes a matter of importance.

The pressure sustained by a caisson worker is usually not greater than five or six atmospheres, a pressure that is not sufficient to produce any *direct* effect upon metabolism. But decompression may have serious *indirect* effects, unless the pressure is reduced very slowly in carefully graduated steps. This precaution is necessary to prevent the formation of gas bubbles in the blood stream. In a caisson, the pressure is transmitted to the body through the surrounding air—rather than through water, as in aquatic organisms. In the caisson, therefore, the high pressure tends to drive excesses of air into solution in the blood and other fluids of the body. During decompression, this gas begins to come out of solution—slowly and without the formation of bubbles, if the decompression is slow. But if the decompression is rapid, gas bubbles are formed in the blood, and these bubbles may choke off circulation in the arterioles and other smaller vessels of the blood system—which accounts for the serious symptoms of **caisson sickness.**

Even at atmospheric pressure fairly large quantities of the atmospheric gases are present in the blood, but ordinarily these gases remain in solution. An ordinary climb to high altitude, for example, is slow enough to permit a gradual escape of blood gases as the atmospheric pressure falls. A modern pilot, however, may climb at a rate approximating a mile a minute. Under such conditions aeroembolisms are sometimes encountered, and a study of the process of **aero-embolism** has become a matter of practical importance in aviation medicine.

Water. No organism can live and grow without water, since water is a main component of all protoplasm. Also it is plain that aquatic organisms can absorb water directly from their surroundings. But most land-dwelling species are constantly losing water to the atmosphere, and such species have developed many adaptations for conserving and augmenting their water resources.

Land-dwelling *animals* display a wide variety of integumental coverings that serve to minimize the loss of water vapor from exposed body surfaces. Thus the skin of terrestrial vertebrates—whether naked or clothed by scales, feathers, or hair—provides an effective barrier against evaporative losses from the tissues and body fluids; and the same is true of the chitinous integuments of insects, arachnids, and other land-dwelling arthropods. In land animals, also, the respiratory organs (for example, the lungs of vertebrates and the tracheae of insects) are deeply recessed within the body, so that the loss of water vapor from the respiratory surfaces is reduced as much as possible. And finally, the excretory organs of typical land animals (for example, the kidneys of man) are able to curtail the excretion of water whenever a dearth of water begins to threaten the welfare of the animal (p. 375).

Terrestrial *plants* likewise display many adaptations that are related to the water supply of the environment. For example, desert plants (**xerophytes**) are apt to have very deep and extensive roots; and the root sap of such plants tends to be very hypertonic, which facilitates the absorption of every possible vestige of water from the soil. Moreover, the stem and leaves of many xerophytes are characteristically modified. Generally, the exposed surface area of a desert plant is sharply reduced; the epidermis is thick, shiny, and heavily cutinized; and the stomata are sparse and deeply sunk below the epidermal surface. In extreme xerophytes

Fig. 30-11. This cactus is one of the extreme xerophytes (see text). (Courtesy of C. J. Alexopaulos.)

(for example, certain cacti) the leaves are reduced to mere spiny structures (Fig. 30-11), and the compact fleshy stem takes over the photosynthetic functions of the leaves. Other xerophytes, however, possess thick fleshy leaves in which large reserves of water may be accumulated.

The **mesophytes** are plants adapted to conditions of moderate moisture. This group includes a number of very quick-growing annual plants that can extend their range into desert regions if a small amount of rainfall occurs each season. For a few weeks each year such deserts may display a rich variety of bright-colored flowers, which mature their seeds very quickly. Then when the drought sets in again, the seeds lie dormant until the next rainy period begins. However, there is an exceedingly wide variety of mesophytes, which, in fact, include a majority of familiar plants in temperate regions.

The **hydrophytes** include all higher plants that live in regions where there is an overabundance of water, and hydrophytes are variously adapted to different local conditions. Some species, like *Elodea,* live entirely under water, in which case the leaves, stems, and roots display a relatively simple structure. In *Elodea,* for example, the roots are scarcely more complex than holdfasts (p. 238), and the stem and leaf cells absorb water directly from the surroundings. Moreover, the vascular and strengthening tissues, especially of the xylem, are almost lacking in the *Elodea,* and since all the cells possess chloroplasts, there is no differentiaton between the epidermis and chlorenchyma.

Other hydrophytes (for example, certain water lilies) have underwater roots and stems, but the leaves and flowers are exposed to the atmosphere. In such cases, usually, only the aquatic parts are simplified. And finally, in swamp-dwelling hydrophytes, only the roots may be submerged. Such roots are not apt to be highly modified, except that *aerial branches,* called **pneumatophores** (Fig. 30-12), are characteristic, especially in the case of large-deep-rooted swamp trees. Probably the pneumatophores fulfill a respiratory function, being designed to transmit air downward through porous channels to the deeper parts of the root system—an important function, since oxygen diffuses very slowly through a swampy soil.

Fig. 30-12. Pneumatophores of the bald cypress; adaptations to a swampy habitat (see text). (Photo by C. F. Hottes.)

ECOLOGICAL SYSTEMS (ECOSYSTEMS)

The ecosystem concept, so named in 1935 by A. G. Tansley, has greatly aided the thinking and researches of modern ecologists. The term designates some particular and characteristic section of the environment that is more or less isolated from other sections; but an ecosystem includes also the sum total of interactions among the species inhabiting the region and all interactions between the species and their abiotic surroundings. A balanced aquarium would be a somewhat artificial and exceedingly miniature example of an ecosystem. Aside from the fact that the aquarium receives light from the outside world, it is virtually a self-sufficient system, which exchanges very little material, either biotic or abiotic, with surrounding environmental areas.

In nature, of course, there are no perfect ecosystems, completely self-sufficient and totally isolated from surrounding systems. However, there are a number of fairly good approximations. Some good examples are to be found in ponds or lakes, and in the central parts of forests, grasslands, salt marshes, and deserts. On the fringes of any such area there are transitional zones, where the particular ecosystem is overlapped by one or more surrounding systems. But disregarding the fringe areas, the ecologist can analyze the main features of the economy of the system and can reach an understanding of how the plant and animal species of the *community* are sustained.

Analysis of any ecosystem reveals that there is a rough sort of balance in the economy of the community. This balance results from interactions among four principal components: (1) an **abiotic base,** which represents the total fund of light and of nutritive substances, provides for the growth of the green plants and other **autotrophic organisms;** (2) a community of **producers,** mainly green plants, provides for the primary synthesis of organic foods; (3) a community of **consumers,** mainly animals, lives upon the available fund of organic food; (4) a community of **decomposers,** mainly bacteria and other fungi, degrades accumulations of organic matter, restoring the abiotic base of inorganic nutrients. In short, each ecosystem represents a microcosm, governed by the same inexorable laws that determine the economy of life upon our terrestrial planet as a whole (Chap. 10).

A pond (Fig. 30-13) will serve to exemplify the economy of a small but definitive ecosystem. Such a system may endure for only a century or two, because an invasion of rooted plants (cattails, water lilies, etc.) will gradually tend to fill the pond, converting it to marshland and finally to "terra firma." But while the pond endures, interactions within the communities of inhabitants can be analyzed with some precision.

The **abiotic base** in a small pond ecosystem is provided partly by the nitrates, phos-

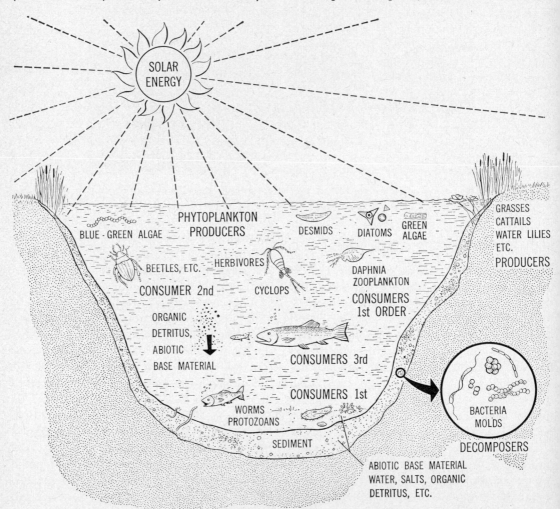

Fig. 30-13.   Ecosystem of a small pond. The system operates upon solar energy and the **producers** are a community of green plants of which the free-floating phytoplankton is of greatest importance. **Abiotic base material**, for supporting the producers, is provided by the water, salts, and carbon dioxide of the pond and by the organic detritus that sediments to the bottom. **Primary consumers** are small crustaceans and other herbivores that feed directly upon the producers; the **secondary** and **tertiary consumers**, respectively, are the smaller and larger carnivorous species. The **decomposers**, which prevent an unduly large accumulation of organic matter, are constituted by the community of fungi—bacteria and molds—that mainly inhabit the bottom sediment. (After E. P. Odum.)

phates, and other inorganic components of the pond water and partly by the **organic detritus** that settles to the bottom. Here it is utilized by bacteria and other fungi, which are the **decomposers;** and, of course, energy for the support of the system comes from the sun. The **producers** are partly the higher plants, cattails, water lilies, etc., which grow along the edges of the pond, but mainly they are the **phytoplankton**—various unicellular and minute colonial algae that float near the surface in easy access to the light. Then come the **consumers:** primary, secondary, and tertiary. Primary consumers are represented mainly by the **zooplankton.** These various protozoans and semimicroscopic crustaceans, such as *Daphnia,* feed directly upon the phytoplankton, although some larger forms, such as tadpoles, may nibble at the larger plants along the margins of the pond. The secondary consumers—larger arthropods, particularly water beetles—feed upon the zooplankton; and finally the largest animals—fish, frogs, etc.—serve as tertiary consumers, which prey upon the secondaries. Meanwhile, organic detritus (excreta, remnants of dead organisms, etc.) keeps silting to the bottom of the pond. Here it may be eaten by scavengers, such as insect larvae. But mainly the organic matter is returned to inorganic form by action of bacteria and other decomposers. Thus each of the various species has its **niche** in any system. Each plays some unique and essential role in the complex business that maintains the economy of the whole community.

Imbalance in an Ecosystem. Sometimes the delicate balance that supports the economy of an ecosystem may be disturbed by some enterprise of man. A case in point is that of the Long Island duck farms bordering the shores of Great South Bay. This has been studied carefully by several ecologists, including particularly John Ryther of the Woods Hole Oceanographic Institution.

Shortly after a group of large duck farms was established along the estuaries at the east end of Great South Bay, the oyster beds, which for years had provided a valuable annual crop of blue point oysters, began to fail. Analysis showed that there had been a profound change in phytoplankton of the bay and that the substituted producers in this ecosystem did not provide a suitable food for oysters. The oysters were literally starving to death, despite the fact that they fed amply on the newly flourishing phytoflagellates (mainly *Nannochloris* and *Stichococcus*). Apparently the enrichment of the bay water by the organic excreta from the many birds had favored the growth of a new flora of phytoflagellates to the exclusion of the old (mainly other phytoflagellates, dinoflagellates, and diatoms). Further experiments showed that the substituted phytoplankton could utilize the *organic* forms of nitrogen, whereas the original flora required nitrates. Thus, even though the total productivity of the bay water had been greatly increased, a shift in the species composition of the producer part of the community had spelled death to the oysters (and certain other shellfish).

Ecological Succession. The community composition of most ecosystems is not static, although sometimes a very stable balance exists such that changes in community structure are exceedingly slow. Frequently, however, an orderly *succession of communities* can be observed and predicted. Such a succession, called a **sere,** may pass through early (pioneering) **seral stages,** before reaching a comparatively stable stage, which is called a **climax.**

A typical seral succession, observed after the abandonment of a large area of cotton farm land in the Piedmont section of the southern United States, is shown in Figure 30-14. The easiest and most accurate observations on ecological successions, of course, are those that deal with plant communities. Census taking among animal populations is sometimes very difficult, because many animals tend to flee and hide from man. It must be remembered, however, that each time a change occurs in the plant part of a commu-

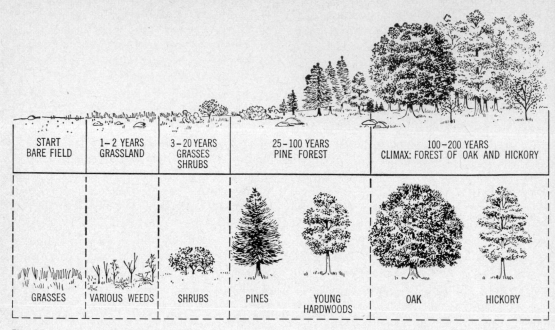

START BARE FIELD	1-2 YEARS GRASSLAND	3-20 YEARS GRASSES SHRUBS	25-100 YEARS PINE FOREST	100-200 YEARS CLIMAX: FOREST OF OAK AND HICKORY	
GRASSES	VARIOUS WEEDS	SHRUBS	PINES	YOUNG HARDWOODS	OAK	HICKORY

Fig. 30-14. An ecological succession, or **sere,** observed after abandonment of farm land in the Piedmont region of the United States. (After E. P. Odum.)

nity an adjustment must be made in the other parts. Thus the animal species fluctuate along with the plants. Indeed, it has been aptly said that when an ecologist enters a field or forest he sees not only what is there but also what will be there in coming generations.

ECOLOGY AND EVOLUTION

In summary, plants and animals display a tremendous variety of adaptation to almost every kind of environment. The natural rate of reproduction gives rise to many more organisms than can survive and creates a pressure for organisms to spread into new environments. Environmental conditions in the different regions of the earth do not directly determine adaptations, but the indirect influence of the environment—through the agency of natural selection— has been decisive in shaping the evolution of the species toward fitness, each to occupy some particular niche in the ecosystem of one or another of the many available types.

TEST QUESTIONS

1. Distinguish between the biotic and abiotic factors of the environment, citing a specific example in each case.
2. Cite three examples to illustrate the observation that changes in the population of one species may bring about changes in the popution of neighboring species.
3. Explain the statement that animal populations in a given region tend to display a "pyramidal" distribution. Cite two examples.
4. Cite examples to show how the prevalence of insects has influenced the evolution of other species.
5. Give two examples of each of the following: (a) offensive adaptations; (b) defensive adaptations; (c) protective coloration; (d) protective mimicry.
6. Specify two adaptations commonly encountered among parasitic species. Discuss.
7. What is an infectious disease? Specify ten such diseases. In each case, give the causative agent and the best curative method (if any).

8. Differentiate between: (a) a vaccine and an antiserum; (b) an antigen and an antibody; (c) antibiotics and other chemotherapeutic agents.
9. Specify three different disease vectors. Explain the relation between a disease vector and an intermediary host.
10. Discuss how each of the following has been important as a factor in natural selection: (a) temperature; (b) light; (c) gravity; (d) pressure; (e) the water supply.
11. What are xerophytes, mesophytes, and hydrophytes? In each case specify some of the distinctive adaptations.
12. What is an ecosystem? Discuss the economy of any one.

FURTHER READINGS

1. *Fundamentals of Ecology,* by E. P. Odum; Philadelphia, 1959.
2. *Elements of Ecology,* by G. L. Clarke; New York, 1954.
3. *Principles of Animal Ecology,* by W. C. Allee and others; Philadelphia, 1949.
4. *Ecology,* by E. P. Odum; New York, 1963.

31-*The Plant Kingdom*

ONE OF THE first attempts to classify all known organisms was made by the great Swedish biologist, Carolus Linnaeus; and by the time of his death in 1778, Linnaeus was able to describe almost 10,000 species. Since then, however, the number of known organisms has increased enormously. Today, in fact, almost 900,000 animals and 400,000 plants are recognized. No one person, of course, can ever hope to learn about all these species. But one person can succeed in *making a broad survey* of the field and can readily learn how to *recognize the principal types of plants and animals.*

The aim of modern **taxonomy** is to *classify organisms according to their evolutionary relationships;* but this represents an exceedingly difficult task. The fossil record (**paleontology**) provides considerable data, though many of the pages and even whole chapters of this record are incomplete and other parts have been badly scarred by time. Often it is necessary to judge relationships on the basis of indirect evidence, derived from a study of the comparative morphology, physiology, embryology, and biochemistry of the organism in question. Consequently, it is not surprising to find that biologists may disagree

on certain questions and that classification may keep changing as more evidence accumulates.

THE PLANT AND ANIMAL KINGDOMS

There are many similarities between plants and animals and these bear witness to a fundamental kinship. In fact, all basic studies on metabolism, growth, responsiveness, reproduction, heredity, and so forth, in plants and animals generally, tend to show this fundamental kinship. Also many similarities of cellular structure are revealed by microscopic studies. All in all, the evidence indicates that plants and animals both originated from a common ancient ancestral stock (Chap. 10). Consequently it is not surprising to find that no single criterion, by itself, can be used to make a sharp distinction between the plant and animal species.

Typically, of course, plants are green and display the holophytic type of nutrition. But there are many exceptions to this rule (Chap. 10). Generally, plant cells possess a cellulose wall, but this is lacking in some lower forms (for example, *Euglena*); and cellulose is possessed by the cells of one animal group, the

592

Tunicata (p. 665). Although most plants display no locomotion, quite a few of the lower forms are motile. The symmetry of most animals is bilateral (p. 624). But many like typical plants, are radially symmetrical. Generally plants can keep on growing, whereas animals stop growing when a certain size is achieved. But again this is not always true. In short, the only basis for placing an organism in a certain category is to consider all available evidence bearing on its origin, morphology, and physiology in an effort to establish its true and natural relationships. At one time quite a number of animals, especially certain Coelenterata (p. 630), which have a plantlike form, were placed in the Plant Kingdom. In fact, the true position of the Coelenterata was determined only later, when they had been studied much more carefully.

Taxonomic Categories. As is shown in Appendix I, modern taxonomy subdivides each kingdom into major and minor categories. These, in descending order of magnitude, are called the **Phylum**, the **Class**, the **Order**, the **Family**, and finally the **Genus** and **Species**. However, various additional *subdivisions may also be employed.*

Each individual kind of organism is identified by a double name. This binomial system, which was introduced mainly by Linnaeus, specifies the genus and species of this organism. The name, **Homo sapiens**, for example, indicates that we humans belong to a small recently evolved group of manlike creatures, the **genus Homo**. Also it shows that we represent only one kind, the **species sapiens**, which is slightly but definitely different from **Homo neanderthalensis**, or **Homo soloensis**—manlike creatures that became extinct just before the dawn of the recent epoch. Or the name **Acer saccharum**, which designates the sugar maple, shows that this plant has maplelike leaves, flowers, fruits, etc., which identify it as a member of a small group, the **genus Acer**. But also the name shows that this plant is of a particular kind (the species **saccharum**), from which maple sugar is derived. Ordinarily, interbreeding can occur only within the limits of one species; but sometimes it also can occur between two different species—if these are related very closely.

In any brief account, the larger categories of the taxonomic system cannot be defined very accurately. Suffice it to say that each **phylum** represents a major subdivision in the plant or animal kingdom. Presumably the members of a phylum originated from the same ancestral stock, very early in the course of evolution. Each phylum, in turn, is subdivided into classes; the classes into orders; the orders into families; and the families into genera; each genus being composed usually of several species. Also there are other categories, such as subkingdom, subphylum, subclass, etc., especially in groups containing a great diversity of forms.

Some Important Questions. Although the main purpose of this survey of the Plant Kingdom is to provide for a recognition of the major groups of plants, a number of other important questions will keep cropping up. What is the structural organization of the group? Is it unicellular, colonial, or truly multicellular? How far has the differentiation of special tissues progressed? How about the vascular tissues that are so essential to the life of land species? How did the higher plants manage to leave the water, which was the age-old environment of the primitive species ever since the beginnings of life? What is the pattern of the reproductive structures and processes, and how does this pattern help one to determine the evolutionary relationships of a certain group or to understand how reproduction became adapted to land conditions? What fossil evidence is available, and how does this bear upon questions of antiquity and relationship? What is the importance of the group in nature and in human affairs? Does it contribute significantly to the supplies of food, construction materials, clothing, drugs, etc.? Is it important in relation to soil fertility, water pollution, or disease? These and many other questions will frequently arise and to some extent they will be answered.

OUTLINE OF THE PLANT KINGDOM

The following outline gives the names of the principal plant groups, with scarcely any mention of their distinctive features. Such a bare map is designed to provide an orientation throughout the subsequent survey. The names, mainly of Greek origin, are difficult, of course. However, they can be mastered with practice, especially by students who look up the derivations.

THE SUBKINGDOM THALLOPHYTA

The Cyanophyta (Blue-green Algae). Several genera of these algae are shown in Figure 31-1. Probably the blue-green algae are

KINGDOM PLANTAE (The Plants)

Subkingdom I: The THALLÓPHYTA (Thállophýtes)—*Primitive plants.* Mainly aquatic; *do not have any embryo* stage in development.

Phylum   1—The CYANÓPHYTA (Cyánophýtes)—*Blue-green algae*
Phylum   2—The EUGLENÓPHYTA (Euglénophýtes)—*Euglena-like algae*
Phylum   3—The CHLORÓPHYTA (Chlórophýtes)—*Green algae*
Phylum   4—The CHRYSÓPHYTA (Chrýsophýtes)—*Golden-brown algae* (diatoms)
Phylum   5—The PYRRÓPHYTA (Pýrrophýtes)—*Flame algae*
Phylum   6—The PHAEÓPHYTA (Phaéophýtes)—*Brown algae*
Phylum   7—The RHODÓPHYTA (Rhódophýtes)—*Red algae*
Phylum   8—The SCHÍZOMYCÓPHYTA (Schízomýcophýtes)—*Bacteria*
Phylum   9—The MÝXOMYCÓPHYTA (Mýxomýcophýtes)—*Slime molds*
Phylum 10—The EÚMYCÓPHYTA (Eumýcophýtes)—*True, or higher fungi*

Subkingdom II: The ÉMBRYÓPHYTA. (Émbryophýtes)—*Mainly terrestrial plants,* more highly developed, *possessing an embryo* stage, in the diploid generation.

Phylum 11—The BRYÓPHYTA (Brýophýtes)—*Mosses and liverworts;* most primitive of land plants.

Phylum 12—The TRÁCHEÓPHYTA (Trácheophýtes)—*Less primitive land plants.* Possess vascular tissues (xylem and phloem).

Subphylum 1—The PSILÓPSIDA—*Ancient group of land plants, now almost extinct;* vascular tissues weakly developed; with no roots and virtually no leaves.

Subphylum 2—The LYCÓPSIDA—*Club mosses, spike mosses, and quillworts.* Dominant group in the Carboniferous period; now diminished to a relatively few species; has roots, leaves, and simple vascular tissues; displays first beginnings of heterospory.

Subphylum 3—The SPHENÓPSIDA—*Scouring rushes.* Another almost extinct group; had zenith in Carboniferous period; has roots, leaves, and vascular tissues, but relatively weak adaptation to land conditions.

Subphylum 4—The PTERÓPSIDA—*Well-adapted land plants,* dominant today; with complex conducting tissues, extensive roots, and large conspicuous leaves.

Class 1—The FILICÍNEAE—*Ferns*

Class 2—The GYMNÓSPERMAE (Gýmnosperms)—*Pines, spruces, cycads, and other cone-bearing, seed-producing plants*

Class 3—The ANGIÓSPERMAE (Ángiosperms)—*Flower-bearing, seed-producing plants*

Subclass 1—The MÓNOCÓTYLÉDONEAE (Mónocotylédons)—The embryo has only one cotyledon (embryonic storage leaf).

Subclass 2—The DÍCOTYLÉDONEAE (Dícotylédons)—Embryo with two cotyledons

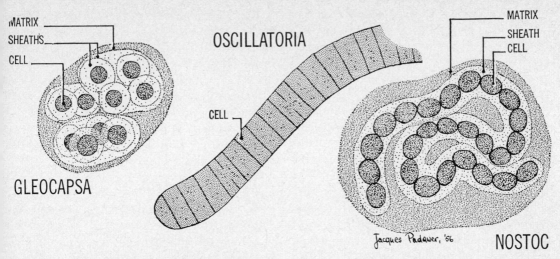

Fig. 31-1. Some blue-green algae (Cyanophyta). Note the absence of nuclei and chloroplasts in the primitive cells. None of the blue-greens reproduces sexually.

the most ancient and primitive of all green plants. Most of the 2000 or so known species display a bluish-green color, owing to the presence of a blue pigment, **phycocyanin,** which is mixed with the chlorophyll. However, red and yellow pigments are also found in the cytoplasm, and some of the species are reddish and a few are brown-green. Many cyanophytes live in fresh waters. In reservoirs and lakes, they sometimes pollute the water seriously by their great abundance. Also there is a large number of marine species. Occasionally a red species, prevalent in the Red Sea, flourishes in such numbers that the water actually becomes colored. A few blue-greens live on damp soil, in moist shady spots; or on the damp outer surfaces of flowerpots in humid greenhouses.

The primitive status of the blue-green algae is indicated by the fact that none of them is multicellular. Many are of solitary, unicellular habit, but others form colonial aggregates, such as are shown in Figure 31-1. Frequently the cells of the colony are protected by one or more gelatinous coverings of pectinous material. The colonies may be threadlike (*filamentous*), or they may be more or less ball-like (Fig. 31-1).

Another primitive feature of the cyanophytes is their extremely simple cell structure. *Definite* **nuclei** *have not been developed* in the cells. The granules of nuclear material **(chromidia)** are not enclosed within a nuclear membrane. They tend to be scattered more or less evenly throughout the cytoplasm (Fig. 31-1). However, in some species (Fig. 2-3), the chromidial granules may be aggregated toward the center of the cell— a sort of transitional stage in the evolution of true nuclei. Moreover, the cells *lack chloroplasts.* The chlorophyll and other pigments appear to be *dissolved,* or at least very finely distributed, throughout all parts of the cytoplasm.

Further evidence as to the primitive status of the cyanophytes is that sexual reproduction has never been found in any of the species. Apparently this group of plants branched off and took an independent line of evolution at a very early date—before sexual reproduction had been evolved by the ancient ancestral organisms (see Fig. 29-11).

The great antiquity of the Cyanophyta is further shown by the paleontological record. Some representatives of the blue-green algae are found in the very oldest of fossil-bearing strata, formed during the Proterozoic era (p. 565). Among all the many fossils formed by green plants in past ages, those of the cyanophytes are by far the oldest.

The Euglenophytes (Euglenoids). *Euglena* (Fig. 10-4) may be chosen to represent this relatively small group of unicellular organisms, which are partly plantlike and partly animallike in their characteristics.

Most of the 250 or so species, like *Euglena,* possess *definite* **chloroplasts.** The Euglenophyta, therefore, can carry on photosynthesis and grow in the manner of green plants generally. But unlike typical plants, the euglenoids do not possess rigid cellulose walls. In fact, the surface covering is very flexible and many forms display active **euglenoid movement** (p. 196) by which the cells may change shape quite drastically. Moreover, euglenophytes have other animallike features. *Active locomotion* is achieved by means of **flagella,** which usually number one or two; and there is always a *gullet,* which serves for the ingestion of solid nutrients in some species, but not in others. The main storage product of reserve organic food is not starch, as in most plants, or glycogen, as in most animals, but an intermediate type of polysaccharide, namely **paramylum.** A definite nucleus, delimited by a membrane, is typical of the group; but no sexual reproduction is found, except in one genus. The usual habitat is fresh water, especially in shallow ponds and lakes containing rich accumulations of organic debris. Many of the species, like *Euglena,* can carry on a saprophytic kind of nutrition, which supplements their growth (p. 178).

Obviously the classification of the Euglenophyta presents a difficult problem; and virtually no fossil remnants are available to help in the solution of this problem. Perhaps the most logical viewpoint is to think of them as an offshoot from a very early stock— the stock that later gave rise to the separately evolving plants and animals. The cellular structure, on the other hand, is distinctly less primitive than that of the Cyanophyta. In any event, the Euglenophyta are often classified as a phylum in the Plant Kingdom, even though the basis for this classification is rather arbitrary.

The Chlorophytes (Green Algae). This fairly large group consists of some 6000 species, which vary widely as to form and habit. Many, like **Chlamydomonas** (Fig. 31-2), are *unicellular* and motile; others, like the **Desmids** (Fig. 31-2), are unicellular, but nonmotile; others, like **Ulothrix** (Fig. 31-2), **Spirogyra** (Fig. 3-17), and **Volvox** (Fig. 3-19), form a variety of colonial aggregates; while a few, like the *sea lettuce,* **Ulva** (Fig. 31-2), take the form of very simple *multicellular organisms.* Most of the species live in shallow fresh or salt waters, although a few grow on damp soil, or even on snow.

Among the green algae the reproductive processes are of great interest because they show how sexual reproduction probably originated. Except for a few forms in which no sexual processes have been found, all the chlorophytes reproduce *both sexually* and *asexually.* Usually, however, there is not a very regular *alternation of sexual and asexual generations,* as is the rule among higher plants.

In the sexual phase of the life cycle, the green algae show a series of gradations which culminates in the production of *true eggs*—which are large nonmotile **female gametes**—and **true sperm**—which are small highly motile **male gametes.** In *Ulothrix* (Fig. 31-2), for example, the fusing gametes are **isogametes,** both of the same size and form, and both motile; in *Pandorina* and *Eudorina* (Fig. 3-19), the **heterogametes,** while still motile, show a progressive difference in size; and finally in *Volvox* (Fig. 3-19), the female gamete is a typical large nonmotile **egg cell** and the male gamete is a small motile **sperm cell,** as in most higher plant (and animal) groups.

Although the fossil evidence is scant, the modern chlorophytes are presumed to represent an offshoot from the ancient stock that gave rise to the higher plants (see Fig. 29-11). The cell structure is generally typical. Each cell is covered by a rigid cellulose wall and typically there are *definite* **nuclei** and *well-defined* **chloroplasts.** Also the pigments

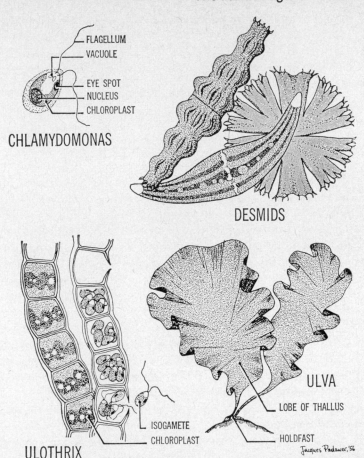

FLAGELLUM
VACUOLE
EYE SPOT
NUCLEUS
CHLOROPLAST

CHLAMYDOMONAS

DESMIDS

ULVA

LOBE OF THALLUS

ISOGAMETE
CHLOROPLAST

HOLDFAST

Jacques Padawer, '56

ULOTHRIX

Fig. 31-2. Some green algae (Chlorophyta). Note the varied form, which may be unicellular, colonial, or multicellular. Also notice the nuclei and chloroplasts in the cells. Most green algae reproduce both sexually and asexually.

(chlorophyll *a* and *b*, carotene, and xanthophyll) are similar in the green algae and higher plants; and true *starch* is usually the intracellular storage product.

The evolutionary status of the Chlorophyta is still quite primitive, however. Only a few of the species can be regarded as multicellular organisms. That is to say, most of the species are either unicellular or merely colonial. And even the multicellular forms display a very limited differentiation of specialized cells and virtually no differentiation of tissues. In the sea lettuce (Fig. 31-2), for example, each large leaflike lobe of the thallus, which resembles a piece of crinkled, green waxed paper, consists of only two layers of cells, all more or less alike; and the holdfast (and stalk) consists mainly of elongate colorless cells arranged in the form of twisted strands. And finally, a relationship between

the unicellular and the colonial species is clearly revealed by a study of the life cycle in forms such as *Ulothrix*. Most of the time this plant takes the form of a nonmotile filamentous colony. But at the time of reproduction, when the zoospores are produced, it reverts to a unicellular motile status, pending the formation of a new colony (Fig. 31-2).

The Chrysophytes (Golden-brown Algae). The most important and widely known members of this group are the **diatoms** (Fig. 31-3). Most of the species are unicellular and nonflagellated, although a few do have flagella, and a few are colonial. Most of the species reproduce both sexually and asexually; and generally the sexual reproduction is **isogamous.**

Diatoms display several unique features. The *cell wall* is *glassy* and brittle, owing to a high content of *silicate*. Also the cell wall

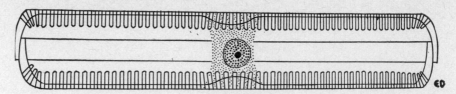

Fig. 31-3. One of the golden-brown algae (Chrysophyta), the diatom, *Pinnularia*. Note the finely etched, glassy cell wall and the overlapping halves of the "capsule." These features are common to all diatoms. (From *The Plant World*, by Fuller and Carothers. Holt, Rinehart and Winston, Inc.)

is formed like a medicinal capsule—with *two symmetrical slightly overlapping halves* (Fig. 31-3). Moreover, the capsule is finely etched with dots and markings of such exquisite delicacy that diatoms are often used by microscopists for testing the resolving power of high quality lenses.

Typical **nuclei** and **chloroplasts** are present (Fig. 31-3). However, in addition to chlorophyll, the chrysophytes possess a brown pigment, **fucoxanthin,** which is likewise found in the brown algae (p. 599) and in the flame algae (p. 598). The intracellular storage product is a fluid lipid, generally referred to as *oil,* rather than solid granules of a carbohydrate nature.

Diatoms occur in enormous abundance and variety in most salt and fresh waters. A cubic foot of ocean water frequently will contain well over a million specimens. In fact, the diatoms, together with the dinoflagellates (p. 599), are sometimes referred to as the "grass of the sea," because they represent such an important food base for fish and other marine animals. By dint of numbers these organisms appear to be responsible directly and indirectly for the synthesis of considerably more than half of all existing organic matter (p. 158). And in past ages, extending back into the early Paleozoic era, diatoms flourished in equal if not greater abundance. Some sedimentary deposits of **diatomaceous earth,** which consists largely of the distinctively marked, silicon-laden capsules of ancient diatoms, display a depth greater than 1000 feet. This material, because of its exceedingly fine abrasive qualities, is used extensively in the preparation of

dentifrices and of metal polishes. Also **diatomaceous earth,** owing to its fine porosity and excellent adsorptive capacity, is very useful in the manufacture of insulating materials and of special filters. And finally, there is considerable evidence that supports the view that much of our present-day **petroleum** owes its origin to the large accumulations of oil in the diatoms of ancient times.

The rich fossil record indicates that the Chrysophyta originated as a distinctly separate group in very early times, and that they did not give rise to any of the higher plants (Fig. 29-11).

The Pyrrophytes (Flame Algae). By far the most abundant and important of the flame algae are the **dinoflagellates,** two species of which are shown in Figure 31-4. These curiously formed unicellular plants are predominantly marine in habitat. In the sea they often generate populations of tremendous density, and thus they provide a food base for a multitude of fish and other marine animals (p. 589).

Dinoflagellates display *typical* **nuclei** and **chloroplasts,** but the cell wall takes the form of a number of *overlapping* **cellulose plates** (Fig. 31-4). Always there are *two* **flagella** (Fig. 31-4), one lying in a groove that tends to encircle the cell and the other trailing posteriorly.

The red color of most Dinoflagellata comes from the pigment **fucoxanthin,** which is present in addition to chlorophyll. Some dinoflagellates synthesize products that are quite toxic to other organisms. Occasionally, indeed, the fish in certain waters (for example, the Gulf of Mexico) may be killed off by

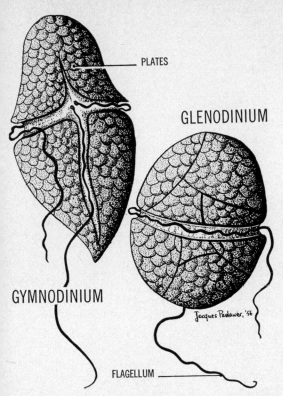

PLATES

GLENODINIUM

GYMNODINIUM

Jacques Padawer, '56

FLAGELLUM

Fig. 31-4. Flame algae (Pyrrophyta). The dinoflagellates (shown above) are the most important of the flame algae. Note the unique arrangement of the flagella and the overlapping cellulose plates. Some dinoflagellates produce toxic substances and are responsible for "mussel poisoning" and "red tides" (see text).

the millions when an upsurging population of dinoflagellates becomes so great that it is described as a "red tide." Also "mussel poisoning" may result when people eat mussels that have been feeding mainly upon toxic dinoflagellates.

The Dinoflagellata and other Pyrrophyta appear to have initiated a separate path of evolution at a very early date, as is indicated in Figure 29-11.

The Phaeophytes (Brown Algae). About 1000 species of these marine algae are found, mainly in shallow coastal waters, although some species extend their range to depths approaching 100 feet. The species vary widely from small branching filamentous forms, such as *Ectocarpus* (Fig. 31-5), to large expansive

plants, such as *Laminaria* (Fig. 31-5). All possess **fucoxanthin** and chlorophyll in varying proportions; and the color ranges from light greenish brown to very dark, almost blackish green.

The larger brown algae, which sometimes are called *kelps,* may show a considerable differentiation of their organs. Characteristically, there is a **holdfast** (Figs. 13-3 and 31-5), a branching stemlike **stipe,** and a number of broad leaflike **blades.** Also there may be a number of **gas bladders** (Fig. 31-5), which buoy up the thallus, so that the blades receive a maximum share of the weak light that filters down through the overlying water. Some brown algae, compared to other algal forms, display a high degree of cellular differentiation. At the center of the stipe in some brown algae, are found a number of elongate cells with perforated end walls, somewhat like the sieve tubes of higher plants; and these probably serve to convey organic materials from the upper to the lower parts of the plant. Also meristem cells, somewhat similar to the cambium of higher plants, are found in a few of the larger phaeophytes.

The brown algae generally display sexual as well as asexual methods of reproduction; and some (for example, *Ectocarpus*) show a regular alternation between diploid spore-forming and haploid gamete-forming generations. And even forms such as *Fucus* (Fig. 31-5), in which the cells of the thallus are consistently diploid, are considered to have a transient unicellular haploid stage, represented by the reproductive cells just before the eggs and sperm are produced.

The brown algae, especially the kelps, are of some practical importance: as a food base for marine fish; as food for cattle, and even man (China and Japan); as sources of iodine and mineral salts; and in the production of **algin,** a carbohydrate derivative quite widely used to improve the "creamy" qualities of ice cream, candies, and hand lotions.

Like other thallophyte groups, the brown algae started an independent line of evolu-

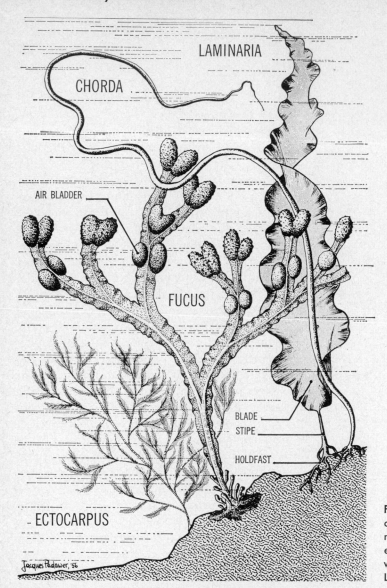

LAMINARIA

CHORDA

AIR BLADDER

FUCUS

BLADE
STIPE

HOLDFAST

ECTOCARPUS

Jacques Padawer, '56

Fig. 31-5. Some brown algae (Phaeophyta). Many of these multicellular marine plants are tough and leathery and can endure the pounding of waves along the shores of the sea. Large brown algae are called kelps.

tion at a very early time, as is indicated in Figure 29-11.

The Rhodophytes (Red Algae). The red algae, of which there are some 2500 species, tend to resemble the brown algae. They are mainly marine and they display a variety of branching forms (Fig. 31-6). However, the rhodophytes generally live in deeper, smoother waters, so that the form, typically, is more delicate and lacy, and their structure is not so tough and leathery. The red pigment (**phycoerythrin**) of the rhodophytes

absorbs heavily at blue-light wavelengths (p. 162), which penetrate more deeply into the ocean. The red algae, therefore, can grow at relatively greater depths, where chlorophyll alone is not a very efficient photosynthesizing pigment.

One group of red algae, the **Corallina**, plays an important part in the building of atoll reefs (p. 634). These forms accumulate calcium carbonate, which finally makes the thallus hard and rigid. Many generations of such algae, each attaching to the bottom and

Fig. 31-6. Two of the red algae (Rhodophyta). Many red algae live in deep quiet waters. These have a delicate form, such as is displayed by *Dasa plumosa* (left). However, some, such as *Rhodomenia palmata* (right), live in the more agitated tidal zone and these are apt to show a sturdier form. (Courtesy of the American Museum of Natural History, New York.)

adding another layer of stony material, may gradually build up and extend a reef enormously. Moreover, the algae provide an effective hiding place for coral animals (p. 634), which likewise deposit vast amounts of calcareous materials.

Some red algae are used as food. The Japanese cultivate one kind (*Porphyra*) in carefully tended submarine gardens; and the Scotch are fond of dulse (*Rhodymenia*, Fig. 31-6), boiled in milk. Moreover, agar, which is so widely used in preparation of bacterial culture media, is derived from two kinds of red algae (*Gelidium* and *Gracilaria*); and **carrageenin**, a material extracted from **Irish moss**, is useful in the preparation of chocolate milk products.

None of the red algae has flagellated reproductive cells, which are so usual among aquatic plants. Typically the nonmotile sperm are carried by the oceanic currents until some are picked up by a sticky protuberance (the **trichogyne**) from the egg-forming organ. Frequently there is an alternation of sexual and asexual generations. The spores of the Rhodophyta are nonflagellated.

The Schizomycophytes (Bacteria). These exceedingly small, unicellular *fungi*[1] were discussed at some length in Chapter 10.

It appears likely that the bacteria originated earlier (p. 566) and that they are more primitive than the blue-green algae, which they tend to resemble. However, bacteria

[1] The term *fungus* (plural, fungi), is a very convenient one, even though it does not designate any single phylum or other taxonomic group. In fact, all relatively simple *colorless* (lacking chlorophyll) plants are called fungi.

lack chlorophyll. Previously it was thought that bacteria do not possess definitive nuclei, but true nuclei have now been demonstrated in many forms. Sexual reproduction may occur, however, at least in primitive form.

In the absence of chlorophyll, bacterial nutrition is saprophytic (p. 174), parasitic (p. 178), or chemotrophic (p. 178). The dominant forms, of course, are spherical (coccus), rod-shaped (bacillus), and spiral (spirillum), as is shown in Figure 10-1. Many bacteria are solitary and unicellular, but many others form colonial aggregates. Often the form of such colonies may be inferred from the name; for example, *Streptococcus* or *Streptobacillus* indicates chainlike formations, and *Staphylococcus* indicates an irregularly bunched colony. Many species are flagellated. This is particularly true of the spirillum forms, which seldom, if ever, form colonial aggregates. Bacterial cells are very small. The average size is about 1 to 3 microns in diameter or length.

As was explained in Chapter 10, the saprophytic bacteria are very important because they are responsible (mainly) for the processes of decay, putrefaction, and fermentation. Vast quantities of organic materials, which otherwise would tend to accumulate in the environment, thus undergo decomposition, liberating their constituents in inorganic form, which can be reutilized by various other organisms (pp. 183–185). Also the saprophytic bacteria are important in relation to food spoilage (p. 178). And last but not least, the parasitic bacteria are very important as disease-causing agents in many plants and animals, including man (Table 30-1).

Some biologists include the *Rickettsia* among the Schizomycophyta, but the classification of these intracellular parasites is problematical. The *Rickettsia* were named after their discoverer, Howard Ricketts, who died in 1910 while studying typhus, which is caused by one of these "organisms." Generally speaking, the *Rickettsia*, like viruses, seem incapable of multiplying except when

they are in the protoplasm of some living cell. Typically, rickettsial bodies are smaller than bacteria, the average size being about half a micron.

About 40 kinds of *Rickettsia,* mainly rod-shaped and ball-shaped, have been observed, particularly in the cells of the intestinal wall and salivary glands of various lice, ticks, and bedbugs. However, only two kinds seem to be associated with common human diseases: (1) The typhus *Rickettsia,* which is transmitted by lice; and (2) the Rocky Mountain spotted fever *Rickettsia,* which is transmitted by ticks.

The antiquity of the Schizomycophyta as a separately evolving group (Fig. 29-11) is indicated not only by the primitive cellular structure and the primitive reproductive status, but also by the fact that bacterial remnants appear to be present in the very oldest fossil-bearing strata.

The Myxomycophytes (Slime Molds). There are about 500 species of these strange fungi. Usually they are found living saprophytically upon rotting wood, fruits, and other masses of organic material.

The vegetative body, or **plasmodium,** of the slime mold typically consists of a lobulated sheet of naked protoplasm (Fig. 31-7), which creeps actively, like a giant amoeba, over the surface of the food material. In some species, the plasmodium may cover an area of several square inches, but in others it may be semimicroscopic. Sometimes the plasmodium may be a multinucleate syncytium, but in a few species it consists of a coordinated mass of uninucleate cells, such as is shown in Figure 2-22 (stage 1).

For many years many slime molds were thought of as animals. Then it was found that each is capable of developing typical multicellular sporangia (Fig. 31-8) in which the cells possess cellulose walls. Each species is best identified, in fact, by the sporangia. These often are beautifully colored, in hues of yellow, orange, brown, red, violet, or purple. However, the sporangia of Myxomycophyta are seldom more than 5 mm in diam-

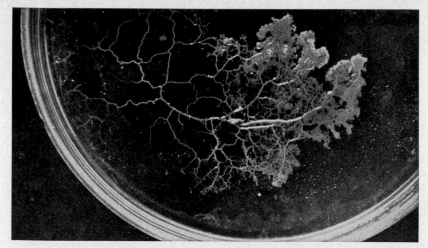

Fig. 31-7. The plasmodium of a slime mold (*Cribraria*) creeping over the surface of an agar nutrient medium in a Petri dish. Note the irregular lobose form of the plasmodium, which is quite typical of the Myxomycophyta generally. (Photo by G. W. Martin; from *The Plant World*, by Fuller and Carothers. Holt, Rinehart and Winston, Inc.)

eter and sometimes they are almost microscopic.

Each spore of the slime mold, typically, gives rise to four naked cells, capable of active amoeboid movement and often possessing one or more flagella. Each of these swarm cells, which are called **myxamoebae,** usually divides a number of times, producing more myxamoebae. Eventually, however, the cells fuse in pairs, each pair forming one zygote. Then the zygote gives rise to the plasmodium of the next generation.

Some myxomycophytes are parasitic and a few are important in relation to plant diseases. For example, the **club-root disease** of cabbages and the **powdery-scab disease** of

Fig. 31-8. Sporangia of two different slime molds, growing on tree bark. Although the sporangium of a myxomycophyte is seldom bigger than a pinhead, the size, shape, colors, and markings are distinctive for each species. Those on the left are of *Badamia foliicola*, and those on the right are of *Physarum globuliferum*. (Photos by Richard Benjamin; from *The Plant World*.)

potatoes are both caused by parasitic slime molds.

The evolutionary relationships of the slime molds represent a puzzling problem. It does seem clear, however, that the Myxomycophyta separated off from all other groups at a fairly early time (Fig. 29-11).

The Eumycophytes (True Fungi). This very large phylum consists of more than 75,000 widely varying species. Most of these higher fungi are saprophytic, although there are quite a few parasitic species. A great majority are multicellular and in most cases the cellular organization is typical (that is, not syncytial). Usually the body, or **mycelium,** consists of a network of branched microscopic threads, or **hyphae,** which collectively may look like a fluffed out piece of absorbent cotton. The "fruiting organ," which usually bears a large number of sporangia, frequently consists of a compactly organized system of hyphae of very definite shape and form. The gametes may be either motile or nonmotile; and sporulation may be either meiotic or mitotic.

Four distinct classes have been evolved among the **Eumycophyta.** There are:
1. *The Phycomycetes,* or algalike fungi
2. *The Ascomycetes,* or sac fungi
3. *The Basidiomycetes,* or basidium fungi
4. *The Deuteromycetes,* or imperfect fungi

The Phycomycetes. The algalike fungi are represented by about 500 species, which generally are smaller and simpler than other eumycophytes. Many Phycomycetes, like the bread mold (Fig. 12-10), are free-living saprophytes. However, there are quite a few parasitic species, such as the downy mildews (Fig. 31-9) and the white rusts. Phycomycetes are generally more primitive than other eumycophytes. Usually the **hyphae** *are syncytial,* the mycelium is rather diffuse, and highly organized fruiting organs are not developed.

The downy mildews (Fig. 31-9) are dangerous disease-producing parasites. They cause considerable damage to tobacco, grapes, lettuce, onions, and potatoes, and they cause "damping off" in a wide variety of

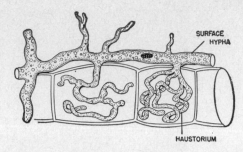

Fig. 31-9. Some parasitic Phycomycetes, such as the downy mildew shown here, possess specialized absorbing hyphae, called *haustoria.* These penetrate into the cells of the host. (From *The Plant World.*)

seedlings. In fact, it was one of the downy mildews (*Phytophthora infestans*) that caused the terrible Irish potato blight in 1845 and led to the immigration of large numbers of famine-ravished people into the United States.

On the basis of the general form and the pattern of their reproductive processes, the Phycomycetes seem quite closely related to the green algae. However, the separation of the two groups seems to have occurred in very early times (Fig. 29-11).

The Ascomycetes (Sac Fungi). This large (35,000 species) *class of* the **Eumycophyta** includes many familiar and important forms. Among the **saprophytic species** are the various blue, green, and yellow molds (usually either **Aspergillus** or **Penicillium**) often seen on spoiling fruit; the red baker's mold, **Neurospora** (p. 529); the various kinds of brewer's and baker's **yeasts** (Fig. 10-2); and the rare but delicious edible **truffle.** And among the **parasitic species** are the **powdery mildews,** which infect leaves, especially in lilacs, roses, apples, and grapes; the **ergot fungus** which infects rye and other cereals; the fungi causing **chestnut blight** and **Dutch elm disease;** and one genus **(Torula)** of yeasts, which may, on rare occasion, invade the skin and nervous system in man, causing a serious infection (**blastomycosis**).

An important distinctive feature of the Ascomycetes is a saclike reproductive structure called an **ascus** (Fig. 31-10). In the ascus, four or (more frequently) eight **haploid**

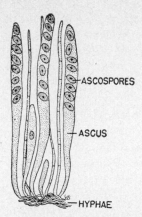

Fig. 31-10. Asci and ascospores are distinctive of the sac fungi, or Ascomycetes. (From *The Plant World*.)

size, shape, and color of their ascocarps, as is shown for a **cup fungus,** in Figure 31-11; and for the **sponge fungus,** in Figure 31-12.

Ascomycetes do much harm, through the spoilage of foods, tobacco, fabrics, and so

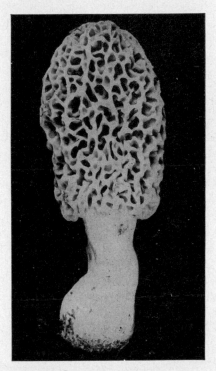

Fig. 31-12. Some Ascomycetes are called sponge fungi, or morels. This one (*Marchella esculenta*) is edible. Moreover, it is considered a rare delicacy. (Photo by C. F. Hottes; from *The Plant World*.)

spores (ascospores) are produced from a single **diploid spore mother cell.** Typically the appearance of an ascus follows immediately after sexual reproduction, when two gamete nuclei fuse to form the diploid nucleus of the spore mother cell. The cells of the mycelium, which grows from an ascospore, are haploid and the haploid condition endures throughout most of the life cycle in Ascomycetes generally.

In many species the asci are formed more or less individually at the ends of certain hyphae. But in others the ascal sacs are borne by a highly organized fruiting organ, called the **ascocarp.** In fact, many of the species are best identified on the basis of the

Fig. 31-11. Some Ascomycetes, such as this one (*Peziza*), are called cup fungi, owing to the shape of the ascocarp. (From *The Plant World*.)

forth, and through their pathogenic effects upon various plants and animals. However, the sac fungi also do much good. Various species of *Aspergillus* are used in the production of alcohol, citric acid, and other organic compounds; *Penicillium roqueforti* and *camemberti* contribute distinctive flavors to roquefort and camembert cheeses; and *Penicillium notatum,* which produces the antibiotic, **penicillin,** has been extremely valuable in helping to cure mastoiditis, syphilis, gonorrhea, and quite a few other previously serious **infections.**

The Basidiomycetes (Basidium, or Club Fungi). This other large (25,000 species) class of the Eumycophyta also includes a number of familiar and important fungi. Among the free-living, saprophytic species are the **mushrooms** (Fig. 31-13), the **puffballs** (Fig. 31-14), and the **bracket fungi.** And among the pathogenic species there are the **rusts** and the **smuts.**

A distinctive feature of the Basidiomycetes is their unique method of forming spores. Following sexual reproduction, a number of large club-shaped diploid cells, each called a **basidium,** are formed on certain reproductive hyphae (Fig. 31-15). The diploid nucleus of the basidial cell divides twice (**meiosis**), giving rise to four haploid nuclei. These nuclei then migrate out into the four spore cells (**basidiospores**) that are budded off at the end of the basidial cell (Fig. 31-15). Each haploid basidiospore can give rise to a new mycelium, in which all the cells are haploid; and the haploid status of the species persists until sexual reproduction occurs again.

Usually the reproductive hyphae, upon which the basidia and basidiospores are formed, are organized into fruiting organs, called **sporophores,** which display a definite shape and color in each of the species. Thus it is possible to recognize each species on the basis of its sporophore—as is shown for the common edible mushroom in Figure 31-13. It should be remembered, however, that the mycelium of the species, which lies buried in the humus-laden soil, or in some other organically rich medium, must have grown for a long time before the sporophore suddenly "mushrooms" and thrusts itself into sight.

Almost 200 edible varieties of mushrooms are known. There are, however, about 30

Fig. 31-13. The commonly cultivated edible mushroom (*Psalliota campestris*) is one of the Basidiomycetes, or club fungi. This is a flashlight photo, taken in a mushroom cellar. (From *The Plant World*.)

Fig. 31-14. Puffballs, another kind of club fungus, growing upon rotting wood. Notice the white strands of the mycelium, which penetrate down into the wood. The mycelium must grow for many weeks before the sporophores (puffballs) appear. (Photo by C. F. Hottes; from *The Plant World*.)

poisonous species (commonly called toadstools). Some of these produce organic toxins of truly high potency. Only an expert, therefore, should be trusted to gather mushrooms from the field. A single large sporophore from the commercial mushroom, **Psalliota campestris** (Fig. 31-13), may produce as many as two billion basidiospores, if it is allowed to ripen completely.

Some of the most devastating crop diseases, such as **wheat rust** (Fig. 31-16) and **corn smut** (Fig. 31-17), are caused by parasitic Basidiomycetes.

The phylogenetic relations of the Eumycophyta are somewhat problematical. However, it is clear that the phylum originated at a very early date (Fig. 29-11).

The Deuteromycetes (Imperfect Fungi). This last class of the Eumycophyta serves as a convenient category into which fungi of obscure relationship may be placed. They are called **imperfect fungi** because they do not seem to display any sexual phase in the reproductive cycle. Possibly such phases may have appeared and were later lost in the course of evolution; or perhaps, at least in some cases, sexual phases do exist, but have never been observed by man. In any event, many of the imperfect fungi are parasitic. Moreover, a few of them are responsible for some troublesome human infections. These include **thrush,** a mouth and throat infection; **sprue,** an intestinal inflammation, not uncommon in the tropics; and several skin infections, namely, **ringworm, barber's itch,** and **athlete's foot.**

The Lichens. These dual organisms (Fig. 10-5) are difficult to classify because each represents a symbiotic association between two species—one a fungus and the other a green alga. There are, however, some 14,000 kinds of lichens, varying in color from the more familiar gray-green forms through a range of yellow, orange, red, brown, and black.

Various lichens can grow on bare rocks and barren soils; and many can withstand extremes of cold and drought. One kind, the **reindeer moss** (Fig. 31-18), provides a staple food for the reindeer herds of Lapland; and other kinds penetrate deep into the Arctic

Circle well beyond the range of other plants. Lichens also provide a source for several dyes. These include **orchil,** a beautiful blue dye, known since ancient times; and **litmus,** the familiar pH indicator, used in the chemistry laboratory.

Probably the lichens were among the first invaders of the land areas in early geological times. Many seem to secrete organic acids, which dissolve and crumble the rocks upon which they grow. Thus lichens probably played a significant part in the creation of

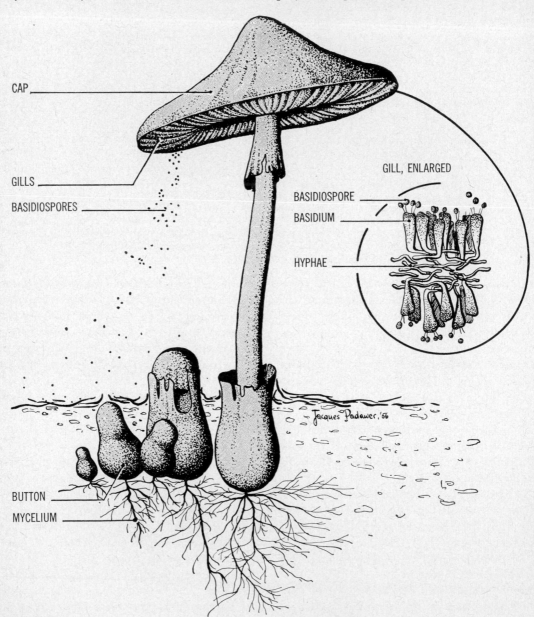

CAP

GILLS

BASIDIOSPORES

GILL, ENLARGED

BASIDIOSPORE

BASIDIUM

HYPHAE

BUTTON

MYCELIUM

Fig. 31-15. Mushrooms are typical representatives of the Basidiomycetes. Note how the spores are produced by the **basidia,** which are borne upon the gills of the sporophore, or "cap." The mycelium, including the button, must grow subterraneously for a number of weeks before the sporophore "mushrooms" upward into the air. One mushroom may produce more than a billion spores.

Fig. 31-16. Wheat rust, growing on wheat stubble (*left*) and on barberry leaves (*right*). This basidiomycete (*Puccinia graminis*) is a very destructive parasite. Summer spores of this rust can pass from wheat plant to wheat plant. But the fall spores, which grow upon wheat stubble, can continue to live only if they manage to infest the leaves of the common barberry bush. Only winter spores, formed in the barberry leaves, are capable of surviving through a cold season. Consequently, it is the winter spores (at least in northern regions) that reinfect the wheat crop when the following spring arrives. The name "rust" derives from the orange color of the summer sporangia, formed on the leaves of the wheat. (Photos by Benjamin Koehler; from *The Plant World.*)

soil and helped to prepare the land environment for the coming of other plants.

SUBKINGDOM EMBRYOPHYTA

Essentially the various groups of **Thallophyta,** which have been described in the foregoing sections, are *relatively simple water-dwelling plants,* despite the fact that a few species show some slight degree of adaptation to life upon the land. The Thallophyta appear to have originated quite early in the Proterozoic era (Fig. 29-10), at which time no terrestrial plants existed. Land plants, in fact, did not begin to appear until well after the early days of the Paleozoic era. At this point, therefore, the question of how plants became adapted to terrestrial conditions becomes pertinent.

Adaptation of Plants to the Land Environment. Land-adapted **nutritional organs,** such as the *leaves, roots,* and *stems* of higher plants, did not spring suddenly full-fledged into being; and the same is true of the **specialized tissues** such as the conducting units of the

xylem and **phloem,** and the well-developed water-proofed **epidermal tissues,** which are so essential to well-adapted land species (Chap. 13). It is interesting to note, therefore, how these nutritional adaptations did arise gradually in the various groups of higher plants.

The land environment also imposes two serious problems upon the *reproductive mechanisms* of the plant. If the plant is not submerged in water: (1) How can the sperm manage to swim to the eggs? and (2) How can the unicellular zygote manage to survive while the new plant is developing its first roots, stem, and leaves? No truly successful land species could appear, in fact, until the reproductive mechanisms became adjusted to meet these basic problems.

The first problem did not reach a truly satisfactory solution in any of the earlier groups. Consequently the more primitive land species are restricted, more or less completely, to areas where, at least periodically, there is an abundance of water in which the sperm can swim. But the highest plant

Fig. 31-17. Corn, infected by corn smut (*Ustilago zeae*), another parasitic basidiomycete. (Photo by Benjamin Koehler; from *The Plant World*.)

groups, especially the gymnosperms and angiosperms, finally did evolve a fertilization mechanism in which the sperm do not need water while they are being transmitted to the eggs (Chap. 12).

Plant Embryos and Their Protection. The second problem—nurturing the zygote during the early vulnerable stages of development—began to reach a solution very early. All Embryophyta (see below) are characterized by the possession of multicellular reproductive organs. Especially important are the **archegonia** (p. 205). In the archegonium, the zygote and the developing **embryo** are protected and *nurtured* until the young plant can shift for itself. This development is the primary basis for grouping all terrestrial species into one large subkingdom—the **Subkingdom Embryophyta.** All members of this large group possess **multicellular archegonia**, in which the **embryos** develop. Also all Embryophyta possess multicellular sperm-forming organs (**antheridia**) and multicellular spore-forming organs (**sporangia**). And lastly, the Embryophyta all display a regular alternation between the diploid asexual **sporophyte generation** and the haploid sexual **gametophyte generation** (Chap. 12).

The Bryophyta (Literally, Moss Plants). This phylum (about 23,000 species) of relatively small *primitive land plants* includes two classes: (1) the **Hepaticae**, or **liverworts** (Fig. 13-4), and (2) the **Musci**, or true mosses Fig. 12-11).

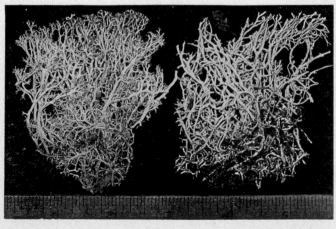

Fig. 31-18. Reindeer moss (*Cladonia rangiferina*). These and other lichens can grow on very poor soil and in very cold regions. (From *The Plant World*.)

The life cycle of the Bryophyta is distinctive. The haploid **gametophyte** generation is **dominant,** whereas the diploid **sporophyte** is relatively small and totally dependent upon the gametophyte (Fig. 12-12).

The bryophytes, undoubtedly, were among the first plants to colonize the land. They show only the most primitive adaptation to land conditions. Bryophyta do not have any well-developed vascular or epidermal tissues. Also the absorbing organs are relatively simple **rhizoids,** rather than complex and efficient **roots.**

Bryophytes were among the first plants to develop a multicellular **archegonium,** which protects and nurtures the zygote and embryo sporophyte. However, the flagellated sperm of the bryophytes, after being liberated from the **antheridia,** must swim through water in order to reach the eggs.

In view of these factors, the biological success of the bryophytes has not been very conspicuous. Such small primitive land plants were not able to offer serious competition to the better adapted, more highly vascularized Tracheophyta, which began to appear upon the evolutionary scene early in the Devonian period.

The Bryophyta seem to have arisen from the green algae (Fig. 29-11). This is indicated by the filamentous **protonema** stage (Fig. 12-2) in the bryophytic life cycle; by the flagellated free-swimming sperm; and by all available paleontological evidence. The evidence also indicates that the Bryophyta represent a terminal evolutionary branch. In other words, the Bryophyta did not give rise to the Tracheophyta. Probably, on the other hand, the Bryophyta and Tracheophyta originated from the same early stock, before the distinctive features of either group had been evolved.

The Tracheophyta (Vascular Plants). This diversified phylum (p. 594) includes virtually all plants commonly seen in the garden, field, and forest. These plants, in fact, have come to dominate most of the land areas of the earth. Today this **phylum** consists of more than a quarter of a million known species. Moreover, the fossil record, which extends back more than 300 million years into the Devonian and even the Silurian periods (Fig. 29-10), reveals many species that later became extinct.

All tracheophytes, as the name implies, possess **vascular tissues,** both **xylem** and **phloem** (p. 244). This development has enabled many species to reach the dimensions of imposing trees. Also all tracheophytes show a regular alternation of diploid and haploid generations. Moreover, the tracheophytes have a distinctive life cycle. The **sporophyte generation** is *relatively large and dominant,* whereas the **gametophyte** is *relatively small and inconspicuous* (see p. 219). In fact, the gametophyte generation, among higher Tracheophyta, is reduced to a microscopically small thallus, which is entirely dependent upon the tissues of the dominant sporophyte for both sustenance and protection (p. 219). Thus when we speak of an individual tracheophyte, such as a fern, a pine tree, or a rosebush, we are referring to the plant during the dominant *sporophyte stage* of its life cycle.

The *Phylum Tracheophyta* displays an evolutionary divergence into four *subphyla:*

Subphylum 1. The Psilopsida: a virtually extinct group.

Subphylum 2. The Lycopsida: dominant in Carboniferous era.

Subphylum 3. The Sphenopsida: almost extinct.

Subphylum 4. The Pteropsida: dominant today.

The Psilopsida (Subphylum 1: Phylum Tracheophyta). Surviving today there are only three species of Psilopsida, including the one (*Psilotum*) that is depicted in Figure 31-19. Fossilized Psilopsida, however, extend back into the Silurian period, at which time they showed a world-wide distribution. Some of these fossils are so remarkably well preserved that even the microscopic structure can be studied.

The Psilopsida, apparently, began to colo-

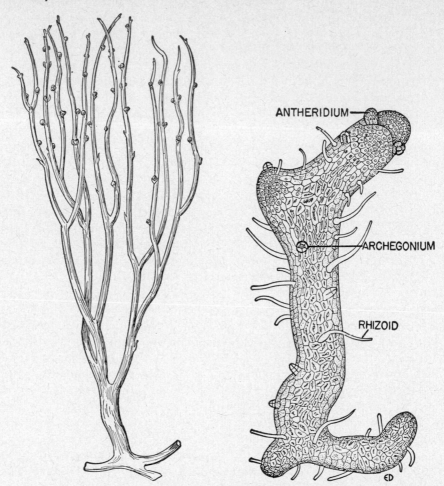

Fig. 31-19. *Psilotum,* one of three surviving kinds of psilopsidan plants. Such specimens, which are only 2 to 3 feet tall, are sometimes exhibited by botanical gardens as "living fossils." Note that the sporophyte (*left*): (1) has a horizontal underground stem without any roots; (2) has very small scalelike "leaves"; (3) displays a primitive dichotomous manner of branching; and (4) bears a number of three-lobed sporangia in the axils of some of the leaves. The gametophyte (*right*) is a semimicroscopic thallus that possesses both archegonia and antheridia. (From *The Plant World.*)

nize the land almost as soon as the Bryophyta. They are, in fact, the most rudimentary of all Tracheophyta. The vascular tissues are very primitive, but the dominance of the sporophyte generation is unmistakable. Typically there is a horizontal underground stem (called a **rhizome**) from which a number of repeatedly forking cylindrical green branches extend up vertically into the air. True roots are lacking and "leaves," when present, take the form of very small "scales" (Fig. 31-19). None of the species appears to have achieved a height of more than about two feet. Probably the Psilopsida arose from a green algal stock. This is indicated by the forking form of the body, the lowly degree of cellular differentiation, and the production of flagellated sperm, which must swim through the water to reach the eggs.

The Lycopsida (Subphylum 2: Phylum Tracheophyta). This primitive group of tracheophytes also reached a climax in earlier times. In the

Carboniferous period, indeed, some Lycopsida achieved the form of gigantic trees (see Fig. 29-13). Moreover, it is known that accumulated masses of these large Lycopsida gave rise to most of the present-day huge deposits of **coal.**

Today the Lycopsida have diminished to just four genera (about 900 species) of small (usually less than 1-foot-tall) relatively unimportant plants. These include the **club mosses** (Fig. 31-20) and the **quillworts.**

The Lycopsida, like other Tracheophyta, have a dominant sporophyte generation, by which the species is commonly identified (Fig. 31-20). But the gametophyte, typically, takes the form of a semimicroscopic, colorless, subterranean thallus, such as is shown in Figure 31-21. Lycopsidan sporophytes, on the

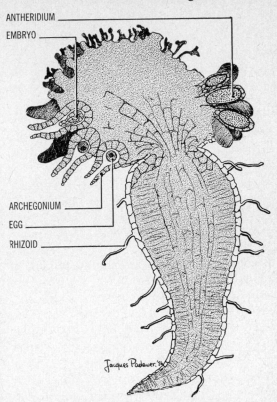

ANTHERIDIUM
EMBRYO
ARCHEGONIUM
EGG
RHIZOID

Jacques Padawer. '5

Fig. 31-21. The haploid gametophyte generation of Lycopodium. This small sexual form of the plant, which is less than ½ inch long, lives almost completely buried on the surface of the soil. The fertilized egg, however, gives rise to the larger dominant diploid sporophyte (Fig. 31-20) as in all of the higher plants (Tracheophyta).

Fig. 31-20. Modern lycopsidans are rather small prostrate plants, such as this club moss (*Lycopodium clavatum*). These plants also may be called "creeping ground pines." Note the dichotomous branching of the stem and the conelike spore-bearing structures. (From *The Plant World*.)

other hand, display well-differentiated vascular tissues (both xylem and phloem); and they have very good root, stem, and leaf systems. The roots and stems tend to branch dichotomously (by successively forking into two more or less equal branches) as growth occurs. The leaves tend to be small and to come off the stem in circlets at regular intervals (giving the plant a "mossy" appearance); and the spore-bearing leaves (sporophylls) tend to be clustered into elongate club-shaped conelike structures (see Fig. 31-20).

Several club mosses belonging to the genus *Lycopodium* (Fig. 31-20) are commonly called creeping ground pines, and frequently these are employed as decorative material at Christmas time. Such species display an elongate, leafy, prostrate stem, from which numerous erect branches extend upwards into the air, and numerous roots extend downward into the soil. Also *Lycopodium* spores, which are produced in great quantity, are sometimes used as a dusting powder (lycopodium powder) in cases of skin irritation. One of the spike mosses (*Selaginella lepidophylla*), which occurs in dry regions from Peru to Texas, is called the *resurrection plant.* During dry spells it rolls up into a brownish, apparently lifeless ball; then quickly and miraculously it unfolds into a delicate green plant as soon as rainy weather comes.

Most Lycopsida produce only one kind of spore (**homospory**), each of which may germinate into a gametophyte in which both archegonia and antheridia are formed. However, a few species in the genus *Selaginella* display **heterospory**. *Selaginella* produces *two kinds of spores*—large **macrospores,** and small **microspores**—as is shown in Figure 12-13. This important feature seems to foreshadow developments that are characteristic of the highest plants (Gymnospermae and Angiospermae).

In Figure 12-13, it may be noted that the **female gametophyte** originates *from the* **macrospore**; whereas a **male gametophyte** comes from each **microspore**. The female gametophyte not only gains protection from the moisture-proof cover of the macrospore, but also it receives nourishment from organic materials previously stored up in this large cell. Then in its turn, the female gametophyte protects and nurtures the next generation, while the egg is being fertilized and while the zygote is developing into the embryo of the new sporophyte.

Despite the fact that heterospory, which is characteristic of the higher plants, had its first incidence among the Lycopsida, the fossil record and other evidence indicates that this group did not give rise either to the gymnosperms or to the angiosperms. The Lycopsida arose, apparently, from an early psilopsidan stock, the Psilophytales, of which

a number of fossil forms have been found. But after a great climax during the Carboniferous period, the Lycopsida have dwindled, and now they seem well along the road toward extinction. The Psilopsida and the Lycopsida tend to resemble each other, especially in regard to the dichotomous branching of the stem and the primitive arrangement of the vascular tissue in the stem.

The Sphenopsida (Subphylum 3: Phylum Tracheophyta). This group, which likewise is represented mainly by fossil species, reached a peak of size and abundance during the Carboniferous period. At this time many species were treelike plants attaining heights up to 100 feet; and Sphenopsida had almost a world-wide distribution. To some extent the Sphenopsida took part in the formation of coal, although most of our large deposits were derived from the Lycopsida.

Today there is only one surviving sphenopsidan genus, namely **Equisetum** (Fig. 31-

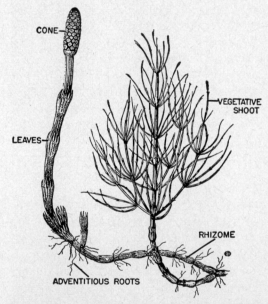

Fig. 31-22. Horsetails (Genus *Equisetum*) are the sole survivors from the ancient Sphenopsida, which in ancient times included a wide variety of treelike species. This species (*Equisetum arvense*) is less than 12 inches tall. Note the horizontal stem (rhizome); the relatively small roots; the small, scalelike leaves; and the conelike spore-forming strobilus. (From *The Plant World*.)

22), and this consists of only 25 species. These living forms are commonly called **horsetails.** Also they may be referred to as the **scouring rushes.** The stems contain many, fine, sharp particles of **silicate.** This made them useful as an abrasive material for cleaning pots and pans, especially in the early Colonial days.

Typically the **dominant sporophyte** (Fig. 31-22) displays well-developed vascular elements (both xylem and phloem). There is a **prostrate stem,** from which **true roots** extend downward into the soil and numerous branches pass upward into the air. The stem and its branches are characteristically hollow, and display conspicuous joints (**nodes**) and longitudinal **ribs.** The **leaves,** at least in modern species, tend to be *very small* **scales,** which come off in whorls at the nodes (Fig. 31-22). Typically the spores are produced by a cone, or **strobilus.** This consists of a compact club-shaped group of sporangium-bearing modified leaves (sporophylls) found at the tip of a specialized branch (Fig. 31-22). Sporulation, as in all higher plants, is meiotic and each spore has the potential of giving rise to a haploid gametophyte. Typically the gametophyte is a semimicroscopic green thallus, nutritively independent of the sporophyte, but poorly adapted to terrestrial conditions. For this reason and because the free-swimming sperm require water if any is to reach an egg, the Sphenopsida tend to be restricted to swampy regions or to unusually rainy localities.

Apparently the Sphenopsida did not provide a direct evolutionary line leading to any of the higher plants. Like other primitive Tracheophyta, the Sphenopsida seem to have arisen from the Psilophytales (p. 563) during the Devonian period. They reached a peak in the Carboniferous period (Fig. 31-23); but by the end of the Paleozoic era, they had almost vanished.

The Pteropsida (Subphylum 4: Phylum Tracheophyta). This highly successful group of land plants is by far the *largest in the Plant Kingdom.* It includes *all* **ferns** and *all* **seed**

Fig. 31-23. Petrified calamite fossil from a Carboniferous formation. Many of the ancient Sphenopsida were large, treelike forms that participated in the formation of coal. (From *The Plant World.*)

plants (Gymnospermae and Angiospermae).

The completely dominant sporophyte generation typically is represented by a sturdy well-adapted land plant. It possesses very *efficient root, stem,* and *leaf systems,* with *highly developed vascular elements* in both xylem and phloem. The leaves tend to be large, complex structures, which have evolved as flattenings at the ends of the stem branches, rather than as small accessory outgrowths, as in the lower Tracheophyta. The sporangia develop on the lower surfaces (or margins) of the sporophylls and the sporophylls usually are so highly specialized that it is difficult to recognize them as modified leaves. The haploid gametophyte generation is very small. Indeed, in higher forms (gymnosperms and angiosperms) both male and female gametophytes are microscopic (Fig. 12-19). The protection and nurturing of the embryonic sporophyte is exceptionally effective.

Three large **classes,** each containing a wide variety of living species, have been evolved among the **Pteropsida.** These are:

Class 1. *The Filicineae*—ferns
Class 2. *The Gymnospermae*—cone-bearing plants
Class 3. *The Angiospermae*—flowering plants

Among the Pteropsida, only the last two classes (Gymnospermae and Angiospermae) produce **seeds.** Formerly these **seed plants** were considered to represent a separate phylum (the Spermatophyta). However, accumulating paleontological evidence has made it necessary to modernize the classification.

THE FERNS (CLASS FILICINEAE). The distinctive reproductive cycle and the general characteristics of this familiar group of plants were described in an earlier section (Chap. 12). During the Carboniferous period a number of large treelike ferns existed and these played some role in the formation of coal. Today, however, ferns seldom exceed knee height, although a few resemble small trees (Fig. 31-24). Among living ferns there are about 250 genera (10,000 species).

The ferns tend to be restricted to environments where water is abundant, at least periodically. The gametophyte (Fig. 12-5), although green and nutritively independent, is small (seldom more than ¼ inch wide) and *not well adapted to land conditions.* Moreover, the flagellated sperm (Fig. 12-4) must

Fig. 31-24. Young tree-ferns, Jamaica. Few modern Filicineae grow to such a size; but many ancient forms were much larger. (From *The Plant World.*)

swim through water in reaching the eggs. The sporophyte generation, on the other hand, is a well-adapted land plant. Often the sporophyte reproduces vegetatively by sending up new clusters of leaves (fronds) and roots from the underground horizontal **rhizome** (Fig. 12-4). Indeed, the **rhizome,** during successive seasons of growth, may continue to reach out from the place where the sporophyte first established itself, thus giving rise to a number of sporophytes within a certain area.

All available evidence indicates that the Filicineae originated from the Psilophytales (p. 563), and in fact, the earliest fossil ferns bear a striking resemblance to this group. Also the evidence indicates that the early ferns, now extinct, represent the stock from which the Gymnospermae and Angiospermae arose (Fig. 29-11).

THE GYMNOSPERMAE (CLASS 2; PHYLUM TRACHEOPHYTA; SUBPHYLUM PTEROPSIDA). This important group (about 750 living species) includes all the **conifers** (pines, spruces, hemlocks, ginkgoes, cycads, etc.). Among the gymnosperms, the reproductive organs are **cones,** rather than flowers. Essentially, each cone is a cluster of **sporophylls** (modified spore-bearing leaves). However, the gymnosperms are **heterosporous;** that is, they produce both **microspores** and **macrospores.** Also the gymnosperms bear two kinds of cones: (1) smaller **staminate cones,** which produce **microspores** (pollen); and (2) larger **pistillate cones,** which produce **macrospores** (Fig. 31-25).

All Gymnospermae (literally, "naked seeds") produce **seeds.** Among Gymnospermae, however, the seeds occupy an exposed position—two on the upper surface of each scale of the **pistillate cone.**

The life cycle of a gymnosperm, such as the pine, resembles that of the angiosperm, which was described in Chapter 12. Typically, two ovules (macrosporangia) are borne on the upper surface of each scale of the pistillate cone (Fig. 31-26); and one **microscopic female gametophyte** develops from the macrospore at the center of each ovule. Here it is protected and nurtured by the surrounding tissues. Each microspore (pollen grain), if it is carried by the wind to an ovule, develops into a microscopic **male gametophyte,** which likewise is protected and nurtured by the ovule tissues. Fertilization occurs when the tip of the male gametophyte (pollen tube) grows into contact with the egg cell—after the female gametophyte (megagametophyte) in the ovule has reached maturity (Fig. 31-26). Finally, **each ovule,** as a whole, *gives rise to* **one** seed and an embryo of the next **sporophyte** generation lies at the center of each seed (Fig. 12-22).

This type of life cycle has many advantages for land plants—as was explained in Chapter 12. It enables the species to achieve fertilization without requiring the sperm to swim through water. Also the protected and nurtured gametophytes are not required to face the hazards of independent life, such as are encountered by the poorly adapted gametophytes of lower land plants. And finally, the new sporophyte, at the center of the seed, is carried to a relatively advanced stage of development before it is forced to shift for itself. Consequently it is not surprising to find that the seed plants (Gymnospermae and Angiospermae) have come to dominate the land environment.

It is difficult to evaluate the tremendous importance of the vast forests of pines and other gymnosperms. They prevent soil erosion; they provide food and shelter for wild animals; they yield vast quantities of lumber and wood products (paper, wood alcohol, turpentine, etc.), and they have many other values. All gymnosperms are woody plants, chiefly trees. Some, such as the California redwoods and big trees, achieve gigantic size. The wood of most species consists mainly of **tracheids** (p. 244); and most species are *evergreens,* with *needlelike leaves.* The adaptation of the sporophyte generation to land life in relatively dry cold regions is excellent; and since sexual reproduction, including seed production, can continue under such condi-

Fig. 31-25.   Pines and other gymnosperms produce two kinds of cones. *Below,* a cluster of **staminate cones** (which produce the microspores, or pollen), surrounded by needlelike leaves. *Above,* two **pistillate cones** (which produce ovules and seeds), flanking a young leaf-bearing shoot, and surrounded by mature leaves. Two very small, young pistillate cones may be seen at the top of the new leaf-bearing shoot. Both photos are of the Austrian pine (*Pinus nigra*). (Copyright General Biological Supply House, Inc.)

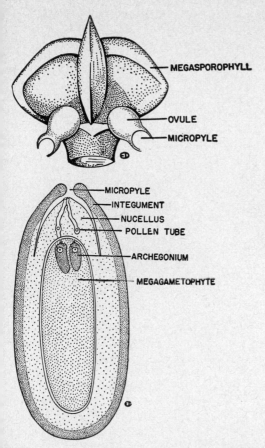

Fig. 31-26. *Above*, one scale (megasporophyll) of a pistillate pine cone, bearing two ovules. *Below*, female gametophyte (megagametophyte) at center of a developing ovule. Note the two male gametophytes (pollen tubes), growing toward the egg cells, in the archegonia. The haploid gametophytes, both male and female, are nurtured by the nucellus tissue and protected by the integument of the ovule while fertilization occurs. Subsequently, the embryo of the new sporophyte, which originates from the fertilized egg, is also nurtured and protected while the ovule (as a whole) is ripening into a seed. (From *The Plant World*.)

tions, gymnosperms have occupied great areas on all continents.

The fossil evidence indicates that the Gymnospermae originated from a now-extinct group, the "seed ferns" (Cycadofilicales), which had a fairly wide distribution in the Carboniferous period. Indeed, the **cycads** (Fig. 31-27), which constitute the most primitive group among surviving Gymnospermae, show many resemblances to ancient "seed

ferns." The **sperm, among cycads, are flagellated,** even though they are carried to the eggs by a pollen tube and never have an opportunity to swim. Also cycads display some other very primitive characteristics.

Ginkgo biloba (Fig. 31-28), on the other hand, represents the only surviving species from an order (Ginkgoales) that previously consisted of many genera and species. This so-called living fossil, a native of China, has recently become quite popular as an ornamental tree in the United States.

THE ANGIOSPERMAE (CLASS 3; PHYLUM TRACHEOPHYTA; SUBPHYLUM PTEROPSIDA). The angiosperms represent by far the largest (250,000 species) group among the land plants of today. Aside from conifers, most plants in almost all terrestrial environments are angiosperms.

As was explained in Chapter 12, **flowers**

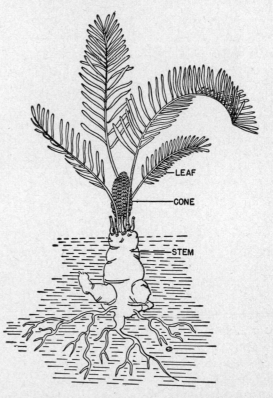

Fig. 31-27. A cycad (*Zamia*). The cycads, a very primitive group of gymnosperms, have flagellated sperm cells. Note one large seed cone at the apex of the short tuberous stem. (From *The Plant World*.)

Fig. 31-28. The ginkgo tree (*Ginkgo biloba*). It is sometimes cited as a living fossil because it is the only species that has survived from a large group (the Ginkgoales) of primitive ancient gymnosperms. (From *The Plant World*.)

(rather than cones) are distinctive of the Angiospermae. Also the *seeds of the angiosperm are enclosed within a* **fruit,** which is a derivative of the basal part of the pistil (**ovule case**).

The life cycle of the angiosperm (Fig. 12-19) is exceedingly well adapted to land conditions. The basic pattern is the same as in the Gymnospermae, except that (1) the gametophytes are even more reduced (Fig. 31-29); (2) the microspores (pollen) are carried mainly by insects (rather than by wind); (3) one of the sperm nuclei participates in an **accessory fertilization,** which forms a **triploid** **endosperm** tissue (p. 221); (4) the growth of the male gametophyte (pollen tube) is supported by the tissues of the upper parts of the pistil (stigma and style), rather than by the tissues of the ovule itself; and (5) the archegonia of the female gametophytes are reduced even further (in fact they are virtually absent).

The sporophyte generation among angiosperms varies tremendously from lowly grasses to mighty oak trees. Generally speaking, however, the tissues and organs are very well adapted to land conditions. The xylem almost always displays well-developed **ducts,**

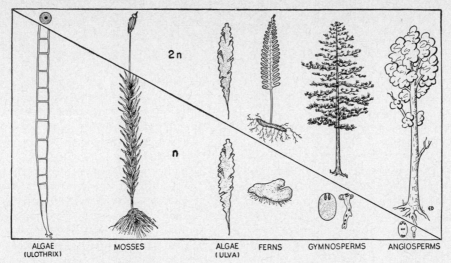

Fig. 31-29. Diagram showing an evolutionary trend in the Plant Kingdom. Progressively the diploid (2n) sporophyte generation has become larger and more dominant; while simultaneously the haploid (n) gametophyte generation has diminished, becoming more subordinate and dependent. Among many algae the diploid generation is represented solely by the zygote. (From *The Plant World*.)

ALGAE (ULOTHRIX)   MOSSES   ALGAE (ULVA)   FERNS   GYMNOSPERMS   ANGIOSPERMS

or **vessels** (Fig. 13-8), and **tracheids** (p. 244) may also be present. Typically the leaves are broad, flat, and very efficient as photosynthesizing structures.

Two important angiosperm subclasses have been evolved. These are: Subclass 1, the **Monocotyledoneae,** and Subclass 2, the **Dicotyledoneae.** Each of these groups displays a number of distinctive features.

The **Monocotyledoneae** include the grasses, palms, lilies, irises, tulips, sedges, cattails, bananas, orchids, cannas, etc. Among all of this wide variety of plants: (1) the embryo displays just **one cotyledon;** (2) the **petals** and other floral parts occur *in groups of three* (or a multiple of three); (3) the **leaves** tend to be *elongate,* narrow, and nonlobulated; (4) the leaf veins run parallel to each other and to the margins of the leaf; (5) the **vascular bundles** *of the stem* do not have a ringlike arrangement but *are scattered;* and (6) **cambium** *is lacking* in the adult stem.

The **Dicotyledoneae,** on the other hand, include: many trees and shrubs (oaks, maples, elms, apples, viburnums, laurels, etc.); most truck garden plants (spinach, broccoli, legumes, tomatoes, potatoes, etc.); many flower garden plants (roses, phlox, geraniums, poppies, sunflowers, etc.); many wild flowers (dandelions, buttercups, violets, hepaticas, etc.), and thousands of other plants, both common and uncommon. All these plants display: (1) *two embryonic* storage *leaves* **(cotyledons);** (2) **petals** and other floral parts occurring in *groups of five* (sometimes four); (3) *broad,* frequently lobulated **leaves;** (4) a *branching network of* **veins** *in the leaves;* (5) a *circular arrangement of* **vascular bundles** *in the stem;* and (6) a *ring of* **cambium** in the *stem.*

The basic nature of flowers and fruits, and how these structures contributed to the evolutionary success of the Angiospermae were considered in Chapter 12. Paleontological evidence as to the precise origin of the angiosperms is somewhat scanty. Probably this great group also originated from the "seed ferns" (p. 563). The first unmistakable fossils of true flowering plants occur in Cretaceous strata, formed about 125 million years ago. These fossils show, however, that many of the modern angiosperms (elms, maples, magnolias, sycamores, poplars, etc.) had become recognizable even in these early times.

TEST QUESTIONS

1. What is taxonomy? What does it aim to accomplish?

2. List the principal types of evidence that may be useful in deciding upon the classification of an organism. Explain why the classification of an organism sometimes may have to be changed.

3. Explain the binomial system of nomenclature. Give four examples. Distinguish between a genus and a species.

4. Who was Linnaeus? How many organisms was he able to recognize and classify? Approximately how many organisms are known today? Is it true that some new species are still being recognized every year?

5. What are some of the principal differences between plants and animals? Can you specify any exceptions to these general rules?

6. What general similarities between plants and animals can be enumerated?

7. How would you explain the fact that plants and animals display many fundamental similarities of structure and function?

8. Distinguish between the Thallophyta and the Embryophyta.

9. Among the various phyla of thallophytes, which two are considered to be most primitive? What evidence can you cite to support this answer? Which of the two probably evolved first? Explain.

10. What group of thallophytes probably gave rise to the higher plants? Explain.

11. Among the twelve phyla of the Plant Kingdom, which are predominantly aquatic and which are terrestrial?

12. What organs, tissues, and reproductive structures would you expect to find among well-adapted land plants? Explain.

13. Explain why the appearance of archegonia represents an important development in the evolution of higher plants.

14. Outline the classification of the Embryophyta, specifying the phyla, subphyla, classes, and subclasses that are mentioned in this chapter.

15. Which group among the Embryophyta displays a relatively dominant independent gametophyte generation and a relatively inconspicuous dependent sporophyte generation?

16. In which group of embryophytes is the gametophyte generation relatively inconspicuous, but nevertheless independent?

17. In what groups of embryophytes is found a relatively inconspicuous and dependent gametophyte?

18. Explain and document the statement that among the Embryophyta the gametophyte generation progressively becomes less conspicuous and more dependent upon the sporophyte generation.

19. Explain and document the statement that among the Embryophyta the sporophyte generation progressively becomes more conspicuous and independent.

20. Among the Tracheophyta:
    a. Which groups, once numerous and dominant in ancient times, have dwindled and become quite scarce and unimportant in recent times?
    b. Which groups are very numerous and dominant today?

21. Compare the Psilopsida, Lycopsida, and Sphenopsida, pointing out at least three similarities and at least one distinctive feature in each.

22. How do ferns differ from other Pteropsida? How are they similar?

23. What is a seed? Discuss the evolutionary antecedents of this reproductive structure.

24. What is a fruit? Discuss the evolutionary relationships of this reproductive structure. In what main group of plants have fruits been evolved?

Note: In seeking to review, students can apply the following questions to each of the plant phyla successively.

25. Name one or more organisms belonging to this phylum and to each of its specified subdivisions.

26. Does the phylum display any unique features, not found in any other plant group?

27. What are the phylogenetic relations of the group? Is the origin of the phylum known? Did it give rise to any other major plant group? What paleontological evidence is available in regard to these questions?

28. Are any of the plants in this phylum important: (a) as a food supply for other organisms; (b) from a medical viewpoint; (c) as sources of economically important materials; (d) from other viewpoints.

FURTHER READINGS

1. *The Plant World,* 4th ed., by H. J. Fuller and Z. B. Carothers; New York, 1963.

2. *Botany,* 3d ed., by C. L. Wilson and W. E. Loomis; New York, 1962.

32-*The Animal Kingdom*

THE PRINCIPLES of classification are essentially the same for both plants and animals. At a very early date, however, animals began to take a different path of evolution. Consequently quite a different set of taxonomic criteria must be employed when one seeks to classify the animals.

SOME IMPORTANT CRITERIA

Active locomotion is much more characteristic of animals than of plants. Consequently the organs of locomotion are apt to be conspicuous among the distinctive features of an animal. One-celled animals (**Protozoa**) are classified primarily on the basis of their locomotor organs; and among multicellular animals (collectively the **Metazoa**) these organs often serve as important taxonomic criteria. Moreover, the sensory-neuromuscular structures, which likewise are instrumental in the fulfillment of the food-getting and other movements of the animal, are apt to be distinctive in the different animal groups.

But in seeking to ascertain the evolutionary status of an animal group, a wide variety of questions must be considered. What is the cellular organization of the group? Is it **unicellular, colonial,** *or truly* **multicellular?** Is the animal **diploblastic** or **triploblastic?** Are there any *special features* that are *distinctive*—in the *embryo,* or in the *adult?* How far has the *differentiation* of special *tissues* and *organs* progressed? What is the *symmetry* of the animal? Is it *spherical, radial,* or *bilateral?* What is the character of the digestive system? Does it consist of *gastric vacuoles;* or is it a *saccular* or *tubular system?* What is the developmental status of the *circulatory, respiratory, excretory,* and *skeletal systems?* How did some higher animal groups manage to invade the land, leaving the age-old aquatic environment of the ancestral species? What is the pattern of the *reproductive structures;* and how have the reproductive processes become adapted to land conditions? What is the *importance* of the group *in nature and in human affairs?* And above all, perhaps, what *paleontological evidence* is available? And what does this evidence indicate as to the *origin, antiquity,* and *specific relationships* of each particular animal group?

624

THE PROTOZOA[1] (LITERALLY, FIRST ANIMALS)

This fairly large (about 20,000 species) phylum includes all **one-celled animal organisms.** Most of the species are of *solitary habit;* but there are a number of *colonial* forms. Typically the nutrition is *holozoic;* but one group, the Sporozoa, is entirely parasitic; and there are some saprophytic species.

Four main *subgroups* (here designated as *classes*) have been evolved:

Class 1.   The **Sarcodina** (Fig. 32-1). Protozoa with pseudopodia.

Class 2.   The **Mastigophora** (Fig. 32-2). Protozoa with flagella (sometimes called the Flagellata).

Class 3.   The **Ciliophora** (Fig. 32-4). Protozoa with cilia (at least during some part of the life cycle).

Class 4.   The **Sporozoa** (Fig. 30-7). Parasitic Protozoa, without distinctive locomotor organs.

[1] Many zoologists believe that the status of the Protozoa should be raised to that of a Subkingdom of the Animalia. In this case, the four classes (see below) of the Protozoa must be designated as phyla. In any event, the paleontological evidence indicates that the four groups of Protozoa initiated separate lines of evolution at a very early date (Fig. 29-11).

The Sarcodina. All these one-celled animals possess pseudopodia. By definition, a pseudopodium is an elongate retractable protrusion of the cytoplasm, which, in most cases, serves for locomotion. However, pseudopodia display a wide variety of forms. They may be blunt and fingerlike (as in *Amoeba* and *Difflugia,* Figure 32-1); slender and needlelike (as in *Actinosphaerium* and *Heliospaera,* Fig. 32-1); stiff or flexible; branched or unbranched; clear or granular. But always a pseudopodium is a *temporary* protrusion, capable of retracting and reforming from time to time.

The **Sarcodina** are quite numerous and varied. Some, like the **Foraminifera,** inhabit perforated calcareous shells; others, like the **Radiolaria** (for example, Heliosphaera, Fig. 32-1), build beautiful intracytoplasmic skeletons of siliceous material; and others, like the **Amoeba,** are unprotected except by a very delicate pellicle.

During past ages, **Radiolaria** and **Foraminifera** populated the sea in great abundance. In fact, the skeletal accumulations of these organisms, collecting on the floor of the ocean, played a dominant part in the deposition of certain layers of sedimentary rock. Accumulations of Foraminifera form a gray-

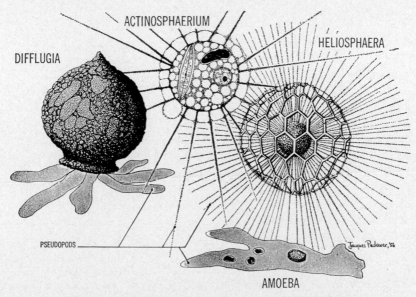

DIFFLUGIA   ACTINOSPHAERIUM   HELIOSPHAERA

PSEUDOPODS

AMOEBA

Fig. 32-1.   Protozoa with pseudopodia: Class **Sarcodina.**

ish mud (**foraminiferous ooze**), which gradually may undergo transformation into chalk. One such deposit is represented by the beautiful "white cliffs of Dover" in which the shells of the original organisms can easily be identified microscopically. And even today foraminiferans and radiolarians are very abundant in the sea.

Accumulations of the Radiolaria, on the other hand, usually undergo metamorphosis into **siliceous rock** (for example, flint). Today, indeed, a study of the distribution of the ancient marine Sarcodina, especially the Foraminifera, is very useful to petroleum geologists who are searching for new oil fields.

Also among the Sarcodina are a few parasitic species. One of these, **Endamoeba histolytica** (see Table 32-1), is the causative agent of **amoebic dysentery,** a rather serious human ailment.

The Mastigophora, or Flagellata. (Fig. 32-2). The flagellates form an extremely varied group. Some, like *Euglena* (Fig. 32-2) and *Volvox* (Fig. 32-2), possess definite chloroplasts and can be classified either as plants or animals. Most are truly unicellular, but a large group, including *Eudorina, Volvox,* and related species, form colonial aggregates of very definite pattern. Such colonies provide a key to how multicellular organisms may have evolved. Indeed, some of these colonies (for example, *Volvox*) display a clear differentiation between the **germ** and the **somatic** types of cells. The germ cells of *Volvox,* as in higher animals, are reproductive cells, which retain the potential of transmitting chromosomes to the next generation. The somatic or body cells, on the other hand, are the nonreproductive cells, in the wall of the colony, and cannot transmit chromosomes to the next generation.

Some flagellates possess collarlike structures surrounding the origins of the flagella (Fig. 32-2). Such cells are strikingly similar to the collar cells (Fig. 16-2) of the Porifera, or sponges (p. 629). Moreover, there is considerable other evidence that indicates that *the flagellates provided a main line of ascent*

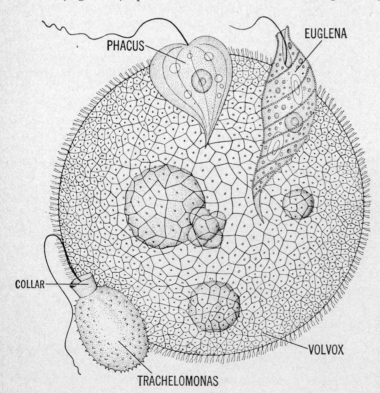

PHACUS
EUGLENA
COLLAR
TRACHELOMONAS
VOLVOX

Fig. 32-2. Protozoa with flagella: Class **Mastigophora**. Note that some forms are colonial. Also note the "collared" species, a Choanoflagellate.

in the evolution of higher organisms, both plants and animals (Fig. 29-11).

In addition to the many free-living species, there are a few parasitic Mastigophora, and some of these, especially the **trypanosomas,** are important medically. The two forms of **African sleeping sickness,**[2] both very serious ailments, are caused, respectively, by *Trypanosoma gambiense* (Fig. 32-3) and *Trypano-*

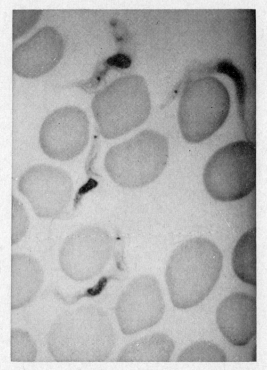

Fig. 32-3. *Trypanosoma gambiense,* a human blood parasite, which causes one form of African sleeping sickness. Four flagellated specimens can be seen among the red blood cells. (Copyright, General Biological Supply House, Inc.)

soma rhodesiense, which are injected into the human blood stream by the bite of the **tsetse fly.** Also two disfiguring diseases, endemic in certain Asiatic and Mediterranean areas, namely **kala azar** and **Oriental sore,** are caused by tissue-invading flagellates of the genus *Leishmania.* A sizable number of other

[2] African sleeping sickness should not be confused with **encephalitis,** which also may be called "sleeping sickness." Encephalitis is one of the virus diseases.

trypanosomes occur as blood parasites in various vertebrate animals. Two cattle diseases of the Orient, **surra** and **nagana,** are caused, respectively, by *Trypanosoma evansi* and *Trypanosoma brucei.* Both of these are transmitted by the tsetse fly, from local game animals, especially antelope, which also harbor the parasites. *Trypanosoma lewisi,* transmitted by fleas, is often found in the blood of rats; and various other *Trypanosoma,* transmitted by leeches, have been found in the blood streams of various fish, amphibians, and reptiles.

The Ciliophora (Fig. 32-4). As the name Ciliophora denotes, all members of this class possess cilia. The group, however, is a diverse one, which is divided into two **subclasses:**

1. The **Ciliata** are forms that possess cilia during all (active) stages of the life cycle.
2. The **Suctoria** are forms that are ciliated during an early stage, but are nonciliated later. The adult suctorian, in fact, is a sedentary animal. It fastens itself to the substratum and feeds by means of suction tentacles (Fig. 32-4, *Podophyra*).

The Ciliata. Although *Paramecium,* undoubtedly, is the most familiar representative, there is a very rich variety of other Ciliata that can be found in fresh, salt, and brackish waters, especially in quiet spots, where strong currents and heavy waves are absent.

Most ciliates display a unique feature. Each cell possesses *two types* of nuclei—one (or more) **micronucleus,** and one (or more) **macronucleus** (Fig. 7-3). This differentiation seems to represent a division of nuclear functions. The **micronucleus,** apparently, determines the hereditary characteristics of the species and transmits these to the next generation; whereas the **macronucleus** is more concerned with metabolic processes in the cell. However, **nuclear reorganization** may occur periodically. At such times a new macronucleus is formed from one of the micronuclei. In *Paramecium,* for example, nuclear reor-

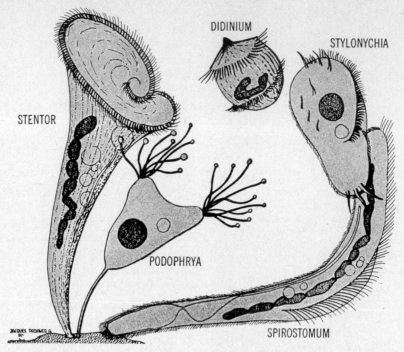

Fig. 32-4. Protozoa with cilia: Class **Ciliophora**. As adults, the Suctoria (e.g., *Podophrya*) have tentacles instead of cilia.

ganization generally occurs following **conjugation,** shortly after the zygote nucleus has been formed. Or it may occur in a single individual—either by **autogamy** or by **endomixis.** Essentially these latter processes of nuclear reorganization are similar, except that autogamy involves a fusion of two micronuclei (within the same individual), whereas endomixis does not involve any nuclear fusion.

The nutrition of most Ciliata is holozoic, but there are a few parasitic species. One mild intestinal inflammation in man is caused by a parasitic ciliate, *Ballantidium coli.* However, this form occurs more frequently in the intestine of the pig.

The Suctoria. Among the Suctoria the offspring are produced by fission or by internal budding; and only the young individuals are active ciliated swimmers. Later each attaches itself to the substratum by a **stalk** or **disc,** loses its cilia, and develops **tentacles** (Fig. 32-4, *Podophrya*). Some of these tentacles possess sticky knoblike tips, which hold the prey (usually some active ciliate), while other sharply pointed tentacles pierce the pellicle of the prey and conduct its cytoplasm into a food vacuole within the suctorian.

The Sporozoa. All Sporozoa are parasitic and they are probably the most widely distributed of animal parasites. In fact, various Sporozoa parasitize almost all other animals, both Vertebrata and Invertebrata; and some of the most devastating diseases of man and other animals are caused by these unicellular parasites. These diseases include the various forms of **malaria,** in man; the **coccidial diseases** of fowl; and the **red-water fevers** of cattle.

The malaria parasites all belong to the genus *Plasmodium,* and like many parasites, these Protozoa display a very complex life cycle. This cycle (Fig. 30-7) includes two reproductive stages, which take place while the parasites are living in the mosquito, and a third very active multiplication (sporulation), which occurs in the blood stream of man and other warm-blooded animals.

THE PORIFERA (LITERALLY, PORE BEARERS)

These **primitive multicellular animals,** which commonly are called the **sponges** (Fig. 32-5), constitute a relatively small (about

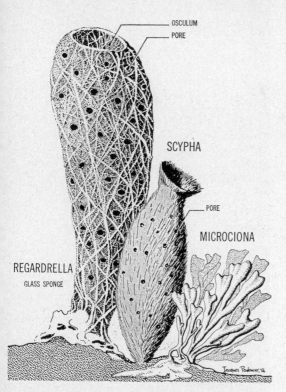

OSCULUM
PORE

SCYPHA

PORE

MICROCIONA

REGARDRELLA
GLASS SPONGE

Fig. 32-5. Some sponges: Phylum **Porifera.**

5000 species) **phylum.** Almost all sponges live in the sea, many in shallow waters. However, some live at depths extending down to four miles; and there is one widely distributed fresh-water family. Most familiar sponges are drab in color; but some of the less familiar species are brightly colored in various hues of red, orange-yellow, blue, and violet.

All sponges display a relatively primitive structure. The **body wall** (Fig. 16-11), which surrounds the central cavity, consists of only two cell layers—an outer **dermal layer** and an inner **gastral layer.** These layers are separated by a thick **gelatinous matrix,** which is strengthened by numerous microscopic **calcareous** or **siliceous spicules,** or by a network

of delicate **fibers,** composed of a silklike protein, **spongin.** Also a number of active amoeboid cells, called **amoebocytes,** can be found wandering through the matrix. Some of the amoebocytes give rise to gametes, or to asexual buds, and thus they must be considered as potential **germ cells.**

The gastral layer consists mainly of collar cells (Fig. 16-2). Individually these cells take small particles of organic food into **gastric vacuoles,** where all the digestive processes of the animal occur. The dermal layer, on the other hand, consists of a poorly differentiated epithelium.

The sponges do not have any excretory or respiratory organs and there are no clearly recognizable nerve or muscle cells. Some of the amoebocytes, however, tend to aggregate around the **pores,** which lead into the gastral cavity. In fact, these amoebocytes possess a fair degree of contractility and collectively they act to regulate the size of the pore openings.

In commercially sold natural sponges (Fig. 16-3), only the spongin part of the matrix remains after processing; and the calcareous and siliceous (glass) sponges are never used for cleaning purposes.

The primitive status of the Porifera is indicated by (1) the **radial** type of **symmetry** (except in the few asymmetrical forms); (2) the **absence** of well-defined **tissues** and **organs;** (3) the **absence** of a **general digestive cavity** (that is, digestion remains intracellular within the gastric vacuoles of the individual collar cells); and (4) the striking resemblance of the collared gastral cells (**choanocytes**) to the collared flagellates (**choanoflagellates**). The dermal and gastral layers probably are not homologous to the germ layers (**ectoderm** and **endoderm**) of higher animals, since invagination occurs from the animal pole of the developing sponge blastula, rather than from the vegetal pole, as in other multicellular animals. The free-swimming larva of the sponge is called, in the blastula stage, an **amphiblastula,** because only the cells in the animal half are flagellated; and it is these flagellated cells that become invaginated when the gastral cavity begins to form.

All in all, the evidence indicates that the Porifera do not represent a main line leading toward the evolution of higher animals. More probably they are a divergent group that originated at a very early date (Fig. 29-11).

THE COELENTERATA

Probably the most familiar member of this relatively small (10,000 species) **primitive metazoan phylum** is *Hydra* (Fig. 3-12). However, the Portuguese man-of-war (Fig. 32-6), the jellyfishes, sea anemones (Fig. 32-7), and coral animals are also coelenterates of fairly common occurrence.

Distinguishing Characteristics of the Phylum. (1) Coelenterates display an essentially **saclike structure** (Fig. 16-4). Only one opening, which is called the **mouth**, communicates between the internal cavity and the outside environment. The cavity itself represents a saccular type of **enteron**, since some digestion occurs here; but also it may be called a **gastrovascular cavity**, because it tends to distribute food particles as well as to digest them. Also the cavity sometimes is called the **coelenteron**, since this one cavity substitutes for the two cavities (coelom and the enteron) of higher animals.

(2) The **body wall** of the coelenterate consists of *only two layers of cells* (Fig. 32-8). However, the outer **ectodermal layer** is separated from the inner **endodermal layer** by an essentially noncellular matrix, called the **mesoglea.** In *Hydra,* this matrix is relatively thin and inconspicuous; but in many other coelenterates (for example, jellyfishes) it constitutes the bulk of the body. Such a **diploblastic organization,** in which only two (ectoderm and endoderm) of the **primary germ layers** are represented, stands in distinct contrast to the **triploblastic organization** of higher animals, in which a **third germ layer,** the **mesoderm,** is always represented.

(3) The cells of the coelenterate show con-

Fig. 32-6. The Portuguese man-of-war, *Physalia pelagica.* Note the gas-filled saillike float, which is about 1 foot long and richly colored in iridescent hues of purple and green. Also note the fish, ensnared in the very long tentacles. Actually this coelenterate represents a colony of multicellular individuals: some specialized for stinging prey, some for feeding, and some for reproduction. (New York Zoological Society Photo.)

siderable differentiation as to form and function but not to the extent found in higher animals. As is shown in Figure 32-8, these cell types include: (a) primitive nerve cells, called **protoneurons;** (b) **gland cells;** (c) **epitheliomuscle cells;** (d) **nematoblasts** (see below); and (e) **interstitial cells.**

(4) The different kinds of cells tend to be

Fig. 32-7.   A sea anemone. Phylum **Coelenterata;** Class **Anthozoa.** This glass model shows one expanded specimen (on the right), with many elongate tentacles surrounding the mouth; and one contracted specimen (on the
left). Both individuals are of the same species (*Megalactis friffithsi*) and both are attached to a rock. (Courtesy
of the American Museum of Natural History, New York.)

scattered rather diffusely throughout the
body of the coelenterate. In other words, the
cells are *not aggregated into clearly recognizable* tissues, such as are found in higher
animals.

(5) The **symmetry** of the coelenterate body
is **radial,** rather than bilateral (as in higher
animals generally).

(6) All Coelenterata possess **nematoblasts**
(Fig. 32-8). These highly specialized cells
enable the animal to capture a variety of
small active food organisms. Each nematoblast contains a tiny bladder, called the **nema-
tocyst,** from which a coiled thread, the **nema,**
can be discharged forcibly and instantaneously. There are several kinds of nema, however. Some are sharply pointed syringes that
can inject a paralyzing substance (**hypnotoxin**) into the prey. But others are merely
coils, which may be single or multiple. Some
such coils are laden with a sticky secretion,

while others are armed with microscopic
barbs, and these structures are very effective
for snaring and holding prey while it is
being paralyzed by the stinging nemae.

(7) Digestion in the coelenterate is partly
extracellular—by means of enzymes secreted
by gland cells into the saccular enteron—and
partly intracellular—in the individual food
vacuoles of the flagellated cells of the enteron. A larger mass of food material soon
disintegrates as it begins to be digested in the
enteron. Then the smaller bits of organic
food are picked up by the flagellated cells.
Thus Coelenterata (and Porifera) seem to
have retained, to a greater or lesser extent,
the digestive mechanisms of their unicellular
forebears.

(8) All Coelenterata possess a number of
tentacles, grouped around the mouth, and
these are armored with an especially heavy
concentration of nematoblasts. *No head* is

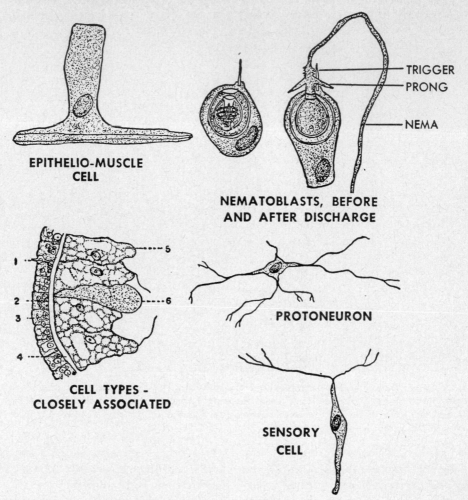

EPITHELIO-MUSCLE CELL

NEMATOBLASTS, BEFORE AND AFTER DISCHARGE

TRIGGER
PRONG
NEMA

CELL TYPES - CLOSELY ASSOCIATED

PROTONEURON

SENSORY CELL

Fig. 32-8. *Hydra*. Diagram of cellular structure. Note the different types of cells and the absence of clearly organized tissues and organs. 1, nematoblast; 2, interstitial cell; 3, ectodermal cell; 4, mesoglea; 5, endodermal cell; 6, gland cell.

recognizable and there are *no other well-developed organs*. Sometimes the body is covered by a horny, but delicately transparent envelope as in the case of *Obelia* (Fig. 32-9). Also many Coelenterata, especially the coral animals, secrete supporting structures at the basal (attached) end of the body. Usually these are composed of calcareous material, but sometimes they have a protein composition.

(9) All Coelenterata are aquatic, chiefly marine.

Classes of the Phylum Coelenterata. *Three distinct classes* have been evolved among coelenterate animals. These may be listed as follows:

*Class 1. The **Hydrozoa** (Hydra, Obelia, and Related Forms).* At some stage in the life cycle, typical Hydrozoa tend to resemble *Hydra*. Many are colonial, however. Also many display an alternation of generations, which is a phenomenon quite rare in the animal kingdom. In the case of *Obelia* (Fig. 32-9), for example, the asexual **hydroid generation** is represented by the colonial form of the organism, in which the individual members of the colony display a hydralike form; whereas the sexual **medusoid generation** takes the

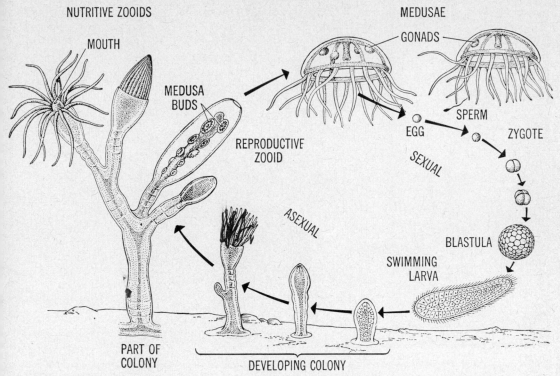

NUTRITIVE ZOOIDS

MOUTH

MEDUSA BUDS

REPRODUCTIVE ZOOID

MEDUSAE

GONADS

SPERM

EGG

ZYGOTE

SEXUAL

ASEXUAL

BLASTULA

SWIMMING LARVA

PART OF COLONY

DEVELOPING COLONY

Fig. 32-9. _Obelia._ This hydrozoan shows a regular alternation of sexual and asexual generations—a rather rare phenomenon in the Animal Kingdom. (By permission, from *General Zoology*, by Tracy I. Storer. McGraw-Hill Book Co., Inc.)

form of a small jellyfish, which is called a **medusa.**

Class 2. The **Scyphozoa** *(True Jellyfishes).* These coelenterates resemble the medusa of *Obelia,* except that they usually are larger and have a greater abundance of gelatinous mesoglea. Also the Scyphozoa do not have any **velum,** the sheet of tissue that partially closes off the subumbrellar space in hydrozoan medusae (see Fig. 32-9). A hydroid form appears very transiently during embryonic development.

The multitude of stinging cells on the long tentacles of some of the larger Scyphozoa may represent a painful hazard for unwary swimmers. The largest kind of jellyfish, *Cyanea,* is a blue and orange giant with a diameter up to 12 feet and tentacles up to 90 feet in length. However, this species is rarely seen along the Atlantic or Pacific coasts of North America, except perhaps in the most northerly parts.

Class 3. The **Anthozoa** *(Sea Anemones and Corals).* No medusoid stage is present. The general form is somewhat suggestive of *Hydra,* except much more complex. A **gullet,** which resembles an **inverted hypostome** (Fig. 16-4), is always present. Also there are sheets of tissue called **septa,** which pass radially inward from the body wall, subdividing the enteric cavity and increasing its digestive capacity. Colonial forms are frequent.

The anemones produce no skeletons but the closely related corals often produce elaborate supporting structures at the basal (attached) end of the body (Fig. 32-10). These may be predominantly calcareous, as in the case of the red *jewel coral,* **Corallium;** or they may be composed of a horny protein, gorgonin, as in the case of the beautiful *sea fan, Gorgonia.*

Some of the colonial corals, which are extremely abundant in warmer (20° C and over) parts of the oceans, have played a domi-

Fig. 32-10.   Skeletal supporting and attaching structures of various coral animals. Coral reefs are built mainly of such structures, which may accumulate enormously through the years. (Courtesy of Ward's Natural Science Establishment.)

nant role in the building of coral reefs. Undoubtedly the greatest of all coral reefs is the Great Barrier Reef, which extends more than a thousand miles along the northeast coast of Australia, at varying distances up to about 80 miles offshore. However, smaller coral reefs are very common in South Atlantic and South Pacific regions. Layer after layer of calcareous deposits, representing countless generations of living animals, tend to accumulate in the warm shallow offshore waters, at a rate (measured under present-day conditions) varying from 5 to 200 millimeters annually (see Fig. 32-11).

Phylogeny of the Coelenterata. Coelenterate fossils extend back into formations of early Cambrian period—which demonstrates a very ancient origin. Also the embryological pattern and other evidence indicate that some of the early Coelenterata represent a main line in the evolutionary ascent of all major groups of higher animals (Fig. 29-11).

THE CTENOPHORA (LITERALLY, COMB BEARERS)

The animals in this small group (only 80 species) of exclusively marine forms resemble

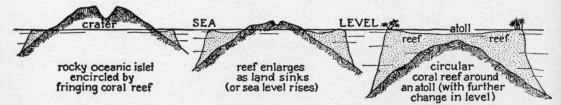

Fig. 32-11.   Darwin's concept of how coral reefs are formed. (By permission from *General Biology*, by Tracy I. Storer. McGraw-Hill Book Co., Inc.)

small jellyfishes, except that they may be of different shapes. In fact, formerly the ctenophores (pronounced—tén-o-fores) were classified as coelenterates. There are, however, a number of important differences, and these seem to justify placing the "comb jellies" in a separate phylum, the Ctenophora.

Distinguishing Features. Ctenophores commonly are called comb jellies, because each displays eight radially arranged rows of cilia, called "combs" (Fig. 32-12). The cilia permit these floating animals to move very slowly through the water. But ctenophores are very feeble swimmers. Great numbers of them often drift together in the tides; and sometimes many are thrown up on the beach when a strong onshore wind is blowing.

Many Ctenophora are also known as sea walnuts, because they are about the size and shape of the common walnut. In the sea, the comb jellies appear as transparent ghosts of rare and delicate beauty. By day they show iridescent hues of blue and rose; and at night they emit a faintly glowing light from eight rows of **luminescent cells,** along the bases of the combs.

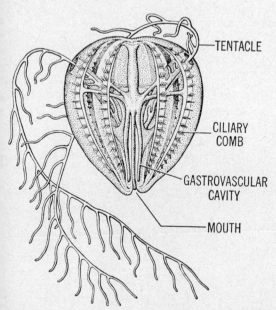

Fig. 32-12. One of the comb jellies: Phylum **Ctenophora.** Note the combs. These animals show iridescent colors by day and a faint luminescence by night.

TENTACLE

CILIARY COMB

GASTROVASCULAR CAVITY

MOUTH

Ctenophora and Coelenterata resemble each other in several respects. Both have a **saccular** (rather than tubular) **enteron** in which the mouth opening serves for egestion as well as for ingestion; both have an abundant, usually gelatinous, **mesoglea** separating the outer **ectodermal** and the inner **endodermal** cell layers. However, the mesoglea of the ctenophores contains well-developed, though scattered, **muscle fibers** and very numerous **amoebocytes.** Many biologists, therefore, consider that the Ctenophora possess a primitive **mesodermal layer,** which would identify them as **triploblastic** animals. Ctenophores have *only two* **tentacles** and *no* **nematoblasts;** and *all species are* **hermaphroditic.** Moreover, the symmetry, while basically radial, shows some tendency toward bilaterality in the placement of some structures. And finally, a greater tendency toward the development of definite organs is found among the Ctenophora. Most species possess an equilibrium organ, or **statocyst** (similar to the one depicted in Fig. 23-7) with nerve connections leading to the muscle fibers; and usually there are definite **ducts** which conduct the eggs and sperm from the internally placed **gonads** to the outside.

Ctenophora do not produce any hard skeletal materials and consequently a fossil record of ancient forms is virtually lacking. However, their general similarity to the Coelenterata, both as to structure and development, leads to the belief that the ctenophore stock was very close to the direct evolutionary line that led to the development of higher animals.

THE PLATYHELMINTHES (LITERALLY, FLATWORMS)

Although it includes only about 7000 species, this phylum is a very important one. Some of the flatworms are small free-living animals such as *Planaria* (Fig. 16-7). These live mainly in quiet waters (both fresh and salt), although there are a few land species, which live in moist, swampy places. But a large majority of flatworms are parasites, in man and many other animals. Moreover there are many pathogenic species. In fact, **intestinal flukes, liver flukes** (Fig. 32-13), **blood flukes,** and **tapeworms** (Fig. 32-14) may cause serious illnesses in the various host organisms which they infect.

Characteristics of the Phylum. Some very important characteristics of higher animals generally appear to have originated at the evolutionary level of the flatworms. These include: (1) **bilateral symmetry;** (2) a tendency toward **cephalization** (differentiation of a definite head region); (3) a clear-cut **triplo-**

blastic organization, in which an unmistakable **mesoderm** is represented; and (4) the development of well-defined **organs** and **organ systems.** However, the Platyhelminthes also have many primitive features: (1) When present, the enteron is of the **saccular** (rather than the tubular) type. (2) **Food vacuoles** frequently are formed by the cells lining the enteron. (3) **No true body cavity,** or **coelom,** is present. (4) No definite skeletal respiratory, or circulatory organs occur. (5) **Locomotion** (in free-living forms) is by means of **cilia.**

Bilateral symmetry probably originated

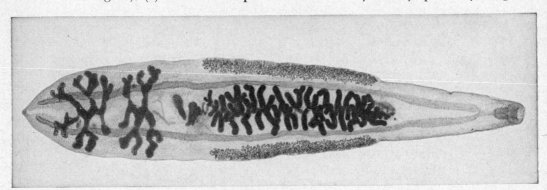

Fig. 32-13. Stained specimen of a parasitic flatworm, the liver fluke (*Clonorchis sinesis*). This adult trematode infests the human gall bladder. Other stages in the life cycle are shown in Figure 32-16. (Copyright, General Biological Supply House, Inc.)

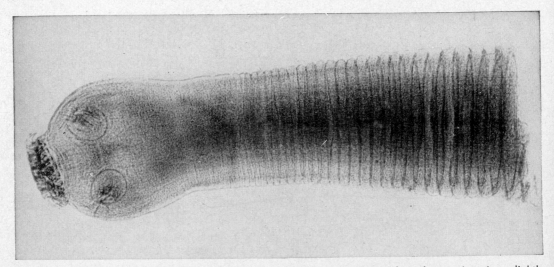

Fig. 32-14. Scolex ("head") and young proglottids (sections) of tapeworm from human intestine, slightly enlarged. Note the ring of hooks (extreme left) and the suckers (immediately to right of hooks) with which the worm fastens itself to the intestinal wall. (Copyright, General Biological Supply House, Inc.)

when animals began to move mainly in one direction and began to maintain a more or less constant orientation of the body. Apparently the forward, or **anterior,** end of the animal, which first encounters changes in the environment, tended to become different from the trailing **posterior** end; and consistent differences in the environment above and below the animal led to a differentiation between the upper **(dorsal)** and the lower **(ventral)** aspects of the body. The right and left **sides,** on the other hand, would encounter approximately the same conditions, and would not become different. Moreover, **cephalization,** which is a tendency toward the development of a "head" part of the body, seems to have resulted from a concentration of **special sense organs** at the anterior end. Thus we find the **light-sensitive eyespots** and the **touch-sensitive auricles** of the planarian (Fig. 16-6) near the anterior, or leading, end of the animal, where most new stimuli impinge.

The bulk of the body of the flatworm consists of tissues derived from the **mesoderm.** The mesoderm intervenes between the **ectodermal** epithelium, covering the outer surface, and the **endodermal** epithelium, lining of the complexly branched gastrovascular cavity (Figs. 16-6 and 16-8). The mesodermal tissues include a complicated set of well-developed muscle fibers, as well as various excretory and reproductive structures and scattered *germ cells* (Fig. 32-15).

The numerous germ cells in the mesoderm give rise to gametes, and also they are responsible for the remarkable regenerative powers displayed by planarians. Between the other mesodermal structures, there is a syncytial network of loosely arranged parenchyma tissue; and the spaces within this network are filled with body fluid, or **hemolymph** (p. 318).

Flatworms are perhaps the simplest animals in which well-defined **organs** and **organ systems** can be recognized. As may be seen in Figure 32-15, these include: (1) the ovaries, testes, and ducts of the reproductive system;

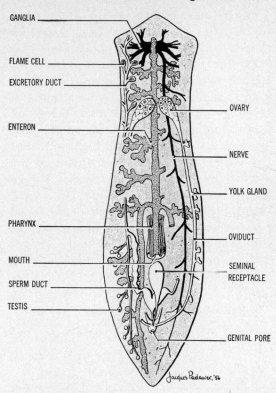

Fig. 32-15. *Planaria,* one of the free-living Platyhelminthes; diagram of internal structures. Flatworms are among the simplest animals that show definite organs and organ systems.

(2) the ganglia and nerve strands of the nervous system; and (3) the **flame cells** and ducts of the **excretory system.**

Classes of the Platyhelminthes. This phylum can be divided naturally into the following three *classes:* (1) the **Turbellaria;** (2) the **Trematoda;** and (3) the **Cestoidea.**

Class 1. The **Turbellaria.** These are mainly free-living flatworms, such as planarians, in which the ectodermal epithelium of the lower surface is ciliated. Generally these animals range between one to three cm in length, although there are a few semimicroscopic species and a few that reach a length of five inches.

Class 2. The **Trematoda,** *or* **Flukes.** (Fig. 32-13). These flatworms are *all parasites,* with adult stages usually found in various vertebrate animals. Cilia are present in a larval stage (the miracidium), but the adult body is covered by a protective cuticle. At least one sucker is present and often one sucker surrounds the anteriorly placed mouth, which leads into the enteron. The food generally consists of the tissues of body fluids of the host, sucked into the enteron by action of a muscular pharynx (Fig. 32-13). A few are external parasites of various fish, amphibians, and reptiles and these tend to have a relatively simple life cycle. Most, however, are internal parasites. They may live in the intestine (**intestinal flukes**), bile ducts, or gall bladder (**liver flukes**), or even in the blood stream (**blood flukes**); and all have a complex life cycle. At least one stage of the cycle is spent in an invertebrate host, usually a snail or other mollusk (Fig. 32-16).

SOME TREMATODE DISEASES. A number of Trematoda are human parasites of consider-

able medical importance. More than half the population in certain parts of China and India carry chronic infections of the **intestinal fluke, Fasciolopis buski.** This parasite infects man (and sometimes dogs and cats) by way of an encysted larval stage found on certain water plants that are eaten raw. Also there is another larval stage found in the tissues of a fresh-water snail.

The commonest human **liver fluke, Clonorchis sinensis,** likewise has a wide distribution in the Orient. This fluke, as may be seen in Figure 32-16, has a larval (**redia**) stage in a snail; but the encysted stage (**metacercaria**) occurs in the skin and muscles of certain fish. Thus human infection occurs when the raw fish is eaten by man.

Various **blood flukes,** of the genus **Schistosoma,** are fairly frequent in certain coun-

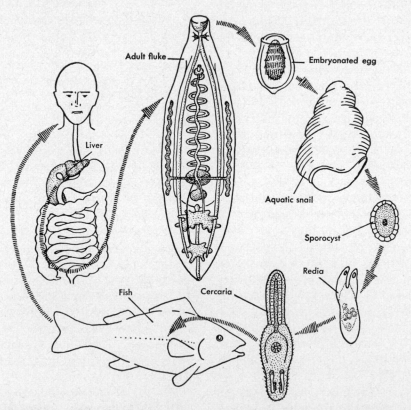

Fig. 32-16. Life cycle of the "Chinese liver fluke" (*Clonorchis sinensis*). Such a cycle, in which the parasite must pass through a mollusk (the snail) before reinfecting a vertebrate, is typical of this group of trematodes. (From *General Zoology,* by Miller and Haub. Holt, Rinehart and Winston, Inc.)

tries; and some of these are found in cattle and domestic animals, as well as in man. Generally, the adult flukes are found clinging to the walls of the large veins of the abdomen; but the eggs leave the human body via the urine or feces. Various snails serve as intermediate hosts for the sporocyst stages and the fork-tailed actively swimming (cercaria) larvae gain entrance into another human host by penetrating the skin of a bather, or via the drinking water. Typically the males and females of *Schistosoma* are never separated from each other. The broadly flattened male is longitudinally folded, forming a groove that encloses the very slender threadlike female.

Class 3. The Cestoidea (Tapeworms). (Fig. 32-14). Some of these elongate parasitic flatworms may measure as much as 75 feet in length. As the common name implies, the Cestoidea display a flattened tapelike form. As adults, all live in the intestinal tracts of various vertebrates (Fig. 32-17). Here they attach themselves to the gut wall by means of (usually) four suckers and a ring of formidable chitinous hooks (Fig. 32-14). The headlike attaching section of the worm, which bears the hooks and suckers, is called the **scolex;** and the rest of the body is made up of sections (not equivalent to the true segments, or somites, of higher animals), which are called **proglottids.** The proglottids near the scolex are relatively small and immature. New ones are continually being budded off from the scolex. Thus the proglottids farther away from the scolex are older, larger, and swollen with eggs. Food substances are absorbed directly into the worm's body from the surrounding intestinal contents of the host; that is, the tapeworm itself does not have any digestive tract. In fact, most of the organ systems tend to be degenerate, except for the reproductive system, which is highly developed. In each ripe proglottid there are dozens of small testes, at least one large ovary, and a complex system of accessory reproductive structures. Flame cells are present, connected to two longitudinal excretory ducts that extend through the successive sections. Also there are six strands of nervous tissue that pass lengthwise through the proglottids.

Cestoidea, compared to Trematoda, have a relatively simpler life cycle. This is indicated in Figure 32-17, which gives the cycle of the pork tapeworm, *Taenia solium,* a rare parasite of man. Ripe proglottids, swollen with eggs (often self-fertilized) pass from the human intestine with the feces (Fig. 32-17). Before it is liberated from a proglottid, each egg develops into a six-hooked embryo, the **onchosphere,** which lies inside a tough envelope (Fig. 32-17). The juices of the pig's intestine digest away the envelopes, liberating the active hooked larvae. These penetrate into the blood stream of the pig, and the blood carries them to the muscles. Here each larva encysts and undergoes metamorphosis into a **cysticercus,** or **bladder worm** (Fig. 32-17). The bladder worm possesses a very small *inverted* scolex, which lies near the center of a fluid-filled bladder; and the bladder, in turn, is enclosed by a cyst wall. If **incompletely cooked** (pink) **pork,** derived from an infected hog, is eaten by a man, the cyst wall digests away, the bladder everts, and the scolex of the young *Taenia* attaches itself to the intestinal wall. The young worm then develops rapidly. In four to five weeks it may become an adult, about 20 feet long, which will produce thousands of ripe egg-laden proglottids in the next generation.

The life cycles of various **other tapeworms** also have been worked out. Perhaps the most important of these are: (1) **Taenia saginata,** the **beef tapeworm** (adult stage in man; larval stages in beef muscle; length up to 75 feet); (2) **Dibothriocephalus latum,** the **fish tapeworm** (adult stage in man and other fish-eating mammals; one larval stage in *Cyclops* and other small fresh-water Crustacea; intermediate stage in muscle (flesh) of carp, perch, and other fresh-water fish; length up to 30 feet); (3) **Dipylidium caninum,** the **dog tapeworm** (adults in dogs, cats, and (rarely) man; larval stage in certain lice and fleas; length,

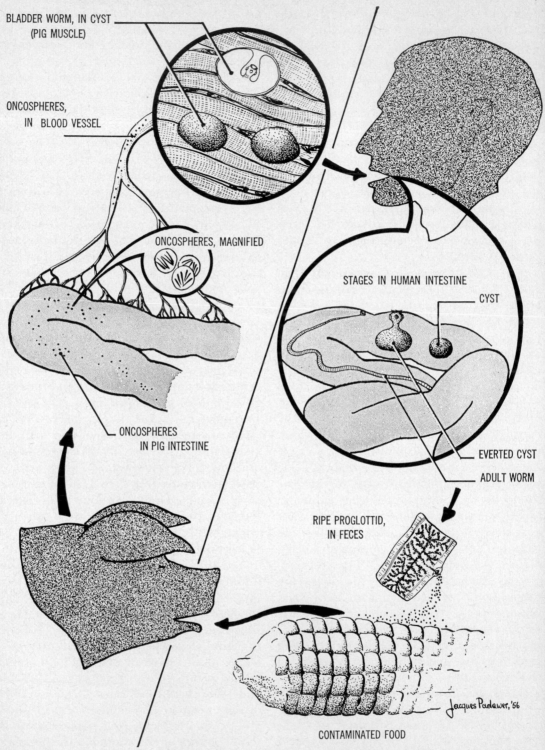

BLADDER WORM, IN CYST
(PIG MUSCLE)

ONCOSPHERES,
IN BLOOD VESSEL

ONCOSPHERES, MAGNIFIED

STAGES IN HUMAN INTESTINE

CYST

ONCOSPHERES
IN PIG INTESTINE

EVERTED CYST

ADULT WORM

RIPE PROGLOTTID,
IN FECES

CONTAMINATED FOOD

Jacques Padawer, '56

Fig. 32-17. Life cycle of the "pork tapeworm" (*Taenia solium*). Careful meat inspection has reduced the incidence of this cestode parasite; but still it is not safe to eat undercooked pork.

only one to two feet); and (4) **Echinococcus granulosus,** the **hydatid worm** (adults, less than one inch long, in dogs, wolves, and other carnivores; huge multiple larval cysts, called **hydatid cysts,** up to two-inch diameters, found in the brain and other organs of man, monkeys, and various domestic animals; cysts may inflict serious damage or even death upon the host; about 500 human cases reported in United States to date).

Phylogeny. Not much definite information is available in regard to the evolutionary origin of the Platyhelminthes. None possesses any skeletal parts and virtually no fossil flatworms have been found in the earlier geological strata. However, judging from other evidence—the symmetry, mesodermal organization, embryological development, and so forth—it seems probable that the early flatworms initially followed the main line that led to the evolution of most of the higher animals (Fig. 29-11), before divergence occurred.

FIVE PROBLEMATICAL PHYLA

There are a number of lowly invertebrate groups,[3] generally considered as phyla, among which the evolutionary relationships are quite obscure. Five of these—the **Nemertinea, Nemathelminthes, Rotifera, Bryozoa,** and **Brachiopoda**—are relatively more important. These will be considered in very brief fashion, more or less collectively.

All representatives of the foregoing groups are **bilaterally symmetrical.** But even more significantly, all possess a **tubular** type of **enteron.** This represents an important advance that becomes established as a standard feature in higher animals generally. Some of these five groups show the first appearance of

a **true body cavity,** or **coelom,** and the first clearly defined **blood vessels**—two other features that are standard in all higher forms.

The **coelom** is a mesodermal cavity. It is important because it separates the body wall from the wall of the enteron. This allows the movements of the body to become independent of the movements of the digestive tract (see discussion, page 279). Moreover, the **tubular** enteron allows the digesting food to follow a "one-way traffic" route; and this in turn permits the successive parts of the digestive tract to become differentiated and specialized in a more efficient manner. Each part of the tube can become uniquely designed to perform some particular part of the work of digestion and absorption, as in the digestive tract of man (Fig. 16-11) and of other higher animals.

The Nemertinea. These animals (Fig. 32-18), which commonly are called **ribbon worms** or **proboscis worms,** are represented by about 500 species, mainly marine, with soft, flat, unsegmented bodies. Sometimes they are white, but more often they are colored (red, brown, green, or yellow). Usually the nemertines are only a few inches long; but there is one species that can reach a length of 75 feet.

Sometimes the nemertines are grouped with the flatworms. The mesoderm consists mainly of loosely arranged tissue in which **no definite coelomic cavity** is present, although there are some **flame cells.** Unlike the flatworms, however, nemertines have a tubular digestive tract; and there are three poorly differentiated "blood vessels" running lengthwise through the mesoderm (Fig. 32-18). Characteristically, the food-catching apparatus is an elongate muscular **proboscis,** sometimes tipped with a sharply pointed **stylet,** which the animal forcibly throws out from its anterior end (Fig. 32-18).

The Rotifera (Fig. 32-19). Most of these "wheel animals" are of microscopic size. In fact they are scarcely larger than most Protozoa, among which they often live. Many different species can usually be found in quiet

---

[3] In addition to the ones mentioned above, there are quite a few other small and obscure groups, for which no generally accepted classification has been worked out. These include: the Mesozoa, Entoprocta, Gastrotricha, Kinorhyncha, Nematomorpha, Acanthocephala, Phoronidea, Chaetognatha, Sipunculoidea, Priapuloidea, Echiuroidea, and, perhaps, one or two others.

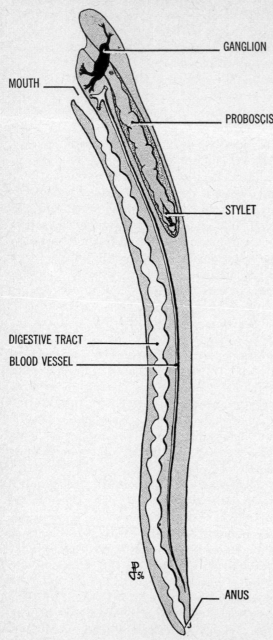

MOUTH

GANGLION

PROBOSCIS

STYLET

DIGESTIVE TRACT

BLOOD VESSEL

ANUS

Fig. 32-18.   A nemertine worm; diagram of essential structures.

streams and ponds, or even in wayside puddles.

The rotifers, nevertheless, are multicellular, bilaterally symmetrical, triploblastic animals, which possess a complete tubular digestive tract (Fig. 32-19). Also there is a body cavity in the mesoderm. However, this cavity is called a **pseudocoel**, rather than a **coelom**, since it does not possess any definite epithelial lining, or **peritoneum** (p. 298). Characteristically, the head end of the cylindrical body bears two circlets of active cilia, which tend to resemble whirling microscopic wheels. The tapered tail usually terminates by forking into two sharply pointed (frequently sticky) **toes**, by which the animal can attach itself to the substratum (Fig. 32-19).

Of the 12,000 or so known Rotifera, almost all are free-living, solitary species, inhabiting fresh water. However, a few live in salt water and a few are parasitic. No fossilized Rotifera have been found, probably because they do not form any mineralized supporting or encasing structures and because they are so very small.

The Bryozoa. These so-called "moss animals" grow in colonies of a size and shape that may have a rough resemblance to clumps of mosses. Encrusting a submerged rock or pile in shallow parts of the sea, they may also look like colonial Hydrozoa (p. 632). Bryozoan colonies, like those of the Hydrozoa, are usually covered by a chitinous or calcareous envelope.

Structurally, however, the individuals of a bryozoan colony are more complex (Fig. 32-20). Each is a triploblastic, bilaterally symmetrical animal. Also each possesses a complete tubular digestive tract and a true coelom, which is definitely delimited by a **peritoneal** lining. Characteristically, the mouth is surrounded by a horseshoe-shaped structure, bearing a number of **ciliated tentacles**, called the **lophophore** (Fig. 32-20). The digestive tract is V-shaped, so that the anal opening discharges the fecal wastes outside the protective envelope in the region bordering the **lophophore** (Fig. 32-20). There is a nerve ganglion situated between mouth and anus, but no circulatory, respiratory, or excretory organs are present.

Fossil remnants of the Bryozoa are widely distributed in geological strata extending back to the Ordovician period; and many

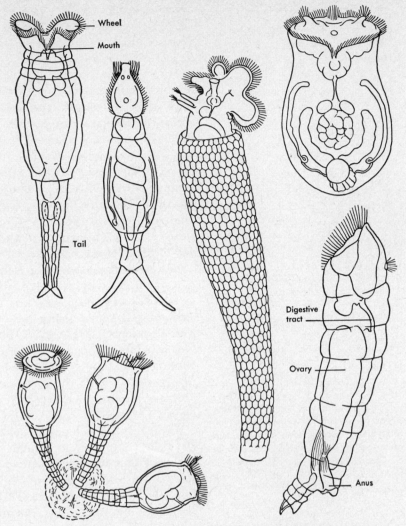

Fig. 32-19. Various rotifers, or "wheel animals." Despite their microscopic size, these are multicellular animals with a fairly complex structure (see text). (From *General Zoology*, by Miller and Haub. Holt, Rinehart and Winston, Inc.)

species, originally prevalent, have since become extinct. The Bryozoa, by forming thick encrustations in shallow marine waters, cooperate significantly with the corals in building **reefs** (p. 634). Petroleum geologists studying core samples obtained from test drillings, find bryozoan fossils very helpful when they are searching for new deposits of oil.

The Brachiopoda or Lamp-shell Animals. Only about 200 species of these two-shelled (bivalved) animals (Fig. 32-21) have survived from the richly varied ancient population

that once attached themselves to the rocky bottom in shallow parts of the sea throughout the world. Superficially the Brachiopoda look like little oysters or other bivalved mollusks. However, the valves of the brachiopods are not placed on the sides of the animal. Rather, there is one **dorsal valve,** which lies above the other **ventral valve.** The name "lamp shell" refers to the shape of the ventral valve. This tends to resemble the ancient *open type* of oil lamp, which once was commonly used by Greek and Roman peoples.

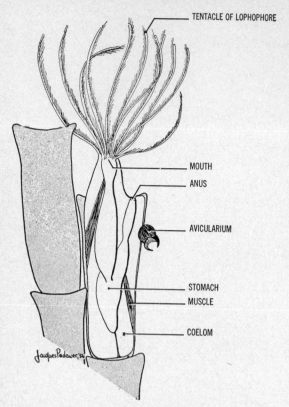

TENTACLE OF LOPHOPHORE

MOUTH

ANUS

AVICULARIUM

STOMACH

MUSCLE

COELOM

Jacques Padawer's

Fig. 32-20. A bryozoan (*Bugula*); part of colony, showing structure of one individual animal. Note the avicularium, a pincerlike structure that serves to clip away debris and encrusting organisms from the surface of the colony. In fossilized Bryozoa, the avicularia (which represent highly modified individuals in the colony) tend to be very well preserved.

Typically, each animal attaches itself to the substratum by means of a fleshy muscular stalk called the **peduncle** (Fig. 32-21).

Much of the space within the shells (Fig. 32-21) is occupied by a coiled many-tentacled **lophophore**. This can be extended forth anteriorly through the gap between the valves, when feeding is in progress. The body proper, which occupies a posterior position within the shells (Fig. 32-21), displays a **bilateral symmetry**, a well-developed **mesoderm**, a complete (usually tubular **digestive tract,** and a fully lined **coelomic cavity**. Also there is a primitive hollow muscular **heart,** which maintains an irregular flowing of the coelomic fluid, even though no blood vessels

are present. Two to four primitive **nephridia** (p. 311) are present as excretory organs, but no specialized respiratory organs have been developed.

Fossilized brachiopod shells (Fig. 32-22) are prevalent in marine rock strata extending back into the Cambrian period; and the record shows that the modern surviving kinds of Brachiopoda are relatively few in comparison with the number of species that have become extinct. One modern genus (*Lingula*) represents perhaps the oldest of surviving multicellular animal groups. This animal has changed very little indeed since it first appeared in the Ordovician period more than 450 million years ago.

The Nemathelminthes, or Nematodes. An amazing number and variety of these elongate cylindrical animals (Fig. 32-23) are found in various fresh-water bodies and in rich moist soils. Among the (roughly) 12,000 species of Nemathelminthes, most are free-living, but there are also quite a few parasitic species. Moreover, some of the parasitic nematodes are very important from a medical point of view.

Typically the elongate nematode body tapers at both ends, although usually the posterior end is more sharply pointed (Fig. 32-23). Many roundworms are microscopic, but a majority range between 1 and 10 mm in length; and one species, the **guinea worm,** which is a subcutaneous parasite of man, may reach a length greater than a meter. The free-living forms, which can easily be seen when one examines almost any sample of good soil under the microscope, display a characteristic thrashing type of movement. The worms keep coiling and uncoiling rapidly and continuously.

Typically the Nemathelminthes are triploblastic, bilaterally symmetrical, nonsegmented animals, with a complete tubular digestive tract (Fig. 32-23). The body cavity is a relatively small unlined **pseudocoel**. No proboscis or lophophore is present; and there are no clearly differentiated respiratory or circulatory organs. One or two nephridia

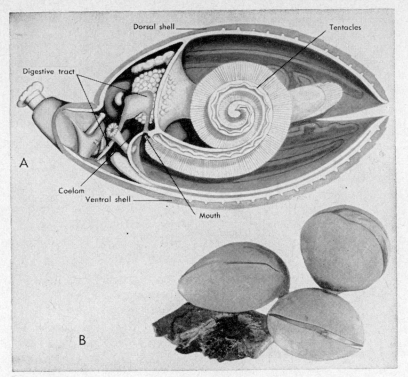

Fig. 32-21. A modern brachiopod (*Tentaculata*). A, diagram of internal structure; B, photo of three clustered individuals. (From *General Zoology*, by Miller
and Haub. Holt, Rinehart and Winston, Inc.; lower photo, copyright, General
Biological Supply House, Inc.)

may be present; and typically there is a ring
of nervous tissue around the esophagus.
Generally the sexes are separate and the
males are distinctly smaller than the females.

Some parasitic nematodes are very harmful, economically and medically. The young
of the common garden nematode (*Hetero-
dera marioni*) penetrate and feed upon the
root tissues of quite a number of garden and
crop plants. These cause **root swellings,** or
galls, which may be very detrimental to the
yield. The "golden nematode" seems to have
entered this country quite recently, but already it is doing considerable damage to
several crops, especially potatoes, in localities where the infestation is heavy.

Among medically encountered Nemathelminthes, **hookworms, trichina,** and **filarial
worms** are perhaps the most important. The
common American hookworm (*Necator
americanus*) stunts the growth and saps the
strength of many unfortunate individuals in
some poorer localities where good sanitation
facilities are lacking and where people tend
to go barefooted. Eggs of the hookworm enter
the soil with the feces, and the active young
larvae penetrate the delicate skin of the victim, usually on the sides of the foot near the
toughened sole. In the body, the larvae migrate to the lungs via the blood stream. Then
they crawl out of the lung, up through the
trachea, and into the digestive tract. The
adult worm, usually about 10 mm long, attaches itself to the intestinal wall. Here it
feeds upon blood, lymph, and bits of tissue,
obtained by means of the cutting action of
the minute teeth of the mouth and the sucking action of the worm's muscular pharynx.
Infection by fifty to a hundred adult hookworms seriously impairs the health of the
host. Internal bleeding from the many small
intestinal wounds is aggravated by an anti-

Fig. 32-22. Fossilized shells of an extinct brachiopod, *Spirifera vanuzemi*. Extinct species far outnumber all modern surviving brachiopods. (Courtesy of the American Museum of Natural History, New York.)

and reach the muscles, where they form a multitude of new cysts. In man, the rare cases of heavy infection (overt trichinosis) involve fever and a very painful swelling of the muscles, with slow recovery. Moreover, if the site of infection includes the diaphragm muscle, breathing may be impaired, even to the point of fatality.

With elephantiasis, on the other hand, the larval filarians are introduced into the blood stream by mosquitoes of the genus *Culex*. Reaching the lymph glands, the larvae mature into adult females about 8 cm long, and males about half that length. In the lymph nodes, the sexually produced larvae may become very numerous. Such an accumulation

coagulant present in the mouth secretions of the worm. Consequently grave anemia may result in heavily infected persons.

Trichinosis, caused by the trichina worm (*Trichinella spiralis*), and **elephantiasis,** caused by a filarial worm (*Wuchereria bancrofti*) are diseases of much rarer occurrence, especially in this country. However, mild infections of trichina, in which scarcely any symptoms are noticed, may occur in some 15 percent of the United States population.

Human infections of trichina may result from eating insufficiently cooked (pink) pork. Cysts (Fig. 32-24) containing dormant trichina larvae may be present in the skeletal muscles of the pig (also of rats, dogs, cats, and certain bears). Liberated by the digestive enzymes of the new host, each larva grows into an adult that lives for a while in the host's intestine, producing a new crop of larvae. Then the active larvae penetrate into the blood stream

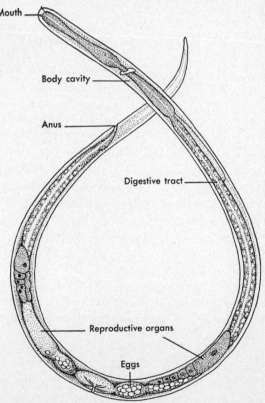

Fig. 32-23. A nematode, or "roundworm," diagram showing internal structures. A rich variety of semi-microscopic nematodes live in the soil. Most nematodes are free-living harmless creatures, but a few are parasites of considerable virulence (see text). (From *General Zoology*, by Miller and Haub. Holt, Rinehart and Winston, Inc.)

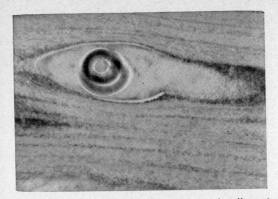

Fig. 32-24. Parasitic trichina worm (*Trichinella spiralis*), encysted in muscle. In man, a heavy infestation of such roundworm parasites causes overt **trichinosis**, a painful and long-enduring disease. (From *General Zoology*, by Miller and Haub. Holt, Rinehart and Winston, Inc.)

of adult and larval parasites may impair the lymph drainage, especially in the lower extremities, causing great swelling in the legs (Fig. 32-25). The disease is restricted almost completely to tropical regions and the incidence is gradually declining as a result of mosquito control.

Phylogenetic Relationships. Among Nemertinea, Nemathelminthes, and Rotifera particularly, the fossil record is scanty; and even though the Brachiopoda and Bryozoa have left many fossils, it is difficult to reach a definite decision as to whether or not one or more of these groups gave rise to others. Most likely all represent early offshoots from the same ancient extinct stock—the stock that also gave rise to most of the higher phyla (Fig. 29-11).

THE ANNELIDA, OR SEGMENTED WORMS

The earthworms (Fig. 21-3), sandworms (Fig. 32-26), and leeches (Fig. 32-27) are perhaps the most familiar members of the **Annelida**. This phylum embraces almost 7000 known species, of which a large majority are aquatic, mainly in marine waters. However, there are some terrestrial forms and a few parasitic species.

Characteristics of the Annelida. Like many other groups, the Annelida are triploblastic, bilaterally symmetrical animals with highly developed tubular digestive tracts (Fig. 16-9) and a clean-cut, fully lined coelomic cavity (Fig. 16-10). The Annelida, however, display a new feature, namely **segmentation,** which does not appear in any of the earlier groups.

Segmentation, or Metamerism. The elongate body of the typical annelid is conspicuously subdivided into a series of **segments,** or **metameres** (Fig. 32-26). Each of the succeeding segments tends to be a close replica of the others, not only as regards the external features, but also as to the form and arrangement of the internal structures. Such a segmented organization is not restricted to the annelids. It also is characteristic of the arthropods and vertebrates. However, the segmenta-

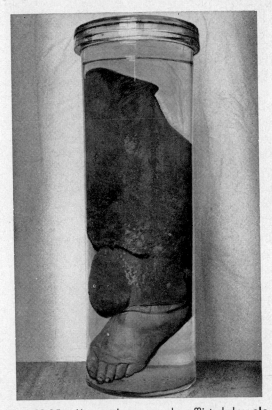

Fig. 32-25. Human leg, severely afflicted by **elephantiasis.** This tropical disease, which is transmitted by various mosquitoes, is caused by a parasitic nematode, the filarial worm (*Wuchereria bancrofti*). The adult parasites live mainly in the lymph vessels and lymph nodes of the body. (From *General Zoology*, by Miller and Haub. Holt, Rinehart and Winston, Inc.)

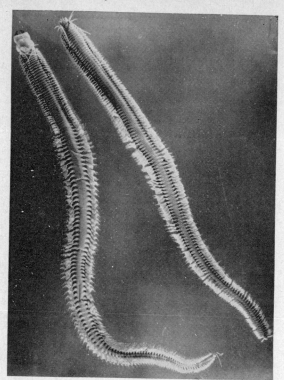

Fig. 32-26. One of the sandworms (*Neanthes*). Phylum **Annelida**; Class **Polychaeta**. Note the unjointed appendages (parapodia) and the numerous bristles (setae). Left specimen, ventral aspect; right specimen, dorsal aspect. (Copyright, General Biological Supply House, Inc.)

ber of pulsating muscular vessels, the **aortic loops** and **dorsal blood vessel** (Fig. 17-9). Hemoglobin usually serves as the respiratory pigment (p. 364) in the annelids. But the hemoglobin of the annelid is dissolved directly in the plasma and is not carried by specialized red cells.

Annelids *do not possess jointed appendages,* such as are characteristic of arthropods and vertebrates. Among annelids, in fact, appendages are often absent; or they may be mere slender, chitinous bristles (called **setae**); or at best, they are short fleshy outgrowths (**parapodia**), usually bearing bristles (Fig. 32-26).

tion in the vertebrates, although very clear in the embryo, may be somewhat obscured in the adult; and there is some tendency for the segments to become fused and modified even among Arthropoda.

Other Annelid Features. The annelids were among the first animals to develop a well-defined **closed circulatory system** (p. 319). In such systems, the *blood* flows through a *continuous* system of *capillaries* and *larger vessels.* The blood does not enter the tissue spaces or come into direct contact with the tissue cells. This efficient type of system, which is well adapted to the nutritive, respiratory, and excretory requirements of larger animals, reaches an apex of development in the vertebrate group, where a centralized pump, or **heart,** is also present. In the annelids, pumping is achieved by a num-

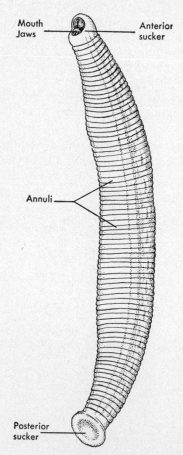

Fig. 32-27. A leech—one of the Hirudinea. This blood-sucking annelid possesses only 34 segments, although the number of external creases (annuli) may be greater. (From *General Zoology,* by Miller and Haub. Holt, Rinehart and Winston, Inc.)

The annelid *excretory system* consists of a series of well-developed **nephridia** (Fig. 20-3). Typically there is a pair of nephridia per segment, each supplied by a network of blood capillaries (p. 371). *Respiration* takes place through the skin (p. 358), although some tube-dwelling Annelida have **gills.**

The well-developed *nervous system* of the annelid is very similar to that of the arthropod. Essentially, the annelid system (Fig. 25-5) consists of a double chain of **segmental ganglia,** which extends longitudinally along the midline, on the inner surface of the *ventral body wall.* The chain connects anteriorly with the two dorsally placed **cerebral ganglia** by way of a pair of nerve connectives, the **circumpharyngeal connectives,** which encircle the digestive tract (Fig. 25-5). In each segment, there are several bilaterally matched nerves that transmit impulses from the receptors and to the effectors of this particular part of the body.

Classes of the Phylum Annelida. The following *four classes* were evolved among the Annelida:

Class 1. The **Archiannelida** *(Literally, "Ancient Annelids").* These are all small marine annelids, usually without any parapodia or setae; segmentation is inconspicuous externally, but well-defined internally.

Class 2. The **Polychaeta** *(Literally, "Many Bristles").* These are the sandworms, tube-worms, etc.; predominantly a marine group with numerous conspicuous segments, each bearing a pair of many bristled paddle-like parapodia, which serve as swimming organs. A well-defined head, with tentacles, is characteristic (Fig. 32-26).

Class 3. The **Oligochaeta** *(Literally, "Few Bristles").* This group includes the earthworms and related forms. They live mainly in fresh water or moist soils; have conspicuous segmentation, no obvious head, and only a few setae per segment.

Class 4. The **Hirudinea,** *or Leeches* (Fig. 32-27). These annelids have a dorsoventrally flattened, pigmented body, with a large sucker at the posterior end, and (usually) a smaller anterior sucker, surrounding the mouth. Externally the body is marked by many transverse creases, but a study of the internal structure reveals only 34 segments. No parapodia are present; a distinct head is lacking; and only one species possesses setae. Most species live in quiet fresh or salt waters; but a few live in damp soil.

Relationship of the Annelida to Other Phyla. Annelida shows some resemblances to other phyla, especially the Mollusca, Arthropoda, and Chordata. The pattern of cleavage, the manner in which the mesoderm arises, and certain larval characteristics are reminiscent of the Mollusca. But the segmentation, the type of cuticle, and the structure of the nervous system all tend to follow the arthropod pattern; and the conspicuous coelom and definite segmentation resemble these features in Chordata. However, the early paleontological record is not clear as to the precise origins of any of these important groups. Most students think that all originated from a common stock subsequent to the development of a coelomic cavity; that the Mollusca branched off before segmentation developed; and that the Annelida and Chordata began to diverge shortly after segmentation appeared in the ancestral animal stock (Fig. 29-11).

THE MOLLUSCA

Mollusks constitute the second largest phylum in the animal kingdom. The group, indeed, comprises more than 40,000 living species; and fossil remnants of more than 35,000 extinct species have been identified at the present time. The many diverse species include: all clams, oysters, and scallops; the chitons, slugs, and snails; and the squids, octopuses, and nautiluses. Also the size range is very great. Some snails measure only 1 mm in diameter; but one great giant squid reaches a length of 60 feet and a weight of several tons—easily the record among invertebrate animals.

Phylum Characteristics. As is shown in

Figure 32-28, all Mollusca, with very rare exceptions, possess one or more shells—which may be chitinous, calcareous, or both. The shell is secreted by a **mantle,** which, essentially, is an outgrowth of the body wall. Also Mollusca have a complete **tubular digestive tract** and a muscular organ, the **foot,** which shows great variation in the different classes (Fig. 32-28). In clams and other bivalve mollusks, the foot assumes the form of a plough-shaped burrowing organ; among snails and related forms, it is the elongate muscular part that enables the animal to attach itself and to crawl along the substratum; whereas in squids and octopuses, the foot is highly modified into a group of powerful tentacles. These tentacles are clad with numerous suction pads, so that the foot may be used for grasping prey, as well as for locomotion (Fig. 32-29).

The symmetry of these triploblastic, **non-segmented** animals is essentially **bilateral,** although some (the snails) display a spiral coiling of the shell and viscera. Also there is a **small lined coelom** limited mainly (in the adult) to the pericardial cavity.

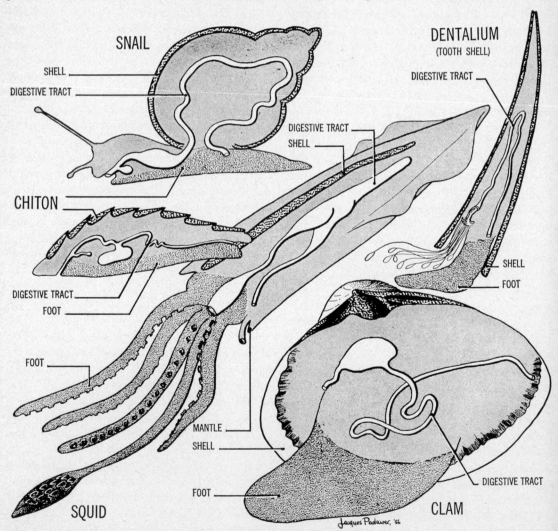

SNAIL

SHELL

DIGESTIVE TRACT

DENTALIUM
(TOOTH SHELL)

DIGESTIVE TRACT

DIGESTIVE TRACT
SHELL

CHITON

SHELL
FOOT

DIGESTIVE TRACT
FOOT

FOOT

MANTLE
SHELL

FOOT

DIGESTIVE TRACT

SQUID

CLAM

Jacques Padawer, '56

Fig. 32-28. Various mollusks. Note that each displays a foot, shell, mantle, and digestive tube—variously modified in the different kinds.

The well-developed circulatory system consists of a heart and definite blood vessels, which lead to the major organs. However, the molluscan system is of the *open type* (p. 319). In most of the organs, the circulatory fluid, or hemolymph, passes directly through the tissue spaces, rather than through clearly delimited capillary channels. Usually the respiratory organs are **gills.** And finally, the sensory-neuromuscular system is highly organized, especially in the squids, octopuses, and other cephalopods. The central nervous system, typically, consists of three pairs of interconnected ganglia: (1) the **cerebral ganglia,** situated anteriorly near the mouth; (2) the **pedal ganglia,** imbedded in the foot; and (3) the **visceral ganglia,** situated posteriorly in the body. The peripheral system, on the other hand, is represented by the numerous sensory nerve fibers coming in from the receptors and the motor fibers going out to the musculature, especially that of the foot.

All Mollusca have tactile and chemical receptors, and many possess **statocysts** (Fig. 23-7), which enable the animal to determine its orientation and equilibrium. Simple light-sensitive "eyespots" are present in some (for example, scallops), and a few mollusks (for example, squids and octopuses) have highly developed eyes, which achieve very accurate *true vision.* In fact, the eye of the mollusk is structurally very similar to the vertebrate eye. However, the manner of embryonic origin—from a folding of the surface ectoderm, rather than from an outgrowth of the brain—indicates that the two organs cannot be homologous. In fact, this is frequently cited as a striking example of **convergent evolution.**

Other Molluscan Features. Clams, oysters, and other bivalves feed upon semimicroscopic particles and organisms. These are carried to the small mouth by a copious (3 quarts per hour for an average oyster) stream of water brought into the shell by an **incurrent siphon** and passed out by an **excurrent siphon.** The mouth, in such cases, is not equipped with any kind of chewing or biting structures; but almost all other mollusks possess several rows of minute chitinous teeth, collectively called the **radula,** bordering the mouth opening. The radula may serve for scraping algae and other encrusting organisms from a rocky surface, as in the case of the sluggish creeping **Chiton** (Fig. 32-29); or it may serve for rasping and boring into the shell of another organism or into the wooden bottom of a ship, as in the case of one very serious marine pest, the "shipworm," **Teredo.** The mouth, in squids and octopuses, is also equipped with two powerful **horny beaks.** These can kill a captured fish or other prey and can tear the food into pieces suitable for swallowing.

Molluscan *shells* vary widely as to form and composition; and some forms (for example, slugs) do not have any shell. Typically, the shell—whether univalved, bivalved, or multivalved—is composed of a dense calcareous material superimposed upon a delicate chitinous framework. Usually it forms a hard external protective covering for the animal. But in the squid, the shell is reduced, and it lies *internally.* In fact, the delicate, chitinous, quill-like shell of the squid is commonly referred to as the "pen" (Fig. 32-28).

Many molluscan shells, of course, are very beautiful. They display a wide variety of lovely forms; and the mother-of-pearl (**nacre**) layer, which lines the inner surface of the shell, is often richly colored in various iridescent hues. Pearllike bodies are apt to form whenever a grain of sand or other small source of irritation becomes lodged on the outer surface of the mantle, where the nacre of the shell is being secreted. But pearls of real value, in which the layers of nacre are exceedingly hard and regular, are produced rarely, and only in certain kinds of oysters. The shell of the "many-chambered nautilus" actually represents a number of shells, formed year after year by the same animal, and fused into a spiral series. The successive shells are larger and larger. Thus each year the nautilus builds itself a "more stately mansion," but always it remains burdened by its older

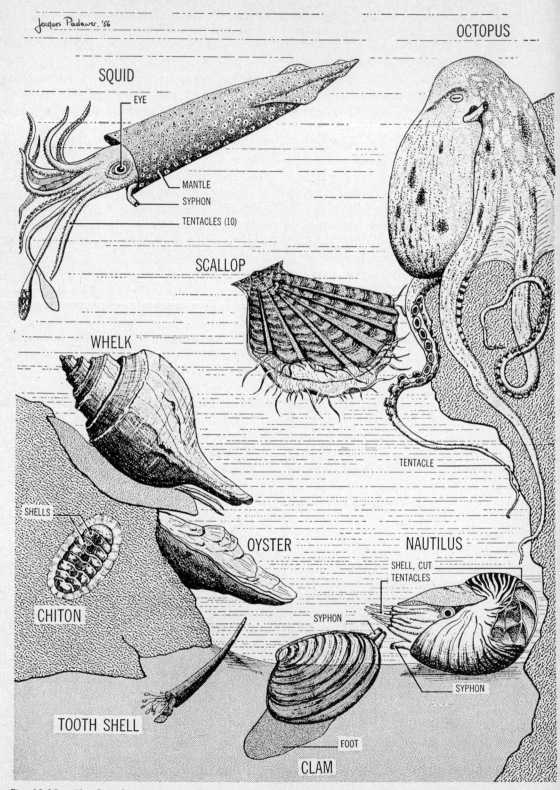

Jacques Padawer '56

SQUID

OCTOPUS

EYE

MANTLE

SYPHON

TENTACLES (10)

SCALLOP

WHELK

TENTACLE

SHELLS

OYSTER

NAUTILUS

SHELL, CUT
TENTACLES

SYPHON

CHITON

SYPHON

TOOTH SHELL

FOOT

CLAM

Fig. 32-29. The five classes of mollusks display a wide variation of form. This picture shows: one of the Amphineura (*Chiton*); three of the Pelecypoda (clam, oyster, and scallop); one of the Scaphopoda (the tooth shell); one of the Gastropoda (whelk); and three of the Cephalopoda (squid, octopus, and nautilus).

houses, which now are empty (Fig. 32-29).

Locomotion among Mollusca also varies widely. Oysters, mussels, and related forms attach themselves to the substratum (Fig. 32-29) and do not move at all during their adult life. Many clams merely burrow into the sand, while others, such as the common edible hard-shelled clam (*Venus mercenaria*), plow along half buried in the sand, slowly extending and retracting the muscular foot (Fig. 32-29). Snails, slugs, whelks, and chitons (Fig. 32-29) creep along the substratum, using an elongate muscular foot, which is closely applied to the surface; and the octopus quickly clambers over a rocky surface, or slithers into and out of a dark crevice by means of the eight powerful tentacles of its highly modified foot. Squids dart forward and backward with flashing speed, using a sort of jet propulsion. The mantle around the body in these animals has become modified into a strong conical muscular sac (Fig. 32-29). When this sac expands, water enters the mantle cavity through the incurrent siphon. Then when the sac contracts forcibly, a strong jet of water shoots out through the excurrent siphon, propelling the animal—in a forward direction if the siphon is pointed backward, or in a backward direction if the siphon is pointed forward. Moreover, the squid guides and steadies its darting movements with fins, at the posterior end of the body, and with its anteriorly placed tentacles (Fig. 32-29).

Phylogenetic Relationships. The rich fossil record of the Mollusca includes more than 35,000 extinct species, localized in all strata from the late Cambrian period to recent times. Nevertheless, the origin of the group remains obscure. The primitive molluscan stock of pre-Cambrian times was devoid of skeletal parts and seems to have left no record. The embryological evidence, based on a comparative study of the cleavage patterns and early larval stages, indicates some relationship to the Annelida. Adult Mollusca, however, are quite different from Annelida, especially as to their lack of seg-mentation and their reduced coelomic cavity. Probably the two groups separated from each other during pre-Cambrian time and the classes of Mollusca became differentiated during the Ordovician, Devonian, and Silurian periods (Fig. 29-11).

Classes of the Mollusca. The Mollusca have evolved as *five* distinctive *classes*, as follows:

Class 1. The **Amphineura** *(Literally, "Two-Nerved").* Chitons (Fig. 32-29) and related forms; body elongate or oval; shell, when present, consisting of eight serially arranged valves; head, reduced, or absent; two pairs of ventral nerve cords; a relatively small exclusively marine group (650 living, 75 fossil species).

Class 2. The **Scaphopoda** *(Literally "Boat-footed").* The "tooth-shells" such as *Dentalium* (Fig. 32-29); shell slenderly conical, open at both ends; foot also cone-shaped; another small marine group (200 living, 300 fossil species).

Class 3. The **Gastropoda** *(Literally, "Stomach-Footed").* Snails, slugs, limpets, and whelks (Fig. 32-29); shell spirally coiled and univalvular, except in a few forms; distinct head; foot is large, flat, and ventrally placed, in contact with substratum; a large group (30,000 living, 13,000 fossil species); mostly marine, but with some fresh-water and terrestrial forms.

Class 4. The **Pelecypoda** *(Literally, "Hatchet-Footed").* Clams, oysters, scallops, and other **bivalved** mollusks (Fig. 32-29). Two valves of shell placed laterally, hinged by dorsal ligament and closed by one or two adductor muscles; no head and almost always lacking a radula in the mouth; a medium-sized aquatic group, mainly in salt water (10,000 living, 14,000 fossil species).

Class 5. The **Cephalopoda** *(Literally "Head-Footed").* Octopuses, cuttle fish, squids, and nautiluses (Fig. 32-29). Shell external, internal, or lacking; "head-foot," bearing tentacles (ten in squids, eight in octopuses); eyes, conspicuous and highly organized; mouth, with horny beaklike jaws, in addition to a radula; an entirely marine group; 400 living and 10,000 fossil species.

THE ARTHROPODA (LITERALLY, "JOINTED LEGS")

This is by far the largest phylum in the animal kingdom. The diverse forms total to more than 700,000 species. In fact, the arthropods outnumber all other kinds of animals by approximately four to one.

The phylum Arthropoda includes: all crabs, shrimps, lobsters, barnacles, and other crustaceans; the flies, bugs, beetles, butterflies, and other insects; spiders, scorpions, ticks, horseshoe crabs, and other arachnids; and all centipedes and millipedes. Also there are some other less familiar forms, such as a small, very primitive genus. *Peripatus* (Fig. 32-30), and a large extinct group, the Trilobita (Fig. 32-31).

The biological success of the arthropods is reflected by their wide range of habitats. They occur almost everywhere—at heights and depths exceeding 20,000 feet; in salt, brackish, and fresh waters; on land and in the air; and on or in other organisms, as ecto- or endoparasites. Moreover, Arthropoda are of tremendous practical importance: as pollinating agents in many plants; as carriers of disease (lice, ticks, flies, mosquitoes); as a food base for fish and birds; as a direct source of food for man (lobsters, shrimps, crabs, etc.); as destroyers of man's food, crops, and clothes; and in many other ways.

Characteristics of the Phylum. In some respects arthropods resemble other complexly organized animals. They display bilateral symmetry, a tubular enteron, and a coelom. The coelom, however, is reduced. It includes mainly just the cavity enclosed within the reproductive organs.

Arthropods, like annelids, are *distinctly* **segmented** *animals*. But unlike annelids, the arthropods, except for *Peripatus* and a few other primitive transitional forms, all display **jointed appendages.** Typically, one pair of jointed appendages is borne by each of the body segments; but among higher forms, especially insects, many of the appendages are missing.

The entire body of the arthropod is covered by a strong **chitinous exoskeleton,** which may or may not be hardened by a deposition of calcareous material. Such a complete encasement of the body does not allow for continuous growth. Consequently arthropods must shed the exoskeleton periodically. This process is called **ecdysis,** or **moulting.** After each moult the animal quickly swallows a large amount of water (or air) rapidly increasing the size of its body before the newly secreted exoskeleton becomes too hard.

In contrast to chordate animals, arthropods generally *do not possess any endoskeleton.* Also the **central nervous system** consists of a double chain of ganglia, which, except for the first pair (cerebral ganglia), lie *ventral to the digestive tract.* Typically there is a *heart* and frequently there are blood vessels leading to the principal organs. But the **circulatory system** is of the *open type.* The **hemolymph** passes through the tissue spaces and comes into direct contact with the cells. Aquatic Arthropoda (chiefly the Crustacea) possess **gills,** except for a few small species that respire directly through the body surfaces. But terrestrial forms have **tracheae** (insects, centipedes, and millipedes) or **book lungs** (spiders and other arachnids).

Arthropoda, compared with Annelida, tend to display a more distinct differentiation of the *principal body parts,* namely **head, thorax,** and **abdomen.** Several **fused segments** can usually be recognized in the head and thorax regions, although the segments of the abdomen tend to be separate. Among Crustacea and Arachnida the head and thorax are frequently fused, forming a body part called the **cephalothorax.**

The exoskeleton of the arthropod not only serves to cover and protect the soft internal structures, but also provides for the muscular movements of the animal. The successive rigid parts of the exoskeleton are hinged together by flexible joints and the muscles stretch from part to part, bridging the joints. Thus each part of the exoskeleton serves as a lever in effecting muscular movement and each joint serves as a fulcrum. Moreover, the arthropod exoskeleton, to which the muscles attach internally, stands in distinct contrast to the vertebrate endoskeleton, to which the muscles attach externally.

Classes of the Arthropoda. The natural groups into which this large phylum can be divided are:

Class 1. The **Crustacea** *(Lobsters, Shrimps, Barnacles, Crabs, etc.).* Typically these are aquatic Arthropoda with gills, two pairs of antennae, and at least five pairs of legs. Usually the body consists of a cephalothorax and abdomen (Fig. 32-30).

Class 2. The **Arachnida** *(Spiders, Ticks, Scorpions, Horseshoe Crabs, etc.).* These mainly terrestrial Arthropoda have four pairs of legs, no antennae, and a cephalothorax. Book lungs are the usual respiratory mechanism, although a few forms have gills and some have tracheae (Fig. 32-30).

Class 3. The **Insecta** *(Flies, Bugs, Beetles, Bees, Butterflies, etc.).* These terrestrial Arthropoda have three pairs of legs, only one pair of antennae, and (usually) two pairs of wings. A **tracheal** *system of air tubes* (p. 657) provides for respiration and typically the body displays a distinct head, thorax, and abdomen (Fig. 32-30).

Class 4. The **Chilopoda** *(The Centipedes).* These are elongate, flattened, terrestrial Arthropoda, with a distinct head, bearing one pair of antennae; there is no thorax and the body consists of at least fifteen segments (usually more), each (except the first) bearing *one pair* of seven-jointed walking legs. The appendage of the first body segment is highly modified, forming a formidable four-

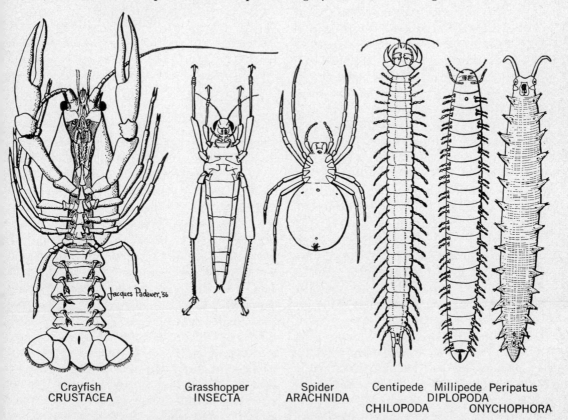

Crayfish CRUSTACEA — Grasshopper INSECTA — Spider ARACHNIDA — Centipede CHILOPODA — Millipede DIPLOPODA — Peripatus ONYCHOPHORA

Fig. 32-30. Phylum **Arthropoda:** a representative animal from each of the six **living** classes.

jointed **poison claw.** A tracheal respiratory system is present (Fig. 32-30).

Class 5. The **Diplopoda** *(the Millipedes, or "Thousand-legs").* These elongate, often brightly colored, terrestrial Arthropoda have a cylindrical body, consisting of a distinct head, with one pair of antennae; a short four-segmented thorax, with one pair of legs per segment; and a many-segmented abdomen, with *two pairs of legs per segment.* A tracheal system is present, but there are no poison claws (Fig. 32-30).

Class 6. The **Onychophora** *(Literally, Claw-Bearing).* This small group of primitive wormlike Arthropoda consists of only 70 scattered species, mainly of the genus *Peripatus* (Fig. 32-30). These forms do not have a distinct head or other body subdivisions; and the segmentation is not very evident, except for the serial arrangement of the stubby claw-bearing legs. The anterior end bears a pair of short antennae and small horny jaws; and the exoskeleton is relatively thin and weak. Respiration is through internal air tubes that seem to represent a primitive type of tracheal system. Cilia, which are absent in all other Arthropoda, are found in the gonoducts of *Peripatus.*

Peripatus and related forms are interesting because they seem to be surviving derivatives of an ancient pre-Cambrian stock that was transitional between the Annelida and Arthropoda. In the list of resemblances to the Annelida are the relative simplicity of the eyes and digestive tract; the presence of cilia and nephridia; and the poorly developed appendages. On the other hand, the dorsally placed heart, the tracheal tubes, the reduced coelomic cavity, and the fact that the jaws represent modified appendages are all features suggestive of Arthropoda.

Class 7. The **Trilobita.** The trilobites (Fig. 32-31) constitute a group of about 2000 **extinct marine species.** Trilobites reached a peak of abundance in the Cambrian and Devonian periods, but died out, mainly in the Carboniferous period. Some fossil specimens, including larval stages, are exceedingly well

Fig. 32-31. Trilobite fossil, from the Devonian period. Note the two longitudinal furrows that divide the body into three sections—one in the center and one on each side. (By permission, from *General Biology,* by Wells and Wells. McGraw-Hill Book Co., Inc.)

preserved and these reveal much of the original structure, internal as well as external.

As the name trilobite suggests, the body is divided by two longitudinal furrows into three lobes, one in the center and two at the sides (Fig. 32-30). There is a distinct head, bearing one pair of compound eyes (usually); one pair of slender antennae, and four pairs of biramous (two-branched) leglike appendages. A number (up to 29) of short separate segments are present in the thorax; but the abdominal segments are fused, forming a **caudal plate.** Each of the segments, except the last abdominal, bears a pair of bristle-fringed biramous appendages. The average size was about three inches, but one species attained a length of more than two feet. The best specimens found so far are from a deposit of Ordovician shale near Rome, New

York, and some of these have been suitable for sectioning and microscopic examination.

Invasion of the Land by Arthropods. The sea, of course, was the "primordial mother of life." In fact, the fossil record shows that no plants or animals succeeded in colonizing any land area until Silurian times. The record also shows that the first animals to display definite adaptations to land conditions were scorpionlike Arachnida that began to occupy the continental edges some 400 million years ago. In other words, the first land arthropods anticipated the first land vertebrates (Amphibia) by more than 60 million years. Furthermore, the Arthropoda are the *only invertebrate group* in which large numbers and a great diversity of terrestrial species have been evolved. A few Annelida, such as earthworms, and a few Mollusca, such as snails, are terrestrial, especially in damp environments; but among living Arthropoda, only the Crustacea are aquatic. In fact, a great majority of centipedes, millipedes, arachnids, and, above all, insects are very well-adapted terrestrial animals.

Arthropod Adaptations to Land Conditions. No organism can live if it loses too much water, and the exposure of a land animal to the drying effects of the atmosphere represents an ever-present hazard. Arthropods, however, are covered most completely by a chitinous exoskeleton that controls the loss of water from the soft internal living parts of the body. In fact, the chitinous, wax-laden exoskeleton of the arthropod stands on a par of efficiency with the integumentary coverings (skin, with scales, feathers, or hair) of various vertebrate animals in protecting the body, not only from desiccation, but also from various other injurious external factors. Moreover, a strong exoskeleton enables the animal to cope with gravitational force, which has a greater effect upon land where the buoyancy of the aquatic environment is lacking.

Respiration in land animals also presents a special problem. The respiratory surface, across which oxygen and carbon dioxide enter and leave the blood, cannot function properly if it becomes too dry. The book lungs and tracheal tubes of terrestrial arthropods, as well as the true lungs of terrestrial vertebrates, represent a deep insinking of the respiratory surfaces to a safely recessed position, where desiccation can scarcely occur. The **book lung,** essentially, consists of a number (usually around twenty) of thin, richly vascularized, leaflike plates, arranged like slightly separated pages in a book, and occupying an inpocketed chamber, usually in the anterior region of the abdomen. The **tracheal system,** on the other hand, consists of an elaborately branching system of air-bearing tubes. The finer (microscopic) tracheal branches permeate the tissues, carrying air to the immediate vicinity of the individual cells. The larger trunk-line **tracheae** communicate with the outside air through paired openings, the **spiracles,** which are present in each typical segment of the thorax and abdomen. Each tube of the system is kept from collapsing by spirally wound chitinous threads which reinforce the wall. A continuous ventilation of the tracheal system (or of the book-lung chamber) is effected by rhythmic expansions and contractions of the abdomen and thus new air keeps reaching the finer branches, where the cells take in oxygen and give off carbon dioxide. The tracheal system, particularly, is well adapted to meet the respiratory requirements of insects. The primitive circulatory system of these very active animals is not designed for carrying large amounts of oxygen, which are needed especially during periods when flight must be sustained.

A few terrestrial arthropods revert to the ancestral habit of depositing their eggs in an aquatic environment; but most lay eggs on or in the soil, or in other places more or less exposed to the drying effects of the atmosphere. Such eggs, typically, are covered by a tough moisture-proof chitinous shell, or integument, which represents an adaptation to terrestrial development. Many such animals, especially insects, resort to copulation. Thus fertilization occurs in the deep recesses of the female reproductive tract, before each egg becomes covered by its shell. Moreover, many insects possess special chambers, **seminal receptacles,** where the sperm derived from one copulation may survive for some weeks, fertilizing new batches of eggs as they reach maturity.

Among insects, which include a great majority of Arthropoda (and of any other animals, too), the development of wings extended the range enormously and led to tremendous diversification of the species (Table 32-1). The vertebrate type of wing, such as is displayed by birds and bats, represents a highly modified forelimb (Fig. 29-1), but this is not true of insect wings. The insect wing essentially represents an outfolding of the chitinous integument. It is cleverly hinged at the body junction and it is operated by an intricate set of striated muscle fibers, which are the fastest acting in all nature. Insect wings, however, are highly diversified as to form and function, as is indicated in Table 32-1.

Insect Societies. Most insects are nonsocial; that is, each individual shifts for itself. Males and females associate only for mating and the parents have little or no concern for the next generation, aside from laying the eggs. However, a few nonsocial forms (for example, earwigs, crickets, roaches) may guard the eggs and young.

Table 32-1—Familiar Orders of Insects

Name of Order	Mouth	Wings	Other Features
Orthoptera (roaches, grasshoppers, etc.)	Chewing mouth parts	Forewing, leathery; hindwing, delicate, folded; wings may be absent	Usually possess cerci, that is, vestigial appendages near posterior end of abdomen
Odonata (dragonflies)	Chewing mouth parts	Both wings filmy; not folded; nearly alike	Body and eyes large; no cerci
Hemiptera (true bugs)	Sucking mouth parts	First wing, leathery in front, membranous behind; second wing, membranous, folded	Piercing beak at anterior tip of head
Lepidoptera (moths, butterflies)	Sucking mouth parts	Both wings covered by delicate overlapping scales	Maxillae modified, forming a feeding proboscis
Diptera (true flies)	Sucking mouth parts	Forewings only	Have "balancer" (highly modified hindwing)
Coleoptera (beetles, weevils, etc.)	Chewing mouth parts	First wing, horny, veinless; second wing, delicate, folded	Large prothorax; reduced mesothorax
Hymenoptera (bees, ants, wasps, etc.)	Chewing or sucking mouth parts	Both wings filmy; sometimes no wings	Abdomen usually tapers to a slender waist, joining the thorax
Isoptera (termites)	Chewing mouth parts	Wingless except for sexual forms, which have four filmy wings	Nonsexual forms white or very pale; sexual forms darkly pigmented

True social colonies of considerable complexity have been developed by all termites and ants, and many bees and wasps. In a termite colony (Fig. 32-32) one large female, the **queen**, may live for several years, producing more than 5000 eggs each day. Meanwhile she is housed in a protected nest, under controlled conditions of temperature and humidity; fed by specialized, nonfertile **workers**; guarded by **soldiers**; and kept fertile by the **king**, a nonworking perfect male. Moreover, problems of food supply are handled on a cooperative community basis. The workers continually collect pollen, and other food and bring it to the nest.

The pastoral ants keep domesticated aphids ("ant-cows") from which they derive "milk" in the form of the honeydew secretions of the aphids; and "farmer ants" (*Atta*) cultivate crops of a selected species of fungus. When another colony is to be established, the new queen transports fungal spores for the planting of a new crop in a special pouchlike outgrowth of her mouth.

A **domestic honeybee** colony houses only one **queen** (diploid fertile female), a hundred or so **drones** (haploid fertile males) and thousands of **workers** (diploid sterile females). After mating, a queen may lay eggs that are either fertilized or unfertilized. Haploid male drones arise from the unfertilized eggs; but diploid females of various kinds can come from the fertilized eggs. A young female larva, fed for about six days on a

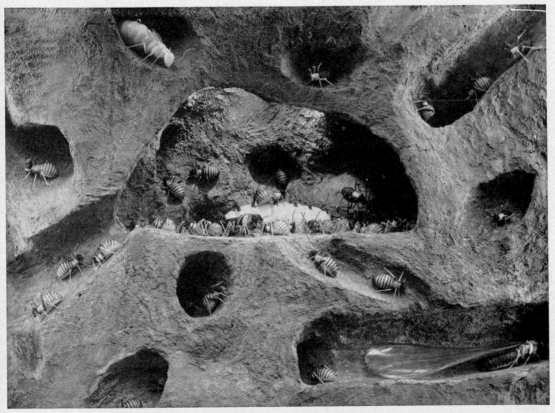

Fig. 32-32.   Royal cell of a termite colony. The queen, surrounded by workers, occupies the large central chamber. Note the king beside the left end of queen. Also note a soldier with "squirt gun" head (right, middle). The chambers and galleries of the nest are constructed of wood particles, cemented together. The winged individual (lower right) is ready to swarm, at which time males and females look alike. The large white individual (upper left) belongs to a supplementary reproductive caste. This termite (*Constrictotermes cavifrons*) is common in British Guiana. (Photo of a model, exhibited in the Schoelkopf Hall of Evolution, Buffalo Museum of Science.)

special mixture, called **royal jelly,** develops into a fertile female, which eventually may migrate and become the queen of a new colony. But if the female larva receives an ordinary mixture of nectar and pollen, she develops into a sterile worker. The youngest of the workers serve as **nurses,** preparing the brood chambers and feeding the larvae; the older ones are **"house workers,"** which clean and guard the hive, make wax for the honey cells, and supervise the storage of food; while the oldest workers are the **"field bees,"** responsible for gathering pollen, nectar, and water for the whole community. Probably the development of the different kinds and castes among socialized insects depends upon a delicate balance between chromosomal, nutritional, and hormonal factors. However, more research must be carried on before this balance can be defined in very precise terms.

Insect Behavior. There is a wealth of evidence that indicates that the behavior patterns of insects (and other invertebrates) are largely "instinctive." The behavior consists mainly of unconditioned (unlearned) responses, performed automatically in the same manner each generation—simply because the animal is born that way, or gets to be that way during the normal course of development (p. 468). Thus a certain kind of solitary wasp always builds a certain kind of nest even though this individual has never had the slightest contact with its parents or any other wasp; and there are many other examples demonstrating such behavior among various invertebrate species.

Despite the well-established fact that insect behavior is largely "instinctive," the extensive experiments and observations reported by the Austrian zoologist Karl von Frisch prove that the honeybee, at least, possesses some capacity to form conditioned reflexes. It thus can learn on the basis of experience. Von Frisch was able to condition worker bees to choose between cards of different colors and to substitute one color for another while seeking the sugar solutions that were used as bait. These studies also show that bees have a fairly elaborate system by which they communicate food information to other members of the colony. The **scout bee,** loaded with pollen or nectar, indicates the direction and distance of his find by performing a series of dancing movements as soon as he gets back to the hive. Dancing in small quick circles indicates that the food is nearby and can easily be found. But for distances greater than about 75 yards, the scout also gives the direction in terms of the position of the sun—by straight-line dances that intervene between the circles. Straight upward movements mean "go toward the sun"; straight downward, "away from the sun"; while various angles toward and away from the sun are given roughly by the angle of the runs, with reference to the vertical direction. Moreover, the communication system works even on cloudy days, since the eye of the bee is sensitive to ultraviolet light, which partly penetrates the clouds.

PHYLUM ECHINODERMATA

The **Echinodermata** constitute a *unique group of entirely marine* invertebrates. **Starfishes** (Fig. 32-33) are perhaps the most familiar representatives, but there are some 5000 other living species. These include the **sea urchins** (Fig. 32-33), **sea lilies** (Fig. 32-33), **sea cucumbers** (Fig. 32-33), and **brittle stars** (Fig. 32-33). Also fossil remnants of *many extinct species* have been found in formations dating from the Cambrian period. Many modern echinoderms are sedentary bottom dwellers; and no terrestrial species have been evolved.

Characteristics of the Phylum. Echinoderms are triploblastic, nonsegmented animals with a well-developed coelom and a mouth-to-anus digestive tract. However, the anus is often rudimentary and it may even be absent. Accordingly, egestion through the mouth is not uncommon, at least among adult echinoderms.

The name of the phylum (Gr., *echinos,* "hedgehog"; *derma,* "skin") refers to the unique structure of the body wall and skin.

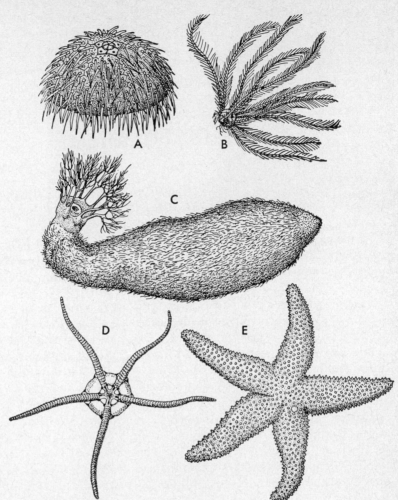

Fig. 32-33. Echinoderms, representing the five classes. A, a sea urchin, Class Echinoidea; B, a sea lilly, Class Crinoidea; C, a sea cucumber, Class Holothuroidea; D, a brittle star, Class Ophiuroidea; and E, a common starfish, Class Asteroidea. (From *General Zoology*, by Miller and Haub. Holt, Rinehart and Winston, Inc.)

Embedded in the body wall there is an **endoskeleton,** consisting of a number of hard calcareous plates, the **ossicles;** and projecting outward from the body there are many calcareous **spines.** Collectively the ossicles and spines, plus a system of interconnecting muscles and strands of connective tissue, give great strength to the body wall.

Usually the ossicles are about the size of very small pebbles, as in the common starfish, or they may be of microscopic size, as in the sea cucumbers. The spines also display considerable variation. Common sea urchins (Fig. 32-33) have strong pronglike spines, usually somewhat less than an inch long; but one semitropical genus (*Diadema*) has sharply

pointed poison spines that may extend more than nine inches out from the surface of the body. On the other hand, the spines of many echinoderms are slender and delicate, as in the sea cucumber (Fig. 32-33).

The symmetry of the echinoderms is another unique identifying feature. Superficially the adults display **radial symmetry,** a development that probably is related to the sedentary history of the group. The body always possesses a central part, the **central disc,** where the digestive tract is found. And surrounding the central disc there are five radially arranged body sections from which, in many species, more or less distinct **arms** (rays) project (Fig. 32-34).

Fig. 32-34. A common starfish (*Asterias forbesi*), lying upside down. Note the many tube feet, each tipped with a suction disc. Four rows of these feet protrude from the groove (ambulacral groove) that extends out into each arm, on the lower surface. Also note the many blunt spines that stud the body wall. (By permission from *Integrated Principles of Zoology*, by C. P. Hickman. C. V. Mosby Co.)

Perhaps more *fundamentally*, on the other hand, the echinoderms may be regarded as **bilaterally symmetrical** animals. All have a bilaterally symmetrical larval stage, and even in the adult there is a remnant of such symmetry in the placement of the **madreporite** (Fig. 32-35).

The **water vascular system** (Fig. 32-35) constitutes another unique feature of Echinodermata. This water-filled system of tubular channels, with muscular walls, connects with a sievelike structure, the **madreporite**, on the one hand, and with a large number of **tube feet** on the other (Fig. 32-35). The madreporite apparently serves to admit new water from the surrounding sea, if the system needs filling. The many tube feet cooperate in achieving a slow and clumsy sort of locomotion and in grasping food material. The tube feet extend outward through the body wall, entirely from the lower surface in the case of the starfish (Fig. 32-34) and related forms, but from other parts of the body, in other echinoderms.

The tube feet are highly extensible and retractible and each may be equipped at its end with a **suction pad**. When a foot contracts, much of its content of water is forced to flow back into other parts of the water vascular system but especially into the bulb, or **ampulla**, which lies directly above (Fig. 32-35). And conversely, when a tube foot is being extended, the ampulla and neighboring parts contract, forcing the water to flow

back into the lumen of the extending foot.

No structure remotely comparable to the echinoderm water vascular system is found anywhere else in nature. Apparently the system serves mainly for locomotion, but perhaps it also helps to carry respiratory gases and other substances. Obviously such a complex and highly specialized system is not well suited to the requirements of a land animal—which probably accounts for the fact that terrestrial Echinodermata have never been evolved.

The respiratory system among echinoderms does not reach a very high state of development. Many possess **dermal branchiae,** which are small hollow blisters, protruding slightly from the body wall near the bases of the spines. Each is filled with coelomic fluid that enters the vesicle through a narrow connection with the coelomic cavity. Thus oxygen can enter and carbon dioxide can leave the body fluid through the delicate walls of the branchiae. Other echinoderms display "respiratory trees," which protrude from the posterior end, and a few respire mainly through the walls of the tube feet.

Typically the central nervous system tends to follow the pattern of the water vascular system. A main nerve ring encircles the mouth and a radial nerve extends out from this ring into each of the body sections. Moreover, there is a system of fluid-filled tubes that lies in close contact with the various parts of the nervous system, but the functional im-

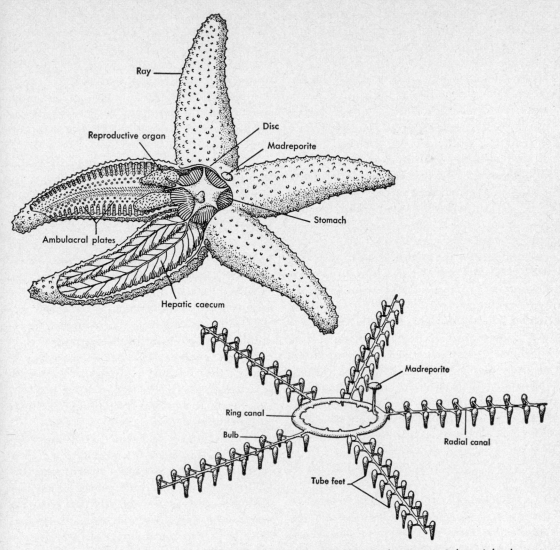

Fig. 32-35. Structure of the common starfish. *Above, left;* diagram of internal structures. *Below, right:* the water-vascular system. (From *General Zoology,* by Miller and Haub. Holt, Rinehart and Winston, Inc.)

portance of this **perihaemal system** has not been ascertained.

Classes of Echinodermata. The major natural subdivisions of the phylum are:

*Class 1. The **Asteroidea** (the Starfishes).* Body, star-shaped; arms, five, single or multiple, not sharply demarcated from the central disc; spines, short and blunt; two to four rows of tube feet, with suckers, extending along undersurface of each arm; distribution, Cambrian period to present time (Fig. 32-33).

*Class 2. The **Echinoidea** (the Sea Urchins,* *Sand Dollars, etc.).* Body, hemispherical, disclike or egg-shaped; no arms; ossicles interlinking and firmly sutured together; spines numerous, relatively long and movable; tube feet, numerous, with suckers; Ordovician period to present time (Fig. 32-33).

*Class 3. The **Holothuroidea** (the Sea Cucumbers).* Body, sausage-shaped; no arms or spines; ossicles, numerous, of microscopic size; mouth, usually surrounded by retractile tentacles; Cambrian period to present time (Fig. 32-33).

Class 4. The **Ophiuroidea** *(the Brittle Stars, etc.).* Body, small, round, distinctly demarcated; arms, five, slender, jointed, and flexible, used for active locomotion; tube feet, in two rows, without suckers, mainly sensory in function; no anus; Mississippian period to present time (Fig. 32-33).

Class 5. The **Crinoidea** *(the Sea Lilies).* Body, cup-shaped, called a calyx, attached to substratum, sometimes by an elongate stalk; five double arms, with numerous side branches, giving a fernlike appearance to the organism; tube feet, suckerless; no madreporite; spines, absent; Cambrian period to present time (Fig. 32-33).

Relationship to Other Phyla. Even the oldest echinoderm fossils, found in early Cambrian strata, clearly show most of the unique characteristics of the phylum. Consequently it is not possible to say precisely when these animals became separated as a distinct group. Echinoderm and chordate animals display several common features, particularly with reference to the embryonic (and larval) stages. In fact, many zoologists believe that Echinodermata and Chordata both evolved from the same stock (Fig. 29-11).

THE CHORDATA

Overwhelmingly this last great phylum of the Animal Kingdom is dominated by the **Vertebrata.** These "back-boned animals" include: all fish, amphibians, reptiles, birds, and mammals—plus some other less familiar forms. Despite their abundance and diversity, however, the Vertebrata are not ranked as an independent phylum. Rather they constitute the subphylum Vertebrata in the phylum Chordata. But the other chordate groups are represented by only a few relatively obscure and unfamiliar animals, namely, the acorn worms, tunicates, and lancelets (see below).

Main Characteristics of the Phylum Chordata. As was stated previously (p. 281), chordate animals display *three unique features.*

1. All chordates develop a **notochord.** This nonsegmented flexible, rodlike structure lies embedded in the body wall along the dorsal midline, and serves as a **functional endoskeleton** in lower Chordata (Fig. 15-10). But in the higher Chordata (Vertebrata), the notochord appears only transiently in the embryo. It is replaced more or less completely in the adult by a **permanent segmented axial skeleton,** the vertebral column ("backbone").

2. All chordates possess a **dorsally placed tubular nerve cord** (Fig. 15-10). This is the **central nervous system.** Usually it exhibits an anterior swollen part, the **brain,** and a slenderer posterior part, the **spinal cord.**

3. All chordates have **pharyngeal gill channels** (Fig. 15-10). Among lower Chordata (up through the fishes) these contain functional gills; but among higher forms (amphibians, reptiles, birds, and mammals) the gill slits are transient embryonic structures that become highly modified in the adult animal.

Other Characteristics. Like other higher forms, chordates are triploblastic, bilaterally symmetrical, segmented animals, with a complete tubular digestive tract and an extensive well-defined coelomic cavity. Typically they have a well-developed **closed circulatory system.** The **heart** occupies an anterior ventral position, whereas the main distributing vessel lies dorsally and conducts the blood in a posterior direction. Generally speaking, the respiratory, excretory, and reproductive organs are highly developed and these systems exhibit many homologies, at least throughout all Vertebrata.

The Lower Chordata: Chordates without "Backbones." In addition to the **Vertebrata,** there are three other **subphyla** in the phylum Chordata. These are: (1) the **Hemichordata,** (2) the **Urochordata,** and (3) the **Cephalochordata.** All these lower groups are small and all consist entirely of marine species possessing *no jaws* and *no paired appendages.* Nevertheless, the lower chordates are very interesting. They provide almost the only clues to the difficult problem of how vertebate animals arose. The later fossil record is quite plain in regard to how the different vertebrates evolved and how the vertebrate classes are related to each other. But the earlier record is very poor. Apparently early chordates did not possess skeletal parts suitable for fossilization and we are left to speculate upon other clues including the study of the few surviving lower chordate forms.

Subphylum 1: The Hemichordata. The **acorn worms,** or **tongue worms** (Fig. 32-36), are the principal representatives of the **Hemichordata.** Typically, such animals possess a stiff tough **proboscis** (for burrowing), behind which lie an acorn-shaped **collar** and an elongate **body** (Fig. 32-36). **Pharyngeal gill slits** are present in the anterior section of the body, but the notochord is short, confined to the proboscis region and not exactly similar, structurally, to the notochords of other chor-

dates. Moreover, there is a ventral nerve cord in addition to the dorsal one; and only the anterior section of the dorsal nerve cord is hollow. The larval stages of Echinodermata and Hemichordata are very closely similar. This may indicate origin from a common early stock.

Subphylum 2: The Urochordata. The **Tunicata** (Fig. 32-37), which collectively comprise the **Urochordata,** can be recognized as Chordata only during the larval stages. The larval tunicate (Fig. 32-37) is an active swimmer, which tends to resemble a good-sized tadpole. Sectioned specimens display a dorsally placed, hollow nervous system, fairly distinct gill slits, and a notochord. The notochord is typical, except that it lies mainly in the tail region. As adults, however, most tunicates become attached to the bottom, develop a tough muscular mantle or tunic around the body, and lose all resemblance to other Chordata, except that gill slits do persist.

Subphylum 3: The Cephalochordata. These tiny fishlike chordates seldom reach a length exceeding three inches. One common group is called **lancelets** because of the slender, tapered form (Fig. 32-38). For many years they were also called **Amphioxus,** but more recently the genus name **Branchiostoma** has received priority. Lancelets are quite widely distributed in tropical and semitropical waters, along the Atlantic and Pacific coasts, and in the Mediterranean area; and in one locality, near Amoy on the southern coast of China, they are caught by the ton and used as food.

As may be seen in Figure 15-10, the lancelet shows the three unique chordate features in unequivocal fashion. The dorsal hollow nervous system, gill slits, and notochord all are typical, and all persist as functional structures in the adult animal. Moreover, these animals display other features that indicate a very close relationship to Vertebrata. These include: (1) a segmental arrangement of the muscles, (2) a segmental arrangement of the spinal nerves, each with a dorsal and ventral

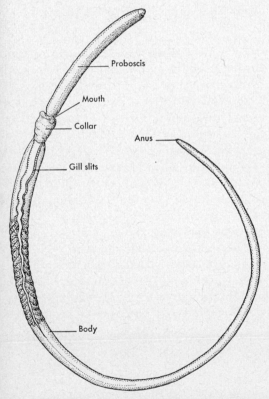

Proboscis

Mouth

Collar

Anus

Gill slits

Body

Fig. 32-36. A hemichordate animal: the acorn worm (tongue worm), *Dolichoglossus*. Perhaps the extinct stock from which the hemichordates arose likewise gave rise to vertebrates. (From *General Zoology*, by Miller and Haub. Holt, Rinehart and Winston, Inc.)

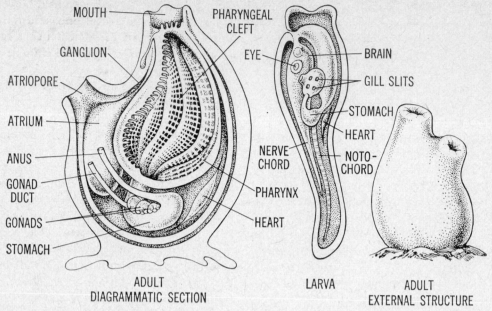

MOUTH
PHARYNGEAL CLEFT
GANGLION
EYE
BRAIN
ATRIOPORE
GILL SLITS
ATRIUM
STOMACH
HEART
ANUS
NERVE CHORD
NOTO-CHORD
GONAD DUCT
PHARYNX
GONADS
HEART
STOMACH

ADULT
DIAGRAMMATIC SECTION
LARVA
ADULT
EXTERNAL STRUCTURE

Fig. 32-37. One of the urochordates (Tunicata). In the larval stage, but not in the adult, this animal appears to be a typical chordate (see text).

root, (3) the origin of the main digestive gland as an outgrowth from the enteron, and (4) the position of the major blood vessels. All in all, therefore, it seems likely that the surviving Cephalochordata originated from the same ancestral stock as did the Vertebrata and that they give the best hints as to what the ancestral vertebrate stock was like.

Subphylum 4: The Vertebrata. Vertebrates (Fig. 32-39) were late starters in evolution. In fact, none of the familiar modern kinds left fossil remnants that can be dated earlier than the Devonian period. Since then, however, their biological success has been impressive. In the aquatic environment, which many vertebrates have not abandoned, the **cartilaginous** and **bony fishes** gave rise to many widely distributed dominant species. But on land the success has been even more spectacular. Many adult **Amphibia** are well-adapted terrestrial species, even though they almost always return to the water to lay their eggs and to spend their embryonic and larval (tadpole) stages.

Vertebrate Characteristics. First and foremost, of course, vertebrates are chordate animals, and all display the classic chordate features. The notochord, however, which can easily be identified in the embryo, is always replaced either partially or completely by a **segmented axial skeleton,** the **vertebral column.** The notochordal material becomes invaded by cartilage- or bone-forming cells, which deposit the new skeletal material in

Fig. 32-38. *Amphioxus.* This primitive cephalochordate animal provides some clues to the problem of how vertebrates were evolved. (By permission from *Integrated Principles of Zoology,* by C. P. Hickman. C. V. Mosby Co.)

Fig. 32-39. The seven vertebrate classes. A, Cyclostomata, a lamprey; B, Chondrichthyes, shark; C, Osteichthyes, sunfish; D, Reptilia, alligator; E, Aves, owl; F, Mammalia, deer; G, Amphibia, frog. (A, C, E, and F by courtesy of Ohio Division of Wildlife Service; D, from Ward's Natural Science Establishment; and G, from Edward S. Thomas. Composite from *General Zoology*, by Miller and Haub. Holt, Rinehart and Winston, Inc.)

blocks, or segments, the **vertebrae.** Each vertebra, typically, displays an archlike section, the **neural arch,** which grows dorsally around the nerve cord. Thus all the vertebrae together form a tunnellike protection for the spinal cord. Moreover, a protective encasement, the **cranium,** composed of either cartilage or bone, always develops around the anterior larger part of the nerve cord, which later becomes the **brain.** In fact, some zoologists prefer to designate vertebrate animals as **Craniata.**

All organs and organ systems throughout the vertebrate group display a progressive series of homologies. (1) The jaws, which are present in all except the lowest group (p. 668), are always derived from skeletal pieces present in the gill arches (between the gill slits). (2) The digestive tract has two major glands, the **liver** and **pancreas,** which arise as outgrowths from the intestinal part of the enteron. (3) The skin, or **integument,** always has a **stratified epithelium,** and always consists of both ectoderm (the **epidermis**) and mesoderm (**dermis**). (4) Except for the lower forms, which have ten, Vertebrata have twelve pairs of *cranial nerves,* each with a characteristic pattern of connections with the various receptors and effectors in the head region, and there is *one pair of double-rooted* **spinal nerves** for each segment of the body. (5) The heart is always derived from a major blood vessel in the anterior ventral part of the body and shows a progressive development from the two-chambered structure of the fish to the three- and four-chambered form of the higher groups. (6) The arterial system displays a number of **aortic arches** (Fig. 17-14), leading from the ventral to the dorsal aorta. (7) The aortic arches vary from five to six pairs in fish down to one single arch in birds and mammals. (8) Erythrocytes, bearing hemoglobin, are always present in the blood. (9) The lungs, when present, originate as outgrowths from the pharynx. (10) Two pairs of jointed appendages, whether fins, wings, or legs, are highly characteristic, and the appendages, which are all homologous as to

their skeletal structure (Fig. 29-1), are suspended to the axial skeleton by girdles, the **pectoral girdle** anteriorly, and the **pelvic girdle** posteriorly. (11) The excretory organs and gonads arise in the dorsal region of the coelomic cavity and show a progressive series of modifications from lower to higher groups. (12) The endocrine glands and their manner of origin are similar throughout. In fact, homologies among Vertebrata are almost limitless, if all phases of the comparative anatomy and embryology are explored completely.

Classes of Vertebrata. (Fig. 32-39). Living vertebrates usually are subdivided into seven groups: Class 1: The **Cyclostomata** (literally, "round-mouthed"); Class 2: The **Chondrichthyes** (literally, "cartilaginous fish"); Class 3: The **Osteichthyes** (literally, "bony fish"); Class 4: The **Amphibia** (literally, "double-lived"); Class 5: The **Reptilia** (reptiles); Class 6: The **Aves** (birds); and Class 7: The **Mammalia** (mammals). Also there are two well-established *extinct classes:* (1) the **ancient jawless fishes** (*Ostracodermi*), which did not have any jaws and usually possessed a heavy armor of large fused scales, covering the head and front part of the body; and (2) the **ancient jawed fish** (*Placodermi*), which had very primitive, incomplete jaws and (usually) a lighter armor composed of smaller scales.

The Cyclostomata (lampreys, hagfishes, and slime eels). These are the most primitive of living Vertebrata. All are small (under three feet long), eellike, aquatic animals (Fig. 32-39). Cyclostomates are unique among living vertebrates because they do not possess any jaws. Moreover, the notochord persists in the adult as a functional skeletal structure; that is, the segmented vertebral column is represented only by a series of cartilaginous **neural arches** protecting the spinal cord. There are no scales, paired fins, or skeletal girdles. Frequently the **Cyclostomata** and **Ostracodermi** are grouped together in a separate category, the **Agnatha** (literally, "without jaws").

Probably the most familiar of the cyclostomes are the lampreys (Fig. 32-39). Unlike other vertebrates, these animals are parasitic. The mouth lies at the center of a circular sucker, which enables the animal to attach itself to a passing fish. Also the mouth is equipped with a sharp-toothed tongue. This bores through the skin of the fish, allowing the lamprey to suck out blood and other body fluids. Then the parasite detaches itself and seeks another temporary host. Thus large numbers of fish may be damaged or even killed, if the lamprey population is abundant. Recently, the lampreys of the Great Lakes of North America have become a serious menace to the fishing industry, especially with reference to the lake trout, a fish of considerable economic value. Previously, there were no lampreys in the Great Lakes, but a marine species (*Petromyzon marinus*) gained entrance via the Welland Canal, an artificially constructed waterway.

The Chondrichthyes. Today the **cartilaginous fish** are represented mainly by the *sharks* (Fig. 32-39), *dogfishes,* and *rays* (skates). However, the group can be traced back to Silurian times when it included many forms long since extinct. All are oceanic and, except for the rays, which are bottom dwellers, all are fast-swimming, voracious predators. One shark, the **whale shark,** has the distinction of being the largest *true* fish, reaching a length of more than 50 feet. Some of the rays (Fig. 24-11) possess high-voltage electric organs with which they stun their prey.

The mouth of the cartilaginous fish displays definite *jaws,* hinged to the cranium and derived from the gill arches; and usually the mouth is located ventrally, some distance behind the anterior end of the animal. The entire skeleton, including the jaws, cranium, vertebrae, and pieces supporting the *paired fins* and gill arches, is composed of **cartilage;** that is, no true bone (p. 289) is present. However, sometimes the cartilage may be partially calcified. Remnants of the notochord are found in and between the vertebrae.

The skin of the typical cartilaginous fish is clothed by a large number of small but uniquely formed, sharply pointed scales, called **placoid scales.** These are minute replicas of the larger *teeth,* many rows of which are found in the anterior part of the mouth cavity of the shark and other forms. **Placoid scales** appear to be homologous to the teeth of higher vertebrates generally, *including man.* Externally each displays a layer of dense hard material, which chemically and histologically is indistinguishable from *enamel* (Fig. 16-14). Then there is a layer of dentine, which encloses a *pulp cavity,* containing a nerve branch, blood vessels, and other soft tissues. Moreover, the fossil record, which favors the preservation of teeth and other hard parts, provides abundant evidence that the teeth of higher vertebrates have been evolved from the placoid scales of lower forms.

The cartilaginous fish (also called *Elasmobranchi*) possess another distinctive feature. All have a complex spiral infolding of the intestinal wall. This *spiral valve* serves to increase the absorbing capacity of the digestive tract.

The Osteichthyes. These familiar bony fishes inhabit salt and fresh waters in tremendous abundance and variety (Fig. 32-39).

Typically the skeleton is composed mainly of true bone (p. 289), although in the embryo, following the notochordal stage, the pattern of the adult skeleton is first laid down in cartilage, as in higher Vertebrata generally. Well-developed *hinged jaws* support the anteriorly placed mouth; the cranium in most forms is very completely ossified; the paired fins have a bony skeleton and are suspended from the vertebral column by girdles. Remnants of the notochord are found in and between the segments of the vertebral column. The scales are of several kinds, but none of the bony fish has placoid scales.

Many bony fish have *swim bladders,* which enable them to regulate their buoyancy in accordance with the depth at which they are swimming. In one group (the **Dipnoi,** or **lung fishes**) the swim bladder retains a tubu-

Fig. 32-40. A lung fish (*Dipnoi*) being removed from cake of mud in which it was shipped from Africa. (Copyright, General Biological Supply House, Inc.)

lar connection with the pharynx and displays a lunglike structure. Such "lungs," in fact, are able to carry on respiration during periods when these creatures are left stranded in mud at the bottom of a dried-up pond or lake (Fig. 32-40).

One virtually extinct group of bony fish (the **Crossopterygii,** or *lobe-finned fishes*) are of particular interest because they gave rise to the Amphibia. These fish tend to resemble

Amphibia, especially as to the pattern of the skull bones, the arrangement of the fin bones, and the structure of the teeth. For many years, the *lobe-finned* fish were considered to be completely extinct. But in 1938, off the coast of South Africa, a five-foot coelacanth (one of the crossopterygian orders) was caught at a depth of about 250 feet by a commercial trawling vessel. And since then the fishermen of that general region, stimulated by generous rewards offered by museums, have succeeded in catching three or four more specimens (Fig. 32-41).

The Amphibia. Three groups of modern Amphibia have been evolved: (1) the **Urodela**—salamanders, newts, mud puppies, and other Amphibia having a distinct tail; (2) the **Anura**—frogs (Fig. 32-39), toads, and other forms that *do not have tails;* and (3) the **Apoda,** a very small group of limbless, burrowing Amphibia, with elongate cylindrical, wormlike bodies.

The ancient Amphibia became extremely abundant during the Permian and Triassic periods. These early forms, in fact, were the first vertebrates to invade the land environment. The Amphibia, accordingly, display a

Fig. 32-41. Model of *Latimeria*, the only surviving representative of the ancient lobe-finned fishes. These crossopterygians, which were very abundant 75 million years ago, were believed to be extinct, until quite recently. Since 1938, however, several specimens of this fish have been caught in deep water off the coast of South Africa. (Courtesy of the American Museum of Natural History, New York.)

limited or transitional sort of terrestrial adaptation. Except for a few, like the midwife toad, which carries its eggs and young embedded in the skin of the female, all amphibians return to the water to lay their eggs and all spend the embryonic and larval stages of their life in the aquatic environment. All have relatively simple lungs; and most carry on a supplemental respiration through the skin, which typically is moist and devoid of scales. On dry land, such a skin permits considerable water to be lost and, except for toads and a few other forms having a cornified skin, most amphibians frequently return to some pond or lake to reabsorb more water.

Typically, the amphibian possesses two pairs of legs, each with four or five toes (webbed in the hind limb). A pair of nasal passages leads from the outside into the mouth cavity. The skeleton is largely bony and there is little or no residual notochordal material in the adult. The heart displays three chambers (two auricles and one ventricle) and usually only one pair of aortic arches is represented in the systemic circulation. Typically the mouth has numerous fine teeth and a protrusible tongue.

The earliest amphibian fossils are found in formations of the Devonian period, a time when periodic droughts prevailed. These ancient Amphibia resembled some of the **lobe-finned fishes.** These fish had lunglike swim bladders, which could be used for aerial respiration, and limblike fins, which enabled them to clamber overland in search of a deeper pool, when a shallower one dried up. On the other hand, another group of ancient Amphibia had a crocodilelike form, large complexly ridged teeth, and a body armored with hard dermal plates, and probably these **Labyrinthodonta** represent the stock from which the reptiles (and hence all higher Vertebrata) took origin.

The Reptiles. Modern reptiles, although numerous and varied, occupy a relatively minor position in comparison with other vertebrates. But during the Mesozoic era, which often is called the Age of the Reptiles, they were the dominant animals. They ranged in size from small lizards to gigantic **dinosaurs.** For example, *Diplodocus* (Fig. 29-8) reached a length of 90 feet and weighed about 30 tons. The ancient reptiles, moreover, usurped almost every type of land habitat, from the lowlands, whether swampy or arid, to the dry highlands; and some, even though air-breathing, lived in the ocean; and a few, the **pterodactyls,** took to the air.

The earliest reptile fossils, found in late formations of the Carboniferous period, are scarcely distinguishable from Amphibia. By the end of the Triassic period, however, fourteen major reptilian orders had evolved. Ten of these became extinct by the end of the Cretaceous period; but the other four gave rise to the four now living groups. These are as follows: (1) turtles, tortoises, and similar forms (order **Chelonia**); (2) crocodiles and alligators (order **Crocodilia**); (3) snakes, lizards, and similar forms (order **Squamata**); and (4) a very primitive type, represented solely by the lizard-type **tuatara** of New Zealand, which has a well-developed median eye and does not have any copulatory organ (order **Rhynchocephalia**).

The success of the reptiles, particularly with reference to their ability to occupy dry areas on the land, derives from a combination of several features. The body is protected by a thick cornified skin, superimposed upon which, usually, there are a number of closely fitting scales, or **scutes.** Usually there are two pairs of limbs, each equipped with five clawed toes, suitable for running, climbing, or crawling. However, in aquatic forms, the limbs are paddlelike; in some extinct reptiles they were wings; and in snakes and some lizards they are vestigial or absent. The lungs and the pulmonary circulation are well developed. The heart is four-chambered, and although the separation of right and left ventricles is not complete (except in the Crocodilia), very little mixing of aerated and unaerated blood occurs (p. 326). The cranium, vertebral column, girdles, and appendicular parts of the skeleton are very well ossified. Copulatory organs have been developed so that fertilization is generally internal. And last but not least, reptilian eggs can develop in dry localities on land. Typically, each is covered by a tough moisture-proofed shell and richly supplied with yolk. Moreover, the embryo possesses an efficient set of extraembryonic membranes (p. 389) with which it meets its respiratory, excretory, and other nutritive needs during development.

The fossil and other evidence strongly indicates that both birds and mammals originated from reptilian stocks during the Triassic period. Fossils of ancient birds, however, are relatively scarce and the bridge to the ancient birdlike reptiles (thecodonts) is not complete.

The Birds: Class Aves. *Feathers,* which represent highly modified reptilian scales, are unique possessions of the birds. All birds have them and no other feathered creature has ever appeared upon the evolutionary scene. Moreover, these light, plane-surfaced integumental structures have played a dominant role in determining the biological success of the many species of modern birds.

The feathered wings and tail of the typical bird are highly efficient as flying mechanisms; and the ability of birds to fly and to migrate long distances has enormously extended and diversified the range of habitats available to the numerous and highly varied species. Moreover, the feathered skin of the bird is even more effective than the hairy skin of the mammal in providing the body with a **thermal insulation.** Such an insulation makes it possible for the birds (and mammals) to maintain a "constant" body temperature (with very slight variation) in the range of 35° to 40° C, which is well above the usual environmental temperature. The **homoiothermic animals** (p. 582), consequently, are able to maintain their metabolic activities at a high pitch of efficiency despite climate and season. They can "stay in business" winter and summer, even in truly arctic regions.

This is in sharp contrast to all other animals, including lower vertebrates, in which the body temperature varies according to the environment. Such **poikilothermic** animals may be very active under warm conditions, but they tend to become sluggish when it gets colder. And finally, most poikilotherms are forced to go into a dormant (hibernating) state if the temperature falls to a critical degree (usually in the range between 0° and 10° C).

In addition to *feathers* and to forelimbs that are modified into wings, birds display some other distinctive characteristics. These, all in all, give birds, compared to reptiles, a higher status. The typically four-toed hindlimbs are adapted for perching, walking, or running; or they may be webbed for swimming. The skeleton is light, but strong and fully ossified. The mouth is equipped with a horny projecting *beak,* but *teeth are lacking,* except in a few ancient species, all extinct. The pelvic girdle, although open ventrally, is firmly attached dorsally to a long series of the vertebrae, and the large sternum possesses a prominent *keel,* from which the powerful wing muscles take origin. The heart is four-chambered with completely separate right and left ventricles, and the persistent **aortic arch,** which becomes the main systemic artery, is on the *right side,* rather than on the left (as in mammals). The lungs are compact and efficient. However, respiration is augmented by a number of *air sacs,* which originate from the lungs and extend out into the spaces between the other organs and even, to some extent, into the bones. The "voice box" is not a single larynx (modified upper part of the trachea) but rather a double structure, the **syrinx,** situated at the fork where the bronchi take origin from the trachea. Fertilization is internal; the eggs are heavily yolked and covered with a calcareous shell; and well-developed embryonic membranes (amnion, chorion, allantois, and yolk sac) provide for the nutritional necessities during development.

Ornithology (Gr. *ornes,* "bird") has always been a popular study. Birds are everywhere and the beauty of their colors and songs and the diversity of their behavior provide an endless fascination. Bird migrations, particularly, have received intensive study, but still they are not completely understood. Some birds, like the quail, are strictly local, while others, like the robin, migrate just a few hundred miles, toward the tropics in the fall and in the opposite direction in the spring. But the arctic tern annually migrates back and forth over a distance of more than 20,000 miles from Alaska to Patagonia. Just how it is guided between its winter and summer quarters is still quite problematical.

The Mammals. If the Mesozoic era can be regarded as the Age of Reptiles, certainly the Cenozoic deserves to be called the Age of Mammals. The oldest mammalian fossils were formed much earlier, in early Triassic formations. These indicate that mammals originated from an ancient reptilian group, the **Therapsida.** Slowly the mammals increased in abundance and diversity, reaching a climax toward the end of the Tertiary period. Subsequently they have shown a small decline but today they are still dominant among land animals. The bony structure of the mammal appears to have been well adapted to fossilization and the lines of connection between the modern and the ancient mammals are quite clear.

Mammals are distinguished by their hairy skin and by mammary glands that produce milk in the female. Typically also there are sebaceous and perspiration glands in the skin, and generally the teeth are of three kinds—incisors, canines, and molars (p. 299). All higher mammals also possess a **placenta** (p. 389). This temporary reproductive organ, in which the capillary circulations of mother and embryo lie in intimate juxtaposition, permits the mother to nourish the embryo and to keep it in the uterus until it reaches a relatively advanced state of development. However, a few primitive mammals (**Monotremata**) still lay eggs; and another small group (**Marsupialia**), also lacking a placenta,

deliver the young from the uterus while they are still exceedingly immature (Fig. 32-42).

Only mammals have a diaphragm (p. 297) separating the abdominal from the thoracic and pericardial cavities; and the mammalian voice box is a single structure, the **larynx,** in contrast to its avian counterpart, the double **syrinx.**

Mammals resemble birds in that they are **homoiothermic** and because they have a four-chambered heart, which does not permit any mixing of aerated and nonaerated blood. However, in mammals the main systemic artery (aorta) is derived from a **left aortic arch** of the embryo, rather than from a *right* one, as it is in birds.

Typically the mammal has four limbs, with five or less clawed, hoofed, or nailed toes, although the hindlimbs are vestigial or absent in a few aquatic forms (for example, whales). Usually the limbs are adapted for walking, running, or climbing. However, a few forms have limbs modified for burrowing (moles), for swimming (seals), or for flying (bats).

Modern mammals occur in three main groups: (1) the **Prototheria** (egg-laying mammals); (2) **Metatheria** (pouched mammals); and (3) **Eutheria** (placental mammals).

THE PROTOTHERIA, OR MONOTREMATA. These are represented solely by the duck-billed platypus (Fig. 21-13) and a very few species of spiny anteaters, all from Australia and neighboring islands. All are very primitive forms, which have retained the egg-laying habits of their reptilian ancestors. The very small, "semiembryonic" young, on hatching from the eggs, feed upon milk lapped up from numerous scattered mammary glands present on the belly of the mother.

THE METATHERIA. These mammals are best represented by marsupials, such as the kangaroo. Marsupials are considerably less primitive than monotremes, but still they *do not possess a placenta.* Fertilization is internal, but the embryos are kept *in utero* for only a short time. Upon delivery the very

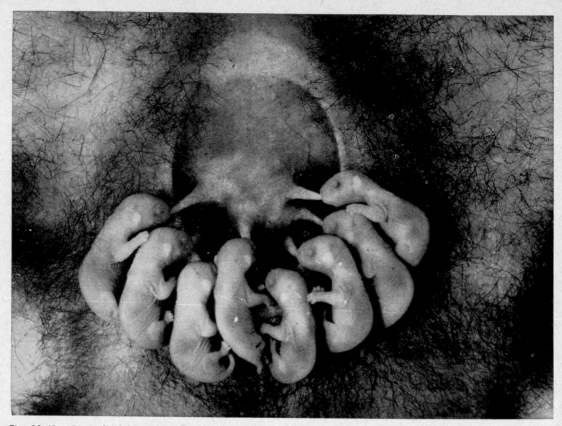

Fig. 32-42. Recently delivered young of an opossum, gently removed from the marsupial pouch of the mother without disturbing their attachment to the mammary nipples. Marsupials, lacking a placenta, deliver the young in a very immature and helpless state. (Copyright, General Biological Supply House, Inc.)

small, incompletely developed, helpless young are placed in the **marsupium,** a pouchlike infolding of skin on the mother's belly. Here they establish an oral connection with the nipples of the mammary glands (Fig. 32-42). In the marsupium the young are carried, nurtured, and protected until they develop into active animals almost ready to fend for themselves.

Monotremes and all marsupials, except the opossum, occur naturally only in the Australian region. Here, however, the marsupials particularly have achieved considerable abundance and diversity. In Australia one finds not only kangaroos, wombats, and wallabies, but also marsupial "cats," "mice," "shrews," "moles," "bears," and even a pouched species resembling the wolf. Appar-

ently these primitive mammals, which once inhabited many regions of the ancient world, escaped extinction in Australia because this large island became isolated from the mainland. The isolation occurred quite early, before the **higher placentate** types had reached Australia. Consequently the evolving marsupials of Australia, unlike those of other regions, were not swamped out by competition from increasing hordes of fitter (placentate) mammals.

THE EUTHERIA, OR PLACENTAL MAMMALS. These higher forms, having a placenta, are able to carry and nurture the embryos *in utero* and to postpone delivery until the young have developed to a relatively advanced state. Sometimes the offspring are able almost immediately to run (horses), climb (monkeys), or swim (whales); but in other species, such as man, the newborn babies must develop even further before they can begin to fend for themselves.

Unquestionably man and many other placentate mammals represent dominant animals in the world of today. There are, to be sure, only about 5000 species, but these are diversely adapted to many sorts of environment (Table 32-2). Moreover, various placentates have had tremendous impact upon man's life, starting long before the dawn of civilization, when game mammals provided primitive man with much of his food and clothing. And in civilized times, man's domesticated mammals alone have been of incalculable importance. Without cattle, sheep, dogs, pigs, horses, donkeys, oxen, llamas, yaks, elephants, and so on—as providers of meat, milk, leather, clothes, and endless other things, including just brute strength for the bearing of burdens—the economic basis of modern civilization would have been very much more restricted.

The Eutheria, or placental mammals, are widely distributed in nature and they include many species that are very familiar and important. In fact, these animals are so abundant and diverse that only the briefest survey of the principal types can be given here (Table 32-2).

Early in the first epoch of the Tertiary period a number of placental mammals quite different from those of today began to appear. But these **archaic placentates** did not survive much beyond the epoch. Their place was quickly taken by a rising tide of modern placentates; and by the end of the fourth epoch (Miocene) all our present-day types, plus some others that did not endure, had been evolved. The earliest primate (Table 32-2) fossils, apparently, came from lemurlike creatures that lived concurrently with the archaic placentates. However, it was not until the third (Oligocene) epoch of the Tertiary that Anthropoidea began to appear; and it seems fairly certain that no member of the genus *Homo* appeared until the Pleistocene epoch of the Quaternary period, about half a million years ago.

Table 32-2—Some Principal Orders of the Eutheria (Placental Mammals)

Order	Common Kinds	Distinguishing Features
Insectivora	Moles, shrews, hedgehogs	Small size; long tapered snout; usually 5-toed; show primitive structures suggestive of the earliest placental mammals; one kind of shrew weighs less than $\frac{1}{2}$ ounce; in moles the eyes are covered, and the feet are spadelike, for tunneling under the earth.
Chiroptera	Bats	Small mouselike mammals, capable of true flight; forelimbs (sometimes hindlimbs also) modified, forming leathery wings; suck blood or eat insects or fruit; flight guided in darkness by echoes of supersonic (to other animals) squeaks—a sort of radar system.
Rodentia	Rats, mice, squirrels, beavers, guinea pigs, chinchillas, etc.	Relatively small gnawing mammals with exposed continuously growing incisor teeth; no canines and well-developed molars; usually with 5-toed clawed feet.

Table 32-2—Some Principal Orders of the Eutheria (Placental Mammals)—Continued

Order	Common Kinds	Distinguishing Features
Edentata	Armadillos, scaly anteaters, sloths	Teeth absent or almost absent, that is, reduced to enamelless vestiges of the molars; often with elongate protrusible tongue (anteaters) or long curved claws (sloths).
Carnivora	Lions, panthers, cats, dogs, foxes, wolves, minks, weasels, skunks, seals, walruses, etc.	Small to fairly large flesh-eating mammals with small incisors, large fanglike canines, and sharp molars; legs highly mobile; usually with five clawed toes.
Ungulata	Group 1. Cattle, sheep, pigs, deer, giraffes, etc. Group 2. Horses, zebras, tapirs, rhinoceroses, etc.	Fairly large hoofed mammals of herbivorous habit; incisors and molars well developed; often fast running, by virtue of elongation of one or more of the toes; in Group 1 (Artiodactyla), the toes are of even number (2–4); in Group 2 (Perissodactyla), the toes are of odd number (1–3).
Proboscidea	Elephants	Generally massive mammals with nose and upper lip modified greatly, forming a long, flexible, muscular proboscis, or trunk; skin thick (pachydermatous), loose, and sparsely provided with hair; two of upper incisors elongated into tusks; heavy molars with deeply ridged grinding surface; the gestation period lasts about 20 months; young weigh about 20 pounds at birth; maximum recorded individual age, about 50 years.
Cetacea	Whales, dolphins, and porpoises	Marine mammals sometimes of great size; forelimbs finlike swimming organs, hindlimbs absent or reduced to vestigial internal remnants; body streamlined, with an extra thick thermal insulation of fatty tissue (blubber); include the largest known animal, the sulfur-bottomed whale, which reaches a length exceeding 100 feet and a weight exceeding 150 tons.
Primates	Lemurs, monkeys, apes, and man	Terrestrial mammals, frequently of arboreal habit; limbs elongate; forelimbs with well-developed five-digited hands, the innermost digit being apposable for grasping and climbing; nails flat or cupped; brain and eyes highly developed; eyes directed forward; usually producing just one offspring with each gestation.

TEST QUESTIONS

1. Explain why the criteria for the classification of animals and plants may be different, although the principles remain the same.
2. Differentiate between Protozoa and Metazoa.
3. Differentiate between the terms given in each of the following groups. In each case provide an example.
   a. saccular vs. tubular enterons
   b. a colony vs. a multicellular organism
   c. spherical, radial, and bilateral symmetry
   d. diploblastic vs. triploblastic organization
   e. open vs. closed circulatory systems
   f. an exoskeleton vs. an endoskeleton
   g. germ vs. somatic cells
   h. Ciliata vs. Suctoria
   i. macronuclei vs. micronuclei
4. Carefully identify and give an example of each of the following: (1) choanoflagellate; (2) gastral layer; (3) spongin; (4) amoebocyte; (5) amphiblastula; (6) nematoblast; (7) hypnotoxin; (8) interstitial cells; (9) protoneurons; (10) cephalization; (11) flame cells; (12) hemolymph; (13) cercaria; (14) scolex; (15) onchospheres; (16) hydatid cyst; (17) pseudocoelom; (18) stylet; (19) lophophore; (20) avicularium; (21) peduncle; (22) nephridia; (23) metamerism; (24) parapodia; (25) setae; (26) cerebral ganglia; (27) radula; (28) spiracles; (29) tracheae; (30) book lungs; (31) seminal receptacles; (32) ossicles; (33) madreporite; (34) tube feet; (35) ampullae; (36) vestigial anus; (37) dermal branchiae; (38) nerve ring; (39) perihaemal system; (40) placoid scales; (41) swim bladder; (42) spiral valve; (43) homoiothermy; (44) syrinx.
5. Specify the classes of the Protozoa and name an organism belonging to each class.
6. Name four pathogenic protozoans and evaluate their medical importance.
7. Differentiate between foraminiferous and radiolarian oozes.
8. Explain why the study of micropaleontology has become quite important in the petroleum industry.
9. Point out two important similarities and two important differences between the Porifera and the Coelenterata.
10. Differentiate among the four classes of the Coelenterata.
11. What is the basis for believing that the coelenterate stock gave rise to many of the higher phyla?
12. Differentiate between coelenterates and ctenophores.
13. Literally, what does the term Platyhelminthes mean?
14. Enumerate the organizational advances displayed by the flatworms. What primitive characteristics do they also display?
15. Differentiate among the three classes of flatworms. Which of the class is the most important from a medical viewpoint?
16. Specify four flatworm parasites and evaluate the medical importance of each. Sketch in the life cycle of each.
17. What is the basis for thinking that the platyhelminth stock provided a main line of evolutionary ascent in the animal kingdom?
18. Differentiate among Nemertinea, Nemathelminthes, Rotifera, Bryozoa, and Brachiopoda. What important organizational advances first appeared in these groups?
19. Among the Nemathelminthes, specify one species that parasitizes plants and three that infest man. Evaluate the importance, in each case.
20. Give two reasons why it is not wise to eat undercooked pork.
21. Are there any *unique* features displayed by Annelida? What combination of characteristics would serve to distinguish Annelida from Vertebrata and other major animal groups?
22. Differentiate among the four classes of Annelida and give an example of each.
23. Explain the basis for thinking that the Annelida stock may have given rise to some of the higher animal groups.
24. What unique features are displayed by Mollusca?
25. Differentiate amongst the five classes of Mollusca and give an example of each.
26. Discuss the various types of locomotion displayed by different mollusks.
27. Apparently the molluscan stock did not give rise to any of the higher groups of animals. Explain and discuss this statement.
28. Differentiate among the seven classes of Arthropoda and give an example of each.

29. Specify four important similarities and two important differences between arthropod and vertebrate animals.
30. In what ways are arthropods similar to and different from annelids?
31. Briefly discuss the adaptations to terrestrial conditions that are found among Arthropoda.
32. Briefly describe the organization of an insect society such as a bee hive or a termite colony.
33. Some insects display a limited capacity to form conditioned reflexes. Explain and substantiate this statement.
34. Briefly discuss the communication system utilized by certain bees.
35. What *unique* features are displayed by echinoderm animals?
36. Differentiate among the five classes of Echinodermata and give an example of each.
37. Hazard an opinion as to why the Echinodermata have not evolved any terrestrial species.
38. What organizational features commonly found among higher animals are also found among the Echinodermata?
39. Specify three *unique* characteristics displayed by chordate animals.
40. Differentiate amongst the four subphyla of the Chordata.
41. How do vertebrates differ from all other chordates? How are they similar?
42. Specify ten characteristics always found in vertebrate animals. Which of these are *unique* to the Vertebrata?
43. Differentiate among the seven classes of Vertebrata and give an example of each.
44. Explain the terms Craniata and Agnatha.
45. Name one parasitic vertebrate animal and evaluate its economic importance.
46. Identify each of the following groups and indicate the relationships of each: (1) Dipnoi; (2) Crossopterygia; (3) Coelacanths; (4) Apoda; (5) Labyrinthodonts; (6) Dinosaurs; (7) Therapsids; (8) Archaic placentates.
47. Discuss the biological significance of: (a) feathers; (b) the placenta; (c) mammary glands.
48. Distinguish among the Prototheria, Metatheria, and Eutheria. Give an example of each.
49. Briefly explain how and why monotremes and marsupials are quite prevalent in Australia but not elsewhere in the world.

FURTHER READINGS

1. *General Zoology,* by D. F. Miller and J. G. Haub; New York, 1956.
2. *General Zoology,* by T. I. Storer; New York, 1957.

APPENDIX

APPENDIX 1
Classification of Organisms

THIS CLASSIFICATION often includes the classes and sometimes also the orders. The phyla within each kingdom, and the classes within each phylum are arranged, *so far as possible,* in order of increasing complexity.

The number of species given for each phylum is the approximate number of living species described and named. In many, probably most, phyla there are undoubtedly many more species still undescribed.

Kingdom **PLANTAE**

Organisms usually having rigid cell walls; nutrition autotrophic, saprophytic, or parasitic. The line between the plant and animal kingdoms is not at all sharp, as explained in the text.

I. Subkingdom **THALLOPHYTA**

Primitive, mainly aquatic plants, with *no embryo* stage in development and no highly differentiated tissues.

Phylum **CYANOPHYTA**: the blue-green algae; no distinct nuclei or chloroplasts; probably the most primitive of existing plants. (2300 species.)

Phylum **EUGLENOPHYTA**: euglenoids; with flexible cell walls; flagellated; sexual reproduction virtually absent; store paramylum; nuclei and chloroplasts well defined. (250 species.)

Phylum **CHLOROPHYTA**: the green algae; including desmids; unicellular, colonial, or simple multicellular forms, with definite nuclei and chloroplasts. (6000 species.)

Phylum **CHRYSOPHYTA**: the yellow-green algae, the golden-brown algae, and the diatoms. (5000 species.)

Phylum **PYRROPHYTA**: the cryptomonads and dinoflagellates. (3000 species.)

Phylum **PHAEOPHYTA**: the brown algae, with multicellular, often large bodies—the large seaweeds. (1000 species.)

Phylum **RHODOPHYTA**: the red algae. Multicellular, usually marine plants, sometimes impregnated with calcium carbonate. (3000 species.)

Phylum **SCHIZOMYCOPHYTA**: the bacteria. (3000 species.)

Phylum **MYXOMYCOPHYTA**: the slime molds. The body consists of a mass of protoplasm containing many nuclei, but not sharply divided into cells. Movement by ameboid motion (2500? species.)

Phylum **EUMYCOPHYTA**: the true fungi. (70,000 species.)

Class *Phycomycetes:* the algal fungi—bread molds and leaf molds.

Class *Ascomycetes:* the sac fungi—yeasts, mildews, and cheese molds.

Class *Basidiomycetes:* mushrooms, toadstools, rusts, and smuts.

Class *Deuteromycetes:* a heterogeneous collection of fungi in which sexual reproduction is unknown, and which are not easily assigned to one of the other classes.

II. Subkingdom **EMBRYOPHYTA**

Plants *with an embryo* stage in development; generally less primitive; more or less adapted to terrestrial conditions.

Phylum **BRYOPHYTA**: multicellular, usually terrestrial, plants, with regular alternation of generations; the sporophyte always dependent on the gametophyte; lack true vascular tissues (xylem and phloem). (23,000 species.)

Class *Hepaticae:* the liverworts; usually simple, flat plants without stem or leaves.

Class *Musci:* the mosses.

Class *Anthocerotae:* the hornworts.

Phylum TRACHEOPHYTA: true vascular plants, having definite xylem and phloem tissues. (265,000 species.)

Subphylum PSILOPSIDA: a mainly extinct group of leafless, rootless, vascular plants.

Subphylum LYCOPSIDA: the modern *club mosses* belong to this largely extinct group; having simple conducting tissues, poor roots, and very small green leaves.

Subphylum SPHENOPSIDA: the *horsetails* are the modern representatives of this previously abundant group; stems display joints and the leaves are small and scalelike; simple conducting tissues.

Subphylum PTEROPSIDA: well-adapted land plants, with complex vascular tissues, an excellent root system, and large, conspicuous leaves.

Class *Filicinae:* the ferns and related forms; numerous extinct as well as living species.

Class *Gymnospermae:* conifers, cycads, etc.; no ovule case or true flowers; no fruits.

Class *Angiospermae:* flowering plants; ovules completely enclosed in an ovule case; seeds enclosed within a fruit.

Subclass Monocotyledoneae: grasses, lilies, orchids, etc.; embryo with a single cotyledon; vascular bundles scattered through the stem; leaves with parallel veins; flower parts in threes or sixes.

Subclass Dicotyledoneae: flowering plants; embryo with two cotyledons; vascular bundles in a ring in the stem; leaves with netlike venation; flower parts in fours or fives.

Kingdom ANIMALIA

Organisms usually without rigid cell walls or chlorophyll; nutrition usually holozoic.

Phylum PROTOZOA: unicellular or simple colonial animals, usually with distinct nucleus and cytoplasm; with or without sexual reproduction. (20,000 species.)

Class *Mastigophora:* the flagellates.

Class *Sarcodina:* protozoans with pseudopodia.

Class *Ciliophora:* protozoans with cilia.

Class *Sporozoa:* parasitic protozoans, usually without locomotive or ingestive organs.

All the following phyla, consisting of multicellular animals, are called collectively Metazoa; the groups Protozoa and Metazoa are sometimes called subkingdoms.

Phylum PORIFERA: the sponges; simple multicellular animals with branched or unbranched, tubular body, perforated by many pores that admit water containing food particles. (4000 species.)

Phylum COELENTERATA: radially symmetrical, diploblastic ("two-layered") animals; possess nematocysts. (5000 species.)

Class *Hydrozoa:* hydralike animals, often colonial, and often having a regular alternation of asexual and sexual generations.

Class *Scyphozoa:* jellyfishes.

Class *Anthozoa* or *(Actinozoa):* sea anemones and corals.

Phylum CTENOPHORA: the comb jellies and sea walnuts; jellyfishlike animals, somewhat more complex in structure than the typical coelenterates; possess eight bands of cilia, for locomotion.

Phylum PLATYHELMINTHES: the flatworms; bilaterally symmetrical, triploblastic ("three-layered") animals, without a true body cavity or anus; excretion by means of flame cells. (6000 species.)

Class *Turbellaria:* nonparasitic flatworms.

Class *Trematoda:* the flukes, parasitic flatworms with an enteron.

Class *Cestoidea:* the tapeworms, parasitic flatworms with no enteron, absorbing nourishment through the body surface.

Phylum NEMERTINEA: the proboscis worms; nonparasitic, usually marine animals with a complete digestive tract and a protrusible proboscis armed with a hook for capturing prey; with a simple blood vascular system. (500 species.)

Phylum **NEMATHELMINTHES:** the roundworms; a fairly large phylum; characterized by elongated, cylindrical, bilaterally symmetrical bodies; live as parasites in plants and animals, or are free-living in the soil or water. (12,000 species.)

Phylum **ACANTHOCEPHALA:** the hookheaded worms; parasitic worms with no digestive tract and a head armed with many recurved hooks. (100 species.)

Phylum **CHAETOGNATHA:** free-swimming marine worms, with a body cavity (coelom) that develops from pouches of the digestive tract (as in the echinoderms and lower chordates). (30 species.)

Phylum **NEMATOMORPHA:** the horsehair worms; extremely thin, brown or black worms about 6 inches long, resembling a horsehair; adults are free-living, but the larvae are parasitic in insects. (200 species.)

Phylum **ROTIFERA:** small, wormlike animals, commonly called "wheel animalcules," with a complete digestive tract, flame cells, and a circle of cilia on the head, the beating of which suggests a wheel. (1200 species.)

Phylum **GASTROTRICHA:** microscopic, wormlike animals resembling the rotifers, but lacking the crownlike circle of cilia. (100 species.)

Phylum **BRYOZOA:** "moss" animals; microscopic organisms, usually marine, which form branching colonies; characterized by a U-shaped row of ciliated tentacles, the lophophore, by means of which they capture food. (1200 species.)

Phylum **BRACHIOPODA:** the lamp shells; marine animals with two hard shells (one dorsal and one ventral), superficially like a clam; obtain food by means of a lophophore. (200 species at present; 3000 extinct.)

Phylum **PHORONIDEA:** wormlike, marine forms that secrete and live in a leathery tube; they have a U-shaped digestive tract and a lophophore. (10 species.)

Phylum **ANNELIDA:** segmented worms, usually with well-developed coelom, head, and blood vessels; appendages, when present, are nonjointed. (7000 species.)

Class *Archiannelida:* marine worms, simpler than other annelids.

Class *Polychaeta:* mainly marine worms, with a distinct head and many-bristled lobose appendages.

Class *Oligochaeta:* mainly fresh-water annelids, with scanty bristles and usually a poorly differentiated head.

Class *Hirudinea:* leeches.

Phylum **MOLLUSCA:** unsegmented animals, usually with one or more shells; a foot, variously modified, and a mantle are characteristic. (75,000 species.)

Class *Amphineura:* the chitons, etc.; simplest type of mollusks, with shell in eight pieces.

Class *Pelecypoda:* bivalve mollusks; clams, oysters, mussels, scallops, etc.; usually with a hatchet-shaped foot and no distinct head.

Class *Scaphopoda:* the tooth shells; mollusks with a conical tubular shell.

Class *Gastropoda:* asymmetrical mollusks, usually with a spiral shell; snails, etc.

Class *Cephalopoda:* octopus, squid, nautilus, etc.; "headfoot" with 8 or 10 tentacles; well-developed eyes and nervous system.

Phylum **ARTHROPODA:** segmented animals, jointed appendages, no endoskeleton. (700,000 species.)

Class *Crustacea:* lobsters, crabs, crayfishes, shrimps, etc.

Class *Arachnida:* spiders, mites, scorpions, etc.

Class *Onychophora:* simple, wormlike, terrestrial arthropods; *Peripatus.*

Class *Insecta:* insects. Example: *Drosophila.*

Class *Chilopoda:* the centipedes; at least 15 segments, each with one pair of jointed appendages.

Class *Diplopoda:* the millipedes; abdomen with many segments, each with two pairs of appendages.

Phylum **ECHINODERMATA:** radially symmetrical in adult stage; with well-developed coelom formed from enteric pouches; with endoskeleton of calcareous ossicles and spines; unique water vascular system; with tube feet. (5000 species.)

Class *Crinoidea:* feather stars; sessile animals often having a jointed stalk for attachment.

Class *Asteroidea:* starfishes.

Class *Ophiuroidea:* brittle stars.

Class *Echinoidea:* sea urchins.

Class *Holothuroidea:* sea cucumbers.

Phylum CHORDATA: animals having at some stage a notochord, gill slits, and a hollow nerve cord on the dorsal side. (60,000 species.)

Subphylum HEMICHORDATA: the acorn, or proboscis worms; wormlike animals with a notochordlike structure in the head end.

Subphylum UROCHORDATA: tunicates, or sea squirts; saclike, usually sessile animals, often forming branching colonies; in the larval stage they have a notochord in the tail region.

Subphylum CEPHALOCHORDATA: lancelets; somewhat fishlike animals, with a permanent notochord the whole length of the body; no cartilage or bone.

Subphylum VERTEBRATA: the vertebrates; notochord surrounded or replaced by cartilage or bone, forming the vertebral column or backbone.

Class *Cyclostomata:* lampreys and hagfishes, eellike vertebrates, without limbs or jaws.

Class *Chondrichthyes:* sharks, rays, skates, and other cartilaginous fish; without air bladders.

Class *Osteichthyes:* the bony fish, including crossopterygians, dipnoians, and ganoids, which are almost extinct; usually with an air bladder or (rarely) a lung.

Class *Amphibia:* salamanders, frogs, and toads; usually breathing by gills in the larval stage, by lungs in the adult stage; incomplete double circulation; skin usually naked; the limbs are legs.

Class *Reptilia:* turtles, lizards, snakes, crocodiles; breathing by lungs; incomplete double circulation; skin usually covered with scales; the limbs are legs (absent in snakes).

Class *Aves:* the birds; warm-blooded animals with complete double circulation, skin covered with feathers, the forelimbs wings.

Class *Mammalia:* the mammals; warm-blooded animals with complete double circulation, skin usually covered with hair, young nourished with milk secreted by the mother; limbs usually legs (forelimbs sometimes arms, wings, or fins).

Subclass **Prototheria:** the monotremes; oviparous mammals with imperfect temperature regulation; only two living species, the duckbill and spiny anteater of Australia.

Subclass **Metatheria:** the marsupials; viviparous mammals without a placenta (or with a poorly developed one), the young carried in an external pouch of the mother for some time after birth; kangaroos, opossums, etc.

Subclass **Eutheria:** mammals with a well-developed placenta, comprising the great majority of living mammals. The principal **orders** of Eutheria are the following:

Insectivora: shrews, moles, hedgehogs, etc.

Edentata: toothless mammals; anteaters, sloths, armadillos, etc.

Rodentia: the rodents; rats, mice, squirrels, etc.

Artiodactyla: even-toed ungulates; cattle, deer, camels, hippopotamuses, etc.

Perissodactyla: odd-toed, hoofed mammals; horses, zebras, rhinoceroses, etc.

Proboscidea: elephants.

Lagomorpha: rabbits and hares.

Sirenia: the manatee, dugong, and sea cows; large aquatic mammals with the forelimbs finlike, the hind limbs absent.

Carnivora: carnivorous animals; cats, dogs, bears, weasels, seals, etc.

Cetacea: the whales, dolphins, and porpoises; aquatic mammals with the forelimbs fins, the hind limbs absent.

Chiroptera: the bats, aerial mammals with the forelimbs wings.

Primates: the lemurs, monkeys, apes, and man.

APPENDIX 2
Glossary

THIS LIST does not include names of taxonomic groups, which are defined in Appendix 1, nor most terms that are used only once in the text and defined there.

ABERRATION. An irregularity of chromosome behavior, resulting in an unusual chromosome complex.

ABSORPTION. The passage of water and dissolved substances into the cell or the organism.

ACID. A substance that dissociates, yielding hydrogen (H⁺) ions (but not hydroxyl (OH⁻) ions).

ACQUIRED CHARACTERS. Somatic modifications; i.e., variations caused by environmental factors.

ACROSOME. Specialized structure found at anterior tip of the head of a sperm cell, concerned with penetration into an egg cell.

ACTION POTENTIAL. A rapid change in the membrane potential, which signifies excitation in cells generally.

ACTIVATION. The stimulation of an egg cell to start development.

ACTIVE TRANSPORT. Any process by which a cell expends energy to foster the entrance or exit of a substance through its boundary membrane.

ADAPTATION. Fitness to live and reproduce. Any characteristic of an organism fitting it to live and reproduce.

ADHESION. Attraction between molecules of different substances.

ADRENAL GLANDS. A pair of ductless glands located near the kidneys.

ADRENALIN. A hormone secreted by the adrenal glands.

ADSORPTION. The accumulation of a dissolved substance at the surface between two phases.

AFFERENT FIBER. A nerve fiber carrying impulses from a receptor toward the central nervous system.

ALGAE. Simple plants (thallophytes) containing chlorophyll.

ALLELES. Genes occupying the same locus in homologous chromosomes, and which, therefore, segregate from each other at reduction.

ALTERNATION OF GENERATIONS. The alternate succession of sexual and asexual forms, each producing the other.

AMICROSCOPIC. Too small to be seen with either the microscope or the ultramicroscope; i.e., less than about 1 mμ in diameter.

AMINO ACIDS. Organic acids possessing both the carboxyl radical (COOH) and the amino radical (NH₂).

AMITOSIS. Division of a cell without the appearance of chromosomes.

AMOEBOID MOVEMENT. Movement of a cell by means of pseudopodia.

AMYLOPSIN. An enzyme, secreted by the pancreas, which partially hydrolyzes starch.

ANAEROBIC METABOLISM. Metabolism without the consumption of free oxygen.

ANALOGOUS ORGANS. Organs having structural similarities correlated with similarity of function and not due to genetic relationship. (*cf.* HOMOLOGOUS ORGANS.)

ANAPHASES. The period of mitosis during which the daughter chromosomes move toward opposite poles.

ANTHER. The part of a stamen containing the pollen.

ANTHERIDIUM. Organ found in most embryophytes, in which the sperm cells are formed.

ANUS. The terminal opening of the enteron.

APHIDS. Plant lice, small sucking insects parasitic on plants.

APICAL CELL. A cell at the apex of the growing point of many thallophytes, bryophytes, and pteropsidans, which by continued growth and cell divisions produces all the tissues of the plant.

ARCHEGONIUM. Organ found in most embryophytes, in which the egg cells are formed.

ARTERY. A muscular, elastic blood vessel, carrying blood from the heart to the capillaries. (*cf.* VEIN.)

ASEXUAL REPRODUCTION. Any method of reproduction not involving fertilization.

ASSIMILATION. The production of protoplasm from food substances in the living cell.

ASTER. A radiate structure surrounding each end of the spindle during cell division.

ATOMS. The elementary particles that enter into chemical reactions.

AURICLE. A relatively thin-walled chamber of the heart that receives blood from the veins and pumps it into the venticle.

685

AUTOCATALYSIS. Capacity of certain substances to catalyze the production of themselves.

AUTONOMIC NERVOUS SYSTEM. A system of neurones innervating the visceral organs, connected with the central nervous system by axons of intermediate neurones of the central nervous system.

AUTOSOMES. Chromosomes that are not sex chromosomes.

AUTOTROPHIC. Able to synthesize all substances required for nutrition from inorganic food substances. (*cf.* HETEROTROPHIC.)

AUXIN. A plant hormone, or growth substance.

AUXOCYTE. A germ cell in the growth period, during which synapsis and tetrad formation occur.

AXON. A long unbranched or sparsely branched nerve fiber, usually carrying impulses away from the cell body of a neuron.

BACKCROSS. A cross between an individual whose genetic constitution is to be tested and one that is homozygous for all recessive genes involved in the experiment.

BACTERIAL TRANSFORMATION. The induction of a new heritable property in bacterial cells by DNA, transmitted via the culture medium.

BACTERIOPHAGE. A virus parasitic in bacteria.

BASE. A substance that dissociates, yielding hydroxyl (OH^-) ions (but not hydrogen (H^+) ions).

BAST. The phloem.

BILATERAL SYMMETRY. Symmetry with reference to a plane. In a bilaterally symmetrical body (e.g., a spoon), only one plane can be found that will divide it into symmetrical halves.

BILE. The external secretion of the liver, secreted through the bile duct to the small intestine.

BIOLOGY. The scientific study of living things.

BIVALENT. A pair of homologous chromosomes joined in synapsis. (*cf.* UNIVALENT.)

BLASTOCOEL. The cavity within a blastula.

BLASTOPORE. The external opening of the enteron of a gastrula.

BLASTULA. An embryo after cleavage and before gastrulation, typically a single layer of cells forming a hollow sphere.

BLOOD. A fluid tissue consisting of the blood cells, or *corpuscles,* and a liquid intercellular material, the *plasma.* A form of connective tissue.

BRAIN. The enlarged anterior end of the central nervous system.

BROWNIAN MOVEMENT. The continual random movement of small particles suspended in a fluid medium, due to their bombardment by the molecules of the medium.

BUD. (1) A young individual produced by budding, before it is completely detached from the parent. (2) The end of a stem or branch, enclosed by young leaves; this may develop into a leafy stem (*leaf bud*) or into a flower (*flower bud*).

BUDDING. The asexual production of a new individual by the splitting off of a relatively small portion of the parent organism.

BULB. A subterranean leaf bud or flower bud.

CALORIE. A quantity of heat required to raise the temperature of 1 kilogram of water 1 degree centigrade; this is the "large Calorie," the unit employed in connection with nutrition.

CALYX. The outermost whorl of parts in a complete flower. Consists of sepals.

CAMBIUM. A layer of embryonic tissue between the xylem and the phloem in dicotyledonous plants.

CAPILLARIES. Very small, thin-walled blood vessels, penetrating the intercellular spaces of all organs, through whose walls exchanges occur between the blood and the tissue cells.

CARBOHYDRATES. Compounds of carbon, hydrogen, and oxygen in the proportions of about 1C:2e:1O; including sugars, starch, glycogen, cellulose, etc.

CARPEL. A macrosporophyll of a flowering plant, one of the innermost whorl of flower parts.

CATALYSIS. The action of a catalyst.

CATALYST. Any substance that modifies the rate of a chemical change without being itself used up in the process.

CELL. A structural unit of protoplasm, consisting typically of nucleus and cytoplasm.

CELL SAP. The fluid in the large vacuoles of plant cells; a watery solution of salts, sugars, etc.

CELL WALL. The rigid external covering of a plant cell.

CELLULOSE. An insoluble complex carbohydrate (polysaccharide), the chief component of most plant cell walls.

CENTRAL NERVOUS SYSTEM. The main part of the nervous system in most animals, containing the cell bodies of most of the neurones.

CENTRIOLES. "Division centers" found at the ends of the spindle during mitosis and meiosis in animal cells; display a complex structure (Fig. 3-5) when studied by electron microscopy.

CENTROLECITHAL EGG. An egg cell containing a large amount of yolk concentrated toward the center.

CENTROSOME. The body or region at the center of an aster.

CEPHALIZATION. The concentration of the sensory and nervous systems at the head end of animals.

CEREBELLUM. An expansion of the dorsal side of the brain near its hind end, the coordinating center for proprioceptive stimuli and complex muscular movements.

CEREBRUM. An expansion of the dorsal and lateral sides of the brain at its front end; the chief center for conditioned, or learned, responses.

CHEMICAL REACTION. A change of one or more substances into different substances, by recombination of their constituent atoms into different kinds of molecules.

CHEMOTROPISM. Movement whose direction is determined by the unequal concentrations of some particular substance on the two sides of an organism.

CHLOROPHYLL. The green pigment of plant cells which catalyzes photosynthesis.

CHLOROPLAST. A plastid containing chlorophyll.

CHOLESTEROL. A sterol found in the cells of many organisms.

CHROMATIN. A substance found in all living cells, which stains deeply with certain dyes; the characteristic component of the nucleus in which DNA is always represented.

CHROMIDIA. Granules of chromatin scattered through the cell, chiefly in cells that have no distinct nucleus and cytoplasm.

CHROMOSOMES. Threads or rods of chromatin (DNA-protein complex), which appear during mitosis (and meiosis).

CILIA. Fine protoplasmic processes that beat in regular fashion to move the cell or move particles over its surface.

CLASS. A taxonomic group, next below a phylum.

CLEAVAGE. The successive cell divisions of the zygote (or parthenogenetic egg) that transform it into a multicellular embryo.

CLOACA. The common posterior opening of the enteron, ureters, and gonoducts in most vertebrates (except mammals).

COARSE. Of microscopic or macroscopic size; i.e., above about 100 mμ in diameter.

COELOM. A mesodermal cavity occupying most of the space between the body wall and the enteron in annelids, vertebrates, etc.

COHESION. Attraction between molecules of the same substance.

COLLOIDAL. Of ultramicroscopic size; i.e., between about 1 mμ and 100 mμ in diameter. Dispersions containing molecules or particles of this size.

COLONIAL ORGANISM. An aggregate of cells all more or less alike in structure and function.

COMPONENTS. The substances making up a mixture. (cf. CONSTITUENTS.)

COMPOUND. A substance containing only one kind of molecule, each molecule consisting of two or more kinds of atoms.

CONDITIONED REFLEX. A habitual response to a particular stimulus determined by the previous experience of the individual; i.e., by the frequent association of this stimulus with a stimulus that originally aroused this response.

CONDUCTOR. A structure specialized for the transmission of excitation.

COENZYME. A. Important cofactor that transmits activated acetyl units to the Krebs cycle, in cells generally. (cf. Fig. 8-5.)

COFACTOR. A nonprotein component of many enzymes; either firmly bonded to the protein, in which case it is called a prosthetic group, or loosely bonded, in which case it is called a coenzyme.

CONJUGATION. The union of two gametes; usually used only in cases where the two gametes are alike.

CONNECTIVE TISSUES. Tissues in which the cells are irregularly distributed through a relatively large amount of intercellular material.

CONSTITUENTS. The elements making up a compound. (cf. COMPONENTS.)

COORDINATION. The production of harmonious interaction of the various parts and processes of an organism.

COPULATION. The introduction of sperm cells into the body of the female by a male animal.

COROLLA. The whorl of parts (petals) just inside the calyx of a complete flower.

CORTEX. The portion of a stem or root between the epidermis and the fibrovascular bundles.

COTYLEDON. Storage leaf of an embryo sporophyte or seedling.

CRANIAL NERVES. Nerves arising from the brain.

CROSS-FERTILIZATION. Union of gametes from different individuals. (cf. SELF-FERTILIZATION.)

CROSS OVER. The exchange of corresponding portions of homologous chromosomes during synapsis.

CRYSTALLOIDAL. Of amicroscopic size; i.e., below about 1 mμ in diameter. Solutions containing molecules of this size.

CYTOCHROMES. A series of iron compounds present in cells generally that relays electrons from level to level, generating useful energy.

CYTOPLASM. The protoplasm of a cell exclusive of the nucleus.

DEATH. Irreversible cessation of the activities and breakdown of the structure of protoplasm.

DEHYDRATION SYNTHESIS. The chemical combination of two or more molecules (of the same substance or different substances) with elimination of water.

DEHYDROGENASE. Any enzyme that catalyzes the transfer of one or more electrons (and hydrogen) from one substance to another.

DENDRONS. Relatively short, usually much branched processes of a neuron, carrying impulses toward the cell body.

DENITRIFYING BACTERIA. Bacteria that decompose nitrogen compounds and liberate free nitrogen.

DEVELOPMENT. The progressive production of the phenotypic characteristics of an organism.

DIFFERENTIATION. The structural and functional specialization of different parts.

DIFFUSION. The spreading of a dissolved substance through the solvent by virtue of the random movements of its molecules or ions.

DIGESTION. The hydrolysis of colloidal, sometimes insoluble, food substances into soluble crystalloidal substances.

DIOECIOUS. Having separate sexes; i.e., the two kinds of gametes produced by different individuals. (cf. MONOECIOUS.)

DIPLOID. The number of chromosomes in the zygote, which is twice the number in each gamete. (cf. HAPLOID.)

DISACCHARIDE. A carbohydrate that can be hydrolyzed into two monosaccharides; i.e., each molecule of the disaccharide yields two monosaccharide molecules (either alike or different).

DISPERSION. A mixture in which one or more substances are distributed (dispersed) throughout another substance (the dispersion medium).

DNA. Deoxyribonucleic acid, in which the sugar of the sugar-phosphate chain is deoxyribose; carrier of the genetic code in cells generally; capable of self-templated synthesis as well as of determining RNA synthesis; closely identified with the genic material.

DOMINANT. A gene whose phenotypic effect largely or entirely obscures that of its allelic gene. (cf. RECESSIVE.)

DORSAL. Pertaining to the upper side (the back in man).

DUCT. (1) A long, hollow, woody tube, in the xylem portion of a vascular bundle (also called a *vessel*). (2) The tubular outlet of a multicellular gland of external secretion.

ECOLOGICAL. Pertaining to the relations of organisms to their environments.

ECOLOGY. Study of the adaptations of organisms to their environment.

ECOSYSTEM. A more or less isolated system constituted by the sum total of interactions between a particular environment and all the organisms inhabiting this environment.

ECTODERM. The outer layer of cells in the gastrula or, less accurately, the tissues derived from this layer.

EFFECTOR. A structure specialized for the production of some particular kind of response; e.g., movement, secretion, etc.

EFFERENT FIBER. A nerve fiber carrying impulses from the central nervous system to an effector.

EGESTION. The elimination of waste material from the digestive cavity.

EGG CELL. A large, usually nonmotile gamete, containing abundant cytoplasm and yolk. (*cf.* SPERM CELL.)

ELECTROLYTE. A substance whose molecules dissociate into ions, especially in aqueous solution.

ELECTRON. A particle of negative electricity; one of the particulate constituents of matter.

ELEMENT. A substance constituted of only one kind of atom.

EMBRYO. A young organism before emerging from the egg, the seed, or the body of the mother.

EMBRYO SAC. The female gametophyte of a seed plant.

EMULSION. A dispersion consisting of small droplets of one liquid in another.

ENDOCRINE ORGAN. A gland of internal secretion, producing a hormone or hormones.

ENDODERM. The inner layer of cells in the gastrula. The tissues derived from this layer.

ENDODERMIS. The differentiated innermost layer of cells of the cortex of stems and roots.

ENDOPLASMIC RETICULUM. A system of double membranes revealed by electron microscopic studies in cells generally; closely affiliated with the ribosomes.

ENDOSPERM. A mass of cells, containing stored food substances, developing from part of the female gametophyte and, unless fully resorbed, filling all the seed outside the embryo.

ENERGY. The capacity to do work; i.e., to produce movement.

ENTERON. The digestive cavity of multicellular animals.

ENZYME. An organic catalyst produced by living cells.

EPICOTYL. The part of an embryonic seed plant, above the point of attachment of the cotyledons. (*cf.* HYPOCOTYL.)

EPIDERMIS. The outermost layer of cells of a plant or animal.

EPITHELIAL TISSUES. Surface tissues in which the cells form one or more regular layers, with very little intercellular material.

EPITHELIUM. An epithelial tissue, covering an external or internal surface.

EREPSIN. A group of enzymes secreted by the intestine, which hydrolyzes peptones to amino acids.

ESOPHAGUS. The portion of the enteron between the pharynx and the stomach.

EUSTACHIAN TUBE. A passage connecting the tympanic cavity (middle ear) with the pharynx; developed from the most anterior gill slit of the embryo.

EVOLUTION. Process by which organisms change, by the origin of new genotypes and phenotypes, with partial or complete extinction of old ones.

EXCITATION. The state of a cell immediately after being stimulated, involving an increased rate of metabolism, increased permeability, and an altered electric membrane potential.

EXCRETION. Elimination of waste products of metabolism (except CO_2).

EXTERNAL SECRETION. Secertion to the outside of the body or into the cavity of the enteron. Any substance or mixture thus secreted.

FAMILY. A taxonomic group, between order and genus; names of plant families end in *-aceae,* those of animal families in *-idae.*

FATS. Lipids that can be hydrolyzed to glycerol and fatty acids, each fat molecule yielding one glycerol molecule and three fatty acid molecules (alike or different). (The term *fats* is sometimes used to include all lipids.)

FATTY ACIDS. Organic acids containing a single carboxyl radical (COOH) and otherwise only carbon and hydrogen; there are many different fatty acids, differing in the number of carbon and hydrogen atoms.

FECES. The material egested from the enteron.

FEMALE. An individual that produces egg cells but not sperm cells.

FERTILITY. Ability to reproduce.

FERTILIZATION. Fusion of two gametes, especially of their nuclei.

FIBRILS. Small fibers or threads within cells.

FISSION. Asexual reproduction by division of an organism into two or more equal, or nearly equal, parts.

FLAGELLUM. A protoplasmic process, longer than a cilium, whose movements usually effect locomotion of a cell.

FLORAL ENVELOPES. The calyx and corolla; i.e., the outer whorls of flower parts, not directly concerned in reproduction.

FLOWER. A group of modified leaves of several kinds, including sporophylls, arranged in concentric whorls; a *complete* flower consists of calyx, corolla, stamens, and carpels, but in many flowers some of these are absent.

FOOD. Any material that the organism obtains from the environment and that can either yield energy for the activities of the organism or supply matter for its growth.

FORMED BODIES. Localized differentiated regions or structures within the cytoplasm.

FOSSILS. Remains or traces of dead organisms preserved by natural processes.

FRUIT. A structure formed from the ovule case (and sometimes other parts) of a flower, containing the seed or seeds.

FUEL SUBSTANCE. A substance that can be metabolized to yield energy in the organism.

FUEL VALUE. The quantity of energy liberated by the oxidation of a substance in the organisms; usually expressed in Calories per gram.

FUNGI. Thallophytes without chlorophyll (often used as including the bacteria).

GALVANOTROPISM. Movement determined by the direction of an external electric current.

GAMETE. A cell that unites with another cell in sexual reproduction.

GAMETOPHYTE. The sexual generation of a plant. (*cf.* SPOROPHYTE.)

GANGLION. A group of nerve cells, especially the cell bodies.

GASTRIC JUICE. The fluid secreted by the gastric glands.

GASTRULA. An embryo in the two-layered stage, consisting of ectoderm and endoderm enclosing the archenteron.

GASTRULATION. The formation of the gastrula from the blastula.

GEL. A mixture of solid or semisolid consistency containing a large proportion of liquid entrapped in the meshes of its solid component.

GELATION. The change of a fluid dispersion into a gel

GENE. A unit hereditary factor, probably a definitive segment of a DNA molecule, capable of self-templated replication and mutation.

GENERATOR POTENTIAL. A change of membrane potential induced by stimulation of a receptor cell, which determines the strength and frequency of its excitational discharges.

GENETIC. Pertaining to internal factors determined by the descent of an organism.

GENETIC CODE. Three symboled system of base-pair sequences in DNA; indirectly determines the amino acid sequence in the enzymes and other protein components synthesized by each organism.

GENOTYPE. The genetic constitution of an organism or a group of genetically identical organisms. (*cf.* PHENOTYPE.)

GENUS. A taxonomic group, next above a species.

GEOLOGICAL. Pertaining to the structure and history of the earth.

GEOTROPISM. Movement determined by the direction of gravitational force.

GERM CELLS. The reproductive cells and all other cells that stand in line of ascent of the reproductive cells (*cf.* SOMATIC CELLS).

GERM PLASM. The germ cells collectively.

GERMINATION. The beginning of growth from a spore or a seed.

GILL SLITS. A series of paired openings from the sides of the pharynx through the body wall to the exterior, found in all chordates, at least in embryonic stages.

GILLS. External respiratory organs of aquatic animals.

GLAND. A cell or organ specialized for secretion.

GLUCOSE. $C_6H_{12}O_6$, the most common monosaccharide, the chief fuel substance of most organisms.

GLYCEROL. $C_3H_5(OH)_3$, a water-soluble compound entering into the synthesis of fats and phospholipids and derived from them by hydrolysis; commonly called *glycerine*.

GLYCOGEN. A complex carbohydrate (polysaccharide), one of the chief stored food substances of most animals and fungi.

GLYCOLYSIS. Anaerobic catabolism of glycogen, down to the level of pyruvic acid (or, in some cases, lactic acid).

GONADS. The essential reproductive organs of multicellular animals, in which the gametes are formed.

GONIA. The germ cells in the period of mitotic multiplication preceding maturation.

GONODUCTS. The ducts through which the gametes reach the exterior of the body, found in most animals above the coelenterates.

GRANA. Small rounded bodies inside chloroplasts, as seen in electronmicrographs.

GROWING POINT. The region at the apex of each filament, stem, or root, to which growth and cell division are largely confined in most plants.

GROWTH PERIOD. The period in the development of the germ cells preceding the meiotic divisions, during which they increase greatly in size and during which synapsis occurs and the tetrads are formed.

GROWTH STAGE. The intermitotic (nondividing) stage of the cell; often called the *resting stage*.

GUARD CELLS. Cells surrounding each stoma, which open and close the stoma.

HABIT. A usually invariable response determined by the previous experience of the individual; a conditioned reflex.

HABITAT. The particular kind of environment inhabited by a particular kind of organism.

HAPLOID. The number of chromosomes in each gamete; i.e., a single "set" of chromosomes. (*cf.* DIPLOID.)

HEMOGLOBIN. An iron-containing protein in the blood of many animals, in combination with which oxygen is transported through the body.

HEPATIC PORTAL SYSTEM. A part of the circulatory system, in all vertebrates, by which blood is carried from the stomach and intestine to the liver; starts and ends in a capillary system.

HEREDITY. The transmission of genes from ancestors to descendants through the germ cells.

HERMAPHRODITE. A monoecious animal, bearing both testes and ovaries.

HETEROTROPHIC. Requiring organic compounds among the food substances taken into the organism (*cf.* AUTOTROPHIC.)

HETEROZYGOUS. Having the two genes of an allelic pair different. (*cf.* HOMOZYGOUS.)

HOLOPHYTIC. Kind of nutrition found in green plants, which utilize light energy for synthesis of organic matter.

HOLOZOIC. Kind of nutrition found in typical animals, which ingest organic foods.

HOMEOSTASIS. Tendency of organisms to maintain structural and functional balance in face of environmental change.

HOMOLECITHAL EGG. An egg cell with the nonabundant yolk uniformly distributed throughout the cytoplasm.

HOMOLOGOUS CHROMOSOMES. The two chromosomes that pair at synapsis.

HOMOLOGOUS ORGANS. Organs having structural and developmental similarities due to genetic relationship. (*cf.* ANALOGOUS ORGANS.)

HOMOZYGOUS. Having the two genes of an allelic pair alike. (*cf.* HETEROZYGOUS.)

HORMONE. An internal secretion having some specific effect on metabolism, development, or response of the organism or some particular part of it.

HYDROLYSIS. Chemical decomposition of a substance by combination with water.

HYPOCOTYL. The part of an embryonic seed plant, below the point of attachment of the cotyledons. (*cf.* EPICOTYL.)

INDEPENDENT ASSORTMENT. The distribution, during meiosis, of the genes of different allelic pairs located in different pairs of homologous chromosomes; the distribution of any such pair of alleles being entirely independent of that of any other such pair.

INGESTION. Process of taking food into the digestive cavity of an organism.

INHIBITION. The stopping of some activity by a stimulus or drug.

INSTINCT. A usually invariable complex response independent of any previous experience of the individual; a complex unconditioned reflex.

INSULIN. An internal secretion of the pancreas essential for the normal metabolism of carbohydrates.

INTELLIGENCE. The ability to learn by experience; i.e., to form conditioned reflexes.

INTERMEDIATE NEURONS. Neurons connecting sensory with motor neurons. Also called *association neurons.*

INTERNAL SECRETION. Secretion into the blood. Any substance or mixture thus secreted.

INTESTINE. The chief portion of the enteron in most animals.

INVERTEBRATE. Any animal that is not a vertebrate.

ION. A part of a molecule, consisting of one or more atoms, with an electric charge.

KIDNEYS. The chief excretory organs of vertebrates.

KINETIC ENERGY. Energy inherent in the motion of a body or of its component particles. (*cf.* POTENTIAL ENERGY.)

KINGDOM. A primary taxonomic division; all organisms are conventionally divided into two kingdoms, plants and animals.

KREBS CYCLE. A regenerative cycle of oxidation-reduction and decarboxylation reactions from which cells derive energy (*cf.* Fig. 8-10).

LACTOSE. Milk sugar, a dissacharide found in the milk of mammals.

LARVA. An active immature animal differing from the adult; e.g., a caterpillar, a tadpole, etc.

LECITHIN. A very common phospholipid, found in many, perhaps all, kinds of cells.

LEUCOCYTES. White blood corpuscles, amoeboid cells of several types, found in most multicellular animals.

LIFE CYCLE. The complete series of forms regularly assumed successively by any particular kind of organism.

LINKAGE. The association in heredity of genes located in the same chromosome.

LIPIDS. Organic compounds insoluble in water but soluble in various organic liquids; consisting chiefly of carbon and hydrogen with a small proportion of oxygen and (in some cases) other elements; including fats, phospholipids, sterols, etc.

LIVER. A large glandular organ of vertebrates with numerous functions, including various special metabolic processes, storage, and secretion of the bile.

LOCUS. A particular position in a chromosome which may be occupied by any gene of a particular allelic series.

LUCIFERASE. Enzyme essential to the reactions that generate light energy in luminescent organisms.

LUCIFERIN. Substrate of luciferase.

LYMPH. A fluid derivative of blood plasma usually containing certain white blood corpuscles and relatively poor in plasma proteins.

LYMPHATIC TISSUE. A kind of tissue, found in various parts of the body, in which some of the white blood corpuscles are formed.

LYMPHOCYTES. One kind of white blood corpuscles, formed in the lymphatic tissue.

MACROGAMETE. The larger of the two kinds of gametes, in organisms that have gametes of two sizes.

MACROSPORANGIUM. A sporangium bearing macrospores.

MACROSPORE. The larger of the two kinds of spores (in plants which have spores of two sizes), which develops into a female gametophyte.

MACROSPOROPHYLL. A sporophyl bearing macrosporangia.

MALE. An individual that produces sperm cells but not egg cells.

MALTOSE. Malt sugar, a disaccharide produced by incomplete hydrolysis of starch.

MARROW. A tissue found in the interior of certain bones, in which red blood corpuscles and some kinds of white blood corpuscles are formed.

MATURATION DIVISIONS. The two final (meiotic) cell divisions in the formation of the gametes (in animals) or spores (in plants), in the course of which the chromosome number is reduced from diploid to haploid.

MEDULLA. The hindmost portion of the brain, adjoining the spinal cord.

MEDULLARY RAYS. Strands of tissue connecting pith and cortex, between the fibrovascular bundles.

MEIOSIS. The two special divisions by which haploid cells are formed from diploid cells, as in the production of the gametes of animals and the spores of plants.

MERISTEM. Embryonic tissue of plants, from which all the other tissues are derived by growth, cell division, and differentiation.

MESENTERY. A thin sheet of tissue connecting an organ, especially the enteron, with the body wall.

MESODERM. The cell layer between ectoderm and endoderm in the embryos of all animals above the coelenterates. The tissues derived from this layer.

MESOGLOEA. A layer of intercellular material between ectoderm and endoderm in coelenterates.

METABOLISM. The sum total of chemical reactions occurring in living cells and organisms.

METAMORPHOSIS. Transformation of a larva into the adult form.

METAPHASE. The stage of mitosis or meiosis, in which the chromosomes lie in the equatorial plane of the spindle.

METAZOA. Multicellular animals.

MICROBE. A microscopic organism.

MICROGAMETE. The smaller of the two kinds of gametes, in organisms which have gametes of two sizes.

MICROSCOPIC. Invisible with the naked eye, but visible with the microscope; i.e., between about 0.1μ and 100μ in diameter.

MICROSPORANGIUM. A sporangium bearing microspores.

MICROSPORE. The smaller of the two kinds of spores (in plants which have spores of two sizes), which develops into a male gametophyte.

MICROSPOROPHYLL. A sporophyl bearing microsporangia.

MITOCHONDRIA. Numerous cytoplasmic organelles having a characteristic (Fig. 2-13) internal structure as seen in electronmicrographs of cells generally; each mitochondrion represents an organized team of metabolic enzymes.

MITOSIS. The usual process of cell division in most organisms, involving a replication of each chromosome and the distribution of the daughter chromosomes to the daughter cells.

MIXTURE. Any material composed of more than one kind of molecule. (cf. SUBSTANCE.)

MODIFICATION. Any variation caused by nongenetic factors.

MOLECULES. The smallest particles into which any substance can be divided without chemical change.

MONOECIOUS. Having the two kinds of gametes produced by the same individual; i.e., not having separate sexes. (cf. DIOECIOUS.)

MONOSACCHARIDE. A simple sugar; i.e., a carbohydrate that cannot be decomposed by hydrolysis into simpler carbohydrates.

MORPHOGENESIS. The production of the characteristic form and structure of a cell or an organism.

MOTOR NEURON. A neuron that transmits excitation directly to an effector.

MUCUS. A slimy fluid secreted by gland cells present in many epithelia, called mucous membranes.

MUSCLE. A tissue specialized for the production of movement by contraction (i.e., shortening) of its cells or fibers. A sheet, bundle, or mass of such tissue.

MUTATION. Change in a gene into another gene.

MYELIN SHEATH. A "fatty" envelope surrounding a nerve fiber.

MYOFIBRILS. Longitudinal fibrils in muscle cells.

MYONEMES. Contractile fibrils in protozoans.

NATURAL SELECTION. The automatic selection of organisms for superior viability and fertility under natural conditions, resulting from the tendency of all organisms to increase in numbers by reproduction and the limitation of this increase by environmental factors.

NEPHRIDIA. Excretory organs found in many invertebrates.

NERVE. A group or bundle of nerve fibers.

NERVE CELLS. A cell specialized for the transmission, generation, or modification of excitation.

NERVE FIBERS. A filamentous cytoplasmic extension of a nerve cell.

NERVE IMPULSE. A state of excitation transmitted along a nerve fiber.

NEUROID TRANSMISSION. The transmission of excitation by cells other than nerve cells.

NEURON. A nerve cell.

NITRIFYING BACTERIA. Bacteria that oxidize ammonia to nitrites, or nitrite to nitrates.

NITROGEN-FIXING BACTERIA. Bacteria that form nitrate $(-NO_3)$ compounds from free nitrogen.

NOTOCHORD. A longitudinal solid rod above the enteron in all chordates, at least in embryonic stages; replaced later, in the vertebrates, by the vertebral column.

NUCLEOLUS. One or more Feulgen-negative, intranuclear bodies, concerned with the synthesis of RNA.

NUCLEOPROTEINS. Conjugated proteins formed by union between protein and nucleic acid; of two principal kinds: (1) deoxyribonucleoprotein (DNA protein), which is closely identified with the genic material, and (2) ribonucleoprotein (RNA protein), varieties of which are concerned with protein synthesis.

NUCLEOTIDES. Sugar-phosphate-base (purine and pyrimidine) units that become bonded into very long molecules, the nucleic acids, by a complex process of polymerization.

NUCLEUS. The clearly delimited portion of a cell containing the chromatin.

NUTRITION. The intake of food substances, their distribution within the organism, metabolism, and elimination of waste products.

OÖCYTES. The auxocytes of the female, which give rise to the egg cells.

OÖGONIA. The gonia of the female, which finally give rise to oöcytes.

ORDER. A taxonomic group, between class and family.

ORGAN. A localized part of an organism, specialized for some particular function.

ORGANIC ACIDS. Organic compounds, usually possessing a carboxyl radical (COOH).

ORGANIC BASES. Organic compounds derived from ammonia (NH_3) by the replacement of one or more of its hydrogen atoms by organic radicals. Organic compounds that dissociate forming hydroxyl (OH⁻) ions.

ORGANIC COMPOUNDS. Compounds of carbon and hydrogen in which some (or, rarely, all) of the hydrogen may be replaced by other elements or radicals.

ORGANISM. An individual living thing.

OSMOSIS. Exchange of solvent (usually water) between two solutions separated by a semipermeable membrane.

OVARY. The female gonad of animals, in which the egg cells are formed.

OVIDUCTS. The female gonoducts.

OVIPAROUS. Laying eggs, either before or shortly after they are fertilized. (*cf.* VIVIPAROUS.)

OVULE. The macrosporangium of seed plants.

OVUM. The egg cell.

OXIDATION. A chemical reaction in which oxygen is accepted or hydrogen is yielded up by a substance. Also includes yielding of one or more electrons by a substance.

PANCREAS. An important digestive gland of vertebrates.

PARASITE. An organism that lives on or in another living organism, from which it derives nourishment.

PARASYMPATHETIC SYSTEM. That portion of the autonomic nervous system which is connected with the brain and the posterior end of the spinal cord, and whose ganglia lie in or close to the organs they innervate.

PARENCHYMA. A relatively undifferentiated tissue.

PARTHENOGENESIS. Development of an egg cell without fertilization.

PELLICLE. A thin, flexible external cell membrane, outside the plasma membrane; characteristic of animal cells.

PEPSIN. An enzyme secreted by the stomach, which partially hydrolyzes proteins.

PERISTALSIS. Rhythmic contraction of the wall of the enteron or other tubular organs, traveling in successive waves in one direction.

PERITONEUM. The membrane lining the abdominal cavity.

PETALS. The separate parts of the corolla.

PETIOLE. The stalk of a leaf.

PHAGOCYTOSIS. The ingestion of solid particles by certain of the cells of a multicellular organism.

PHARYNX. The portion of the enteron of vertebrate animals, immediately behind the mouth cavity.

PHENOTYPE. A type of organism judged on the basis of its visible characteristics. (*cf.* GENOTYPE.)

PHLOEM. That portion of the fibrovascular bundles which contains the sieve tubes, usually the outer portion of the bundles. (*cf.* XYLEM.)

PHOSPHOLIPIDS. Lipids containing phosphorus and nitrogen, found in all cells; essential components of protoplasm.

PHOTOPERIODISM. Processes by which the flowering and other responses of plants are regulated by seasonal (and experimental) changes in exposure to light and dark.

PHOTOSYNTHESIS. The formation of carbohydrates and other compounds from carbon dioxide and water by the absorption of radiant energy of sunlight by chlorophyll.

PHOTOTROPISM. Movement determined by the direction of incident light.

PHYLOGENY. The line of descent of a major group of organisms.

PHYLUM. A taxonomic group, next below a kingdom.

PHYTOHORMONES. Auxins and other plant hormones.

PISTIL. A separate carpel or a group of carpels united to form a single compound organ.

PITH. The parenchyma in the center of a stem or root.

PITUITARY GLAND. A ductless gland on the ventral side of the brain, above the roof of the mouth, composed of two lobes having different origins and different secretions.

PLACENTA. An organ of most mammals, by which the embryo is attached to the wall of the uterus and through which exchanges occur between the blood of the embryo and that of the mother.

PLASMA MEMBRANE. The differentiated film at the outer surface of the cytoplasm, of ultramicroscopic thickness.

PLASTIDS. Cytoplasmic formed bodies in which occur special constructive metabolic processes.

POLAR BODIES. The very small, functionless cells that are produced, with the mature egg cell, by the meiotic divisions of the oöcyte.

POLLEN GRAIN. The microspore of seed plants.

POLLEN TUBE. The male gametophyte of seed plants.

POLLINATION. The transfer of pollen grains to the stigma.

POLYEMBRYONY. The production of two or more embryos from one, by fission.

POLYSACCHARIDE. A carbohydrate, each molecule of which yields, by hydrolysis, many monosaccharide molecules.

PONS. A region on the ventral side of the hind part of the brain; an important intermediate station between the cerebrum and the cerebellum.

POPULATION. Any group of individuals, considered as a whole, especially with reference to numbers and statistics.

PORTAL VEIN. A vein that starts and ends in capillaries.

POTENTIAL ENERGY. Energy inherent in the position or configuration (relative positions of component parts) of a body. (*cf.* KINETIC ENERGY.)

PROPHASES. The early stages of mitosis or meiosis, preceding metaphase.

PROPRIOCEPTORS. Special receptors for internal stimuli due to the positions and movements of the parts of the body.

PROTEINS. Complex organic compounds of C, H, O, N, and often other elements, yielding amino acids by hydrolysis; essential components of protoplasm.

PROTHALLIUM. The gametophyte of vascular plants, especially ferns.

PROTONEMA. An early stage in the development of the gametophyte in mosses.

PROTON. A particle of positive electricity, one of the particulate constitutents of matter.

PROTOPLASM. Living matter, a complex system of organic and inorganic substances, having an intricate microscopic and ultramicroscopic structure and certain characteristic activities; i.e., metabolism, liberation of energy as movement, heat, etc., responses to stimuli; growth and reproduction.

PSEUDOPODIA. Temporary projections of the protoplasm of a cell, effecting locomotion of the cell and phagocytosis.

PTYALIN. An enzyme secreted by the salivary glands, which partially hydrolyzes starch. Also called *salivary amylase.*

PUPA. A quiescent stage of many insects, between the larval and adult stages.

RADIAL SYMMETRY. Symmetry built around a *line.* In a radially symmetrical body (e.g., a cylinder), any plane that passes through the line of the central axis will divide the body into symmetrical halves.

RADIANT ENERGY. Energy transmitted through "empty" space (i.e., space devoid of matter); including light, x-rays, etc.

RADICAL. A group of atoms that acts as a unit in many chemical reactions.

RADICLE. Tne root of an embryo plant within the seed.

RECEPTACLE. The base of a flower, to which all other parts of the flower are attached.

RECEPTOR. A structure specialized for the reception of some particular kind of stimulus.

RECESSIVE. A gene whose phenotypic effect is largely or entirely obscured by that of its allelomorph. (*cf.* DOMINANT.)

RECOMBINATION. A new combination of genes brought about by the normal processes of crossing over, reduction, and fertilization.

RECTUM. The terminal portion of the enteron.

REDUCTION. Chemical reaction in which hydrogen is accepted or oxygen is yielded up by a substance. Also the acceptance of electrons by a substance. In genetics, the change of chromosome number from diploid to haploid.

REFLEX. A response to a particular stimulus; a reflex may be simple or complex, unconditioned or conditioned. When not otherwise qualified the term *reflex* usually means a simple unconditioned response; i.e., one involving only a single action and independent of any previous experience of the individual. (*cf.* CONDITIONED REFLEX, HABIT, INSTINCT.)

REFLEX ARC. A series of neurons transmitting excitation successively from a receptor through the central nervous system to an effector; comprising one sensory and one motor neuron with or without one or more intermediate neurons.

REFRACTORY STATE. The state of a cell for a brief period immediately following excitation, during which it cannot be excited again by another stimulus.

REPRODUCTION. The production of organisms from those already living.

RESPIRATION. The intake of oxygen and elimination of carbon dioxide. (Often used as including oxidation in the cells.)

RESPONSE. Any change of activity resulting from a change of external or internal conditions. (*cf.* STIMULUS.)

RESPONSIVENESS. The property of responding to changes of conditions by changes of activity.

RESTING STAGE. The intermitotic, or growth, stage of the cell.

RHIZOID. A rootlike organ of simple structure; distinguished from a true root by not containing vascular bundles.

RIBOSOMES. Numerous fine granules seen bordering the endoplasmic reticulum in electronmicrographs of cells generally; rich in RNA; associated with the the synthesis of enzymes and other proteins.

RNA. Ribonucleic acid, in which the sugar of the sugar-phosphate chain is ribose; occurs in three fractions: (1) ribosomal, (2) messenger, and (3) transfer RNA, all concerned with protein synthesis.

ROOT HAIRS. Filamentous projections of the epidermal cells of roots shortly above the growing point.

SALIVARY GLANDS. Glands located near the mouth, which secrete saliva into the mouth.

SALT. A substance that produces positive ions other than H^+ and negative ions other than OH^-.

SAP. The watery solution of salts, etc., in the ducts and tracheids of a plant.

SAPROPHYTIC. A mode of nutrition in which the organism absorbs organic food directly from the environment.

SARCOPLASM. The liquid portion of the cytoplasm of a muscle cell, between the myofibrils and filaments.

SECRETIN. An internal secretion of the duodenum, which stimulates the pancreas to secrete pancreatic juice.

SECRETION. The liberation from cells of substances that have been synthesized or accumulated in these cells. Any substance or mixture thus secreted. (Often used as including also the synthesis of such substances in the cells.)

SEDIMENTARY ROCKS. Rocks formed by the deposition in water of sand, clay, mud, etc., which subsequently hardens.

SEED. An embryo sporophyte surrounded by the remains (if any) of the mother gametophyte (endosperm) and external integuments derived from the ovule of parent sporophyte.

SEGREGATION. The separation of the two genes of an allelomorphic pair into different germ cells during meiosis.

SELECTION. Any process tending to favor the preservation and reproduction of one type of organism rather than another.

SELF-FERTILIZATION. Union of gametes both derived from the same individual. (*cf.* CROSS-FERTILIZATION.)

SEMIPERMEABLE MEMBRANE. A membrane through which some, but not all, of the components of the separated solutions can diffuse.

SENSE ORGAN. A multicellular receptor organ, including sensory cells and accessory structures associated with them.

SENSORY CELL. A unicellular receptor.

SENSORY NEURON. A neuron that either acts as a receptor itself or receives excitation directly from a receptor that is not a neuron; its axon usually runs into the central nervous system.

SEPALS. The separate parts of the calyx.

SEX CHROMOSOMES. A particular pair of chromosomes that (normally) determines the sex of an organism.

SEX-LINKED GENE. Genes in the sex chromosomes, which are therefore linked in heredity to the genes determining sex.

SEXUAL REPRODUCTION. Reproduction involving the fusion of two cells (gametes), especially of their nuclei.

SIEVE TUBES. Tubular structures in the phloem portion of vascular bundles, composed of elongate cells whose walls are perforated by fine pores giving direct protoplasmic continuity from cell to cell.

SOLUTE. A substance dissolved in another.

SOLUTION. A mixture in which one or more substances are dispersed in the form of separate molecules or ions throughout another (usually liquid) substance.

SOLVENT. The substance in which another is dissolved.

SOMA. The somatic cells collectively.

SOMATIC CELLS. The body cells of an organism, which do not stand in the line of ascent of the reproductive cells. (*cf.* GERM CELLS.)

SPECIES. A taxonomic group, supposed to be a group of individuals that do not differ from each other more than offspring of the same parent may do, and all of which may interbreed freely; in practice, however, the lines between species are often drawn arbitrarily.

SPERMARY. The male gonad, in which the sperm cells are formed.

SPERMATIDS. Germ cells of the male after the meiotic divisions but before assuming the specialized form of the sperm cells.

SPERMATOCYTES. The auxocytes of the male, which give rise to the spermatids.

SPERMATOGONIA. The gonia of the male, which give rise to the spermatocytes.

SPERMATOZOÖN. A sperm cell.

SPERM CELL. A small, usually motile gamete, containing very little cytoplasm and no yolk. (*cf.* EGG CELL.)

SPERMIDUCTS. The male gonoducts.

SPHERICAL SYMMETRY. Symmetry built around a *point*. In a spherically symmetrical body (e.g., a ball), any plane that passes through the central point will divide the body into symmetrical halves.

SPINAL CORD. The central nervous system, exclusive of the brain, of vertebrates.

SPINAL NERVES. Nerves arising from the spinal cord.

SPINDLE. A spindle-shaped group of fibers, converging toward opposite ends of the cell, which appears during mitosis and meiosis.

SPORANGIUM. A hollow structure in which the spores are formed.

SPORE. An asexual specialized reproductive cell.

SPOROCYTE. A cell from which four spores are formed by the two meiotic divisions.

SPOROPHYLL. A modified leaf bearing sporangia.

SPOROPHYTE. The asexual generation of a plant that has an alternation of generations. (*cf.* GAMETOPHYTE.)

STAMEN. A microsporophyll of a flowering plant.

STARCH. A complex carbohydrate (polysaccharide), the chief stored food substance of most green plants.

STEAPSIN. An enzyme secreted by the pancreas, which hydrolyzes fats and some other lipids.

STEREOTROPISM. Movement whose direction is determined by contact with a solid body.

STEROLS. Complex lipids, not susceptible to hydrolysis, found in all cells.

STIGMA. A moist, sticky surface at the tip of the pistil, on which the pollen grains germinate.

STIMULUS. Any change of external or internal conditions that results in a change in the activities of the organism. (*cf.* RESPONSE.)

STOMA. An opening from the intercellular space of a leaf or stem to the outer air, surrounded by two guard cells.

STYLE. The elongate portion of a pistil, between the stigma and the ovule case, through which the pollen tube grows.

SUBSTANCE. Any material composed of only one kind of molecule. (*cf.* MIXTURE.)

SUBSTRATE. A substance acted on by a catalyst.

SUCROSE. Common sugar, a disaccharide found in many plants; e.g., sugar cane, sugar beets, etc.

SUGAR. Any monosaccharide or disaccharide.

SUSPENSION. A dispersion consisting of solid particles in a liquid medium.

SWARM SPORE. A motile spore, characteristic of some thallophytes.

SYMBIOSIS. A mutually beneficial relation between a parasite and its host.

SYMPATHETIC SYSTEM. That portion of the autonomic nervous system which is connected with the anterior and middle regions of the spinal cord, and whose ganglia lie close to the spinal cord or in the abdominal cavity.

SYNAPSE. The point of contact between two successive neurons.

SYNAPSIS. The intimate conjunction of homologous chromosomes that occurs during the prophase of the first meiotic division.

SYNCYTIUM. A continuous mass of protoplasm with several or many nuclei.

SYNTHESIS. The formation of a more complex substance from simpler ones.

TAXONOMIC. Pertaining to the classification of organisms.

TELOLECITHAL EGG. An egg cell with abundant yolk concentrated toward the vegetal end of the cell.

TELOPHASES. The final stages of mitosis, during which the daughter nuclei are formed and the cytoplasm is divided.

TESTIS. A spermary.

TETRAD. A group of four chromosomes consisting of a pair of homologous chromosomes each having divided into two daughter chromosomes; formed after synapsis.

THALAMUS. The part of the brain just behind the cerebrum; an important intermediate station between all other parts of the nervous system and the cerebrum.

THYROID GLAND. A ductless gland located in the throat region, below the pharynx, in vertebrates.

THYROXIN. A hormone secreted by the thyroid gland.

TISSUE. An aggregate of cells of a particular type, or at most a few types, with more or less intercellular material of a particular type.

TRACHEIDS. Elongate hollow units (dead cell walls without protoplasm), with oblique, perforated end walls, in the xylem portion of vascular bundles.

TRANSPIRATION. A controlled elimination of water vapor from plants, especially through the stomata.

TRIPLOID. Having three haploid sets of chromosomes.

TROPISM. A movement, of growth, orientation, or locomotion, whose direction is determined by the direction from which the stimulus impinges on the organism.

TRYPSIN. An enzyme secreted by the pancreas, which catalyzes the hydrolysis of proteins.

TUBER. A short, thick, subterranean stem with numerous buds; e.g., a potato.

TURGOR. The taut condition of a cell due to absorption of water to the limit of distensibility of the cell wall.

TURGOR MOVEMENTS. Movements effected by local changes of turgor.

ULTRAMICROBE. An ultramicroscopic organism.

ULTRAMICROSCOPE. A microscope in which light is thrown onto the object from the side, so that particles appear as bright specks against a dark background.

ULTRAMICROSCOPIC. Invisible with the ordinary microscope, but visible with the ultramicroscope; i.e., between about 1 mμ and 100 mμ in diameter.

UNIVALENT. A single member of a pair of homologous chromosomes. (*cf.* BIVALENT.)

UREA. A simple organic compound, $CO(NH_2)_2$, the chief nitrogenous waste product of mammals.

URETERS. The tubes carrying urine from the kidneys to the cloaca or to the urinary bladder.

URETHRA. The tube carrying urine from the bladder to the exterior in mammals.

URIC ACID. A nitrogenous waste product, more complex than urea.

URINARY TUBULES. The tubules making up the kidney, which produce the urine; nephrons.

URINE. The fluid excreted by the kidneys; a solution of various waste products.

UTERUS. An enlargement of the lower end of the oviduct, in which the eggs are retained temporarily or in which the embryo develops; in some mammals (e.g., man) there is a single uterus formed by coalescence of the two oviducts.

VACUOLE. A droplet of watery fluid within the cytoplasm, bounded by a membrane.

VAGUS NERVES. The tenth pair of cranial nerves, composed of parasympathetic fibers innervating most of the internal organs.

VARIATION. Differences among organisms related by descent.

VASCULAR BUNDLES. Strands of tissue containing woody fibers and tubular vessels, running lengthwise through the stems, roots, and leaf veins of all tracheophytes.

VASCULAR PLANTS. Plants having vascular bundles; i.e., pteropsidans, gymnosperms, and angiosperms.

VEIN. A relatively thin-walled, distensible blood vessel, carrying blood from the capillaries back toward the heart. (*cf.* ARTERY.)

VENTRAL. Pertaining to the belly side of an animal.

VENTRICLE. A very thick-walled chamber of the heart, which receives blood from the auricle and pumps it into the arteries.

VERTEBRAE. The series of short bony or cartilaginous segments making up the vertebral column, or backbone, of vertebrates.

VESTIGIAL ORGAN. A degenerate, useless remnant of an organ.

VIABILITY. Ability to live.

VILLI. Small cylindrical projections of the inner surface of the small intestine.

VIRUSES. Ultramicroscopic intracellular infective agents.

VITAMINS. A heterogeneous group of relatively simple organic food substances required by animals and some other organisms in very small amounts.

VIVIPAROUS. Giving birth to fairly well-developed young. (*cf.* OVIPAROUS.)

WARM-BLOODED ANIMALS. Animals whose body temperature is (normally) practically constant and usually higher than that of the environment; including the birds and the mammals.

X CHROMOSOMES. The sex chromosomes of which there are a pair in the female but only one in the male, in most dioecious diploid organisms.

XYLEM. That portion of the vascular bundles which contains the ducts and tracheids, usually the inner portion of the bundles; constituting the wood in woody plants. (*cf.* PHLOEM.)

Y CHROMOSOME. A chromosome in the male, which pairs with the X chromosome at synapsis, and which often contains few or no active genes.

YOLK. Stored food substances in egg cells.

ZOÖSPORES. Flagellate spores, in many algae.

ZYGOSPORE. A thick-walled, resting zygote, in many algae.

ZYGOTE. The cell formed by the union of two gametes in sexual reproduction.

INDEX

Index

Bold face numbers indicate either a main reference or an illustration. Italics indicate scientific names of taxonomic groups (species, genera, etc.). Page references to Appendixes 1 and 2 are not included.

A

Aberration, **513–16**
Abortion, 402
Absolute zero, 112
Absorption, 128, **130–31**, 310, 313, **339–40**; in bread mold, 176; in unicellular and colonial plants, **167–68**
Acceptor compounds, 145
Acceptors, electron, 162; hydrogen, 145; primary, **145–46**, 161
Acetylation, 154
Acetylcholine, 193, 414, **455**
Acetyl CoA, 149 n.
Achromatium, **181**
Acid solutions, **73–74**
Acids, 71, **74–75**; acetic, **82**, 177; amino (*see* Amino acids); ascorbic, 347, **349**; butyric, 177; carbonic, **75**; citric, 153; deoxyribonucleic (*see* Deoxyribonucleic acid); fatty, 81, **82**, 340; gibberellic, 265; homogentisic, 506; lactic, 100, 177; nucleic, 10 n., **88**, 90, 137; organic, **82**; oxaloacetic, 153; palmitic, **82**; pantothenic, 353; parascorbic, 265; phosphoglyceric, 165; pyruvic, 145; ribonucleic (*see* Ribonucleic acid); stearic, **82**; uric, 342
Acini, 441
Acromegaly, 410–11
Acrosome, 273
Acrosome filament, 273
ACTH (*see* Adrenocorticotrophic hormone)
Actin, 436, 439
Actinosphaerium, **625**
Action potential, **190, 191, 192–93,** 260, **428, 429,** 448
Activation, **276;** fertilization vs., **274–76**
Active transport mechanisms, **112–13, 121–24;** ionic transport, **123–24;** phagocytosis, **121–22;** pinocytosis, **121–22;** water transport, **123**
Actomyosin, 439
Adaptation, **543–44,** 573; arthropod, to land conditions, **657–58;** external, 543; internal, 543; of species to species, **575**
Adenine, 134, 521; derivatives, 265
Adenosine diphosphate (ADP), 144, 151, 155, 162

Adenosine monophosphate (AMP), 144
Adenosine triphosphate (ATP), 89, **90,** 135, **143–44,** 151, 155, 162, 163, 155, 187, 436, 439, 442
ADP (*see* Adenosine diphosphate)
Adrenal glands, 398, **406–08;** cortex, 407–08; medulla, 406–07
Adrenal virilism, 408
Adrenalin, 341, 406–07, 444; in protoplasm, 89
Adrenocorticotrophic hormone (ACTH), 411, 413
Adsorption, **93**
Alveoli, **359, 363**
African sleeping sickness, 627
Afterbirth, 393
Agammaglobulinemia, 505, **507**
Agglutinins, 325
Agglutinogens, 325
Agnatha, 668
Agranulocytes, **322**
Air, alveolar, **362–63;** atmosphere and alveolar, comparison between, **362**
Alanine deaminase, 102
Albinism, 504, 505
Alcohol, 117; ethyl, 152; fermentation, **151–52**
Aldosterone, 407
Algae, 55, 179; blue-green, 16, 17, **49,** 187, **208, 594–95;** brown, 210, **599–600;** flame, **598–99;** golden-brown, **597–98;** green, **30,** 57, 59, 62, 164, **167–68, 596–97;** nutrition of, **236–38;** red, **600–01**
Algin, 599
Alkaptonuria, 505, **506,** 529
Allantois, **389, 390**
All-or-none law, 435
Alveolar air, **362–63;** atmosphere and, comparison between, 362
Amblystoma punctatum, 358
Aminases, **102**
Amination, **152–53**
Amino acids, **84–85, 86,** 135, 136, 138, 139, 152–53, 186, 312, 314, 339, 341–42, 346, 405, 412, 507, 526. *See also* Essential amino acids; Nonessential amino acids
Amino radical, 84
Aminopeptidase, 103, 108, 314

699